Lawrence Rieser
826 Burton Judson
1005 E 60th St
Illinois

4-47

D0394731

UP FROM THE APE

MACMILLAN AND CO., LIMITED

THE MACMILLAN COMPANY
NEW YORK · BOSTON · CHICAGO
DALLAS · ATLANTA · SAN FRANCISCO

MACMILLAN AND CO., LIMITED
LONDON · BOMBAY · CALCUTTA
MADRAS · MELBOURNE

THE MACMILLAN COMPANY
OF CANADA, LIMITED
TORONTO

YOUNG FEMALE CHIMPANZEE (PHOTOGRAPH BY FRED JOHNSON)

UP FROM THE APE

BY EARNEST ALBERT HOOTON, PROFESSOR OF ANTHROPOLOGY, HARVARD
UNIVERSITY; CURATOR OF SOMATOLOGY, PEABODY MUSEUM OF HARVARD UNIVERSITY

ILLUSTRATED — REVISED EDITION

THE MACMILLAN COMPANY · NEW YORK · 1946

Revised Edition Copyrighted, 1946, by The Macmillan Company

All rights reserved—no part of this book may be reproduced in any form without permission in writing from the publisher, except by a reviewer who wishes to quote brief passages in connection with a review written for inclusion in magazine or newspaper.

PRINTED IN THE UNITED STATES OF AMERICA

FIRST EDITION COPYRIGHTED 1931 BY THE MACMILLAN COMPANY

TO THE MOST SOCIAL OF SOCIAL ANTHROPOLOGISTS

TO THE MOST HUMAN OF HUMAN ANATOMISTS

TO THE MOST ADVANCED INTERPRETER OF
PRIMITIVE INDUSTRIES

IN SHORT

TO MY TEACHERS OF ANTHROPOLOGY AT OXFORD

Preface to Second Edition

PREFACE TO SECOND EDITION

In the fifteen years that have elapsed since the publication of the first edition of this work, masses of new data on human evolution have accumulated. In the field of human and primate palaeontology, the remains of numerous extinct forms of apes and men have been brought to light. I think it is safe to assert that the finds of fossil man since 1931 exceed in number and importance all that had been made in the whole period before that date. There have also been tremendous advances in knowledge of the anatomy, physiology, and psychology of the great apes and the lower primates. At length we have acquired also some substantial information on the social habits of apes and monkeys in the wild. On the whole, I am afraid that we have advanced farther in our knowledge of extinct men and living infrahuman primates than in the taxonomy of present human races and in the general biology of *Homo sapiens*. Human genetics is still a thinly cultivated field, sporadically scratched. Endocrinology is advancing slowly from quackery and speculation to an experimental science, but its part in human evolution is still a matter of hypothesis and dialectics.

On the whole, I should say that the greatest progress has been made in the study of the physical anthropology of the individual in its relationship to his physiology, psychology, and behavior. The study of the human constitution opens up to the physical anthropologist a field of immediate, vital, and almost universal usefulness, but only when he works in close cooperation with the physician, the physiologist, the psychologist, the psychiatrist, and the social anthropologist. We have to begin to study the total man, even when we have not yet completed the dissection of his *disiecta membra*. It is certain that the study of the whole man will yield great human dividends.

I have tried to bring this work up to date by rewriting nearly all of it and adding several new sections. Unfortunately, new data do not always bring a better understanding of such vast subjects as man's evolution. Processes that seemed simple and explicable to us in our ignorance have turned out to be exceedingly complex and mysterious. Cocksureness has had to yield to humility. I do not think that anyone can be complacent about the present status of man if he is at all aware of the direction of trend and the accelerated pace of human evolution. However, I have kept this book clear, for the most part, of biological preachments. I have done enough of that elsewhere (and mostly to deaf ears).

When I was preparing the original edition of *Up from the Ape,* I was still naïve enough to think that I was writing a "popular" book on human evolution. In the sense of being comparatively non-technical and simple it has been "popular," but it has been read principally by students. Since I am now wholly reconciled to the task of writing unpopular books, I have tried to add to the academic usefulness of this work by appending to the college edition a brief description of some of the more important techniques used in physical anthropology.

In the course of this revision many obligations have been incurred. I am indebted to Professor R. Ruggles Gates for advice and help in the section upon human genetics and for allowing me access to his great work on human inheritance, *Human Genetics.* Professor William C. Boyd has patiently discussed with me problems of serology and I have drawn upon his many excellent publications in this field for most of the material I have presented on this subject. Dr. William H. Sheldon has helped me in the preparation of the section on "The Anthropology of the Individual," and has allowed me to publish in the Appendix his instructions for posing subjects for the photographs involved in somatotyping. Finally, he and his publishers, Harper & Brothers, have granted me permission to reprint the Scale for Temperament and to summarize many important parts of his works. I am grateful also to Dr. Alice M. Brues, Dr. P. B. Candela, and Mr. H. R. Glodt for the use of unpublished material. A glance at the Bibliography and the turning of the pages will make the reader realize how generously I have drawn in the preparation of this work upon the researches of many learned colleagues here and abroad. To mention all of them here would unduly prolong this preface. Let it be understood, however, that my sincere thanks are implicit in every reference cited in the Bibliography. The merits of this book, such as they are, derive from the scientific contributions of others, of which I am merely a reporter.

I am particularly grateful to Stanley M. Garn for letting me use his admirable photomicrographs of human hair and for the photographs from which were made the drawings that illustrate anthropometric technique. Most of the new drawings in this edition were made by Dr. Oliver G. Ricketson. Some of the new illustrations of racial types are the work of Dr. Henry M. Field (reproduced through the kindness of the Chicago Museum of Natural History), Dr. Joseph B. Birdsell, and

Dr. C. Wesley Dupertuis. All of these men are past or present pupils of mine to whom I owe much. I have also used in this edition new drawings and fresh data derived from the works of Adolph H. Schultz, W. K. Gregory and Milo Hellman, Sir Arthur Keith, and Franz Weidenreich.

Finally, although not noticeably inarticulate, I cannot find words to express my gratitude to Dorothea Kelly (wife of my valued colleague, Dr. William H. Kelly). Mrs. Kelly voluntarily, gratuitously, and with an incredible semblance of pleasure in the task, has helped me prepare the manuscript and read the proofs of this lengthy work. She has compiled the Index and the Bibliography, checked the references, corrected many of my inaccuracies, and made countless wise and helpful suggestions. I might have undertaken this revision without her services, but I do not see how I could have finished it. Anticlimactically, I thank her.

EARNEST A. HOOTON

Preface to First Edition

I began to write this book in a summer vacation because I was tired of turning out "contributions to knowledge," full of tables and technical terms, to be perused by a few yawning, carping specialists. I thought it might be more amusing to try to write something which could be read. I have succeeded in getting a certain amount of fun out of the writing, whether or not anyone may derive pleasure from the reading. I have simply sat down and typed out the stuff which I deliver each year, more or less extemporaneously, to a class of Harvard students most of whom have had no previous instruction in the subject. Some of these students endure the lectures in obvious boredom, but a good many are genuinely interested, or, at any rate, successfully simulate that desirable state of mind.

There are plenty of problems of human evolution which I have not attempted to solve here. For that matter, my mental juices are not sufficiently potent to dissolve the solid difficulties of the subject. Nothing in this volume seems to me to be particularly original or revolutionary. I have utilized freely the thoughts and investigations of many scientists. If I have not always given them credit specifically, it is not because I wish to appropriate their glory, but rather because I have assimilated so completely the nourishment which they have provided that identification of the raw materials has become difficult. So I gratefully acknowledge my indebtedness to anyone who may think that he reads in this book an exposition of his own ideas, however distorted their reflection. Of course one fondly imagines that he has an occasional idea of his own, but too often such "original" ideas are merely the few drops which have not rolled off the duck's back, rather than his own exudations.

Nevertheless I am acutely and pleasurably conscious of my obligation to the works of many students of primate and human evolution. Among these I may mention Professor William K. Gregory's profound studies of primate palaeontology, which have been a most sure-footed guide; the brilliant researches of Professor G. Elliot Smith upon the evolution of the brain, and Professor Frederic Wood Jones' ingenious deductions regarding the effects of arboreal life upon man's ancestors, which are always stimulating and often convincing; the intensive inquiries into the mental life of the anthropoid apes carried on by Professor Robert M. Yerkes and Professor Wolfgang Köhler; Sir Arthur Keith's masterly analyses and reconstructions of the anatomy of fossil man; the late Professor Rudolf Martin's great thesaurus of anthropological knowledge; the sound scientific work of Hrdlička, Schultz, Boas, and many other of my colleagues whose names appear frequently in the pages which follow.

This book does not presuppose on the part of the reader any knowledge of geology, biology, anatomy, or anthropology. It is intended primarily for the more or less educated layman and not either secondarily or more remotely for the overeducated professional. Indeed I rather hope that not many of the latter class will read it, because the most favorable opinion of a general book which can be extracted from a specialist is that it is good enough except where it touches his particular subject.

If the tone of this book seems at times to belie my Christian name, it is not because I take my subject lightly, but rather because of a conviction that science need not be clothed in sackcloth and ashes and that knowledge is not necessarily expounded in accents of lugubrious pomposity. One ought not to be cheaply flippant in describing nature's marvels, but he need not always deport himself as if he were in church.

I do not hesitate to assert that some of the things in this book are very good. I refer to the drawings which are the work of Mr. Elmer Rising, and to the photographs of primates, most of which I owe to the skill of Mr. Newton H. Hartman and to the courtesy of the Philadelphia Zoological Garden, and the remainder to the artistry of Mr. Alvin Sanborn and the kindness of the New York Zoological Society, to the cooperation of the Pathé Exchange, or to the friendly assistance of Mr. Frederick Johnson and Mr. Fred Orchard of the Peabody Museum.

I am indebted to a number of colleagues and scientific institutions for permission to reproduce photographs illustrative of racial types: first and foremost to Dr. Harry L. Shapiro and to the American Museum of Natural History, also to Dr. Carleton S. Coon, to Professor Frederick Starr, to the Museum National d'Histoire Naturelle of Paris, to the Peabody Museum of Harvard University, and to the United States Geological Survey. A number of authors and publishers have kindly allowed me to use reproductions or modifications of drawings in their published works. These include Professor William K. Gregory and the Journal of Dental Research; Sir Arthur Keith, Williams and Norgate, and the J. Lippincott Company; Professor Marcellin Boule and Masson et Cie. of Paris; Herr Gustav Fischer of Jena, publisher of Rudolf Martin's *Lehrbuch der Anthropologie*. Courteous permission to quote from copyrighted works has been granted me by various publishers: John Bale, Sons, and Danielsson, Ltd.; Bureau of American Ethnology, Smithsonian Institution; Cambridge University Press; Carnegie Institution of Washington; Century Co.; Harcourt, Brace and Co.; Paul B. Hoeber, Inc.; Longmans, Green and Co.; Oxford University Press; G. P. Putnam's Sons; Science Press; Wistar Institute of Anatomy and Biology; Yale University Press.

Professor Glover Allen and the Museum of Comparative Zoology of Harvard University, Dr. Edward Reynolds and the Peabody Museum of Harvard University, have put at my disposal, for study or for drawing, their invaluable skeletal collections.

Mrs. Pearl B. Hurwitz, my indispensable research assistant, has labored intelligently and painstakingly upon the manuscript and index. Mr. H. S. Latham of the Macmillan Company has given expert advice and assistance.

If this book is not good, no one is to blame except the author.

CAMBRIDGE, MASSACHUSETTS,
FEBRUARY 6, 1931.

Table of Contents

Part I. Man's Relations

Part II. The Primate Life Cycle

Part III. The Individual Life Cycle

Part IV. Fossil Ancestors and Collaterals

Part VI. The Anthropology of the Individual

List of Text Figures

List of Plates

(Plates 1–20 follow p. 40; Plates 21–39 follow p. 648)

List of Tables

UP FROM THE APE

Part I. Man's Relations

Recognizing Relationship

When you see a two-legged, feathered animal flying through the air, you identify it as a bird and distinguish it from the four-legged, hair-covered animal that you notice drawing a cart through the street. The latter animal you recognize as a horse or a mule. But you must observe more closely to distinguish the horse from the mule, because they resemble each other more than do the bird and the horse. When you see two human beings walking together, you may judge one of them to be a Negro from his skin color, the curl of his hair, and the thickness of his lips, and the other to be a White from opposite variations of the same bodily features. If you meet two men who look very much alike, you suspect that they may be "related" to each other. Two persons who are almost identical in appearance will be judged to be twins. Thus you distinguish one kind of animal from another by observing their anatomical differences and you determine their degrees of relationship one to the other by recognizing the closeness of their mutual resemblances.

In this everyday process of distinguishing and identifying animals and men you are unconsciously passing zoological judgments. You are subscribing to the agreement of scientists that general anatomical resemblances imply relationship and that detailed similarities of face and form mean that the individuals possessing them have in common all or nearly all of their ancestors. But it is not always true that persons who look alike are, in the ordinary sense, "blood relations." They may show similar combinations of bodily features by chance, without being akin to each other. Such accidental resemblances we regard as coincidences. We do not expect striking individual likenesses to occur very often, even in groups of people that exhibit in general the same complexions and similar bodily features. We do not expect them to occur at all in physically diverse groups. One might meet an Englishman who bears a very close personal resemblance to a Swede or even to an Italian. We should not be willing to admit that a "pure" Englishman could by chance so closely resemble an individual of "pure" Negro blood as to be mistaken for him. It is highly improbable that chance could effect even one combination

1

of features in a "pure" Englishman that would lead him to be mistaken for any Negro or to be classified as a member of the Negro race. It is wholly inconceivable that a horse and a man could resemble each other in any intimate or detailed way, even though many men have "horse faces" and some horses are said to have "human intelligence." It is then apparent that striking resemblances due to chance are likely to occur within physical groups that share similar bodily attributes. If we assume that these bodily attributes are inherited, it becomes clear that chance resemblances of individuals are, in a broad sense, due to their common ancestry, and "chance" merely effects the intensity of the individual likenesses by selecting similar or identical combinations of characters from the ancestral store.

We may then affirm that detailed resemblances between animals indicate their common descent, or, to state the matter from another point of view, that "heredity is resemblance based upon descent." But it is quite apparent that in applying such a principle we must not be misled by superficial likenesses that may result from causes other than relationship. If you see a large creature flitting about in the dusk, you will not hastily adjudge it to be a bird; you will consider the possibility of its being a bat. And if you examine a bat and an owl, you will perceive that having wings and flying about at night constitute practically the sole detailed resemblances between these two animals. The bat has neither feathers nor bill and is fundamentally distinct in form and structure from a bird. The wings of the bat consist of membranes stretched between the fore and hind limbs, but the wings of a bird consist of feathers arranged upon tissues that are supported by the fore limbs alone. The wings of both animals are organs of flight, but the resemblance ends there. Similar or identical functions of organs in two different animals do bring about resemblances, but not the deep-rooted structural resemblances from which it may be inferred that the animals are related.

Organs that have the same function are said to be analogous. But relationships must be based upon fundamental identities of structure and development, not upon analogous functions. The foot of the ape is a grasping organ with a great toe set off from the lesser toes like a thumb. It looks more like the hand than the foot of man, and it was for this reason that the great apes were formerly called the Quadrumana—"four-handed." Man's foot is a supporting foot with short and non-prehensile toes, but, if its structure be compared with that of the ape foot, it will be seen that the two organs correspond bone for bone, whereas the human hand, which superficially and functionally resembles the ape foot, is quite differently constructed from the latter. The fundamental resemblances of structure and development upon which the zoological relationships are based are called homologies.

Basic similarity of form that indicates relationship may be obscured by differences in the habits and functions of two related animals. A whale lives in the sea; its hind limbs have been lost and its fore limbs have become converted into paddles; but the examination of the structure of the whale shows very clearly that it is not a fish but a mammal, and as such is closely related to higher forms of land-dwelling quadrupeds. Animals have to get along in the world somehow, and similar living conditions often force very remotely related types of animals to adopt similar habits. Their bodies modify themselves in conformity to habit and the exigencies of existence, and the limited number of ways in which the requirements of the situation may be met often forces quite dissimilar animals into identical modifications of certain bodily parts. An animal that lives in trees has to develop some means of maintaining its arboreal position; in some way or other it has to keep from falling off the tree. In the New World several very different and only remotely related animals, such as opossums, monkeys, kinkajous, and some kinds of anteaters have met this need in the same way by developing their tails into grasping or prehensile organs. Such similar functional modifications or adaptations must not be confounded with basic structural resemblances.

Often an organ or part of an animal that is changed or adapted during life by use or disuse—that is to say function—shows, in the prenatal or embryonic development of the animal, clear indications of its original form and primitive structure. Man has no external tail after birth, but at a certain period of foetal development a tail plainly projects beyond the body of the embryo. Before birth, however, that caudal remnant has been bent underneath and with its ligaments and muscles serves a new and essentially human purpose—to close the pelvic aperture and help support the viscera by forming part of the pelvic floor. In tracing relationships it is often helpful to study the embryology of different animals, since fundamental similarities of structure are often obscured in later life by different functions with consequent modifications in the form of the parts affected by those functions.

Another clue to relationship in embryology is found by observing the similarities and differences in the *manner* of development of animals before birth. It is a matter of common knowledge that the young of birds are hatched out of eggs, as are also young reptiles. On the other hand, the offspring of all higher animals including man are born alive from their mothers' wombs. Both the manner of reproduction and the processes of prenatal development are most significant in tracing relationship, and it is very obvious that an animal that lays eggs is not as closely akin to man as an animal the young of which are suckled at the breast.

Thus the process of tracing relationship is no more than the examination and recognition of fundamental resemblances in structure and development. The more detailed and far-reaching these resemblances are, the more closely related are the animals that manifest them. The science of taxonomy or zoological classification is simply the logical arrangement of animals into groups according to their mutual similarities. And these groups show relationship. But all criteria of relationship must be based upon essential identities of structure and development, which are called homologies, not upon the deceptive similarities due to function, which are called analogies.

Why Man is a Mammal

With a knowledge of the principles of zoological classification and of the outstanding physical characteristics of the various animals of the earth, it is simple enough to determine man's relationships in the animal kingdom. We cannot do better than adopt the point of view indicated by Huxley many years ago, when he suggested that we imagine ourselves scientific Saturnians, who, already acquainted with the animal life on this earth, are called upon to determine the affinities of "an erect and featherless biped, which some enterprising traveller . . . has brought from that distant planet for our inspection, well preserved, may be, in a cask of rum." [1]

Examining dispassionately our preserved specimen of a human being, we should ask ourselves whether it is "animal, vegetable, or mineral." And having decided that it belongs to the animal kingdom, and observing that it is an organism consisting not of one cell only but of many cells, we should classify it as one of the Metazoa. Turning the specimen so that the back is visible, we should observe the relief of the spinal column showing through the fleshy parts and would therefore not hesitate to say that this animal belongs to the vertebrate rather than the invertebrate subkingdom. We should then recall that the vertebrates consist of five classes: namely, fishes, amphibians, birds, reptiles, and mammals. But it would be obvious to us at once that our specimen could not be a fish, because it lacks gills through which to breathe and fins with which to swim. We should then consider the Class of Am-

[1] Huxley, *On the Relations of Man*, p. 95.

phibians, of which the young usually breathe for a time through gills and in which the paired fins of the fish are replaced by pectoral and pelvic limbs. The amphibians, we should remember, include such animals as frogs, toads, newts, and salamanders. Plainly, we should have to exclude our human specimen from this class on the basis of general anatomical resemblance, a decision that would be verified by the study of the reproductive organs. The absence of scales would lead us to eliminate the Class of Reptiles from the consideration of possible groups to which our specimen of man might be assigned. We should know, of course, that the blood of reptiles is cold and that of birds and mammals warm, but our preserved specimen of a man would tell us nothing of the temperature of its blood in life. A very cursory glance at our biped would impress upon us its lack of feathers—a fact which would inform us immediately that the animal is not a bird.

By a process of elimination we should now have arrived either at the conclusion that our specimen is a mammal or at that of the rustic at the zoo, who, upon seeing a kangaroo for the first time, exclaimed, turning away in disgust, "You can't fool me; there ain't no sich animile!"

Before having recourse to the latter desperate alternative, however, we should review the characteristics of the Class of Mammals. Mammals are warm-blooded, air-breathing animals with an epidermal covering of hair. Applying these tests to our specimen, we should have to pass over the matter of blood temperature, but would satisfy ourselves from the presence of the lungs that the animal in life breathed air, and we should also notice that the hairy covering, though scanty, is unmistakably present. To proceed a little farther, we should examine the lower jaw to find out whether it is hung directly from the skull as in mammals, or whether it articulates with the skull by the intervention of a separate quadrate bone as in reptiles or amphibians. Here again an examination would convince us that our canned human example exhibits in this respect the typical mammalian condition. If we were to follow out and examine our specimen with reference to every one of the known characters of mammals, we should find each one of them typically developed. But in our cursory examination we should have to observe only the presence of breasts on the ventral side of the body to conclude immediately that man is a mammal. For the most characteristic feature of the class and that from which it derives its name is the method of reproducing and nourishing the young. Birds and reptiles lay eggs and hatch them out or leave nature to incubate them, but the young of mammals are not developed within eggs but in the body of the mother. For a considerable period of time the embryo grows within the mother's womb and is then born in a relatively helpless condition and for some time is nourished by suckling at the mother's breasts (*mammae*). It is for this reason that the presence of breasts on the human specimen tells us at once that man is a mammal.

Having decided that man is a mammal, let us abandon our pretense of being "scientific Saturnians" and consequently confined to the examination of one preserved specimen in our attempt to classify man. While still maintaining a Saturnian impartiality, let us utilize for the further determination of man's affinities a fuller knowledge of his development, structure, and functioning, than could be gained from an isolated cadaver. The only point in pretending that we are inhabitants of another planet in classifying man is to ensure a rigidly judicial and impersonal attitude in our analysis. It is most essential that we forget that man is something "a little lower than the angels" and apply to the determination of his zoological affinities the same cold-blooded reasoning that we should employ in trying to trace the relationships of some new kind of bug. If we fail to attain this attitude of scientific detachment, of relentless quest for the truth wherever that search may take us; if we allow ourselves to be swayed by our emotions, by human vanity, or even by a realization that we ourselves are men, we cannot hope to eat of the fruit of the tree of knowledge without getting a very bad stomach-ache.

The Class of Mammals may be divided into three subclasses: the Prototheria, the Metatheria, and the Eutheria. The Prototheria entirely, and the Metatheria in large part, are confined to the Australian zoological region, which was cut off from Asia at a period before higher mammals had developed, and consequently preserves in its fauna some very archaic types. This region includes also New Guinea, Tasmania, and some other islands. The Prototheria consist of two living families, the duckbill, or Ornithorhynchus, and the spiny anteater, or Echidna. These animals represent in some respects a transition between reptiles and mammals, for they lay eggs and hatch them out and then suckle the young at the breast. The duckbill looks like a muskrat with a duck's bill and webbed feet. It is an aquatic animal. The Echidna is covered with quills. Both exhibit marked reptilian reminiscences in structure, in addition to their curiously mixed method of reproducing and nourishing the young. Obviously, man has no close affinities with these animals.

The Metatheria, or marsupials, are the pouched mammals, such as the kangaroo, opossum, bandicoot, et cetera. In the higher forms of Eutherian mammals the young are nourished in the uterus or womb of the mother by means of a special arrangement of the embryonic structures called the placenta ("cake"). This is a disk-like organ, one side of which is embedded in the wall of the maternal uterus, while the other side gives origin to the umbilical cord through which nourishment is carried to the foetus. After the young are delivered the placenta usually becomes detached and is also expelled. For this reason it is called "the after-birth." This reproductive arrangement, typical for higher mammals, is entirely lacking in animals that lay eggs and hatch them out. In marsupials the placenta is either undeveloped or functions for a few days only. The young are born in a foetal condition and after birth are transferred to a marsupium or pouch in the abdomen of the mother, where they remain until about a quarter grown, imbibing their nourishment from nipples conveniently placed in the inner side of this natural vest pocket. In the case of the kangaroo, an animal that may stand almost six feet high when fully grown, the young at birth are less than an inch long. The mother picks them up in her lips and puts them in her pouch. Marsupials are most instructive from an evolutionary standpoint, representing, as they do, an archaic method of reproduction and nourishment of the young. They are obviously no close relatives of ours.

The remaining subclass of the mammals is the Eutheria, or placental mammals. Clearly, man belongs somewhere in this group, because the foetal structure known as the placenta is well developed in the process of human reproduction. Eutherian mammals usually have two sets of teeth, a deciduous or milk set, and a permanent set. The milk teeth allow the young to chew at a time when the jaws are still too small to accommodate the permanent set of teeth.

Zoological classes are divided into subclasses and the subclasses into orders. Each successive subdivision contains animals more nearly alike and consequently more closely related. By a process of elimination we can determine man's nearest relations among the orders of Eutherian mammals. There are at least nine such orders. Let us begin with those that seem least like man.

First of all, then, we may consider the Edentata, including such animals as sloths, anteaters, and armadillos. This order derives its name from the fact that in some of its species the teeth are very degenerate and lack enamel, but few of them are really edentulous or toothless. In some respects this order seems to be very primitive, and the armadillo recalls reptiles in its development of a carapace made of horny plates. Rudyard Kipling recognized the anomalous position of the armadillo in his *Just So Stories*, where he accounts for that animal by making the tortoise (a reptile) learn to bend his back and curl up, and the hedgehog (a mammal) learn to swim and develop scales. Clearly, the animals of this group are very far removed from man.

The Cetacea include the whales. They are sea-dwelling mammals with large heads and fish-like bodies almost devoid of hair. The fore limbs have become paddle-like and the collar bones (clavicles) are absent. The hind limbs have disappeared entirely, and the pelvis is represented by a vestige only. The teeth may be absent and be replaced by sheets of baleen (whalebone). I remember when this whalebone was used for stiffening in ladies' corsets, but now the lady's waist has gone the way of the whale's pelvis. Perhaps the "noble and generous Cetacean" is now allowed to strain his food through his baleen in peace, like our grandfathers with their "cavalry" moustaches.

The Sirenia are also aquatic mammals with porpoise-like bodies and a scattered covering of hairs. In the arrangements of their limbs they are similar to the whales, but they have teeth. They include such uncommon animals as the manatee and the dugong. They are herbivorous. In spite of their poetic-sounding name, they are ugly, awkward creatures not a bit like Lorelei, and very remote from man.

The Ungulata are four-footed, ground-dwelling animals. The end segments of the digits usually terminate in solid, horny hoofs upon which the weight of the body falls. The hoofs are homologous with our finger and toe nails. The number of digits is often reduced. These animals frequently have horns and they are usually herbivorous. The order includes all sorts of familiar quadrupeds: deer, antelope, cattle, swine, horses, rhinoceroses, et cetera. The hoofed and horned animals are especially adapted for habits unlike ours and in their general structure diverge widely from the human type.

The name of the next order, the Carnivora, implies that these animals usually live on flesh. Generally they have a furry covering and the digits of hands and feet are not less than four in number and provided with claws which, in some families, may be extended or retracted at will. The canine or eye teeth are often very long and it is by means of these teeth and claws that the animal holds and tears its prey. Like the whales and ungulates, the carnivores have no collar bones. Among them are all the members of the cat and dog families, bears, seals, and others. A few years ago some enthusiastic but zoologically ill-informed medical men attempted to recognize two types of man, a "carnivorous" type— tall, slender, nervous, and prone to flesh-eating—and a "herbivorous" type—squat, stolid, paunchy, and phlegmatic, perhaps almost ruminative. The "herbivorous" type was not supposed to feed upon grass like Nebuchadnezzar, as the name would imply, but upon vegetable food. It was even hinted that the carnivorous type might have descended from cats and the herbivorous type from cows. But these efforts to trace a relationship between man and the carnivores and ungulates have not been well received in scientific circles. When a lady is referred to as a "cat" or a gentleman as a "bull," the appellations must be considered metaphorical, not phylogenetic.

The Order Rodentia includes rats, rabbits, squirrels, and their ilk. They are vegetable-feeding animals, usually small in bulk, with furry or spiny covering and provided with claws. The incisor teeth are chisel-shaped and very large, and are used for gnawing into wood. These incisor teeth grow out as fast as they are worn down by usage. Evidently man is not a rodent, not even if he has "buck" teeth.

The Order Cheiroptera is devoted to the bats. Their fore limbs are modified so as to support wings, the bones being greatly elongated and a broad web of skin extending to the hind limbs. The collar bones are well developed, but the inner bone of the forearm, the ulna, is reduced to a vestige. Apart from the wing modifications, the body of a bat is astoundingly like that of a monkey, and some of the early classification-ists mistakenly grouped the bats with the apes and monkeys. We now leave the bats to themselves.

The Order Insectivora includes, as the name implies, a group of mammals that, ordinarily, are insect-eaters. They are usually small and nocturnal in their habits. Most of them live on the ground, but some of them are arboreal (e.g., tree shrews), and some of them burrow (e.g., moles). Shrews, hedgehogs, and moles are the best known of this very diversified group. The insectivores show in many respects very primitive mammalian characteristics. The brain is exceedingly simple; the nose is prolonged into a short muzzle; the integument is furry or spiny, and there are usually five digits on the hands and the feet. Collar bones are present. One would scarcely select such a grubby animal as a mole or a hedgehog for his ancestor. A dear old lady who wandered into one of my summer-school courses listened to a somewhat detailed deduction of man's zoological relationships and then asked me if it were not possible that man had descended from the lion, "because he is such a noble and kingly beast." But it is hardly safe to trace relationship by soul affinities. Insectivores are lowly little brutes and far removed from man as he is today, but it is highly probable that some extinct, primitive, and generalized members of this order stand in our direct ancestral line, though very far back. From the early insectivores were descended the bats and also the earliest of the Order of Primates, to which we are now reduced in our search for man's nearest relations.

Why Man is a Primate

The most outstanding characteristic of the Primate Order is the possession of prehensile hands and feet, adapted for arboreal life. Most arboreal animals maintain themselves in the trees by embedding their claws in the bark. Primates grasp the branches by opposing the thumb to the fingers and the great toe to the lesser toes. When you grasp an iron pipe of so large a diameter that your fingers cannot span it, you place the four fingers on one side of the pipe and the thumb on the other side and grip the pipe between fingers and thumb. The ability to oppose the thumb to the fingers in this way, and not only to grip rounded surfaces in the circlet of the thumb and fingers, but also to bring the ball of the thumb into contact with the tips of the fingers, is a prime requisite for all the delicate movements of the hands that have resulted in the mechanical supremacy of man.[2] The primates can, as a rule, oppose the great toe to the lesser toes in a similar fashion. But man cannot do this. Savages and people who go barefoot often retain a considerable mobility of the toes and to some extent the power of prehension. But they are never able to oppose the great toe to the lesser toes. Nevertheless, as we shall see, the foot of man gives evidence in its structure and development of having been derived from a grasping foot such as the primates possess.

Another general characteristic of the Primate Order is a well-developed clavicle (collar bone), a concomitant of the great mobility of the forearms.

The clavicle serves as a strut or brace to keep the shoulders fixed in lateral movements of the arms. If you break your collar bone, the shoulder joint slumps down over the chest. Man has this well-developed collar bone and so also has the bat. The bat's clavicle is necessary as a brace for the wing joint in the movements of flight.

The digits of primates are provided with flat nails, instead of hoofs or claws. This development is evidently connected with the grasping function of the hands and feet. Claws would be out of place on opposable digits and would destroy the efficacy of movements of opposition of the thumb and the great toe to the lesser digits. All of the primates have developed the flat finger and toe nails, with a few exceptions that will be noted. Insectivores and arboreal rodents usually have claws, and some

[2] I retain the term "opposability" in spite of the conscientious objections of Professor F. Wood Jones (*Man's Place*, pp. 197–198), who would restrict its use to such thumbs as may be rotated so as to be placed in the palm of the hand with the nail facing directly upward from the palm. I cannot "palm" my thumb in this fashion and such a movement, if possible, would be useless. Yet I can and do "oppose" my thumbs to my fingers and so do most primates.

of the lowliest primates preserve on one or more digits reminiscences of their lower mammalian origin. Man evidently conforms to the primate description with respect to his nails. The flatter and broader your nails, the more human you are.

The breasts of primates are usually two in number and placed high up on the thorax; that is to say, they are pectoral in position. A few of the lowlier members of the order have more than one pair of breasts, the lower pair being situated far down on the abdomen or in the groin. Supplementary pairs of breasts occur occasionally in man also, but only as anomalies or freaks of reversion.

The brain in the Primate Order varies widely in its development, but may attain great size and intricacy of pattern. The lowest of the primates have somewhat simple brains, but the higher forms show a large development of the forebrain or cerebrum, the surface of which is folded and wrinkled into extensive convolutions. These folds and wrinkles increase the area of the cerebral cortex (bark), which is the seat of nervous activity. Man has an essentially primate brain in form and pattern, really a super-primate brain, the development of which is approximated only by the great anthropoid apes.

It will be noted that these outstanding characteristics of the Primate Order are quite generalized and variable. They even seem a trifle vague. The primates remained for a long period of time in a relatively generalized and unspecialized state of development. This lack of specialization kept them adaptable and made possible the ultimate high development of the more progressive members. Early specialization and overspecialization is likely to lead to extinction in the animal world. For, changing conditions of food supply, climate, or other factors of physical environment find the overspecialized animal unable to cope with them. We find it more profitable to keep our children in school and learning for a long period of time, rather than to force their development by casting them upon their own resources at a tender age. One of our educational principles is that a child will go farther by developing his body and mind in school and by learning to profit by the experience of others during the period of childhood and adolescence, than by exhausting himself during the growth period in earning his living and in learning by his own experience. The primates went to school for a long period. This school was in the trees. It was arboreal life that provided for them their elementary and secondary education. But man was the only primate that went to college, although the anthropoid apes may be said at least to have flunked the entrance examinations.

Excepting the non-prehensile character of his foot, man answers to the general description of a primate. It would not be in accordance with principles of zoological classification to exclude man from the Primate Order because of this one divergent character, for almost any family or species is likely to show one or more exceptional features due to specializations or to variation. It should be understood that zoological classifications are based upon a totalling up of significant morphological hereditary resemblances, not upon any single character. Of course, if man laid eggs instead of producing his young alive, that single feature would make us hesitate to include him in the Class of Mammals. But if, as in the case of the duckbill, the young were hatched from eggs and then suckled at the breast, we should have to conclude that man was a primitive and transitional form of mammal in whom the full development of the features that characterize the class had not yet taken place. Transitions from one zoological group to another are often gradual. And it is the continuous character of animal differentiation that leads to the hypothesis that one animal group has developed from another by the process called evolution. Zoological groupings are significant combinations of bodily homologies which indicate close relationship in those that possess them; they are qualitative judgments of similarity, but they are not mathematical equations, incorrectness in one element of which destroys the validity of the whole. The development of a new feature, or the loss of an old organ, or the modification of an old part to serve a new function—any one of these changes sets apart the animal group that possesses it from a kindred group that lacks it, but sets it apart only to the extent of indicating that the relationship between the groups is more remote by reason of their difference with respect to the character. The implication is that in course of time the two groups have grown away from each other.

We may then assign man provisionally to the Order of Primates, which, apart from other considerations, is the court of last resort, since he obviously cannot be admitted to any other known order. However, to say that man is indeed a primate on the basis of his conforming in general to the description of that order is not enough for the seeker of exact relationships. Such a genealogist must trace in detail the lineage that he wishes to reconstruct; he must, at any rate, become more definite and adduce more truths, the more specific he becomes in his statements of relationship. If I say that I am a descendant of Abraham, you will perhaps accept the statement as true on my face value. But, if I assert that I am a descendant of Abraham Lincoln, you will require of me more specific genealogical evidence.

The Order of Primates may be divided into three suborders: the

Lemuroidea, the Tarsioidea, and the Anthropoidea. The Lemuroidea are distinguished from the higher suborders by certain peculiarities. The bony ring that surrounds the eyeball and is called the orbit has no back wall in the lemurs, whereas in the Tarsioidea and the Anthropoidea this back wall is almost complete. In the Lemuroidea the eye may be compared with a ball within a ring; in the Tarsioidea and the Anthropoidea it is more like a ball within a bowl. In the Lemuroidea, moreover, the eyes are directed outward (Fig. 4, A, B); the field of vision is distinct for each eye; whereas in the Anthropoidea the eyes are directed forward and the fields of vision overlap to such an extent that a stereoscopic image results. In the Lemuroidea the opening of the tear duct is on the facial surface, outside of the bony orbit of the eye, but, in the Anthropoidea, this orifice, called the lachrymal foramen, is within the orbit. This has nothing to do with weeping, however. Lemurs do not weep. Neither walruses nor crocodiles weep. I think man is the only cry-baby in the animal kingdom.

The number and form of the teeth are very important in zoological classification, because the teeth are fairly rigid and conservative parts of the body and are not easily modified away from their ancestral patterns. Lemuroids usually have, on each side, above and below, two incisors or biting teeth, one canine or piercing tooth (often called the "eye tooth"), and in the grinding series three premolars, or bicuspids, and three molars. The higher families in the suborder Anthropoidea invariably have but two premolars, above and below on each side. In the lemuroids also the lower incisors are usually directed almost horizontally forward. These "procumbent" incisors may be connected with the alleged habit of combing the fur with the lower front teeth, but, since these teeth are so close together that they cannot go through the fur, it is more probable that the so-called incisor comb is used rather for scraping. In the higher primates the incisor teeth tend to be more nearly vertical.

The brains of lemuroids are usually rather simple. The cerebral hemispheres are not developed backward sufficiently to overhang the cerebellum and the frontal lobes are very small. The skull does not balance upon the spinal column as in man, but is suspended from occipital condyles (bony knobs) that are situated far back on the skull base as in other lower mammals. The hind limbs of the lemuroids are in most cases somewhat longer than the fore limbs and the animals are usually pronograde, that is, they go on all fours. Some of them, however, have adopted a hopping gait. Hands and feet have each five digits provided with opposable thumbs and great toes, and flat nails. The second toes of the hind feet, however, usually bear claws. Some think that these claws have been retained for toilet purposes (i.e., scratching). The members of this suborder are all arboreal and generally nocturnal in their habits. The word "lemur" signifies "ghost" and the lemurs are so called from their habit of flitting ghost-like among the trees by night.

Whereas the higher primates, with the exception of a single family, usually bear but one young at a birth, some kinds of lemurs are said to produce litters of two or three offspring. Accommodating nature has provided the female of such species with an extra pair of breasts situated in the groin, in addition to the usual pair on the thorax. Lowly animals usually produce large numbers of young at a birth or lay numerous eggs, which are hatched out by incubation or by the heat of the sun. Many of the eggs may fail to mature; the majority of the young may perish; the continuance of the species is assured by the prodigal number of offspring produced. But, in higher forms, such as mammals, the young develop for a longer time within the body of the mother and after birth require maternal care because of a longer period of infancy. This protracted infancy implies an ultimately higher development of the animal. In higher types of mammals, the prolonged period of embryonic development and the large size of the brain of the embryo may limit still further the number of young produced at a birth, since the size of the maternal uterus may preclude the possibility of simultaneous development of several foetuses. It is apparent then that the retention of multiple births is, in the lemuroids, an indication of lowly organization.[3]

[3] Professor Frederic Wood Jones, a chronic insurgent among students of primate evolution, has revived the earlier opinion that the lemurs should be removed from the Primate Order and relegated to a group with the tree shrews whom they closely resemble. (Jones, *Man's Place*, pp. 69–144). Following Pocock, he separates the Lemuroidea from the Tarsioidea and the Anthropoidea on the basis of the retention by the first-named group of a primitive naked snout or rhinarium. This naked and moist muzzle of the lemurs is continued to the upper lip by a middle strip of hairless skin, underlying which the upper lip is closely tethered to the upper jaw by a bridle or frenulum. It is, therefore, not protrusive or eversible. The nostrils of this primitive mammalian snout are semicircular clefts, directed sideways. In the tarsioids and all of the rest of the primates the nostrils are completely ringed around with naked skin, but the moist, glandular muzzle is absent, and the upper lip is not so tightly attached to the jaw. Wood Jones says that this latter feature allows the tarsioids and other primates to drink by sucking instead of by lapping. Other distinguishing features of the lemuroids mentioned by him are: (a) the bony tube or ring leading to the interior of the ear is enclosed in a large inflated spherical chamber, whereas in higher primates this bony ring (the tympanic annulus) is entirely outside of the chamber (auditory bulla); (b) lemurs have placentae that are bell-shaped or diffuse and are not expelled after birth, whereas other primates have disk-shaped placentae that are deciduate (i.e., they come away after birth). These and other features Wood Jones regards as lemurine specializations that prevent these animals from being regarded as ancestral forms to the tarsiers, monkeys, and apes. In most or all of these features, the lemurs agree with the tree shrews, who closely resemble them but are more primitive. He therefore unites the lemurs with the tree shrews and dismisses them from the assemblage of primates.

This interesting but academic argument has little importance for purposes of this

None of the lemurs are large. They range in size from that of a cat to that of a mouse. They have furry coverings and, usually, long bushy tails.

Lemuroids are mostly omnivorous in their habits. Their diet consists of insects, fruit, nuts, berries, leaves, shoots, birds' eggs, et cetera. The importance of a generalized diet is that it permits an animal to survive under more varied conditions of food supply than are possible for animals specialized in this respect. Any one who has ever lived in a boarding-house will recognize the truth of this principle.

The present-day lemuroids are found only in the Old World. The majority inhabit the tropical forests of Africa and of the island of Madagascar. They are also found in the Indonesian islands and as far east as the Philippines. They do not occur in the continent of Europe nor in most parts of Asia.

Although it is obvious that man is not of the Suborder Lemuroidea, it is worth while to study these humble primates because they represent perhaps the nearest approach to the "contemporary ancestors" of all of the more highly developed families of the order. The lemuroids consist of several families, including the true lemurs, the galagos, the indrises, the lorises, pottos, et cetera. The true lemur has an elongated snout and facially looks something like a fox; its ears are erect and pointed; it is very active in the trees and when running along the boughs uses its opposable thumbs and great toes for grasping and clinging (Plate 1a). The lorises are notable for their slowness of movements and for the absence of tails. The large and practically tailless indri lemur of Madagascar is said to walk upright. One kind of lemur, the mouse lemur, has developed a habit of aestivation, apparently unique among primates.

---

work. Most authorities agree that monkeys, apes, and man have developed from tarsioids rather than lemuroids, and whether the tarsioids developed from primitive lemuroids rather than from some primitive type of insectivore need not concern us deeply. For purposes of this book, we may adhere to orthodox opinion and leave the Lemuroidea as a suborder of the primates.

An anonymous correspondent of mine, who writes me from Hugh Town, Scilly Isles, and calls himself "The Rhyming Taxonomist," offers me the following from his fortunately unpublished lucubrations:

THE LEMUR

The lemur is a lowly brute;
His primate status some dispute.
He has a damp and longish snout
With lower front teeth leaning out.
He parts his fur with this comb-jaw,
And scratches with a single claw
That still adorns a hinder digit
Wherever itching makes him fidget.
He is arboreal and omnivorous;
From more about him, Lord deliver us!

Aestivation is equivalent to hibernation, except that the former implies sleeping through the summer or dry season. The mouse lemur has developed a mass of fat at the base of the tail, and during the dry season it remains in a state of partially suspended animation, subsisting upon this reserve larder.

The most aberrant member of the lemuroid suborder is the aye-aye, which belongs in a family by itself, the Cheiromyidae. This animal is found only in the island of Madagascar. The aye-aye is about the size of a cat. It has become specialized in a rodent-like manner. The front teeth are reduced to two above and two below, and these are long and chisel-shaped as in rodents. The fingers of the hand are thin and elongated, especially the second finger, which resembles a piece of bent wire. Observation of this animal in captivity seems to show that the wire-like middle fingers and the chisel-shaped incisors are functional adaptations to a specialized habit of feeding. The aye-aye lives on grubs. With its chisel-like teeth it bites down into a grub hole, then introduces its wire-like middle finger into the hole and impales the grub upon it, just as a tree-man pokes a piece of wire into a hole in a tree and extracts therefrom a leopard-borer. But the aye-aye eats the grub.[4] Here is an example of narrow specialization that effectually limits the possibility of higher development.

Very different from the lemuroids is the little animal called Tarsius spectrum. It is usually classified by modern taxonomists in a separate suborder called the Tarsioidea. The tarsiers are diminutive animals living in the East Indies. They are about the size of a small rat and are completely arboreal and nocturnal (Plate 1b). The features that distinguish them from lemurs are: the more nearly frontal position of the eyes and the fact that the back walls of the bony orbits are almost

---

[4] Here is another of the prosodic misdemeanors of my eccentric correspondent, who sometimes refers to himself as "The Scilly Linnaeus":

THE AYE-AYE

In Madagascar dwells the Aye-Aye,
Who would be better named the Why-Why.
His chisel teeth recall a rabbit
And are connected with the habit
Of digging grubs out from their holes
In boughs of trees or even boles.
He pokes his wirelike middle finger
Into the ends where larvae linger,
Impales them on this one-tined spear,
And forks them in with right good cheer.
By now you doubtless have surmized
The Aye-Aye is too specialized
For living on one kind of grub.
If this should fail—"Aye, there's the rub."

complete as in the higher primates; a larger development of the occipital lobes of the brain so that these overlap the cerebellum to a greater extent than in the lemuroids; a more anteriorly situated foramen magnum and occipital condyles, such that the skull is more nearly balanced upon the spinal column (Fig. 4, p. 78); a less diffuse and more discoidal placenta. The placenta in the tarsier is also deciduate (that is, it comes away after birth), whereas in lemurs this is not the case. In the features that distinguish the tarsiers from lemuroids, the former approach the characteristics of the higher suborder, the Anthropoidea, and by some classificationists the tarsiers are assigned to that suborder. In some respects they are more primitive than the lemuroids and in others more advanced and specialized. As we shall see, there is good reason for supposing that the higher developments in the Primate Order have occurred through the advance of a group of tarsioid ancestors.

The existing tarsiers are adapted for hopping in the trees. The tarsus, which forms the arch of the foot, is enormously elongated in these animals. The digits of the hands and feet are provided with sucker-disk pads which enable the animal to get a good grip as it leaps from bough to bough. The tarsier usually assumes a semi-erect position. Its hands are used not only for grasping but also to convey food to its mouth. Its snout, possibly in conformity with this habit of hand-feeding, is very much shortened, and its eyes are of enormous size (Plate 1b). The enlargement of the eyes, which is connected with nocturnal vision, has involved the growth forward of outer rims of the huge orbits, so that the fields of vision overlap, although the animal has probably not attained stereoscopic vision. However, the displacement of eyes from the sides of the head toward the front is associated with a narrowing of the nasal space between the orbits, so that the olfactory sensitiveness of the animal is probably decreased. Smelling is not as important for an arboreal animal as is seeing, and in the higher arboreal primates the visual areas of the brain are developed at the expense of the more primitive olfactory areas. The tarsier sits up and takes notice to an extent that lemurs do not. It can turn its head directly backward. It foreshadows higher primate development.

It is evident that man's place in the Primate Order must be sought beyond the Lemuroidea and the Tarsioidea. In the Suborder Anthropoidea the eyes are swivelled still farther forward toward the frontal plane, and the back wall of the bony orbit is almost complete. The tear duct is within the orbit of the eye. The occipital lobes of the cerebrum overhang the cerebellum; only one pair of breasts, pectoral in position, occurs; and, except in one family, the digits are never clawed. The brains are relatively larger than those of lemuroids, and the cerebrum is usually wrinkled or convoluted, in contrast to its primitive smoothness in the tarsier and in some lemurs.

The living members of the Suborder Anthropoidea include the New World monkeys, the Old World monkeys and apes, and, provisionally, man. The New World primates are often called the Platyrrhini, or "broad-nosed," because their nostrils are usually separated by a wide septum and are directed outward. The Old World monkeys are called Catarrhini, because their nostrils are usually directed downward and the nasal septum is narrower.

The American monkeys consist of two families: the Hapalidae and the Cebidae. Like the lemurs, they have three premolar or bicuspid teeth on each side and in both jaws.

The small, squirrel-like marmosets (Plate 2a) of the family Hapalidae are either the most primitive or the most degenerate of monkeys. They have claws on all of their digits except the great toe, and they run spirally up and down the trunks of trees, digging these claws into the bark. The thumb is not opposable. Many details of marmoset anatomy recall lemuroids or even tree shrews. The tail is non-prehensile in contrast with its grasping specialization in many of the Cebidae. It will be remembered that the marmoset is also the only primate higher than a lemur that ordinarily produces more than one offspring at a birth. Gregory, however, calls attention to the typically New World monkey characteristics of marmoset teeth and especially the shortening of the dental arch and the suppression of the third molars. The diminished projection of the jaws gives the marmoset a straighter profile than any other primate below man. Gregory argues that the claws of the marmoset are only secondarily bent-up nails and that by virtue of the dental reduction and for other reasons this little monkey must be considered degenerative and reversionary. Yet a larger group of primatologists, including J. Beattie, Wood Jones, and Le Gros Clark, maintain that the marmoset's claws are real claws and offer a good deal of collateral anatomical evidence of the primitive structure of the beast. They seem to have the better of the argument, but the real lesson for the student of primate evolution is that a single group in the order may remain primitive and generalized in most respects, recalling preprimate types, and, at the same time, acquire very advanced and specialized features in one or more bodily parts.

The Family Cebidae includes the rest of the American monkeys, of which there are many kinds. Like the Hapalidae, they have an additional premolar tooth in each jaw. Their brains are relatively large and very well developed. Unlike any of the rest of the primates, the Cebidae often have prehensile tails, adapted for grasping. These tails are long, and the free end is curved. In the concavity of the curve there is no hair, and this portion is used as a fifth grasping member and for suspending the animals from trees (Plate 2b). This is evidently an arboreal adaptation peculiar among the primates to this family. Strangely enough, however, prehensile tails are extremely common among the arboreal animals of South America, in orders far removed from the primates. The opossum had a prehensile tail, and the opposum is a marsupial. The raccoon and the kinkajou, which are carnivores, likewise possess this grasping tail. So do certain anteaters, which are edentates, as well as does the armadillo, also a member of that lowly order of mammals. Then there are the arboreal and prehensile-tailed porcupines of South America—rodents. Finally, there are prehensile-tailed snakes which do not belong to the Class Mammalia at all. In the Old World, on the other hand, prehensile-tailed arboreal animals are very rare. One may mention the chameleon —a reptile—certain snakes, and the long-snouted phalanger—an arboreal marsupial from Australia. Why should prehensile tails have been endemic in many classes, orders, and species in South America and so rare elsewhere? Dr. W. K. Gregory has suggested to me that a significant fact in this connection is the flooding of the land surface in the tropical forest area of South America. Lack of dry ground beneath the trees may possibly have been associated with extraordinary adaptations for arboreal life in the forest-dwelling animals.

There are a number of genera and species of Cebidae. Perhaps the most typical are the capuchin or cebus monkeys. These are the common or garden variety of hand organ monkeys oftenest seen in captivity. Their snouts are short, their faces pensive and intelligent, their braincases rounded and well developed; they have opposable thumbs and great toes and slightly prehensile tails. They have long, projecting canine teeth, and the hind limbs are somewhat longer than the fore limbs. All of the Cebidae are completely arboreal, but the most highly specialized for aerial gymnastics are the spider monkeys (Ateles) (Plate 3). These animals have most completely prehensile tails, which are so strong that the entire body may be suspended by them. They even serve as a fifth hand to convey objects to the mouth. Spider monkeys have slender bodies and long limbs, the arms exceeding the legs in length. They have developed a habit of swinging from bough to bough by their arms. The elongation of the arms is related to this form of progression. The fingers are long and hooked, and the thumb is rudimentary or absent. It is apparent that an animal using its hands for swinging from bough to bough would be likely to stub its thumbs in such movements if its thumbs were long. Certainly, it is in connection with the hook-like specialization of the fingers that the thumbs have atrophied and disappeared, as is also the case with some of the Old World monkeys. However, the thumbless Old World monkeys are not arm-swingers, or brachiators.

The largest, most brilliantly colored, most vociferous, and perhaps the stupidest of the American monkeys are the howlers (Mycetes, Alouatta). These are stocky brutes with prehensile tails and jaws developed, apparently, at the expense of their brain-cases. The throat has a goiterous and swollen appearance, owing to an expansion of the hyoid bone and of the larynx. The sides and hinder angles of the lower jaws are greatly enlarged to accommodate this vocal apparatus (Fig. 5C, p. 85). The howlers make a most prodigious and terrifying noise but are quite harmless. Why is it that loud voices go with meager wits, even in monkeys? I suppose that the howler bluffs his way through life by bellowing and roaring. He scares off animals that bite by his formidable bark.

Other American monkeys are the squirrel monkeys, the woolly monkeys, the teetees, et cetera. Most of these animals live in troops and are vegetarian or frugivorous.

The presumption that American primates, because of their superior brain development, are more intelligent than the lemuroids or the tarsier is supported by almost no experimental work, but is probably valid. There is a marked difference of opinion between psychologists who have worked with New World and Old World monkeys as to which group is the more intelligent.

Some years ago, there appeared in various popular periodicals accounts of the discovery of a new anthropoid ape in the forests near the Tarra River, in the Motilones districts of Colombia and Venezuela, South America.[5] A Frenchman, Dr. Francis de Loys, was travelling in this region in 1917 when his party was attacked by two great tailless apes, who advanced to the assault defecating in their hands and hurling this disagreeable ammunition at their foes. One of these apes, an adult female, was shot. The other escaped. The body was said to measure more than five feet in height (157 centimeters), and its weight was guessed to be more than 112 pounds. Unfortunately, the skin and bones were not brought out. The cook used the skull for a salt box, and the salt is said to have

    5 Honoré, "Un nouveau singe," p. 451.
    de Loys, "A Gap Filled," p. 1040.
    Montandon, "Un singe actuel," p. 268–269.
    Joleaud, "Remarques sur l'evolution," pp. 269–273.

dissolved the bones! A picture alleged to represent this anthropoid shows it sitting on a box. It looks suspiciously like a spider monkey and seems to have rudimentary thumbs. The tail is either missing or behind the box. There is no scale in the photograph. We shall have to secure better evidence than has been presented before we receive this scatological relative into the anthropoid family.

There are persistent reports of the existence of a giant spider monkey, provided with the usual prehensile tail, in the area of Colombia and Venezuela. An American engineer, who worked for oil companies in this region, sent me a picture postcard showing an alleged specimen of this giant monkey sitting on a stump with its prehensile tail in plain sight. In its hand this animal held a hen's egg—supposedly to give an idea of the size of the hand and of the whole beast relative to this familiar object. This monkey was stated to measure 3 feet 6 inches in height and to weigh 72 pounds. Our informant expressed his willingness to try to shoot a specimen of this monkey, embalm it in formaldehyde, and ship it to us for study. Up to the present, no pickled giant spider monkey has been forthcoming. Meanwhile, another engineer has asserted that the photograph was faked, in so far as the egg held in the monkey's hand is not that of an ordinary domestic hen but of a much smaller fowl. The problem awaits clarification.

The higher primates of the Old World, aside from man, consist of three families, the Cercopithecidae or Old World monkeys, the Hylobatidae, or gibbons, and the Simiidae, or anthropoid apes. These families have the same number and kinds of teeth as has man: two incisors, one canine, two premolars, and three molars, on each side of both jaws.

The Cercopithecidae include many genera and species. All have callous areas on the buttocks, devoid of hair, which are called ischial callosities. The ischium is the haunch bone upon which the body rests when the animal sits. These callosities of the skin occur at the points beneath which the haunch bones are flattened into broad tuberosities. Athough it seems that these areas are primarily sitting pads and are sensory in function, like callous places on the palms and soles, they seem to have been modified into secondary sexual characters in some of these monkeys. In baboons, mandrills, macaques, and some others of the Cercopithecidae, the callosities are brilliantly colored—pink, red, or purple—and are involved in the cyclic changes of the sexual skin. The latter is a naked area of the perinaeum around the anal and genital region that reddens and swells in females, mainly during the first half of the cycle, under the activation, probably, of a secretion of the growing ovarian follicle. The swellings are often enormous, turgid, and bright red and extend to, surround, or even include, the ischial callosities.

The Cercopithecidae usually have cheek pouches in which food may be crammed for subsequent and leisurely swallowing. The front limbs are shorter than the hind limbs; the whole sole of the foot is applied to the ground in walking. Wood Jones says that the nails on the hands and feet are less arched in the Old World monkeys than in the New World monkeys and that the former have greater mobility of the thumbs and great toes than the latter. The tail in the Cercopithecidae may be very short or very long. It is never prehensile. There are two subfamilies of the Cercopithecidae: the Semnopithecinae and the Cercopithecinae.

The Semnopithecinae include langurs, guerezas, proboscis monkeys, snub-nosed monkeys, et cetera. Usually these monkeys have no cheek pouches; the ischial callosities are small, and the thumb is vestigial or absent. Most of them feed upon leaves and have pouched stomachs, recalling the arrangements in animals that chew the cud. Old World monkeys that possess cheek pouches have simple stomachs, and it has been suggested that the first compartment of the sacculated stomach replaces the cheek pouches. The Semnopithecinae are arboreal and usually have long tails. Some of these monkeys are brilliantly colored. The langurs live in southeastern Asia and the neighboring islands, whereas the guerezas are inhabitants of Africa. A remarkable member of this subfamily is the proboscis monkey of Borneo, which is a large chestnut-colored beast. Males of this genus have the tip of the nose enlarged and overhanging the upper lip. This protuberant nasal tip is capable of dilation. However, an elevated nasal root is confined to man and the gorilla among the primates, and man alone has a high nasal bridge. In northwestern China, Tonkin, and eastern Tibet, there is a snub-nosed monkey of the langur type which lives in mountains where snow lies the greater part of the year. The tip of its short nose is decidedly retroussé.

The Cercopithecinae are the second subfamily of the Cercopithecidae. They include baboons, mandrills, drills, the so-called black apes of Celebes, macaques, guenons, mangabeys, and patas monkeys. In this subfamily, the tail is of variable length; cheek pouches and ischial callosities are always present; the thumb is well developed. The guenons, which constitute the largest genus of the primates with more than 80 species or races, are brilliantly colored, arboreal monkeys found in most forested areas of Africa. Not much is known of their habits, but they are said to go about in companies of a dozen or less, led by an old male who gives signals. Mangabeys and patas monkeys are also African tree-dwellers. The "black ape" of Celebes is a little-known monkey that seems to be intermediate between macaques and baboons. It has a markedly protruding snout, but its nostrils open some distance back from the tip, contrary to their position in true baboons. The tail is said to be reduced to a mere tubercle. This monkey resembles macaques in being fruit-eating and arboreal.

The macaque is the commonest monkey of southeastern Asia and the Indo-Malayan archipelago and the favorite laboratory animal for medical experimentation. The species are very numerous, and the island forms differ considerably from each other. Macaques usually have stout, compact bodies with tails of varying lengths and relatively short limbs with well-developed thumbs and great toes. The snout is projecting, and the nostrils open short of the tip of the muzzle. Cheek pouches and ischial callosities are present, the latter often large. The sexual skin is well developed in most macaques and has been extensively studied in its cyclic changes. It has been said that more is known of the reproductive mechanisms of the macaque than those of man or of all of the rest of the primates put together. Much is also known of the intelligence of this animal, which is considerable, and of its social behavior, which is nasty.

The Barbary "apes" are really macaques—the only western survivors of that group. They dwell in the mountains of Morocco and Algeria and in a preserve on the Rock of Gibraltar as unwilling emigrants from across the Strait. They are particularly notable for the fact that their tails are reduced to a mere rudiment without any vertebrae—presumably the excuse for the misnomer "ape." It is said that the ancients derived their knowledge of human anatomy from dissections of this monkey.

The baboons, mandrills, and drills are big, powerful monkeys with bestially elongated snouts and large ischial callosities. The sexual skin is remarkably developed and in females undergoes pronounced changes during the sexual cycle. The various kinds of baboons inhabit rocky and treeless sections of East Africa and South Africa, but some are found in Arabia. The mandrill and the drill live in West Africa. Both the mandrill and the drill are distinguished from ordinary baboons by the reduction of the tail to a mere stump and by the development of longitudinal bony swellings on both sides of the nose. In the mandrill, these rostral ridges that flank the nose are covered with bright blue hair, while the top of the nose is red, the tip scarlet, and at the other end of the animal there is a similar color combination—violet ischial callosities and a scarlet sexual skin. The drill is more restrained in coloration. Its face is black and its callosities only are red. Mandrills and drills exaggerate the tremendous muzzle, huge canine teeth, deep lower jaws, and small, flat brain-cases with overhanging bony brow-ridges that generally characterize the baboon group. All of these animals walk flat on the palms of their hands and the soles of their feet and have well-developed thumbs and great toes. They seem to have been secondarily adapted for quadrupedal gait upon the ground by the equalization of length of fore and hind limbs and by re-elongation of the snout. Little is known of the habits of the mandrill and drill in the wild, and they certainly dwell in areas that ought to have an abundance of trees. The baboons, however, are terrestrial perforce.

Baboons live in large troops, and an extensive folklore has grown up about their social organization. They have been reported to make forays upon the crops and orchards of African farmers, moving in regular formations, with advance guards, rear guards, and flanking parties of old males, and with the females and young in the center. They are also supposed to post sentinels at strategic spots when robbing orchards so that an alarm may be given when danger threatens. It is also asserted that baboons attack flocks and tear open the stomachs of young lambs to eat the curdled milk therein. Almost all of this lore has been discredited by modern scientific observers. There is one possibly authentic story of a legless railway signalman in South Africa who trained a baboon to push him down to his signal box on a handcar and then to pull the levers that threw the switches. There is another of a bricklayer who had a baboon hod-carrier until the labor unions objected. The statement that the ancient Egyptians taught baboons to pick dates is probably true, since the natives of Sumatra train macaques to pick cocoanuts. My favorite tale is of the pet baboon who was left by his master to watch a pot of chicken stewing over a campfire. Tempted by the appetizing smell, this delinquent primate first extracted a chicken leg from the pot and ate it, then a wing, and finally ended up by eating the entire contents of the stew pot. Then, struck with remorse or realization of impending punishment, the worried baboon resorted to the following expedient. First he knelt with his head to the ground and his scarlet, raw-beef-looking ischial callosities presented to the sky. Then he waited until a hovering vulture spotted these twin steaks from aloft and swooped down to seize them. Thereupon the baboon seized the bird, wrung its neck, deposited it in the stew pot over the fire, and sat back virtuously to await his master's homecoming. The present writer would like to believe this story but can offer in support of its credibility only the fact that Maslow and Harlow, two of the most skillful students of primate intelligence, found 12 baboons with which they experimented definitely superior to the rest of the Old World monkeys.[6] It seems that an elongated snout and a generally bestial appearance are not inevitably associated with stupidity in monkeys. The baboons have taken an evolutionary path divergent from man in that their ancestors, when descending to the ground, went down on all fours and have converged upon the terrestrial quadrupeds in snoutiness and bodily form. Nevertheless, the baboon is no monkey moron. The baboon and the macaque are the only Old World monkeys whose social life and sex behavior have been adequately observed by modern scientists. The fascinating work of S. Zuckerman on a captive colony of Hamadryas baboons and the most instructive monograph of C. R. Carpenter on rhesus macaques cannot be summarized here.[7] Both baboons and macaques are brutal and domineering animals. They behave like Nazis.

The manlike or anthropoid apes include the gibbons, the orang-utan, the chimpanzee, and the gorilla. Their principal distinctive features are: the excess of arm length over leg length, which is associated with their brachiating (arm-swinging) method of progression through the trees; their adaptation for an erect position of the trunk, which involves the flattening and broadening of the chest and the suspension of the viscera in the body cavities in such a way as to prevent their sagging toward the hinder end; their enlarged and highly organized brains. The anthropoid apes are distinguished from most lower primates by the absence of external tails; they differ from most of the Old World monkeys in lacking cheek pouches and (excepting the gibbons and a minority of aberrant individual great apes) ischial callosities.

These long-armed, flat-chested, tailless, and big-brained apes may be assigned to two families: the Hylobatidae, including the gibbon and the siamang; the Simiidae, consisting of the three great apes—the orang-utan, the gorilla, and the chimpanzee. The gibbon family consists of two slightly different types of small apes: the gibbons proper and the siamang. The siamang is somewhat larger than a gibbon, has a more advanced webbing of the second and third toes, possesses a laryngeal air-sac, and shows certain variations from typical gibbonoid form in shape of skull and jaws. In some respects the siamang may represent a form intermediate between the little gibbons and the giant apes. The siamang is found only in the island of Sumatra, whereas gibbons of several species range through southeastern Asia and many of the islands of the Indo-Malayan archipelago.

[6] Maslow and Harlow, "Comparative Behavior of Primates," pp. 97–107.

[7] For summaries of these important works the reader may be referred to my book, *Man's Poor Relations*, pp. 177–220. References to the original monographs may be found in the Bibliography of this book.

Gibbons average about 27 centimeters (10.6 inches) in trunk length and probably do not stand as high as 3 feet. Adults range in weight from about 11 to 15 pounds, as contrasted with an average of almost 24 pounds for siamangs. There is no reliable size difference between male and female gibbons nor any secondary sexual differences that are easily discernible. Skin color is ordinarily black, and most parts of the body are covered with a fine, woolly hair, which contrasts with the coarse hairy coats of the great apes (Plate 5). The coat color ranges from black, through tan and gray, to a silvery white. Animals of the same species and even in a single family often differ in coat color. In the individual, the coat color is often variegated. Commonly, the almost naked black face is surrounded by a circle of white hairs. A white band across the brow is a frequent marking. Gibbons have small ischial callosities, but there is apparently no development of a sexual skin. These small apes have broad shoulders, flattened chests, and high-lying nipples. Both limbs are relatively much longer than those of monkeys, but the length of the arms is truly prodigious. It is commonly said that when a gibbon stands erect, its finger tips reach the ground. Relative to trunk length, the gibbon's leg length is 147 and its arm length 238 per cent, according to Professor Adolph H. Schultz, the foremost student of the anatomy of the anthropoid apes.[8] In relative length of the leg, the gibbon stands next to man. The hand of the gibbon is very long and narrow, with a hairless black palm. The relatively short thumb branches from the palm very close to the wrist and is unique among the primates in that the larger part of the first metacarpal bone, which is ordinarily embedded in the palm, is a "free" thumb. The thumb is imperfectly opposable and has a flatter nail than the claw-like, transversely arched nails on the other digits.

The foot of the gibbon is also long and narrow and has a deep cleft between the great toe and the outer digits. This wide separation gives increased flexibility to the foot and is of great advantage in grasping branches.

The brain-case of the gibbon is relatively large but somewhat flattened downward, with a low forehead elevation. The large, oval eye-sockets are surmounted by thickened bony rims, but there is no great supra-orbital bar of bone or torus, such as is found in the gorilla, the chimpanzee, and in many of the larger monkeys. The face is short but protrusive, with a flat, inhumanly shaped nose and thin lips. Long spike-like canine teeth interlock at the corners of the jaws and constitute deadly weapons with which vicious animals inflict deep, slashing wounds upon their fellows, or upon you if you are unwary and accessible.

8 Schultz, "Characters Common to Higher Primates," p. 445.

Scientific analyses of the posture and gait of the gibbon and admirable descriptions of the behavior of these apes in the wild have been made recently by Dr. C. R. Carpenter.[9] The fundamental motion in brachiation or arm-swinging is that of a pendulum. When the gibbon stops brachiating, it oscillates before coming to rest. Beginning a swing, it drops to one side of a branch, extending the near hand and arm, gliding smoothly downward and checking the glide at its bottom by grasping the limb with its fingers, thereby establishing the fulcrum for the first half of the swing. As the gibbon swings down, it raises its body up near the branch by contracting its arm muscles. Then the free arm and hand are brought round to grasp the branch three or four feet beyond the first grasp in a second contact, which may not be taken for an instant after the first has been loosed. In the swing, the legs are drawn up close to the body. A gibbon covers about 20 feet in two or two and a half swings. If it has to jump, it anticipates the leap by a forceful swing and then hurtles through the air with the trunk bent forward and the arms flexed above the head ready to grasp the next branch. Altitude is generally lost in these jumps, which may clear spaces of 35 to 40 feet. If an animal lands on a solid branch after a leap, it may walk along the top of the branch with the knees bent and the arms held out for balancing. Carpenter estimates that about 90 per cent of gibbon locomotion is brachiating. On the ground gibbons may walk upright, with arms uplifted or extended for balancing, the knees bent, the trunk inclined forward, and the feet and legs turned outward. The soles of the feet are applied flat to the ground, but the great toe is extended inward at a wide angle with the axis of the foot. Other methods of ground progression are going on all fours, with the knuckles of the hands resting on the ground; and using the arms as crutches, swinging the legs between them.

About 80 per cent of gibbon food is fruit, with the fig as the most important single item. Leaves, buds, and flowers make up most of the remainder of the diet, but birds' eggs, young birds, and insects provide the necessary protein. Gibbon families usually consist of parents and two young, but solitary animals of various ages are seen occasionally. Each gibbon family has its fairly well-defined territory in which it stays, using well-known arboreal pathways, food trees, and lodging trees. The area occupied by a group may vary from 30 to 100 acres. When gibbon groups approach each other, they engage in vocal battles. They are very vociferous animals and do a good deal of calling in the morning hours.

---

[9] Carpenter, *A Field Study in Siam.* This monograph is summarized in Hooton, *Man's Poor Relations,* pp. 148–174.

Carpenter has recorded nine types of vocalizations, each of which probably has a definite communicative function. Gibbons roost in trees, but make no nests as do the great apes.

Comparatively little work has been done upon gibbon intelligence, and results are conflicting. Several experimenters have found the gibbon by no means superior, and perhaps inferior, to monkeys in solving the kind of problems ordinarily required of primates in the laboratory. This conclusion fits in fairly well with the judgment of students of primate brains that the gibbon is intermediate in cerebral development between the Old World monkeys and the great apes. Wood Jones says that the gibbon has "a glorified langur brain."

The orang-utan is confined to the islands of Borneo and Sumatra in the Indo-Malayan archipelago. It is a bulky and very powerful animal, but, because of the extreme shortness of its legs, it does not measure much more than four feet in height from crown to heels. The girth of the body, however, may be nearly two-thirds of its height, and the span of the long arms may attain from seven to eight and a quarter feet. Thirteen full grown males weighed by Schultz averaged about 165 pounds, with a maximum of 200 pounds. The females are smaller and lighter; eight adults averaged only 81¼ pounds. (Plate 6). The abdomen is very prominent; the chest is barrel-like, and the buttocks are not well developed. The arms are so long that the finger tips reach to the ankles when the animal is made to stand erect, which it ordinarily does not. The hand is extremely long and narrow, with especially elongated fingers, but with a diminutive thumb. All of the digits are provided with flat nails. The forearm is disproportionately long and very powerful. The legs are very short and seem degenerate. The foot is extremely long and narrow; the lesser toes are long and curved toward the sole; the great toe is set off at an angle like a thumb and is opposable. It is, however, small and often lacks a nail.

The head is very large but consists of a relatively small brain-case and enormous and protrusive face and jaws. The forehead is, however, high and rounded, and the ridges of bone above the eyes are small. The root of the nose is very narrow, and there is no elevation to the bridge. The tip of the nose is not developed as in man. The upper and lower lips are very long and protrusile and are stretched over the bulging jaws. The mucous portions of the lips are not rolled outward and are thin. The ear is small and folded. The adult males often have cheek pads, which are absent in other apes (Plate 16a). Sonntag describes these as "semi-lunar or triangular blinker-like appendages which widen the face; and they may be so large that the external ears are concealed behind them. During life they are turgid, but they collapse somewhat after death. Their basal parts are thick and fixed, but their peripheral parts are thinner and slightly mobile. They are composed of fat and connective tissue and the skin which covers them is naked." [10] Underneath the chin is a fold of naked skin that covers the laryngeal sac, which can be inflated with air, giving the animal a goiterous appearance.

The jaws of the orang-utan are extremely large and projecting, especially in the adult males, which greatly exceed females and immature animals in this respect. The canine teeth are tusk-like and interlocking. In adult males, a crest of bone usually extends along the middle of the skull from front to back. This joins a similar crest that extends across the back of the head or occiput. These bony crests provide attachment for the tremendous muscles that work the jaws and for the muscles and ligaments that hold up the head, the latter being badly overbalanced by the protruding jaws.

The body of the orang-utan, with the exception of face, ears, palms, and soles, is sparsely covered with long reddish-brown or carroty hair. The skin is brownish. In adults, the brow and the cheek pads are hairless. The breasts are situated laterally and high, with the nipples in adults just in front of the armpits. The breasts of the nursing female may be large and similar to those of man.

Orang-utans have 12 pairs of ribs, as has man; the gorilla, chimpanzee, and gibbon have 13 pairs. The orang-utan, like the gibbon, has an extra bony element in the wrist, the os centrale, which does not exist as a separate mass in the other large anthropoids and in man. There is probably but one species of orang-utan.

In its natural haunts, the orang-utan is an almost exclusively arboreal animal; it keeps to thickest portions of the Borneo and Sumatra jungles. On account of its great weight, the movements of the orang-utan in the trees are said to be slow and deliberate, and it tests out the strength of branches before entrusting its weight to them. In the daytime it may be found in the tops of the tallest trees, but at night it descends to the lower and more sheltered branches and builds itself a nest, laying small branches crosswise to form a supporting framework and covering them with the large leaves that abound in the jungle. If the night is cold, rainy, or windy, it covers itself with leaves, especially its head, and in captivity it will cover itself with straw or newspapers, if these are placed in its cage.

Orang-utans have the reputation of being slow, sluggish, and morose animals, which may not be altogether deserved, since solitary confine-

[10] Sonntag, *Morphology and Evolution,* pp. 76–77.

ment in a zoo is not conducive to cheerfulness. The writer has watched
two half-grown orang-utans and an adult playing together in the same
cage in the primate house of the New York Zoological Society. So far
from being sluggish and morose, these animals were romping about the
cage, indulging in all sorts of acrobatic feats, wrestling, pretending to
fight, and, to all appearances, having a glorious time. One of the young
orangs had a most ingenious way of devising a substitute for a rope. It
would gather up an armful of long straws from the floor of the cage, as-
cend to a swinging trapeze, loop a handful of straws around the trapeze
bar, and twist them into a fairly substantial rope, by means of which it
would descend. This process was repeated several times.

On the ground, the orang-utan goes on all fours (Plate 12), but it can,
if it desires, straighten up and walk upright, though with extreme difficulty.[11] The arms are so much longer than the legs that the upper part
of the body is elevated when the animal walks resting on the knuckles of
the fingers and toes, with the weight supported on the outside of the
sole of the foot and on the inner edges of the hand. The great toes project inward from the long axis of the foot, like thumbs.

The orang-utan lives upon wild fruit, leaves, and shoots and is especially fond of the spiny fruit of the durian. It has been asserted that the
orang-utan, if attacked by a crocodile, jumps upon the back of the
reptile and wrenches its jaws asunder with its powerful arms. But I do
not know where an orang-utan would meet a crocodile, unless the former
goes down to the rivers to drink, or the latter climbs trees. It is also said
to disable pythons by biting.

The orang produces but one offspring at a birth. The infant clings
to the hair of the mother's chest. These animals are not very sociable,
and the males apparently keep apart from the females, except in the
mating season. A female is often seen with an infant and one or more
partially grown animals. The span of life of the orang-utan is probably
about 40 or 50 years and the period of growth is perhaps between 10
and 12 years.

The chimpanzee is found throughout a wide range of the tropical
forests of Africa. It occurs from Gambia in the north to Angola in the
south and as far east as Uganda in the Lake Region.

There are at least three species of chimpanzee: the common, more or
less white-faced type; the black-faced, bald-headed chimpanzee; and a

---

11 Sokolowsky and Yerkes have known captive orangs to adopt this bipedal gait, though it
is not habitual. The arms are usually held above the head and the toes are curved inward
with the weight resting chiefly on the outer edge of the foot. (Yerkes and Yerkes, *Great Apes*,
p. 116).

pygmy chimpanzee, as yet little known. Most available information pertains to the common chimpanzee.

The average weight of a series of captive adult male chimpanzees was approximately 110 pounds, and of females 88 pounds. The heaviest male at the Yerkes Laboratories of Primate Biology, Orange Park, Florida, weighs only a little more than 132 pounds, but there is an outsize and obese female, named Mona, who tips the scales at more than 176 pounds.

Data on the standing heights of chimpanzees are few. Various authorities estimate the maximum stature of males from about 5 feet to 5 feet 7 inches, and of females from 4 feet to 4 feet 3 inches. (Plate 7.)

Probably the strength of chimpanzees has been exaggerated. One observer, Bauman,[12] tested male and female chimpanzees by getting them to pull on a rope attached to a dynamometer fixed outside the cage. From these tests Bauman suggested that the male was 4.4 times and the female 3.6 times as strong as physically well-developed and fit young men. However, Dr. Glen Finch's recent careful tests with specially devised apparatus at Orange Park indicate that male chimpanzees are not absolutely stronger than male human beings, although the apes are superior in pull relative to weight.[13] The maximum pulls of four subjects ranged from 338 to 525 pounds. Both male chimps and male men were stronger than adult female chimpanzees. It should be noted, however, that the heaviest male chimpanzee weighed only 122 pounds and was 13 pounds lighter than the lightest man (who, incidentally, recorded the lowest pull). The man who pulled 525 pounds weighed 190 pounds. The male chimpanzees pulled from 3.5 to 4.6 times their body weight, and the human beings from 2.5 to 3.4 times their own weights.

Chimpanzee legs are longer than those of the orang-utan, and the arms are shorter. When the animal stands erect, the finger tips reach above the knees. But these limb proportions seem quite variable.

The hand of the chimpanzee is long and narrow, with coarse, elongated fingers and a small thumb which scarcely reaches the base of the index finger. The knuckles beyond the finger bases are covered with callosities, since they are applied to the ground in walking. The fingers are also webbed to a variable extent. There is no hair on the palms of the hands.

The foot of the chimpanzee is also long and narrow, but the great toe

[12] Bauman, "Strength of the Chimpanzee," pp. 432–439; "Observations on the Strength of the Chimpanzee," pp. 1–9.
[13] Finch, "Bodily Strength," pp. 224–228.

is short and thick and projects inward from the middle of the inner margin of the foot, being separated from the other toes by a wide interval. This great toe is opposable to the other toes, and the foot is essentially a grasping organ. The lesser toes are very long and are partially webbed. The heel is poorly developed. The trunk is thick and the abdomen rounded. The body is covered with black hair except the face, hands, and feet, and, in the case of the bald-headed chimpanzee, the top and sides of the head. In the common chimpanzee, the hair on the top of the head parts in the center and, continuing down on the sides of the face, forms whiskers; but in the bald-headed species, the top and sides of the head and the face are nearly naked. In the ordinary chimpanzee, the skin of the face and hands is pink or nearly white, while in the bald-headed chimpanzee these parts are dark brown or nearly black. Many chimpanzees have mottled faces.

The head is low-vaulted with a poorly developed brow and bony brow-ridges, which are prominent but not as massive as those of the gorilla (Plates 13b, 14b). The nose is flat, depressed in the middle, and inhuman in the shape of its tip. The jaws project forward, and the thin lips of the animal are stretched over the bulging alveolar arches which lodge the powerful teeth. The chin is absent. The canine teeth are massive and projecting but not as large as those of the orang and the gorilla.

The chimpanzee typically has very large ears which stand out from the head "like port-sails of a steamer in the tropics." These ears are pale in color and have no lobes. Only the upper part of the free margin of the external ear (the helix) is rolled. Bald-headed chimpanzees are said to have smaller ears, set closer to the head.

Chimpanzees are expert climbers and swing from limb to limb with great agility (Plate 10a). They build nests for themselves in the branches of the trees, as does the orang-utan. Apparently, however, they spend a good deal of their time on the ground, where they run about on all fours, resting the body anteriorly upon the knuckles of the fingers, with the toes partially flexed, the weight supported on the outside of the soles of the feet, and the great toes projecting inward (Plate 10c). Sometimes, however, the feet rest flatly on the ground, or the toes may be partially bent. Chimpanzees are also capable of standing and walking erect for short times and distances (Plate 11a). Yerkes states that upright walking takes place when the hands are full, when the ground is wet and cold, or when the animals are excited in various ways.[14]

Our best information on the habits of wild chimpanzees has been secured by Dr. Henry Nissen, of the Yerkes Laboratories, who stalked

14 Yerkes and Yerkes, op. cit., p. 216.

these animals in the forests of French Guinea for 64 days.[15] The chimpanzee groups that he watched ranged in number of individuals from 4 to 14, with an average of 8.5. In a number of instances, there were at least two mature males in the group and often more than one adult female. As far as Nissen could distinguish the sex of the animals, the groups seemed to be composed of about 65 per cent of females. About half of the animals in any group seemed less than half of the size of the largest, and a quarter of the groups included infants that had to be carried. Chimpanzees rise early and move about from food tree to food tree, doing most of their travelling on the ground. In the middle of the day they pick out shady places, usually on the ground, and take a siesta. At dusk they build their nests in the trees, but they do not go to bed until dark. The nests average about 38 feet from the ground and are made by breaking back and intertwining branches. Only one animal sleeps in a nest, with the exception of mothers and infants or very young animals. Animals of a single group nest in one tree or in neighboring trees.

Nissen lists 34 foods eaten by chimpanzees during the dry season in a limited area of French Guinea. Twenty-eight of these foods are fruits— usually sour and unripe. About three to six hours per day are spent in feeding. The food concentration is so low that a large bulk has to be swallowed. Chimps are wasteful and messy feeders.

Nissen could not get near enough to chimpanzee groups to make detailed observations on their social habits He saw no evidence of despotic domination of the group by any large male, although he noticed several times that a large adult (once a female) seemed to be leading. A good deal of play among the young was observed. These apes make tremendous noises when on the ground, usually by beating with hands and feet upon hollow logs or the buttresses of trees. Nissen classifies their vocal sounds in five categories, but these sounds cease when a human observer approaches. Nissen thinks that chimpanzee noises not only express emotion, but are also a rudimentary means of communication and signalling.

Gorillas are found in two limited equatorial regions of Africa, separated by an area of the Upper Congo basin that is about 650 miles wide. The western, coastal, or lowland gorilla is found principally in the Cameroons and the Gaboon, while the mountain gorilla inhabits a narrow strip of the eastern Congo west of Lake Edward and Lake Kivu. The mountain gorilla, which has been known for a comparatively short time, differs from the lowland animal in having a narrower skull, a

[15] Nissen, *A Field Study of the Chimpanzee.*

longer trunk, shorter limbs, broader and shorter hands, longer face, thicker and blacker hairy covering, and in numerous other details. The lowland gorilla inhabits a thick, rain-saturated, primaeval forest, whereas the mountain variety lives in a volcanic country covered with a mixed bamboo forest and ranging in altitude from 7,500 feet to more than 12,000 feet. (Plate 8.)

Measurements on short series of freshly killed gorillas give a range of total body length from about 5 feet to 6 feet for lowland gorillas and 5 feet 3½ inches to 5 feet 10½ inches for mountain gorillas. However, the over-all length of a male mountain gorilla that recently died in the San Diego zoo was 6 feet 5 inches. The span of the outstretched arms, from finger tip to finger tip, enormously exceeds stature in the gorilla. The San Diego gorilla had a span of 8 feet 1½ inches. Chest girths are also enormous—in males roughly from 50 to 69 inches. Weights of adult males or nearly full-grown males in American zoos range from 360 to 618 pounds. However, Armand Denis, whose experience in hunting and capturing wild gorillas has been extensive, tells me that he believes that the gigantic and overgrown specimens raised in captivity are rarely encountered among the animals in a state of nature. Four female gorillas in captivity in this country range from 180 pounds to 438 pounds in weight, but the 180-pound animals (there are two of them) have estimated ages of only seven years and are certainly not full grown. The heavyweight M'Toto, affianced of Gargantua in the Ringling Circus, was about ten years old in 1941 when the weight was recorded. Roger Conant of the Philadelphia Zoological Garden tells me that it is easy enough to put 50 pounds or more on a gorilla by allowing the animal to overeat.

Here are a few comparative measurements of the cadaver of an adult male mountain gorilla and of a living heavyweight wrestling champion, Maurice Tillet.[16] The human subject suffers from acromegaly, a condition of the pituitary gland that sometimes causes gigantism, but, in

	Wrestler	Mountain Gorilla
Age	36	?
Weight	276 lbs.	460 lbs.
Stature	174.4 cm.	177.8 cm.
Chest circumference	120.5 cm.	148.8 cm.
Leg length (stature minus sitting height)	78.6 cm.	69.2 cm.
Arm length	79.3 cm.	109.6 cm.
Span	202.3 cm.	276.0 cm.
Average diameter of head	172.7 mm.	157.0 mm.

[16] The measurements on the gorilla were taken by Professor Adolph H. Schultz and those on the wrestler by Professor Carleton S. Coon. For further details of this comparison, cf. Hooton, *Man's Poor Relations*, pp. 71–75.

this instance, has not affected stature. This endocrine disturbance, however, has increased enormously the size of M. Tillet's head and face, has thickened his hands and feet, and has probably broadened his torso. The result is an extraordinary body build that offers a particularly interesting comparison with the gorilla. (Plate 15.)

The gorilla was about 1½ inches taller than the Angel (as M. Tillet is called) but 84 pounds heavier. The wrestler has a prodigious torso, but it is small beside that of the gorilla. The long and massive arms of the Angel are short and puny in comparison with those of the gorilla, but the man has longer legs, broader feet, and a bigger brain-case, especially in height.

Although the Angel is an intelligent man, enormously strong, and skilled in the complicated technique of wrestling, I am afraid that he would fare very badly in a contest with an adult male gorilla, even if the latter did not bite. The best human wrestler might be able to take on a half-grown female gorilla with a fair prospect of emerging alive. There have been no adequate tests of the strength of gorillas. Yerkes secured some crude measurements of the strength of the arms in a young female gorilla estimated to be about five or six years old. Working with both arms and with feet braced, this animal, which weighed 128 pounds, recorded a pull of 240 pounds without maximal effort. This pull is below the maximum of female chimpanzees 25 to 46 pounds lighter than the gorilla. Relative to body weight, it is less than any of the maximum pulls recorded by Finch for either sex of chimpanzees and for adult male men. However, it seems probable that Congo, Yerkes' little girl gorilla, "did not half-try." (The vulgarism is mine, not Professor Yerkes'.)

The legs of the gorilla are relatively short. When the animal stands erect, its finger tips reach below the knees. The segments of the arm are more human in their proportions than in other anthropoid apes. The forearm has not the exaggerated length of that of the orang-utan, and the upper arm is longer. The hand is relatively shorter and wider than in the other apes, and the thumb is larger and better developed, although relatively smaller than that of man. The fingers are webbed almost up to the first joints. The hand of the gorilla resembles that of man more closely than it resembles the hand of any other ape.

The foot of the gorilla also shows an approximation to the human form. The great toe is set off from the other toes like a thumb and is opposable to the other digits. The lesser toes are much shorter than those of the chimpanzee and are not curled underneath. The heel is moderately well developed. The whole foot of the gorilla is less adapted for arboreal prehension than those of other apes, and as the animal be-

comes adult and tends to remain more and more upon the ground, the
foot becomes less prehensile in its form and a better supporting organ.

Long hair of a black color covers the whole of the body except the
face and the palms and soles. The hair on the head is often chestnut-
colored in old males, and the back is light. This hair becomes grizzled
with age. The hair on the breast, however, is likely to be thin.

The gorilla has a massive head, the greater part of which is face and
jaws and chewing muscles (Plates 13a, 14a). The portion of the skull
that lodges the brain is small and, in adult males, is provided with
fore-and-aft and transverse bony crests, a sort of scaffolding to which the
masticatory and supporting muscles are attached (Fig. 15). The vertex
of the head in living adult gorillas seems to rise high, but most of
this cranial altitude is masticatory muscle and bony crest, with a
thickened callous pad surmounting the crest. This pad of connective
tissue is supposed to be characteristic of old male mountain gorillas but
probably occurs in both varieties of gorillas and in both sexes of each.
The forehead of the gorilla is very low, and great supraorbital ridges
overhang the eyes like a cornice. The jaws are prolonged forward and
downward in a snout-like fashion. The nose is long, low, and narrow
at the root, but it has a faint suggestion of a bridge. The nostrils are
broad and open directly forward; they are surrounded with cartilaginous rings, which are somewhat like the nasal wings (alae) in man but
merge with the upper lip. The tip of the nose is not extended forward
and downward, as in man, but is relatively undeveloped. The lips
are long and overlie the prognathous or projecting jaws; but the mucous membrane is visible to a slight extent only. In short, the gorilla,
like the other anthropoids, has "thin" lips. The chin is conspicuous by
its absence.

The ears of the gorilla are small and have little or no lobules. The
teeth, especially in adult males, are enormous, notably the canines, which
exceed in size those of the orang-utan, although they are not so long
as the canines of baboons or gibbons.

The skin color of the gorilla is typically black but may vary toward
dirty gray or dark brown. The eyes range from a bright hazel color to
a dark brown. Gorillas have abundant sweat glands in certain parts of
the body and are said to emit a musky odor.

It is well established that gorillas live mostly upon the ground, although they frequently climb trees. At night they sleep in nests, usually
built on or very near to the ground in the case of the eastern or mountain
gorilla, but sometimes upon low-lying branches of trees in the case of the

lowland or western gorilla. The gait upon the ground is habitually quadrupedal, with the body bent forward and the weight of the head and
shoulders supported on the closed knuckles of the hands. All authorities
seem to agree that the gorilla walks upon the sole of the foot, with the
toes extended and not flexed as is the case with orangs and chimpanzees.
When attacked or attacking, gorillas sometimes rear up and walk in the
erect posture, but bipedal gait is unnatural and difficult for them. When
a gorilla becomes enraged, the ridge of hair that runs over the crest of
the head from front to back is pulled downward over the brow; his
enormous jaws are widely opened, his under lip hangs down over his
chin, and he presents "an aspect of indescribable ferocity." The young
and females quickly disappear, and the male advances to the attack utter-
ing terrific yells. That the attacking gorilla thumps on his chest like a
drum, as Paul Du Chaillu claimed, is now well established. If he does
this often, it is no wonder that he has little hair on that region of his
body.

The late Carl Akeley expressed the opinion that the gorilla is not a
ferocious animal, as he is usually described, but is timid and peaceable
and is not disposed to attack man. Mr. Akeley's observations may apply
to the eastern or mountain gorilla, but they are not in accord with the
evidence in respect to the Cameroon gorillas of West Africa. Mr. George
Schwab, for more than 40 years a missionary in the Cameroon and a
careful observer of the habits of anthropoid apes, tells me that his native
hunter was walking along a path just outside of a village one evening
when a big gorilla jumped out from behind a bush, said "Woof!" and
grabbed the man by the leg, tearing off the flesh down to the bone. Of
course, as Mr. Schwab said, the gorilla may have been simply playful,
but this seems a trifle rough. Mr. Schwab believes that the gorillas, like
human beings, vary tremendously in temperament and pugnacity, and
that it is unwise to generalize about their dispositions.

No modern scientific studies of the gorilla in the wild have been made,
with the exception of one that yielded little more than a description of
the abandoned nests of the mountain gorilla. The size of the gorilla
group or family has to be estimated from the count of the number of
nests placed together or from reports of hunters and natives. The largest
number of nests in one group seems to be 16. One observer states that he
has seen as many as 13 nests together, but ordinarily they are placed in
groups of 2 to 4, with the groups 8 to 15 meters apart. Mr. Schwab counted
14 sleeping places in one spot. Plants had been broken and trampled
down to make the beds. Four of the beds, wider than the others and

with bulges on the sides, were stated by natives to be the places for children with their mothers. One of Mr. Schwab's native hunters told him of a band of gorillas in the Cameroons that included 12 mothers, 4 children, 2 adolescent males, and "the father." Mr. Schwab thinks that the adult male gorilla maintains his position as the patriarch as long as he can defeat competing males. He is ultimately driven out and leads a solitary life. Schwab has seen many of these lone males. He also records the case of an adult female repeatedly seen in company with a male about one-third grown, but otherwise unescorted.

Information on the diet of wild gorillas is also scarce. It is generally agreed that they live on fruits, leaves, vegetables, and shoots. The low-land gorilla is a notorious raider of native gardens. The mountain gorilla apparently likes bamboo shoots. In zoological gardens, several gorillas have thrived upon diets of fresh, uncooked vegetables, with the occa-sional addition of grains, seeds, milk, and eggs. Some captive gorillas have relished the addition of liver and ground beef to their vegetarian diets.

With respect to size, man is to be classified as one of the giant primates, along with the gorilla, the chimpanzee, and the orang-utan. But no one would think of assigning man to the Primate Order on the criterion of size alone. A kangaroo is about the size of a man, but this fact does not necessarily indicate relationship. Let us enumerate the more important external and internal features in which man differs from the anthropoid apes and from other primates, so that we may decide whether or not these distinctive characters are important enough to justify us in re-moving man from the Primate Order. Man is distinguished from the apes, monkeys, and lemurs principally in the following respects: (1) the human nose has a prominent bridge and a well-developed, elongated, and peculiar tip; (2) there is a median furrow in the upper lip of man, and the lips are out-rolled so that the mucous membrane is visible as a continuous red line; (3) man has a chin; (4) man's spine has a forward convexity in the small of the back that is called the lumbar curve; (5) the great toe in man is not opposable to the other toes and is in line with them instead of being set off on the inside like a thumb; (6) man's foot is arched both transversely and antero-posteriorly; (7) man's body is relatively hairless and is completely devoid of "feelers" or tactile hairs; (8) man's brain is from two and one half to three times as large as that of the gorilla, which has the largest brain of any ape; (9) the canine teeth in man project slightly, if at all, beyond the level of the other teeth, and the upper and lower canines do not interlock so as to make gaps in the upper tooth arch for the reception of the lower canines and in the lower tooth arch for the reception of the upper canines.[17]

These are the principal anatomical characteristics whereby man differs from all other primates. Some of them are quantitative rather than qualitative differences, as, for example, the amount of hair on the body and the pronounced lumbar convexity of the spine, which is dimly foreshadowed in the anthropoid apes. The depressed tip of the nose peculiar to man is caricatured in the proboscis monkey of Borneo, whose nasal tip is enlarged, depressed, and capable of dilation. The essentially supporting type of foot that man possesses is closely approached by that of the adult male gorilla, although in the size, position, and non-opposability of the great toe we must recognize a specifically human character. The enormous size of the brain is the pre-eminently human feature, but as we shall see, the form and pattern of man's brain is essentially that of a higher primate.

We recall that organs which owe their distinguishing form to adaptation, that is, to the moulding of the body in conformity with habits, are not safe criteria upon which to base conclusions as to relationship. Such an adaptative organ is the human foot, the principal distinctive features

[17] Schultz, "Characters Common to Higher Primates," p. 550, gives a much more elaborate list of characters that are peculiar to man and differ in degree of specialization from all of the great apes, as follows:

". . . in all probability the greatest increase in the duration of postnatal growth; the greatest weight at birth in relation to body weight in adult life; the largest relative brain size; complete bipedal walk and erect posture; greatest reduction in density of hair (except on scalp) and occurrence of wavy and curly hair; universal absence of ischial callosities; probably earliest disappearance of an independent *os centrale;* rarity and lateness of fusion of nasal bones; by far the earliest obliteration of the facial sutures between maxillary and premaxillary bones; by far the latest closure of the great fontanelle; complete lack of penis bone; presence of *ossicula mentalia,* of a true inguinal ligament, and of a transverse metatarsal ligament between toes I and II; unique structure of kidney; highest total number of vertebrae; highest average numbers of thoraco-lumbar and coccygeal vertebrae; longest cervical and lumbar regions of the spine; the least approximation between thorax and pelvis; least increase in average stoutness of the trunk; by far the lowest shoulders; lowest placed nipples; greatest average relative length of lower limbs and shortest average relative length of upper limbs; by far the lowest intermembral index; by far the longest thumb in proportion to the length of the hand and the relatively longest free portion of the thumb; straightness of fingers with extension of palm; by far the shortest relative length of the phalangeal portions of II to V; complete and permanent adduction of hallux; the shortest height of the face in relation to trunk height and, particularly, to size of brain part of head; by far the shortest height of the pelvis, particularly the ilium, in relation to the trunk height and the ilium breadth; the greatest enlargement of the sacral surface of the ilium; the unique position of the pelvis in regard to the longitudinal axis of the trunk; the unique direction of the *fossa iliaca;* the equality of the sexes in regard to the size of the canine teeth."

Schultz says that this list is of course very incomplete, but the present writer feels that it ought to be enough to enable students to distinguish their friends from the apes, providing that said students know enough human anatomy. The reader, unversed in this subject, would do well to defer a careful reading of this list until he has perused Parts II and III of this book.

TABLE 1. RESEMBLANCES AND DIFFERENCES BETWEEN MAN, THE ANTHROPOID APES, AND AN OLD WORLD MONKEY

(Adult males. Data mostly derived from Adolph H. Schultz) [18]

Character	1 Man	2 Gorilla	3 Chimpanzee	4 Orang-utan	5 Gibbon	6 Macaque
Approximate average weight	143 lbs.	495 lbs.	110 lbs.	165 lbs.	13 lbs.	20 lbs.
Body Proportions						
Chest breadth in % of chest depth	129	135-146	129	126	118	87
Chest girth in % of trunk height	162	207-223	176	185	149	103
Upper limb length in % of lower limb length	88	137-140	137	170	162	111
Lower limb length in % of trunk height	171	112-131	128	119	147	96
Hand						
Hand breadth in % of hand length	41	49-58	35	33	24	37
Thumb length in % of hand length	68	50-52	47	44	54	56
Foot						
Foot breadth in % of foot length	25	28-32	27	25	22	22
Great toe length in % of foot length	100	86-89	86	55	84	74
Opposability of great toe	Absent	Present	Present	Present (?)	Present	Present
Length of heel	Long	Medium	Short	Shorter	Shortest	Short
Skeleton						
Cranial capacity	1300-1450 cc.	549 cc.	400 cc.	416 cc.	98 cc.	103 cc.
Brow-ridges	Large to absent	Very large	Large	Small	Large	Large
Frontal sinus	Variable in size, rarely absent	Always very large	Usually large	Sometimes present, small	Absent	Absent
Elevation of nasal bones	Small to great	Very slight	Absent	Absent	Absent	Absent
Positive chin projection	Usually present	Absent	Absent	Absent	Absent	Absent

PLATE 1

Courtesy of the Philadelphia Zoölogical Garden. Photograph by N. H. Hartman

a. A LEMUR

Courtesy of the Museum of Comparative Zoölogy, Harvard University. Photograph by F. P. Orchard

b. THE SPECTRAL TARSIER

PLATE 2

Courtesy of the Philadelphia Zoölogical Garden. Photograph by N. H. Hartman

a. A MARMOSET

Courtesy of the New York Zoölogical Society. Photograph by E. R. Sanborn

b. A PREHENSILE–TAILED AMERICAN MONKEY

PLATE 3

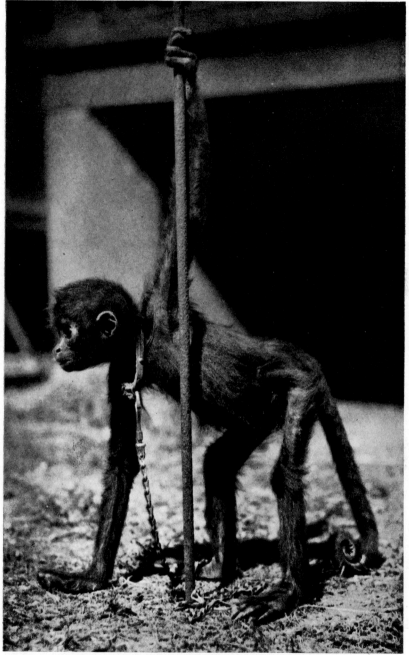

Courtesy of the Philadelphia Zoölogical Garden. Photograph by N. H. Hartman

SPIDER MONKEY, ONE OF THE CEBIDAE,
A NEW WORLD FAMILY

PLATE 4

Courtesy of the Philadelphia Zoölogical Garden. Photographs by N. H. Hartman

b

OLD WORLD MONKEYS. MACAQUE MOTHER
AND CHILD

a

BABOON

PLATE 5

Courtesy of the Philadelphia Zoölogical Garden. Photograph by N. H. Hartman

A GIBBON, THE SMALL ANTHROPOID APE

PLATE 6

Courtesy of the Philadelphia Zoölogical Garden. Photograph by N. H. Hartman

ORANG–UTAN MOTHER AND CHILD

PLATE 7

Courtesy of the Philadelphia Zoölogical Garden. Photograph by N. H. Hartman

CHIMPANZEE

PLATE 8

Courtesy, Zoölogical Society of San Diego

b

a

NEARLY ADULT MALE MOUNTAIN GORILLA, M'BONGO

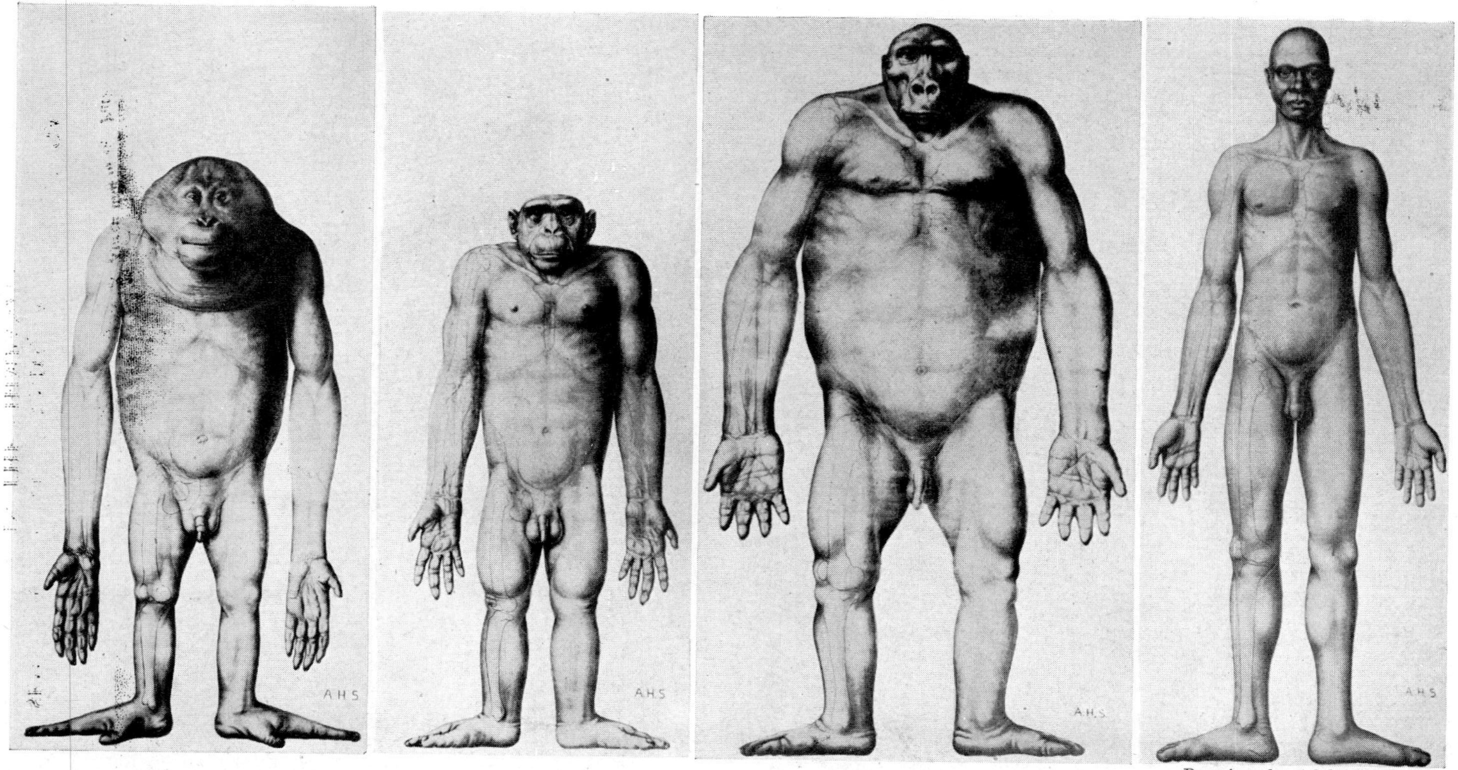

PLATE 9

Orang-Utan

Chimpanzee

Gorilla

Drawings by Adolph H. Schultz

Negro

COMPARATIVE PROPORTIONS OF GREAT APES AND MAN

PLATE 10

a   b

BRACHIATING CHIMPANZEE   CLIMBING CHIMPANZEE

Courtesy of Mme. R. Abreu and of the Pathé Exchange

c

**SEMI-ERECT POSTURE AND QUADRUPEDAL GAIT
IN THE CHIMPANZEE**

PLATE 11

Courtesy of Mme. R. Abreu and of the Pathé Exchange

BIPEDAL GAIT OF THE CHIMPANZEE

Courtesy of the Philadelphia Zoölogical Garden and of the Pathé Exchange

GIBBON RUNNING

PLATE 12

Courtesy of the Philadelphia Zoölogical Garden. Photograph by N. H. Hartman
MOTHER ORANG–UTAN AND BABY. QUADRUPEDAL POSTURE

PLATE 13

Courtesy of the Philadelphia Zoölogical Garden. Photographs by N. H. Hartman

a   b

YOUNG GORILLA   CHIMPANZEE

PLATE 14

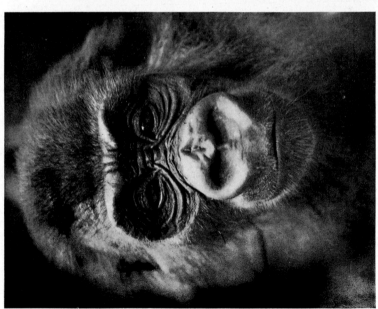

Courtesy of the Philadelphia Zoölogical Garden. Photographs by N. H. Hartman

a. YOUNG GORILLA   b. CHIMPANZEE

PLATE 15

Courtesy, Zoölogical Society of Philadelphia. Photograph, Zoölogical Park

BAMBOO, ADULT MALE LOWLAND GORILLA

PLATE 16

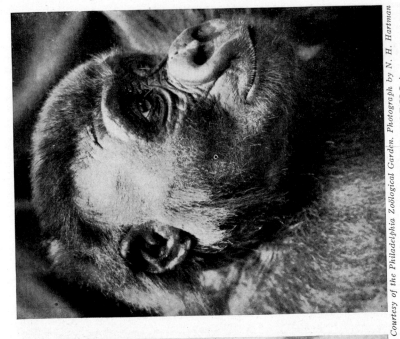

Courtesy of the Philadelphia Zoölogical Garden. Photograph by N. H. Hartman

b. YOUNG MALE GORILLA

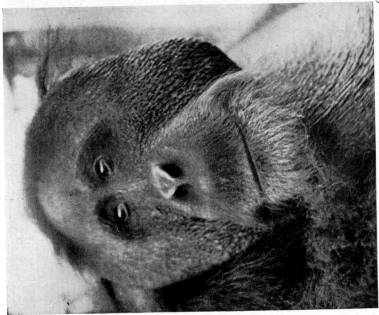

a. OLD MALE ORANG–UTAN

PLATE 17

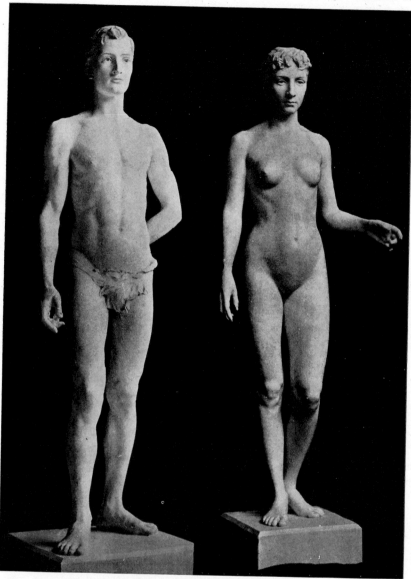

DR. DUDLEY A. SARGENT'S COMPOSITE FIGURES OF COLLEGE
STUDENTS OF THE "GAY NINETIES." MADE FROM AVERAGE
MEASUREMENTS. THE PRESENT GENERATION OF AMERICAN
STUDENTS IS CONSIDERABLY TALLER AND MORE SLENDER

PLATE 18

Courtesy of the Philadelphia Zoölogical Garden. Photographs by N. H. Hartman

CHIMPANZEE MOTHER AND CHILD. MEALTIME FOR BABY

PLATE 19

Courtesy of the Philadelphia Zoölogical Garden. Photograph by N. H. Hartman

CHIMPANZEE MOTHER AND CHILD. MEALTIME FOR MOTHER

PLATE 20

Courtesy of the Philadelphia Zoölogical Garden. Photograph by N. H. Hartman

ORANG–UTAN MOTHER AND CHILD

Projection of canine teeth	Great	Very great	Great	Moderate	Great	Absent
Pairs of ribs	12	13	12	13	13	12
Lumbar curve	Absent	Trace	Trace	Trace	Trace	Pronounced
External tail	Present	Absent	Absent	Absent	Absent	Absent
Pelvis		Progressively higher and narrower in order: 2, 4, 3, 5, 6				Broad, low, basin-shaped
Penis bone	Present	Present	Present	Present	Present	Absent
Hair						
Distribution	Very thick on head and body	Thickest on head and body	Thin on head, medium on body	Thin on head and body	Thick on head, medium on body	Thick on head, very thin on body
No. of hairs per sq. cm. in scalp	910	2035	158	112	440	312
No. of hairs per sq. cm. in back	866	1727	176	48	127	0
No. of hairs per sq. cm. in chest	172	499	107	21	5	1
Form	Straight	Straight	Straight	Straight	Straight	Woolly to straight
Tactile hairs	Present	Present	Present	Present	Present	Absent
Color	Variable	Black, white, variegated	Ginger, foxy red	Black	Black, chestnut patches	Ash, golden, red, brown, black
Skin						
Color	Variable	Black	Red-brown darkening to purplish black	Whitish, mottled brown to black	Black	White, yellow-brown, brown, black
Ischial callosities	Present, large	Present, small	Rare and small	Rare and small 10%	Rare and small	Absent
Changing sexual skin in females	Present	Absent (?)	Absent	Present in 38%	Absent	Absent
Relative ear size $\dfrac{\text{(Ear length} \times \text{breadth)}}{\text{(Head length} \times \text{height)}}$	14	13	3	16	4	5

[18] Schultz, "Characters Common to Higher Primates," pp. 444–446; "Die Körperproportionen,"

of which may be referred with certainty to the function it performs in man. Its general architecture is that of a primate and originally prehensile organ. Many authorities consider even the size of man's brain as essentially the result of function and adaptation, but this is not demonstrable.

In classification, it is necessary to take account of both resemblances and differences in bodily form. If the resemblances are more numerous and more important than the differences, we are led to conclude that the animals manifesting a majority of homologous features are related, and the larger the majority, the closer the relationship.

The most outstanding resemblances and differences between man and the anthropoid apes may be set forth crudely in tabular form. With these may be compared also the macaque, a member of the family Cercopithecidae. In each case the basis of comparison is the adult male.

The table above summarizes only the gross anatomical resemblances and differences between man and the anthropoid apes and the baboon. It does not pretend to enumerate the hundreds of morphological characters that man shares with some or all of these primates, nor to describe in detail the many minor differences.

Man is evidently most like the chimpanzee in chest proportions. The gorilla has hands, feet, and pelvis most like those of man and, in size of brain, is closest to the human type. The skull of the chimpanzee is more like that of man than the skull of any other ape, and the pigmentation of the chimpanzee shows a humanoid range. The orang-utan is most like man in his possession of the same number of pairs of ribs and in his high forehead. The gibbon approximates the human type in the relative length of his legs. In posture and gait upon the ground, the gibbon most nearly resembles man; the gorilla comes next, then the chimpanzee. The orang is a clumsy quadruped on earth and wisely stays aloft. Lack of adaptability has left him up a tree.

The gorilla departs farthest from man in the enormous development of his jaws, the orang-utan in the shortness and degenerate character of his legs and in the adaptation of his feet for suspension; the gibbon differs most from the human type in excessive arm length, general size, conformation of the lumbar spine, pelvis, hands and feet, character of hairy covering, size of brain, and length of canine teeth.

Professor Adolph H. Schultz,[19] in an analysis of characters common to the higher primates and characters specific to man (upon which I have drawn extensively in compiling the preceding table), finds that, in 23 of 57 characters considered, man resembles the gorilla most closely. He

19 *Ibid.*, p. 449.

resembles the gibbon or the siamang most closely in 15 characters, the chimpanzee in 12 characters, and the orang in only 7 characters. Such a numerical summary is open to the objection that it gives equal weight to anatomical, anthropometric, and physiological resemblances of varying significance. However, if we insist upon having an answer to the question, "What anthropoid ape is physically closest to man?" this method of counting characters affords the only scientific answer. It is unsafe, nevertheless, to attempt to establish degrees of difference in genetic relationship from such arrays of isolated anatomical characters. The fact that man is closest to the gorilla in the majority of characters enumerated by Schultz does not necessarily indicate that the gorilla is man's closest blood relation, because many points of resemblance may be the result of convergent adaptations rather than items of a common inheritance. Thus the resemblance of human and gorilla feet, which is closer than that between the human foot and any other anthropoid ape foot, may conceivably be attributed to the fact that man and the gorilla have independently adapted themselves to a plantar gait (a method of progression on the ground that involves walking upon the sole and the heel of the foot rather than upon the knuckles of the toes). Similarities or identities of function, we recall, often result in anatomical resemblances that are analogous rather than homologous.

In this same enumeration of resemblances, Schultz points out that the gorilla is closest to the chimpanzee in 30 of 57 characters, the chimpanzee to the gorilla in 28 characters, the orang-utan to the chimpanzee in 19 characters, and the gibbon family to the orang in 23 characters. On this basis, the gorilla and the chimpanzee resemble each other more closely than either resembles the Asiatic apes, and man resembles the gorilla more closely than the orang resembles the chimpanzee, which is the ape nearest to the former in this count of characters. Evidently, this method is likely to lead to a good deal of confusion if one attempts to use it as a measure of genetic relationship, which Schultz does not. However, this warning seems necessary.

Also in this very illuminating study Schultz remarks that, in a total of 82 characters showing highest degrees of specialization, man possesses 27, the gorilla 17, the orang-utan 16, the gibbon family 16, and the chimpanzee only 6. One might suppose that the animal showing the fewest highly specialized characters would be the most generalized and hence closer to the common ancestor of the group. I am afraid, however, that to deduce that the chimpanzee is closest to the prototypical ape that was the ancestor of man and the anthropoids would be a very precarious business.

Huxley, in his epochal essay "On the Relations of Man to the Lower Animals," demonstrated that "whatever system of organs be studied, the comparison of their modification in the apes series leads to one and the same result—that the structural differences which separate man from the gorilla and the chimpanzee are not so great as those which separate the gorilla from the lower apes." [20] He therefore concluded that man must be classified as one of the primates.[21] The implications of such a decision are weighty; if man is classified as a primate, he is descended from a primate and is nearly or remotely related to every other primate. To say that man is a primate is tantamount to a declaration that the gorilla and the chimpanzee are our nearest blood relations, since in the sum total of classificatory characters they are most like man.

How Blood Tells

Fortunately we do not have to abide by a decision based upon the comparison of gross anatomical features only. Since the time of Huxley, a new field of study has been developed—serology, or the study of blood. This enables us to determine quantitatively and qualitatively the nearest blood relations of man in a literal physiological sense.

The serum precipitin reactions afford a conclusive method of testing blood relationships. Rabbits are immunized against human, ape, and monkey blood by receiving at intervals intravenous injections of one or another of these bloods. The rabbits are then killed, and their blood is allowed to coagulate. The clear fluid that surrounds the clotted cells (the serum) is then found to have developed anti-bodies against the foreign blood with which the animal has been inoculated. Thus anti-human, anti-chimpanzee, and other sera are obtained from the immunized rabbits. These sera are then tested with the sera of various primates, and the amount of precipitate thrown down is observed or measured. When bloods mingle harmoniously, there is no precipitin reaction, but when sera of markedly different properties are mixed, a precipitate of varying density is formed. In general, anti-human sera give virtually as marked precipitates when mixed with chimpanzee blood as they do with human blood. Taking the human reaction to anti-human sera as 100, the precipitate produced by mixing anti-human serum with chimpanzee blood is 130 (but the precipitate is less compact). Anti-

[20] Huxley, *op. cit.*, pp. 143 ff.

[21] Jones (*Man's Place*, pp. 56 ff.) objects to this line of reasoning as in earlier days anti-evolutionary anatomists have objected. But Wood Jones wishes to derive man directly from a tarsioid ancestry with no intervening monkey or anthropoid stage. This theory, not accepted here, necessitates the disregarding or minimizing of most structural resemblances between man and all other primates except Tarsius.

human serum with gorilla blood gives 64, with orang and mandrill blood 42, with those of the Guinea baboon and spider monkey 20. The bloods of Old World monkeys generally show slighter precipitin reactions to anti-human sera than do those of the great apes; the bloods of New World monkeys produce only the faintest reactions; and those of the true lemurs and the tarsier none whatever.

The differential cross-reactions of the anti-sera and sera of pairs of animals are used by Von Krogh to indicate not only comparative nearness of relationship, but also the extent to which the blood of each animal has presumably differentiated from the primate prototype.[22] Thus human blood gives the maximum reaction with anti-human serum, chimpanzee blood 84.5 per cent, orang 70.6 per cent, and so on down the list of primates. But with anti-chimpanzee serum, the full reaction is given with chimpanzee blood; the orang gives 84.9 per cent, macaque 74 per cent, baboon 72.4 per cent, and man only 62.9 per cent. Continuing this process with the anti-sera of various primates, it is deduced that the animal whose anti-serum gives, on the whole, the largest reactions with a whole primate series of different animals has retained the highest proportion of ancestral blood substances, and those giving smaller reactions are progressively more differentiated from the prototype. On this basis, man is farthest differentiated from the ancestral serological type of primates; the chimpanzee farther than the orang, macaque, or baboon. Man has most blood substances in common with the chimpanzee and vice versa. The orang is closest to the chimpanzee, somewhat farther from man, and much farther from the macaque and the baboon. The baboon and macaque are closer to man and the chimpanzee than to the orang. The weak similarity of the orang to other species suggests a lengthy process of separate development for this animal and its early branching off from the stock of chimpanzee and man.

It has been found that the blood of a human being cannot be transfused indiscriminately into that of any other human being, since agglutination or clotting is likely to result because of the presence in the blood serum of substances called iso-agglutinins. Similarly, the red blood corpuscles contain iso-agglutinogens or receptors that cause them to clot under the stimulus of alien sera. There are four main blood groups in man: O, A, B, and AB. Group O blood has neither agglutinogens in the red cells nor agglutinins in the serum. The other groups have, respectively, the agglutinogen A, the agglutinogen B, and both. There are two other iso-agglutinogens, M and N, that exist in human bloods quite independently of the other series. Further, there are several subvarieties

22 Krogh, "Serologische Untersuchungen," pp. 240–247.

of the agglutinogen A and there are substances in human blood serum called hetero-agglutinins that clot the corpuscles of apes and must be absorbed before human blood can be compared with ape blood.

In spite of all these complications, carefully checked researches have demonstrated that the gorilla, orang-utan, and gibbon have A and B, but no O, and the chimpanzee has an A agglutinogen, probably identical with the human A, and also O, but no B and consequently no AB. Candela's experiments suggest that gorillas have two kinds of B, one comparable with the human B, and another that he calls B_2, which may be comparable with the A_2 group in man. Among the lower primates also specific group factors are present in the body tissues and secretions, accompanied by the appropriate agglutinins in the blood sera, but these factors are rarely identifiable in the red blood cells of New World monkeys and never in those of Old World monkeys. This absence has caused difficulty in identifying the blood groups in monkeys. Without going into details about various genera and species, it may be said that macaques seem to have all of the blood groups, as do also various other Old World monkeys and also New World monkeys. However, Candela emphasizes the fact that the A and B factors in many of these lower primates do not react exactly like the corresponding human blood group factors.[23]

The interpretation of these recent findings concerning blood groups in infrahuman primates is not altogether clear. Obviously the common possession by man and the apes of the various blood groups in which the factors seem to be identical demonstrates still further their intimate relationship. Possibly the slightly different blood group factors in monkeys indicate more remote relationship. A tempting explanation of the community of blood groups among human beings and anthropoid apes is to refer man's possession of these factors to inheritance from ape precursors. However, it seems barely possible that the agglutinogens have arisen, by the evolutionary process known as mutation, independently in various human stocks and in the several apes.

If there were no evidences of human evolution other than those proved by zoological classification and by blood tests, these alone would be sufficient to convince every impartial thinker that man and the anthropoid apes have evolved from some common ape-like ancestor. It is not going too far, perhaps, to surmise that, from a knowledge of the morphology and physiology of the anthropoid apes and of the lower primates, Huxley's scientific Saturnians would be driven to postulate the existence of

23 Candela, New Data.

man. For man is logically the next evolutionary step beyond the gorilla and the chimpanzee, or perhaps one should say the next *jump.*

In the foregoing pages, I have attempted to show that a simple comparison of homologous structures in existing animal forms, with recognition of the principle that structural resemblances mean relationship, leads any fair-minded observer directly and inevitably to the conclusion that man is an animal, a member of the Class of Mammals, and one of the Eutherian or Placental Subclass; that he belongs to the Order of Primates and to the Suborder of Anthropoidea, and that among the Anthropoidea he resembles most closely in structure and in size, and is consequently most nearly related to, the Family Simiidae, or the anthropoid apes. The lemur insinuates that he is our remote relation; the monkey asserts his kinship with us; the anthropoid ape proclaims it from the treetops. Man shows his primate origin in every bodily character, and, if he is a rational being, he must admit this self-evident relationship.

No qualified person thinks that man is descended from any existing anthropoid ape. We need not go beyond saying "Cousin Gorilla." The differences between man and the great apes are enough to justify us in recognizing a separate family for man, the Hominidae. For the present it is unnecessary to concern ourselves with the question as to the number of genera or species that the family of man includes. No type of present-day man can cry "Ape!" at another without an answering echo. When "flu" rages among the chimpanzees, all the races of man may worry.

man. For man is logically the next evolutionary step beyond the gorilla and the chimpanzee, or perhaps one should say the next jump.

In the foregoing pages, I have attempted to show that a simple comparison of homologous structures in existing animal forms, with recognition of the principle that structural resemblances mean relationship, leads any fair-minded observer directly and inevitably to the conclusion that man is an animal, a member of the Class of Mammals, and one of the Eutherian or Placental Subclass; that he belongs to the Order of Primates and to the Suborder of Anthropoidea; and that among the Anthropoidea he resembles most closely in structure and in size, and is consequently most nearly related to, the Family Simiidae, or the anthropoid apes. The femur insinuates that he is our remote relation; the monkey asserts his kinship with us; the anthropoid ape proclaims it from the treetops. Man shows his primate origin in every bodily character; and if he is a rational being, he must admit this self-evident relationship.

No qualified person thinks that man is descended from any existing anthropoid ape. We need not go beyond saying, "Cousin Gorilla." The differences between man and the great apes are enough to justify us in recognizing a separate family for man, the Hominidae. For the present it is unnecessary to concern ourselves with the question as to the number of genera or species that the family of man includes. No type of present-day man can cry "Ape!" at another without an answering echo. When "Ette" rages among the chimpanzees, all the races of man may worry.

Part II. The Primate Life Cycle

Tracing Evolutionary Steps

We cannot study family history unless we know our past and present relatives. An orphan foundling is unlikely to become a genealogist. Having recognized contemporary relations, we are ready to delve into our common past and find out who our ancestors were and how they got along in life. It will be more profitable to begin by sketching the life cycle of the Primate Order, as reconstructed from the study of fossil ancestors and living members, than to display at once the raw data from the town records and the church-yards. The biographies of individual ancestors must come after the chronicle of the group.

The next sections will describe the stages whereby the primates emerged from lower animal forms, how they grew up and diversified, what lives they led, and how they became slaves or masters of their environment; what were the short and simple annals of the poor relations and how the more richly endowed fought their way upward. It will be shown how each part of the body evolved in different primate groups toward or away from the human end-product. By combining a family history with an account of the changes of bodily parts, it may be possible to gain a clear conception of human evolution. The family history of a zoological group is more like the stages in the life history of an individual than a family chronicle in the ordinary human sense of the phrase. For, zoological families and species are born, pass through periods of infancy, develop inherited and acquired bodily characters as they grow, reproduce their kind or produce some other slightly different kind, grow old, and die.

A reconstruction of the stages of primate evolution necessitates combining the evidence of several distinct scientific fields. The first of these is palaeontology, which deals with the development of animal life as revealed by the fossil remains of creatures in the beds of rock laid down during successive periods of the earth's history. This "record of the rocks" is necessarily fragmentary but is the real backbone of our evolutionary skeleton. For the interpretation of fossil data we must utilize the results of geology in order to ascertain the time sequences of the various forms. In the reconstruction of incomplete skeletal remains, great assistance is derived from the comparison of living animals. Fortunately for the student of evolution, all types of animals have not evolved at the same rate of speed, but some have tended to become fixed in their physical type and habits at almost every successive evolutionary stage. Many of these animals represent primitive phases of development but have, nevertheless, survived almost unchanged in their habits and organization to the present day. Thus the palaeontologist can reconstruct the fragmentary skeletal remains of fossil animals by comparing them with the complete skeletons of existing forms that have become hardened or set at about the same evolutionary stages as those represented by the fossils. The study of the soft parts of these living animals provides the knowledge for clothing fossil skeletons with the tissues that are never preserved in the rocks. The zoologist studies the environment and habits of existing animals, experiments with their physiological processes, and gains a knowledge of their potentialities as living organisms. His results may be applied with caution to the reconstruction of the life and surroundings of extinct ancestral forms.

Physiologists and pathologists, who are endeavoring to extend knowledge as to the functioning of the human organism, often prefer to conduct their experiments upon monkeys or, even better, upon anthropoid apes. The reason for this preference is that the animals in question resemble man most closely in form and function and can be utilized for experimental purposes more readily and with less regard for consequences. Similarly, the study of an existing animal provides the firmest basis for a knowledge of the structure and organization of an allied but extinct precursor. Actually, the dissection of the body of a modern lemur probably furnishes a more reliable basis for the reconstruction of the fossil lemuroid than immunization experiments upon monkeys afford for judging the effects of sera upon human beings. For the differences between recent and extinct lemuroids are probably far less than those between the present higher apes and man, to say nothing of monkeys.

Students of animal psychology contribute to the reconstruction of the life cycle of the primates by investigating the mental processes of the present primates and of lower animals. Thirty years ago, one could only speculate upon the intelligence of anthropoid apes. Now there is an invaluable mass of scientific evidence bearing upon this most important subject. We are, as a result, in a position to sketch out roughly the limits of the mental processes of ancestral forms, the living representatives of which have been investigated by psychologists.

A general knowledge of the sequence of formations deposited upon the earth's surface and of the forms of life contained in these rocks is essential for the understanding of primate evolution. In large measure, the various layers of the earth's crust have arranged themselves in a chronological order, the oldest lying at the bottom and the newest at the top. For example, an ancient land surface may be overlaid by a vanished sea floor, which is again surmounted by another land surface, over which may be deposits of a freshwater lake. The remains of plants and animals preserved in these rocks enable geologists to infer the changes in climate, geography, flora, and fauna that have taken place since the hardening of the earth's crust. Fossil remains of plants and animals are not found in igneous rocks, which have cooled from a melted state or have been subjected to great heat. They occur almost exclusively in rocks that have been formed by slow deposition in water of mud, sand, clay, or lime. The sediment carried by streams into a lake or the ocean sinks gradually to the bottom and there becomes hardened by pressure into rock. This is called sedimentary or stratified rock.

The earliest sedimentary rocks contain no certain traces of life. For this reason they are often called the Azoic (lifeless) rocks, although some geologists prefer to style them the Archaeozoic rocks, on the assumption that the first living matter was so soft as to leave no recognizable fossil traces. The second stratum of rocks is called the Proterozoic series (earlier stages of life) and contains a few vestiges of simple plants and possibly skeletons of minute animals called radiolaria. With the Palaeozoic or Primary era (the era of ancient life), traces of living things in the rocks become common. Among the lower forms of spineless animals in the basal rocks of this era are sponges, sea-urchins, starfishes, and ringed worms. Higher in the scale of organization are the Crustacea —shelled animals such as the extinct trilobites, crabs of different kinds, —and a number of molluscs or shellfish. The first period of this era, the Cambrian, yields nothing higher than spineless (invertebrate) animals. In the second period, the Ordovician, the first traces of vertebrate fishes appear in the Colorado beds. In the following Silurian period, ancestors of the shark and dogfish are found—vertebrates with cartilaginous rather than bony skeletons. In the Devonian rocks, which are next in order, occur the ancestors of the present-day air-breathing lungfishes, as well as sharks and a variety of true bony fishes. Transitional forms from the fish to the four-footed land-dwelling vertebrate, represented by the footprints of a supposed amphibian, have been found in the upper levels of the Devonian strata.

The Carboniferous rocks are those from which coal is mined. About seven hundred species of fishes of this period have been described. Insects are abundant, and primitive amphibians, some as long as seven or eight feet, appear in considerable numbers in the upper strata of the series. The first remains of reptiles of the earliest type are also found in the Upper Carboniferous. These animals lived in swamps. The uppermost system of stratified rocks of the Palaeozoic era is called the Permian. Land-dwelling reptiles were common at this period, and some of them succeeded in raising their bodies well off the ground in walking.

The Mesozoic or Secondary era is commonly called the "Age of Reptiles." Its duration was probably not more than one-fourth that of the Palaeozoic era. The Mesozoic witnessed a tremendous evolution and differentiation of reptilian forms, including the various kinds of dinosaurs. More important for our purposes is the fact that this era gave rise to the first mammals. The periods of the Mesozoic are the Triassic, Jurassic, and Cretaceous. In the Upper Triassic of North America, Europe, and South Africa are found fragmentary remains of small mammals, probably insectivorous in habit and belonging perhaps to the marsupials or pouched mammals. Possibly the small banded anteater of Australia is a present-day form akin to these ancestral mammals. In the following Jurassic period, reptiles reached their highest development. Some of them flew; some were aquatic; and the most striking were the dinosaurs, ranging in size from that of a rabbit to the Atlantosaurus, 100 feet long. Fishes began to approach their modern forms; the earliest known bird, the reptile-like Archaeopteryx, was flying about. Mammals were still few, small, and insignificant. They appear to have been insect-eating and were probably marsupials.

In the Cretaceous rocks, the period of the chalk formation, the reptiles were still dominant, but they were intensely specialized; the assemblage was not as numerous as in the preceding Jurassic, and many distinctive Mesozoic forms had passed away before the end of the period. Mammals were still rare and puny. Six skulls of small Cretaceous mammals, discovered by the Third Asiatic Expedition of the American Museum of Natural History, indicate that the mammals had already split up into monotremes, marsupials, and placentals. The placental mammals are represented by diminutive forms, suggesting in some instances insectivores and in others carnivores. In both the brain-cases are smaller than those of modern insectivores or marsupials of the same size. By the end of the Cretaceous period, many existing forms of trees, such as beech, walnut, tamarisk, plane, laurel, had developed, as well as junipers, pines, sequoias, ivy, ilex, et cetera. The flora was widespread and uniform and generally subtropical in aspect.

The Cainozoic era is the age of mammals and of man. It is divided into the Tertiary and the Quaternary epochs. At the end of the Tertiary began the glaciations, but throughout most of the epoch the climate was warm. The first period of the Tertiary, called the Eocene, witnessed the development of the Mammalian Orders. The early Eocene mammals were only obscurely differentiated into types which presaged the carnivorous, herbivorous, and other groups. Before the end of the period, most of the great orders had been clearly defined, but none of the Eocene genera survive today. The only primates developed in this period were lemuroids and tarsioids. In the succeeding Oligocene period, the ancestors of the Old World monkeys and the common ape ancestors of the present anthropoid apes and man were already flourishing in the Old World. The New World monkeys were developing from lemuroids or tarsioids of the New World.

The Miocene period is notable in primate evolution because of the discovery of ancestral forms of the gibbon, giant apes of a generalized chimpanzee-gorilla type, and some also that may have been human precursors. Probably before the end of this period, man's ancestors had descended from the trees and had assumed the erect posture.

The last period of the Tertiary epoch, the Pliocene, has yielded remains of primates closely akin to existing species. Archaic humanoid forms were certainly in existence also, but none of these, actually dated to that period, has been found. Our human precursors probably began to use stone for tools and weapons before the end of the period. Some of them may have been giants, in bones and teeth, but not in brains.

The Pleistocene, or Quaternary, is the epoch of glaciations. Four times the ice sheet descended from the polar north and covered large portions of the northern hemisphere. Early forms of man, some of them now extinct, inhabited the unglaciated areas of Europe and the more genial climes of Africa and of Asia. Before the close of the glacial period, the modern types of man had been differentiated and were developing their material cultures. All were hunters or fishers.

The Holocene or Recent period extends from the retreat of the last glaciation down to the present day. Its opening millennia are marked by the transition from glacial to recent climates and corresponding changes in flora. The fauna becomes completely modern. Agriculture and the domestication of animals were the first great steps in man's progress toward civilization. By 5000 b.c. great centers of culture had developed in Mesopotamia and shortly thereafter in Egypt and India. Writing was invented, and history began in these areas.

Getting a Backbone: The Vertebrate Stage

The simplest known animals, and presumably the earliest to develop, are the Protozoa, whose bodies consist of a single cell, in contrast to all other animals that are multicellular and are called Metazoa. These fundamental divisions between unicellular and multicellular animals are called "grades." All of the higher animals belong to the grade Metazoa. The grades are divided into phyla ("tribes"), of which there are at least ten. For example, jellyfish, anemones, corals, belong to the phylum Coelenterata; flat worms belong to another phylum; shellfish are mostly included in the phylum Mollusca. Ringed worms, centipedes, insects, trilobites, spiders, scorpions, et cetera, are all members of the phylum Appendiculata (with limbs). Every animal that has a backbone or an elastic rod or cord in place of a backbone belongs to the phylum Chordata and is a chordate. Fishes, amphibians, birds, reptiles, and mammals are all chordates and belong to the vertebrate division of that phylum.

If we assume that animal life has been continuous and that all existing complex forms have evolved from those of simpler organization, it is obvious that the vertebrates have developed from simpler spineless animals. But the stages of this evolutionary process are very obscure, and transitional forms, either recent or fossil, are, to a great extent, lacking.

True vertebrates have a tubular central nervous system running along the back, the nerve cord of which is enclosed in a segmented backbone. They also possess a closed circulatory system containing blood carrying a special type of corpuscle charged with respiratory haemoglobin, a heart that contracts, situated on the belly (ventral) side, and a spacious body cavity. The throat is pierced or nearly pierced at some stage of the animal's existence by paired gill slits.

The animals that possess some but not all of these characteristics are Chordata but not Vertebrata. They are simpler in organization than the vertebrates. One class of chordates, the sea-squirts, lose the notochord (the supporting back rod) when they become adults, as a result of adopting a sedentary life fixed to such objects as rocks or piers. In the tadpole stage, this structure is present.

Another class of Chordata is occupied by a single animal, Amphioxus, or the lancelet. This animal probably represents an approximation to the ancestral form of the chordates. It is a cigar-shaped marine creature, an inch or two in length, with no skull, jaws, nor limbs, but a back fin expanded at the tail. A flexible gelatinous rod, the notochord (back rod), stretches along the back from snout to tail. This is the only skeleton the animal possesses. It is thus more primitive than a fish. The nervous system is represented by a hollow tube running along the back above the notochord. It has no brain swelling at the front end of this tube, as in fishes and all higher vertebrates, and it possesses only two pairs of sensory nerves instead of the 10 pairs found in vertebrates. It has a patch of pigmented cells constituting an eye-spot and a doubtful smelling organ, both applied to the undifferentiated front end of the nerve cord. The alimentary canal is not coiled and has but one digestive gland; the throat is pierced with gill slits that are not much like those of fishes. There is no heart and no colored blood corpuscles, but the circulatory system is closed.

All vertebrates are essentially segmented animals. The spine consists of repeated homologous parts, the vertebrae. From the level of each of these vertebrae pairs of spinal nerves are thrown off from the nerve tube. The body muscles are segmented similarly, and each transverse segment of the body develops from one of the series of embryonic blocks which, at a certain stage of development, extend from head to tail. Now this segmentation of the body is similar to that found in ringed worms (annelids), of which earthworms are an example. The only difference between the vertebrate and the annelid segmentation is that in the former only the back is involved and not the walls of the body cavity, whereas in the latter the whole body cavity is divided into repeated transverse compartments. Of course, in the annelid, or ringed worm, each compartment or segment may carry a complete set of organs, including limbs, nerves, excretory organs, et cetera, so that, apart from head and tail, the animal consists merely of a repetition of identical parts.

In Amphioxus, the segmentation is more clearly marked than in vertebrates, and excretory organs are also found in each segment as in annelids. Amphioxus therefore seems to represent a primitive form closely related to the higher vertebrates but strongly recalling the annelids. These facts have led some authorities to postulate an annelid descent for vertebrates, but there is a serious difficulty in the way of this view. In annelids, the brain ending of the nerve cord is on the back side (dorsal side) of the digestive tube, but the nerve cord itself is on the belly side (ventral). In vertebrates, on the other hand, both brain and nerve cord are on the dorsal (back) side of the digestive tube. The only way to get around this difficulty is to suppose that the back of the vertebrate represents the belly of the annelid; that the mouth of the annelid has shifted from the belly side over the snout end to the back side, and that the brain of the vertebrate is not the brain of the annelid but has developed from that portion of the nerve cord which in annelids is on the belly side, the terminal nerve swelling just below the gullet.

Geoffrey Smith amusingly says of this hypothesis: [1] "It may seem a revolutionary, almost impious, idea that what we have been accustomed to look upon as the back and the front of ourselves and all other Vertebrates, have all along been diametrically the opposite; that, when, for instance, we imagined that we were exhibiting a bold front to our enemies or turning our back in reprobation, we were really acting in a manner unworthy of our ancestry. A kind of moral value has come to be associated with the ideas of back and front, and we allow this moral value to influence our morphological conceptions. But if we put ourselves in the position of a worm which for some reason is forced to adopt a more erect attitude, or at any rate to forsake its creeping habit, we should be hard put to it to know which surface to present to a hostile and not incurious world."

Many authorities are unable to accept this hypothesis of an annelid descent of the chordates and vertebrates because of the assumption of the reversal of front that it entails, because segmentation occurs independently in many groups of animals and in different organs and for other reasons.

As a matter of fact, every phylum except the molluscs has been suggested as the ancestor of the vertebrates. An obscure animal called the acorn worm (Balanoglossus), which burrows in the seashore, has gill slits, a dorsal nerve cord in the collar region, and a structure in the proboscis that may be a rudimentary notochord. This animal is decidedly below the lancelet in organization and is highly specialized and off the main line of vertebrate descent, but it is certainly related to the chordates.

The echinoderms (starfishes, sea urchins, et cetera) are wholly unlike vertebrates in their adult form. They lack internal skeleton, notochord, nerve cord, and gill slits and are radially rather than bilaterally symmetrical. However, their larvae are bilaterally symmetrical, and certain of the body cavities develop as in the embryos of primitive vertebrates. Some of their larvae closely resemble the acorn worm. Hence, some zoologists support the theory that the chordates sprung from simple and generalized ancestors of the echinoderms that retained bilateral asymmetry and acquired gill slits, notochord, dorsal nerve chord, and the other appurtenances of the chordates.

Other zoologists have considered that the chordates arose from the arthropods, which include, among other forms, crabs, and have selected

[1] Smith, *Primitive Animals*, p. 85.

the Limulus, or king-crab, as the closest living representative of what the ancestors of vertebrates may have been. Gaskell thinks that the brain and spinal cord of vertebrates have been formed around the original digestive tracts of the arthropods and that a new digestive tract has developed in vertebrates.

In both the ringed worms (annelids) and the arthropods (insects, spiders, crustacea, et cetera), there are two ventral (belly side) bands of nervous tissue, which tend to unite down the middle ventral line, and a collar going around the gullet. In the chordates, there is a back side (dorsal) band, which tends to migrate inwards and become tubular. In any of the above types and in other phyla of invertebrates, there is a tendency in more highly organized individuals for the specialized areas of nervous matter to be further massed and consolidated, and, especially in bilaterally symmetrical animals that move forward, there is likely to form an important mass at the head end.

Thus, in a general way, it becomes reasonable to suppose that the development of the spinal cord is an effect of the migration into the back region, and of the concentration and fusion there of various longitudinal nerve bands, the brain mass being formed at the prow.

All this is complicated, obscure, and dubious. Anyhow, there evolved from the invertebrates a tribe of animals that, by hook or by crook, had acquired backbones. When we call a person "spineless," we offer him a deadly zoological insult.

Scrambling: Land-dwelling Quadruped Stage

It is generally agreed that land vertebrates must have developed from marine animals with all of the essential characteristics of fishes. But between the amphibians, the lowest of the terrestrial vertebrates, and the fishes, there is a serious palaeontological and anatomical gap. Comparatively little is known about the evolution of the limbs except that the paired pectoral and pelvic fins of fishes are almost certainly the fore-runners of the fore and hind limbs of terrestrial vertebrates. However, the paired fins of fishes do not resemble in any detail the limbs of land animals. When the amphibians (frogs, newts, et cetera) first appear, they are already provided with perfectly formed limbs, each one having an upper segment consisting of a single bone, the humerus or femur, attached to a pectoral or pelvic girdle; a lower segment of paired bones, the radius and ulna in the arm and the tibia and fibula in the leg; a number of small bones constituting the wrist or ankle; and hands or feet each with five digits—the fingers and toes. Such limbs are possessed of a high degree of mobility in tailed amphibians and in some reptiles, but do not support the weight of the body, although they are used for propulsion.

According to Wood Jones, with the exchange of an aquatic for a terrestrial life, the limbs took on a new function, since they were now used, not only to propel the body, but also to lift it during the act of propulsion. This demanded the development of a new limb property—*stability*—added to the original *mobility*.[2]

Certain of the less specialized reptiles and tailed amphibians of to-

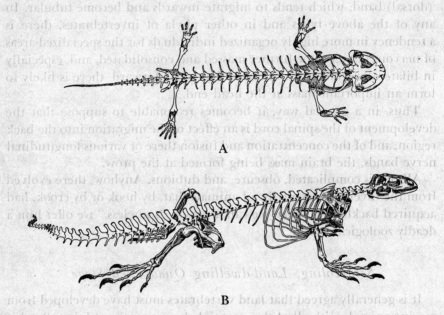

Fig. 1. A, skeleton of an amphibian. Giant salamander of Japan (Megalobatrachus maximus). B, skeleton of a reptile. Common iguana (Iguana iguana).

day exemplify perfectly the stage in the development of land-living vertebrates in which the primitive limbs enable the animal to walk about under water and to drag itself about on land. Wood Jones says, " 'On thy belly shalt thou go' applies to the pioneers of the land-living vertebrates; for their limbs are not yet adapted to supporting their bodies and carrying them sheer of the ground."[3]

The first land animals possessing these stable and propulsive limbs were probably early, mammal-like reptiles such as Moschops of the Permian epoch and the Therapsida of the South African Triassic, which

2 Jones, *Arboreal Man*, p. 10.
3 *Ibid.*, p. 10.

seem to have been able to raise their bodies well off the ground in running.

Breathing

Much clearer than the evolution of supporting and propelling limbs are the stages in the development of respiratory organs, which, in terrestrial adaptation, had to cease drawing oxygen from the water and take it directly from the air. Typical fish secure their supply of oxygen from the gas dissolved in the water, a fresh stream of which is continually passing over the thin, blood-charged walls of the gills. The blood, oxygenated in the gills, is carried back and distributed over the body. The gills are a series of pouches in the throat opening to the exterior. These pouches, which are supported by cartilaginous bars or gill arches, have folded walls produced into fine filaments in which the blood circulates. Modern bony fishes (teleosts) have four pairs of gills, but in the primitive cartilaginous fishes such as sharks, dogfishes, rays, et cetera, there may be as many as seven gill pouches. In these fishes, the skeletons of which are not calcified into bone, the gill pouches open to the exterior by clefts, except the first gill pouch, which is modified to form a special tube, the spiracle, that opens immediately behind the eye. This spiracle contains only rudimentary gills and serves under certain conditions for the intake of water into the throat. In other fishes, the first gill cleft or spiracle does not open externally, and in land vertebrates it has been converted into the cavity of the middle ear, and the opening into the throat survives as the Eustachian tube.

Ordinary fishes die from asphyxiation a short time after their exposure to the air. But some fresh-water fishes, which live in the tropics, have chambers adapted for air-breathing leading from their gill pouches. These fishes are in the habit of coming up periodically from the muddy and stagnant pools in which they live to take gulps of fresh air. Many bony fishes have a thin-walled sac filled with air leading off from the gullet (oesophagus) and often connected with the throat by a duct. This air bladder is usually behind, or dorsal to, the oesophagus. In modern bony fishes, the lining of the air bladder secretes a mixture of oxygen and nitrogen and gives the organism the power of counteracting the effects of pressure at varying depths of water. It has no respiratory function.

The air bladder is transformed into a lung in the Dipnoi or lungfishes. In these curious animals, the air bladder lies back of the oesophagus, but its walls are vascular and honeycombed like a lung, and it is supplied with blood by a pair of arteries that arise from the sixth branchial (gill-

TABLE 2. OUTLINE OF GEOLOGICAL PERIODS AND FORMS OF LIFE

Palaeontological Period	Geological Period	Typical Rock Deposits	Characteristic Forms of Animal Life (Fauna)	Vegetation (Flora)	Climate
QUATERNARY — Age of Man	Holocene or Recent	Uppermost river, lake, and sea sediment; surface soil	Present-day animals and races of man	Present day	Present
	Pleistocene (Quaternary) the Glacial Epoch	Boulder clays, moraines, interglacial river gravels of North America and Europe	Early forms of modern man; extinct apelike forms of man; other primates of existing forms; alternation of warm and cold fauna; some extant and some extinct mammals; early stone implements	Repetition of arctic, tundra, temperate, and subtropical cycles of flora	Repetition of damp, cold, dry cold, temperate, damp warm, and damp cool cycles
CAINOZOIC ERA (Era of Recent Life) — TERTIARY — Age of Mammals	Pliocene	Forest beds and crags of East Anglia, England; clays and sands of Belgium and Holland; sands, marls, marine beds of other countries	Undiscovered ancestral types of man; humanoid types; generalized ancestors of present anthropoid apes; many existing and some extinct mammals; 36–95% of living molluscs; gradual change from southern to northern types	At first subtropical; gradual change to flora similar to that today: palms, camphors, sequoias, bamboos disappear from Europe	Gradual lowering of temperature from warm to cool presaging glaciations
	Miocene	Lake, river, sea beds of shelly sands, sandstone marls, conglomerates in Europe and West Asia. Period of mountain building	Undiscovered ground-dwelling biped-humanoid forms; early generalized anthropoid ancestors of great apes and possibly of man also; mammals of Europe assume African aspect; herbivores; marsupials disappear; herbivores increase. Fossil monkeys	Increase of deciduous trees—oaks, maples, willows, poplars, palms flourished together	Equable and moist subtropical, slowly cooling
	Oligocene	Gypsum beds of the Paris Basin, various freshwater and marine deposits in Europe and South America. Fayum lakebed in Egypt	First small and primitive anthropoid apes; ancestors of Old World monkeys; forerunners of living genera of mammals: carnivores, insectivores, rodents, ruminants, camels, marsupial-placental transitional types	Evergreens with characters akin to those of tropical India, Australia, and subtropical America	Tropical or subtropical

OUTLINE OF GEOLOGICAL PERIODS AND FORMS OF LIFE (continued)

Palaeontological Period		Geological Period	Typical Rock Deposits	Characteristic Forms of Animal Life (Fauna)	Vegetation (Flora)	Climate
		Eocene	Sands, clays, limestones of London - Paris - Belgian basins; Gulf of Mexico coastal rocks	Earliest lemuroids, tarsioids, insectivores; early generalized placentals; marsupials abundant but secondary. Reptiles few	Mixed assemblage of tropical and mild temperate trees	Temperate or subtropical
MESOZOIC	SECONDARY (Age of Reptiles)	Cretaceous	British chalks; Southern European limestones; North American deposits	Small puny mammals, mainly marsupial; greatly specialized reptiles—aquatic, aerial, terrestrial—birds, bony fishes, sharks, and rays	Rise of modern forms of trees such as beech, walnut, plane, laurel, ivy, etc.	Subtropical
		Jurassic	Central Europe and elsewhere; sandstones, clays, limestones	Numerous diversified reptiles; small insectivorous marsupials; fishes approaching modern forms; first birds	Cycads, ferns, conifers; no flowering plants	Warm
		Triassic	German Trias: conglomerates, sandstones, marls, clays, etc. Alpine calcareous and dolomitic strata	First small mammals; great development of reptiles—early crocodiles, dinosaurs, etc. Amphibia and fish numerous	Cycads, ferns, conifers	Dry and warm in north; moist and warm in south
PALAEOZOIC	PRIMARY Amphibians	Permian	Russian province of Perm; many deposits in Europe, India, North America. Red rocks, sandstones, marls	Large amphibians, mammal-like reptiles, fishes, molluscs, last of the Trilobites	Northern flora, and southern tongue-fern flora. Conifers, ferns, cycads	Arid, evidence of glaciations
		Carboniferous	Coal Measures, limestones in many areas, marine and continental deposits	In the upper strata, earliest amphibians and traces of reptiles; numerous insects, bony fishes, molluscs. In the lower strata, sharks, ganoids, molluscs, crinoids, corals, foraminifera, brachiopods	In the upper strata, conifers, ferns, tree ferns, algae, fungi: in the lower, horsetails, club mosses, etc.	Moist and generally mild, but some glaciations

OUTLINE OF GEOLOGICAL PERIODS AND FORMS OF LIFE (continued)

Palaeontological Period		Geological Period	Typical Rock Deposits	Characteristic Forms of Animal Life (Fauna)	Vegetation (Flora)	Climate
PALAEOZOIC	**PRIMARY** Fishes	Devonian	Dark gray, sandy and shaly rocks of Central Europe; Old Red Sandstones in South Britain; rocks in South America, etc.	Corals, brachiopods (type of shell fish), molluscs, crustaceans, insects, lungfish, bony fishes, sharks, foot-prints of amphibians	Earliest well-defined land plants — lycopods	Temperate, local glacial conditions
		Silurian	Sedimentary marine deposits in Northern Hemisphere	Molluscs, trilobites, corals, sponges, sharks, obscure bony-skinned fishes.	Some land plants and sea-weed	
		Ordovician	Large deposits in Europe and North America	Molluscs, trilobites and other crustacea, first traces of vertebrate fishes, insects	Few land plants	
	In vertebrates	Cambrian	Muds, sands, grits, conglomerates — North America, Europe, Asia	Molluscs, trilobites, crustacea, worms, sponges, corals, star-fishes	No land plants	
PROTEROZOIC		Pre-Cambrian	Sedimentary and igneous rocks	Evolution of invertebrates, molluscs, worms, etc.		
ARCHAEOZOIC		Archaean	Metamorphosed and igneous rocks, some sedimentary	No definite traces. Unicellular life?		

62

arch) arteries and by a pair of veins that empty directly into the heart. The structure, position, and blood supply of the air bladder in these lungfishes is essentially the same as that of the lungs in land-dwelling vertebrates, and there is no doubt that this air bladder is the homologous precursor of the lungs and that it serves the same function in supplying oxygen to the blood. There are three species of lungfishes, one in Australia, one in West Africa, and one in South America. The last-named, Lepidosiren, inhabits the reedy swamps of the Gran Chaco, where in the dry season the standing water may disappear almost completely. This fish comes up for air as often as the condition of the foul and dirty water requires, sometimes at intervals of only four or five minutes. In the dry season Lepidosiren burrows into the mud and fashions for itself a sort of cocoon with a lidded opening to the air. Here it remains, breathing entirely with its lungs, until the return of the rainy season when the water floats it out.

The lungfishes, or Dipnoi, are probably not the modern representatives of the ancestors of land vertebrates. A more progressive group of fishes, the Crossopterygians (lobe-finned), became adapted for air-breathing through lungs, began to use their paddles for crawling, and evolved into land-dwelling quadrupeds, in the Upper Devonian period. But the lungfishes of today and their Devonian ancestors, already somewhat specialized, exemplify most beautifully a stage that, in another stock, was transitional between the acquatic and the terrestrial vertebrate.

In structure of the jaws and skull, the lungfishes differ from all other fishes and resemble the amphibians (frogs, newts, et cetera), which are the lowest class of land vertebrates. In ordinary fishes, the upper jaw is loosely suspended from the skull by the hyomandibular cartilage, the upper portion of the first gill arch, which is firmly attached to the skull near the internal ear. In the Dipnoi and in all land vertebrates, the upper jaw is fused to the skull so that it cannot be moved without moving the whole skull.

Hearing

A fish has no auditory use for an ear, and only land vertebrates and certain terrestrial insects can hear. In fishes, the canals in the skull corresponding to the ear constitute a balancing organ. In land vertebrates, the original balancing organ is retained in the inner ear, and there has also been developed a mechanism for collecting and transmitting sound waves to a sensitized part of this organ. This organ of hearing consists of an external ear, which may be absent or rudimentary, an eardrum upon

which the sound waves strike, and a middle ear cavity through which
the sound waves are conveyed to the inner ear by means of a chain of
small bones, the auditory ossicles, one end of which is attached to the
eardrum and the other to the internal ear. The middle ear is developed
from the first or spiracular gill cleft, which no longer opens to the
exterior, but is closed by the tympanic membrane or eardrum. From
the middle ear to the throat runs the Eustachian tube, which is the old
opening into the throat of the spiracle or first gill cleft.

In the lower forms of land vertebrates—the amphibians, reptiles, and
birds—the hyomandibular cartilage, which in fishes suspends the upper
jaw from the skull, has been transformed into the little bone that
transmits the sound waves into the inner ear (the auditory ossicle). In
mammals, two additional auditory ossicles (the incus and malleus) have
been derived from the quadrate and articular bones, which, in the lower
land vertebrates, intervene between the lower jaw and the skull base
(Fig. 2).

The earliest land vertebrates seem to have developed from air-
breathing fishes provided with stout paddles, one pair behind the throat
and another pair in about the middle of the body. Some of these
progressive air-breathers struggled out of the swampy pools in which
they lived and took up their abodes on dry land. The eggs and the
young of these pioneers continued to pass through a water-living, fish-
like stage of development, breathing through gills like the tadpoles of
frogs. These first land-dwellers were amphibians, and their comparatively unmodified descendants are the frogs, toads, newts, and salamanders of today. The first traces of supposed amphibians appear in the
Upper Devonian strata far back in the Palaeozoic Era. (Table 2). Fossil
remains of these earliest amphibians are common in the Carboniferous
period. They are called Stegocephalia (roof-heads) and their skulls
retain most of the bones found in the crania of certain fishes from which
they probably descended. They had short extremities, each with five
digits, and were tailed, lizard- or snake-like animals. In some of them
the notochord (back rod) persisted through life and was not entirely
replaced by the spine, as in higher animals. Some were large and others
small; some were fairly close to the modern frogs, and others suggest
reptiles. One type had a shell or carapace recalling that of the armadillo.

In these earliest amphibians, as in those of the present day, the young
were hatched out in the water and breathed through gills in the tadpole stage, while in adult years they became metamorphosed into true,
air-breathing land-dwellers. Some of the modern amphibians, although
possessing lungs, breathe through gills throughout the whole period of

their lives; some forms are devoid both of gills and lungs and breathe
through the skin and the mucuous membranes of the mouth. In a few
amphibians, the whole development takes place within the egg or within
the body of the mother, and there is no metamorphosis. In the tailed

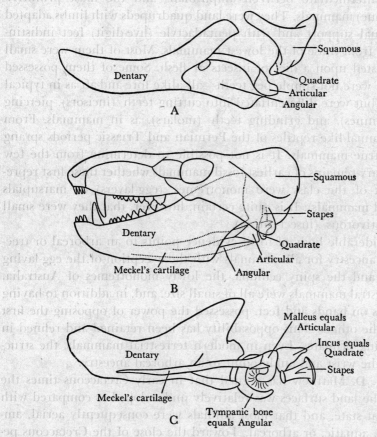

Fig. 2. Fate of the extra bony elements intervening between the lower jaw (dentary)
and the temporal region of the brain-case; transformation into the auditory ossicles
of mammals. A, primitive reptilian type with extra bony elements unreduced. B, fossil cynodont condition, a reptilian jaw of sub-mammalian type; reduction of extra
elements, stapes in contact with quadrate. C, mammalian embryo (marsupial) seen
from the inner side. Extra elements now function as ear bones. (After Gregory,
Origin and Evolution of the Human Dentition, Fig. 13, by permission of the
Journal of Dental Research.)

amphibians, three external gills on each side persist until the close of
metamorphosis, while in some others they exist only in earlier stages and
are afterwards replaced by internal gills.

In the Upper Carboniferous, some progressive amphibians succeeded in suppressing entirely the larval stage of the development of young and, without passing through a gill-breathing aquatic phase, accomplished their entire embryonic and postnatal life cycle on land. Thus the reptiles developed from the amphibians. These earliest reptiles showed features intermediate between amphibians and the most primitive (monotreme) mammals. They were land quadrupeds with limbs adapted for habitual support and with pentadactyle (five-digit) feet indistinguishable from those of the lowest mammals. Most of them were small and subsisted upon a diet of insects or flesh. Some of them possessed teeth that were not simple peg teeth—all alike fore-and-aft as in typical reptiles—but were differentiated into cutting teeth (incisors), piercing teeth (canines), and grinding teeth (molars), as in mammals. From these mammal-like reptiles of the Permian and Triassic periods sprang the first true mammals. It is not possible to determine from the few fragmentary remains of earliest fossil mammals whether these first representatives of the class were monotremes (egg-layers) or marsupials (pouched mammals). It is quite certain, however, that they were small and insectivorous (insect-eating).

A considerable body of fossil evidence points to an arboreal or tree-dwelling ancestry for all mammals with the exception of the egg-laying duckbill and the spiny echidna, the lowly monotremes of Australia. The ancestral mammals were all of small size, and, in addition to having five digits on hands and feet, possessed the power of opposing the first digit to the others. This opposability has been retained and refined in the existing primates. Even in modern terrestrial mammals, the structures of the wrist and ankle point to an arboreal ancestry.

Dr. W. D. Matthew has argued that in early Cretaceous times the flora of the land surfaces was relatively undeveloped as compared with its present state, and that most animals were consequently aerial, amphibious, aquatic, or arboreal. Toward the close of the Cretaceous period, when the chalk was being deposited, a great upland flora developed, which tremendously increased the territory available for mammalian life. It was at this period that many small insectivorous ancestral mammals forsook the trees and took to the ground, developing, on the one hand, into carnivorous and other groups in which the digits are provided with claws and, on the other, into the hoofed and herbivorous group of ungulates. The insectivore ancestors of the primates were among those that remained in the trees.

Our arboreal preprimate ancestors must have been very closely similar to the existing tree shrews of the Order Insectivora. Insectivores are small placental mammals with teeth adapted for an insect diet. Their general organization is very low, and in many respects they recall the marsupials. They are found in the temperate and tropical parts of both hemispheres with the exception of Australia and South America. While most of them live on the ground, some are aquatic, and only a few are tree-dwellers. Tree shrews are somewhat squirrel-like in appearance. They are covered with fur, and their long tails are adorned with a fringe of hairs. They apply the soles of the feet to the branches in walking, and there are usually five digits on hands and feet, terminating in claws. In the modern tree shrews, thumbs and great toes are not opposable to the other digits. The snout is long and pointed, and the eyes are directed sideways. The brain is very small, and its hemispheres are smooth and not intricately wrinkled or convoluted as in higher forms. Two sets of teeth erupt successively—a milk set and a permanent set. Several young are produced at a birth and fostered for a time in a nest.

Climbing the Family Tree: Arboreal Preprimate Stage

Some very important developments marked the adoption of a tree habitat on the part of the primitive insectivore ancestors of the subsequent primates. Wood Jones has expounded these changes most brilliantly and convincingly in his book *Arboreal Man,* and I shall embody his deductions in the account of this early phase of mammalian evolution. The ability of the primitive terrestrial mammal to adopt an arboreal life was probably dependent, to a great extent, upon its success in clambering over obstacles that lay in its path on the ground. This skill in clambering and even in tree-climbing is beautifully exemplified in vertebrates as low down in the scale as the tailed amphibians; indeed, Wood Jones thinks that the tree frogs are perhaps the most skilled tree-climbers in all the vertebrate series. A less talented amphibian or unspecialized reptile, such as the water newt, ascends an obstacle by applying its feet to the surface without attempting to grip it with its nails or claws. As it progresses upward, it repeatedly reaches ahead with one of its fore limbs for a new hold, and the weight of the body is temporarily thrown upon the hind limbs. The part of the fore limb that corresponds to our forearm has the power of rotation, which allows the palm of the "hand" to be applied to any surface that may offer a new hold, at almost any angle. The supporting of the weight upon the hind limbs and the reaching for holds with the fore limbs brings about the first specializations in function of these limbs. The fore limbs are on the way to becoming arms, and the hind limbs are doomed to remain supporting members—legs.

The third segment of the limbs in primitive mammals retains the five mobile digits found in modern, unspecialized reptiles and in extinct, generalized reptiles and amphibians. In the fore limbs, these five mobile digits are attached by a flexible wrist to a rotating forearm. The possibilities of grasping by means of such a fore limb are almost unlimited. The fingers may be flexed toward the palm or extended; the thumb may be opposed to the other digits; the whole hand may be bent upward or downward at the wrist and turned inward or outwards by means of the rotation of the outside bone of the forearm (the radius) over the inner bone (the ulna). Combinations of these varied movements of the fore limb in its several parts render it a perfect prehensile organ.

Wood Jones has pointed out that the retention of this primitive and mobile fore limb is a prerequisite for a perfect adaptation to life in the trees. Any considerable utilization of the fore limb as a supporting organ in walking upon the ground inevitably results in a stiffening and stabilization of its mobile elements. Loss of freedom of movement and reduction of digits accompanies this four-footed, ground-walking specialization. Animals that have become adapted in this quadrupedal direction may attain great skill in tree-climbing as a secondary modification by developing specialized claws with which to dig into the bark of trees. But only the animal that retains the primitive vertebrate arrangement of five flexible digits can close its fingers over branches and attain a perfectly adjustable grasp. The development of this prehensile limb in tree-climbing makes possible the eventual utilization of the hand and arm for the skilled movements that have brought about man's unique position as the master mechanic of the animal world. At a much earlier stage than that of tool-using, the power of grasp developed by primitive mammals in tree-climbing was employed for seizing fruit, leaves, insects, or what not, and conveying them to the animal's mouth. When the insectivorous preprimate became a hand-feeder and a manipulator of objects, it opened up for its decendants a new route of evolutionary progress which eventually led to man. However, this route was not mandatory; many hand-feeders did not take it.

The head end points the way in progression of vertebrates and quadrupeds; the fore limbs go first and the hind limbs follow after. The fore limbs are nearer to the central part of the nervous system—the brain—and to the organs of sight and smell: The hind limbs are nearer to the center of mass of the body and are in the neighborhood of the excretory orifices of the body rather than those which are ingestive and respiratory. The fore limbs are situated for purposes of investigation and defense conveniently near to the front door; the hind limbs support the rearward openings.

In the early tree-climbing mammal the fore limb was an exact counterpart of the hind limb. The differentiation of the fore and hind limbs was brought about by their separate functions in climbing, as affecting the head end and tail end positions of the respective pairs. The fore limbs in an arboreal climber tend to take on a suspending as well as a grasping function. The suspensory function does not appertain to the hind limbs, unless the animal forms a habit of hanging head downward. On the other hand, as Wood Jones shows, the weight of the body is supported by the hind limbs during the intervals of reaching out for new holds by the fore limbs. But this supporting function of the hind limbs is not identical with that of the limbs of ground-dwelling animals. For, in the tree-climber, the legs, though extended, are not straightened out and stiffened into stable props; they are kept in a partially bent or flexed position. The soles of the feet are turned inward against the rounded surface of the branch, and the great toes are directed inwards and in opposition to the lesser toes, which are curved to accommodate themselves to the outer convexity. Thus, a grasping function of the feet tends also to be developed, which, in some cases, may attain a perfection equal to that of the hands. In some of the lemurs, the New World monkeys, and in the orang-utan, this grasping function of the foot has been combined with a habit of hanging by the feet, which renders these primates truly quadrumanous or "four-handed."

But, in most of the lower primates and in the Old World monkeys, the hind limbs have sacrificed some of their mobility to stability in supporting the body during the climb, and, in many arboreal animals, they have been strengthened and specialized for springing and leaping. Taking off from the hind legs in leaps from bough to bough tends to strengthen and to stabilize these members but also to restrict their lateral flexibility.

The development of a suspensory function in the hind feet tends to prevent the clear differentiation in function of the fore limbs. In this connection Wood Jones observes that lemurs and American monkeys climb up a tree head foremost and climb down again head-first, whereas the higher primates, in whom the stabilizing and supporting function of the hind limbs has developed, like man, climb up a tree head-first and walk down or back down, stern foremost.

The thigh bone, or femur, in the hind limb corresponds to the humerus, the bone of the upper arm (Fig. 3). The paired bones in the leg are homologous with those in the forearm—the tibia, or shin bone,

with the radius, or outer bone of the forearm; the fibula, or outer bone of
the leg, with the ulna, or inner bone of the second segment of the fore
limb. In the fore limb, the radius rotates over the ulna, thus allowing the
palm to be turned forward or backward. A similar power of rotating the
tibia over the fibula existed in the primitive land vertebrates, but this
mobility of the lower segments of the hind limb was sacrificed, to a great
extent, even before the arboreal stage, in order that the hind end of the

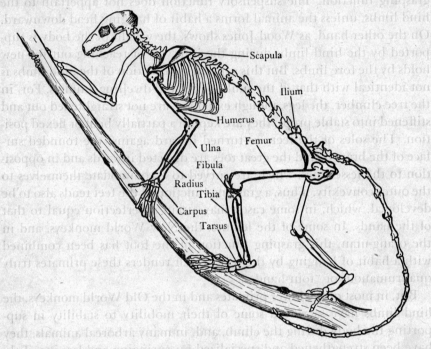

Fig. 3. Skeleton of lemur, showing homologies of fore and hind limbs.

body might be supported clear of the ground. In the tree shrews and in
the primates, because of the grasping function of the feet in climbing,
the two segments of the lower limb have been retained in a separate
and well-developed state, and some slight power of rotation has also
survived. In some of the arboreal marsupials, the power of rotation of
the tibia over the fibula rivals that of the bones of the forearm. However, in terrestrial quadrupeds, the power of movement between the
paired bones of the second segments of both fore and hind limbs is early
lost, and the ulna in the fore limb and the fibula in the hind limb tend to
become fused with the surviving bone or to disappear entirely. Thus,
power of movement is sacrificed to firmness of support, and the possibilities of a grasping organ are lost.

Smelling and Handling

Even more important than the modifications of the limbs that resulted from the adoption of an arboreal habitat were the changes that took place in the organization of the brain. In its early embryonic condition the latter consists of three hollow expansions of the neural tube, called the forebrain, the midbrain, and the hindbrain. The cerebrum constitutes the larger part of the forebrain in adult life; the cerebellum, pons Varolii, and medulla oblongata are the principal parts of the hindbrain. The midbrain forms only a small part of the whole.

The cortex ("bark") of the brain is the layer of gray matter investing the cerebral hemispheres, which is also called the pallium ("cloak"). The development of higher types of brains is largely a matter of the increase in size of this cerebral cortex. In general terms, the primitive mammalian brain must have consisted of a collection of ganglionic masses, each one allotted to a particular sense or a particular function. Impressions from various sense organs come to the different parts of such a brain, which are in free communication with each other, each impression passing through a definite channel to a specific area of the brain. In addition to these ganglionic masses, there is, on each side of the brain, a small cerebral hemisphere, within the cortical covering of which lie all the possibilities of evolution. The function of the cortex is to receive, sort out, and store away impressions that come to it from the sense organs, not only in order to modify present behavior, but also to serve as a recording apparatus for reviving in memory the impressions received in association with other simultaneous impressions and their responses. It is, in short, an organ of associative memory, into which pathways from all the sense organs lead and are blended in such a way as to evoke consciousness and memory and to provide a basis for judgment and subsequent behavior. This unitary organ of the physical processes, which corresponds to the psychic state of consciousness, has been called by Sir Grafton Elliot Smith the neopallium.[4] "Neopallium" signifies the newer part of the cerebral covering that develops with the growth of higher sensory and associative brain functions.

The various sense impressions receive representation in the cerebral cortex, one by one and in a definite order. The sense of smell, or the olfactory sense, was first to receive cortical representation. Sharks have large olfactory bulbs separated by long stalks from the cerebral hemispheres. The roof of the latter, or pallium, has no cortical structure but

[4] Smith, *Evolution of Man,* p. 32; also Smithsonian Report for 1912, pp. 553–572; "The Natural Subdivision," p. 431.

is composed of nervous tissue. In bony fishes, the smelling apparatus is suppressed, but the visual apparatus is greatly developed. The pallium is non-nervous. In amphibians, the brain is of a low type, but there appears, probably for the first time, a small mass of cells in the median wall of the pallium that is the rudiment of a cortex. This earliest cerebral cortex is formed in connection with neurone chains coming into the central nervous system from a patch of olfactory cells on the surface of the head. The region of the cerebrum thus developed and consisting of the olfactory lobe and the hippocampal formation is called by Elliot Smith the archepallium because it is the most ancient portion of the pallium or cerebral cloak. As has been noted, the olfactory lobe of the archepallium is well formed in sharks. The reptilian cerebrum possesses, in addition, the marginal hippocampal formation of the cerebrum, but both parts are olfactory in function. Only in the mammals has the new part of the brain, the neopallium, any extensive development. The primitive mammal was provided with an olfactory cortex of the cerebrum but probably little more. Smell impressions are the most important for such a lowly mammal, and the guidance of the olfactory sense is most useful to a small "land-grubbing" animal, whether in a search for food or in recognition of friends or enemies. Sir Grafton Elliot Smith says:

"Thus the small creature's mental life was lived essentially in an atmosphere of odors, and every object in the outside world was judged primarily and predominantly by its smell. The senses of touch, hearing, and vision were merely auxiliary to the compelling influence of smell.

"Once such a creature left the solid earth and took to an arboreal life all this was changed, for away from the ground the guidance of the olfactory sense lost much of its usefulness. Life amidst the branches of the trees limits the usefulness of the olfactory organs, but it is favorable to the high development of vision, touch, and hearing. Moreover, it demands an agility and quickness of movement that necessitates an efficient motor cortex to control and coördinate such actions as an arboreal mode of life demands (and secures, by the survival only of those so fitted) and also a well-developed muscular sensibility to enable such acts to be carried out with precision and quickness. In the struggle for existence, therefore, all arboreal mammals, such as the tree shrews, suffer a marked diminution of their olfactory apparatus and develop a considerable neopallium in which relatively large areas are given up to visual, tactile, acoustic, kinaesthetic, and motor functions, as well as to the purpose of providing a mechanism for mutually blending in consciousness the effects of the impressions pouring in through the avenues of these senses."[5]

Wood Jones points out that in the primitive terrestrial insectivores there is found a bewildering complexity of scent glands, but, in the stocks that are arboreal, these glands diminish in number because of their uselessness. Thus the result of the preprimates' adoption of an arboreal life was a cessation of the habit of "nosing" and sniffing through life and a higher development of the visual, auditory, and tactile areas of the cerebrum.

Another effect of the waning importance of the olfactory sense in the newly arboreal mammal was a loss of the functions of the projecting snout that is typical of lower mammals. It is obvious that a primitive land-dwelling quadruped needs a snout or muzzle: first, because, if it is guided largely by the sense of smell, its nose should point the way. The nose should come first, and the eyes should follow after at a respectful distance. Secondly, if all of the primitive creature's four extremities are engaged in locomotion, its nose must be used also for touching things and conveying tactile impressions to the brain. The animal finds out about things firstly by "nosing" them—bumping into them with its nose—secondly by smelling them. Wood Jones says that the anterior tip of the body is used for "feeling out" objects in lower forms of animal life long before a real nose develops. He therefore considers the tactile function of the snout as primary and the olfactory function as secondary. It is well known that special tactile organs are lodged in the snout region —among them the "feelers," "whiskers," which are specialized tactile hairs. Another reason for the projecting muzzle lies in the necessity of the animal's grasping its food with its jaws—the grazing or browsing habit. If a creature is to seize its food with its teeth, it is obvious that the jaws should project well forward from the visual plane. Otherwise the animal will get its eyes in its food and will be a blind feeder. It must see what it is eating, and it must not only keep its eyes on its food (rather than in its food), but also keep a lookout for enemies without interrupting the feeding process.

The free use of the hands for touching objects and conveying them to the nose, where they may be smelled, and to the mouth, where they may be tasted, relieves the snout of its tactile, grazing functions. The utilization of the hands for the examination of objects also extends the employment of the visual sense, since the objects in question may be held up before the eyes and brought more easily into the field of sight. Once

[5] Smith, *op. cit.*, 1912, pp. 561–562. Also quoted by Wood Jones, *Arboreal Man*, pp. 153–154.

the primitive mammal became arboreal and began to sit up in the trees or to squat upon its hind legs, the forelimbs were to some extent freed for these tactile and food-conveying functions. But the preliminary step to this "emancipation of the fore limbs," as Wood Jones calls it, was the utilization of the fore limb in reaching ahead for holds in climbing, the developing of the power of opposition of the thumb to the other fingers, and the resting of the body weight upon the hind limbs while the fore limbs and proto-hands were exploring ahead and above.

Such specialization of the hands as tactile organs and food-conveyers has been partially realized in the proto-primate insectivores and in other arboreal stocks, including such rodents as the squirrels. In the latter animals and in others, the paws are used to convey food to the mouth and to bring objects into the line of vision for examination, but, because of the absence of opposable thumbs and the presence of claws, the fore limbs have not attained perfection as grasping organs; nor can they be used to the same extent for tactile information.

Another result of the adoption of an arboreal life by the preprimate was the reduction in the number of offspring produced at a birth. Lower vertebrates, such as amphibians and reptiles, produce numerous litters. The females lay many eggs and deposit them in sand or in water, leaving them to be hatched out by the heat of the sun or by some other means. The young receive little or no parental care and are born well-developed so that they are able to fend for themselves. Survival is that of the fittest. Primitive ground mammals, in spite of the fact that the young are born in a more helpless condition and must be nursed at the breast and otherwise require parental care, also produce large litters. The ground-dwelling insectivores have large families. Centetes, the Madagascar hedgehog, according to Wood Jones, produces twenty offspring at a birth.

But life in the trees is incompatible with multiple births. If the activity of an arboreal life during pregnancy is not conducive to the reduction of the number of offspring, at any rate the difficulty of caring for a large number of young simultaneously in a tree might effect such a limitation of numbers. The arboreal insectivores (tree shrews) beget three or four young at a birth, as contrasted with the much larger litters of the ground-dwelling members of the same order. The lowest primates, such as lemurs, often produce two young at a birth; the lowliest of the New World monkeys, the marmosets, usually have three young at once; but in the rest of the monkeys, and in the higher forms, one young at a time is a rule. The number of pairs of breasts on the mother's body is reduced in accordance with the diminishing number of offspring produced at a single pregnancy. Only illiterates have litters.

The principal changes in the insectivorous preprimate that resulted from taking to a life in the trees have been described. Such an insectivorous preprimate would be small, furry, with a long tail and a projecting, pointed snout; the females would have two or three pairs of breasts; the limbs would be pentadactyle or five-digited, with the retention of some power of opposition of the first digit to the others and no specialized claws; the second segment of each limb, but particularly of the fore limbs, would be capable of rotating; the teeth would already have been differentiated into incisors, canines, and molars; the brain would be small, with little or no development of the neopallium, the largest area of the cerebral cortex being devoted to the sense of smell. However, as compared with the ground-dwelling insectivore, much larger areas of the growing neopallium would be allotted to the representation of the visual sense, hearing, and feeling because of the growing demands made upon these senses by arboreal life.

The transition between the tree-dwelling, unspecialized insectivore and primitive lemuroids is so slight that often there is doubt whether Eocene fossils are insectivores or primates. The recent tree shrews have feet and limbs less specialized for arboreal life than had probably the pre-Tertiary ancestors of the primates, but a number of fossil Palaeocene forms seem to be intermediate between insectivores and lemuroids.

The earliest fossil primates clearly identified as such are the lemuroid families of Notharctidae from the base of the Lower Eocene in America and the related European Adapidae, also from the Eocene deposits. The earliest American Notharctidae were tiny beasts, smaller than the existing tree shrews. Their brains were smaller than those of present lemurs, but otherwise they had much the same structure. Certain features of the teeth of the European Eocene lemuroids make them more probable ancestors of the existing lemurs than the contemporaneous American lemuroid group. By the middle of the Eocene period in America, some of the lemuroids had become as large as the modern howler monkeys, which are the biggest of the New World primates.[6]

The modern lemurs have descended from these Tertiary primates with some few modifications, usually further developments of tendencies already foreshadowed in the Eocene ancestors.

[6] With the possible exception of the incompletely authenticated giant spider monkey.

Sitting Up and Looking Around: Tarsioid Stage

The tarsioids are first found in the deposits of the Lower Eocene period in Europe and North America. They represent a stage of primate development almost, if not quite, as primitive as that of the lemuroids, but they constitute that more progressive primate group from which higher forms and perhaps (ultimately) man were derived. Both the modern Tarsius and the fossil tarsioids are diminutive in size, not much larger, in fact, than a mouse. Their most noticeable external characters are their shortened snouts and their immense eyes, which are not so lateral in position as in lemurs and lower mammals but are brought more to the front of the head as in the higher primates and man.

In the modern tarsier, as in the fossil tarsioids, this snout reduction and the more frontal position of the eyes seem to be associated with the emancipation of the fore limbs, with hand-feeding, and with the diminishing importance of the olfactory sense.

A freedom of the fore limbs sufficient to stimulate the formation of a habit of hand-feeding seems not to have been attained in ordinary lemuroids because of their retention of a quadrupedal, pronograde position and mode of progression in the trees. The tarsiers went beyond the lemurs in adaption for arboreal life by adopting a sitting-up posture and a hopping mode of progression. As has been mentioned in a preceding section (p. 16), the modern tarsiers hop from bough to bough like miniature kangaroos. Their hind limbs are modified for this method of locomotion in that the tarsus (foot-arch) is tremendously elongated, and the toes are provided with sucker-disk pads to enable the animal to secure a firm grip upon the boughs. It is not, however, the leaping habits of the animal that are probably responsible for the adoption of hand-feeding, but rather the habit of sitting erect in the branches instead of remaining upon all fours. Nevertheless, it is reasonable to suppose that freeing the fore limbs entirely from the locomotor function is likely to result in an improvement of their prehensile utility, providing that the hands have not been previously specialized for locomotion as they have been, for example, in certain squatting and hopping rodents, marsupials, and other animals.

One is here faced with a constantly recurring difficulty of interpreting evolutionary changes—that is the distinguishing between cause and effect. For example, in the present instance, we do not know whether tarsiers use the hands for feeding because the latter have been emancipated from locomotor functions or whether, on the other hand, the sitting-erect position and the hopping gait have resulted from the formation of a habit of hand-feeding promoted or necessitated by a reduction in snout length that may have been a spontaneous non-adaptive variation in the stock. Some authors tend to regard evolution as essentially a process of cumulative functional adaptations, but there are grave biological difficulties in the way of the general acceptance of such a view. Others adhere to a theory of multiple spontaneous variations in the evolving stocks, hereditarily transmitted and miraculously selected through sur- viving generations in such a way as to simulate direct morphological adaptation. A complete dependence upon such a theory of evolution involves one in incredible absurdities. Clearly, both views must be combined in some way or other, and usually it is quite impossible from available knowledge to dogmatize as to the causation of an observed morphological change in any direction. Who can tell which is the cart and which is the horse?

While it is entirely probable that hand-feeding resulted from Wood Jones' "emancipation of the fore limbs," it is by no means inevitable that arboreal life brings about such an emancipation, nor that hand- feeding is a necessary result of release of the hands from the locomotor function.

Again, the disuse of any part of an organ is likely to result in the atrophy and shrinkage of the part disused, but it is perfectly conceivable that a reduction in size or an alteration in form of an organ may originate as a variation, non-adaptive and quite dissociated from func- tion. The greater freedom of the fore limbs in tarsioids and the adoption of hand-feeding, as contrasted with the more quadrupedal habits of the lemur, may be the result of the tarsioid organism's following a line of development which, in the first place, was marked out by inherent morphological peculiarities and thus conditioned a habit.

Associated with the reduction of the tarsioid snout is the displace- ment of the eyes from the lateral toward the frontal plane—a change that is a prerequisite of stereoscopic vision (Fig. 4 C, D). It seems to me, however, that it would be very rash to assert that the frontal position of the eyes is, in any sense, an effect of the shortening of the muzzle. Nor is it apparent that the closing of the back wall of the orbital opening, which is characteristic of tarsioids and of all higher primates but is absent in the lemuroids, is mechanically consequent upon the recession of the snout region. In the baboon, there has been a secondary and tremendous elongation of the snout, quite unaccompanied by any lateral displacement of the orbits or by any reduction in the bony hinder wall of the orbit. If I were to evoke any mechanical factor to explain the frontal position of the tarsioid orbits as contrasted with those of lemurs,

I should be inclined to lay emphasis rather upon the reduction of the inter-orbital space that may have been associated with the diminution of the olfactory sense, since the upper portion of the nose is the seat of that sense. As a matter of fact, certain short-nosed lemurs, such as lorises and galagos, exhibit a displacement of the orbits toward the frontal plane

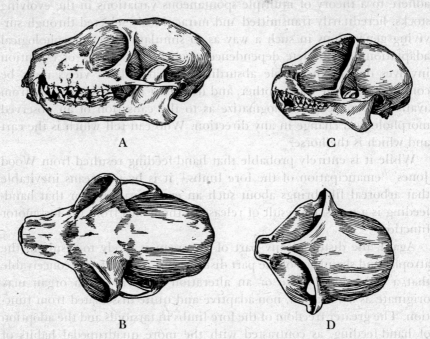

Fig. 4. Snout projection and brain case development in the lemur and tarsier. A, side view and B, top view of lemur skull showing protrusive snout, laterally directed orbits, small brain case. C, side view and D, top view of a tarsier skull showing reduced snout, enlarged and frontally directed orbits, large brain case.

equal, or almost equal, to that shown in the tarsiers, without, however, any concomitant growth of the post-orbital partition.

It seems more reasonable to ascribe the frontal shift and the enlargement of the eyes in Tarsius to an increase in importance and a special development of the visual sense and to an associated reduction of the olfactory sense. Tarsius does not possess completely frontally directed orbits, although the displacement toward the frontal plane and the enlargement of the eyes is so marked as to make it probable that the fields of vision in the two eyes overlap in this animal.

In the higher primates there is always a yellow spot (macula lutea) on the back of the retina almost directly in line with the center of the pupil—the optic axis. Within this yellow spot is the area of most acute vision. When we look at an object with both eyes having the optic axes parallel, the image of the object falls upon the two yellow spots, and it is seen as one object. In order to see a single object with the two eyes as one image, it is not necessary, however, that the two images fall upon the two yellow spots; an object is single if its images fall upon corresponding points of the retinae of the two eyes. The higher primates have yellow spots on the retinae of the eyes and incomplete crossings of the fibres of the optic nerve that enable them to focus objects on corresponding points of the retinae by moving their eyes alone. Tarsius has no yellow spots, and the crossings (decussations) of the optic nerve fibres are complete, so that it moves its head as a whole in order to see objects properly. Tarsius can rotate its head so that it looks directly backward, but it apparently does not move its large eyes.

The specialization of vision in Tarsius and its large eyes, perhaps consequent upon its nocturnal habits, are connected also with a very much enlarged visual area in the brain cortex (as compared with lemurs or tree shrews). As the visual areas are situated in the hinder or occipital portions of the neopallium, the increased cortical area devoted to this sense impression brings about a prolongation backward of the occipital lobes of the brain so that they overhang the cerebellum, as in higher primates and in man. This overhang of the occipital lobes is absent in lemurs and in lower mammals. The olfactory bulbs of the brain are smaller in Tarsius than in lemurs and relatively larger than in the higher primates. Evidently, the sense of smell has degenerated. Hearing, however, has a larger cortical representation in the brain of the tarsier than in that of the lemur. This is thought by some authorities to be a result of the increased mobility of the head in the erect-sitting or hopping animal, which enables it to turn its head with greater facility to catch sound waves than is possible in the case of a long-snouted, pronograde animal. Perhaps head-swiveling is more efficient than ear-cocking.

Wood Jones has suggested that, when any definite area of the brain is the seat of a well-defined sensation or sensibility, the motor center that governs the movements of the parts most intimately related to that sensibility will be in close proximity to that area of the brain in which the sensory center lies. Accordingly, he supposes that, since olfactory sensations are first to receive cortical representation in the neopallium, the snout-tactile area will be in immediate proximity to the olfactory area, and, since the mouth is associated with the snout, the sense of taste and the snout-movement center will also be in the same neighborhood. He then reconstructs a hypothetical primitive neopallial area—a cortical region near the olfactory archepallium containing centers devoted to the "storing, sorting, and association of impressions of taste, snout sensa-tions, and snout movements."

When the hand is added to the snout as a tactile organ, it is probable that a hand-tactile area will be developed on the neopallium beyond that devoted to snout touch, with a corresponding motor area in prox-imity to it. It is the opinion of Wood Jones that the development of the hand as a tactile organ will be correlated with an increased power of vision and an increased visual area in the brain cortex, since the hands are used for bringing objects into closer proximity to the eyes so that a clearer impression of them may be gained. Add to this fact the very reasonable assumption that visual impression and tactile impression from the hands will be simultaneous and correlated and will give rise to associations of touch and sight that were previously tactile-olfactory sensations.

The same author emphasizes the fuller realization of its own anatomy gained by an animal that can move its head easily and readily in almost any direction, so that it can see most parts of its body and can also use its hands for tactile exploration of all of its bodily parts. Such an animal as a horse can have but a limited knowledge of its external anatomy, since this knowledge is restricted by the parts it can touch with its nose and see with its eyes. On the other hand, in an aboreal animal with emancipated tactile hands, with a free moving head, and with stereo-scopic vision, a complete knowledge of its own bodily parts is naturally acquired. Wood Jones, therefore, supposes that certain "association" areas of the brain, that develop in the arboreal mammal in conjunction with the enlargement of the cortical areas devoted to sight, touch, and movement, are "pictured movement areas" in which are represented movements of those parts of the body of which the animal has a concrete and definite knowledge. And, as in man, for example, certain areas of the neopallium are devoted to sensory and motor areas of the forearm, the leg, the thigh, the knee, et cetera, so to these centers the impressions of "pictured parts" are added. Movements of different parts only are represented in the brain cortex, since it is generally agreed that muscles are not in themselves either realized by the animal or represented in the cortex. The higher the development of the brain, the more com-pletely are the conscious movements initiated in these areas that associate sensory impressions with movements of the part realized to be concerned. In man all voluntary or pictured movements are affected by injury to these areas of the brain. In the lower animals this is true to a diminishing extent in correlation with the reduction of these cortical areas and with the decrease in the animal's knowledge of its own external anatomy.

This theory, then, supposes that the pictured movement areas of the brain have developed largely as a result of the arboreal primate's using its hands for touching and exploring itself, and moving its head about so that it can see and feel and appreciate all parts of its body.

In the Eocene period of the Tertiary epoch, the tarsioids were already differentiated into American and European groups, each comprising several different genera. All were, at first, very small in size, and some had begun a precocious specialization that rules them out from the direct ancestral line of higher forms. Indeed, it is not certain that the existing Tarsius spectrum is descended from any fossil tarsioid form hitherto discovered.

But from some similar large-brained, short-jawed, arboreal-hopping tarsioid, which used its hands for prehension and feeding, and which had already developed the visual and auditory parts of the neopallium at the expense of the olfactory archepallium, the Anthropoidea, including New World and Old World monkeys, anthropoid apes, and man, have certainly evolved.

Branching Out: Monkey Stage

At the end of the Eocene period, the primitive tarsioids suddenly branched out and grew up into higher forms both in America and in the Old World. Some of the American tarsioids wandered into South America and there gave rise to the existing families of New World primates—the Cebidae, or American monkeys, and the Hapalidae, or marmosets.

There are only two or three fossil monkeys from the Miocene deposits of South America that serve to bridge the gap between the modern New World primates and the early Eocene fossils. The most important changes in the tarsioid ancestors leading to the development of the modern American monkeys were a rapid expansion in the size of the brain, especially in its breadth and in the development of the frontal region, and a growth forward of the outer borders of the orbits so that the eyes were brought into an almost completely frontal position. The face was shortened and retracted under the orbits, which are smaller than those of tarsioids and with more nearly complete back walls. Up to this point, the changes that produced the American monkey from the tarsioids are substantially identical with those that must have taken place in the development of the higher Old World forms. But the ancestors of the American Cebidae began to develop very long canine teeth, and in many of them the tails began to be adapted for coiling about boughs, thus providing them with a fifth prehensile organ very useful in arboreal life but restrictive in the postural habits that were a consequence of this new development. The truly prehensile tail, found in the American monkeys alone of all the primates, has a curved tip, the concavity of which is naked and serves as a tactile as well as a prehensile organ. The development of the caudal member for this purpose encouraged a habit of hanging by the tail head-downward, which tended to make of the feet suspending rather than supporting members and militated against the possibility of a biped gait or an erect posture.

In the spider monkey (Ateles) alone of all the Cebidae, the habit of swinging by the arms from bough to bough brought about certain bodily modifications that suggest those of the anthropoid apes. Results of this arm locomotion are the elongation of the fore limbs, strong development of the collar bones, and a tendency for the chest to be flattened from front to back. However, the habit of swinging from bough to bough by use of the arms was followed by unfortunate effects upon the hands. The fingers became elongated and curved in a hook-like fashion, and the thumb, no longer opposed to the other digits in the swings from one branch to another, degenerated and became reduced to a mere vestige. Thus the tactile delicacy of the hand and the precious power of opposability of the thumb were sacrificed to a suspensory and locomotor function. None of the anthropoid apes, although using the arms to a great extent for tree locomotion, have similarly lost the thumb, although it is small and perhaps degenerate in all of them. The possession of a perfectly prehensile tail, in the case of the spider monkey, tended to transfer to that caudal member some of the tactile functions usually retained by the hands. The tail is also used, it is said, both to convey objects to the mouth and as a pioneer prehensile organ, being held before the face and often grasping boughs before the hands take hold. In this animal the tail may be said truly to "wag the dog," and, although useful in the trees, it brings about bodily specializations that limit evolutionary possibilities.

The New World families of primates are often called "Platyrrhini" because their nostrils are widely separated at the base and tend to look outward, whereas in the higher primates of the Old World series the opposite nostrils are close together and look downward, whence these latter are called the "Catarrhini." These differences are probably not due to adaptation but are inherent stock variations that have no bearing upon the respiratory, olfactory, or tactile functions to which the noses in the two groups are put. Such non-adaptive variations are significant in proclaiming diversity of descent.

The American monkeys and marmosets represent a higher stage of primate evolution than the lemurs and the tarsier in that the brain is enlarged and stereoscopic vision is fully realized. But in other important features, such as the development of a prehensile tail and, in the case of the marmosets, the retention or redevelopment of claws, they have strayed away from the paths of progress that lead toward the highest primate forms. They do not offer an example of a stage through which man's ancestors passed, nor can they be said to be, in any sense, forms ancestral to man.

While the American monkeys were evolving from tarsioid ancestors in the New World, a much greater and more important differentiation of the more progressive tarsioids of the Old World was giving rise to the Cercopithecidae (the Old World tailed monkeys), the Hylobatidae (gibbons), and to the Simiidae (great apes). The earliest ancestral catarrhine monkey occurs in the deposits of the Lower Oligocene in the dried-up lake bed of the Fayum, Egypt. Palaeontologists are certain that this ancestral catarrhine was derived from a tarsioid form. Parapithecus, the fossil monkey in question, is represented only by a lower jaw and some teeth. The size of the parts preserved indicate an animal smaller than any existing Old World monkey. Its teeth and jaws are about half as large as those of the gibbon, the smallest of the anthropoids. It is fortunate that the mandible or lower jaw is the most time-resisting bone in the body, because from it and from the even more durable teeth a palaeontologist can obtain a better idea of the general form and habits of an animal than from any other skeletal parts. Probably the reason why fossils are so often represented by teeth and jaws is that these are peculiarly inedible morsels and are almost certain to be rejected even by powerful carnivores that are able to crunch up and digest ordinary animal bones.

Dr. William K. Gregory, one of the most competent students of primate palaeontology, regards Parapithecus as by far the most primitive of all known Old World apes and monkeys and, in its known characters, standing in or quite near to the line of descent leading to the anthropoid apes and eventually to man. The teeth of this animal consisted of two incisors, one canine, two premolars, and three molars, above and below, and on each side. This is the dental formula of the Anthropoidea (including man) and is generally written thus: $I\frac{2}{2}C\frac{1}{1}P\frac{2}{2}M\frac{3}{3}$. The canines are small and the grinding teeth are low-cusped; the incisors incline gently forward. The form of the teeth indicates a mixed diet, possibly of insects, fruit, birds' eggs, and small reptiles. The chin region is narrow, and the sides of the mandible flare out behind. The face of the animal must have been short and the brain case broad.

The family Cercopithecidae, the tailed monkeys of the Old World, differentiated from the primitive catarrhine stock of which Parapithecus is the first fossil representative. This development took place during the Oligocene and Miocene periods. The Cercopithecidae are generally arboreal and very agile, rivalling the lemurs in activity, and with specialized eyes, the fields of which overlap so that vision has become binocular. They are not nocturnal like lemurs but move abroad in the daylight. The sense of smell and probably the sense of hearing have degenerated to a considerable extent, but the brain is superior in general development and possibilities to the brains of the Cebidae. The principal characteristics of this family have been described on pages 21–25 and need not be repeated here.

There are, however, two interesting and diverse specializations in this family that merit further attention. The first of these has to do with the ground-dwelling habits of the baboons. These animals live in the rocky, hilly country of Africa and Arabia, rarely ascending trees. They have retained the primate limbs with five digits and grasping thumbs and great toes. The power of opposability is unimpaired, and they walk upon the palms of their hands and soles of their feet like quadrupeds. Evidently their terrestrial life was adopted after their arboreal and prehensile limbs were perfected. Their pronograde gait upon the ground is a continuation of a similar method of progression in trees. When their ancestors took to the ground, they must have been monkeys whose size and strength rendered them fit to cope with the greater dangers of a terrestrial habitat and whose bodily adaptations did not permit an erect posture.

It seems difficult to avoid the conclusion that the long, dog-like snouts of these animals and their projecting, sabre-like canine teeth are a secondary adaptation developed because of the necessity of using all four limbs principally for locomotion, which, therefore, throws back upon the snout the grazing and defensive function that it subserves in terrestrial quadrupeds. The tree-dwelling cercopiths have neither this excessive snout-length nor the tusk-like canines of the "dog-faced" baboons. It is significant that even in the ground-dwelling cercopiths the eyes remain in the frontal plane, the visual areas of the cortex are extensive, and the sense of smell remains degenerative (Fig. 5 A, B). Thus the arboreal heritage in this respect is retained. The brain in the dog-faced baboons, possibly as a result of the secondary elongation of the facial skeleton, is relatively very small but, apparently, not inferior in organization to that of more arboreal Old World monkeys. These animals, nevertheless, frequently assume an erect-sitting posture and convey things to their mouths with their hands. There is, then, no perfect correlation between hand-feeding and snout regression.

The other interesting specialization in the family Cercopithecidae is the sacculated stomach that has been developed in the Semnopithecinae. Instead of a simple stomach, these animals have a series of pouches, which are regarded as modifications caused by their herbivorous diet and especially by leaf-eating. Since monkeys that possess sacculated stomachs

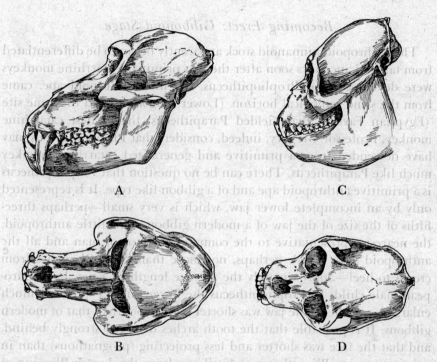

Fig. 5. Secondary enlargements of the jaws of Old World and New World primates. A, side view and B, top view of a baboon skull, showing elongated snout, tuck-like canines, and small brain case (Family Cercopithecidae). C, side view and D, top view of howler monkey skull, showing enlarged hinder parts of lower jaw connected with vocal specialization, and relatively small brain case (Family Cebidae).

have no cheek pouches, it is possible that the cheek pouches replace the first compartment of the stomach. In man, anomalous instances of the occurrence of a sacculated stomach have been recorded, and there are traces of this sacculation in human foetuses. The sacculated stomach found in the Semnopithecus monkeys may be capable of providing for rumination. This is an instance of the apparent effect of physiology upon morphology, of function upon form.

Neither the present-day tailed monkeys of the Old World nor their fossil ancestors, with the possible exception of Parapithecus of the Egyptian Oligocene, represent a stage in human evolution. They have specialized along lines divergent from those that lead to the humanoid type. Such specialization can hardly be attributed to chance alone. It must be due, in a measure, to the inherent limitations and hereditary tendencies that manifested themselves at an early period in the ancestral stock of this group of primates.

Becoming Erect: Gibbonoid Stage

The anthropoid-humanoid stock apparently began to be differentiated from tarsioid ancestors soon after the first primitive catarrhine monkeys were developed. For Propliopithecus, the first anthropoid ape, came from the same geological horizon (Lower Oligocene) and the same site (Egyptian Fayum) that yielded Parapithecus, the earliest catarrhine monkey. Professor Gregory, indeed, considers that Propliopithecus may have descended from a primitive and generalized catarrhine monkey much like Parapithecus. There can be no question that Propliopithecus is a primitive anthropoid ape and of a gibbon-like type. It is represented only by an incomplete lower jaw, which is very small—perhaps three-fifths of the size of the jaw of a modern gibbon. This little anthropoid, the nearest representative to the common ancestor of man and all the anthropoid apes, stood, perhaps, not more than 20 or 21 inches from crown to heel—approximately the average length of a new-born European male child. In Propliopithecus the lower canines were not much enlarged, and the whole jaw was shorter and deeper than that of modern gibbons. It is probable that the tooth arches diverged strongly behind, and that the face was shorter and less projecting (prognathous) than in existing species. Pliopithecus, a fossil ape from the Lower Pliocene of Germany, is probably a descendant of Propliopithecus and is an almost full-fledged gibbon. In this ancestral gibbon, the elongated, sabre-like canines have not yet developed, and the jaw is deeper than that of modern forms.

Although the brains of gibbons represent some advance over those of the catarrhine monkeys, they are not as extensively convoluted as those of the great anthropoid apes. The gibbon is the specialized descendant of small, generalized, arboreal anthropoids, which were the precursors of all the great apes of today and of man also. Especially in posture and mode of locomotion, the gibbon exemplifies a most important step in the humanoid direction, and it will be profitable to discuss in some detail these gibbonoid modifications which may have taken place even in such a remote ancestral anthropoid as Propliopithecus.

Tarsiers, lemurs, and monkeys frequently adopt an erect-sitting posture in the trees, but it was not until the evolution of the primitive gibbonoid apes that the modifications of the body for the upright posture began in the primate order. We are likely to think of the erect posture as pertaining to man only, but in so doing we confuse posture with gait. Man is an erect biped walker, but the gibbon is an erect tree climber and frequently an erect biped when on the ground. The adaptations that have made possible the human attitude and human form of progression began in early anthropoids before the giant primates were evolved.

In an animal that goes on all fours, the spine and the long axis of the body cavities are approximately parallel to the ground. The internal organs are packed in these body cavities in such a way that they are supported by the rib cage or chest wall, by the abdominal wall, and by the front portion of the pelvis, which is greatly elongated fore-and-aft. When such a pronograde animal stands upon its hind legs, it soon becomes uncomfortable, because the viscera tend to sag down into the pelvic cavity, no longer being supported by the ventral body wall. In an animal adapted for an upright posture, the abdominal contents must be so fixed and suspended that they will not slip downward.

The present gibbons and the ancestral anthropoids adopted an erect arboreal posture partially as a result of the habit of swinging from bough to bough by means of the arms rather than running along the branches and leaping from the hind legs as do lower primates. This arm locomotion (brachiation), common to all anthropoid apes, involves the suspension of the body with its spine and long axis perpendicular to the ground instead of parallel to it. All trunk-climbing necessitates a similar attitude, but the smaller arboreal animals, when at rest, are usually found upon the more or less horizontal boughs. The larger an arboreal animal becomes, the more closely is he likely to confine himself to the strong and thick branches near the trunk of the tree, since the smaller branches and the tips of the branches are not strong enough to support his weight. Consequently, an increase in the size of an arboreal primate is likely to result in the animal's maintaining more or less continually an erect, climbing posture, with its backbone parallel to the tree trunk rather than to the ground. This again puts the animal in a position where it is constantly using its arms for suspension and for locomotion.

Gibbons of today are not large or heavy animals, and the ancestral forms recovered from fossil deposits were still smaller. It seems probable, therefore, that erect posture and arm locomotion in the trees may have been adopted originally through inclination rather than through necessity. At any rate, the changes in the mode of fixation of the viscera that upright posture necessitates are already present in the modern gibbons and were certainly complete in their fossil ancestors. The small bowel in pronograde animals is loosely attached by a fan-like sheet of membrane called a mesentery. The upright primates, including the gibbon, the great anthropoids, and man, have the bowels and the other viscera closely bound to the back wall of the abdominal cavity or suspended from the head-end. Occasionally a human individual is born with a pronograde type of mesentery, and, in such persons, the bowel is likely to twist upon itself, causing obstructions. In the development of the human embryo, the earlier stages show the pronograde attachment of the viscera, but later these are modified in accordance with the requirements of the erect posture.[7]

The muscles that serve to depress the tail in lower primates are adapted to a new function in the anthropoid apes and in man. A dog, when frightened or in disgrace, will tuck his tail between his legs. The tail is a shutter that closes the back orifices of the body, and, by depressing his tail, the animal secures for himself a certain physical, if not moral, support. Already in the gibbon, the external tail has disappeared entirely. Its vertebral remnants are bent underneath the pelvic opening, and the muscles that formerly were tail depressors are spread out to form the pelvic floor and thus assist in supporting the pelvic viscera.

The diaphragm is a muscular and tendinous partition which, in mammals, separates the chest cavity from the abdominal cavity. In the orthograde or upright primates, the heart rests upon the diaphragm and is supported by it. In pronograde monkeys, a process or lobe of the right lung (the azygos) occupies a space between the heart and the diaphragm. A rudiment of this lobe, occupying a similar position, is sometimes observed in man. In the gibbon, the azygos lobe is usually present.

The chest or thorax of the typical mammalian quadruped is a narrow rib cage slung between its fore limbs. It is flattened from side to side and very deep from the keel-like breastbone (sternum) to the backbone. The ribs are heart-shaped hoops with the apices downward and attached to the segments of the spine at their bases by movable articulations and to the sternum at their points by flexible cartilages. The thoracic cavity is completely filled by the heart, lungs, and other vessels. In primitive land vertebrates, air is drawn into the lungs by the ribs being pulled forward toward the fore limbs, creating a suction within the body cavity. In all

[7] Keith, *The Human Body,* pp. 82–83.

pronograde animals in which the fore limbs are usually planted firmly
on the ground or on boughs of trees, inspiration is accomplished mainly
by the muscles that are attached to the immovable shoulder girdle, pulling the flexible rib cage forward and downward. But, when the axis of
the body is changed so that the spine is perpendicular to the ground, an
internal method of respiration develops whereby the thorax is enlarged
for the drawing in of the air by the lowering of the diaphragmatic floor
of the thoracic cavity. Wood Jones suggests that the animal sitting erect
or brachiating in the trees no longer has its fore limbs fixed so that the
muscles that elevate the ribs in inspiration act upon an immovable point
of attachment. These muscles in the animal with emancipated fore limbs
also serve, in part, to move the shoulder girdle. The diaphragm, therefore, has to function more actively in order to enlarge the thoracic cavity
so that the air may be drawn into the lungs. In pronograde mammals, it
acts in inspiration chiefly by compressing the abdominal contents and
resisting suction upward into the chest cavity. This diaphragm in upright animals is a muscular dome projecting upward into the thoracic
cavity, its tendon being the top of the dome. The sides of the dome are
in contact with the thoracic walls. When a breath is taken, the curved
muscular fibers, which are like ribs of the dome, contract and straighten
out so that the dome becomes more conical; the heart and lungs sink
downward with the falling of the diaphragmatic dome, while the ribs
are elevated by the pull of the inspiratory muscles. The lungs then take
in air and expand to fill the enlarged thoracic cavity. In expiration, the
diaphragm expands or relaxes, and the rib cage is dropped so that the air
in the lungs is expelled by the pressure. It is quite obvious that diaphragmatic breathing takes on an increased importance with the weakening
of the muscular pull upon the ribs caused by the mobility of the fore
limbs.

It is not quite so easy to explain the flattening of the thorax from
front to back, which, in erect animals, replaces the lateral flattening
characteristic of quadrupeds. Man has a broad, shallow chest, and this
antero-posterior flattening begins to be marked in the erect-sitting arboreal primates and culminates in the human stock. It seems probable
that breathing functions have little to do with this change of form, which
is already manifested in the gibbon. The alteration in the shape of the
thorax is partly due to the shift in the direction of gravity that takes
place with the change of the body axis. In quadrupeds, the weight of the
thoracic contents tends to bear down upon the ventral chest wall increasing the depth from the vertebral column to the breast bone. The
fore-and-aft movements of the fore limbs may have also the effect of com-

pressing the thoracic cage laterally. In the erect animal, on the other hand, the pull of the thoracic contents is downward, and the lateral movements of the arms outward from the body tend to broaden the shoulder girdle and to increase the length of the collar bone or clavicle, which acts as a strut to hold the shoulder blade and arm away from the center of the body. We recall that in typical quadrupeds, such as carnivores and ungulates, the clavicle is absent.

The lateral position and the bracing of the shoulder joints in the erect animal eliminate the side-to-side compression of the thoracic cage and permit its transverse expansion in the taking in of air. The pectoral muscles, which in man and the anthropoids cover the upper part of the chest and are attached to the upper part of the arm bone and the shoulder blade, depress the shoulder and, when the arm is raised, bring it down to the side and across over the chest. The use of these muscles in lateral arm movements probably tends to flatten the chest and to increase its breadth.

It therefore appears that the shape of the thorax in man and the anthropoids is effected by the free lateral movements of the prehensile fore limbs and by the change in the direction of the gravity pull of the thoracic contents. Diaphragmatic breathing is rendered necessary by this altered gravity pull and by the greater resistance to the raising of the rib cage in the erect posture, as well as by the loss of stability of the points of attachments of the rib-raising muscles due to the mobility of the fore limbs.

The vertebral column or spine of a typical mammalian quadruped is bow-shaped, with the highest point of the arch in the middle of the back, with the concavity of the bow directed downward, the head end bent upward, and the tail end flattened. The weight of the body is suspended from this springy arch. The bony spines of the vertebrae usually converge upon a center of motion in the spinal column, the head end vertebrae and the tail end vertebrae having their spines sloped toward one with an erect spine called the anticlinal vertebra. The position of this anticlinal vertebra is at the point of greatest flexure, the spine being bent and straightened like a spring, when the animal is in motion, by the long muscles attached to the opposed spinous processes. This erect or anticlinal vertebra occurs in all of the pronograde primates; in the lemurs and the Old World monkeys it is usually the tenth rib-bearing or dorsal vertebra; in the New World monkeys, it is variable but always in the lower dorsal series; it is absent in the anthropoid apes and in man, in whom all of the vertebral spines slope downward in varying degrees. Evidently, the disappearance of the anticlinal vertebra and of the opposed slopes of the vertebral spines in the higher primates is an effect of the erect climbing and sitting posture and of the loss of the quadrupedal springing and jumping method of progression.

When an arboreal animal adopts an erect-sitting or a squatting posture in the trees, resting its weight upon its haunches, the simple bow curve of the quadrupedal spine is altered. In the monkeys and other arboreal animals that sit or squat with a curved back and drawn-up knees, this alteration is merely a flattening of the bow curve in the lumbar region—the region between the rib-bearing vertebrae and the pelvis. But in animals that straighten out or extend the legs in climbing, such as anthropoid apes, the flatness of the spine in the lumbar region gives way to a reversed curve or slight forward convexity of this part of the spine. This change takes place because the extension of the legs bends the front part of the pelvis downward and pushes the back part of the pelvis, where it articulates with the spine, and that portion of the spine itself, upward and backward. Thus we see in the gibbon and in the other anthropoid apes the beginning of a lumbar curve, which is accentuated in man as a result of the erect posture and biped gait on the ground. Traces of this lumbar curve may be seen even in the vertebral columns of erect-sitting monkeys when these are in a fresh state with the intervertebral disks of cartilage preserved. In the gibbons, the curve begins to show in the vertebrae themselves.

When the spine of the erect-sitting or squatting animal is perpendicular or nearly perpendicular to the ground, the cervical curve upward of the quadruped becomes an anterior convexity, and the depressing of the tail, or the clamping of it between the buttocks, makes a forward concavity in the sacral region (the region of the spine upon which the pelvic girdle is hung). Hence, the sitting arboreal animal already displays from head to tail the following spinal curves: (1) a forward convexity in the neck region, (2) a forward concavity in thoracic and abdominal region, (3) a flattening or slight forward convexity in the lumbar region (the small of the back), (4) a forward concavity in the sacral region within the pelvic cavity. With the loss of the external tail in the anthropoid apes, the few remaining tail vertebrae are bent underneath the pelvis and continue and accentuate the sacral concavity. The body weight is now suspended vertically from the spine, instead of horizontally as in pronograde animals, and the spine has become a somewhat S-shaped vertical spring instead of a horizontal bow spring.

In a quadrupedal mammal, the skull is suspended from the end of the spine by two knobs or condyles on the occipital or back surface of the cranium. These occipital condyles rest in depressions in the first vertebra or atlas, and between the condyles is the occipital foramen, a circular or oval orifice through which the spinal cord passes to unite with the brain. The head of the animal is in no sense balanced on the end of the spine but is supported by powerful muscles and ligaments that are attached to the long spines of the vertebrae and elswhere (Fig. 6). The mammalian snout projects along the line of the vertebral column. But when such a pronograde mammal as a dog squats upon its haunches or sits up on its hind legs, it lowers its muzzle so that the head rotates for-

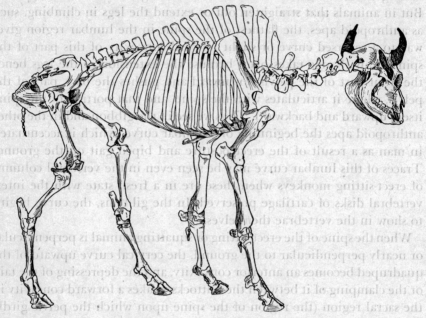

Fig. 6. Skeleton of an American bison, an ungulate, to illustrate specializations for pronograde, digitigrade posture.

ward and downward through almost a quarter of a circle, and the long axis of the snout and skull is now perpendicular to the axis of the spine. This nodding of the head is accomplished by the skull rocking forward upon its occipital condyles. In erect-sitting arboreal animals the change in the position of the head tends to be permanent, and the condylar knobs and the occipital foramen between them migrate from their original position on the back of the skull to a new site in the base of the skull, so that the head now may be said to "rest" upon the spinal column instead of being suspended from it. Yet the head does not balance upon the spine because of the great forward projection of the muzzle and the lack of rearward development of the occipital parts of the brain to offset the protrusion of the snout.

With the recession of the snout, however, which seems to be associated with the emancipation of the fore limbs and the habit of hand-feeding, there is a simultaneous backward growth of the occipital lobes of the brain in order to give cortical representation in the neopallium to the increasingly important sense of vision. In Tarsius and in the lower monkeys, the recession of the snout, the shifting of the eyes to a frontal plane, the backward growth of the occipital lobes of the brain, and the migration of the foramen magnum and the condyles from the back to the base of the skull are associated changes. These become more and more evident in the higher primate forms, are particularly noticeable in the upright anthropoids, and culminate in man.

Practically all mammals have seven cervical or neck vertebrae, regardless of the length or mobility of the neck.[8] The giraffe has seven cervical vertebrae, and the whale, which appears to have no neck at all, also has seven. Differences in neck length depend upon the height of the bodies (centra) of the vertebrae. The more the snout protrudes, the longer are the spines of the cervical vertebrae, which, projecting backward from the vertebral column, give attachment to the muscles supporting the head. In the upright primates, the decrease in the size of the vertebral spines accompanies the recession of the snout region and the backward growth of the occipital lobes of the brain. In Tarsius, the cervical spines are undeveloped except on the second neck vertebra. In man, the skull is so nearly balanced upon the spinal column that the cervical spines have become very degenerate and are forked or bifid, except the sixth and seventh. In the anthropoid apes, the projection of the jaws and smaller development of the hinder parts of the brain preserve the horizontal and long spines (Fig. 10). The nearest approach to man in this respect is found in the gibbon.

The number of rib-bearing (thoracic or dorsal) vertebrae in the primates probably ranges from 12 to 17 in the Lemuroidea and from 11 to 15 in the Anthropoidea. The loris appears to have the largest number, but several species of lemurs have only 12 pairs. American monkeys also appear to vary in number of dorsal vertebrae from 12 to 15, but cebus, spider, and howler genera most commonly have 14, with reduction commoner than increase. Macaques usually have 12 pairs of ribs, and other Old World monkeys 12 or 13 pairs. Man and the orang ordinarily have 12 dorsal vertebrae and the other anthropoid apes 13. Schultz thinks that 14 and 15 dorsal vertebrae probably represent the

---

[8] The four exceptions are the American manatee with six cervicals, and three types of South American Sloth, one with six, one with eight, and one with nine cervicals. Sloths hang upside down, but not by their necks, Kingsley, *The Vertebrate Skeleton*, p. 50.

primitive primate condition, with 11 (found only in man and more frequently in the orang) the most specialized condition.[9] Evidently, the number of ribs is not affected by the shift to the upright posture in the trees on the part of the anthropoid-humanoid stocks. There is no doubt, however, that man and the orang-utan for different reasons have lost each a pair of ribs, since 13 pairs is the ancestral number in the anthropoid-humanoid stocks. The diaphragm always has an attachment to the rib process of the twentieth vertebra, however vestigial that proc-

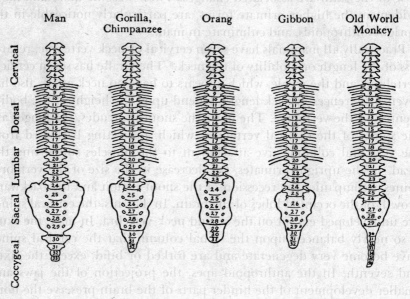

Fig. 7. Diagram showing approximate average number of segments in the various regions of the spine in different primates.

ess may be. The twentieth is, therefore, the last respiratory segment. The reason for such loss has to do, however, with method of progression rather than upright posture in the trees and will be considered in its proper place.

The lumbar column is that part of the spine between the rib-bearing portion and the sacral region to which the pelvis is articulated. Pronograde primates usually have a long, rod-like lumbar column upon which the pelvis is flexed in leaping from the hind limbs. Thus, in the lemuroids the number of lumbar vertebrae seems to vary from 6 to 9, with 8 and 9 quite common in some genera. Schultz found a majority of macaques to have 7 lumbars, cebus monkeys 6, howlers 5, and spider monkeys 4.[10] Evidently, specialization in the primates commonly leads to a reduction

9 Schultz, "Skeleton of the Trunk and Limbs," pp. 303–438.
10 *Ibid.*, p. 314.

in the number of segments in the lumbar part of the spine. With the evolution of the anthropoid-human stock, the number of lumbars was probably reduced to 5, which is the commonest number in the gibbons and siamangs. In the giant apes, a further reduction takes place, with the orang-utan and chimpanzee usually possessing 4 lumbar vertebrae, and the gorilla having 4 or 3 lumbar segments, Schultz found 60 per cent of 75 lowland gorillas with 4 lumbars, 38.7 per cent with 3, and 1.3 per cent with 5 lumbars. A very short series of mountain gorillas (7) had a majority with 3 lumbars. Man is the most stable of the high primates with 5 lumbar vertebrae in about 92 per cent of cases, but apparently the howler monkey shows equal stability, and the spider monkey (20 specimens) was invariable with 4 lumbars.

Schultz thinks that the original and most primitive number of combined thoracic and lumbar (thoraco-lumbar) vertebrae in the primates was probably 20, and that some of the lemuroids have tended to increase this number and the higher primates to reduce it. The reduction ordinarily affects the lumbar region exclusively. It has proceeded farther in the gibbon family (average 17.8) than in any of the monkeys; farther still in man (average 17.0) and farthest in the great apes (chimpanzee 16.8, gorilla 16.6, orang-utan 16.0).

The sacrum consists of a number of vertebrae fused together, to which the pelvic girdle which carries the legs is articulated. In the lower primates, the number of sacral vertebrae ranges from 2 to 4, with such Old and New World monkeys as have been studied showing very high percentages of 3 sacral segments.

In the gibbon family the commonest number of sacrals is 4, but almost 39 per cent have 5 segments. In the orang, over 68 per cent have 5 sacral vertebrae and nearly twice as many animals have 6 segments as have only 4. In man, the percentage of five-segmented sacra rises to about 78, with nearly all of the rest having 6. In the chimpanzee series examined by Schultz, the percentages of five- and six-segmented sacra were equal, and in gorillas it seems probable that slightly more than half have 6 vertebrae in the sacrum. The averages of the high primates are: Hylobatidae 4.4, orang-utan 5.1, man 5.2, chimpanzee 5.4, gorilla 5.5.

At the end of the spine are the caudal or coccygeal vertebrae. The maximum in the primates is 34 (observed in one spider monkey) and the minimum one (found often in gibbons, siamangs, and orangs). In the anthropoid apes and man, who lack external tails, the coccygeal vertebrae vary from 1 to 6. Man averages 4.2 coccygeal vertebrae (with 61 per cent having 4). The chimpanzee is very unstable and shows a range from 2 to 6 caudal vertebrae; its average is 3.3. Gorillas most commonly have 3 coccygeal vertebrae, but nearly one quarter of these animals have 4 and about the same proportion 2. Thus, in man, the terminal or tail portion of the spine tends to be less reduced than in any of the anthropoid apes.

All of these tedious statistics about the number of segments in the different parts of primate spines bear upon the process of evolution. Sir Arthur Keith,[11] following Rosenberg, points out that in the anthropoid apes and man there has been no addition or suppression of segments in the dorsal, lumbar, or sacral regions of the spine, but only in the tail or caudal region. Any shortening of the lumbar region is effected by the pelvis shifting up the spine so that lumbar vertebrae are transmuted into sacral vertebrae, sacral vertebrae into tail (caudal) vertebrae, and the elimination of the segment occurs at the end of the caudal series. In other words, the pelvis climbs up the spine, and excess vertebrae are "shucked" off the tail end.

The shortening of the lumbar region has been considered by Keith as the result of the new method of locomotion (arm-swinging) adopted by the higher upright primates, since the long, rod-like lumbar column of pronograde leapers is no longer necessary. The brachiating spider monkey, which is the only lower primate that uses this form of progression, fits in with this explanation in that it seems to have usually only 4 lumbars. However, another New World monkey, the cebus, and still another, the howler, show reduced lumbar regions but do not brachiate. The cebus most commonly has 6 lumbars and very frequently (35 per cent) only 5. The howler has 5 lumbars in 92 per cent of cases. It is possible that these animals and the spider monkey also have undergone a diminution of the lumbar spine in connection with their habit of suspending themselves by their prehensile tails. Whether an animal hangs from its hands or from its tail, it is mechanically desirable to shorten the interval between the rib cage and the pelvic girdle by reducing the length of the lumbar region and thus consolidating the trunk.

The incorporation of additional lumbar segments into the sacrum, which begins with the gibbon and is increasingly manifested in man and the great apes, can be explained in the case of man and the gibbon partly by the fact that in biped walkers the pelvis must transmit all of the body weight to the lower limbs and consequently requires a stronger sacro-iliac articulation. The heavy bodies of the great apes seem to demand increased strength of the sacro-iliac articulation, although they are quadrupeds when on the ground.

11 Keith, "Suppression and Transmutation," p. 18.

The reason for man's retention of a greater number of caudal or coccygeal vertebrae than have been preserved by any of the anthropoid apes is connected with his erect posture, as is also his loss of a pair of ribs. We may defer discussion of these matters until we deal with the evolution of giant primates.

Here, however, we may inquire into the probable causes of the disappearance of the tail in the higher primate stocks. The tail is, of course, an ancient vertebrate inheritance. It is dispensed with in adult life by such amphibians as frogs and toads, possibly as a result of their leaping habits of progression. In a small arboreal mammal, a tail may be useful for prehensile purposes or as a balancing rod. In a terrestrial quadruped, the tail may be useful for brushing off flies and other insects from parts of the body that are out of reach of the mouth. In an erect-sitting animal with free prehensile limbs, any part of the body can be reached easily with the hands. The tail is thus deprived of its fly-switching function, its rudder function having long since disappeared with the adoption of a life on dry land. Arboreal animals with bushy tails use these tails as a sort of comforter to keep themselves warm at night. But such animals are small; the tail cannot be of use in this way to a large animal. Certain terrestrial hopping animals, such as the kangaroo, use the tail as a third leg of a tripodal base of support when sitting up and at rest. But such a heavy tail would be a very serious incumbrance to an arboreal animal.

It is evident that the tail has lost its function in the higher primates. But that does not explain why and how it disappeared. In some of the ground-dwelling pronograde primates, such as the mandrill, drill, black "ape" of Celebes, and certain macaques, the tail is very short and stumpy. In these animals the last few vertebrae of the tail are rudimentary, and the end of the tail is calloused and rough. Darwin thought that this projecting stump of a tail was reduced by friction. He favored the view that when the monkey sat down the short tail was depressed into the interspace between the ischial callosities to escape being pinched between them and the ground and that in time the curvature became permanent. Under these circumstances the end of the tail may have been lost by a process of attrition and the basal part permanently curved underneath where it served to close the pelvic aperture and to support the pelvic viscera. Whether or not this naïve Lamarckian view is correct, it seems probable that the disappearance of the external tail in the anthropoid apes and man is in some way connected with the upright posture in the trees and with the new function the caudal remnant subserves in the erect or semi-erect posture. The entangling tail has become a moral and visceral prop.

However, a tendency toward shortening and eventual disappearance of the tail may have manifested itself in certain branches of the primate stock as an independent and non-adaptive variation, in no way influenced by use or disuse. The tail is also absent in the slow loris (Nycticebus tardigradus), a lemur that is an arboreal clinger and does not leap but crawls along the branches and shuffles along the ground, and, like man, has all of its vertebral spines sloped in one direction. All of the existing lorises in Asia and the allied pottos in Africa are tailless. They belong to the Suborder Lemuroidea but closely parallel the tarsioids in the forward shifting of the eyes and the enlargement of the brain-case. The snout is, however, projecting, and, according to Gregory, the dentition shows no human possibilities. It is, in my opinion, perfectly possible that the anthropoid apes and man may have descended from tarsioid ancestors, which, like the lemuroid or pseudo-tarsioid lorises, lacked tails or, at any rate, lost them before they evolved into catarrhines and anthropoids.

Let us recapitulate the principal modifications in the human direction that took place in the common ancestors of man and the great apes at the gibbonoid stage of evolution before the development of giant primates. These are the assumption of an erect-sitting posture as the habitual position of the animal at rest; the broadening and flattening of the thorax connected with arm locomotion and altered gravitational pull; an increasingly marked tendency (already initiated at the tarsioid stage of development) for the skull to be poised on the vertebral column from a basal articulation rather than suspended from an occipital articulation; the reduction of the lumbar column by one segment, owing to an upward shift of the pelvic articulation; the foreshadowing of a lumbar curve; and a greater power of extending or straightening out the legs.

The extension of the legs will be discussed in detail later, but here it may be mentioned that a habit of arm suspension and arm progression is likely to involve the straightening out of the trailing hind limbs. However, the gibbon swings from bough to bough with the knees bent up close to the body and not with trailing legs. That the gibbon can extend its legs is shown by its erect biped method of progression on the ground. The gibbon, when walking, does not, however, completely extend the leg upon the thigh (i.e., he walks with his knees bent).

The modern gibbons have, of course, become tremendously specialized for brachiating by the elongation of the arms, and their canine teeth have also become projecting and spike-like. These and other modifications probably belong especially to the gibbonoid heritage and were acquired after the giant primate stock branched off from the primitive small anthropoid stem.

Outgrowing the Nursery: Giant Anthropoid Stage

During the Miocene period, the giant primates developed from the small and primitive anthropoids of the preceding Oligocene period. Teeth and fragmentary jaws of great anthropoid apes have been discovered in the Siwalik hills of India, in northern Egypt, in Kenya Colony, East Africa, and in several European sites. The characteristics of these early great apes can be deduced only from the intensive study of their teeth and such parts of their jaws as have survived. The Middle Miocene anthropoids had advanced far in structure toward the orangs, chimpanzees, and gorillas and, probably in some cases, toward man. Palaeosimia, an Indian fossil from the Middle Miocene deposits of India, is almost certainly an ancestor of the orang-utan, and a lower jaw from the Upper Pliocene series in the same region shows essentially orang characters. It seems probable that the orang-utans became differentiated from the primitive giant anthropoid stock in the Lower Miocene somewhere in northern India and subsequently migrated southward to their present habitat in Borneo and Sumatra. There is reason for believing that the orangs separated from the common, giant anthropoid-humanoid stock before the latter differentiated into chimpanzee, gorilla, and human lines. The evidence for such conclusions rests mainly upon dental characters and will be developed later in this narrative. Sivapithecus indicus is an Upper Miocene Indian genus which Gregory regards provisionally as an early offshoot between the Palaeosimia-orang group and the Dryopithecus group. Dryopithecus is a fossil family or subfamily represented by many fragmentary specimens, differing greatly in size and considerably in details. Some species of Dryopithecus seem to lead directly to the gorilla or the chimpanzee; others are intermediate between the two; all of them, and especially the earlier and more primitive forms, show characteristics that ally them more or less remotely to man. Some of the best palaeontological authorities of today regard man as having been derived from a primitive Dryopithecus stock, but this opinion cannot be substantiated or refuted until more complete fossil evidence is available.

Groups of animals, in their evolution through successive geological periods, simulate to some extent the life of an individual. Periods of infancy, childhood, adolescence, maturity, and senescence are often followed by the ultimate extinction of the group. An increase in size of the members of the animal group throughout successive periods often seems to be a part of this growing-up process. But this is not as constant a phenomenon as is bodily growth in individuals. Some geologically ancient groups have decreased in size and others have remained relatively stationary. At a certain period in the life cycle of an animal phylum, relatively gigantic forms are often produced. The classic example, of course, is found in the Age of Reptiles. Mammals began as very small animals and, as a class, increased in size throughout the Tertiary epoch, although this increase does not manifest itself in every order, family, genus, and species. Among the primates, the lemuroids have shown a comparatively slight increase in size during their evolution, although the modern indris is as large as a terrier, and an extinct lemuroid, the remains of which were found in a cave in Madagascar, is said to have been as large as a donkey. In the Primate Order, the higher groups are usually of larger size than the less highly evolved groups—the American monkeys are larger than the tarsiers; many of the Cercopithecidae are bigger than any of the Cebidae and Hapalidae; and the Simiidae and man are largest of all. There are, however, exceptions in individual genera and species. Gibbons, for instance, are smaller than baboons and some other cercopiths. The extent to which an increase of size takes place in any evolving group is probably dependent upon a complexity of environmental and organic factors, such as abundance of food supply, habitat, secretions of the ductless glands in the organism, et cetera. Natural selection may operate to increase or diminish the size of animals in eliminating those that are too small or too large for their environmental habitat. Beyond these inadequate generalizations, I am unable to offer any explanation for the development of the giant primates. Probably in the last analysis any increase in size of an animal is an effect of an accumulation of stored-up bodily energy in excess of that expended.

If we take the approximate average weight of a gibbon of either sex to be 13 pounds, an adult male chimpanzee weighs about 8 times as much as a gibbon, an adult man about 11 times as much, a male orang nearly 13 times as much, and an adult male gorilla roughly 38 times the mean gibbon poundage. It is mechanically impossible to increase the size and bulk of an animal greatly without altering its proportions. Otherwise, the enlarged animal would be likely to fall apart. This limitation depends upon the mechanical law of cubes and squares, which is: "if the shape and proportions of any material body remain the same, but its size increases, its strength increases as the square of any one dimension, while its weight increases as the cube." [12]

---

[12] Reynolds, *Evolution of the Human Pelvis*, p. 256.

In the light of this principle, it is easy enough to understand why in man and the great apes the pelvic girdle requires a firmer articulation to the spine than in the featherweight gibbon; why, other things being equal, it is desirable for the giant primates to have shorter lumbar columns, thus reducing the length of the weak and unbraced segment of the spine between the rib cage and the pelvis; and why the construction of the pelvis itself has to be altered profoundly.

We have noted that the gibbon, as contrasted with most pronograde monkeys, has a lumbar spine shorter by one segment, so that the number of lumbar vertebrae is now 5 or 6. The greater bulk of the giant apes renders explicable their tendencies to reduce further the lumbar segments, until in the massive gorillas the proportion of animals with only 3 lumbars is exceeded slightly, if at all, by those that possess 4. Again, while the gibbon has increased the number of its sacral segments from the 3 common and usual in monkeys to 4 and often 5, it is understandable that the larger primate, man, should have less than 5 sacral vertebrae very rarely, 5 sacral vertebrae predominantly, and 6 in more than one fifth of cases. This enlargement of the sacrum reaches its logical climax in gorillas, which are likely to show a slight majority of individuals with six-segmented sacra.

However, there are usually dangers in over-simplified explanations of changes in form by alteration of function or of size and weight. In this case it is to be noted that chimpanzees are, on the average, smaller and lighter than human beings and yet display shortening of the lumbar spine and increased sacralization of vertebrae not much less marked than in the heavier orangs and the vastly more weighty gorillas. Again, man, who is much larger than the gibbon, has the same number of lumbar segments, but less than 40 per cent of the gibbon family have 5 sacral segments (as in man) instead of the modal 4. We can get over this difficulty in the case of the lumbar parity of man and the gibbon by evoking in the former the modifications required by completely erect posture and bipedal gait on the ground. Man's lumbar spine has undergone a secondary elongation in order to provide enough space between his rib cage and his pelvis to accommodate the lumbar curve. This is a marked anterior convexity of the lumbar spine that permits the torso to be bent to a vertical position directly in the long axis of the pelvic girdle and the legs. If we had this forward kink of the lumbar spine with our original 13 pairs of ribs and the reduced lumbar region found in the giant apes, our lowermost ribs might scrape against our pelvic brims, and there would be no space for lateral bending of the upper part of the trunk upon the pelvis. Thus it appears that the re-elongation of the human lumbar region is a functional necessity, and that it is attained by the suppression of the thirteenth pair of ribs, which were presumably a part of the ancestral heritage of man and all of the apes.

Certainly, the orang-utan, which regularly has only 12 pairs of ribs and not infrequently only 11, cannot have suffered this reduction to provide for a secondary enlargement of the lumbar column, because this ape usually has only 4 lumbars and has the shortest spinal column, taking all of the segments together, that is found among the higher primates. This animal is the least terrestrial of the anthropoid apes and probably the least adapted for erect, bipedal walking. The orang frequently hangs by its feet in the trees, and, since it is a heavy ape, such upside-down suspension from the lower extremity would render advantageous a shortened lumbar region but not necessarily the loss of the lowest pair of ribs. As a matter of fact, there are evidences of degeneration in the lower limbs of this ape (in their extreme abbreviation, in the absence of the *ligamentum teres* that holds the head of the femur in its socket, and in the frequent reduction of the great toe). So it is possible to refer the spinal shortening of the Asiatic great ape to its "being dead from the waist down." However, that is hardly a satisfactory explanation. Habitual suspension from the feet ought to hypertrophy rather than atrophy the lower extremity.

When we consider as a whole the phenomena of lumbar shortening, addition of sacral segments, and reduction of coccygeal segments in all of the apes, beginning with the gibbon, it is hard to evade the conclusion that inherent tendencies toward these changes must be present in the anthropoid stock quite aside from functional adaptation or increase of weight or degeneration. We must not be deceived into adopting the view that man is very close to the gibbon in that both separated from the common ancestral anthropoid-humanoid stock before lumbar reduction had proceeded to the extent found in the giant apes. For man has a shorter thoraco-lumbar spine than the small anthropoid, and the re-elongation of lumbar region that makes the number of segments (5) the same as that found in gibbons is due, in the human species, to the loss of a pair of ribs. Man rather shares most of the reduction tendencies in the lower spine that are common to the great apes.

Man has retained the caudal vertebrae in a less vestigal condition than have the great apes, because his erect biped gait and his more capacious pelvic aperture require the support of the caudal muscles and vertebrae to sustain the weight of the viscera, whereas in the anthropoids the pelvic opening is constricted, and the semi-erect atitude and the use of the fore limbs for support when on the ground renders this retention of the caudal vertebrae unnecessary. It is not surprising, therefore, that in man the caudal part of the spine normally consists of 4 and not infrequently of five vertebrae, whereas in the anthropoids the number tends to be reduced, and the segments are far more amorphous and vestigial than in the case of man. The commonest number of tail vertebrae is 3 in the great apes and 2 or 3 in the gibbon. In the gorilla the caudal portion of the spine (coccyx) is scarcely discernible. In the human foetus from the fourth to the eighth week the coccygeal region of the spine protrudes, and the vertebral segments in it number from 8 to 11. Subsequently, the surrounding parts grow out and cover this protruding tail tip, but in a new-born child there can always be observed a post-anal pit or depression, which marks the point where the coccyx disappears below the surface early in the third foetal month. There are a few instances recorded of human individuals born with true tails, in which the coccyx, instead of being bent under, is continued along the axis of the spine and contains a variable number of vertebrae. Vestiges of the extensor and flexor muscles of the tail are found on the dorsal and ventral aspects of about 10 per cent of human bodies dissected, according to Keith, and occasionally there occur also small nodules of bone spanning the continuation of the middle sacral artery and representing the chevron bones of tailed mammals, to which are attached the muscles depressing the tail. I am not aware of any recorded instance of an anthropoid ape with an external tail. Such a manifestation would be much more remarkable as a reversionary fact than it is in man.

The principal changes in the human direction that seem to have taken place at the time of the rise of the giant primates were a further shortening of the lumbar spine by one segment, an enlargement of the sacrum to knit the pelvis more firmly to the spine, and a broadening of the pelvic girdle.

Coming Down to Earth: Terrestrial Anthropoids

A tree is no suitable abiding place for a large and bulky animal. Arboreal life offers an existence of relative security to small and weak creatures and a sufficient food supply to satisfy their small demands. When the preprimate insectivores climbed the trees in the Cretaceous period, they were tiny, defenseless animals. For them tree life offered a means of escape from the dangers of the ground, an adequate basis of subsistence, and a chance of development.

When one group of the Primate Order attained a relatively gigantic size, it forfeited most of the advantages offered by tree life. A tree can scarcely be said to offer an existence of security or comfort for an animal so heavy that it must keep to the larger branches or test out the strength of the smaller before it entrusts its weight to them. Such an animal, however agile, has to waste a good deal of time and effort to keep from falling off the tree. Then consider also the problem of sleeping. I am not aware that any of the smaller primates actually build nests in the trees as sleeping quarters for themselves and their young. However, the chimpanzee and the orang certainly perpetrate this primate anachronism, and the gorilla builds nests both in trees and on the ground. However big the tree, and however tough and broad its leaves, a nest is a no more satisfactory sleeping place for a 150-pound animal than a go-cart as a means of conveyance for a grown-up man.

There is also the matter of food supply. A diet of fruit, nuts, leaves, shoots, insects, birds' eggs, et cetera, is adequate for a small and very agile animal living in a tree. In order to obtain enough of that provender to satisfy its bodily needs, a giant primate must range over a considerable forest area, handicapped by the difficulty of arboreal progression that his great bulk entails. Apparently the orang-utan and the chimpanzee spend most of their time pursuing their appetites and never quite catching up with them. A huge mass of such unnutritious green stuff must be consumed daily by such animals. With this prospect, contrast the possibilities of food-getting on the ground. Here are all sorts of creeping and crawling things which may be caught and devoured, as well as the animals that run and jump. Here one may grub for roots and hunt for eggs, pick berries, and even go fishing. And if one wants nuts or fruit or birds' eggs, it is still possible to climb a tree.

The gorilla is probably mainly a ground-feeder, but in a state of nature a rigid vegetarian. The fourteen-year-old male mountain gorillas in the San Diego zoo were fed about 35 pounds of food apiece per day —all choice fruits, vegetables, and cereals. A gorilla in his native haunts would be hard put to it to find that amount. The San Diego gorillas became fat, but wild gorillas probably get few chances to overeat.

On the ground the barriers to free migration and the pursuit of prey are not so numerous as in the trees; almost any spot on *terra firma* is a more comfortable sleeping place than the crotch of a tree. If an animal of great size falls out of a tree, other animals come and pick its bones; but if an animal on the ground falls, it picks itself up and goes on.

Living on the ground involves, of course, danger from the attacks of other animals. Burrowing habits, speed in locomotion, quills, poison fangs, unpleasant scents, horny hides, inconspicuous coloration—all of these and others are acquisitions of protective value. But the best defense against enemies is to be large, strong, and formidable, unless it is to be clever. The giant primates were and are both powerful and intelligent. And the most intelligent of them and the most powerful have taken to the ground. The gorilla is the largest and strongest of the primates. He is probably also the most ferocious. It seems very unlikely that the gorilla has much to fear from the attacks of any beast of prey except man. There is very little reason to doubt that the gorilla has been driven to descend from the trees in adult life owing to his great size and large appetite. However, his gigantic strength of jaws and arms relieves him of worry in his terrestrial habitat. If the story about the orang-utan and the crocodile is true, it may be inferred that the auburn-haired ape has remained in the trees from motives of conservatism and prudence rather than because of impotence.

There is some difference of opinion as to the geological period and the evolutionary stage at which man's ancestor took to the ground. Some writers think that this crucial step was taken as early as the Oligocene period and before the giant primates had evolved. This necessitates the supposition that our prehuman ancestors became terrestrial bipeds when they were no larger, if as large, as the present-day gibbons. But such a small humanoid would scarcely have been able to cope with formidable land animals of the period either by strength or by wile. Even today man is a relatively slow-moving creature on the ground if he be compared with most terrestrial quadrupeds, and he is not equipped with any efficacious weapons, either defensive or offensive. Further, there is abundant evidence that the erect posture and biped gait became a fixed habit in the humanoid stock before the brain attained its present great size. And it is a reasonable assumption that man's ancestors did not reach their present position of mental dominance until their brain size largely surpassed that of other animals.

Yet, it would be unwise to prejudge this matter of the time of the proto-human descent and the body size of this enterprising ancestor until we have examined in some detail the anatomy of the erect posture and biped gait in man. By a comparison of structures and proportions involved in this human posture and gait with those of the brachiating anthropoids and of pronograde monkeys, it should be possible to obtain evidence as to the derivation of man from giant brachiator or small ground ape. Here, however, we may inquire into the probable causes that impelled these promising anthropoids to such a radical change of habitat. There are those who feebly postulate a deforestation of the area in which our anthropoid ancestors dwelt, supposing that they descended to the ground because the trees died under them or burned up or otherwise became non-existent. In my opinion, this hypothesis is ridiculous. Any change of climate involving deforestation of the ancestral area would either be sufficiently gradual to permit our arboreal ancestors to migrate to other forest zones or, if of a sudden or cataclysmic nature, would have destroyed both the trees and the apes perching thereon. When the climate changes, most animals follow their congenial environment to a place where it remains fixed and constant. A cat does not become a walrus because of an inundation; it either drowns or scuttles away to dry land. But an ostrich might abandon an arboreal life because it found itself too large for the trees and might give up flying because it became too heavy. And an unusually intelligent anthropoid ape might take a chance on the ground when an arboreal life became too cramping, especially if that anthropoid ape were provided with mighty hands and powerful jaws.

Let us suppose, then, that man's ancestors neither fell out of the trees nor fell with the trees but descended to the ground on their own initiative, leaving their more cautious and conservative anthropoid relatives glaring at them disapprovingly from the branches. These radical ancestors of ours saw and accepted the chance of a larger, more varied, and fuller diet; they wanted to live their lives more abundantly.

An ingenious but somewhat improbable theory of ape and human evolution has been sketched by J. R. de la H. Marett.[13] He attempts to refer the erect posture, the expansion of the brain and skull, and the loss of body hair to the results of rapid reactions to iodine deficiency. The common Dryopithecine ancestors of both man and the present apes are thought by Marett to have been small, light-boned, physiologically efficient apes, which brachiated. The branch that diverged toward humanity moved into mountain areas above the tree line and was there subjected to severe mineral deficiency—especially of iodine. The result was not only cranial expansion and denudation of the hairy coat, but a sort of achondroplastic shortening or crippling of the specialized brachiating arms that necessitated dependence upon the lower limbs for locomotion and, hence, an erect posture. The giant body size, Marett thinks, may have developed independently in man and in the apes that remained arboreal, as a result of iodine economy supposedly promoted by large body surfaces. This view envisages the first men as virtually hairless, achondroplastic (a term denoting failure of normal cartilaginous development in the skeleton), and hydrocephalic ("water on the brain") pygmies. Some of us may not admire man inordinately but still may hesitate

---

[13] Marett, *Race, Sex and Environment,* chap. VI and *passim.*

to attribute his origin to a series of pathological accidents resulting from
deficient mineral supplies.

Standing Up and Walking: The Bipedal Humanoid Stage

When the proto-human ancestors of man took to the ground, they
were offered a theoretical choice of several different postures and modes
of locomotion. They could become pronograde and go on all fours;
they could adopt a squatting posture with the knees bent and develop
a hopping mode of progression; or they could stand erect and walk upon
the hind limbs. The ancestors of the baboon took to the quadrupedal
gait and posture. The indri lemurs hop when on the ground like the
tarsiers in the trees; the gibbon moves along the ground in the erect
posture, holding its arms up and walking on its two feet with the legs
incompletely extended. Actually, the way a primate progresses on the
ground may be predetermined by the bodily adaptations effected by its
posture and its method of locomotion in the trees.

The ancestors of the baboon were pronograde tree monkeys, running
along the branches and leaping with their hind legs. They occasionally
sat up or squatted in the trees with the knees drawn up toward the body
(flexed), but they were not really upright primates, and they did not
brachiate (swing from bough to bough by means of the arms). Their
fore and hind limbs were of approximately equal lengths, and, when they
took to the ground, they naturally and inevitably assumed a pronograde
posture and continued to use a quadrupedal gait. These proto-baboons
probably went to earth as a result of their large size, which rendered
them ill-fitted for arboreal life, while strength exempted them from
most of the dangers of attacks by other animals when on the ground.
Baboons live in rocky and treeless or scantily forested areas. But I doubt
that they were driven to the ground by dearth of trees. Perhaps, however, one should concede less to initiative and more to body bulk and to
the environment as causes of their change of habitat than in the case of
man's ancestors.

A hopping gait requires specialization of the hind limbs. The tarsus
or vault of the foot may be greatly elongated, and a long and heavy
counterpoising tail is desirable. No changes in this direction during the
aboreal period prepared man's ancestors for such a gait on the ground,
unless, as Wood Jones may think, man springs from a hopping tarsioid.
Hopping involves a take-off from a position of rest in which the legs are
flexed, the femur being perpendicular to the erect spine or the knees
drawn up toward the abdomen. However, man does not hop.

Dr. Dudley Morton [14] has argued that posture is a biomechanical interaction between the organism and gravity. The more massive the head and fore parts of an animal, the farther removed from the hind quarters is the center of weight, and the more difficult is the elevation and maintenance of the spine in a vertical position, not to mention the problem of balancing the top-heavy body on the hind legs. On the other hand, the nearer the center of gravity approaches the pelvis, the more easily can the body be erected. In the case of the kangaroo and of some extinct

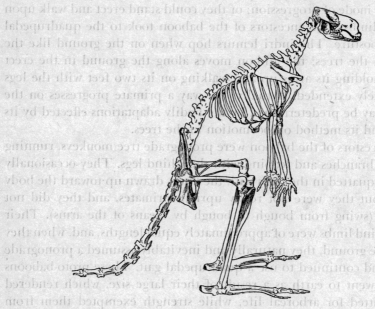

Fig. 8. Skeleton of a kangaroo—to illustrate hopping posture, use of the heavy tail in the tripodal stance, and flexed position of the thigh bones.

reptilian forms, a heavy counterpoising tail helps the animal to assume an erect position (Fig. 8). The gorilla, chimpanzee, and orang all have such massive heads and chests and such heavy arms that the weight of the forepart of the body necessitates the support of the fore limbs when moving upon the ground (Fig. 9). Dr. Johnson said: "Sir, a woman's preaching is like a dog walking on his hinder legs; it is not well done, but you are surprised to find it done at all." The latter part of this statement may be applied aptly to the occasional erect bipedal movements of the gorilla and the chimpanzee. These animals are too top-heavy to become erect bipeds. Their hind limbs are too weak to support the full

[14] Morton, "Evolution of Man's Erect Posture," pp. 148 ff.

weight of the body, and their pelves are not adapted for the transmitting of that weight to the legs. They therefore bend forward and rest the weight of the forepart of the body upon their long arms. Because these arms are so much longer than their legs, the spine is not parallel to the ground but is carried in a semi-erect position. The gibbon, however, does not always adopt a quadrupedal gait when on the ground (Fig. 10; Plate 11, a, b). According to Carpenter's observations, gibbons have three methods of walking on the ground. The first is quadrupedal, with

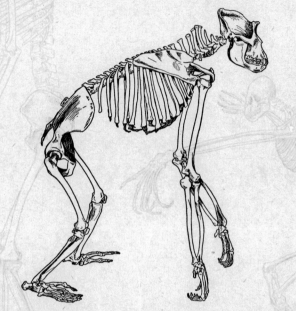

Fig. 9. Skeleton of male gorilla—to illustrate semi-erect posture and quadrupedal gait, elongation of spines of neck vertebrae to support unbalanced cranium.

the legs fairly straight, the trunk semi-erect, and the arms spread widely apart, fingers extended and weight borne on the palms. The second is using the arms as crutches and swinging the legs through them. The third, the upright bipedal gait, is easily learned by young captive animals and may be the preferred natural method of locomotion on the ground. I doubt that it is ordinarily the result of human tuition. The gibbon is a light and slender animal and has not the huge bulk of head, arms, and torso that characterize the giant apes. The center of weight is nearer to the pelvis. Again, the arms are so long that the finger tips touch the ground when the animal stands erect, so that it is inconvenient to use them as forelegs. Finally, the legs of the gibbon are long relative

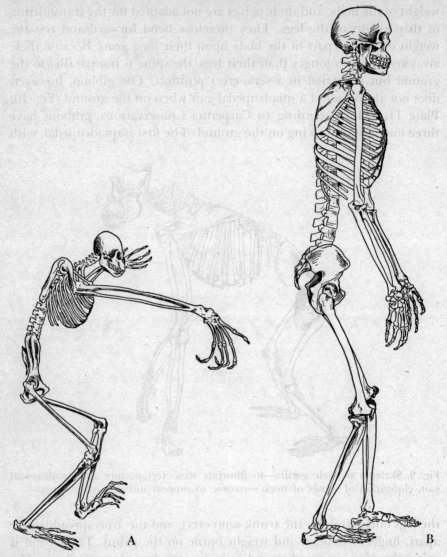

Fig. 10. The upright posture and biped gait. A, running gibbon; B, walking man (Australian).

to its trunk length; they are capable of more or less complete extension and are strong enough to bear the weight of its body in the erect posture. Nevertheless, the gibbon is not an easy walker or runner and usually takes but a few steps in the erect posture without squatting down to rest.

A somewhat misty light on the posture and gait of man's prehuman ancestors has been shed by the researches of the late Dr. Aleš Hrdlička upon children "who run on all fours." [15] This veteran anthropologist over a period of years collected and studied some 387 cases of children who used this quadrupedal posture and gait, usually beginning between the seventh and twelfth months and for an average duration of four months. In general, these were strong, healthy, and bright children. They were not clumsy and achieved quite amazing speed, ordinarily working one arm with the opposite leg and placing the flat of the palm on the ground with the fingers fully extended. However (and this may be important), in some instances the fingers were more or less flexed and "use of the dorsal part of the fingers or of the knuckles" is recorded. In this gait, the legs may be fully extended or bent at the knees. Both Schultz and Straus lay great emphasis upon this use of the palms and extended fingers in human walking on all fours because it is matched in the pronograde gait of the macaque and other monkey walkers, whereas the three great apes usually rest their weight on the backs of the middle phalanges of the fingers with the basal phalanges and the rest of the hand and wrist practically in a line with the forearm. On the other hand, the gibbon, when it goes on all fours, places its palms flat on the ground with its fingers extended, as do man and the monkeys. Straus points out that the great apes, because of the shortness of certain muscles that flex or bend the fingers, cannot bend the hand back on the wrist (hyperextension or dorsiflexion) without simultaneously bending or flexing the fingers.[16] Hence they cannot walk on all fours with the palms flat and the fingers stretched out. He thinks that the great apes have acquired this limitation in straightening the fingers with dorsiflexion of the hand in connection with brachiation, since a slight bending back of the wrist hooks the fingers and enables the apes to hang by their hands without the expenditure of great muscular energy. At the same time, the limited dorsiflexion of the hand keeps it aligned with the forearm both in hanging and in walking on the ground.

Now, the important conclusion that Straus draws from these facts is that man's ancestor never was a brachiator but went from a pronograde monkey gait straight to the status of an erect biped walker. He does not overlook the fact that the gibbon, who is also a palmar walker when going on all fours, is the most gifted brachiator among the primates, but he alleges that this small ape has become adapted to arboreal brachiation in quite a different manner from the giant apes, shows wholly peculiar alterations in certain muscles of the upper extremity, and has not suf-

[15] Hrdlička, *Children Who Run on All Fours.*
[16] Straus, "Posture of the Great Ape Hand."

fered the physiological degeneration of the thumb that has overtaken the giant brachiators. Straus concludes that the upper extremity of man is fundamentally closer to that of an Old World monkey than to that of any ape.

There are several small points in the evidence that seem to have been disregarded by Straus and Schultz in this argument. The first is that Hrdlička records a fair number of cases in which the human children walking on all fours actually rest their weight upon their knuckles, their bent fists, or their flexed fingers. The second is that Reichenow, in describing the first attempts of a young gorilla to walk on all fours, states that he began to walk on his palms (apparently with extended fingers), but soon began to double his fingers and walked on the hinder part of his palm and the last joints of his fingers, then finally upon the middle phalanges with the palm free and in line with the wrist. The third is that Yerkes has also noticed that the baby chimp begins by walking on the palms with the fingers extended and only later walks on the knuckles of its fingers. It would, therefore, appear that the limitation of finger extension with dorsiflexion of the hand in the great apes is a postnatal acquisition. If this is so, the fact that human children who run on all fours usually have their palms flat and fingers extended carries with it no implication whatsoever as to whether their ancestors brachiated or not, any more than in the case of the gibbon.

However, Straus and Schultz are certainly right in holding that brachiation in the trees is no necessary prerequisite for bipedal walking on the ground or, at any rate, does not fore-ordain that terrestrial posture and gait.

The changes in bodily form resulting from erect biped gait, which man's ancestors certainly adopted in some way or other, were numerous and important. Let us first consider the pelvic modifications, according to Reynolds.[17] The pelvic girdle consists in mammals of two irregularly-shaped bones—the innominate bones—the dorsal portions of which are articulated to one or more sacral vertebrae, and of which the lower, anterior ends curve around to meet together in the mid-ventral line (the symphysis), thus enclosing an oval or circular pelvic cavity. Each of these pelvic halves consists of three fused parts: a dorsal section called the ilium, which is articulated to the sacrum; a superior, anterior part called the pubis, and an inferior, posterior portion called the ischium. The pubis and ischium are united to form the ventral arch or symphysis where the halves of the pelvis join together in the middle line of the body. The flattened bases of the ischia form the bot-

17 Reynolds, *op. cit.*

tom part of the pelvis, the haunch bones, upon which the sitting animal rests its weight. The hind limbs are attached to the pelvis by ball-and-socket joints where the three portions of the innominate bones—the ilium, ischium, and pubis—unite.

In mammalian quadrupeds, the pelvis may be likened to a bony cylinder flattened from side to side, with its long axis parallel to the spine, its dorsal surface composed of the sacrum and its caudal prolongation,

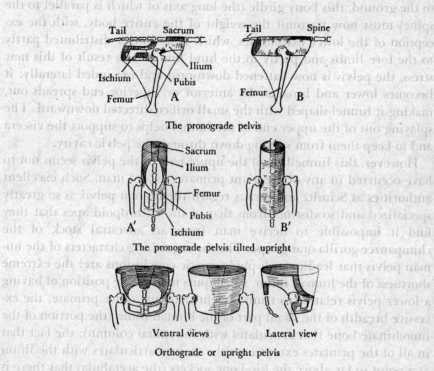

Fig. 11. Diagrammatic sketches to illustrate evolution from pronograde to orthograde types of pelvis.

the ventral surface cut away for the anterior half of its length and the dorsal surface similarly cut away for the posterior half of its length (Fig. 11).

This pelvic cylinder, elongated fore-and-aft and compressed from side to side, contains the rectum, the bladder, and the internal reproductive organs. Its posterior opening contains the orifices of the rectum and urogenital system, and this opening is covered by the tail, when present.

The elongation of this pelvic cylinder affords mechanically advantageous attachments for the muscles to act upon the thigh bones, which are slung from the middle points of the lateral surfaces of the cylinder about half way along its axis and almost perpendicular to that axis. The elongated ventral symphysis (the lower and posterior part of the arch) supports the pelvic viscera, which are disposed along the central tunnel. The anterior and dorsal part of the wall of the cylinder knits the pelvic girdle with its appended limbs to the spine.

When an animal stands up with its spine more or less perpendicular to the ground, this bony girdle (the long axis of which is parallel to the spine) must now transmit the weight of the entire body, with the exception of the lower extremities, which is no longer distributed partly to the fore limbs and partly to the hind limbs. As a result of this new stress, the pelvis is now flattened downward and expanded laterally; it becomes lower and broader. Its anterior or superior end spreads out, making it funnel-shaped with the small orifice directed downward. The splaying out of the upper end of the funnel helps to support the viscera and to keep them from sagging down through the pelvic cavity.

However, this funnelling of the upper part of the pelvis seems not to have occurred in any of the giant primates except man. Such excellent authorities as Schultz and Straus regard the human pelvis as so greatly specialized and so distinct from that of the anthropoid apes that they find it impossible to derive man from an ancestral stock of the chimpanzee-gorilla-orang type. The distinguishing characters of the human pelvis that lead to such phylogenetic conclusions are: the extreme shortness of the human ilium, which puts man in the position of having a lower pelvis relative to trunk height than any other primate; the excessive breadth of the sacral part of the human ilium (the portion of the innominate bone that articulates with the spinal column); the fact that in all of the primates except man the sacrum articulates with the ilium at a point so far above the hip-bone sockets (the acetabula) that there is no fixed bony structure opposite the pubic bones such as exists in man in the form of the lower part of the sacrum; the proportionately much larger and thicker acetabular or joint-socket region of the human pelvis, as contrasted with that of other primates, implying that the head of the human thigh bone is proportionately much larger than that of any of the quadrupedal primates.

Schultz argues that the comparative shortness of the human ilium represents a primitive condition in which man equals the macaque, and that it is safer to conclude that man has preserved this primitive condition than that he at first participated in the trend of the anthropoid apes toward increasing the length of the ilium and then very recently experienced a secondary and extensive shortening of this part of the pel-

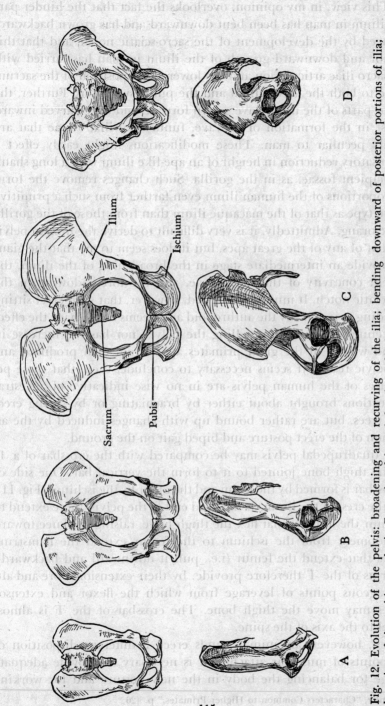

Ilium

Ischium

Pubis

Sacrum

A

B

C

D

Fig. 12. Evolution of the pelvis: broadening and recurving of the ilia; bending downward of posterior portions of ilia; lowering of the pubic symphysis. Frontal and lateral drawings of pelves of A, gibbon; B, chimpanzee; C, gorilla; D, man.

vis.[18] This view, in my opinion, overlooks the fact that the hinder part of the ilium in man has been bent downward and has grown backward, as evinced by the development of the sacro-sciatic notch, and that this posterior and downward growth of the ilium in man has carried with it the sacro-iliac articulation and has lowered the position of the sacrum relative to both the acetabulum and the pubic symphysis. Further, the anterior parts of the ilium have grown forward and have curved inward to assist in the formation of concave, funnel-like iliac fossae that are virtually peculiar to man. These modifications might easily effect a compensatory reduction in height of an ape-like ilium with a long shank and incipient fossae, as in the gorilla. Such changes remove the form and proportions of the human ilium even farther from such a primitive primate type as that of the macaque ilium than from those of the gorilla and the orang. Admittedly, it is very difficult to derive the human pelvis from that of any of the great apes, but it does seem to me that the giant apes provide an intermediate stage in the broadening of the ilium, the incipient concavity of the iliac fossae, and the foreshadowing of the sacro-sciatic notch. It must be confessed, however, that such erect sitting or standing as is done by the anthropoid apes seems not to have the effect of flattening down and funnelling the pelvis, nor has the increase in size and weight in the giant primates apart from man produced any such pelvic result. It seems necessary to conclude, then, that these peculiarities of the human pelvis are in no wise indicative of ancestral modifications brought about either by brachiating or by sitting erect in the trees, but are rather bound up with changes induced by the assumption of the erect posture and biped gait on the ground.

The quadrupedal pelvis may be compared with the crossbar of a T, with the thigh bone jointed to it to form the vertical bar. One side of the crossbar is formed by the ilium and the other by the ischium (Fig. 11). From the crest of the ilium, at the head end of the pelvis, there extend to the femur the muscles that flex the thigh bone, raising the knee toward the abdomen; from the ischium to the femur extend the hamstring muscles that extend the femur (i.e., pull it downward and backward). The arms of the T therefore provide, by their extensions fore-and-aft, advantageous points of leverage from which the flexor and extensor muscles may move the thigh bone. The crossbar of the T is almost parallel to the axis of the spine.

When, however, an animal stands erect, a different disposition of these points of muscular attachment is necessary to provide adequate leverage for balancing the body in the new posture and for working

[18] Schultz, "Characters Common to Higher Primates," p. 426.

efficiently upon the limbs in its movements. The attachments of the muscles that elevate or flex the thigh must be anterior to, or in front of, their insertions in the femur in order to obtain a good purchase upon the thigh, and the extensor muscle attachments must be back of their points of insertion. These requirements necessitate an antero-posterior extension of the pelvis. Since the axis of the lower limb is now parallel to the spine instead of being perpendicular to it, the points of pelvic attachment must now bear upon the leg from an axis more or less perpendicular to the spine.

In the pelvis of man, this new requirement is partly met by a marked flexure of the spine in the lumbar region that tilts the front part of the pelvis downward and backward, while the sacrum is bent upward and backward, until the hip joint falls into the axis of the erect spine. Simultaneously, the iliac bones, which are blade-like in quadrupeds but already expanded laterally in the large anthropoids, grow downward in their dorsal portions and also develop forward in a curve toward the middle line, until the ventral ends of their crests are anterior to the hip joint and well above it so as to afford advantageous leverages for the muscles that flex the thigh (Fig. 12). The inlet of the pelvis now is framed in the expanded and curved iliac bones (the false pelvis), which drop away rapidly in front to the low symphysis where the median halves of the true pelvis come together. The upper part of the pelvis is like a bottomless basin tilted forward and with the front broken away. The hollowed inner sides of the basin support the pelvic viscera, and the rim, the front broken edges, and the convex outer sides give attachment to the muscles that move the limbs and erect the trunk.

The lateral view of the pelvis is now somewhat like a solid wheel (Fig. 13). The upper half of the rim is almost complete, being formed by the iliac crest and the recurved sacrum and coccyx. Almost the entire lower anterior quadrant is cut away, and the posterior lower quadrant is hollowed out where the shank of the ischium is separated from the posterior rim of the ilium and the recurved sacrum by the sacro-sciatic notch. The thigh bone socket is near the center of the pelvic wheel. When you bend forward and touch your fingers to the ground (Fig. 13A), the thigh is fixed, and the flexor muscles of the thigh, pulling from the front surfaces of the fixed limbs upon the anterior points of the pelvic rim, bend the trunk downward or flex the spine and pelvis upon the lower limbs. When you straighten up again, the extensors of the thigh, working again from the hinder surfaces of the fixed limb, erect the trunk by pulling at the points of attachment upon the posterior and upper portions of the pelvic rim and sacrum.

The broad pelvic basin in man is tilted downward and forward so that the plane of the superior aperture makes an angle averaging from about 35° to 55° with the horizontal. The symphysis is lowered, since it no longer sustains the weight of the viscera. The front wall of the pelvis is

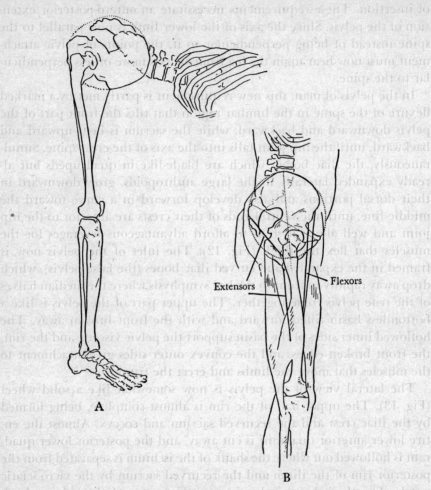

Extensors   Flexors

A

B

Fig. 13. The pelvic wheel. A, the pelvis flexed on the thigh. B, approximate relations of the flexor and extensor muscles to the rim of the pelvic wheel.

very much broader in man than in the anthropoid apes, partially because the whole pelvis is laterally expanded to support and transmit the weight of the body to the thigh bones, and partly in conformity with the antero-posterior, or front-to-back, flattening of the trunk that has been one of the consequences of the erect posture. There is no doubt that the extension of the thighs and the lowering of the pelvic symphysis have rendered man liable to hernia—the escape of the abdominal contents.

Professor Schultz [19] offers arguments against the view, presented above, that the erect posture in man has involved a tilting downward and forward of the pelvic brim and upward and backward of the sacrum in order to bring the hip joint beneath the vertical axis of the spine. By studying the natural position of the pelvis within the trunk (exposing one side and leaving the other imbedded in the flesh), Schultz concludes that the position is the same in all primates except man. He states that in the brachiating and, therefore, erect gibbon, the pelvis has the same position in the trunk as in the largely quadrupedal chimpanzee, and the upright position is attained solely by the turning of the leg in the acetabulum or hip socket joint. In man, the lower part of the pelvis is retained in the characteristically quadrupedal position, and the human trunk becomes erect only above the sacro-iliac articulation, chiefly by the bending of the spine in the lumbar region. However, on Schultz's own showing, the pubic or brim angle forms roughly a right angle with the trunk axis in the chimpanzee (but *not* in the gibbon, in spite of his assertion), and one of about 150° in man. In any event, whether the entire pelvis has been tilted forward and downward by the bulging forward of the lumbar spine and for the purpose of bringing the acetabula directly beneath the axis of the spine, or whether the turning to the erect posture is exclusively above the sacrum, the effect has been to raise the tip of the sacrum and tilt the pelvic brim forward and downward. The importance of Schultz's argument lies in its contention that the comparative morphology and relation of the pelvis in man and the apes does not validate the view that brachiation with its vertical posture opened the way automatically for the erect posture of modern man. In this he is probably correct, since the gibbon—at once the most specialized brachiator and the most efficient upright walker among the apes—shows little, if any, modification of the pelvis in a human direction, whereas the great apes, which do at least show some approximation to a human type of pelvis in the lateral expansion of the iliac blades, ordinarily walk on all fours when on the ground.

The curves of the human spine in the erect posture are easily explicable if one imagines the spine as a vertical, elastic rod upon which pressure is exerted downward. In the thoracic region, the elastic spine is reinforced by the shoulder girdle and the rib cage; in the pelvic region it is reinforced by the pelvic girdle (Fig. 10B). At the caudal end it is

[19] Schultz, "Skeleton of the Trunk and Limbs," pp. 346–360.

again free. The forward flexures of the spine come in the free and unbraced cervical (neck) and lumbar (loin) regions, which buckle forward,
making anterior convexities. The free tail end is recurved underneath
to support the viscera, being held in this position by strong ligaments
attached to the haunch bones.

The lower portions of the pelvic symphysis, instead of meeting as in
the apes, now curve away from each other to form a subpubic arch, so
that the external reproductive organs, instead of being situated at the
posterior opening of the pelvis, are now placed anteriorly, beneath the
subpubic arch.

With the specialization of the lower limbs for support and locomotion, the legs become very much longer and stronger. Thus, Schultz [20]
gives the following figures for leg length relative to trunk length in adult
primates: Old World monkeys, 106; mountain gorilla, 112; orang-utan,
119; chimpanzee, 128; coastal gorilla, 131; siamang, 131; gibbon, 146;
man, 171. However, in the new born, the relative leg length in gibbons
ranges from 137 to 164; in orangs, 124 to 128; in chimpanzees, 114 to 119;
gorillas, 119 to 123; and in man averages 116. Thus, in the proportion
at birth and, presumably, in the foetal period, man stands closer to the
great, brachiating apes than to the small gibbon.

The great group of muscles that cover the front of the femur and are
attached along a line that extends down the middle of its posterior surface is called the Quadriceps extensor femoris (Fig. 14). The knee cap
is embedded in the tendon of these muscles, which is attached to the upper
part of the shin bone (tibia) just below the knee. This muscle group, in
addition to its function of helping to flex the pelvis on the thigh when the
leg is fixed and to flex the femur on the pelvis when the leg is free, serves
to extend the leg on the thigh and is of great importance in walking and
in preserving the upright posture. Similarly, the hamstring muscles,
which are attached at one end to the extremity of the haunch bones and
run down the back of the thigh, are inserted in the upper portions of the
leg bones (the tibia and fibula) on their posterior surface. These muscles
flex or bend the leg on the thigh when the lower limb is in motion and
from the standing position help to balance the body. The superficial
muscles of the calf of the leg are the chief extensors of the foot at the
ankle joint. They are characteristically large in man, since they are used
constantly in running, walking, leaping, and standing. In walking, these
muscles raise the heel from the ground, and in standing, they steady the
leg upon the foot and keep the knee from giving way. The deep muscles
of the calf and the anterior muscles of the legs are all strongly con-

20 Schultz "Die Körporproportionen," p. 168.

cerned in the erect posture and the biped gait, acting in two different ways, according to which point of the extremity is fixed and which is free.

The effect of the great functional demands made upon the lower limbs

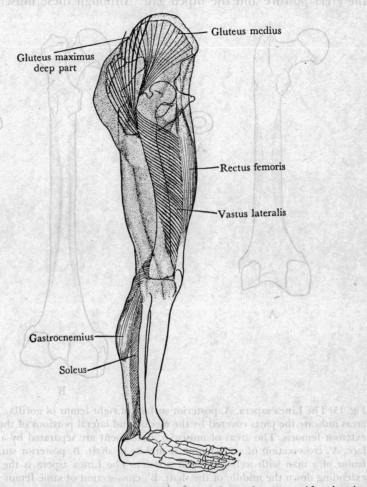

Fig. 14. Schematic dissection of the right leg, viewed from the outer side, showing approximately the positions and relations of the gluteal muscles, the extensor muscles of the thigh, and the superficial muscles of the calf.

by erect posture and biped gait is to increase the whole members in size, especially the muscle masses and the bones to which they are attached. Man's leg bones are much longer and the ridges for muscle attachments are much more sharply defined and differentiated than in the anthropoid apes. Along the back of the human femur, or thigh bone, is a rough ridge (the linea aspera) which often stands out like a buttress or pilaster (Fig. 15). This characteristically human feature is an effect of the great development of the extensor muscles of the thigh, which are attached to this roughened line and are of primary importance in the erect posture and the biped gait. Although these muscles exist in

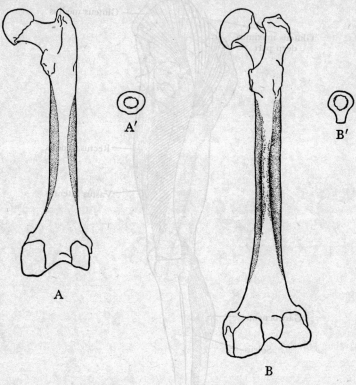

Fig. 15. The Linea aspera. A, posterior surface of right femur of gorilla. The stippled areas indicate the parts covered by the medial and lateral portions of the Quadriceps extensor femoris. The areas of muscular attachment are separated by a smooth surface. A', cross-section of same femur at middle of shaft. B, posterior surface of right femur of a man with well-developed pilaster. The Linea aspera is the rough ridge extending down the middle of the shaft. B', cross-section of same femur at middle of shaft.

apes, they are much less strongly developed, and their attachment on the back of the femur is scarcely discernible. The great development of this ridge gives to the human femur a prismatic cross section with the apex of the prism pointing backward, whereas in apes the cross section of the bone is round or oval. Similarly, in other bones of the extremities, the human shaft shapes tend to be prismatic and, in the apes, round or oval.

The most profound changes that took place in our primate ancestor when ground-dwelling became a fixed habit affected the foot. That member had to be changed from a grasping to a supporting organ. In order to appreciate these changes we must describe the form and function of the foot in various primate groups.

Dr. Dudley Morton has enumerated the various kinds of foot grasp employed by different primates.[21] Small lemuroids and tarsioids use a clinging or perching grasp because of the small size of their feet relative to the circumference of the boughs. If you attempt to grasp a pipe or tree trunk of very large diameter, you will find that the most effective grip is that between the thumb and the outer digits of the hands, because the width of the palm helps to cover the increased span. Hence, in small primates, the clinging or perching grasp involves large development of the great toe and of the outside toes and little development of the second and third toes. In such a clinging or perching grasp, the fulcrum of the foot (the point at which leverage is applied) is the middle point of the tarsus (the group of small bones in the foot corresponding to the wrist in the hand and constituting in man's foot the "instep"). In such a grasp the great toe is almost perpendicular to the long axis of the foot. Some few of the primates, especially the orang-utan, employ a suspension grasp in which no use is made of the great toe, and the weight is hung from the curved or hooked digits of the lesser toes. In the marmosets, a regression toward a rodent type of foot is observed in that the great toe becomes rudimentary and loses its power of opposability, and the lesser toe nails take on a claw-like appearance and are dug into the bark of the trees to give the animal a grip. But most of the primates employ the feet in a type of grasp that Morton calls "hallucial" (hallux, the great toe). This consists of a flexion of the opposable great toe toward the outer digits, which are simultaneously bent toward the great toe. In other words, the great toe is curved around one side of the bough, and the four lesser toes are curved around the other side of the bough. This converging flexion affects not only the toe bones but also the long bones of the foot behind the toes (the metatarsals), which correspond to the long bones in the palm of the hand (the metacarpals). With the development of the larger primates, the grasp of hands and feet upon the boughs is essentially similar to what your hand grip would be if you were to stand on a branch with your back to the tree trunk and, bending down, grasp the bough in front of you with both hands, one in advance of the other, supporting the weight of the fore part of your body upon the grasping arms. The monkeys and apes, in progressing along boughs with such a

21 Morton, "Evolution of the Human Foot," Vol. V, pp. 305–336; Vol. VII, pp. 2–52.

hand and foot grasp, employ the distal or farther ends of the metatarsal bones as the fulcra upon which the feet are raised in walking. We employ these same points (the bases of the toes)—the "ball of the foot"—in a similar fashion, rising upon the ends of the metatarsals as we step off from each foot alternately.

Many terrestrial quadrupeds are digitigrade—that is they walk upon their toes; but the primates are plantigrade—they walk on the soles of their feet.

In the smaller primates, whose feet are too tiny to encircle the boughs upon which they walk, the long axis of the foot and the principal line of leverage pass through the middle toe. In the great anthropoids the foot is large enough to grasp the boughs efficiently so that the four lesser toes are flexed against one surface of the bough and the great toe against the opposite surface. This changes the line of leverage so that it now runs between the great toe and the second toe, the fulcrum now being the web between these toes. The shafts of the metatarsal bones are also twisted, those of the lesser toes inward and that of the great toe outward, so that they face each other in conformity with the curved surfaces of the boughs that they grasp. Dr. Morton has shown that the functional axis of the human foot likewise passes between the great toe and the lesser toes, and, since the primitive mammalian line of leverage invariably passes through the third digit, it is not possible to explain the axis of the human foot except by the assumption that it has been derived from a large, grasping anthropoid foot.

When biped gait was assumed upon the ground, the proto-human foot was a large, prehensile organ similar to that of a chimpanzee or of a young gorilla. The great toe was opposable to the other toes and set off on the inside of the foot like a thumb; the lesser toes were longer than those of man and were probably curved downward to some extent, or partially flexed. The first metatarsal, which carries the great toe, was twisted to face the four lesser metatarsals. The tarsus, which now forms the instep and contributes to the foot arches, was an assortment of loosely articulated and mobile bones like those of the wrist; the heel bone was only slightly developed.[22] Put your hand down on the table, resting it on the

22 Dr. Morton argues that the ancestors of man must have been small animals when they took to the ground because of a lack of crushing or shortening of the mid-tarsal region of the human foot. He asserts that in the great apes these bones are considerably shortened as compared with the condition in the gibbon and in the monkeys. Man retains the unshortened tarsus; hence, he must have separated from the anthropoid stock and taken to the ground before he became a large animal and the more because the bearing of the weight on the tarsus is assumed to have shortened the bones in the giant primates. I am not at all sure of the reality of this alleged "crushing" of the mid-tarsus in the great apes. Schultz ("Characters Common to Higher Primates," p. 446) gives the following lengths of the entire tarsus in proportion

outside of the palm and the inside of the thumb and let the interval between your curved fingers and thumb make a C. You now have the
approximate resting position of the prehensile anthropoid foot.

The changes necessary for modifying this grasping foot into an organ
capable of supporting the weight of the body are fairly clear. First of
all, the great toe and its supporting metatarsal bone must be brought
into the line of the long axis of the foot; for a divergent toe, sticking out
like a thumb, would be a hindrance to ground walking, since it would
be "stubbed" almost constantly. Put your palms down upon the table
with the thumbs pointing inward and bear down with your weight.
Keeping the same position of the hands, draw in the thumbs toward the
index fingers, so that the thumb–first finger interspace is obliterated and
the thumb is brought into line with the other fingers. Observe that this
movement of adduction of the thumb makes a transverse arch of the
palm of the hand. Notice also that, when your thumb is parallel with
the other digits, it rests upon its side so that the palmar surface of the
thumb is opposed to the side of the index finger. When the foot was
transformed into a supporting organ, the great toe was brought into
line with the other toes and lengthened to become a principal basis for
support of the body weight. The pulley joint at the base of the originally
opposable great toes was flattened out so that the great toe no longer
could be opposed directly to the other digits. The converging twists
of the metatarsals of the lesser toes were obliterated to a great extent by
flattening, whereas, in the great toe, the outward twist of the supporting

of trunk lengths: Old World monkeys, 12; gibbon, 15; orang, 16; chimpanzee, 18; gorillas, 21;
man, 23. The same authority ("Skeleton of the Trunk and Limbs," p. 397) cites these figures
for tarsal length relative to total foot length: lower primates, 30; gibbon and siamang, 28;
orang, 26; chimpanzee, 35; gorilla, 40; man, 49. In a Negro foetus of the tenth week, this relationship is only 37. The extreme length of the human tarsus is a slow, postnatal development. Further, the gibbon seems not to have an elongated tarsus as contrasted with lower
primates, whereas the chimpanzee and gorilla closely approach man in this feature. Assuming,
however, the correctness of Morton's observations, I doubt that the shortening of the tarsus in
the great apes was effected by "crushing," due to the weight's being placed on this part of the
foot. I should regard it rather as an adaptation for greater mobility of the tarsus in grasping.
Putting stress and weight on bones does not "crush" them; if it did, the human tarsus would
be crushed. On the contrary, strain on a bone is likely to bring about its enlargement and
hypertrophy. Retention of a primitive, unshortened tarsus in man may prove that his ancestors diverged from the anthropoid stock before the great apes had "crushed" their tarsals;
but it does not prove that those ancestors were homunculi. Man's ancestors may have grown
to a large size in the trees without suffering the degeneration of the lower limbs and the
intense specialization of the foot that have fallen to the lot of the giant primates. A long
tarsus is a short peg upon which to hang such an important hypothesis. Further, this theory
is in direct contradiction to the main thesis of foot evolution developed by Dr. Morton himself, since he makes the shifting of the axis of leverage from the middle of the foot to the
web between the great toe and the lesser toe an effect of the great increase in size of the
anthropoid foot enabling it to span large branches. This he calls the "humanoid line of
leverage."

metatarsal was retained, but the toe itself was turned out so that the nail was directed upward and the plantar surface rested upon the ground. The adduction of the great toe contributed toward the formation of the transverse arch of the foot. The four lesser toes, being no longer used for grasping, now underwent a process of shortening and degeneration, which has proceeded so far in civilized man that the little toes often lack nails and sometimes have lost a whole segment. The great toe retains its length because its base, together with the head of the supporting first metatarsal, constitutes one of the main points of support of the foot. But the great toe has sacrificed its opposability.

The tarsal bones become strong, wedge-shaped bones firmly articulated to form the springy arch of the foot and are no longer loose and mobile like the corresponding wrist bones. Mobility is sacrificed to stability. The small and insignificant heel bone of the grasping primate foot becomes greatly enlarged and elongated. Its length constitutes the power arm of the lever to which is attached the tendon of Achilles, which, by the contraction of the calf muscles, lifts the heel off the ground in walking. The foot is, then, a lever of the first class, the fulcrum being at the ankle joint, the weight on the ball of the foot, and the power applied to the posterior end of the heel bone.

The process of conversion of a prehensile foot to a supporting foot may be observed in an incompleted state in the gorilla, which in its infancy is largely arboreal, but in adult years becomes almost exclusively terrestrial because of its great size and weight. Dr. Morton has shown that the growing gorilla undergoes a gradual reduction in the torsion or twisting of the metatarsals, a retardation in the growth of the outer digits, and an increase in the length of the great toe. The gorilla also displays better development of the heel bone than does any other anthropoid. These changes in the foot of the gorilla, in consequence of its descent to the ground, are similar in kind but not so marked in degree as those that must have occurred in the evolution of the modern human foot. But the gorilla has not lost the power of opposability of the great toe and has not developed the completely supporting foot that man possesses. The gorilla is half-heartedly terrestrial, semi-erect, and only occasionally bipedal. Each individual gorilla becomes painfully and imperfectly adapted for a terrestrial gait late in life. The gorilla represents a stage of evolutionary vacillation, a postural and locomotor compromise.

We have now arrived at a point where the human line of descent is represented by an erect, ground-dwelling biped, whose lower limbs and feet have become specialized for support and locomotion. No such radical transformation as that which metamorphosed the lower extremities when man stood erect upon the ground took place in the arms and hands. Professor Frederic Wood Jones has been at much pains to show that the skeleton of the fore limb in man is almost identical with that of such a primitive aquatic vertebrate as a tortoise. It is a mobile limb, with its grasping function developed by arboreal life. We have seen that the "emancipation of the fore limb" followed the assumption of an erect sitting posture in the trees. But this emancipation in the arboreal primates was incomplete and transitory because of the growth of the habit of brachiating, i.e., using the arms for the purpose of locomotion in swinging from bough to bough. The effect of this new habit was, of course, to curtail the prehensile function of the fore limbs, since these were now used to a great extent in suspending and moving the body. In the anthropoid apes, the arms became elongated in a fashion quite analogous with the lengthening of man's legs.

Since there is a difference of opinion concerning the existence of a brachiating, giant ape stage in man's ancestry, it is important to note the position of the human stock with reference to relative length of the upper extremity—whether man is allied to the monkeys in this feature or to be arm-swinging apes. Schultz [23] presents the following data for total arm (including hand) length relative to trunk length: Old World monkeys, 118; gibbon, 238; orang, 182; chimpanzee, 175; coastal gorilla, 184; mountain gorilla, 154; man, 150. These figures speak for themselves. Schultz notes the case of a Negro whose relative arm length (174) exceeds that of mountain gorillas and falls into the chimpanzee range.

Another result of brachiating is a disproportionate lengthening of the forearm. In the anthropoid apes, this segment of the upper limb is greatly elongated, whereas in man it is comparatively short. Sir Arthur Keith has explained this difference by calling attention to the way anthropoids grasp a branch and draw upward the weight of the body by flexing the arm, (i.e., their habit of "chinning themselves"). In such a lever movement, the fulcrum is at the elbow joint, the power is applied to the upper arm by the biceps and anterior brachial muscles, and the weight is suspended from the shoulder joint. It is, therefore, a lever of the third order, with the short brachium or upper arm the moveable lever. In man, on the contrary, the typical use of the arm is to lift a weight held in the hand; the fulcrum is at the elbow and the power is applied to the forearm by means of the same muscles, but in this case the short and moveable lever is the forearm. In the anthropoid, the short upper arm is the

[23] Schultz, "Die Körporproportionen," pp. 168–169.

moving lever and affords by its shortness a greater purchase; in man, the forearm is the moveable lever and is, therefore, short, relative to the length of the upper arm.

The brachial index (radius expressed as a percentage of length of humerus) gives the length of the forearm relative to that of the upper arm. Schultz found it to be 104 in two lemurs, 95 in ten New World monkeys, 101 in twelve Old World monkeys, 113 in twenty-four gibbons, 101 in sixty-six orangs, 93 in twenty-nine chimpanzees, 81 in fifty-one lowland or coastal gorillas, 86 in five mountain gorillas and 75 to 77 in various human groups. This index increases with age and is much lower in foetal life in all primates except the lowland gorilla. Man is closest to the gorilla in proportion of forearm to upper arm. Both have very short radii. Individual human specimens can actually exceed the range of the lowland gorilla. Schultz found an index of 87.6 in a perfectly normal Negro woman, whereas the highest figure for the lowland gorilla was only 85.2. [24]

Thus the abbreviation of the forearm has proceeded farthest in man but is also marked in the gorilla, the least arboreal of the anthropoid apes.

Suspending the body by the arms also elongates the hand and especially the fingers and the metacarpal bones of the palm. In such a hooked suspension, the thumb is not used to any extent, the weight being supported by the four flexed fingers. These consequently become long and coarse, and the muscles and ligaments between them extend downward so that the digits of anthropoids are "webbed" almost to the first joint. The disuse of the thumb tends to result in its atrophy and diminution; in the spider monkey and some of the semnopitheques, the external thumb has disappeared entirely. Clearly such a suspensory grasp interferes with the opposability of the thumb to the other digits. It militates against skilled manual movements. When the hand is made an organ of locomotion, the perfection of its prehensile power is sacrificed. Conversely, in an erect biped animal with fully emancipated fore limbs, the more primitive grasping function of the hand and the opposability of the thumb tend to be retained and further developed. The thumb becomes long enough to be opposed conveniently to any of the outer digits. The manipulation of objects and the tactile use of the free prehensile hands both promote manual dexterity, as contrasted with the coarsening effect of brachiation upon the hand as a supporting member. The human hand tends to be given over to independent movements of the fingers, whereas the use to which the human foot has been put has resulted in the loss,

[24] Schultz, "Skeleton of the Trunk and Limbs," pp. 362–363.

to a great extent, of independent movements of the toes. The foot is a specialist, the hand a general practitioner.

In recent years, the studies of Schultz have cleared up a good deal of confusion that has existed about the extent to which the human hand resembles and differs from the hands of apes and lower primates. This subject has to be elucidated here because it bears again upon the disputed question of man's descent from a large, brachiating tree ape or from a ground ape that diverged from the common ape-human stock when still a small animal.

In the first place, hand length relative to trunk height is longer in all adult higher primates than in macaques, but it is proportionately shortest in the mountain gorilla, second shortest in man, and relatively the longest in the most extreme brachiators—the orang and the gibbon. Orangs, chimpanzees, and apes of the gibbon family have proportionately narrower hands than the macaque, but man and the gorilla have very broad hands, and the mountain gorilla notably exceeds man in relative hand breadth. These differences are illustrated by the hand breadth expressed as a percentage of hand length: Old World monkeys, 33; gibbons, 24; orang-utans, 33; chimpanzees, 35; lowland gorillas, 49; mountain gorillas, 58; man, 41.[25] In all of these primates except the gorilla, relative hand breadth decreases with age. Since the gorilla has a comparatively slender hand during middle foetal life, Schultz concludes that the great relative breadth of the gorilla hand is a late phylogenetic (or ancestral) acquisition, but that man's hand breadth was probably acquired at an early stage of evolution, and the human stock probably never possessed the typically long and slender brachiator's hand. The total length of the thumb relative to hand length is greater in man than in the macaque, but less in the anthropoid apes than in that common Old World monkey (macaques, 55; gibbons, 54; orangs, 44; chimpanzees, 47; lowland gorillas, 52; mountain gorillas, 50; man, 68.)[26] These facts have lead to the assertion that the thumbs of the apes have been atrophied in consequence of their disuse in brachiating, or that man's thumb has elongated. However, Schultz points out that it is hardly fair to consider thumb length only in relation to total hand length, since the latter has been greatly increased in the extreme brachiators by suspension and the process of stretching involved therein. If thumb length be expressed as a percentage of trunk height, it is found that all higher primates have relatively longer thumbs than the macaque and man stands in the middle of the apes (macaques, 14; gibbons, 34;

25 Schultz, "Die Körporproportionen," p. 172.
26 Schultz, ibid., p. 172.

orangs, 23; chimpanzees, 24; gorillas, 22; man, 24).[27] In gibbons only, the free part of the thumb, beyond its branching from the palm, includes a large part of the first metacarpal bone, whereas, in some gorillas, only the farther part of the basal phalanx of the thumb is free. In all higher primates, the relative foetal length of the thumb is greater than in adults, but this postnatal decrease is much more marked in chimpanzees than in man. The rotation of the thumb that facilitates opposition to the other digits is much more developed in higher primates than in monkeys and is not present in the foetal life of any primate. Schultz says that this rotation in some chimpanzees is more advanced than in the average man.

Finally, with respect to the hand of man and those of the apes, we may revert again to Straus' conclusions concerning the absence of brachiating specializations in the human hand, such as the alteration of the short hand muscles in the gibbon; the restriction of manual dorsiflexion, the shortening of the long digital flexors, and the degeneration of the long flexor tendon of the thumb in chimpanzee, orang, and gorilla. These considerations made Straus conclude (with the apparent concurrence of Schultz) that the upper extremity of man is closer to that of a catarrhine monkey than to that of any anthropoid ape.

It appears, then, that man is closer to all of the apes than to the monkeys in thumb length relative to trunk length and in rotation power of the thumb and is nearer to the gorilla and chimpanzee in relative hand breadth than to the macaque, but approximates the hand musculature of the more primitive monkeys rather than the specialized myological arrangements of the apes (which are quite different in the gibbon from those of the big brachiators). Evidently, the process of drawing phylogenetic deductions from comparative study of the hands is most precarious.

Were Man's Ancestors Arboreal Arm-Swingers or Pronograde Ground Apes?

We must now come to grips with the main problem that has been worrying us in our survey of the development of an "erect and featherless biped" from the common ancestral stock of man and the apes. Did man's ape ancestors remain in the trees until they had attained giant size and prepare themselves for the erect posture on the ground by brachiating in the trees? Or did they forsake arboreal life before the development of great tree apes and run along the ground on all fours, insignificant in

[27] Schultz, "Characters Common to Higher Primates," p. 446.

size and monkey-like in posture, until they got their hands so filled with food, weapons, or mischief that they had to stand up and walk on their hind legs?

The arguments may be summarized according to the various anatomical parts that are alleged to show changes supporting one theory or the other according to physiological, psychological, or other topics of consideration that may offer apposite evidence. Under each heading the pro-giant ape brachiator and pro-small ground ape arguments may be listed.

1. Lumbar Spine
   Pro-brachiator
   Suggestions of lumbar curve in great apes; reduction of number of lumbar segments and increased tendency to incorporate lumbar vertebrae in sacrum in great apes and man.
   Pro-ground ape
   Common possession of five lumbar segments in gibbon and man (but in man an extra segment has been added above by suppression of a pair of ribs).
2. Pelvis
   Pro-brachiator
   Lateral expansion of iliac blades foreshadowed in great apes; consolidation of sacrum.
   Pro-ground ape
   Unreduced height of ilium in great apes and shortening in man; alleged quadrupedal position of true pelvis (lower portion of pelvic girdle) in man; large size of acetabulum (socket for head of thigh bone) in man; lack of clear transitional forms between human and ape pelves; retention of less vestigial caudal vertebrae in man than in the apes.
3. Proportions of Lower Limbs
   Pro-brachiator
   Human resemblance to great apes in short relative leg length in embryonic period and at birth and divergence from gibbon proportions at this time.
   Pro-small ground ape
   Human resemblance to gibbon in relatively long legs in postnatal period, supposed to indicate that lower limb in man has not undergone degeneration and reduction as in giant brachiators.
4. Foot
   Pro-brachiator
   Shift of axis of foot from third digit to between great toe and second digit in man and great apes (Morton's "anthropoid-humanoid line of leverage"), supposed to be attributable to large increase of foot size in giant brachiators.
   Pro-ground ape
   Alleged "crushing of mid-tarsal region" in great apes, absent in man

and the gibbon; general resemblance of human foot musculature to that of baboon (Wells).

5. Rib Cage and Body Cavities
   Pro-brachiator
   Suspension of viscera in body cavities by type of mesenteries supposedly developed in gibbons and other apes as result of upright posture; flattening of the chest and back as in brachiators.

6. Upper Limbs
   Pro-brachiator
   Great relative length of fore limb in which man approaches the giant apes and vastly exceeds the lower primates (except the brachiating spider monkey); lack of any of the muscular or bony specializations found in typically quadrupedal mammals; frequent occurrence in man of one or more extra heads of the biceps, as is regular in the gibbon, but uncommon or absent in giant apes.
   Pro-ground ape
   Lack of pectoralis-biceps-sublimis union and other specialized muscular features of gibbon upper limb; general resemblance of upper limb musculature to that of monkeys.

7. Hand
   Pro-brachiator
   Power of rotation of thumb, approximated only in great apes.
   Pro-ground ape
   Lack of manual specializations of great apes, such as limited dorsiflexion with extension of fingers; walking on palms in infants "who go on all fours."

8. Teeth
   Pro-brachiator
   Inheritance of Dryopithecus (generalized great pattern) of molar tooth form in man.

9. Brain
   Pro-brachiator
   Detailed resemblances of brain pattern between man and great apes.

10. Psychology
    Pro-brachiator
    Results of psychological tests showing closest approximation to human intelligence in great apes.

11. Physiology
    Pro-brachiator
    Common possession of the blood groups by man and apes.

On the whole, the evidence pro and con seems to be often equivocal and generally inconclusive. In recent years, there has been a strong trend toward the small ground ape theory and away from the giant brachiator hypothesis. An imposing list of authorities inclines to the belief that the human stock separated from the common anthropoid-humanoid trunk at about the same time that the gibbon family branched off or possibly only slightly later. Such a separation prior to the development of the giant primates would have to be referred to the Oligocene period or, at latest, the lower Miocene, and would postulate a divergence beginning some 27 millions of years back. It necessitates the belief that the detailed resemblances of man to the great apes are largely to be referred to the evolutionary phenomenon called "convergence." Among the students who adhere to this view, or something close to it, are: F. Wood Jones, Sir Arthur Keith, Adolph H. Schultz, W. L. Straus, Jr., Le Gros Clark. They constitute an eminent and influential majority. The principal adherents of the giant brachiator theory are W. K. Gregory and Hans Weinert. None of these students of human evolution except Wood Jones has the slightest doubt of man's descent from an ape stock, and all except him recognize the closeness of human relationship with the great apes. Wood Jones would bring man up from a progressive tarsioid ancestor without the intervention of ape or monkey stages.

To me, the most reasonable solution of the problem, as the evidence now stands, lies in a compromise between the two extreme views.

Indubitably, the earliest ancestor of man at the ape stage, when the common anthropoid-humanoid stock had already topped the Old World monkey level, was some kind of an arboreal ape not yet of modern giant primate size. There is no reason whatsoever for supposing that man's ancestor became a ground dweller while still a monkey. Otherwise, it would be reasonable to expect man to show far more intimate resemblance to the mainly terrestrial monkeys, such as baboons, mandrills, and drills, than he actually does, if only through "convergence." Under such circumstances, he could hardly resemble the anthropoid apes, large and small, in the intricate way that he in fact does. Walking on all fours ought to be at least a regular, and not a rare, method of infant progression, if a pronograde gait had been directly superseded by erect, biped walking.

Next, if man had an early tree ape ancestor, what was the putative arboreal posture and method of locomotion of that precursor? There can be little doubt that this prehuman arboreal ape sat up habitually and climbed tree trunks with the long axis of the body perpendicular to the ground or vertical. If the fixation of the viscera by suspension from the head end was acquired in arboreal life, which I think is very probable, if not certain, our ancestor might well have acquired these modifications without having previously become a confirmed brachiator. Since the human ancestor in ape form must certainly have been more versatile and less given to cramping specializations than the progenitors of the present great apes, it would appear probable that the proto-man brachiated in moderation, walked the branches sometimes as a biped (as does also the gibbon), and perhaps even on occasion went on all fours along the boughs. The elongation of the arms in man of today suggests a preference for brachiation over arboreal pronograde progression, but Straus, Schultz, and others appear right in denying to man's ancestors any such extensive brachiating specialization of the upper limb as affected the ancestors of the gibbon family or those of any of the other great apes. Let us, then, suppose that tree ape-man was a habitual erect sitter, an occasional bough biped, with a penchant for brachiating and an inclination to go on all fours when the going was difficult. In other words, man's ancestor was perhaps a somewhat generalized tree ape in posture and gait. He exhibited a catholic taste.

According to Carpenter, about 90 per cent of gibbon locomotion is brachiating. On the other hand, wild chimpanzees in West Africa, as observed by Nissen, move along the ground from tree to tree. They rarely if ever progress by brachiating from one tree to another. The adult gorilla probably spends most of his time on the ground. The transition from a mainly arboreal life to a predominantly terrestrial habitat was probably made gradually by man's ancestors, and there is nothing in the anatomical evidence that seems to me to weigh heavily in favor of the hypothesis that an exclusively terrestrial abode and a completely ortho-grade gait were attained at a small ape stage. If man's ancestors had gone to ground in the Upper Oligocene, before the gibbon was separated from the giant brachiators-to-be, I suspect we should have turned out to be quadrupeds. At any rate, such a protracted terrestrial sojourn might reasonably be expected to produce a further specialization of the hind limbs and the feet away from the generalized primate type than actually is evident. Fusion of the fibula with the tibia and most of the cursorial specializations of terrestrial mammals are lacking in the hind limb as well as in the fore limb of man, although, of course, one could not reasonably look for the development of a digitigrade form of progression in a biped.

However, it seems to me that the strongest argument in favor of man's having reached giant status before he forsook the trees is, as stated above, that the actual handicap of large size and great weight to an ar-boreal animal may well have been a deciding factor in causing our ape ancestor gradually to change his habitat. It is true enough that, of the two confirmed brachiators and almost exclusively arboreal apes, the gib-bon is small and light, the orang big and heavy. Yet the latter shows clearly enough in the degeneration of his nether parts the penalty paid by the animal that outgrows the trees and still remains there. A combination of increasing bulk and superior initiative may have impelled our early ancestors to take this crucial step. I do not think that a small Oligocene ape would have had much chance of survival on the ground. He would have been too weak, too slow, and too stupid. Practically no archaeologist today credits the Oligocene, Miocene, or even Pliocene "eoliths"—the stone tools or weapons thought to have been shaped and used by our ancestors before stereotyped and recognizable tool and weapon forms had developed. But no Oligocene ground ape with a human destiny could have survived without such aids to his feeble organic equipment for defense or offense. On the other hand, it is incredible that any Oligocene primate could have reached a stage of brain development that would permit him to be a tool-making animal. So I conclude that approximately modern human size (which is giant primate size) and a brain bulk and nervous organization that could scarcely have been attained before Middle Miocene times were probably antecedent to, and prerequisite for, man's career as a terrestrial biped.

Making Things and Using Tools: The Arms and Hands

The indirect effects of the emancipation of the fore limb on other parts of the body are far more important than the modifications brought about in the arms and hands by the new uses to which they are put. O. G. S. Crawford has given a brilliant exposition of the diverse results of tool-using and tool-growing.[28] He explains that most animals grow their own tools out of the limited materials provided by the substances of their own body; they use no other tools.

Man was the first animal to grow a limb outside of himself by making tools out of wood and stone. This was a great achievement. In the first place, because it takes much less time, say, to make an eolith or sharpen a stake than to grow canines or flatten your tail into a trowel. Moreover, once made and the principle grasped, however dimly, the external limb is capable of an infinity of modification, self-suggested by its very inadequacy as a tool. There is no time for automatism to set in before the possibilty of fresh use occurs, prompted sometimes accidentally by the tool itself.

Crawford further stresses the importance of an intelligent brain control in the use of an "external limb," which is unnecessary in cases where the tools are unchangeable because they are a part of the animal's own body and are linked to the brain by a nervous system and learn their jobs so well that they never require to be prompted.

[28] Crawford, *Man and His Past*, pp. 1–19.

The invention of extracorporeal limbs put a stop to progressive structural modifications, for thenceforth such modifications took place *outside* the organism instead of within it as before.

The importance of tool-using may then be said to lie in the fact that it eliminates the necessity of constant functional adaptations in the body by employing external objects to fulfill an environmental requirement, and at the same time it imposes upon the senses and the intelligence the necessity of coping with changing conditions, and of controlling movements that can never become automatic because they involve the utilization of an inanimate and unintelligent mass in a purposeful and skilled manner.

The tool-using and tool-making capacities of animals are limited not only by the acquisition of free and prehensile fore limbs, but also by their intelligence. In this connection, it is important to describe the extent to which anthropoid apes are able to utilize and to make implements, as determined by the experiments of psychologists. For these tests should show whether the limitations of the animals are those of physical or of mental capacity. Köhler tried a series of experiments with chimpanzees in which a desired object, such as some form of food, could be reached only by the employment of some tool or implement.[29] In one such experiment, the chimpanzee was tied so as to limit its range of movement, and the objective was placed on the ground outside of this periphery, while a string attached to it was left within reach. Although in some cases the string was three meters long, the animal never failed to use it and to pull the object to itself, always gazing at the object and never at the rope. In this case, both motor ability and intelligence were adequate for the solution of the problem.

A similar experiment involved the use of a stick for dragging within reach of the animal in the cage some desired object placed outside of the bars, such as a banana. When the stick was left within the field of vision of the chimpanzee, it was quickly and handily utilized for securing the object, but, if the stick was out of sight, no effort would be made to search for it. On the other hand, if the ape happened to turn around and notice the stick, it would then seize and use it. Often the chimpanzee would attempt to drag the object outside the bars within reach by using such obviously unsuitable tools as straws, green plant stocks, stones, et cetera. It is obvious here that the limitation of the use of the tool is prescribed by the animal's lack of intelligence and not by physical incapacity.

A problem frequently set for apes involves the suspension out of reach

29 Köhler, *Mentality of Apes*, pp. 25 ff.

of a banana or some other desired object and the provision of one or two boxes with which the animal is required to reach the objective. The animals apparently learn with comparative ease to push a box beneath the objective, climb upon the box, and thus secure the prize. The quickness in the solution of the problem seems to depend again upon the intelligence of the individual ape rather than upon its agility. Such problems are easily solved by chimpanzees and with more difficulty by orang-utans and gorillas.

Professor Köhler's chimpanzees easily developed for themselves the use of sticks as levers.

The tank, which received the waste water used to wash out cages, was closed by a thick wooden lid and iron bolts. But there were cracks, and it became a perfect mania with the apes to squat beside the tank, armed with straws and sticks which they dipped in the foul liquid and then licked. Of course things would have been much easier if the lid had been removed, and, either because it moved easily under the groping hands, or because it was easy to understand the situation, *this* obstacle was removed "early and often" either with the naked hand of a creature whose strength is capable of bursting open an iron bolt bedded in cement, or, later, as we increased the solidity of the structures, prized open by means of a stick, which had formerly functioned as a spoon, but was extremely popular on its promotion to the dignity of *lever*. The chimpanzee uses a lever in exactly the same manner as man.[30]

These chimpanzees also developed the use of sticks as digging tools, employing them in a variety of ways. Sometimes both hands and teeth were used to thrust the stick into the hard ground, while as often the tough sole of the foot was pressed hard against one end of a stick held diagonally in both hands, thus driving it into the earth. These digging sticks were used to lay bare roots for food.

A chimpanzee will often use a stick to poke at things or to touch things that it is afraid to investigate with the naked hand. It always prefers to wipe off filth, moisture, or what not from the surface of the body by using leaves, twigs, handfuls of straw, paper. These animals strike with sticks and poke with them in play, but, when they actually "mean business," they drop the sticks and use their hands, feet, and teeth as weapons. Nevertheless, Köhler's pets developed a great fondness for creeping up to the wire netting of the cage and stabbing unsuspecting animals or persons with pointed sticks or bits of wire. Sticks and stones and other objects of various shapes, sizes, and weights were also thrown with varying precision and, unlike the usage of sticks in hitting and thrusting, were employed as missiles of attack when enraged.

[30] *Ibid.*, p. 77.

The chimpanzees were also very fond of carrying things about on the body: ropes, strings, sticks, tin cans, stones.

The making of implements is far more significant than the mere utilization of objects lying about. A chimpanzee accustomed to the use of sticks will sometimes break off the branch of a tree and use it as a stick when no loose tool is available. Under similar circumstances, it will pull a board loose from a box and use it as a stick. But, if the chimpanzee does not see the board or the branch as a "separable part," it will not attempt to detach or utilize it. If, for instance, a table is placed with its corner in the right angle of a room, and flat against the walls, the chimpanzee will pass it by in the search for an implement because the table seems an integral part of the wall.

One of Professor Köhler's anthropoids succeeded in making a double stick by thrusting a smaller bamboo section into a larger one in order to reach an object unattainable by means of either of the separate pieces. The same animal developed a method of making a jointed stick by sharpening the end of a board by biting until it was small enough to fit into the opening of a bamboo stick. Any chimpanzee will use an inclined plank or stick as a ladder, and most of them will pile up boxes into two- or three-story edifices in order to reach an objective.

The foregoing facts indicate that chimpanzees on the ground tend to develop tool-using and tool-making habits to a limited extent. Clearly, an arboreal life would militate against such habits, regardless of the capabilities of the animal, because of the restricted use to which implements could be put in a tree. But a ground-dwelling animal, with prehensile fore limbs and the habit of sitting up and, occasionally, of standing erect and walking, is almost certain to employ its free prehensile members in random and eventually purposeful handling of objects. From this point, the use of implements and the making of tools seems to depend more upon the intelligence of the animal than upon the structural modifications of the fore limbs. Of course, so long as a quadrupedal gait is employed, there are obvious restrictions upon the development of "external limbs." But observation of the anthropoid apes does not make it seem probable that their tool-using abilities are strictly limited by the conformation of their hands or arms, in spite of the relative coarseness of these members, resulting, no doubt, from the locomotor and suspensory uses to which they are put. Köhler's apes in Tenerife were fond of handling strings and straws. They would often sit beside a column of ants holding a straw among the insects, and, when the ants ran up the straw, the latter would be drawn through the ape's mouth and the ants eaten. This unique fishing process would then be repeated many times. Such a sport surely requires skilled and fairly delicate manipulation. I do not believe that the anthropoid apes are manually incapable of most of the ordinary movements in which man employs his hands. Their lack of a material culture is to be traced rather to their lack of brains.

We must remember, however, that an anthropoid ape, torn from its natural arboreal life and forced to live in captivity on the ground, cannot be expected to progress in the use of artifacts as did our own ancestors when they voluntarily came down to earth. The great apes are "die-hard" Tories; that is why they have persisted in their outgrown leafy abodes. Our ancestors were Radicals; they "took a chance" on the ground. There is no doubt that the first erect-walking, ground-dwelling (and therefore "human") primates were far more intelligent than any of the present anthropoid apes.

Without insisting too much upon the obvious, let us consider the new uses to which the fore limb was put at this beginning period of human existence. Hand-feeding, hand-feeling, and hand-fighting had already developed to some extent in arboreal life. The new functions seem to have been confined to making things and using tools and weapons.

The principal weapons of primates are their teeth. In the larger members of the order, the jaws are very powerful and the canine teeth are greatly elongated. The ground-dwelling baboons show the most extreme development of snout and canine teeth, and there seems little reason for doubting that their canines function principally as weapons.

Now it seems clear that the development of external weapons for the manual use of early human ground-dwellers transferred to the hands once and for all the defensive and offensive functions that previously fell to the lot of the jaws and especially of the canine teeth. The question at issue is whether or not this loss of function of the jaws was a primary cause of the recession or shrinkage that is such an important human characteristic as compared with the protrusive condition in anthropoid apes. I must confess that I find this development of hand weapons a somewhat inadequate cause for such a tremendous effect. The gorilla has the most powerful arms and hands of any primate and, if reports are to be credited, uses these members in fighting. Yet the gorilla has the most projecting jaws and the largest canine teeth of any of the anthropoid apes. Again, some authorities claim that the orang-utan fights only with his hands and does not use his teeth at all; yet the size of the jaws and the development of the canines in orangs is prodigious. This Asiatic ape far outstrips the chimpanzee in size of jaws and canines, although the latter is stated to fight with its teeth only. The elongated canine teeth of the gibbon are used in fighting. The aggressor attacks quickly and viciously, holding his opponent with his hands, plunging in the sharp canine teeth, then pulling with the neck muscles like a carnivore. The result is a deep, clean cut. Carpenter thinks that some of the healed bone fractures observed in collected gibbons have resulted from canine bites. Many gibbon males, and some human beings who have got too close to captive gibbons, bear scars attesting the efficacy of the gibbon canines as weapons. Apparently, they are not much used in the preparation of food.

While the use of hand weapons may have resulted in some diminution in size of the canine teeth, it would appear that the preparation of food by the hands and by tools must have been far more important as a cause of the reduction of the dentition. The diet of the anthropoid apes is principally frugivorous, and the long canines are used, sometimes, at any rate, to tear away the tough rinds of the fruits that they eat. Early man was omnivorous; in fact, he probably took to the ground principally to enlarge his diet. There he was able to secure a greater variety of food that was at the same time more nutritious and less tough than the vegetable fare of the arboreal anthropoids. Moreover, he very soon developed implements with which to prepare his food by chopping it into small bits, crushing it, or otherwise reducing it to pieces of such a size as would obviate the necessity of tearing at it with long canines and grinding it up with powerful molars. It is reasonable enough to ascribe the reduction of the canines and the recession of the jaws to these functional transfers, but there is no absolute proof that such was the case.

There may have been operative in the human stock in the early ground-dwelling stage and in the previous arboreal existence certain progressive and non-adaptive hereditary forces making for jaw reduction. Long, tusk-like canine teeth are a specialization that some of the ape ancestors of man may never have developed. Recently, there have been discovered in South Africa fossil anthropoid apes of late Pliocene or early Pleistocene date that had very small, non-projecting canines. Yet they also had small brains and were indubitable apes. The evidence of finds of early human fossils suggests that some lines were developed with tusk-like canines, which were gradually reduced, whereas others may have lacked them. Some primates come with tusks and tails, and others come without one, or the other, or either.

Thinking: Brains and Jaws

The pre-eminent bodily attribute of man is the great size of his brain. Only an intellectual colossus could write an *Origin of Species;* but an idiot may have a brain as large as that of a Darwin. Yet, Darwin could not have told you why the brain of a genius surpasses that of a mediocrity. Far less could he explain the greater gap that yawns between ordinary human intelligence and that of the anthropoid apes. Since the time of Darwin, much has been learned concerning the evolution and functions of the brain. But even now nobody knows whether man's brain is so large because he is so intelligent, or whether he is so intelligent because his brain is so large. Listen to what one of the greatest authorities on the evolution of the brain, Sir Grafton Elliot Smith, has to say on this subject: [31]

Man has evolved as the result of the continuous exploitation throughout the Tertiary period of the vast possibilities which the reliance upon vision as the guiding sense created for a mammal that had not lost the plasticity of its hands by too early specialization. Under the guidance of vision the hands were able to acquire skill in action and incidentally to become the instruments of an increasingly sensitive tactile discrimination, which again reacted upon the motor mechanisms and made possible the attainment of yet higher degrees of muscular skill. But this in turn reacted upon the control of ocular movements and prepared the way for the acquisition of stereoscopic vision and a fuller understanding of the world and the nature of things and activities in it. For the cultivation of manual dexterity was effected by means of the development of certain cortical mechanisms; and the facility in the performance of skilled movements once acquired was not a monopoly of the hands, but was at the service of all the muscles. . . . The sudden extension of the range of conjugate movements of the eyes and the attainment of more precise and effective convergence were results that accrued from this fuller cultivation of muscular skill. They were brought about as the result of the expansion of the prefrontal cortex, which provided the controlling instrument, and also by the building up in the mid-brain of the mechanism for automatically regulating the complex coordinations necessary to move the two eyes in association in any direction.

This seems to mean that the use of the eyes guides the hands in skilled movements, which react upon the brain to bring about increased control of ocular movements, which again result in better manual efficiency, which develops the controlling mechanism of the brain, and so on around, ad infinitum, in a beneficent evolutionary cycle, which is never-

---

[31] Smith, *Essays on the Evolution of Man*, pp. 145 ff.

theless a vicious circle of reasoning. It would appear that man owes the large size of his brain to his intelligence and owes his intelligence to the large size of his brain. It seems to me rather that we are driven to postulate certain inherent differences in the ancestors of man, on the one hand, and of the chimpanzee, on the other, which determined the development of a large brain and a large intelligence in one and a smaller brain and a lesser intelligence in the other.

There is, however, no doubt that some sort of causal relationship obtains between the size of the brain and the size of the mind. It is true that any man with a brain larger than that of Darwin could not write a better book than the *Origin of Species*. But it is certain that a man with a brain the size of that of a chimpanzee could not even *read* the *Origin of Species*. And I doubt that any chimpanzee or any descendant of a chimpanzee could ever read any book, even if his ancestors had been brought up for untold generations in the Library of Congress. I do not believe that any gorilla will ever invent a knife and fork; and if he did invent them and use them, I doubt if his jaws would shrink.

We must credit man's prehuman arboreal ancestors with larger brains and more active intelligence than that of their contemporary anthropoid apes; otherwise they would not have descended to the ground. If our first ground-dwelling forbears had not been more intelligent than the chimpanzees of today, nothing they could have done with their hands would have increased the size of their brains. The hands manipulate objects, fashion tools, and use them; the jaws recede, the brain grows, and man begins to think. But handling things does not necessarily produce thought, nor do tools make the brain grow. Not every treelorn ape blunders into intellectuality.

These pseudo-philosophical ruminations are merely intended as a warning to the reader against facile, mechanistic interpretations of observed or deduced evolutionary changes. He must be on his guard against those who readily evolve an entirely new species out of a new habit. Let us now consider the plausible and possible theory of the influence of external factors upon the evolution of the human head and face.

The skull consists of two parts—the brain-case and the facial skeleton. The upper jaw is immovably hafted to the brain-case, to which the lower jaw is also jointed just in front of the opening of the external ear. The most important muscles concerned in the shutting of the jaws and in cutting or grinding objects held between the teeth are the masseter and temporal muscles. The masseters arise from the lower edges of the malars or cheek bones and are attached to the outside of the ascending portions of the lower jaws. Put your fingers to your cheeks back toward the angles of the jaw. Now open and close your jaws, putting pressure upon the closed teeth. You will feel the masseter muscles contract and become hard when you close your mouth, and the harder you bite the more these muscles will swell out. The temporal muscles arise from fan-shaped areas

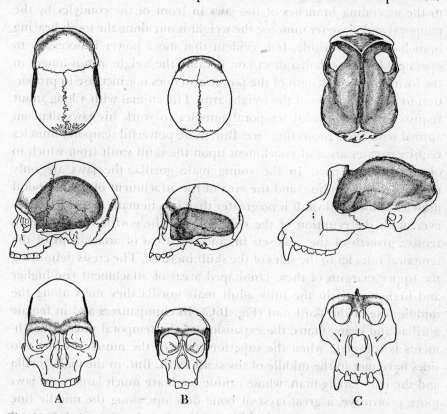

Fig. 16. Relation between area of temporal muscle attachment to brain case and size of brow-ridges in A, an adult male Australian; B, an infant gorilla; C, an adult male gorilla. (The heavily stippled areas are those covered by the temporal muscles. The relief of the brow-ridges is shown by light stipple.)

on both sides of the skull vault, behind above, and in front of the ear. The fibers of these fan-shaped muscles converge and pass down through the temporal fossae (the channels between the malar bones and the sides of the skull) and are attached to the inner surface of the ascending parts of the lower jaw. Place your fingers on your temples and close your jaws firmly. You will feel the contraction of the temporal muscles. Put your fingers against your head farther back and above the ears. When you close your jaws tightly, you will still be able to feel the swelling of the temporal muscles. You can delimit their area of attachment to the skull by exploring with the fingers the sides of the skull vault while working the muscles. When you close your jaws, the lower jaw is a lever of the third order. The fulcrum is at the condyles (the knobs that joint the mandible to the skull just in front of the ears); the power is applied to the ascending branches of the jaws in front of the condyles by the temporal and masseter muscles; the weight is out along the tooth-bearing branch of the mandible. It is evident that more power is necessary to operate a long jaw than a short jaw, because the weight arm is longer in the former and the length of the power arm does not increase in proportion to the elongation of the weight arm. The animal with a long snout requires more powerful temporal muscles to work his jaws than an animal with a less projecting face. But, more powerful temporal muscles require greater areas of attachment upon the skull vault from which to operate on the jaws. In the young male gorilla, the jaws are only moderately protruding, and the area of the attachment of the temporal muscles to the skull vault is no greater than it is in man (Fig. 16B). However, with the eruption of the second set of the gorilla's teeth, an intensive growth of the jaws sets in, and the areas of attachment of the temporal muscles to the sides of the skull increase. The crests delimiting the upper margins of these fan-shaped areas of attachment rise higher and higher until in the fully adult male gorilla they meet along the middle line of the skull roof (Fig. 16C). In chimpanzees and in female gorillas and orang-utans, the expansion of the temporal muscle attachments is complete when the superior edges of the muscles of the two sides have met in the middle of the skull vault. But, in the male gorilla and the male orang-utan, whose canine teeth are much larger and jaws more protrusive, a great crest of bone develops along the middle line of the skull in order to afford additional purchase for the great temporal muscles that operate their mighty jaws.

As the jaws of the adolescent gorilla become more and more projecting and his temporal muscles climb higher and higher up the sides of the skull, the weight of the jaws and face overbalances more and more the brain-case, which is poised upon the end of the spinal column. Since the facial parts and the portion of the skull base to which they are attached grow much more rapidly than the posterior parts of the skull vault and brain-case, the juncture of the skull with the vertebral column is displaced farther and farther backward until it comes to occupy a position that is occipital rather than basal, and in which the plane of the occipital foramen (the opening through which the spinal cord enters the skull to unite with the brain) is directed backward instead of downward. As the head becomes more and more overweighted with increased snoutiness, the muscles and ligaments that are fastened to the back of the head and extend down the neck enlarge and expand their attachments to support the greater weight of the jaws. The areas of attachment of the occipital and nuchal supports, which in the young gorilla and in man are mostly confined to the skull base behind the occipital foramen, rise higher and higher up the occipital bone (the back of the head), until in the male gorilla they reach the temporal muscle areas, where a transverse bony crest is developed similar to the median longitudinal crest that separates the two temporal muscles. Thus, in the adult gorilla or orang, the entire skull vault is covered with muscles that operate the jaws or support them.

Now the brain-case in a growing mammal is not made of one continuous vault of bone but of several bones that join each other at the edges, forming long interlocking sutures with irregularly serrated, or toothed, edges. When the brain is growing, these sutures or seams are open, and the expansion of the brain is accompanied by the growth of its bony covering, especially along these sutural lines. When the brain has completed its growth, the sutures begin to be obliterated from the inside, so that in adult animals the skull vault ultimately becomes one continuous bony shell. Such a process of sutural obliteration also takes place in man, but much more slowly than in most other animals, and complete obliteration of the sutures of the cranial vault is rare, even in aged persons.

In the young gorilla, the sutures begin to close when the jaws start their intensive growth during the eruption of the permanent dentition. By the time the temporal muscles have mounted to the summit of the cranial vault, the sutures have become entirely obliterated, and the growth of the brain has ceased. Sutural obliteration and brain growth in anthropoid apes are complete at an age varying from twelve to sixteen years, perhaps less. But in man, sutural obliteration does not begin until the eighteenth or nineteenth year and is not completed until old age, if then. The brain in man continues to grow long after the last teeth are erupted. Probably human brain growth proceeds until the twenty-fifth year of life, if not longer. It is easy to see that the overlying of the skull vault and occiput with powerful muscle attachments may exert a compressing and restricting influence upon the expansion of the brain in the anthropoid apes. Are we then to suppose that the early stoppage of brain growth in apes is the result of external pressure exerted by the muscles upon the skull? Only in the most indirect way. The sutures of the skull normally close because the brain has stopped growing; the brain does not stop growing because the sutures have closed. Sutural obliteration begins internally, at least in man.

There is a type of human idiocy called microcephaly, in which brain growth ceases at an early stage through some pathological cause. Microcephalic idiots often have brain cases as small as, or smaller than, that of a chimpanzee, but their faces are of nearly normal size. The areas of attachment of the temporal muscles on their under-sized brain cases are comparable with those of the chimpanzee, and the cranial sutures show premature obliteration. On the assumption that it was this premature obliteration of the sutures that stopped the growth of the brain in such idiots, a number of operations were performed in which the sutures of microcephals were opened. But none of these operations resulted in any subsequent growth of the patient's brain. You cannot enlarge the brain by prying apart the sutures of the skull.

Presumably the size of the jaws influences that of the brain in so far as a hypertrophy of the jaws probably results in a lessened blood supply for the brain. The growth energy that is available in the body is directed to its different portions and if one receives a disproportionate supply, some other must suffer. If you run to jaw development, you are scarcely likely to excel in brain size also. In man, the brains have developed at the expense of the jaws, and, in the anthropoid apes, the jaws have grown to the detriment of the brain.

A strictly mechanical view of skull evolution in man regards the great human brain as a direct result of reduction in size of the jaws. According to this opinion, the complete emancipation of the fore limbs in our early, erect-walking, ground-dwelling ancestors, transferred the defensive functions of the canine teeth, the cutting functions of the incisors, and a part of the grinding function of the cheek teeth to the hands and to manual tools. Consequently the jaws began to atrophy and to shrink back. In particular, a recession of the front portions of the jaws and a decrease in the size of the canines resulted from their loss of function. The diminution in jaw projection and jaw size brought about decreased areas of the temporal muscle attachments to the skull vault. This relieved pressure upon the brain-case and gave the brain a chance to expand.

Now, it is probable that the changes described did take place at about the same time, but it is altogether unlikely that jaw reduction caused brain growth. When we consider the skeletal remains of the early types of man, it will be seen that great jaw projection actually is found in specimens in which the brain had already attained its modern size. If you do not use your teeth, they will not develop properly, and disuse of the jaws undoubtedly will bring about a shrinkage of these parts. But a liquid diet will not increase the size of your brain. If you make your living by doing feats of strength with your teeth, such as lifting pianos on the vaudeville stage, you will unquestionably develop very large jaws and very powerful jaw muscles. You will probably also have a small or, at any rate, a feeble brain. But the inferiority of your brain will not be caused by the use to which you put your teeth. Rather your occupation will have been determined by your simultaneous possession of strong jaws and weak intelligence.

It would be more reasonable to conclude that man's jaws have shrunk because he began to use his brain than that his brain has grown because he has stopped using his jaws. It was the activity of the brain in inventing weapons and methods of preparing more easily masticable food that relieved the jaws of a heavy portion of their burden. Yet I am of the opinion that this relationship between jaw recession and manual preparation of food has been tremendously exaggerated. Instead of using rude and inefficient implements to cut their food into small bits, our savage ancestors probably held large chunks of food up to their mouths and tore at them with sharp and efficient teeth. It is easier to crack a nut between your teeth than between your fingers, and I do not believe that you begin trying to crack it with a stone until your teeth have begun to degenerate.

The growth of the neopallium in the arboreal ancestors of man has been discussed (pages 71–73). The development of visual, auditory, motor, and sensory areas of cortical representation seems to have been associated with the increased use of these senses brought about by the life in the trees, the erect-sitting posture, and the freedom of the hands for tactile and prehensile uses. The cerebrum consists of right and left hemispheres, each of which is subdivided by long and deep depressions called fissures (Fig. 17). The main fissure of each hemisphere, which is called the central fissure, or the fissure of Rolando, begins behind the eye and beneath the temple and passes diagonally upward and backward across the cerebral hemisphere. It separates the frontal lobe from the parietal lobe. The fissure of Silvius begins immediately behind the eye and runs backward and a little upward toward the posterior part of the brain. It separates the parietal lobe above from the temporal lobe below. The occipital lobe is also more or less clearly separated from the other lobes by fissures or sulci.

The cortical representation of sight is an area in the occipital lobe. Removal of this area in a tortoise produces little or no obvious defect in vision. In a bird such a lesion greatly impairs the vision of the eye on the opposite side, but the impairment does not amount to blindness. Destruction of the visual cortex of one hemisphere in a dog or in man causes a visual defect in half of the field of vision of both eyes. Destruc-

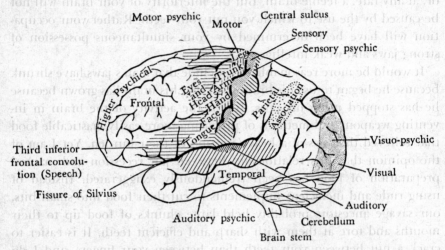

Fig. 17. Lateral surface of left hemisphere of the human brain, showing areas of localization.

tion of the visual areas in both hemispheres in man causes virtual blindness. But a dog or monkey whose visual areas have been destroyed still avoids obstacles as it walks. In man, the destruction of the visual cortex causes a loss of memory of localities and of the position of objects that are visually appreciated; whereas those who lose their sight through disease of the retina retain good memorial pictures of positions and objects known by sight. The area of visual memory is probably an area zonal to that of vision proper and has been called the *visuo-psychic* area. Adjoining this in the parietal and temporal lobes is an area that includes the so-called angular gyrus, a diseased condition of which impairs the power of understanding *written* words.

The auditory area of cortical representation has been located in the temporal lobe. Destruction of this area is said to cause "word deafness" —the inability to recognize familiar words when heard, although they are recognized when seen. In dogs, such a lesion affects the ability to recognize their masters' call.

The olfactory bulb is underneath the cerebrum and is greatly reduced in man. Disease of these parts has been accompanied by a disturbance of the sense of smell.

The area immediately in front of the great central fissure, called the precentral area, is given over to the localization of movements of various parts of the body; the sequence, beginning at the top, being: perineum, foot, knee, hip, abdomen, chest, shoulder, elbow, wrist, hand, eyelids, ear, mouth, and tongue. Just back of the central sulcus are probably the areas of sensation relating to these same parts of the body. It is a remarkable fact that the centers for the movements of the eyes themselves, as contrasted with the eyelids, occupy a position in the frontal lobes removed from the precentral area. It has been suggested by Tschermak that the eyeball movements of the frontal region are of a reflex nature to carry the visual field in various directions in response to sensory data, as for example, the touch of an object by the hand. The movements of the eyeballs arising from the occipital cortex are, according to this view, such as would direct the gaze toward something seen in the periphery of the visual field.

Apart from the foregoing areas, the functions of the cerebral cortex are as yet almost unknown. This much, however, is certain; the portions of the neopallium not given over to motor and sensory functions are "association areas," in which are received and blended the impressions from the different receptive areas. Here are stored the memories of sensory and motor experiences. Here are the seats of the higher intellectual functions. The frontal association areas of the brain begin to differentiate in the tree shrews and increase throughout the primates, culminating in man. These areas underlie the forehead or brow. Man is the "high-brow" member of the Primate Order. Now, these frontal lobes of the brain are generally assumed to lodge the higher mental faculties: memory, judgment, imagination, et cetera. If this is true, it is remarkable that they should border upon the motor areas that occupy the precentral region. Professor Wood Jones [32] offers an ingenious explanation of this juxtaposition of the higher association areas with those that represent the movements of different parts of the body. He assumes that the so-called motor area is one given over to what he calls "pictured movements," i.e., those movements an animal can see and feel itself doing. The frontal areas anterior to these "pictured movement areas" he

[32] Jones, *Arboreal Man*, pp. 192 ff.

conceives to be an extension of this field in which memories of the movements are stored and sorted and in which the movements may be imagined or idealized. Here, perhaps, may originate conceptions of hypothetical movements of the body under imaginary circumstances— in other words, conceptions of conduct or behavior.

The animal without a neopallial kinaesthetic area performs all its actions in the absence of any pictured consciousness of the action. An animal with a kinaesthetic area performs actions of which it has a definite mental pictured conception. *It knows what it is doing.*

An animal with a developing prefrontal association area has, in addition, memories of its past actions. *It knows what it is doing, and it remembers what it has done.* An animal with an elaborated prefrontal area has, in addition, the faculty for building up pictures of possible future actions. *It knows what it is doing, it remembers what it has done, and it can estimate what it might do.*[33]

Wood Jones' conception is, in short, that reason and intelligence may be the perfection of cortical representations of the several senses and the development of ample association areas, whereas the origin of higher ideals of conduct are particularly dependent upon the growth of the frontal or prefrontal regions.

As a matter of fact, the examinations of brains of intellectually distinguished men seem to indicate that the development of the parietal and occipital association areas are of equal importance with the frontal areas. The skulls of Kant, Gauss, and Dirichlet showed marked developments of the parietal region; those of Bach and Beethoven, of the posterior and central region, while in the last two named the prefrontal lobes were of insignificant proportions. Helmholtz's brain showed a remarkable development of the parietal region, while the skulls of Gauss and Richard Wagner exhibited striking developments of both the parietal and pre-frontal association areas.[34]

Evidently, man's intelligence is intimately related to his possession of a large neopallium, the cortex of which is intricately folded and wrinkled in order to afford the maximum nervous surface area. In general, the size of the neopallium, the cortical representations of the senses, the association areas, and the complexity of the folds (convolutions) and wrinkles (sulci), increase from the lemuroids and tarsioids up to the great anthropoid apes, although there are individual exceptions in various families and species. In the lemurs, in conjunction with their nocturnal habits,

[33] *Ibid.*, pp. 192 ff.
[34] Sonntag, *op. cit.*, p. 278, quoting Luciani, *Textbook of Physiology.*

the motor and visual areas of the cortex are exuberantly developed, while the association areas are small. In Tarsius, the neopallium is smooth, the visual cortex is relatively larger than in lemurs, and the association areas are small. In the New World monkeys, the neopallium is much more voluminous than in lemurs. A Pithecia monkey has a brain three times as large as that of a loris (Suborder Lemuroidea) of the same body weight.[35] The Old World monkeys (Cercopithecidae) have reduced olfactory lobes but very large neopallia with increased association areas. The visual area is more complex than in Tarsius. The surface of the cerebrum is not always extensively convoluted. The brain of the gibbon is intermediate in character between those of the Old World monkeys and those of the larger anthropoids. The orang-utan has a more voluminous brain with a more convoluted and fissured surface than that of the gibbon. The brain of the chimpanzee is still larger, but that of the gorilla is largest of all the anthropoids and in its pattern approaches most closely to that of man. Nevertheless, the brain of man is very much larger than that of the gorilla and weighs about two and a half times as much as that of the great ape. The human brain is about 1/50 of the entire body weight, while that of a gorilla varies from 1/150 to 1/200 part of that weight.[36]

The neopallium in man is from 3.4 to 6 times as large as it is in the gorilla and chimpanzee.[37] Tilney states that by actual planimetric measurement the frontal area in man covers 47 per cent of the entire lateral surface of the brain, in chimpanzee 33 per cent, in gorilla 32 per cent, in baboon 31 per cent, and in lemur 23 per cent.[38] Duckworth points out that the gorilla's brain is to be regarded as showing the amount of surface area requisite for the reception of general sensory impulses arising from a body of that size, since there is probably no great difference between man and the gorilla in the development of special senses.

The evolution of the neopallium in the primates is marked by a great increase in the motor areas, which is most marked in man. The great size of these areas in the human brain probably represents an increase in range and variety of movements rather than an accession of strength. In skilled movements of the hands, lips, tongue, and vocal apparatus, the higher apes are greatly inferior to man. Destruction of the motor cortex in the brain of a dog does not impair the ordinary use of the limbs, but it renders the dog unable to perform skilled movements with

[35] *Ibid.*, p. 45, quoting Elliot Smith.
[36] Duckworth, *Morphology and Anthropology*, p. 190.
[37] Sonntag, *op. cit.*, p. 275, quoting Elliot Smith.
[38] Tilney, *Brain*, pp. 783–784.

the limbs, such as offering its paw to its master, steadying a bone with its paws when gnawing, standing or walking on its hind legs, et cetera. When the arms become trained in the use of tools, as in man, these skilled movements suffer most heavily from lesions to the motor cortex. Consequently, the primates are most affected by such injuries and man pre-eminently so. The area of motor representation in the cortex of a given part of the body seems to depend not so much upon the size of the part involved as the range and variety of movement. In man, the cortical area for the thumb is greater than the combined areas of chest and abdomen, and the tongue has a larger area than the neck.

But, as a factor determining the pre-eminent size of the human brain, the association areas are by far most important. Their increase in man seems to extend to the outlying areas of general and special sensibility. Man has a larger and heavier brain than any of the other animals except the elephant and the whale, and there is not the shadow of a doubt that human intelligence, individually and collectively, is most intimately related to extension of motor, sensory, and association areas in the brain cortex. If we do not know the details of this delicate and intricate relationship, it is, nevertheless, apparent that such a relationship obtains.

We have already discussed the tool-using capacities of anthropoid apes in connection with the function of the emancipated fore limbs. Professor Köhler's chimpanzees in their handling of objects and use of tools seemed to be handicapped not so much by motor inability as by lack of intelligence necessary for purposeful direction of such activity. We must now examine the extent to which anthropoid apes behave with "insight" or intelligence when confronted with the various problems set before them by experimental psychologists.

Suppose you make a blind alley out of chicken wire and place a hen inside at the blind end, with some food on the other side of the wire fence just out of the hen's reach. The hen will beat helplessly against the obstruction or rush back and forth in front of it aimlessly. Eventually, in its purposeless meanderings, the fowl may get outside of the blind alley and reach the objective by running round the curve. But some particularly ungifted specimens will keep beating against the obstacle, even when the necessary detour is short. A dog, under the same circumstances, with the food on the other side of the obstacle, turns round and dashes out of the blind alley in a smooth curve round the fence to obtain the food. Professor Köhler tried this experiment on a little girl of one year and three months, able to walk alone for a few weeks. First she pushed against the partition, then looked round slowly, let her eyes run along the blind alley, laughed joyfully, and trotted around the corner toward the objective.[39] In the case of the hen, the objective, if attained at all, is gained by a series of pure coincidences; in the case of the dog and the child, the result is a genuine achievement. A successful chance solution consists of an agglomeration of random movements; a genuine achievement takes place as a single, continuous occurrence. The animal makes for the objective directly and smoothly. Usually, when the true solution is struck, there is a jerk on the part of the animal, a sudden turn, or, in the case of the child, a lighting up of the face.

Köhler used a variation of this type of experiment with chimpanzees. A desired object was suspended out of reach in a basket. The basket was weighted and swung like a pendulum so that at the end of its swing it almost reached a perch high up on the side of the cage. A chimpanzee faced with this problem surveyed the situation quietly for an instant; then ran to the perch and climbed up, waited for the basket with outstretched arms, and caught it. Experiments with other animals led Köhler to conclude that every chimpanzee could solve this problem. If variations were introduced, the animal always selected the right place from which the objective could be secured.

Another experiment consists of placing a desired object beyond the bars of the cage with a string tied to it and leading to the bars. A number of other strings, beside the "right" one to which the object is attached, are placed on the ground running in a similar direction and crossing the "right" string and one another. The chimpanzee in these circumstances will always pull at the string that touches the objective, even if it is not attached to it; he will not usually pull at a string the end of which is obviously some distance from the objective. But when very hungry, the chimpanzee will pull at a rope that quite apparently does not reach the objective, as Köhler says, like the proverbial drowning man who clutches at a straw. It seems doubtful whether the concept of "connection" signifies to the chimpanzee anything more than contact.

Another test consisted of hanging a desired object in such a position that it could be reached from the top of one of a number of closed doors, if the right door was opened at a full right angle to the wall. The chimpanzees readily selected the right door and either opened it to the proper angle and climbed up it, or climbed up the door and pushed themselves and the door away from the wall into the proper position.

The chimpanzees, however, could not grapple with a problem involving the necessity of fastening a rope to a crossbar in order to swing toward an objective and were even unable to arrive at a solution of a similar kind by unwinding a rope coiled round a crossbar in order to

[39] Köhler, *Mentality of Apes*, pp. 14–15.

make it long enough for them to take the required swing. They seemed to regard a carefully coiled rope as a mere tangle. In placing boxes one on top of another in order to climb upon them to reach a desired object, it appears that the conception of placing a second box on top of the first is very difficult for the ape to grasp; for the second box has to be placed so that it will be stable. "There is practically no statics to be observed in the chimpanzee." The animals pile up an altogether wobbly and ill-balanced structure, because the boxes are not properly selected and carefully placed; but often they succeed in climbing up and reaching the objective because of their own masterly balancing abilities. A chimpanzee, attempting to use a ladder, will place it flat against the wall rather than prop it with the base planted out from the wall. Or one edge of the ladder may be placed against the wall with the other edge and the rounds projecting into space. Probably this lack of an appreciation of statics is to some extent a result of an incomplete optical realization of situations, but it also may be due to the varying positions in which the animal holds its head. If the head were always held upright, as in man, the fixed "above" and "below" orientation might be acquired.

Mrs. Ladygin Kohts trained a young chimpanzee to match objects and colors and discovered that up to 15 seconds after the sample was removed from sight the chimpanzee could match it successfully. Professor R. M. Yerkes experimented with two monkeys and a young orang-utan on a problem the solution of which required the animals to select always the middle object, or an object in some specific relation to others. The monkeys gradually learned by a process of trial and error. The orang-utan worked for 23 days without the slightest improvement and then suddenly and finally solved the problem over night. It was the opinion of the experimenter that the orang solved his problem ideationally, by insight.[40]

Köhler concludes that "chimpanzees manifest intelligent behavior of the general kind familiar in human beings. This type of intelligent conduct extends to the least gifted of the species." He is inclined to the opinion that in intelligence *too,* the anthropoid ape is nearer to man than to the lower apes and monkeys. He thinks it very probable that the chief difference between anthropoids and human beings lies in the limitation of the time "in which the animal lives"—that is to say, the extent to which the animal remembers back and considers forward. Furthermore, the lack of speech and the limitation of those important components of thought—"images"—are among the causes that prevent the chimpanzee from developing the rudiments of a culture. The chimpan-

[40] Yerkes, *Almost Human,* pp. 115 ff.

zee also suffers from a defective optical apprehension of many situations and will often begin to solve a problem from too purely a visual point of view. Often, therefore, when this animal ceases to behave with "insight," it may be the result of his being unable to get "the lie of the land." With respect to memory in chimpanzees, Köhler found that his apes were able to solve correctly problems in form perception and in color values after intervals of from 13 to 18 months. However, he regards these successes as after-effects of previous performances rather than as achievements necessitating images of the past. He himself tested memory by burying fruit in the presence of the animals and, after obliterating the marks of the excavation, allowing them to range about in the neighborhood of the concealed objects a day or several days afterward. In most cases, they went to the right spot and dug up the fruit. He also was able to secure a large proportion of successes in tests involving the selection of a photograph showing a *full* box of bananas in preference to one in which the box was empty.

Very little experimental work has been done with the gibbon. Boutan tested one of these animals, particularly with various problems involving the opening of "trick" boxes in order to secure food. She acquired independently a few new ideas and retained for months their memory and the movements requisite to successful solutions. She foresaw her objective but lacked "prevision" of the proper movements. The gibbon seems to be inferior in manual dexterity to the other great apes. In two more recent studies, the performance of the gibbon has been matched with those of Old World and New World monkeys. At solving laboratory problems the small anthropoid ape seems certainly no better than monkeys and may possibly be inferior to them.

The most extensive scientific studies of the orang-utan have been those of Yerkes. This animal shows "behavioral adaptivity" in a variety of ways: by imitation; by trial of various responses and gradual elimination of those that are unprofitable; by perceptually selecting suitable responses and eliminating useless ones without trial; adaptation by understanding, insight, or ideation. The orang is obviously more intelligent than the gibbon. Aerial gymnastics require coordination, not cerebration.

Yerkes again has conducted, apparently, the only modern "psychobiological" investigation of the gorilla. The specimen he studied was a young female mountain gorilla, Congo, which lived for two and a half years in captivity in Florida. This animal was apparently deficient in inquisitiveness or curiosity and was not imitative, profiting very little by human tuition. Congo showed some very perplexing inhibitions.

For example, a problem was set for her designated by Yerkes as the "wound-chain experiment." This involved winding the animal's mooring chain in a complex fashion about various trees and posts and leaving her to disentangle herself. By chance, in the setting of this problem, the gorilla was tied, not to her customary mooring tree, but to a nearby tree. She failed completely to solve the problem. Subsequently, it was discovered that she had no difficulty whatsoever in disentangling herself when she was tied to her familiar tree but would refuse to attempt the problem when she was tied to the adjacent tree. "Having initially failed of success in that particular situation, she tended to be inhibited thereafter whenever that particular situation was used." [41]

In the manipulation of sticks for the getting of food, Congo showed little ability, either native or acquired. In attempting to sweep a piece of apple within reach by means of a stick, she would often grasp the stick and sweep it away from the food, or sweep the food away from, instead of toward, herself. After considerable practice, however, she succeeded. Professor Yerkes thinks that she had her objective clearly in mind but lacked the ability to make hand and eye work together. On the whole, she was mechanically inept to a high degree and learned only very slowly and imperfectly. It seems to follow from these experiments that the gorilla has very little mechanical ability and shows practically no tendency to utilize objects as tools. On the other hand, chimpanzees are highly gifted in this way.

Yet this gorilla evidenced definite powers of memory. When, after an absence of ten months, Professor Yerkes resumed his experiments with Congo, she not only recognized him but resumed her work where she had left it the previous winter and even seemed to have improved in the interval. Buried food was remembered for several days. She was able to remember either by location or by color of the container in which the food was placed. In the memory responses to color, the gorilla showed quicker adaptation to the problem than do chimpanzees.

Congo showed decidedly less "insight" in dealing with problematic situations than Professor Yerkes had observed in the case of chimpanzees and orangs. He is, nevertheless, confident that the gorilla possesses both insight and foresight. In attempting to get the experimenter to leave her cage in order that she might have a mirror to herself or secure for herself food that had been placed on a platform, Congo exhibited qualities that made Professor Yerkes suspect her of a development of cunning and craft far beyond anything else he had previously noted in anthropoid apes. Yerkes thinks that Congo was trying to conceal her

[41] Yerkes and Yerkes, *op. cit.*, p. 505.

"insights" rather than to reveal them. In spite of the mechanical and other deficiencies of Congo, Yerkes is inclined to rank the gorilla next to man in intelligence.

The following table, adapted from this investigator, shows his estimate of the ranking of the various anthropoids in nearness to man in several criteria of intelligence.

	Gorilla	Chimpanzee	Orang-utan	Gibbon
Curiosity	2	1	3	4
Imitation	3	1	2	4
Teachableness	3	1	2	4
Attention	1	2	3	4
Adaptation with insight	2	1	3	4
Attention with foresight	2	1	3	?
Memory—temporal span	1	2	2	3
Imagination	2	1	2	3
Instrumentation	3	1	2	4
Adaptation of environment versus self-adaptation	3	1	2	4
Mechanical ability	3	1	2	4
Behavioral adaptability	3	1	2	4
Psychological resemblance to man	1	2	3	4

On the basis of mean rating, the chimpanzee easily is closest to man, but Professor Yerkes, certainly the most experienced student of anthropoid intelligence, concludes his summary of the subject thus:

Were correspondingly varied and satisfactory data available for the gorilla, it might command first place in psychological resemblance to man even if less alert, docile, imitative, and suggestible than the chimpanzee.[42]

The above accounts of experiments designed to investigate the intelligence of anthropoid apes may appear to the reader trivial and of little significance. The successes of the animals in such psychological tests are in no sense spectacular. A chimpanzee roller-skating on a vaudeville stage is a much more impressive sight. But the tricks animals learn under physical compulsion do not afford the slightest scientific evidence as to their intelligent behavior. It is easy to *read* intelligence into the actions of animals. However, an animal or a human being is not acting intelligently when it attains its objective by a direct route that arises naturally out of its own organization, as when, for example, a monkey climbs a tree to secure fruit. Intelligence is called into play only when circumstances block the way of an obvious course of procedure, and the animal, confronted with the problem, then chooses a roundabout path whereby the difficulty may be surmounted. Such behavior with "insight" or "intelligence" is not restricted to man and the anthropoid apes, as was

[42] *Ibid.*, p. 550.

formerly believed. All of the monkeys display it in some degree and even the few lemurs that have been tested. Some of the monkeys do as well as, or better than, the apes. Furthermore many kinds of lower mammals and birds demonstrate performance ability in laboratory tests.

Perhaps the most important reason why anthropoid apes do not "behave like human beings" is because they are not really "teachable." Köhler says of the chimpanzee: [43]

It is a continuous source of wonder, and often enough of vexation, to observe how every attempt to re-mould his biological heritage "runs off" an otherwise clever and ductile animal of this species "like water from a duck's back." If one is able to produce a very temporary type of behaviour which is not congenial to the chimpanzee's instincts, it will soon be necessary to use compulsion if he is to keep to it. And the slightest relaxation of that compulsion will be followed by a "reversion to type"; moreover, while such pressure lasts, his behaviour expresses offensive unwillingness and indifference to the essence of what has been demanded of him.

The orang-utan and the gorilla are said to be even less receptive of humanizing influence than the chimpanzee.

The first ground-dwelling ancestors of man must have handled objects and experimented in the use of tools much as do the present anthropoid apes when observed in captivity. But our human ancestors were on the ground through initiative and not through compulsion, by choice and not by necessity. They were "free agents." They had the ability of profiting by experience. No ethnologist today can offer an adequate reason for the vast disparity of culture that obtains between, let us say, the native Australians (perhaps the most primitive physically, if not culturally, of modern races) and the Australians of British descent. The native Australian is almost as incapable of absorbing civilization as the chimpanzee of adopting the method of life and tribal customs of the aboriginal Australian. Yet the native Australian is a human being and behaves with insight. He is, nevertheless, almost as culturally inert as an anthropoid ape. The brain of the average Australian is somewhat smaller than that of the European, but the differences in size are not commensurate with the differences in culture. We have no scale for comparing the intelligence of a native Australian with that of a European; still less have we any really adequate means of comparing the intelligence of an anthropoid ape with that of any man. Yet we are fairly safe in assuming that the Australian is far less intelligent than is the Englishman, and that the chimpanzee is much farther removed in his mental capacity from the

[43] Köhler, *op. cit.*, p. 70.

native Australian. The Australian has had as much time to develop a culture as has the Englishman; so has the chimpanzee. If environmental circumstances make progress unfavorable, the progressive animal attempts to shift his habitat to a more favorable environment. The pygmies of Africa inhabit the same area as do the gorillas; many Bantu Negroes also live in these African forests. The gorilla is a brute without any vestige of a culture; the pygmy has a few weapons, no habitations worth mentioning, no language of his own, so far as is known, and very little else in the way of material or immaterial culture. The Bantu Negro has domesticated animals and plants, has acquired the use of iron, and has an intricate social organization and some fairly well developed arts, as well as a useful language. Why is the pygmy more advanced than the gorilla? You may reply, "Because the pygmy is a man and the gorilla is an ape." Very well, but why has the Bantu Negro a culture the pygmy lacks? Both are men; both live in the same environment, as does also the gorilla. You may say, "Because the Negro is more intelligent than the pygmy." Why? Because the Negro is hereditarily endowed with a superior mentality, initiative, brain, or whatever you may choose to call it.

I can see no reason why the gorilla should not have become man, no reason why the pygmy should not have acquired a culture, except inherent lack of mental capacity—which in terms of gross anatomy means an inferior brain.

The most primitive humanoid form discovered up to the present is the fossil ape-man of Java, Pithecanthropus erectus (the "erect ape-man"). We shall have occasion in a later section to discuss more fully the anatomical characteristics of this remarkable specimen; at present, we are particularly concerned with his brain. Pithecanthropus lived at the beginning of the Middle Pleistocene period, perhaps half a million years ago. The cubic capacity of this animal's brain-case, as estimated from the skull cap, must have been about 900 cc. The mean for gorillas is 549 cc, and for adult human males racial averages range from about 1200 to 1500 cc. This Javanese fossil was in size of brain transitional between modern man and the anthropoid apes and, in bodily size and posture, so far as known, completely human. Pithecanthropus may well represent a late and unprogressive survival of one of the earliest forms of ground-dwelling human primates. He may have been the "native Australian" of his day. His brain was more than half again as large as that of the gorilla, a third or more smaller than that of the more primitive men of today. The frontal lobes of the brain were very low and narrow, as judged from the cast of the skull interior, and only about half as large as those of the average modern European, but at least twice as large as those of a chimpanzee or an orang-utan. The area of the frontal lobes that is connected with speech foreshadows in Pithecanthropus its modern human development. The association areas of the parietal lobes between the centers of sight, hearing, and of common sensation are simple, small, and ape-like. Nevertheless, Pithecanthropus undoubtedly behaved "with insight" upon most, if not all, occasions. Since the chimpanzee can fit together sticks, Pithecanthropus erectus must have been able to make rude implements; since the orang and chimpanzee can solve some few and simple problems ideationally, Pithecanthropus must have grappled successfully with much harder mental tasks; and if the chimpanzee remembers for a few days or weeks, this early humanoid form must have had a vastly longer span of memory. We may reasonably conjecture that the Java ape-man used rude implements of stone and wood, constructed shelters, perhaps nest-like on the ground, and made vocal sounds by which he conveyed to his fellows some simple meanings. Although the actual specimen found in Java probably represents a late survival of a conservative humanoid stock which scarcely attained the lowest level of human intelligence and culture, nevertheless, when the first Pithecanthropidae walked among the forests, man, erect in posture and dominant in brain, had arrived.

Talking: Getting a Chin

A few months before the death of the Honorable William J. Bryan, I was called upon to introduce him to a Harvard audience. His topic for the evening was "Evolution." Mr. Bryan's opinions on the subject and his reputation for oratory and wit made the task of introducing him somewhat embarrassing for a humble student of evolution. I extricated myself as best I could from this situation by saying simply, "Man is said to be distinguished from the anthropoid apes principally by his power of articulate speech; if this is true, there is no living human being who has a better right to disclaim any relationship with the anthropoids than the speaker of this evening."

As a matter of fact, there have not been lacking those who have claimed for the anthropoid apes the use of some sort of a language. R. L. Garner studied and professed to understand the language of chimpanzees.[44] He described sounds that seemed to stand for words and contended that the vocal language of monkeys and apes differs from ours only in its complexity and degree of development. Boutan, on the contrary, concluded that gibbons had no real speech but only a pseudo-

[44] Garner, *Apes and Monkeys.*

language in which the sounds are spontaneous or instinctive.[45] The sounds of a true language are, on the other hand, acquired or learned. Boutan's gibbon made sounds of four categories: a group expressive of satisfaction; a second expressing discomfort or fear; a group intermediate between the two; and a group expressive of excitement. Each of these groups consisted of several sounds. But the gibbon acquired no new sounds during captivity.

The orang-utan expresses its emotions by grunts, whines, screams, and other vocalizations, but is not known to have any articulate language. Yerkes says that the chimpanzee has a sign language in which "no" is expressed by a movement of the head, and definite positions or movements of the arm and hand signify affirmation. Nissen classified chimpanzee vocalizations into five categories; Carpenter recorded nine types of gibbon sounds. Köhler says that the gamut of chimpanzee phonetics is entirely subjective; they can only express emotions, never designate objects. Yerkes tried vainly to teach two young chimpanzees to speak. Dr. William H. Furness, after six months of daily training, succeeded in teaching a young orang-utan to say "papa" and to recognize it as his teacher's name. By dint of almost superhuman efforts, he also taught the same animal to say "cup." But Dr. Furness concluded that orang-utan language, if existent, is restricted to a few sounds of merely emotional significance.

Yerkes is inclined to ascribe the lack of speech in anthropoid apes to a disinclination to imitate sounds. They have plenty of things to talk about but no gift of vocal expression. They may have ideas, but they cannot exchange them.

According to Elliot Smith, the full appreciation of objects and events in the external world was dependent upon developments of the brain cortex that did not take place until man became human. Realization of space and time, recognition of objects by their form, color, texture, size —all of these are human attainments that promote the development and use of language with all that it implies in the way of stimulating thought by the exchange of ideas. Therefore, the initiation of language is directly the result of the development of certain areas of the brain cortex. Clinical investigation shows that injury to any part of the brain cortex disturbs attention. The sensory cortex records past impressions which modify the effects of new ones. It is also concerned with the appreciation of weight, size, shape, and texture of objects, and of spatial reference. It derives this last-named power from connection with the visual cortex, because it is dependent upon the coordinated movements of the eyes.

[45] Yerkes, *Almost Human*, pp. 169 ff.

The cast of the interior of the brain-case of Pithecanthropus shows a pronounced enlargement of the posterior part of the second temporal convolution. This, according to Elliot Smith, can mean only that there was a sudden expansion of the auditory or acoustic area for the appreciation of some sort of speech. Paul Broca, a great French anthropologist, discovered that the third inferior frontal convolution was a speech area. It is now recognized, however, that this is only one of a number of cortical areas connected with speech, and that, of these, perhaps the most important is the acoustic area in the temporal region, which has to do with the reception of sounds. The area concerned in the production of words is probably that frontal speech area adjacent to the motor centers for lips and tongue. An intensive cultivation of the temporal acoustic area was required in order to link these sounds into sentences so as to express a meaning. This is, then, the syntactical area. The parietal cortex, which is between the sensory, acoustic, and visual areas, associates the sensations from these areas in such a way as to give a wider understanding of the sounds and symbols as expressed in sentences—a true comprehension of the significance of speech, thought, and action. This is the *semantic* area, which is the area of "meaning." Similarly, the parts of the cortex immediately bordering upon the occipital area constitute the *nominal* centers, since visual perception is intimately related to the recognition and naming of objects. All of these areas are linked together and coordinated in the reception, understanding, and production of speech. They constitute the "central exchange."

The prefrontal area is generally cultivated in the performance of skilled movements. It is especially associated with the power of exact convergence that is essential for the fixation of the eyes upon an object so that its images are focused upon corresponding spots in the two retinae. Connections of this focusing area with other parts of the brain enable the individual to concentrate upon the object itself rather than upon the effort of looking at it. It may then be understood that the development of the prefrontal cortex is a prerequisite of stereoscopic vision, without which there is no depth of perspective, no spatial appreciation, no visual basis for the giving of names to objects.

All of the anthropoid apes are vocally and muscularly equipped so that they could have an articulate language, if they possessed the requisite intelligence. They express their emotions by a variety of sounds, as our prehuman ancestors must have done. There is nothing about a snout that prevents its possessor from speaking, but there is something about the brain that goes with a snout that makes speech impossible.

There are, however, certain modifications in the jaws of man that seem to be connected with the habit of speech. To understand these we must consider the evolution of the human face from its previous anthropoid condition. Here we are on firm ground, for we have early fossil forms of man to demonstrate the various changes that have taken place. The face of an anthropoid ape protrudes and forms the semblance of a snout, but it is not a real snout because its long axis is not produced in a horizontal line almost continuous with the long axis of the skull base but

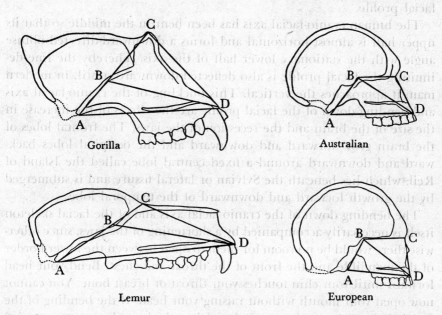

Fig. 18. Median longitudinal sections of skulls showing the extension of the face upon a straight cranio-facial axis in the lemur and the gorilla, and upon a bent axis in man. A, the middle of the anterior border of the foramen magnum. B, the anterior point on the sphenoid bone (where the chiasmatic groove is cut by the sagittal plane). C, the juncture of the nasal and frontal bones (nasion). D, the most anterior point on the upper jaw between the middle incisor teeth (prosthion).

is bent sharply downward. In logitudinal section, the facial skeleton of a gorilla has roughly the form of an equilateral triangle of which the base is formed by a line extending from the middle point between the upper central incisor teeth back to the foramen magnum; the posterior side is formed by the attachment of the facial skeleton to the cranio-facial base, and the anterior by the line marking the facial profile from the middle point between the brow-ridges down the nose to the incisors (Fig. 18).

The most protruding part of the lower jaw of a gorilla is the incisor region, and from that point it slopes downward and backward so that there is no chin prominence at all. It is evident that the jaws and face of the gorilla are already bent downward on the cranio-facial base in such a way that the level gaze of the animal is not directed along the snout but out from it. The snouted animal sights along its nose; the gorilla can look *down* its nose, but in modern man, the jaws have receded so far and the facial skeleton is bent down under the cranio-facial base to such an extent that the eye-level axis is almost perpendicular to the facial profile.

The human cranio-facial axis has been bent in the middle so that its upper half is almost horizontal and forms a downward-directed obtuse angle with the stationary lower half of the axis. Thereby the line delimiting the facial profile is also deflected downward, until, in modern man, it approaches the vertical. This buckling of the cranio-facial axis and bending down of the facial profile are the effects of the increase in the size of the brain and the recession of the jaws. The frontal lobes of the brain grow forward and downward and the occipital lobes backward and downward around a fixed central lobe called the Island of Reil, which lies beneath the Sylvian or lateral fissure and is submerged by the growth forward and downward of the temporal lobe.

The bending down of the cranio-facial axis and of the facial skeleton itself is necessarily accompanied by a shortening of the jaws, since otherwise there would be no room for them to open between the lower border of the mandible and the front of the throat and chest. Bend your head forward until your chin touches your throat or breast bone. You cannot now open your mouth without raising your head. If the bending of the facial skeleton upon the cranio-facial base had not been accompanied by a recession of the jaws, it would be necessary for the head to be thrown backward and the nose elevated before the jaws could be opened.

If the bending downward of the cranio-facial base was a progressive development caused by the growth of the neopallium, the recession of the jaws must have been, in large measure, a regressive change owing to loss of function. Fossil human skulls clearly show that in some cases, at least, this process of jaw shortening was first effected by a reduction in size of the canine teeth, so that they no longer protruded above the level of the other teeth, and the upper and lower canines ceased to interlock as they do in anthropoid apes (Fig. 19 A, B). The incisor teeth also became smaller and were no longer inclined forward, as in the apes, but assumed a nearly vertical position. The portions of the upper and lower jaws in which the teeth are embedded (the alveolar processes) shrank back, carrying with them the reduced teeth. You have noticed how, in old people who have lost their front teeth, the lips fall in and the chin is left sticking out, owing to the absorption of the alveolar processes that formerly lodged the teeth. A somewhat similar process of shrinkage of the jaws must have taken place when, in the course of evolution, the

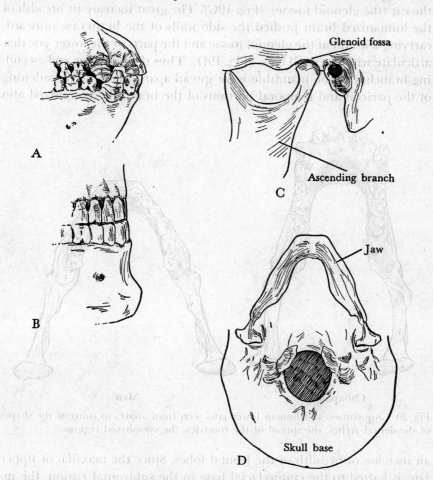

Fig. 19. A, the anterior portions of a chimpanzee's jaws showing protrusive alveolar processes and chinless condition. B, the anterior portions of a European's jaws showing retracted alveolar processes and positive chin eminence. C, the left glenoid fossa of a human skull. D, human lower jaw and skull base, showing how the condyles of the jaw are spread and the dental arches made to diverge posteriorly by the broadening of the skull base.

canines and incisors became reduced to modern human dimensions, although, of course, the teeth in question were not lost but merely reduced.

The jaws of an ape are long and relatively narrow; the dental arches are U-shaped, but broadest across the canine teeth and somewhat narrowed in the region of the molar or grinding teeth (Fig. 20). The lower jaw is hinged to the skull base by ascending branches ending in knobs or condyles that fit into hollows of the temporal bones just in front of the ear (the glenoid fossae) (Fig. 19C). The great increase in breadth of the humanized brain pushed the side walls of the brain-case outward, carrying with them the glenoid fossae and the parts of the lower jaw that articulate with the skull base (Fig. 19D). Thus the posterior and ascending branches of the mandible were spread apart. With the broadening of the parietal and temporal portions of the brain, there occurred also

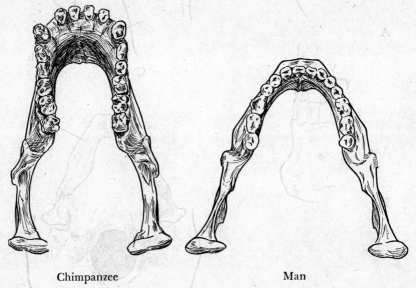

Chimpanzee   Man

Fig. 20. Chimpanzee and human lower jaws seen from above, to contrast the shapes of the dental arches, the spread of the condyles, the symphysial regions.

an increase of breadth of the frontal lobes. Since the maxilla, or upper jaw, is hafted to the cranio-facial base in the subfrontal region, the increase of the breadth of these lobes tended to broaden the posterior parts of the palate, making the dental arches diverge posteriorly instead of being parallel or convergent, and changing them from an inverted U-shape to a parabolic shape. Hence, the jaws become shortened anteriorly and narrowed in front by the reduction in size of the canines and incisors, and spread out in the rear by the increased breadth of the brain.

The lower jaw consists of two halves joined together in front. This region is called the symphysis. The line of juncture of the two halves disappears in the first year of life. The symphysis has to be strong enough to withstand considerable strains, since it is situated at the extreme anterior end of the jaw, which is employed in biting and tearing. In the anthropoid apes, the two horizontal branches of the jaw are held together firmly by the thick bony symphysis which slopes downward and backward from the incisor teeth. There is no chin eminence, and when one looks at the lower jaw of an anthropoid from above, it is seen that the two halves of the jaw are not only united at the symphysis, but also strapped together by a horizontal plate of bone that is continuous with the lower and posterior part of the mandibular symphysis and forms

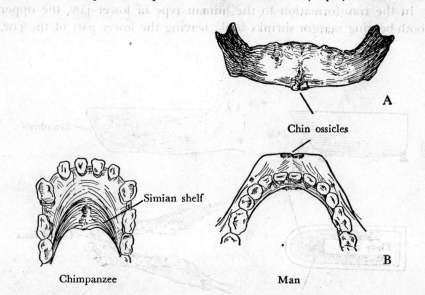

Chin ossicles

Simian shelf

Chimpanzee   Man

Fig. 21. Form of the symphysial region of the lower jaw in chimpanzee and man. In the ape, the symphysial region slopes inward and is reinforced below by the simian shelf or plate. In man, the symphysial region slopes outward and is reinforced by the chin eminence. The latter is formed in part by a pair of chin ossicles best shown in foetal jaws, A; it is not discernible in adult jaws, B.

an integral part of it. This transverse plate of bone is often called the simian shelf. Inside of the jaw and back of where the chin should be, there is a hollow or fossa at the juncture of the simian shelf with the sloping mandibular symphysis. From this fossa in apes there springs a pair of muscles that spread out fanwise and are inserted in the whole length of the under surface of the tongue. These genio-glossus ("chin-tongue") muscles are of great importance in the movements of the tongue in speech. From the hinder margin of the simian shelf, there arise two other pairs of muscles: the genio-hyoid, which draw the larynx forward in swallowing, and the digastric muscles, which depress the lower jaw and assist in the opening of the mouth. The horizontal part of the lower jaw of an anthropoid ape is, then, a good deal like an old-fashioned bath tub with rounded sides and a sloping end (Fig. 22). In the interior of the tub the sloped end represents the inside surface of the mandibular symphysis. The bottom of the bath tub is all cut away except a little piece next to the sloping end. The piece that remains at the foot of the sloping end is the simian shelf. The tip of the tongue rests on the sloping end and the origins of the fan-shaped muscles that move the tongue are at the juncture of the shelf with the slope.

In the transformation to the human type of lower jaw, the upper tooth-bearing margin shrinks back, leaving the lower part of the jaw,

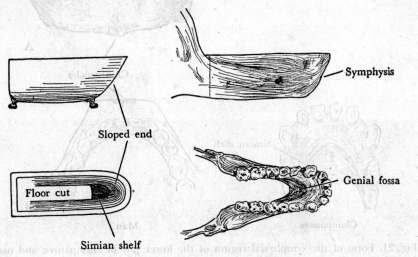

Fig. 22. How the body of a chimpanzee's jaw resembles an old-fashioned bath tub.

to which the tongue muscles are attached, protruding forward as a chin. But the chin does not originate merely as a projecting and isolated vestige; the floor of the jaw is opened out, and the chin is thrust forward to provide more room for the tongue and greater freedom for its movements in speech. The simian shelf disappears from the *inside* of the chin region with this spreading of the sides of the jaw, and on the outside or front of the chin there grow up bumps of bone (usually two of them—you can feel them), which contribute positively to the forward jutting of the chin (Fig. 21 A, B). These chin bumps (the mental ossicles) serve exactly the same function as did the simian shelf on the interior of the ape symphysis; they serve to bind together and strengthen the two halves of the jaw. If these two ossicles grow together completely, you have a rounded chin eminence; if they remain separated, you have a cleft chin or a bilateral chin. The cleft chin is much commoner in males than in females because the chin region in the male is broader and squarer and heavier than in the female.

The genio-glossus muscles, which work the tongue and, in the ape, arise from a pit or fossa just in front of the simian shelf, now in the human type take their origin from spines of bone projecting backward from the interior of the chin region where the fossa used to be (Fig. 23). These spines of bones are called the genial tubercles and are found only in man. The presence of well developed genial tubercles is the surest anatomical evidence of articulate speech that the skeleton affords. But a poor development of these bony spines to which the tongue muscles

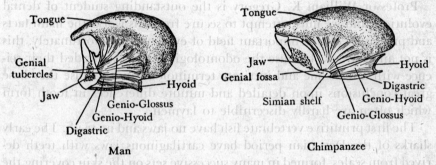

Fig. 23. Sections through the middle of symphysis of lower jaw to show differences in attachment of tongue muscles. (Modified from Keith, *Antiquity of Man*, II, Figs. 176, 177, by permission of Messrs. Williams and Norgate and the J. B. Lippincott Company.)

are attached is no evidence at all that the possessor is or was unable to speak. The writer has examined hundreds of human mandibles in which the genial tubercles are very small and not a few in which they are absent; but probably none of the original owners of these jaws was dumb, and many of them may have been excessively loquacious. Women have smaller genial tubercles than men.

The modifications of the jaws associated with the development of articular speech are then: (a) an opening out and broadening of the floor of the jaws to give more freedom of movement to the tongue; (b) a pushing forward of the chin for the same purpose and a transfer of the bony braces of the symphysis from the inside to the outside of the chin region; (c) a development of bony tubercles as the seat of origin of the tongue muscles, replacing the pit in the backward-sloping ape symphysis.

The slang expression "chinning," meaning "talking," seems to have a certain evolutionary justification.

Chewing: The Evolution of the Teeth

During life, we are more likely to lose our teeth through wear, disease, and decay than any other part of the body; yet after death, the teeth, when present, outlast all the rest of the body. When all other marks of personal identity have been destroyed, the dentist is often able to recognize a body by the repair work he has done on the teeth. Palaeontologists identify the species and genera of extinct animals largely by the form and number of their teeth, partly because the patterns of teeth are distinctive in zoological groups and partly because teeth are the bodily parts most likely to be preserved in geological deposits. The most complete record of vertebrate evolution is furnished by series of fossil teeth.

Professor William K. Gregory is the outstanding student of dental evolution, and we must attempt to secure from his works the main facts and principles of this important field of evidence.[46] Unfortunately, this is not an easy task, because the odontologists have barricaded their science with a fearsome and intricate terminology and because they base great conclusions upon detailed and minute differences in tooth form which often are hardly discernible to laymen.

The first primitive vertebrate fish have no jaws and no teeth. The early sharks of the Devonian period have cartilaginous jaws with teeth derived from scales, formed in many successive sets on the skin covering the jaws. When one set of these scaly teeth is worn out, another grows up to take its place. The whole surface of the throat is covered with this denticle-bearing skin, which is also carried around to the inner side of the mouth. There are no sockets for the teeth in the upper and lower jaws, which are made of cartilage. In the progressive bony fishes, the descendants of which became land-dwelling vertebrates, and in other bony fishes, the teeth have become sharply differentiated from scales and cover the margins and inner sides of the jaws and roof of the mouth. These teeth are often set in sockets or grooves in the jaws. The teeth are pointed, but their bases are elaborately folded in to strengthen their hold on the tough bony skin that bears them. In the first land-dwelling vertebrates, the teeth were still of this character. In the early stem reptiles, this infolding of the bases of the teeth is gradually lost as they become embedded in separate sockets. These reptiles have simple peg-shaped teeth, all alike fore-and-aft in the jaws, several sets in the lifetime of an animal, each set replacing the preceding. In the mammal-like reptiles of the Permian and Triassic periods, the multiple sets of teeth are no longer developed; there are but two sets, corresponding to the milk teeth and

---

[46] Gregory, *Origin and Evolution.*

the permanent teeth of mammals. The teeth are no longer all alike and peg-shaped but are differentiated into incisors or biting teeth at the tips of the jaws, followed by long canine or piercing teeth, behind which come premolars and molars, the latter with several points or cusps on the crown. Evidently, in the shutting of the jaws, the incisors and canines sweep through a large arc and, by reason of their velocity, are best suited for cutting and piercing, whereas the back teeth or cheek teeth, being nearer the fulcrum and the application of power, are in the best position for crushing and grinding. Consequently, their crowns become widened for this purpose. Also, in these mammal-like rep-tiles, the upper teeth overhang, or bite outside of, the lower teeth, and the upper and lower teeth alternate, each lower lying between two uppers. All these features foreshadow the mammalian condition.

A

Simple peg teeth

B

Development of
three-cusped form

Fig. 24.

The primitive insectivorous mammals of the Upper Triassic have molar or grinding teeth con-sisting of three cusps or cones arranged in a fore-and-aft line, the middle cone being much larger than the anterior and posterior cones. The upper and lower molars interlock as in Fig. 24B, the large central cusp of each being opposed to the lower anterior and posterior cusps of two teeth above or below. These smaller cusps seem to have grown up to fill the interspaces between the interlocking teeth. All of the cheek teeth are now supported by two roots.

In the next stage of development of mammalian molar teeth, the crowns become widened transversely, and the upper and lower molars consist each of two parts, a shearing V or triangle with three cusps and an overlapping and crushing heel. The heel, or talonid, is especially developed on the posterior part of the lower molars; in the uppers, the crushing part extends medially, or inward. The triangles of Vs are re-versed in their relationship, the apex of the upper V being directed in-ward and of the lower V outwards. The shearing Vs interlock, and the crushing heels oppose each other, the upper teeth biting outside of the lower teeth (Fig. 25). The crushing heel or basin of the lower molars now becomes much enlarged.

In the early Eocene primates, the triangular shape of the upper molar has been lost by the addition of a fourth main cusp, so that the upper molar is now quadrangular. The crushing heel of the lower molars has increased in size so that it now surpasses the cutting V. This heel also grows backward, crowding out of existence the antero-internal cusp of the lower molar behind it (Fig. 26D). The heel, previously basin-shaped, now develops an internal and external cusp, with a small one at the rear and between the two. Thus the original V is reduced to an outer and an inner cusp, and three more cusps develop behind, giving the lower molar a total of five cusps. The upper molars are now four-cusped and the lower ones five-cusped, which is the ordinary primate cusp formula.

With the development of the Old World catarrhine primate stock, the number of premolars on each side above and below is reduced from three to two, and they show a strong tendency to become two-cusped or

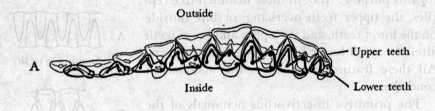

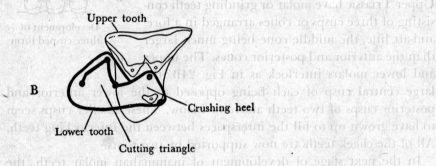

Fig. 25. A, diagram illustrating probable origin of molar teeth patterns in primitive placental mammals; also, the correlated evolution of upper and lower teeth. (After Gregory, by permission of the *Journal of Dental Research*.) B, enlargement from the above, showing how an upper molar opposes a lower molar.

biscuspid. In the primitive anthropoid, Dryopithecus, the cusps of the upper molars have lost their crested shearing form and become bluntly conical (Fig. 26A). The width of the lower molars has greatly increased in proportion to their length, and the cusps have become large and conical, arranged in two pairs, with a rearmost single cusp behind the second pair. The surface of the crown has become flattened to a great extent; the sharp-edged, shearing blades have disappeared. There is less alternation between the upper and lower teeth than in the primitive stages; the reduction of the V and the increase of the heel tend to make each lower molar articulate more with the correspondingly numbered upper molar than with the preceding upper tooth.

In the earliest fossil human types (Sinanthropus), of which both the upper and lower molars are known, the molar tooth pattern of Dryopithecus is retained. The number of cusps on each cheek tooth corresponds to that of the fossil anthropoid, and the arrangement of ridges and cusps is identical. The relations of the opposing molar teeth in the upper and lower jaws are also the same. In the lower molars, the broadening of the crowns has progressed much farther. The formerly projecting canines have their tips reduced to the levels of the other teeth, the incisors become erect, and all of the premolars are definitely biscuspid.

In modern man, the second and third molars are much reduced in size as compared with the first. The third molars, or wisdom teeth, erupt late and are often degenerate. In the reduction of the size of the teeth, the upper molars often lose a cusp and revert to the triangular shape that

Fig. 26. Anthropoid heritage in the lower molar teeth in man. A, *Dryopithecus chinjiensis*, left third molar. B, Indian child, left first molar. C, adult Australian woman, left first molar. (After Gregory, by permission of the *Journal of Dental Research.*) D, loss of antero-internal cusp of lower molars.

formerly characterized the primitive V. The fifth cusp on the lower molars is also lost in many of the more civilized races, but it is likely to be preserved in the first molar.

Although the decrease in size in human teeth is partially attributable, no doubt, to the loss of function of the canines and to the use of the hands in preparing food, as well as to the invention of cooking, the major part of the story of the evolution of teeth has no functional moral running through it. The flattening of the molar crowns was doubtless brought about by the change from a mainly insectivorous to a frugivorous and then an omnivorous diet. But there are no facile explanations available for the numerous modifications and changes that took place in patterns of the molar teeth in the course of this long process of evolution. Human molar patterns are so completely those of the Dryopithecus anthropoids, even today, that Professor Gregory has suggested that some progressive group of these extinct Miocene anthropoids gave rise to man.

Since 1925, South Africa has yielded the remains of fossil man-like apes that probably lived during the Early Pleistocene period, when primitive human forms of several types were already in existence. Hence, these South African apes could not be ancestors of man. Yet they have small, non-projecting canine teeth and molars of patterns derived from the Dryopithecus type. Their entire dentitions resemble those of early fossil men much more closely than do those of contemporary apes or fossil Dryopithecids. Since Nature can endow out-and-out apes with dentitions hardly distinguishable from those of men, it is evident that we must be very cautious in tracing human descent exclusively from details of form and pattern of the teeth.

The reduction of the canine teeth in man opened the way for development of new chewing movements. In the gorilla, the great projecting canines act as guides for the powerful jaws and prevent them from "skid-

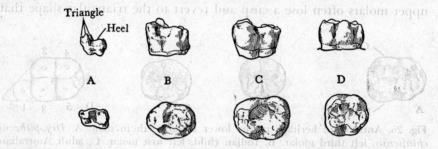

Fig. 27. Man's affinity to other primates in molar tooth pattern. A, permanent molar of an Eocene tarsioid. B, lower second milk molar of *Dryopithecus rhenanus.* C, lower second milk molar of chimpanzee. D, lower second milk molar of a man. (After Gregory, by permission of the *Journal of Dental Research.*)

ding." They also prevent lateral movements in chewing. With the shortening of the canines the human stock developed certain rotary movements of mastication which may be observed in any gum-chewing stenographer. Instead of moving simply up and down in a hinge fashion, the lower jaw performs a complicated series of motions involving alternate advance and retraction of the two sides, since the condyles by which they are jointed to the skull base move in and out of their sockets (the glenoid fossae). The mechanism of this mandibular rotation is too intricate for description here, but it depends largely upon the alternate contraction and expansion of the pterygoid muscles, which are attached to the inner surfaces of the posterior jaw angles and take their origin from bony processes running upward from the back of the palate.

These lateral or rotary movements in chewing were probably instrumental in spreading the palatal arches posteriorly, although the broadening of the brain was perhaps the primary cause of this increase in hinder breadth of the palate and dental arcades.

Physiognomy

Literary people and physiognomists make much ado about the form of the mouth and the expression of the eyes as indications of individual character. The person who has full, red lips is sensual, and the thin-lipped, tight-mouthed individual is avaricious, according to romantic conventions. "Long upper lips" and "short upper lips" also mean something or other. No anthropologist or anatomist believes that there is any relationship between the form of individual features of the face and the character or abilities of the owner. One grants that the expression of a countenance may give indication of the temperament and emotional nature of its possessor, but hardly that these are in any way manifested by shape of the individual features, except, perhaps, in certain definitely pathological cases. People who profess to be able to diagnose character and ability and to determine vocational fitness by studying the "concavity or convexity" of a profile, or by any other method of divination from form and feature, are not scientists but quacks. An act of Queen Elizabeth (1579–1598) declared "all persons fayning to have knowledge of Phisiognomie or like Fantasticall Ymaginaccions" liable "to be stripped naked from the middle upwards and openly whipped until his body be bloudye."

An impecunious instructor, newly engaged to be married, was once taken to be looked over by the uncle of his intended, a very successful but comparatively unread business man. When asked about his profession, the young man endeavored to explain that he was a student of human development, especially of man's physical evolution from lower animal forms and of the significance of bodily differences in human groups. The hard-headed uncle gave him this advice: "Cut out all that stuff about man and the apes; it annoys people and will never get you anything. Concentrate on trying to find out the relation between facial features and abilities; see if you can't discover whether a man with a Roman nose and a lantern jaw should be a parson or a plumber; when you have got something really definite in that line, incorporate and sell it. That's what people want; there's money in that." But the young man went away sorrowing and remained impecunious.

The two preceding paragraphs, written in 1929 for the first edition of this book, still represent the consensus of conservative scientists—anthropologists, psychologists, and anatomists. Nevertheless, I should be guilty of sacrificing candor to caution were I to allow them to stand unqualified now (as of 1945).[47] The study of constitutional anthro-

---

[47] For I was that young man, and the old devil was right!

pology—the relation of physical characteristics in the individual to his psychology, temperament, to his physiological and pathological peculiarities—has advanced in the past dozen of years so rapidly that I venture to predict that another couple of decades may establish, upon a rigorously scientific base, some rather astounding associations of physiognomy with behavior. At present, most of our reliable data pertain to the relationship of body build to individual capacities—physical, mental, and social. As yet there have been no satisfactory investigations correlating the intricate mosaic of hereditary units that comprises the individual human face with variations in temperament or behavior. There is, however, a normal conformity of general face form and head form with type of body build, frequently absent in this or that individual feature owing to independent inheritance of organs, or small details of their form, in numerous small units. Occasionally, there is to be observed a complete disharmony between the type of an individual's head and face and his general body build, just as there are hereditary disharmonies or dysplasias in the conformation of different areas of the trunk and limbs in certain persons. The skeptic may deny that the inherited or acquired form of details of the human anatomy can ever provide any useful clue to the personality of the individual that possesses them. I think that such correlations may eventually prove to be existent, although I must emphasize that virtually no sound observations on this subject have been made up to the present. If the behavior of an individual arises principally from the structure and functioning of his own organism and is only secondarily modified by his cultural environment, there is some hope for a future science of individual anthropology of which physiognomy would be a part. If, however, as many believe, the mentality, personality, and behavior of individuals and groups are determined almost wholly by environment—if, in short, there is no relation between body and behavior—the study of the human face in its wealth of variations is still of interest to the geneticist, the physiologist, the pathologist, and the feeble aesthete. Here we are concerned only with the evolution of the face in man.

MOUTH

In the more advanced, lobe-finned, ganoid fishes (crossopts), the outer surface of the jaws is rough, indicating that they were covered with tough, thick skin. The same is true of early amphibians and reptiles. In some of the more recent reptiles there is a small muscle at the corner of the mouth, but the lips are not fleshy.

In that archaic mammal, the duckbill, the mouth is surrounded by a leathery bill, possibly the remnant of tough reptilian skin. In the other monotreme, the spiny anteater, the lips already approach the typical mammalian condition, being supplied with muscles and covered with hair rather than scales. Gregory thinks that the evolution of true lips "was a part of the general transformation of reptiles with unstable body temperature and low-grade metabolism, into mammals living at high pressure." [48]

The primary function of the lips, which are present in most mammals except whales, is to seize the food. For this purpose they are usually endowed with more or less prehensile power. In the lower primates, as in carnivores, the two opposite sides of the upper lip hang down and scarcely meet in the center, if at all, but in the anthropoids and in man, the juncture is broad and the mouth is completely encircled by the orbicularis oris muscle. Wood Jones has pointed out that in lemuroids the upper lip is closely tethered to the gum of the upper jaw, which determines the method of drinking by lapping rather than by sucking. In Tarsius and the Anthropoidea, the upper lip is relatively free and mobile.

The lips of the great apes are stretched over their bulging jaws, or rather suspended over their jaws, for they are loose and protrusive. In the orang-utan, the under lip is said to be a great organ of touch and to play a very important part in drinking, being thrust out like a trough to catch the falling rain or to receive liquid poured into it. When giving out high notes, this animal is reported to thrust out his lips into a funnel-shape; but when the tone deepens, the mouth is widely opened. The chimpanzee also has long, mobile, and protrusive lips, but the upper lip of the gorilla is somewhat shorter than in the other anthropoids. The gorilla is said to elongate his lower lip and let it drop over his chin when enraged. Evidently, the lips are constantly used to express emotions, as well as for tactile purposes and in eating. In the ordinary sense of the phrase, anthropoid apes have "thin" lips, since only a small part of the red mucous margins of the lips is exposed when the mouth is closed. The integumental portions of the lips are those upon which the moustache and goatee grow in men; that is to say, those parts of the lips that extend from the nose downward to the mucous lips on the upper jaw, and from the boundary of the mucous lips down to the chin eminence on the lower jaw.

In anthropoid apes, the integumental lips are poor in fat and are moulded to the form of the protruding alveolar portions of the jaws. The integumental upper lip in man shows a central furrow (the philtrum) running down from the nasal septum to the edge of the membranous

---

[48] Gregory, *Our Face*, p. 132. The above account of the earlier stages of lip evolution is summarized from this work.

lip, the boundary of which is elevated at the edges of this furrow. This furrow is peculiar to man and gives to him his characteristic upper lip profile. Below the skin of the integumental lips is a circular muscle (the orbicularis oris), which surrounds the membranous lips. This varies considerably in thickness in man. In its ordinary action, it closes the lips; by its deep and oblique fibres, it applies them closely to the alveolar arch and, by its superficial fibres, brings the lips together and protrudes them forward.

The evolution of the human type of lips from the anthropoid type is not as yet clearly understood. It is evidently connected with the shrinking back of the anterior teeth and of those parts of the jaw that lodge them (the alveolar processes). One of the theories involves the supposition that, with the recession of the alveolar processes, the lips were rolled outward, exposing the mucous parts. The greater development of the circular muscle around the lips and the eversion of its fibres is held partially responsible for this. Such a process of eversion would be partially analogous to the tightening of a drawstring around the neck of a sack, which would tend to turn outward the inner surfaces of the free edges. In the most strongly everted lips, some of the fibres of a small muscle called the rectus, which lies at the boundary of the integumental and mucous lips, are very strongly developed. These muscle fibres pass more or less perpendicularly down through the diagonal fibres of the circular muscle and help to evert the lips. This little muscle appears first at a late period of foetal life and is thought to be a progressive development. An opposed theory accounts for the exposure of the mucous lips in man by the supposition that originally integumental parts of the lips have taken on a secondarily mucous character. This theory is based partially upon the occurrence of sweat glands in the mucous (membranous) parts of the exposed lips. It is also stated that in new-born children the membranous portions of the lips show hairy zones at the upper portion of the upper lip and the lower portion of the lower lip.

The strongly everted lips of Negroes seem to be in part a result of the shortening of the integumental lips and the great volume of musculature and underlying fat (Plate 28). The swollen and everted Negro lips are not connected with the protrusion of the jaws. Nor has it been possible to relate the development of the mucous lips to the use of the lips in speech. There is some reason, however, for considering that the more pronounced eversion of the lower lip is connected with the act of suckling, which is protracted in the human species as compared, perhaps, with other primates.

NOSE

In the sharks, the smelling apparatus consists of two small olfactory capsules, one on each side of the head, from which nostrils open and a groove connects with the mouth cavity. In the lungfishes, this groove has worked its way inside of the mouth so that there are two openings, a nostril on the outside and a hole in the roof of the mouth. In both these air-breathing fishes and in amphibians, air may be sucked through the nose or gulped in at the mouth. In the mammal-like reptiles of the South African Triassic, the nasal capsules are elongated fore-and-aft, and, in some, the median bony partition supports scroll-like outgrowths on which are spread the olfactory membranes. These correspond to the turbinate bones of mammals.

In amphibians, reptiles, and primitive mammals, a small extra pair of cartilaginous scrolls near the bottom of the middle partition contain a fold of olfactory membrane and communicate with the mouth cavity by a fine tube. This "Jacobson's organ" allows the food taken in the mouth to be smelled. It is absent or vestigial in the adults of higher primates and of man but is found in foetal life.

The internal arrangements of the nose in man are the same as in the other higher primates, especially the chimpanzee and the gorilla.[49]

The nose is a characteristically human feature—not that it is peculiar to man as an olfactory and respiratory organ but because of its distinctive external form. One may admit at once that in man there is no obvious connection between the form of the nose and its functions. Aristotle says that persons with thick bulbous noses are insensitive and swinish; that sharp-tipped noses belong to irascible persons like dogs; large, rounded, obtuse noses are found in magnanimous, lion-like individuals; hooked, eagle-like noses in the noble but grasping, et cetera.[50] If the modern study of the physiology of the brain does not permit us to be definite about the localization of higher functions of the mind, certainly we are unable to say anything at all about the relation of temperamental peculiarities to the sense organs. Possibly no such relationship exists. The nose in man shows many variations of form that apparently are due to a sort of degenerate flamboyancy in an organ, the shape of which has little to do with its function. Perhaps sexual selection has played some part in the evolution of various nasal forms, but this seems hardly likely in view of the extreme commonness of all kinds of noses.

[49] Ibid., pp. 153–163.
[50] Macalister, "Physiognomy," p. 550.

Among the primates, the nose of man is distinguished by the elevation of its bridge and the prolongation of its tip.

In the lemurs, the nose is a naked glandular "rhinarium" or muzzle, the middle portion of which extends right down to the mouth opening. The nostrils are comma-shaped slits, with the points directed toward the eyes. The specialized skin of this rhinarium is moist. In Tarsius, there is only a narrow margin of bare skin around the nostrils; there is no naked central strip on the upper lip; most of the muzzle is covered with fine hairs. The nostrils are not slit and are far apart. Tarsius shares with the Anthropoidea the possession of a nose with nostrils that are not cleft laterally but completely ringed around with naked skin, and that lacks the median naked strip.[51]

The New World monkeys are called the Platyrrhini because the septum between the nostrils is usually broad and these look outward. The nostrils are comma-shaped, S-shaped, or circular, but completely surrounded by bare skin. The Old World monkeys are often given the name Catarrhini because their nostrils open downward. The septum between them is narrow, as a rule.

To understand the differences in architecture between the noses of anthropoids and of man, one must study the nasal and facial skeletons. If you look at the skull of a gorilla, chimpanzee, or orang-utan, you notice that the orbits of the eyes are so close together as to leave only a very narrow space for the root of the nose. This reduction in interorbital space is especially marked in the orang. The roof of the nose is formed in the primates by two parallel bony plates, united by a suture along the middle line. In the orang-utan, these bones are so narrow as to be splint-like and lie edge to edge in such a way that there is no nasal "bridge"; they are quite flat. Sometimes they are fused together and do not extend even as far down as the nasal aperture. In the chimpanzee, the nasal bones are hour-glass shaped and narrow but not so pronouncedly as in the orang; nor are they so long as those of the gorilla. The suture between them is often depressed so that, instead of a "bridge," the nasal skeleton actually has a furrow. In the gorilla, again, the nasal bones are extremely long and narrow, and a lancet-like point projects upward between the massive brow-ridges into the frontal bone. However, in the gorilla, the surfaces of the paired nasal bones are not quite plane one with the other, but are elevated slightly along the suture or middle line, so that there is a very sharp and narrow ridge down the upper half of the nose, either a rudiment or a vestige of a nasal bridge (Fig. 16C). This ridge projects slightly so that the gorilla, alone of the

[51] Jones, *Man's Place*, pp. 79–80; 86–88.

anthropoids, may be said to show a nasal bridge in profile. In general, then, the anthropoid apes have very long, narrow nasal bones which lie flat against the face. These great apes have undergone a decrease in the breadth of the upper parts of the nose, possibly in conjunction with the lateral compression of the skull brought about by the pressure of their great temporal muscles.

The aperture of the nose in the skull of all the anthropoids is relatively narrow when compared with the great length of the face. In the gorilla, the absolute breadth of the aperture is, however, great.

In all of these apes, the nasal aperture resembles the mouth of a cave in the sloping face of a hillside (Fig. 28). The top of this cave mouth is

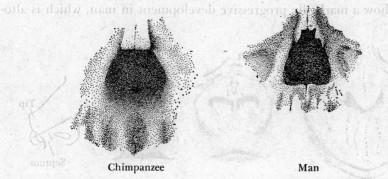

Chimpanzee   Man

Fig. 28. Nasal apertures.

formed by overhanging and downward projecting sharp slabs (the nasal bones); the side walls are simply the rounded edges of the cliff face (the upper jaw bone); there is no threshold at the cave mouth, for the rounded talus slope of the hillside is continuous with the floor of the cave, entering it without transition. Now suppose that the cliff face is eroded on both sides of the cave mouth, and the rounded talus at the foot of the cliff is washed away. The slabs forming the top of the cave mouth and sloping up the hill are thrown into relief by the hollowing out of the cliff face on either side of the cave. The cutting away of the rounded talus makes a sharp edge or sill at the mouth of the cave. Similarly, by the recession of the alveolar processes and the falling in of the supporting side walls of the face, the roof of the nose and the side walls of the nasal aperture are thrown into relief in man and a definite sill to the nasal aperture makes its appearance. The most primitive human noses show only faint traces of this sill and the nasal bones are still almost flat, but, in the more highly evolved types, the falling in of the lateral parts of the upper jaw seems to have pinched up the nasal bones along the middle suture, so that their median portions are elevated and they become arched, forming the bridge of the nose. It should be explained that the portions of the upper jaw that support the palatal arch and flank the nose are not solid but hollow, and enclose, on either side of the nasal aperture, cavities or sinuses (bays), which are lined with mucous membrane. As the alveolar portions of the upper jaw shrink backward, these sinuses become smaller; they are deflated, so that the facial skeleton below the eyes and on both sides of the nose develops deep hollows or suborbital fossae, which first make their appearance in the more advanced human types.

But the nose, like the chin, is not a mere vestige, isolated by the falling away of surrounding parts. The cartilages that constitute its tip and wings show a markedly progressive development in man, which is alto-

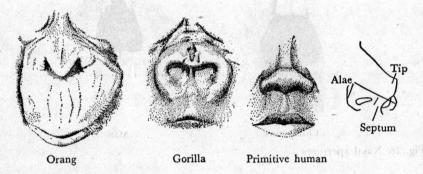

Orang   Gorilla   Primitive human

Fig. 29. Form of the external nose.

gether lacking in the anthropoids. The orang shows very slight development of the nasal wings or alae (the cartilaginous parts that form the outer walls of the nostrils), and these are very small also in the chimpanzee. In the gorilla, on the other hand, the nasal wings are very large and extend round below the nostrils, forming ring-like, swollen growths separated by a furrow in the middle line below the nasal septum. None of the anthropoids has any considerable development of the cartilages forming the tip of the nose. In the chimpanzee and the orang, they are thin and pointed, with a distinct furrow running down the center. In the gorilla, they converge to a sharp point above the nasal septum and are a little thicker than in the other great apes. In man, these cartilages are greatly thickened and have grown down so that the tip of the nose is a thick bulb that overhangs the septum and is supported by the underlying septal partition of cartilage and also by a bony nasal spine. The wings of the nose in man are also strongly developed, but do not grow round beneath and form the lower borders of the nostrils as in the gorilla.

The primitive form of the human nose must have been much like the ordinary infant's nose. It was broad and had a low bridge; the tip was elevated but bulbous, and the nostrils circular and visible from the front, the wings being rather thick and encircling the outer halves of the nostrils. In the process of growth, the cartilages forming the nasal tip extend downward so that the fleshy end of the nose often conceals from view the nostril openings, which are directed downward. In maturity and old age, the nasal cartilages seem to continue their growth so that the tip of the nose becomes definitely depressed. There is, however, much racial and individual variation, as everyone knows. Certainly, the flat nose, with the elevated tip and the nostril openings presented to the frontal plane, is the most primitive type.

Two of the Old World monkeys have prominent noses, not, as in man, partially because of the elevation of the skeleton of the nasal bridge, but wholly because of an overgrowth of the cartilages of the fleshy end. These are: the snub-nosed monkey, the tip of whose nose is turned up, and the proboscis monkey, whose nasal cartilages are so elongated that the tip of the nose bends down and overhangs the upper lip.

The peculiar form of the nose in man is, thus, the result in part of the regression of the jaws and in part of a progressive development of the cartilages forming the soft parts. The latter growth can be set down as a mere exuberant variation of no functional significance. The great constriction of the nasal bones in anthropoid apes must be considered a degenerative feature. This may be connected with the atrophy of the sense of smell. Köhler states that chimpanzees are so obtuse in this respect that they cannot smell a hidden pear or tomato a couple of decimeters away.[52] Not much is known about the sense of smell in the orang-utan and the gorilla. The orang is said to touch objects first, then to raise them for visual examination, then to smell them, and finally to taste them. This perhaps indicates that smell is less developed than sight. Gorillas are quick to notice unfamiliar or disagreeable odors and test novel food both by sight and by smell.

EYES

Professor Gregory has summarized the evolution of the eye from the invertebrate beginnings, and we may well paraphrase from his account

---

[52] Köhler, *Mentality of Apes*, p. 292.

a few important conclusions.[53] Eyes owe their beginnings to the sensitivity of protoplasm both to the injurious and to the beneficial effects of light. In early prevertebrate stages, they seem merely to have served as directional organs to orientate the animal's movements with reference to the light, being at this stage on the inner side of the brain tube. When the brain grew out to contact with the epithelium, true vision resulted. Various accessory organs then appeared for regulating the focus of the lens, either by changing its position with reference to the opening or by altering its curvature. These devices were improved when the air-breathing fishes crawled out of the swamps. They culminate in mammals, in which, however, the olfactory apparatus is usually the dominant sense organ. The primates, however, show a progressive reduction of the sense of smell and a concomitantly increasing importance of vision. This is particularly emphasized in the brachiating anthropoids. Man retains all of the ocular advantages won by the earlier vertebrates together with certain improvements resulting from the arboreal life of his primate ancestors.

Vision is highly developed in all of the anthropoid apes. Two kinds of visual sensation are known in man: color (chromatic) sensations and light (non-chromatic). Kohts and Köhler have demonstrated color discrimination in the chimpanzee. The former investigator taught a chimpanzee to match colors from both halves of the spectrum and concluded that degree of accuracy in discrimination of 40 chromatic stimuli depended upon relative nearness in hue rather than brightness. Both of these investigators also concluded that achromatic stimuli, with the exception of black and white, are not as readily distinguished by the chimpanzee as are chromatic. Monocular, binocular, and stereoscopic vision have likewise been demonstrated for this anthropoid. In short, it is indicated that the vision of the chimpanzee is in many respects essentially the same as that of man. Yerkes' gorilla was able to select food by color of the containers, and he gained the impression that vision was the dominant sense in Congo's life. He was impressed, however, with a radical difference of the animal's "visual configurations" from those of man. The gorilla, for example, placed a rectangular box on its corner in order to reach suspended food and, on another occasion, held the box in midair and tried to climb up it. These may be instances, however, merely of a defective conception of statics or mechanics. Size, form, and depth perception have also been demonstrated for the chimpanzee. Experimental analysis of vision in the other anthropoids is lacking.[54]

[53] Gregory, *Our Face*, pp. 173–201.
[54] Yerkes and Yerkes, *op. cit.*, pp. 169, 319, 332, 483, 486, 547.

No marked changes take place in the eyes in the evolution of the human from the anthropoid type. The shifting of the eyes to a frontal plane and the attainment of stereoscopic vision occur in a lower primate stage. The horizontal opening of the eyelids is greater in man than in any other primate, and the bony sockets or orbits of the eyes are relatively and absolutely smaller in man than in the great anthropoids. The human orbits are especially reduced in height, as a result, no doubt, of the shortening of the face in man, which is brought about by the decrease in the size of the jaws. The eyes of man are much farther apart than in the great apes, in whom, as previously noted, the nasal root is very constricted.

The eyebrows and the eyelashes are found to some extent in foetal and immature apes but are not usually discernible in adults. Their presence in adult human beings is perhaps the retention of an infantile condition. In connection with the recession of the jaws and the high vaulting of the forehead, there is a strong contrast between the brow-ridges of man and those of most primates. In the gorilla and the chimpanzee the upper edges of the orbits are surmounted by heavy rims of bone which, to some extent, overhang the eyes. These are called the brow-ridges or supraorbital ridges. Their functions are twofold: in primates whose frontal cerebral lobes do not rise above the orbits, they afford protection to the eyes by forming penthouses over them; they also serve as buttresses to resist the tremendous upward stress exerted by the jaws in chewing. When, however, the jaws recede and the frontal bone rises in a curve above the orbits, the brow-ridges lose their function. Since the jaws are no longer large and projecting, the upward stress of chewing is diminished and is resisted with perfect efficiency by the high vaulting of the forehead. Moreover, the greatly overhanging brow-ridges are no longer needed for the protection of the eyes, since the newly developed frontal overhang serves that purpose. Consequently, in man, the brow-ridges shrink in conformity with the development of a frontal vault and a diminution in the size of the jaws.

The orang-utan, however, has greatly protruding jaws, hafted to a brain-case in which the forehead is highly arched and the brow-ridges are small. The necessity for large brow-ridges in the orang seems to have been eliminated, partly by the frontal vaulting and partly by the fact that his jaws are tilted upward and backward in such a way that the stresses of chewing are not directed vertically from the molar teeth up to the supraorbital region but are carried back diagonally to the skull vault (Fig. 30C). In man, the individuals or races with the most projecting jaws either have very large brow-ridges and retreating foreheads or, much less commonly, strongly vaulted frontals. With tremendously projecting jaws and neither frontal vault nor brow-ridges, an animal like the gorilla would be likely to break its face off when closing its

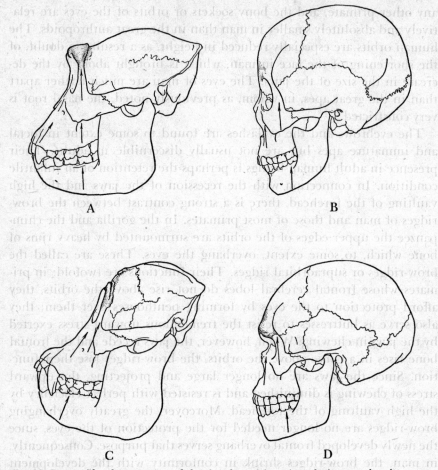

Fig. 30. Brow ridge buttresses and forehead vaultings in relation to chewing stress (shown by arrows). A, skull of female gorilla with great jaw protrusion; brow ridge buttress. B, skull of Chinese with no jaw protrusion; chewing stress resisted by frontal vaulting. C, skull of male orang-utan with great jaw protrusion; jaws tilted upward directing chewing stress upward and backward; resistance afforded principally by frontal vaulting. D, skull of male Australian with considerable jaw protrusion; combination of buttress and vaulting to resist chewing stress.

powerful jaws. But nature does not make mistakes in her engineering arrangements. In the gorilla and the chimpanzee, one may compare the orbits and the brow-ridges with porches protecting the eyes; the supra-orbital ridges form the roofs of the porches (Fig. 31). In man, however, a second story is built out over the roof of the porch—the vaulted frontal bone that covers the frontal lobes of the neopallium. The gorilla's skull is a bungalow with a long flight of steps, a big porch, and no upper story; man inhabits a two-story house with short steps and a small recessed porch that has a well-filled chamber over it.

Phrenologists used to identify the prominence just above the root of the nose and between the brow-ridges as the bump of "God-fearingness."

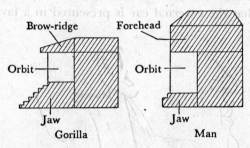

Fig. 31. Profiles and porches.

As a matter of fact, this prominence either overlies the frontal sinus, a cavity in the frontal bone lined with mucous membrane, or, in some cases, there is a solid bar of bone in that region. In no case does this prominence correspond to any elevation on the frontal lobes of the brain. Someone has remarked that the male gorilla has the largest bump of "God-fearingness" of any known animal.

EARS

Hearing begins with the evolution of land-dwelling vertebrates. In a previous section, I have discussed the origin of the ear passages from the spiracular gill cleft of fishes and the transformation of certain bony elements of the reptilian jaw into the ossicles that transmit the sound waves to the inner ear (p. 64). There is little or nothing about the ear in man that is characteristically human. Most of the stages of auditory evolution are completed in the monkeys of the Old World.

The organ of hearing is lodged in the temporal bone, a portion of which projects wedge-like toward the center line of the skull and forms an important component of the skull base. It is in this petrous (rocky) portion of the temporal bone that the middle and internal ear are situated. In man, the anthropoid apes, and the Old World monkeys, the passage leading into the ear is surrounded by a bony ring (the tympanic bone) immediately behind the socket to which the lower jaw is hinged. This tympanic ring is expanded to enclose a chamber and forms an auditory bulla (knob) at the side of the skull base in New World monkeys, tarsioids, lemuroids, whales, and many lower mammals.

In man there are blunted, conical, bony processes of the temporal bone extending downward just behind the ear. These are called the mastoid processes. To them are attached muscles that run obliquely down the side and front of the neck and take their origins from the breast bone and the collar bone (Fig. 32). In addition to other functions, these sterno-cleido-mastoid muscles serve to rotate the head in one direction or the other, so that the external ear is presented in a favorable position

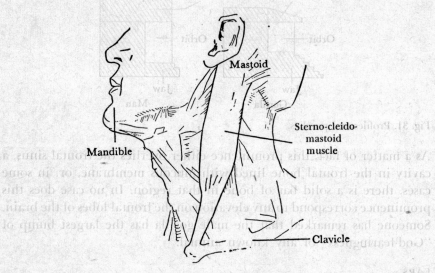

Fig. 32. Diagrammatic dissection to show the attachments of the sterno-cleido-mastoid muscle.

to catch sound waves. These muscles are present in some form or other in all of the primates but reach their highest development in man. The conical processes of the temporal bone to which they are attached, the mastoid processes, are found only in the gorilla and in man, being well developed in the latter and rudimentary in the former. The free poise of the human head upon the spinal column as a result of the recession of the jaws, the backward growth of the brain, and the erect standing posture, are, no doubt, responsible for the development of the mastoid processes and for the great mobility of the head in rotating movements. Man has also acquired a potential disability with the growth of this new feature. The bone cells inside the mastoid processes sometimes become infected from the ear or in some other way and cause the very serious disease, mastoiditis, to relieve which it is necessary to chisel away the hard bony covering of the mastoid region in order to drain the infected bone cells.

The first appearance of an external ear is represented by a fold of skin in certain lizards and owls. In many mammals, the ears are long and pointed or covered with a flap of skin. The ears of lemurs and tarsiers are erect and more or less pointed and conform in general to the mammalian type. They can be "cocked" in one direction or another to catch sound waves. In the higher primates, the habit of sitting erect and the free rotating movements of the head are thought to have brought about a reduction in size of the external ear and, to a great extent, the loss of its mobility. This is presumably because the head is now turned so that sound waves strike directly upon the ear, instead of the ear itself being moved. However, Tarsius can swivel its head around 180° and thus surpasses most, if not all, other primates in cephalic mobility. Yet the ears of this animal are very large. Their hinder rims are flattened, not rolled. The ears can be reduced in size by folding and laid flat against the head. When the tarsier is listening intently, the ears are opened widely and moved back and forth, one pointing to the front and the other to the rear, alternately. Thus the tarsier appears to turn both head and ears with unsurpassed facility. This circumstance hardly supports the theory that ear-cocking diminishes as head-turning power increases.

The only degenerate part of the external ear in man is the portion that represents the ear flap or free tip of the ear in mammals. This flap originally served not only to catch sounds but to close the auditory passage. The external ear in apes, monkeys, and man is composed of a fibrocartilaginous framework covered with skin. In man, a rolled rim passes up from the anterior root of the ear over the top and down its hinder surface. This is called the helix. Concentric with the helix and inside of it is a ridge called the antihelix. The latter is generally forked in its upper portion. Inside the antihelix is the deep concha (shell of the ear) from the anterior part of which the auditory passage enters the skull. A flap called the tragus overlaps the auditory opening in front, and below and behind it is a smaller flap called the antitragus. The lowest part of the ear is the lobe, which contains no cartilage. In the process of evolution, the root of the ear, which is attached to the side of the head, has not been reduced but has increased in area (Fig. 33). The free tip, on the other hand, has been progressively shortened until, in man, the orang-utan, and the gorilla, it has disappeared or is represented only by a tubercle or point on the inner edge of the rim of the helix, known as Darwin's point. In monkeys, only the portion of the helix just above its root shows any rolling or infolding, and the free point of the ear is still distinguishable. Among the anthropoid apes, the helix is least rolled in the chimpanzee and shows the deepest infolding in the orang-utan (Fig. 34). Both the orang and the gorilla have relatively and absolutely smaller and more degenerate ears than man, but the chimpanzee usually retains fine, large ears. A progressive feature found in the human ear and in that of the orang-utan is the elevation of the antihelix so that it protrudes to catch the sound waves. The lobe is absent or rudimentary in the anthropoids and best developed in civilized races of man. It is a

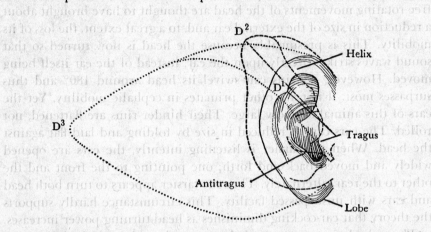

Fig. 33. Reduction of the external ear in man. D^1, remnant of the free tip of the mammalian ear in man (Darwin's point). D^2, remnant of the free tip in a monkey ear with identical implantation. D^3, free tip of a cow's ear drawn to same scale. (Modified from Schwalbe and Martin, by permission of Gustav Fischer.)

new feature that apparently serves no useful purpose, unless it is pierced for the carrying of ornaments, tobacco tins, or what not.

Elder, experimenting with chimpanzees, found their auditory acuity greater than that of man. They are capable of responding to high tones inaudible to human beings.[55] Sound discrimination in the gorilla and in the chimpanzee has been definitely noted by Yerkes.

The ear shows many individual variations in man, as is to be expected in an organ of which portions show distinct degeneration. Some persons have large, outstanding, "chimpanzee" ears, with little roll of the helix, and the free tip still visible as a nodule on the unrolled rim. More have the "orang" type of ear, which is small, with a deeply rolled helix and a prominent antihelix. A helix pointed at the top is called a "Satyr point" and occurs in some human beings and occasionally in the gorilla (Fig.

[55] Yerkes, *Chimpanzees*, pp. 96–98, quoting J. H. Elder, "Auditory Acuity of the Chimpanzee," *J. Comp. Psychol.*, vol. 17, 1934, pp. 157–183; "The Upper Limit of Hearing in Chimpanzees," *Amer. J. Physiol.*, vol. 112, pp. 109–115.

54). The muscles that move the ears in lower animals are reduced in size in the higher primates and are often impotent. Some talented persons are able to move their ears forward and backward as a result of these muscles' being less vestigial than in the ruck of human beings. I have been told that one can recover the power of moving one's ears by volition and unremitting effort, but it has never seemed worth while to me to try very long and hard.

The organ of hearing in man takes on a new and increased importance in the reception of the sounds of articulate speech. But the auditory apparatus is no longer of primary use in detecting sounds made by

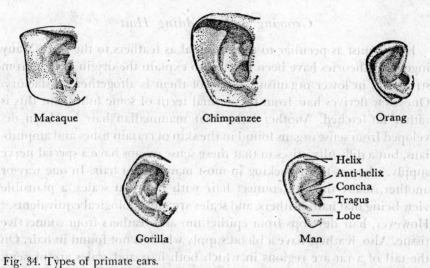

Fig. 34. Types of primate ears.

enemies. Perhaps one may conjecture that the greater reduction of the ear in the gorilla and in the orang-utan, as compared with man, may be connected with their failure to use their ears as receptors of speech and with the fact that their size and strength make it unnecessary for them to bother about hostile sounds. But what about the chimpanzee? Does that anthropoid hear better or find it necessary to hearken to threatening sounds? Probably the differences between the various anthropoids and between them and man are, to a great extent, the result of hereditary, non-adaptive modifications.

Ears seem to be the least noticed of human features, unless they are unduly prominent. Ordinarily, we look at the faces of people, not at their ears. It used to be the fashion, however, among students of criminal anthropology, to pay minute attention to the variations of the form of the external ear in criminals. There was a theory that people with warped minds and anti-social tendencies were likely to have misshapen or peculiar ears, on the general supposition that degeneracy was likely to manifest itself externally in the form of this organ. Examination of criminal ears does show a great number of malformations and anomalies; but examination of the same organs in respectable, law-abiding, and eminent citizens indicates very clearly that almost any kind of an ear is likely to occur in the best of families. The form of the external ear is a variation of little or no functional importance; hence any particular ear form is not likely to interfere with its possessor's chance of survival. Consequently, all forms occur and are transmitted with impunity.

Growing and Shedding Hair

Hair is just as peculiar to the mammal as feathers to the bird. Many ingenious theories have been evolved to explain the origin of hair from structures in lower organisms. None of them is altogether satisfactory. One view derives hair from the dermal teeth of some fishes, but this is rather far-fetched. Another holds that mammalian hair has been developed from sense organs found in the skin of certain fishes and amphibians, but a difficulty arises in that these sense organs have a special nerve supply, whereas this is lacking in most mammalian hair. In one way or another, many theories connect hair with reptilian scales, a plausible view being that hair, feathers, and scales are morphological equivalents.[56] However, hair develops from epithelium and feathers from connective tissue. Also, feathers have a blood supply which is not found in hair. On the tail of a rat are regions in which both hair and scales are present. Ordinarily, a group of three hairs projects from under the free margin of each scale. Similar hair groups occur where scales are absent—a fact which suggests that the hair groups in mammals mark the site of ancestral scales. In general, it is certain that mammalian hair is akin to tactile organs, placoidal scales, teeth, claws dermal scales, and feathers; but it has not yet been demonstrated conclusively that hair is fully homologous with any of these structures. It may be, and probably is, a new formation in mammals.

Hair grows out of the epidermis, which is the uppermost layer of skin. A hair shaft consists of cuticle on the outside, cortex under that, and a medulla or pith in the center. The cuticle is made of overlapping scales of various shapes. The hair shaft grows out of a follicle or sheath set obliquely in the skin (Fig. 35). At the base of this sheath is a bulb en-

---

[56] In this section I have drawn largely upon the work of Professor C. F. Danforth, *Hair, with Special Reference to Hypertrichosis.*

closing a papilla from which the hair grows. A sebaceous gland empties into the follicle just below its mouth, providing the secretion that oils the hair. A few muscle fibers, called the arrector pili muscle, are stretched from the follicle below the sebaceous gland diagonally upward toward the surface of the skin. When this muscle contracts, it pulls the follicle into a more vertical position, making the hair "stand on end" and causing "goose-flesh."

Hairs are of two kinds: tactile and protective. Tactile hairs have spaces filled with blood (blood sinuses) round the follicle and have a special nerve supply. They are sense organs of great delicacy and generally are

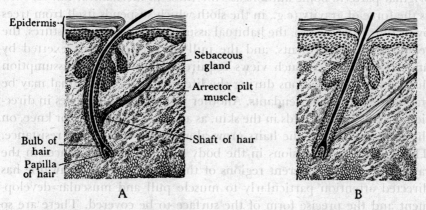

Fig. 35. Sketches of longitudinal sections of hair follicles. A, negro's head hair; B, the head of a European.

found on the lips, cheeks, and brow regions. Some of them, such as the whiskers on the upper lip of a cat, are under voluntary control. Protective hairs may be grouped, according to size and rigidity, into spines, bristles, awns, wool, fur, down, in descending order.

Whales and dolphins are the least hairy of mammals, but the sea-cows are close rivals. Such thick-skinned animals as the elephant, the rhinoceros, and the hippopotamus have also lost most of their hair. Where the hairy covering is scanty, it is either replaced by a subcutaneous layer of fat, or the animal inhabits a warm climate. But there is no direct evidence that a warm climate necessarily brings about a hereditary decrease in hairiness. In animals with sparse hair, that remaining is likely to be coarse and of a bristly character.

The distinctive feature of man's hairy covering is not its scantiness but the complete absence of tactile hairs ("feelers"). In this respect he is unique in mammals. Most of the hair on the human body never develops beyond fine and more or less rudimentary down. The adult human being has only about one-fourth as many hairs per square centimeter in the scalp as has the gibbon, less than half of the number in the siamang's scalp, about one-third less than the mountain gorilla, twice as many as the orang, and almost three times as many as the chimpanzee. (Table 1, p. 41.)

In the evolution of human hair the direction and pattern of hair tracts are of interest. Because the hair follicles are always set obliquely in the skin, the hairs slope according to the direction of the follicles. Apparently, the primitive arrangement of the hairs is a uniform backward slope from the head to the tail. But there are many modifications of this original pattern. Some authors ascribe these to mechanical causes, such as the force of gravity (e.g., in the sloth which suspends itself from trees by its four extremities), the habitual assumption of certain postures, the repetition of movements, and the pull on certain points exerted by underlying muscles. Such views require the questionable assumption that bodily modifications during the lifetime of the individual may be transmitted to his descendants. Another view refers differences in direction of hair slope to folds in the skin, as at the elbow, throat, or knee, on the supposition that the hairs grow along the lines of least resistance. There are also depressions in the body surfaces and differences in the rate of growth of different regions of the skin. Professor Schwalbe has directed attention particularly to muscle pull and muscular development and the precise form of the surface to be covered. There are so many variations in different primate species in the hair tracts and slopes and in the arrangements of vortices, spirals, et cetera, that any detailed interpretation of them is most difficult. That the direction of hair in the individual is in some way affected by his habits as well as his form is, however, entirely probable.

It is a well known fact that the hair on the upper arm in man is directed downward and that of the forearm upward, so that the hair tracts converge at the elbow. Since the time of Darwin and Wallace, this peculiar arrangement has been explained as the result of our arboreal ancestors' habit of crouching in the trees during rain storms, holding on to boughs above their heads. The rain would then drip down from the hairs converging at the elbows. The gorilla and the orang are said to adopt such positions. One of the objections to this theory is that the hair tracts similarly converge at the elbow in the quadrupedal lemurs, which presumably do not adopt this attitude in the trees, as well as in many of the Old World monkeys, which are also pronograde. They do not so converge in the tarsiers nor in one type of gibbon.

The beard is not peculiar to man, although the absence of tactile hairs in it is. The growth of hair on the face of the orang-utan is most suggestive of the human condition, especially since the moustache in this animal develops most definitely toward the corners of the mouth. But in the orang and in all other apes, the presence of a large proportion of tactile or sinus hairs in the beard makes it difficult to accept their growths of facial hair as homologous with the human beard. However, it is said that the beard of the orang shows transitional forms of hair from the vascular sinus type to the non-vascular, non-tactile, protective type of beard found in man.

Most areas of the human body grow hair, but it has been reduced to a fine vellus or down over the greater part of the body surface. Careful examination, either with the naked eye or with a microscope, reveals definite tracts, partings, spirals, or whorls, and lines of convergence. Most of those found in human beings can be traced back to the other primates. It has been stated that two hair partings that extend down the front of the body about in a line from the nipples downward are new features in man and must be ascribed to the erect posture. Wood Jones says that in man the hairs of the back converge upon a midline whereas in the anthropoids they diverge.[57] The definite hair line on the forehead is a human feature, the nearest approximation to which occurs, apparently, in the orang-utan and in the bonnet macaque.

From the sixth to the eighth month of foetal life, the human baby is almost completely covered with a fine hairy down, the lanugo, most of which is shed before birth. Just above the aperture of the rectum (the anus), there may often be observed in new-born infants a slight depression in the groove between the buttocks. This marks the point at which the end of the coccyx (the tail remnant of the spine) has sunk beneath the surface. Usually in this dimple or depression there is a whorl or spiral of hairs; but both of these features usually disappear in the first few days of life.

There are a number of fairly well authenticated cases of "hairy men," in whom it is thought that the foetal lanugo has been retained and has run riot. About 30 families are on record in which this anomaly has been observed in one or more members. Whether or not such cases of excessive hairiness ("hypertrichosis") are to be interpreted as pathological conditions or as anomalies of a reversionary character, it is certain that, somewhere in the course of evolution, man or his ancestors underwent a great reduction in hairy covering and a change in its distribution. It has been suggested by Elliot Smith that there is a correlation between the disappearance of the hairy covering and the evolution of the brain.

[57] Jones, *Man's Place*, p. 298.

Sensory nerves link up the brain with every papilla of the skin, and the thinner and more naked the skin, the greater its sensitiveness, and the larger the number of messages sent to the brain.[58] Keith points out that both hair and deposition of fat beneath the skin are probably influenced by the secretions of the thyroid gland. Anthropoid ape babies differ from human babies in that the former are hairy and have little subcutaneous fat. These two conditions are probably correlated, and it seems possible that the loss of hairy covering in man is associated with his higher nervous organization and that the protective covering of hair is replaced by the subcutaneous layer of fat which similarly preserves the warmth of the body. Keith also suggests that the human infant is better nourished than the anthropoid infant, since a first effect of the humanization of a higher primate was to insure a richer variety and more ample command of food all the year round than was possessed by any arboreal or pre-human primate. Such an improvement in pre- and post-natal nutrition would probably have its effect upon the thyroid gland and upon the other glands of internal secretion and may well have brought about the changes in fat deposition and in hair covering that distinguish man from the other primates.

Although elephants and rhinoceroses are almost hairless, species of these animals that inhabited Europe during the glacial epoch were covered with long hair or wool. One may possibly infer from this fact that the hairy covering was acquired in order to preserve the heat of the body. I believe, however, that none of the existing hairless species is derived from the hairy Pleistocene forms of these animals, so that it would hardly be possible to argue that a secondary denudation has taken place as a result of a sojourn in warm tropical climates. Darwin suggested that the retention of hair in the human male on the face and chest, and in both sexes at the juncture of the limbs of the body, favors the supposition that hair was lost before man became erect, for the parts now retaining the most hair would then have been those most protected from the heat of the sun.[59] He recognized, however, that the abundant hirsute covering of the giant anthropoids and other primates that still inhabit the tropics renders improbable any supposition relating the denudation of the human skin to tropical heat. Darwin also rejected the theory that the loss of the hair may have been a result of natural selection in enabling man to divest himself of the multitude of ticks and external parasites that would otherwise infest the body. He thought it improbable that this evil would be of sufficient magnitude to bring into operation the forces

58 Keith, *The Human Body*, p. 204.
59 Darwin, *Descent of Man*, p. 85.

of natural selection, especially since other fur-bearing animals in the tropics seem to have acquired no specialized form of relief. Darwin concluded that, on the whole, the loss of a hairy covering is disadvantageous to man, even in the tropics, since it exposes his body to the scorching of the sun and to the sudden chills of wet weather. It is, then, improbable that this denudation could have come about through natural selection.

The author of the *Descent of Man* emphasized the importance of sexual selection in bringing about the relatively hairless condition of man, the elongation of the head hair in the human female, and of the beard hair in the male. He argued that, in most species, the female is less hairy than the male, and that the added exposure of the naked skin in the female could constitute a special sexual attraction. Thus, the less hairy females would be selected as mates by the more powerful and vigorous males and would transmit to their offspring the hairless condition, both sexes being to some extent affected. In like manner, the male with the longest beard and the female with the longest head hair would acquire advantages in the selection of mates and in the perpetuation of their kind, by reason of the possession of these special characters which would enhance their sexual attraction and permit them to secure the most desirable mates.

This ingenious theory of Darwin is, however, inadequate. There are few indications that preferential mating could have brought about such profound modifications in the amount and distribution of body hair. We can neither assume that in all human and pre-human races the least hairy women have always been the most desired, nor that, if they had been, they would necessarily have transmitted their relative hairlessness to their descendants.

The variation in the amount of body hair in existing races of man will require further discussion when we come to deal with racial characteristics. But it may be stated at this point that there is no appreciable relationship between the climate in which various human groups live and the amount of body hair that they possess. The most plausible theory accounting for the denudation of the human body is that of Elliot Smith and Keith, which connects it with increased sensitiveness of the skin, deposition of a layer of subcutaneous fat, and an altered functioning of the glands of internal secretion. Possibly the nutritional factor is also important.

J. R. de la H. Marett, a brilliant but speculative anthropologist, has suggested that man's loss of hair was due to an iodine deficient diet in our early hominid ancestors. It is established that iodine deficiency can cause a lack of hair in domesticated animals. Since the growth of hair demands cell proliferation that otherwise need not have taken place, Marett infers that iodine economy may cause a loss of hair. However, proof that such a loss can conserve iodine or promote physiological efficiency in any other way is admittedly lacking.[60]

Man's relative hairlessness cannot be brought into any causal relationship with the erect posture, the free prehensile function of the fore limbs, nor with the extremes of cold or heat encountered in different latitudes.

There may be some force in the argument that the loss of body hair in man must have taken place in a tropical climate, since Negroids and Mongoloids are less hairy than the white races, and since it would appear that such a diminution of "pelage" would scarcely take place in a cold environment. If, however, the decrease in the amount of hair is assumed to be accompanied by an increase in the amount of subcutaneous fat, this argument loses its force.

Perhaps the only documentary evidence as to the time of the disappearance of man's hairy covering is offered by an engraving from one of the Upper Palaeolithic sites in France. This engraving was found at Laugerie Basse in the Dordogne and has been attributed to the Aurignacian period. It apparently represents a nude pregnant woman. Hatchings on the ventral surface of the body and on the limbs certainly represent an abundant covering of hairs. A conservative estimate of the age of this engraving is 30,000 years. Taken at its face value, this would mean that essentially modern types of man, such as prevailed at that period, retained, in some instances at least, a considerable covering of body hair under sub-Arctic climatic conditions. There is, however, comparatively little reason for interpreting thus literally the Aurignacian Venus of Laugerie Basse. In the first place, palaeolithic drawings and engravings of human beings are in general so poorly executed that little reliance can be placed upon anatomical details. Again, even if the subject is represented accurately, the excess of hair may represent a temporary condition associated with pregnancy. Danforth states that there is a considerable literature indicating an increased growth of hair on the face and body at this time.[61] Thus, the palaeolithic woman depicted may have been an exception to the ordinary condition of relative hairlessness. Anthropomorphic representations of one sort or another and of palaeolithic age have been found in more than 63 European sites,[62] but

---

[60] Marett, *Race, Sex and Environment*, p. 160.
[61] Danforth, *op. cit.*, p. 133.
[62] MacCurdy, *Human Origins*, p. 265.

the Laugerie Basse engraving is the only one in which the body is shown as hairy. Finally, the Laugerie Basse engraving may not represent a human being at all.

I should be inclined to think that man's ancestors became divested of the greater part of their hairy covering at a much earlier period than the Aurignacian, indeed at the very beginning of the essentially human stage in development. It is perfectly possible, however, that some human groups may have retained, or even redeveloped, body hair at a much later period of human evolution. In fact, we know little or nothing about this subject.

Touch Pads and Friction Skin

Pads that serve as cushions in walking develop on the under sides of the extremities of many mammals. The absence of hair on these pads is an adaptation to their locomotor function in quadrupeds. In such animals, the pads are ordinarily devoid of ridged skin, unless the hands and feet are used for grasping. This ridged skin ("friction skin") develops on the palmar and plantar surfaces and on the tips of the fingers and toes as a structural specialization to counteract slipping by heightening frictional resistance and also to enhance tactile acuity. It forms, in the first instance, over the walking or tactile pads and extends thence over the undersurfaces of the extremities. Ridged skin is also found on the business part of the grasping tails of New World monkeys—the naked area on the inside of the curve near the tip. These friction skin areas yield finger prints, toe prints, palm prints and sole prints, and (presumably) tail prints, as a result of the patterning of the ridges. The study of these patterns has been given the gruesome name of dermatoglyphics ("skin-carving").[63]

The palmar or volar pads and those on the underside of the finger tips are both evident as localized bulges at the close of the second foetal month in man and become rounder and individualized during the ensuing four weeks. From the thirteenth week onward they regress. On the palm, there are four interdigital pads lying just below the spaces between the thumb and the fingers. There are also pads on the ball of the thumb (thenar) and on the heel of the palm opposite the thumb (hypothenar). Similar pads develop on the toes and the soles of the feet, but

---

[63] This whole section is abstracted from the standard work on the subject: *Finger Prints, Palms and Soles, An Introduction to Dermatoglyphics*, by Harold Cummins and Charles Midlo.

they are retarded by two weeks in comparison with those of the upper extremity, both in appearance and in regression. Old World monkeys retain prominent pads in adult life, but these are lower than in the foetal stage. In adult anthropoid apes, the definition and elevation of pads are comparable with those of man, although the gibbon falls below man in their development.

The ridged skin develops over the pads and other areas of the palm, sole, and digits in an irregular and patchy fashion, with the fingers most precocious and the sole most delayed. The ridges are not evident on the surface of the skin until the eighteenth foetal week. They are developed and moulded upon the rows of papillae in the dermis, each ridge corresponding to a double row of papillae. On the summits of the ridges open the pores—the apertures of the sweat glands. Once developed, the ridge patterns are unchanged throughout life. Epidermal ridges are modified scales, primitively imbricated, and each associated with one hair, or a group of hairs, and one sweat gland. The lowest stages of ridge evolution are illustrated in the lemurs, whose pads bear fully developed ridges, whereas other regions have incomplete ridges represented by minute elevations, warts, or islands, with the orifice of a sweat gland duct in the center of each, or epidermal rings that are annular conglomerations of such warts. In lower primates that have ridges developed continuously over sole and palm, the zones of junction between the ridged skin and the unspecialized skin of the dorsum show transitions from ridges to islands.

The basic pad system is discernible in all of the primates and consists of an apical pad on the terminal segment of each digit and marginal and central series on the palms and soles. The marginal series consists of four interdigital pads and the thenar and hypothenar pads (the latter divided into two, the distal and proximal hypothenar pads). In the sole, the thenar pad may be similarly subdivided. The central pad system has three elevations in palm and sole, and rarely there may also be accessory interdigital pads. However, a full complement of the volar pads is almost never expressed; the central pads are usually absent, and the marginal pads may be variously modified.

Ridge systems in the lemurs are diversely developed. In the galago or bush baby, they are found only on the pads; in the slow loris over all the palmar and plantar surfaces except the flexion creases and occasional areas of the center of the palm. There is also considerable variation in the New World monkeys, with Aotus, the night monkey, showing the least extensive ridge formation, confined to pads, islands and short

ridges, and with the marmoset and capuchin or cebus monkey occasionally showing incomplete ridge formations in the center of palm or
sole. Other New World monkeys, all Old World monkeys, together with
apes and man, have complete ridge systems. The foot is less advanced
than the hand, in that the ridge systems are oftener incomplete in the
former.

It is assumed that the evolutionary progression of friction skin patterns is from whorl to loop to arch, since a primitive volar pad is an
elevation with a circumscribed base and a more or less pointed summit
developmentally correlated with the presence of a whorl. A whorl is a
concentric design in which the majority of the ridges make circuits
around the core. This latter is a pivotal feature in the center of the
pattern. The pattern area is framed by lines that meet at the lower or
proximal corners in tiny triangles, each of which is called a triradius.
The second principal pattern is the loop, in which the ridges course
around one head and flow toward the margin of the pattern, which is
open. If the loop opens toward the inside of the hand, it is called an ulnar
loop; if toward the outside, a radial loop. A loop has only one triradius.
The arch is hardly a pattern at all because it consists of a system of ridges
gently convex toward the tip, and there are no defining triradii. Evidently, the evolutionary progression from whorl to loop to arch conforms with the lowering or regression of the volar pads.

Apical (finger and toe) patterns are substantially similar in monkeys
and apes to those that exist in man, but statistical data resulting from
surveys of the various genera and species are lacking. The lemurs and
New World monkeys show some apical patterns dissimilar to those of
higher primates. The galago has longitudinal or vertical lines enclosed
by looped ridges; in the lemur, the looped frame is shifted to the dorsal
side of the digit tip and does not show on the volar side. Aotus, the
night monkey, shows longitudinal ridges that converge toward each
other at each extremity, like series of parentheses— ((((|))).

The chimpanzee, whose dermatoglyphics have been studied by Cummins and Spragg,[64] has pattern size and distribution quite comparable
with that of man. In round numbers, the chimpanzee frequencies of patterns are: whorls, 50 per cent; ulnar loops, 40 per cent; radial loops,
9 per cent; arches, 2 per cent. As may be seen from Table 6, p. 524, where
racial differences in finger print patterns are listed, this chimpanzee
count is almost indistinguishable from that of Japanese. However, the
chimpanzee patterns show some peculiarities. The whorls are more

[64] Cummins and Spragg, "Dermatoglyphics in the Chimpanzee," pp. 457–511.

evenly distributed on the digits, and certain subclasses of the general whorl pattern—twin loops, lateral pocket loops, and accidentals—are commoner than in man. About four-fifths of human whorls are mono-centric, as compared with one-third in the chimpanzee. Chimpanzee pattern distributions show other deviations from the human type that cannot be detailed here.

Human variations in the patterns of palms and soles will be described under the sections devoted to racial differences (pp. 523–529). In general, each of the pattern areas of the palm is likely to be bounded wholly or partially by triradii and their radiants. The palms and soles of lower primates show much diversification and individual variation, with deviation from the fundamental morphological plan of the order usually more marked in the sole than the palm. These departures from the basic primate plan indicate specializations.

Cummins and Midlo state that Tarsius is the most specialized of the lower primates, as indicated by absence of whorls and infrequency of other true patterns. New World monkeys are contradictory; some lack complete ridge formations over palm and sole. The most advanced is the spider monkey. Old World monkeys usually show whorl patterns, and departures from the fundamental primate plan ordinarily are confined to fusions of the thenar (thumb) and first interdigital areas. The order of increasing modification of the basic plan in the higher primates is: man, orang, gorilla, chimpanzee, gibbon.

Number and complexity of pattern can be evaluated largely on the basis of counts of the number of triradii that define the pattern areas. The higher the pattern intensity, the more primitive is the group. In the primates, Tarsius and the lemuroids are widely variable, and, as a group, Old World monkeys show the highest pattern intensity. New World monkeys have lower pattern intensity and apes and man lower still. Man is peculiar in that the pattern intensity of his sole is greater than that of his hand, indicating advanced specialization of the latter.

Cummins and Midlo attempt some phylogenetic interpretations of primate dermatoglyphics. They note the heterogeneous character of the lemuroids and suggest that this field of study "contraindicates" origin of monkeys from a tarsier-like stem. Except the langur, Old World monkeys are exaggeratedly primitive in their dermatoglyphics or, at any rate, unspecialized. The langur is more like some New World monkeys than other Old World monkeys. New World monkeys are most diverse, with the night monkey and the marmoset-like monkeys most primitive and the spider monkey most advanced. The gibbon is the most specialized ape, while the great apes and man stand in the following order of increasing specialization: orang, gorilla or chimpanzee, man. However, man is more primitive in adherence to basic configurational plan than even the orang. Therefore, in view of the fundamental importance of plan, these dermatoglyphologists (which is certainly a hard name to call them) conclude that man stemmed from an ancestral stock more primitive than any existing apes and with dermatoglyphic traits more closely allied to those of monkeys.[65]

[65] Cummins and Midlo, *Finger Prints*, p. 177.

ape, while the great apes and man stand in the following order of increasing specialization: orang, gorilla or chimpanzee, man. However, man is more primitive in adherence to basic configurational plan than even the orang. Therefore, in view of the fundamental importance of plan, these dermatoglyphologists (which is certainly a hard name to call them) conclude that man stemmed from an ancestral stock more primitive than any existing apes and with dermatoglyphic traits more closely allied to those of monkeys."

Cummins and Midlo, Finger Prints, p. 174.

UP FROM THE APE

and are present in enormous numbers in the seminal fluid. Each consists of an oval flattened head, a neck, a rod-like body, and a long, thread-
like tail. The total length of a human spermatozoön varies between 52
and 62 one-thousandths of a millimeter. The whip-like tail of the minute
spermatozoön propels it through the seminal fluid and enables it to move about freely.
The male sperm cell matures in the testicle in a way similar to the
maturation of the ovum, but, in the process of ripening, the primary
male cells give rise to four cells instead of one, each of which
is capable of fertilizing a mature ovum. The sperm cells of the large

Part III. The Individual Life Cycle

Being Born: Prenatal Development

The internal reproductive organs of the female consist of the uterus
and a pair of ovaries, each connected with the uterus by a tube or ovi-
duct. The ovaries in the human female are two small, almond-like
bodies situated on either side of the uterus near the lateral pelvic walls.
Each of the uterine tubes is about 10 centimeters long and empties into
the upper part of the uterus or womb. The uterus is a hollow, thick-
walled, muscular organ about the size and shape of a pear with the apex
pointed downward and backward. It is situated in the pelvic cavity between the bladder and rectum. Below, its cavity communicates with that
of the vagina (the sheath-like canal leading to the exterior) (Fig. 36).

In the Monotremata, the lowliest of mammals, the oviducts open
separately into the common excretory duct, or cloaca, and do not fuse
to form a uterus. In the marsupials or pouched mammals, there are
two uteri, each opening into a short cloaca by means of its own canal.
In the lemurs and tarsiers, there is but one uterus, but it is forked above
and has two horns for the reception of oviducts. All of the higher primates, including man, have a simple uterus.

The development of a new being takes place in vertebrate animals
when the female germ cell (ovum) has been fertilized by a male germ
cell (spermatozoön). The ova or eggs are developed in follicles or pockets
of the female ovaries. The human ova, although the largest cells of the
body, are very minute, measuring about 0.2 millimeters in diameter. In
the female of child-bearing age, a mature ovum is liberated each month
and conveyed through the uterine tube into the cavity of the uterus.
Here it undergoes no further development and is discharged, unless
fertilized. If it is fertilized, it is retained within the uterine cavity and
develops into an embryo. Before the ovum can be fertilized, it must
mature or ripen. This maturation of the ovum takes place within the
ovarian follicle or immediately after its escape therefrom. It consists of
a process of subdivision of the ovum into two and then four cells. Only
one of these four cells develops into a mature ovum.

The spermatozoa, or male germ cells, are developed within the testicles and are present in enormous numbers in the seminal fluid. Each consists of an oval flattened head, a neck, a rod-like body, and a long, thread-like tail. The total length of a human spermatozoön varies between 52 and 62 one-thousandths of a millimeter. The whip-like tail of the minute spermatozoön acts as a propeller and enables it to move about freely. The male sperm cell matures in the testicle in a way similar to the maturation of the ovum, but, in the process of ripening, the primary male cells give rise by subdivision to four spermatozoa, each of which is capable of fertilizing a mature ovum. The sperm cells of the large anthropoid apes each have special characteristics, the orang-utan being most aberrant in this respect. In the form and proportions of the different

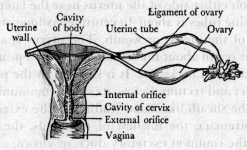

Fig. 36. The posterior half of the human uterus and upper part of the vagina, with the left uterine tube and ovary.

parts of the male germ cell, the gorilla approaches most closely to the human condition.

Although the fertilization of the human ovum has not been observed, the general outline of the process may be deduced from knowledge of various stages in other animals. The ovum is probably fertilized in the lateral portion of the uterine tube. The head and connecting piece of one sperm cell penetrate the ovum, and the tail of the sperm cell breaks off. The fertilized ovum probably takes seven or eight days in moving through the uterine tube to the cavity of the uterus. During this time the ovum undergoes segmentation or subdivision.

The ovum before fertilization contains a minute body of circular or oval shape embedded in the protoplasm. This is the female pronucleus. The part of the male germ cell that pierces the ovum forms the male pronucleus. The male and female pronuclei unite to form a segmentation nucleus. This multiplies by division into two, then four, then eight, then sixteen cells, et cetera, until the ovum is filled with a mulberry-like mass of closely packed cells (the morula). These soon separate into an outer peripheral cell mass called the trophoblast, which makes a covering but does not contribute to the formation of the embryo proper, and an inner cell mass from which the embryo is formed. Fluid accumulates between the outer covering and the inner cell mass, so that the ovum is now transformed into a vesicle (little vessel). The inner cell mass remains in contact with the outer covering or trophoblast at one pole of the vesicle. The latter is now called the blastula. In most animals the blastula, a hollow sphere with its walls made of a single layer of cells, then caves in, as one can push in the side of a hollow rubber ball, so that nearly half of the original exterior becomes the inside of the cup. It is then called the gastrula, and the mouth of the cup, called the blastophore, gradually grows together. Thus there is developed an inside germ layer, the entoderm, pushed in against the outside layer, the ectoderm. However, in mammals, this process of gastrulation is not so simple, because the fertilized ovum is early embedded in the wall of the maternal uterus. After the trophoblast, or outer sphere for the interpenetration of the maternal tissue, has been formed, some sort of gastrulation apparently occurs in the inner cell mass that is in contact with one pole of the blastodermic vesicle. At any rate, the entoderm and ectoderm are now differentiated.

The inside layer of the inner cell mass (entoderm) becomes differentiated into a small sac, the yolk-sac. The cells of the embryonic mass migrate toward the inner wall of the cluster leaving a space between it and the covering of the vesicle. This free space gradually develops into the amniotic cavity (Fig. 37A). The inward migration of the cells forms a layer constituting the inner floor of the cavity. This layer is the embryonic disk from which the body of the embryo will be formed. It consists of prismatic cells known as the embryonic ectoderm (outside layer), on the back side, and another layer, the entoderm, on the belly side.

The embryonic disk becomes pear-shaped with the wider end directed forward, and an opaque streak makes its appearance at the middle of the disk extending downward to the narrow end. This is called the primitive streak. Along its surface there appears the primitive groove, which, at its upper end, communicates with the yolk-sac by an aperture. The two original layers of the embryonic disk, the ectoderm (outer germ layer) and the entoderm (inner germ layer), now apparently separate where the thickened primitive streak formed of ectoderm grows down into the entoderm. On either side of this thickened streak, the layers draw apart and a third layer, the mesoderm (middle germ layer), differentiates between them. Just how this differentiation of the three germinal layers occurs in the human embryo is not known. Eventually,

however, from the outer layer are formed the nervous system, the
epidermis of the skin, the lining cells of the sweat glands, oil glands, and
mammary glands; the hair, nails, lining membranes of the nose and
mouth, external parts of the eyes, and some other organs. The entoderm
or inside layer forms the lining of most of the digestive tube and of all
the digestive glands that open into it, the lining of the auditory tubes,
the lungs, the bladder, and parts of the thyroid and thymus glands. The
mesoderm, which develops between the ectoderm and entoderm, gives

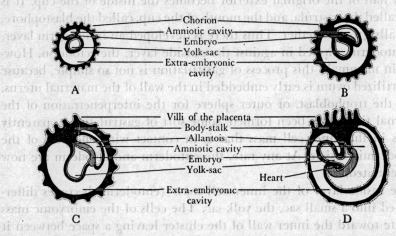

Fig. 37. Diagrams showing development of foetal membranes and the placenta in
man. A, an early stage of the human ovum; B, the formation of the allantois and of
the body-stalk; C, constriction of the yolk-sac; D, expansion of the amnion and definition of the navel.

rise to the remaining structures of the body, including skeleton, muscles,
circulatory system, et cetera.

Above the primitive streak, there now develop two longitudinal folds
of ectoderm, which extend up to the head end. These are called the
neural folds, and the groove between them is called the neural groove.
The groove deepens, and the folds close over it to form the neural
(nervous) tube. The coalescence of the neural folds begins at the region
of the hind brain and extends in both directions. Toward the end of
the third week, the anterior opening closes at the site of the future brain,
and three swellings appear at this end of the tube corresponding to the
future forebrain, midbrain, and hindbrain. The rest of the tube forms
the spinal cord.

Along the front of the neural tube, there develops a thickened ridge,
which soon becomes converted into a rod of cells called the notochord

(back chord). It extends from the anterior end of the midbrain down the entire length of the future vertebral column. It soon becomes separated from the neural tube by surrounding mesoderm cells from which develop the skull, vertebral column, and brain coverings. Toward the end of the second week, the mesoderm, lying on either side of the neural tube and notochord, begins to divide into cubical masses, which are called the primitive segments. These extend along the whole trunk from the base of the head downward. Eight of these segments are cervical (neck segments); twelve are thoracic (corresponding to the future ribbed vertebrae); five are lumbar, five sacral, and from five to eight are coccygeal (corresponding to the tail region of the vertebral column). There is some reason for believing that the head region is also segmented, but in mammals the primitive segments can be recognized only in the occipital region (the back part of the head.)

The embryo grows rapidly, and a part of the yolk-sac becomes enclosed within it at the site of the future navel; this constitutes the primitive digestive tube (Fig. 37 C, D). Since the growth in length is greater than in width, the head and tail ends are curved toward each other, and a blind end of the yolk-sac is enclosed within the body toward the head end forming the fore gut and another at the tail end forming the hind gut. The embryo is connected by a band of mesoderm, called the body stalk, to the chorion, which is the outermost foetal envelope enclosing the embryo and in contact externally with the walls of the maternal uterus. This body stalk, which at first is at the tail end of the embryo, comes to occupy a ventral position with the folding of the head and tail ends toward each other.

The yolk-sac is filled with the vitelline fluid, which may be utilized for the nourishment of the embryo during its earlier stages. At the end of the fourth week, it is a small, pear-shaped vesicle, opening into the digestive tract of the embryo by means of a long narrow duct. By the seventh week, the duct has usually become obliterated, but the yolk-sac may be seen in the after-birth as a minute, oval-shaped body, varying in diameter from one to five millimeters. In certain mammals, the yolk-sac provides nutrition for the embryo for a considerable period. In most primitive mammals, the yolk-sac forms a complete lining to the whole of the blastodermic vesicle (the membranous envelope that contains the embryo). In the higher apes and man, the yolk-sac touches only a small part of the wall of the blastodermic vesicle, and that for a short time only. In marsupials, the yolk-sac comes into contact with the walls of the uterus of the mother and sends out processes that draw nutriment from the maternal system, but, in man and the higher apes, the yolk-sac plays no such important part and has only a transitory and insignificant nutritive function.

The allantois is a blind tube that arises from the posterior part of the yolk-sac and is carried backward with the development of the hind gut in the embryo and opens into its terminal part (Fig. 37). Eventually, it grows out into the body stalk that connects the embryo with the wall of the blastodermic vesicle near its tail end. In birds, reptiles, and many mammals, the allantois develops into a vesicle. In birds, it ultimately surrounds the yolk and becomes applied to the membrane immediately inside the shell. By means of allantoic veins and arteries, oxygen is taken from the atmosphere, and carbonic acid is given off through the egg-shell. Thus, in birds, the allantois is an important means of foetal respiration. Even in a rabbit, the allantois is a large vesicle in contact with a considerable area of the blastodermic wall. But, in man and the higher primates, it is a mere rudiment that becomes lost in the body stalk.

The amnion is the membranous sac, which, at a very early period, expands round and encloses the embryo. At its earliest observed stage in man, it is a closed cavity, its inner floor being formed by the dorsal (back) surface of the embryonic disk (Fig. 37A). With the curvature of the embryo, it expands and extends round the head and tail ends until it adheres to the chorion (the outermost foetal envelope). About the fourth or fifth week, fluid begins to accumulate in the amnion. At the end of pregnancy, it amounts to about one liter. This fluid protects the foetus from injury and allows its free movements during the later period of pregnancy.

The amnion is developed in reptiles, birds, and mammals but not in fishes or amphibians.

The fertilized ovum reaches the uterine cavity after seven or eight days in the uterine tube. It digs itself into the mucous membrane lining the uterus. This membrane is called the "decidua" because it is sloughed off monthly during the menstruation of the female and then renewed. The trophoblast, or covering of the fertilized ovum, has the power of dissolving and absorbing the uterine lining tissues. It forms a network of branching processes which open into the maternal blood vessels so that the spaces between the network are filled with blood. The chorion, which is the outermost foetal covering, consists of two layers, an outer one formed from the trophoblast and an inner from the mesoderm (middle germ layer.) With this latter the amnion is in contact. Processes from the chorion—the villi—invade the tissues of the uterine walls and absorb from them the nutritive materials for the growth of

the embryo. These villi are supplied with blood from the arteries leading out of the embryonic navel, and, after circulating through the capillaries of the villi, the blood is returned to the embryo through the
umbilical vein. At first the villi cover the entire chorion (Fig. 37 A, B, C),
but, after the end of the second month, they atrophy, except at the site
of the placenta (Fig. 37 D). The rest of the chorion becomes smooth.
The placenta (cake) is the disk-like formation whereby the foetus is
connected with the wall of the maternal uterus and through which the
nutritive, respiratory, and excretory functions of the foetus are carried
on. The foetal portion of the placenta consists of enlarged villi of the
chorion, which are bathed in maternal blood. The maternal portion
consists of uterine tissues modified to form the intervillous spaces and
supplied with blood from the mother. The foetal blood stream passes
through the villi, and the maternal blood currents traverse the intervillous spaces. The delicate walls of the villi separate the foetal from the
maternal blood, and through these walls the foetal blood absorbs oxygen
and nutritive materials from the maternal blood and gives off waste
products. The purified blood is carried back to the embryo. The placenta
is usually attached at the top of the uterus between the uterine tubes.
The umbilical cord connects the foetus with the placenta, its length being about equal to that of the foetus. It develops from the body stalk, the
mass of tissue connecting the embryo with the wall of the fertilized ovum
(the chorion) (Figs. 37, 38). When the amnion has expanded round the
foetus, the umbilical cord includes the remnant of the duct leading to
the yolk-sac and the allantois, as well as the umbilical arteries and
veins.

When the child is born, the placenta and umbilical cord are expelled
as the after-birth. The orifices of the torn uterine vessels are closed by
contraction of the muscular fibers of the uterine walls, and hemorrhage
is thus checked. The expelled placenta is a discoidal mass with a diameter
from seven to eight inches and average thickness at the center of one
and one quarter inches, and a weight of about one pound. The umbilical
cord is attached at about the center and leads from there to the navel
of the child.

The placenta is a structure characteristic of the higher mammals.
Analogous embryonic structures are found sporadically among vertebrates even as low down in the scale as the sharks. Monotremes and
marsupials are said to be non-placental, but this only means that they
possess no allantoic placenta, i.e., that the allantois does not establish a
vascular connection with the maternal uterine walls. Such a connection
is, however, established between the walls of the yolk-sac and the uterine

membranes. In most of the lower placental mammals, the allantois is more developed than in man, and the primitive type of placenta is called "diffuse" because the villi develop over all of that surface of the chorion projecting into the horns of the uterus and invade the maternal uterine membranes (the decidua). At birth, these villi are withdrawn, leaving the decidua behind in the uterus; hence these placentae are called "non-deciduate," while those that carry the maternal tissues with them in the after-birth are "deciduate." In Tarsius, the monkeys, and the apes, as well as in man, the villi of the chorion get their blood supply

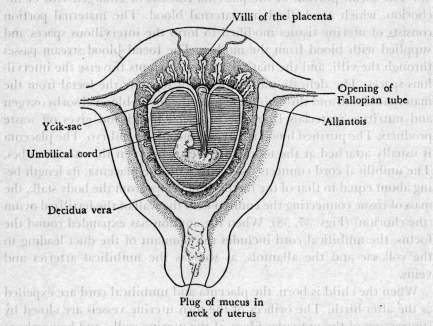

Fig. 38. Diagrammatic section of the uterus in the early months of pregnancy.

through the body stalk and persist only in the area of the future placenta; in the lemurs, on the contrary, the villi persist all over the chorion and are vascularized through the allantois, which, in man, is merely a "blind alley." The ungulates and other Eutherian mammals belong with the lemurs in the class with allantoic placentae. In the lemurs, the placenta is diffuse (spread over a large area of the chorion) and non-deciduate. There is also a transitory yolk-sac placenta, but this is absent in Tarsius and in the suborder Anthropoidea. Tarsius differs from the higher primates in that the villi of the placenta are indistinct and not as deeply imbedded in the maternal tissues as in the cases of the apes and man. The single, disk-shaped placenta of Tarsius is taken to be a strong indication of the ultimate tarsioid descent of the Anthropoidea and man. The Carnivora have a zonary placenta that extends like a girdle round the embryo. The Old World monkeys usually have two disk placentae, which Keith considers of zonary origin. The Cebidae, or New World monkeys, have a single disk placenta, like man, the anthropoids, and Tarsius. The double placenta occurs as a rare anomaly in man. In the development of these foetal structures, man shows the closest resemblances to the great anthropoid apes.

By the end of the second week, the head and tail ends of the embryo are distinguishable, and it is well separated from the yolk-sac; the mesoderm on either side of the axis is being divided into cubical segments. At the end of the third week, the embryo is strongly curved, and there are about 30 of these primitive segments. The primary swellings indicating the various parts of the brain are marked, and the capsules that ultimately give rise to eyes and ears may be distinguished. In the throat region, there now appear certain structures of great interest from an evolutionary standpoint. These are the branchial (gill or visceral)

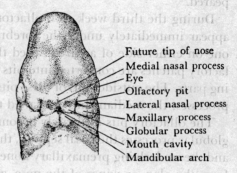

Fig. 39. Head of an embryo seven weeks old. (After His.)

arches. The upper part of the fore gut is indented to form five throat pouches. In fishes, these indentations, or branchial grooves, ultimately open into gill slits by means of which the animal breathes. These openings do not occur in birds or mammals. The grooves separate rounded bars or arches of cartilage, which are attached to the sides of the head and extend round to meet in the middle ventral line of the neck. Altogether six arches appear, but only four are visible externally (Fig. 40B). Each arch is supplied with blood from the great aorta artery, exactly as in the gill arches of fishes. The first branchial arch gives rise to the lower lip, the lower jaw, the masticatory muscles, and the forward part of the tongue. The ends of the cartilaginous bar forming this arch are connected with the ear capsules, and the extremity of each is ossified to form the malleus, the outermost of the auditory ossicles (cf. p. 64). Probably the second ossicle, the incus, is also developed from the end of this arch. From the second branchial arch, the hyoid arch, are formed the sides and front of the neck, and from its cartilage is developed a part of the hyoid bone at the base of the tongue. The third arch also contributes to the hyoid bone and to the posterior part of the tongue. The fourth, fifth, and sixth arches form the cartilages of the larynx, of the trachea, and the bronchi (the organ of the voice and the respiratory tubes). From the first branchial groove the entrance into the ear is formed, and cartilaginous swellings around the auditory entrance give rise to the external ear. The first gill pouch, or pharyngeal pouch, forms the tube of the middle ear (the spiracular gill cleft of certain fishes), and the closing membrane between the mandibular, or first gill arch, and the hyoid, or second gill arch, develops into the ear drum (tympanum). The inner part of the second gill pouch is the site of the development of the tonsils. By the end of the sixth week, the gill arches, those fishy reminiscences, have disappeared.

During the third week, two olfactory patches of thickened ectoderm appear immediately under the forebrain and above the mouth cavity, one on either side of an area called the fronto-nasal process. These olfactory patches are converted into pits by the upgrowth of the surrounding parts. The outside rims of these pits are formed from the lateral nasal processes; the median rims are called the globular processes (Fig. 39).

The olfactory pits ultimately become the nasal cavities, and from the globular processes the nasal septum, the middle portion of the upper lip, and the underlying premaxillary bone are formed. The lateral processes form the alae, or wings of the nose, and a raised median area between and above the olfactory pits becomes the nasal tip. Two triangular processes, the maxillary processes, grow toward the middle line of the face from the dorsal ends of the maxillary arch. These form the lateral walls and floor of the orbits of the eye, the cheek bones, and the greater part of the maxilla (the upper jaw).

The maxillary processes with associated shelf-like palatine processes fuse with the lateral nasal and globular processes and form the floor of the nose and roof of the palate. Incomplete union in the center line of the globular and maxillary processes produces the condition known as hare-lip, while cleft palate is caused by the failure to unite of the palatine processes that form the roof of the mouth. Hare-lip is found as a normal condition in adult vertebrates only in sharks and rays. The complete palate, such as occurs in man, is a mammalian structure enabling an animal to chew or suck and to breathe through the nose freely at the same time. The upper lips and underlying structures are normally completely united by the end of the eighth week, but the palatine roof is not complete until the ninth week and the soft palate at the end of the eleventh week. In amphibia, reptiles, and birds, the open cleft between the mouth and the nose persists in the adult condition.

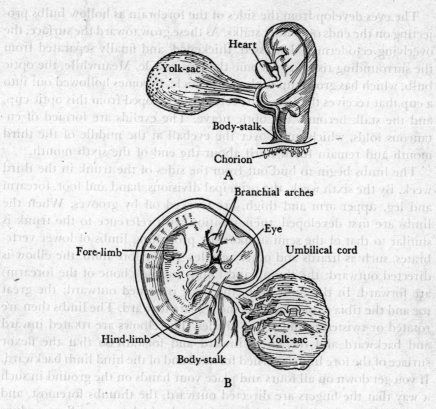

Heart

Yolk-sac

Body-stalk

Chorion

A

Branchial arches

Eye

Fore-limb

Umbilical cord

Hind-limb

Yolk-sac

Body-stalk

B

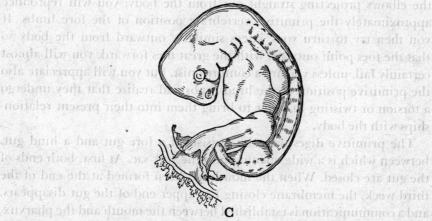

C

Fig. 40. Form of the human embryo at various stages of growth. (After His.) A, about twelve days old, length 2.5 mm. B, about four weeks old, length 7.5 mm. C, four to five weeks old, length 10 mm.

The eyes develop from the sides of the forebrain as hollow bulbs projecting on the ends of slender stalks. As these grow toward the surface, the overlying ectoderm is depressed, thickened, and finally separated from the surrounding tissue to become the lens vesicle. Meanwhile, the optic bulb, which has grown up to the lens vesicle, becomes hollowed out into a cup that receives the lens. The retina is developed from this optic cup, and the stalk becomes the optic nerve. The eyelids are formed of cutaneous folds, which unite over the eyeball at the middle of the third month and remain fused until about the end of the sixth month.

The limbs begin to bud out from the sides of the trunk in the third week. By the sixth week, the principal divisions, hand and foot, forearm and leg, upper arm and thigh, are marked off by grooves. When the limbs are first developed, their position with reference to the trunk is similar to that of the semi-supporting, propelling limbs of lower vertebrates, such as lizards and other reptiles. In the fore limb, the elbow is directed outward; the thumb and radius (outside bone of the forearm) are forward. In the hind limb, the knee is turned outward; the great toe and the tibia (inside bone of the leg) are forward. The limbs then are rotated or twisted round at the girdles. The elbows are rotated inward and backward and the knees inward and forward so that the flexor surface of the fore limb is turned forward and of the hind limb backward. If you get down on all fours and place your hands on the ground in such a way that the fingers are directed outward, the thumbs foremost, and the elbows projecting straight out from the body, you will reproduce approximately the primitive vertebrate position of the fore limbs. If you then try to turn your knees similarly outward from the body so that the toes point outward with the great toes forward, you will almost certainly fail, unless you are a contortionist, but you will appreciate also the primitive position of the hind limbs and realize that they undergo a torsion or twisting in order to bring them into their present relationships with the body.

The primitive digestive tube consists of a fore gut and a hind gut, between which is a wide opening into the yolk-sac. At first, both ends of the gut are closed. When the mouth has been formed at the end of the third week, the membrane closing the upper end of the gut disappears, and a communication is established between the mouth and the pharynx, which latter is formed by a swelling of the upper part of the tube in association with the development of the branchial (gill) arches. The wide opening from the gut into the yolk-sac is gradually narrowed to a tubular duct. About the fourth week, a dilation of the digestive tube marks the site of the future stomach. An outgrowth for the liver appears;

the stomach becomes further expanded and takes on a double curvature. The gut below the stomach is greatly elongated, and a great loop extends forward, from the summit of which the yolk-sac duct passes to the navel. For a time, a considerable part of this loop protrudes beyond the abdominal cavity into the umbilical cord, but by the end of the third month it has been withdrawn. The rest of the gut increases greatly in length, is coiled upon itself, and ultimately is disposed in the positions that are maintained throughout life, being bound by sheets of membranes called mesenteries.

The permanent urinary and generative organs are developed only after the appearance and disappearance of several purely embryonic structures. There are three forerunners of the kidneys, and the permanent organs make their appearance about the beginning of the second month. One of these precursors of the kidneys is the Wolffian body, which persists as a kidney in fishes and amphibians, but in birds, reptiles, and mammals disappears almost completely with the development of the permanent kidneys. In the male, the duct of the Wolffian body, which opens into the cloaca, persists as a part of the genitary organs. Soon after the formation of the Wolffian ducts, another pair of ducts, the Mullerian ducts, are formed, each on the outside of the corresponding Wolffian duct but crossing over to the inside toward the posterior end of the embryo. In the male, these Mullerian ducts atrophy and disappear; in the female, the lower portions fuse together and form the vagina and uterus, and the upper parts remain separate as the uterine tubes. From plates of epithelium called the genital ridges lying near the upper extremities of the Wolffian and Mullerian ducts are formed the genital glands—the ovaries in the female, the testes in the male. In the female, the ovaries come into apposition with the ends of the Mullerian ducts (the uterine tubes); in the male, the testes become connected with the Wolffian tubes, which ultimately form their efferent ducts. At first the testes are at the back part of the abdominal cavity, but by the end of the eighth month they have descended into the scrotum. The permanent kidneys develop partly as offshoots of the lower portions of the Wolffian ducts and partly from one of the embryonic structures antecedent to the kidneys. The bladder is also formed partly from the cloaca and partly from the ends of the Wolffian ducts. Ultimately, the dorsal part of the cloaca or common sewer is separated from the ventral part; the former becomes the rectum and the latter the urogenital aperture.

The first rudiments of the heart appear as a pair of tubular vessels called the primitive aortae, which soon establish a communication with the yolk-sac, from which each receives a vein. Dorsal prolongations of these primitive aortae are continued downward through the body stalk to the placental villi. From the placental villi, the blood is returned through the body stalk to the heart by means of a pair of umbilical veins. It seems that the placental or chorionic circulation is established before the yolk-sac circulation. At first the rudiment of the heart lies above the yolk-sac and just below the mandibular arch and is not closely applied to the main mass of the embryo. By the development of the head and tail flexions, the heart is gradually drawn within the thorax; at first it lies in the middle line, but toward the end of the pregnancy it becomes oblique in position. A single tubular heart is formed by the fusion of the two primitive aortae in the pericardial region. The posterior end of this primitive tubular heart receives two veins, the vitelline veins, from the yolk-sac, and, from its anterior end, two aortae arise which form six pairs of arches supplying the six gill arches. The contraction of the tubular heart forces the blood through the vascular area, and it is returned to the heart by the vitelline veins after nutriment has been absorbed from the yolk. When the yolk-sac atrophies, the vitelline circulation disappears, and an increased amount of blood is carried through the umbilical arteries to the villi of the placenta and is returned to the heart by the umbilical veins. The simple tubular heart becomes elongated and bent upon itself to form an S-shaped loop. Constrictions in the tube divide it into five parts: a venous sinus at the opening of the vitelline veins, an atrium or auricle that receives the blood, a primitive ventricle, from which it issues into a bulb, thence into an arterial trunk. When the gill arches begin to disappear and the lungs to develop, the first chamber, the venous sinus, becomes incorporated in the right side of the auricle; the bulb is included within the ventricle, and partitions or septa grow up which divide the heart into right and left halves. The right side receives the venous blood and passes it on to the lungs and the placenta; the left receives the blood from the lungs and placenta and supplies it to the rest of the body. An aperture called the foramen ovale allows free communication between the auricles until the end of foetal life. The heart has now become a four-chambered pump.

Each of the primitive aortae has a dorsal and ventral portion springing from a trunk common to the aortae of both sides. At first, both run backward separately on either side of the notochord, but about the third week, they fuse to form a single descending trunk. Above, six aortic arches are formed on each side to supply the six gill arches (Fig. 41). The anterior branches persist on both sides to form the internal and external carotid arteries. The third arches form portions of the internal carotid arteries; the right side of the fourth, a part of the right subclavian; the left side of the fourth, the aortic arch; and the left side of the sixth arch forms the ductus arteriosus, which allows the blood from the pulmonary artery to pass into the aorta. Since the lungs of the foetus are inactive, only a small amount of blood passes through the pulmonary artery; but at birth, when respiration is established, the ductus arteriosus begins to contract and is completely closed at about the fourth to the tenth day. The placental circulation is now cut off, and the blood is pumped through the pulmonary artery to the lungs instead of through the aorta to the placenta.

We have seen that the nervous system is of ectodermal origin, and that

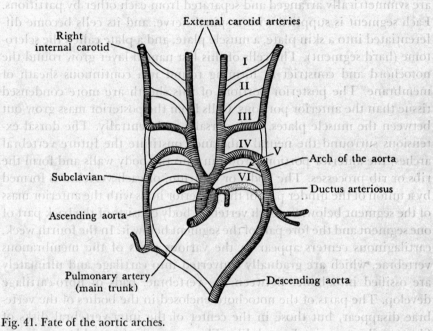

Fig. 41. Fate of the aortic arches.

its first rudiment is the neural groove that appears on the back of the embryo. By coalescence of the folds, this groove becomes the neural tube, at the head end of which three swellings form the primary vesicles of the forebrain, the midbrain, and the hindbrain. Cavities of these vesicles become the ventricles of the brain, and the neural tube develops into the spinal cord. The three brain vesicles become curved forward in a somewhat S-shaped fashion with the development of the cephalic or head flexure. The cerebral hemispheres of the forebrain are at first small, but they increase rapidly in size until they overlap the structures developed from the mid- and hindbrains. This rapid increase of the cerebral hemispheres is a typically mammalian feature. At first, the surface of the cerebrum is smooth, but, during the sixth and seventh months of foetal life, ridges, or convolutions, and sulci, or furrows, appear on its surface.

The skeleton develops from mesoderm. The notochord is a solid rod of cells that forms on the ventral side of the neural tube. In Amphioxus it persists and is the only representative of a skeleton. In vertebrates, it is an embryonic structure, which largely disappears before the end of foetal life. The notochord reaches from the upper end of the midbrain down to the extremity of the tail region. On both sides of the notochord, the mesoderm becomes divided into primitive cubical segments. These are symmetrically arranged and separated from each other by partitions. Each segment is supplied with a spinal nerve, and its cells become differentiated into a skin plate, a muscle plate, and a plate called the sclerotome (hard segment). The cells of this last named layer grow round the notochord and constrict it, forming round it a continuous sheath of membrane. The posterior portions of this sheath are more condensed tissue than the anterior portions. Cells from the posterior mass grow out between the muscle plates, both dorsally and ventrally. The dorsal extensions surround the neural tube and constitute the future vertebral arches; the anterior portions grow out into the body walls and form the ribs or rib processes. The body, or centrum, of each vertebra is formed by a union of the hinder part of the posterior mass with the anterior mass of the segment below. So, each vertebral body consists of the back part of one segment and the fore part of the segment below it. In the fourth week, cartilaginous centers appear in the various parts of the membranous vertebrae, which are gradually converted into cartilage and ultimately are ossified into bone. Between the vertebrae, pads of fibro-cartilage develop. The parts of the notochord enclosed in the bodies of the vertebrae disappear, but those in the center of the inter-vertebral disks of fibro-cartilage persist through life. The sternum is formed by two longitudinal bars of cartilage that unite the ventral ends of the ribs opposite the first seven pairs. These bars fuse in the middle line to form the breast bone.

The notochord extends up to the fore end of the midbrain and becomes partially surrounded with mesoderm in the head portion. This mesoderm grows over the brain vesicles so that a mesodermous envelope covers the entire brain. From the inner layer of this, the coverings of the brain and the bones of the skull are developed; from the outer layer, the scalp, muscles, and soft parts. In sharks and dogfish, the membranous cranium becomes converted into cartilage, but in mammals, only the skull base is laid down in cartilage, the sides and vault of the cranium remaining membranous until converted into bone. That part of the skull base developed round the notochord shows segmentation similar to that in the region of the vertebral column. Parts of the notochord persist in the dorsal wall of the pharynx. All skeletal elements, whether formed from cartilage or from membrane, are gradually calcified or ossified and become converted into bone. This process begins at definite centers of ossification in each bone and is not completed in all portions of all bones of the body until the individual becomes adult.

In the fourth week, the embryo is so strongly curved upon itself that it seems almost circular in profile. The limb buds appear, and in the next week their segments are discernible. The embryo now begins to uncurl. By the end of the eighth week, the face is more or less completed, the eyelids are present, and the ears are distinguishable. By the third month, the limbs are well developed, and sex may be distinguished from the external organs. At the end of the month, the foetus is about 9 or 10 centimeters long from crown to heel. In the fourth month, hairs begin to make their appearance, and in the fifth month, the movements of the foetus may be observed. In the sixth month, the body is covered with fine hairs (lanugo). During the next month, the eyelids open, and, in the male, the testes decend into the scrotum. In the eighth month, the lanugo begins to disappear, and the foetus is coated with a cheesy substance called the vernix caseosa. The skin becomes pink, and the foetus gets plump. At the end of the ninth month, delivery takes place. The baby at birth weighs from 6½ to 10 pounds and is about 50 centimeters from head to heels.

Our present interest in the development of the individual—embryology—is concentrated upon the evidence of evolution that this process presents. The most controversial subject in embryology is the so-called recapitulation theory, which holds that the embryonic development of the individual is to some extent an abbreviated record of the zoological history of his species—that the individual "climbs up his own family tree." This theory is based upon the appearance in the embryo of structures found in the adults of lower forms of animal life that disappear before birth or are replaced by other structures in the fully developed animals whose embryology is being studied. The assumption is that such embryonic structures represent ancestral features lost in the process of evolution. Thus, to cite the most familiar example, the presence of gill arches and gill grooves with their associated blood supply as transient embryonic structures in the higher vertebrates leads to the conclusion that these vertebrates are the ultimate descendants of fishy ancestors having functioning gills, by means of which respiration was carried on.

In this instance, it seems that the conclusion stated is irrefutable, since no other reasonable explanation can be given for the appearance of gill arches in the embryos of land-dwelling vertebrates. There are a number of such examples in which embryonic structures seem to be undeniable survivals of stages of evolution through which our ancestors have passed.

But it is a long step from the recognition of the evolutionary significance of such atavistic survivals to the conclusion that the process of embryonic development is a complete or trustworthy record of the various stages of ancestral evolution. It is obvious that many foetal structures are quite *sui generis* and are by no means survivals or modifications of organs formerly possessed in adult life by some remote ancestor. For example, the placenta, amnion, and yolk-sac can have no such atavistic significance. They could never have been adult structures in any animal. There is ample reason for supposing that mammals developed from reptiles, reptiles from amphibians, amphibians from vertebrate fishes, and the last named from invertebrates. But in the embryonic history of no higher mammal can there be recognized stages in which the developing individual closely resembles successively an invertebrate animal, a fish, and a reptile. There may be a number of temporary structures which, at one time or another in embryonic development, recall or suggest reptilian or piscian ancestry. It is certain that similar embryonic processes in different animals must be regarded in a general sense as indicative of a common ancestry. However, to suppose that any sequential account of evolution of the species may be derived from the study of individual development alone is obviously nonsensical.

We cannot assume that structures found in the embryo as transient survivals were necessarily the permanent adult organs of ancestral forms. Still less can we admit that a vestigial organ must necessarily have had, in an ancestral form, the function of the homologous organ when fully developed in another animal. Otherwise we should have to suppose that the presence of the vestigial mammary glands in the male indicates that the ancestral males had functioning breasts and suckled the young. It is equally irrational to suppose that any hypothetical reconstruction of less remote ancestral forms can be made from a study of embryology. For instance, the large and rounded head of the human foetus does not indicate that the remote ancestors of man had large and rounded brain cases; they almost certainly had not. Nor can we deduce from the absence of the opposable great toe in the human foetus that no ancestor of man ever possessed such opposability of the hallux.

Thus, embryology does not give a complete picture of the evolution of the race in the development of the individual; it merely contributes scraps of evidence that evolution has taken place. These are, as someone has said, like disconnected cuttings of a cinema film, pieced together more or less in the order of their taking, but with many of the crucial scenes omitted and others given a prominence that reflects their final importance rather than the order of their occurrence. Professor Adolph Schultz, who has made valuable studies upon the foetal growth of primates, classifies the embryological observations that bear upon human evolution in two categories: those pertaining to normal structures of passing embryological duration which can be interpreted only as transient repetitions of ancestral features, and those that show such close similarities in the details of the process and structures of embryonic life that they prove evolutionary relationship, without, however, contributing in any way to a hypothetical reconstruction of ancestors.[1]

Let us for the moment consider only the vestigial organs that appear in foetal life. We have already referred to the presence in the human foetus of an external tail (page 88). For a considerable time this appendage projects well below the level of the rump, but it is soon overgrown by the neighboring parts, so that in the adult the last caudal vertebra is high above the level of the rectal aperture. Schultz reports a case in which a human embryo with a crown to rump length of 7.5 millimeters had an external tail length of 1.2 millimeters, or 16 per cent of the entire body length. The length of the coccygeal or tail vertebrae in the adult is only 3.5 per cent of the corresponding measurement, the sitting height. This difference indicates the tremendous reduction of the human tail that takes place during growth. A still greater reduction occurs in the spinal cord, the lower end of which reaches beyond the thirty-eighth vertebral rudiment in the early embryo but only as far as the twenty-first vertebra in the adult.

In this category of vestigial features belongs also the lanugo, the foetal covering of hair found on the body of the embryo between the sixth and the eighth month. It can be interpreted only as a fleeting reproduction of a condition that must have been permanent in the adult life of some of our ancestors.

All of the lower primates and the gibbon and orang-utan have nine wrist bones, whereas man, the gorilla, and the chimpanzee usually have only eight, arranged in two rows. The extra bony element in the carpus, or wrist, of most primates is called the os centrale. This element regu-

1 Schultz, "Embryological Evidence," p. 248.

larly appears in the foetal human being as a cartilaginous nodule that usually fuses with the navicular bone but sometimes remains a separate element through life.

On the inside of the forearm, close to the wrist, tactile hairs occur in many arboreal animals, implanted in an elevation of the skin that receives a special branch of the ulnar nerve. This is called the carpal hillock. It is found in adult lemurs but not in the adults of tarsiers or of higher primates. Schultz has discovered these carpal "feelers" in the foetuses of American marmosets and in those of the Old World monkeys of the genus Colobus. No trace of these hairs is found in the adult. In the human foetus, the hillock of skin, with no sinus hairs implanted in it, has been observed by Schultz, but it disappears during the ninth week of foetal life, at which age no hairs could be expected.

Many of the foetal structures, that may be designated as atavistic because they belong properly to an ancestral stage of development, nevertheless persist in the adult as vestigial organs. One of the best known of these is the vermiform appendix, a long, narrow, worm-shaped tube opening from the blind end (caecum) of the large intestine. It varies in length in the adult from 2 to 20 centimeters, averaging about 8.3 centimeters. About the sixth week, a diverticulum or offshoot of the gut appears just behind the opening of the vitelline duct which leads to the yolk-sac. Below this diverticulum, the tube increases in size and becomes the large intestine. Until the fifth month, the caecal diverticulum is of uniform diameter, but from this time onward the terminal portion remans rudimentary and forms the vermiform appendix, while the part above it expands to form the caecum. The appendix is present in some lemurs and absent in tarsiers, New World and Old World monkeys; in the anthropoid apes, it is larger and better developed than in man. The function of the appendix is unknown, but Keith has observed that in anthropoids and children the contents of the caecum pass freely into it. and that, in the gibbon, fruit seeds as big as cherry stones are found in the appendix during normal and natural digestion. Anthropoid apes are not known to suffer from appendicitis in a state of nature but may acquire it in captivity when fed upon a human diet. Keith favors the supposition that the appendix is not a vestigial organ but rather one of which the function is unknown.[2]

The azygos lobe of the lung is a process at the base of the right lung that fills the space between the heart and the diaphragm in pronograde animals. In upright animals, such as man and the anthropoid apes, the heart comes to rest upon the diaphragm, and the azygos lobe disappears,

2 Keith, *Human Body*, pp. 49, 236.

but, according to Keith, a rudiment of it can always be seen, and occasionally it projects between the heart and the diaphragm, occupying the same position as in the pronograde apes. According to the observations of several anatomists, the gibbon possesses an azygos lobe of the lung. One case has been observed in a gorilla, but normally the gorilla and chimpanzee lack this lobe, as does man. The orang-utan resembles sloths and marsupials in that its lungs are usually undivided.[3] It is reasonable to infer from the rudiment of the azygos lobe of the lung in man that he is descended from pronograde ancestors.

At the top of the scapula or shoulder blade, just above and inside of the socket to which the bone of the upper arm is jointed, there is a hooklike bony process called the coracoid process (like a crow's beak). This process ossifies from two separate centers and does not become united to the scapula until about the seventeenth year of life. The coracoid process is the vestige of a bone that, in the lowest mammals—the monotremes—and in reptiles and birds, stretches from the shoulder blade to the middle line of the shoulder girdle, where it meets a bone above the sternum, or breast bone, called the episternum. Occasionally, in man, two bony ossicles are found at the top of the sternum between the medial ends of the clavicles or collar bones. These suprasternal ossicles are probably the vestiges of the episternum of lower animals. In the primates, bats, and some other mammals, the clavicle extends from the scapula to the sternum, acting as a strut to support the shoulder joint. It is the first bone to ossify in the human foetus. The clavicle is well developed in those mammals that have the greatest freedom of movement of the fore limb but is usually absent in such mammals as employ only a pendulum movement in walking or swimming, as ungulates, whales, et cetera. Vestiges of the reptilian shoulder girdle, such as the coracoid process and the suprasternal ossicles, are explicable only in the light of the examination of the cumbersome shoulder girdles of lower vertebrates. Some remote ancestors of man must have had coracoid bones reaching to the middle line of the body and articulating there with a flat bone surmounting the top of the sternum. You can put your finger on the place where this suprasternal structure must have been, by feeling for the notch at the top of the breast bone between the inner ends of the collar bones.

Many of the features in man that recall his origin from lower animal forms are observed only occasionally or rarely. Some of these are merely temporary structures in the embryo; others, when present at all, persist through life. One of the most interesting of these is a small hook-like

---

[3] Sonntag, *Morphology and Evolution*, pp. 262–263.

process—the supracondyloid process—not infrequently found attached to the inner side of the bone of the upper arm—the humerus—just above the elbow. When the supracondyloid process is present, the main artery and nerve of the upper arm pass under it. Very rarely it is not a process but a complete bony arch bridging a foramen, or hole, through which the nerve and artery pass. This supracondyloid foramen is found in many reptiles and lower mammals and in the lemurs, tarsiers, and most American monkeys. It does not occur in the Old World monkeys, the anthropoid apes, or man, except in the last named as a rare anomaly. The hook-like supracondyloid process, which is a remnant of the supracondyloid foramen, is, however, suggestive of a condition that must once have been general in man's preanthropoid ancestors.

There are other reminiscences of the lower animal forms from which man has sprung, in the occasional malformations that occur in human beings because of some disturbance of the normal course of embryonic development. Cleft palate is an example of such a pathological anomaly, as is also the occasional webbing of fingers or toes.

A number of vestigial muscles are also to be observed in man, sometimes as a normal occurrence and sometimes as more or less rare anomalies. Those of most interest are the climbing muscles. These have been described by Keith and other anatomists.[4] Some of them are found in foetuses; others persist in the adult. The lifter of the collar bone (levator claviculi) is a muscle that passes from the neck to the shoulder and, in pronograde monkeys, advances the shoulder in running. In the higher apes, it becomes modified in form and attachments, and, in man, it disappears or occurs as a rare anomaly.

There is usually found in man a fibrous slip, sometimes a small muscle, in the back of the arm pit, which connects the broad triangular muscle of the back (latissimus dorsi) with the long head of the triceps muscle passing from the shoulder to the back of the arm. This muscle is well developed in apes, since it is useful in climbing.

In man, the biceps muscle is ordinarily used to flex the forearm in lifting or pulling, but, in climbing apes, the whole body weight is often lifted by the flexing of the arm. In gibbons, according to Keith, the biceps is usually provided with extra parts or heads, two or three in number. One of these extra heads appears in 10 per cent of human bodies, and occasionally a third and even a fourth is observed. In the larger apes, two heads (biceps) occur as in man, but in the lemurs usually there is but one head.

In the wrist of man is usually found the remnant of a muscle passing

4 Keith, *Human Body*, pp. 85 ff.

from the forearm to the palm, which, in pronograde monkeys, acts upon the skin and pads of the palm to give firmness of grasp in the foot-like use to which the hand is put. This muscle—the palmaris longus—is vestigial or absent both in the anthropoids and in man. Correspondingly, in the leg of pronograde primates, a long muscle runs from the knee joint through the calf of the leg under the heel to spread out in a tough membrane under the sole of the foot. This muscle—the plantaris longus—helps the foot to grasp the bough firmly. Monkeys' feet bend in the mid-tarsal region, just in front of the ankle joint, so that, when they run along the boughs, their heels are lifted off the ground. In the anthropoids and man this mid-tarsal joint disappears, and the tarsus is welded into a stout arch to support the weight of the body. The heel is prolonged backward, and the whole sole of the foot is applied to the ground in walking. Consequently, in the anthropoid apes and in man, the plantaris muscle is cut through by the heel bone where its tendon passes underneath the heel, and has lost its attachment to the sole of the foot. Both in man and the orthograde anthropoids, this muscle is inserted in the heel bone or is lost in the leg. Often in man (5 per cent of cases according to Keith) and, according to Sonntag, usually in the anthropoids, it is missing.

Another vestigial muscle is the psoas minor, which arises from the backbone in the lumbar region and is inserted in the pelvic brim behind the abdominal wall. In pronograde apes, it flexes the pelvis on the spine in jumping, but, in man and the anthropoids, its function has been lost. In man, it has often disappeared entirely.

One of the so-called laws of embryology, that of von Baer, states that the embryos of different species of the same group resemble each other more closely than do the adults, and that the younger the embryo examined the closer the similarity. This is not altogether true, since the embryos of different species are usually quite easily distinguishable, and many of the differences of specific importance in adult life are already marked in foetal development. In spite of these objections, it seems undeniable that the postnatal period of growth brings about many features of divergence between man and the anthropoid apes that do not distinguish the foetuses of these several species. To state the case the other way, there is a certain parallelism in foetal growth between man and the great apes, both in the proportions and form of bodily parts, which is succeeded by a divergence in their respective courses of development subsequent to birth. While some of these embryonic similarities are undoubtedly caused by the common limitations of mammalian foetal environment, it is undeniable that many of them are explicable only upon the supposition that these animals are of a common descent and that many of the distinguishing adult characteristics are comparatively recent acquisitions.

Schultz points out that in early embryonic stages man and all of the primates possess deep and relatively narrow thoraxes, with transverse diameters about equal to the antero-posterior diameters. The deep and narrow chest in the lower primates, and in quadrupeds in general, is due to the action of gravity upon the thoracic viscera, which exercises a constant pressure downward upon the flexible cartilaginous ends of the ribs and the breast bone. In man and, to a lesser extent, in the upright anthropoids, the weight bears not upon the front of the thoracic cage but upon the diaphragm. Consequently, in man and the anthropoids, the chest is free to expand laterally in conjunction with the free movements of the arms and shoulders. Man and the anthropoid apes show, in early foetal stages, the deep, narrow, quadrupedal thorax, but, in later stages of development, their chests become proportionately much broader and flatter, whereas, in the monkeys and lemurs, a change in the opposite direction takes place, and the chest becomes further constricted and deepened.

All primates except man have high standing shoulders with collar bones directed upward and nipples placed near the armpits. Man shows in the very young foetus a similar position of these parts, but in adult life the shoulders descend in most human races, so that the clavicles are horizontal or nearly so and the nipples are very low in position. On the other hand, in such primates as the orang and the howler monkey, the position of the nipples in the adult is, if anything, higher than in the foetus. Consequently, Schultz regards the axillary position of the nipples in these primates as a recent specialization and concludes that the common ancestors of man and the other primates must have had nipples situated between the two extremes.[5]

In many of the changes in size and proportion of bodily parts during foetal life, man shows a close similarity to the other primates and particularly to the anthropoid apes. Although the brain case of man is absolutely the largest of any primate, the size of the human head relative to the length of the trunk is well within the range of primate variation. Indeed, according to Schultz, the new-born gibbon and the orangutan both have relatively larger heads at birth than does the human infant. The relative size of the head diminishes in growth up to adult years, not only in man but in all of the other primates. Hence, the great size of the head during the embryonic period and at birth is a primate

5 Schultz, "Embryological Evidence," p. 252.

condition rather than a human condition. Similarly, the eyes of the human embryo are so far apart in the early stages of development that they are almost lateral in position, and, in the course of foetal growth, the interocular space becomes progressively narrower. In this narrowing of the space between the eyes, the anthropoid apes exceed man.

In most primates, the ear grows faster than the rest of the head during the foetal period, thus increasing in its size relative to the head. In a gibbon foetus, 21 millimeters long from crown to rump, the index expressing this relative ear size is 1.7; in a new-born gibbon, this index is almost six times as great (9.9), and in an adult it is eight times as large as in the foetus of 21 millimeters (13.6). But in man, the gorilla, and the orang-utan, the relative ear size increases up to birth and then diminishes. The average relative ear size of human foetuses of nine weeks is 1.3, of human infants at birth, 5.9, and of adults, 4.7. In an orang foetus 145 millimeters in length, the index was 2.5; of an infant, 5.3; and of an adult, 1.4.[6]

The adult human being has arms comparatively shorter than those of any anthropoid ape and legs much longer. Relative to anterior trunk height, arm length in man is 150 per cent; in the lowland gorilla, 184 per cent; in the mountain gorilla, 154 per cent; in the chimpanzee, 175 per cent; in the orang-utan, 182 per cent; in the siamang, 233 per cent; and in the gibbon, 238 per cent.[7] Thus, in this proportion, man and the mountain gorilla resemble each other more closely than do the two kinds of gorillas. Some Negroes have relative arm lengths greater than those of mountain gorillas and equalling those of chimpanzees. The length of the upper extremity relative to trunk length (or height) tends to be greater in adult years than at birth in all higher primates, but the gibbon family shows such an enormous postnatal increase of this proportion that it must be considered a new phylogenetic acquisition. Relative to the length of the upper arm, man has the shortest forearm of all higher primates, both at birth and in adult life, and this shortened forearm is more marked at maturity than at birth. In this proportion, man and the lowland gorilla are very closely allied (77 per cent and 78 per cent, respectively), and here again Schultz thinks it probable that we are dealing with new phylogenetic acquisitions, independently acquired in the two species. The marked postnatal elongation of the forearm in the gibbon family is a new specialization in the opposite direction.

The new born human being has relatively the shortest and broadest hand among the higher primates, but, in adult life, the hand of the

[6] *Ibid.*, pp. 254–255.
[7] Schultz, "Die Körporproportionen," p. 168.

mountain gorilla is proportionately even shorter. Relative hand length increases in these primates during postnatal growth—most in such extreme brachiators as the gibbon and the orang. Schultz deduces from the breadth and shortness of the foetal human hand that it was acquired at a comparatively early stage in evolution, and that man never had the typically long and slender hand of the brachiator. On the contrary, the gorilla has a relatively long and slender hand up to middle foetal life, so that his manual breadth and shortness may be a recent evolutionary acquisition. Relative width of the hand continues to decrease in the period after birth in all primates except the gorilla.

Again, in all primates, the relative length of the thumb decreases during the foetal period, and, in some monkeys, it almost or completely disappears. Man retains the longest thumb but is closely approached in this proportion by Cebus monkeys and baboons. During growth, the attachment of the thumb, originally at the base of the index finger, shifts up towards the wrist. This upward shift of the thumb is most marked in the orang-utan, less in the other anthropoid apes and man, still less in the Old World monkeys, and does not take place at all in the New World monkeys, but does occur in some lemurs. (Schultz.)

The legs of man in adult life are relatively and absolutely far longer than those of any other primate. However, in the prenatal period, this excessive length of the human lower limb is lacking. All of the apes, according to Schultz, surpass the new-born infant in leg length. Possibly one may argue from this fact that the leg length of the human animal is phylogenetically a relatively late acquisition—later than the acquisition of the characteristically long arms of the anthropoid apes.

In all foetal primates, the soles of the feet are at first turned inward so that they face each other but, in the course of growth, rotate until the soles are directed downward. In man, this rotation of the soles has proceeded farther than in the other members of the order.

The great toes of young primate embryos are considerably shorter than the second toes and separated from them by a wide interval. As growth continues, man's great toe becomes proportionately longer, but those of the other primates decrease in relative length. Eventually, in many human individuals and groups, the great toe becomes the longest of all the toes, but it is shorter than the second toe in a considerable proportion of Whites and Negroes. Usually, in apes and monkeys, the middle toe is the longest, and this is observed occasionally as a transitory feature in the second or third foetal month of human beings. The lateral toes in man decrease in relative length during foetal development but increase in other primates.

Just as the thumb in all primates springs at first from the hand at the base of the second finger, so also the great toe springs from the base of the second toe in early foetal life. In man, this position of the great toes is maintained throughout adult life, whereas, in all other primates, the base of the great toe shifts toward the heel. This backward displacement of the great toe has proceeded farthest in the orang-utan and is least marked in the gorilla, who walks on the soles of his feet in adult life. In this the gorilla is nearer to man than to the orang-utan, and the chimpanzee is intermediate between the gorilla and the great ape of Asia. In the last-named animal, the degeneracy of the great toes is indicated by the frequent absence of a nail and the loss of one phalanx or segment. Similar manifestations are frequently found in the little toes of man.

Webbing of the toes is an early embryonic condition in primates. The web between the second and third toes is more extensive and lasts longer than any other. It persists as a normal adult character in many marsupials, insectivores, and lemurs, in some of the Old World monkeys, and in individual gibbons (regularly in the siamangs). This condition appears occasionally in man and persists through life. It must be regarded as an example of atavism or reversion to an ancestral type.

In the foregoing similarities of foetal growth trends in man and the other primates, there is striking conformation of the hypothesis that the great apes and all human types have diverged from a common anthropoid precursor, each specializing in different directions. Man in some characters has retained the primitive ancestral condition less altered than have the anthropoid apes, whereas in other features the reverse is true.

There are many gaps in our knowledge of the comparative embryology of man and the higher primates because of the great difficulties inherent in the acquisition and observation of foetal material of known age representing all stages. The interpretation of foetal changes from an evolutionary standpoint is also a most precarious process. There is, however, no real doubt that the evidence of embryological development by itself is enough to establish the kinship of man with the primates and his most intimate relationship with the great apes.

Growing

It takes such a long time for human beings to grow up that few scientists have had the patience to study individual subjects from birth to maturity. I can testify that it is a tiresome task even to measure one's own modest quota of offspring, month after month and year after year. Persistence and longevity are essential for such research. It is almost impossible to do that job on anthropoid apes. First you have to catch your apes alive—two of them of different sexes. Then you have to keep them happy, or they will not live. If you succeed in mating them, and an infant is born alive, then you have material for a growth study, if it can be raised to maturity. But it is not very accessible or submissive material. It is hard enough to pacify a suspicious human mother so that you can measure her squalling, kicking infant. How would you like to try it on a full-grown chimpanzee mother and her sharp-toothed offspring? For my part, I am content to obtain such scientific data at second hand from Professor R. T. Yerkes of Yale or from any other intrepid investigator who is bold enough to wrench the infant anthropoid from its maternal bosom. The only adequate data on the growth of live anthropoid apes pertain to the chimpanzee. In the Yerkes Laboratories of Primate Biology, at Orange Park, Florida, new-born chimpanzee babies are taken from their mothers within a few hours of their births and raised on the bottle in the chimpanzee nursery. Here they are weighed, measured, and X-rayed at regular intervals. The results of these growth studies on infant chimpanzees afford most valuable data for comparison with human growth phenomena. Dr. Adolph Schultz has also contributed largely to our knowledge of the growth of the chimpanzee and the orang-utan by making studies and measurements of dead specimens from the foetal period to maturity. However, in most of these cadavers, the age is not accurately known.

The period of human infancy extends from birth to the time when all of the milk teeth have been cut or fully erupted, roughly until the end of the second or the middle of the third year of life. The most remarkable feature of this period is the rapid growth of the brain-case, which, as we have seen, outstrips other parts of the body in prenatal growth. In newborn infants, the girth of the brain-case is from 64 to 68 per cent of the bodily height, whereas in adult males between twenty and twenty-five years of age, the circumference of the skull is only about 33 per cent of the stature. From birth to maturity stature increases about 3½ times, while head girth is only 1.6 times its initial size.

During the entire prenatal period, the girth of the head is greater than that of the chest. Chest circumference first exceeds head circumference in the third year and ultimately is more than 1½ times as great. The head is heaviest relative to body weight in the second foetal month when it attains 45 per cent, a proportion which has decreased to about 26 per cent at birth. The brain weight of the newly-born infant is about

12.6 per cent of the entire body weight but, in adult years, is only 2.2 per cent.[8]

This precocity of brain growth is not an exclusively human characteristic, as we have seen, but is equalled and even surpassed by some of the anthropoid apes. The human head, however, continues to increase in size after the brain-cases of our anthropoid cousins have stopped growing. The girth of the head increases more in the first year of life than in all of the remaining period of growth. By the end of the second year, according to Keith, the child's brain has attained more than half of its adult size, by the end of the fourth year over 80 per cent. In the gorilla, on the other hand, the head at birth is about 65 per cent of its ultimate size and continues to increase at a steady and uniform rate until adult years, without manifesting the sudden spurts in infancy characteristic of human brain growth.

The face does not share in the mushroom growth of the brain-case. At birth, it is very short and relatively broad, being only 42 per cent of its adult length and 47 per cent of its ultimate breadth across the cheek bones. The root of the nose and the space between the orbits of the eyes, however, have already attained 48 to 49 per cent of their adult breadth. The greatest increase in the face after birth is in its length, in the breadth of its lateral portions, and in the elevation of the nose and the elongation of its tip. The advanced development of the nasal root and the orbital region of the face at birth is partially the result of these facial portions' being the seat of the visual and olfactory organs, which are already well formed. Another factor contributing to this precocity is the great breadth of the frontal lobes of the brain, the bony coverings of which carry outward with them in their growth the lateral portions of the facial skeleton. The shortness of the face during infancy is caused by the slow development of the teeth and the jaws. The intensive growth of the face sets in when the permanent set of teeth begins to erupt. The face then becomes greatly elongated as the jaws increase in depth. A lesser expansion in breadth also takes place because of the necessity of stronger and more extensive attachments of the masticatory muscles to the cheek bones (malars), which are thrust outward, carrying with them the hinder portions of the jaws.

In man, the face begins growing rapidly after most of the growth of the brain-case has been completed. From infancy to adult years, the brain-case becomes longer and (usually, but not invariably) relatively narrower, and a similar change in proportions is characteristic of the face. There is also a thrusting forward of the face and jaws, which seems to

[8] Martin, *Lehrbuch*, p. 596.

result from their growing more rapidly than the cranio-facial base to
which they are hafted.

In the anthropoid ape, the growth of the face after birth is much
greater than in man. The brain-case increases slowly in capacity after
the first year, but, with the eruption of the permanent dentition, the
jaws and face become enormously longer and are protruded. The skull
base increases greatly in length to provide the larger basis of attachment required by the massive jaws. The foramen magnum is displaced
backward; the temporal and occipital muscles mount the skull vault;
great brow-ridges and bony crests for muscular attachments make their
appearance in the maturing apes. Thus, the greater part of the differences between man and ape in facial development relative to brain-case
development is due to excessive facial growth in apes during adolescence
and long continued expansion of the cranial envelope in man.

In the human baby, the first milk teeth are usually cut between the
sixth and seventh months after birth, although there is great individual
variation. Occasionally, a child is born with one or two teeth already
erupted. All of the milk teeth, 20 in number, are usually in place by the
end of the second or the beginning of the third year. There is little exact
information on the age of eruption of the milk teeth in lower primates.
The macaque apparently has this dentition completely in place in 25
weeks or less. One little American monkey (Aotus) had all of its deciduous teeth in the tenth week after birth. There are only two records on
the gibbon, but these indicate that the milk teeth of this ape begin to
erupt slightly later than those of the macaque. Scanty evidence also indicates that the orang's deciduous dentition is completed by the end of
the first year, the chimpanzee's by the middle of the second year.

Schultz has gathered all available data concerning the age of the eruption of the permanent dentition in primates.[9] Unfortunately, these data
are confined to the macaque, the chimpanzee, and man. The macaque
begins to erupt his second teeth at the age of 1½ years, the chimpanzee
at twice this age, and man at twice the age of the chimpanzee, namely,
at 6 years. All of the permanent teeth of the macaque are erupted at the
age of about 7 years, those of the chimpanzee by the end of the tenth year
or beginning of the eleventh year, whereas, in man, the wisdom teeth,
or third molars, when present, are usually in place by the end of the
nineteenth year. After the completion of the milk dentition, there is a
resting phase before the permanent set erupts, which amounts, in all
three primates, to roughly 15 per cent of the ages between birth and
dental maturity. In all of these three primates, also, there is a long resting

[9] Schultz, "Eruption and Decay."

phase before the eruption of the last molars. In all primates studied by Schultz except man, there is a considerable period after the eruption of the first molars in which no teeth are added to the permanent dentition.

Judging from the eruption of teeth, lower primates, such as the monkeys, complete their growth earliest, whereas the great apes mature somewhat more slowly, and man is most retarded in his physical development. However, in recent years new material on ape growth has been collected that permits comparison with man of other processes than merely time and sequence of tooth eruption. These new facts will be considered in their proper place.

Human growth is not a steady and uniform process of accretion in which all parts of the body enlarge at the same rate and the increment of one year is equal to that of the preceding or succeeding years. Growth takes place by fits and by starts, some portions of the body increasing rapidly for a period while others lag. We have already noted the examples of the precocious brain-case and the backward face. There is, however, a certain method in this irregularity, such that a growth "rhythm" may be recognized, which is applicable, so far as known, to all of the races of man. This is most clearly and crudely manifested in stature, or bodily height, the largest and most composite human measurement. The first and most rapid movement of the growth rhythm extends in both sexes from birth to the fifth or sixth year. It is most intense and rapid during the first two years. There follows a slower increase, terminating in boys about the tenth to twelfth years and in girls no later than the tenth year. Then both sexes enter upon another period of accelerated growth—adolescence—which is completed in girls between the fourteenth and the sixteenth years but extends in boys through the sixteenth or eighteenth year. Since the girls enter upon the pubertal period a year or two earlier than the boys, it naturally follows that between the eleventh and fourteenth years they outstrip their brothers in size and weight. Girls also attain their full growth earlier than boys because the final period of slow growth ends between the eighteenth and twentieth years in the female sex but does not terminate in boys until about the twenty-fifth year. Excepting a short period during the adolescent growth stage, girls are at all times smaller and lighter than boys.

Until recently, it was generally believed that tropical peoples enter precociously upon the several stages of the growth rhythm, mature early, and complete their growth before the inhabitants of more northerly climes. The evidence of such a "forcing" effect of equatorial light, heat, and moisture was largely presumptive but was partially deduced from insufficient and possibly incomparable data on growth of various peoples in diverse climes and upon inadequate records of the onset of menstruation in northern and southern countries. Formerly, growth studies were usually conducted by measuring samples of children of different age groups and calculating the growth increments by taking, for example, the average stature of a group of seven year olds and subtracting from it the average stature of another group of children of the age of six years. Now the only approved method is called "longitudinal" (presumably as contrasted with "cross-sectional") and involves repeated measurements of the same individuals as they grow, year after year. This method, though onerous and time-consuming, has corrected many of our misconceptions about racial, ethnic, climatic, and nutritional factors that influence growth.

Dr. Morris Steggerda has conducted a unique growth study over a period of 8 to 10 years, which has involved measuring each year Maya Indian children in Yucatan, Negro children in Alabama, Navajo Indian children in Arizona, and White children of Dutch stock in Michigan. Steggerda goes from one area to the other, measuring the same children every year. His results are of great importance because they involve three races living under strikingly diverse environmental conditions. The Navajo live in a semi-arid region at an altitude of 6,000 feet, the Maya in a subtropical region nearly at sea level, the Dutch Whites in the northern United States, and the Negroes in the south. The food habits of these groups are very diverse. The Navajo are chiefly protein eaters, living on mutton when they can get it; the Maya diet consists of 75 to 80 per cent maize products; and the difference between the food of Alabama Negroes and Michigan Dutch is undoubtedly great. Nevertheless, Steggerda found that the growth rhythms of the Maya are identical with those of the other races selected for comparison; that physical differences that distinguish the Mayas from the adults of other races are present from early childhood and do not develop during growth; and the Maya boys grow at relatively the same rate at fifteen, sixteen, and seventeen years of age as do Navajo, Negro, and White boys. There *are* physical differences between the four stocks, and particularly in body build and stature they are markedly dissimilar, but the growth patterns are the same, in spite of wide diversities of heredity and environment.[10]

The growth rhythms of anthropoid apes are unknown, with the exception of some data (not altogether adequate) on the chimpanzee age changes in weight. The chimpanzee rhythm agrees with that of man in

[10] Steggerda, *Maya Indians,* pp. 162–195.

showing an initial infantile period of rapid but diminishing growth (to about the age of four years) and a prepubertal growth phase. The latter is marked in males but not in females, and reaches its maximum in males in the eighth year, whereas it achieves a rather poorly defined maximum in females during the seventh year. At this period, the male definitely secures the lead over the female in weight and holds it. There is no precocious adolescent spurt on the part of the females that puts them temporarily ahead of the males in weight, as regularly is observed in man. Finally, in chimpanzee weight curves, there is a terminal growth phase that drops off rapidly in males from the eighth year to zero in the twelfth year, but may continue into the thirteenth year in females. In man the female terminates growth before the male—usually at about the age of eighteen years.

Schultz [11] has shown that in the macaque the duration of postnatal growth is only 15 times greater than the duration of prenatal growth, whereas in man it is 27 times greater. In the chimpanzee, postnatal growth is 15.7 times as long as prenatal growth. Taking the entire growth period from conception to full eruption of the permanent dentition, 6.2 per cent represents life *in utero* in the case of the macaque, 6 per cent in the chimpanzee, and only 3.5 per cent in man. Thus it would appear that the chimpanzee in respect of these divisions of the growth period is much more like the macaque than like man. Schultz thinks that the orang finishes growing between the tenth and twelfth year, but data are lamentably few. There are no complete records of gorilla growth, partly because no gorillas have been born in captivity. It can be deduced, however, that, as in the case of the chimpanzee and the orang-utan, growth takes place at a moderate rate until the apes begin their preadolescent spurts—probably in the seventh or eighth year. They then grow very much more rapidly than does man (about twice as fast in the case of the chimpanzee). Figures are available for the gorilla in several isolated instances that indicate simply prodigious growth between the eighth and thirteenth year. M'Bongo, a male mountain gorilla in the San Diego zoo, weighed 172 pounds at the estimated age of seven years, 270 pounds at ten years, and 602 pounds at thirteen years. Female gorillas fall far behind the males in growth during this terminal phase.

The average weight of a new-born European boy is about 7¼ pounds or a little less (3.3 kilos). Girls are usually a trifle lighter. Birth weights of nine chimpanzees average only 1.89 kilos (4.17 pounds), and of three orangs, 1.5 kilos (3.31 pounds). The youngest gorilla captured, at a guessed age of two weeks, weighed only 2 kilos (4.41 pounds). The birth

---

[11] Schultz, *Growth of Chimpanzee*, p. 10.

weight of chimpanzees is roughly 4 per cent of their adult weight, as against 5.5 per cent for man and 6.7 per cent for the macaque. Thus the babies of the great apes appear to be absolutely and relatively much smaller than the human infant.

Bodily proportions in man change greatly from infancy to maturity. The extremities increase relatively more than the trunk. During foetal life, the development of the head segment plays the most important rôle and is especially characteristic of the first few months. At the end of the second foetal month, the embryo has an absolute length of about 40 millimeters, of which half is the head height. In the course of the second month, the trunk and extremities double in length, and the head does not keep pace, so that stature at the end of the fifth month is 3 head heights and at the end of pregnancy 4 head heights.

During the entire embryonic period, arm length exceeds leg length, and it is not until birth that the extremities are of approximately equal length—about 1½ head heights; the trunk and neck being 1¾ head heights.

Postnatal changes are much slower than the growth of foetal life. During the intra-uterine period it takes from 3 to 5 months for the body to increase by one head height, but a similar change after birth requires from 2 to 8 years. An adult finally reaches a stature of 7½ to 8 head heights. During this period the trunk increases from 1¼ to 3 head heights and the lower extremity from 1½ to 4 head heights. Between the sixth and ninth years, the lower extremity begins definitely to exceed the upper in length. The relatively great length of the arms in the foetal and infantile period is, of course, an anthropoid reminiscence. Ultimately, the ratio of arm to leg length is about 4 to 5.

During growth, the center of mass descends from below the chin in the two months foetus to just above the navel at birth, and finally to the level of the pubic symphysis in the adult European.

In the foetal period, breadth development alternates with length development of the trunk. During the first three years of life, the broadening of the trunk is a distinctive growth feature. After that time, relative trunk breadth changes but little. Man has the widest shoulder breadth relative to trunk length of all animals except the gorilla, but an approximation to the human condition is found in the other anthropoid apes. Similarly, the human pelvis is relatively very broad.

In the foetal period and in early infancy, the thorax of man is narrow and deep like that of the anthropoid apes and remotely resembles the condition found in lower mammals; but, when the erect posture is assumed, the thorax expands more transversely than in depth, the ratio of breadth to depth increasing from 113 in new-born infants to 139 in adults.

At birth, the arms of human infants are about the same length as the trunk; in the second year, arm length is almost 115 per cent of trunk length; in the sixth year, about 123 per cent and, in adult life, almost 153 per cent. Males have relatively longer arms than females. The anthropoid apes show a much greater postnatal growth of the arms than man. Relative to trunk length, man has the shortest upper arm and forearm of any primate. Girls have relatively longer upper arms and shorter forearms than boys. In both sexes, the forearm is relatively longer in childhood than at maturity—again a reminder of anthropoid ancestry. In adult years, the forearm is about 78 per cent of the upper arm length in adult South Germans, but only 76 per cent in their wives.

Relative to his trunk length, man's legs are longest of all the primates, among which the gibbon and the spider monkey rank next. This specifically human length of the legs is attained relatively late. During foetal life, the legs are from two to seven months behind the arms in growth; at birth, the extremities are about equal—about 40 per cent of stature and 96 per cent of trunk length—after which the upper extremities increase until, in adult life, they are about 153 per cent of trunk length, whereas the legs attain about 190 per cent (e.g., in the Swiss [Schwerz]). This great postnatal growth of man's lower extremities is connected with his upright biped gait.

Both segments of the lower extremity—the thigh and the leg—share in the characteristically human elongation. Women have relatively longer thighs and shorter legs than men; so have the great apes. The entire lower extremity tends to be relatively shorter in the fair sex. If, however, women are closer to apes in leg proportions than are men, men are more anthropoidal in arm length.

The human foot, like the hand, is short and broad. Relative to trunk length, the foot length is 49.8 per cent in South German women and 52 per cent in men; in gibbons, the ratio is 52.7 per cent; in chimpanzees, 50.1; in gorillas, 40.9; and in orang-utans, 64. In the last named animal, the foot undergoes a secondary elongation, perhaps because of its habit of hanging from the toes.

We have seen that man and the anthropoid apes strongly diverge from each other during the postnatal growth period. The human species exaggerates leg length and size of brain-case; the anthropoids accentuate jaw growth and arm length; man develops long thumbs and great toes, short lesser toes and fingers; human hands and feet remain relatively short and broad; the anthropoid apes grow long and slender hands and feet, but their thumbs and great toes are short. No human race preserves simian proportions, but races with short stature, long trunks, long arms, and short legs are closest to the anthropoid type.

The mechanism of growth is controlled by the secretions of certain glands, especially the thyroid, pituitary, and sex glands. These are among the so-called glands of internal secretion or endocrines. They discharge, directly into the blood, *hormones,* or chemical messengers—powerful drugs that stimulate and regulate growth.

These endocrine secretions individually determine the alternations of rapid and slow development of the various parts of the body at different times. Collectively, they establish the growth rhythm that is so notable a feature of human development.

The thyroid is a bi-lobed gland in the throat. When it is deficient in children, it gives rise to the condition known as cretinism, in which stature is stunted, the limbs are short and thick, the skin dry and hairless, and the sex glands retarded in development. This condition may be helped by the feeding of thyroid extract.

The pituitary gland is about as large as a hazel nut and rests in the Turkish saddle, a depression in the sphenoid bone at the base of the brain. The pituitary has two lobes, an anterior and a posterior. The anterior lobe is of ectodermal origin, and its secretions are associated with growth and sexual development. An over-functioning, or hypertrophy, of the anterior lobe probably causes gigantism, in which there is an abnormal continuation of growth of the bones, especially the long bones, of which the cartilaginous caps or epiphyses fail to unite to the shafts at the proper time.

Among the famous and authenticated cases of gigantism is that of Charles Byrne, the "Irish giant," whose skeleton is preserved in the Museum of the Royal College of Surgeons in London. He was born about 1761 and died at the age of twenty-two years. His skeleton, according to Keith, has a height of 7 feet, 8.4 inches (2.358 meters), but he is said to have stood 8 feet, 2 inches, in life. The bones of the lower extremity are disproportionately long and pronouncedly knock-kneed. Many giants seem to be sufferers from acromegaly, a disease probably caused by an overgrowth or tumor affecting the pituitary gland. This affliction involves the enlargement of the lower jaw and of the extremities of the body, especially the hands and feet. The brow-ridges become immensely thickened, the face and nose greatly elongated; the chest becomes barrel-shaped, and, if the disease sets in before the epiphyses have ossified, great stature is likely to result.

Cornelius MacGrath, another giant, was born in Tipperary in 1736.

His parents were of ordinary size. When he was sixteen years of age, he visited the city of Cork and was followed by crowds of people because of his great stature, for he then measured 6 feet, 8.75 inches. In the preceding year, he is said to have been afflicted with violent pains in his limbs, which were aptly called "growing pains," for he grew from a little over 5 feet to the above mentioned stature in the space of a year. In 1753, he is said to have stood 7 feet, 3 inches, without his shoes, and upon his death in 1760, his body, when dissected, measured 7 feet, 8 inches. It was rumored that MacGrath was an example of experimental gigantism, having been specially fed with a view of producing this effect by Bishop Berkeley. This is probably untrue, unless, perhaps, the good bishop, anticipating the endocrine quacks by one hundred and fifty years, fed him upon extract of the anterior lobe of the pituitary. MacGrath's pituitary is stated to have been the size of a hen's egg; his hand was as large as "a middling sized shoulder of mutton, which joint he could cover with that member." His lower jaw was greatly enlarged, and his feet are variously stated to have been 12 or 15 inches long.[12] He probably suffered from acromegaly.

Glandular disturbances are also known to cause precocious senility. Thomas Hall, born in Willingham, near Cambridge, England, at the age of three years and two months, was 4 feet in height, and was said to have had limbs nearly as long and strong as a man's. His voice was deeper than that of most men. He died of extreme old age on September 3rd, 1747, at the age of less than six years. He was then 4 feet, 6 inches, in height and weighed about 98 pounds. "He presented a piteous spectacle, having several bald places on his head, and his visage and whole appearance being those of a decrepid old man, worn with years." Hall was buried in the churchyard in Willingham, where a stone bears his Latin epitaph, the English translation of which is as follows:

Stop, traveller, and wondering know here buried lie the remains of Thomas, the son of Thomas and Margaret Hall: who not one year old had the signs of manhood; not three was almost four feet high; endued with uncommon strength, a just proportion of parts, and a stupendous voice; before six died as it were of advanced age. He was born in this village October 31st, 1741; and in the same departed this life September 3rd, 1747.[13]

Another case of this compression of the natural span of growth and life is that of Charles Charlesworth, born at Longnor, in Staffordshire, in 1729.

12 Wood, *Giants and Dwarfs,* pp. 152–156.
13 *Ibid.,* pp. 145–147.

At his birth he was under common size; but he grew so amazingly fast, that by the time he was four years of age he was nearly four feet in height, and in strength, agility, and bulk was equal to a fine boy of twelve years old. At the age of five years he was four feet seven inches high, weighed eighty-seven pounds, could with ease carry a man of fourteen stone weight (196 pounds), had hair on his body as a man, and every sign of puberty, and worked at his father's business. From this time, however, he gradually declined in strength and bulk; and at the age of seven years his vigour was gone, his body became totally emaciated, his eyes were sunk, his head was palsied, and he died with all the signs of extreme old age.[14]

However, Craterus, the brother of Antigonus, caps the climax by telling us that he knew one "who in the space of seven years was an infant, a youth, a mature person, an old man, a husband, a father, and a corpse." Such abnormal growth cycles are, in general, the result of improper functioning of the ductless glands, but their exact causation is as yet unknown.

Dwarfism or nanism, the arrest of growth, is possibly caused by defective development and general atrophy of the thyroid and pituitary glands. Dwarfs are of two kinds, a well proportioned but diminutive type, which is called ateleotic, and a type in which the trunk length is virtually normal, but the extremities are stunted and thick. This type is called achondroplastic. Dwarfs vary in stature from about 2 to 4 feet. They are usually born of normal sized parents and are often sterile. Jeffrey Hudson, one of the most famous, was born in 1619 at Oakham, Rutlandshire, England. His father was a person of "lusty stature" and all of his children except Jeffrey were of full size. His mother was "of no mean altitude." Jeffrey was presented by his father to the Duchess of Buckinghamshire when he was between seven and nine years of age, "without any deformity, wholly proportionable, and scarce a foot and a half in height." When Charles I was entertained at Burleigh, Jeffrey was served up to table in a cold pie, armed and accoutred. He was kept at the court for many years, and the king bestowed knighthood upon him in frolic. "Hee was high in mind, not knowing himself, and hee would not knowe his father, for which by the king's command he was soundly corrected." According to his own statement, Hudson remained at the height of 18 inches from the age of eight until the age of thirty years. Ultimately, he increased to 3 feet, 9 inches. He seems to have been an achondroplastic, if he is accurately described by Sir Walter Scott in *Peveril of the Peak* as having disproportionately large hands, head, and feet, and a very thick body. Jeffrey Hudson had many adventures; he was taken to sea by

[14] *Ibid.*, pp. 140-141.

Dutch privateers, sold as a slave by Barbary pirates, was a captain of horse in the royal army, killed an antagonist in a duel, and was finally imprisoned in Westminster on suspicion of complicity in a Popish plot. He died in 1682 in the sixty-third year of his age.

The so-called pygmy races of Africa and Oceania are perfectly fecund, and the children inherit the stature of their parents. Whether or not their small size is connected with endocrine functioning has not as yet been determined, but, as we shall see in our later discussion of racial differences, it is by no means improbable that race differences in size and proportions, as well as in morphological features, are ultimately due to inherited variations in the balance and functioning of the ductless glands.

There exists no extensive literature upon the ductless glands of anthropoid apes. It is probable, however, that many of the morphological and physiological differences that distinguish man from the anthropoids are brought about through the endocrines.

Adolescing: Sex Differences

Sex is probably determined at the time of the fertilization of the ovum. It is distinguishable in the human foetus as early as the seventh week. The pelvis of the female foetus in the third month differs from that of the male in that the inlet is more rounded, the outlet larger, and the subpubic arch wider. These differences become accentuated during post-natal growth, especially during adolescence (Fig. 42). Thus, the most outstanding sex differences in the skeleton are established before birth. Boys are taller and heavier than girls at birth and continue to be until the girls catch up and temporarily outstrip them by an earlier entrance upon the adolescent phase of growth. The bones of the feet, hands, wrists, and ankles, ossify from cartilage somewhat earlier in girls than in boys, and the females are perhaps slightly more precocious in the cutting of teeth. The human infant usually begins to walk between the twelfth and eighteenth months of life, but the girls, who are smaller and lighter, generally learn before the boys. Chimpanzees are known to walk (on all fours) at six months of age, and a young gorilla began to stand up at seven months of age and learned to walk during the eighth month.

Even before the beginning of the adolescent stage, girls have more rounded limbs and, especially, fuller thighs and buttocks than have boys. When puberty sets in, the pelvis and hips of the girl rapidly become broader, and the female characters of the pelvic basin become more marked. Greulich and Thoms studied the changes in size and shape of the pelvic brim in 107 girls ranging in age from five years to fifteen years.

The pelvis of each girl was photographed by X-ray at approximately annual intervals. The majority of the prepubertal girls had long, oval pelves (dolichopellic—with the antero-posterior diameter of the brim exceeding 95 per cent of the transverse). The pelvic brim also showed a constriction where the walls projected inward at the site of the hip joint (acetabulum). Before puberty the superior pelvic aperature grows slowly and symmetrically. At puberty the pelvis begins to widen more rapidly than its antero-posterior diameter increases. Especially the fore-part becomes broader and more rounded and the hip joint constriction

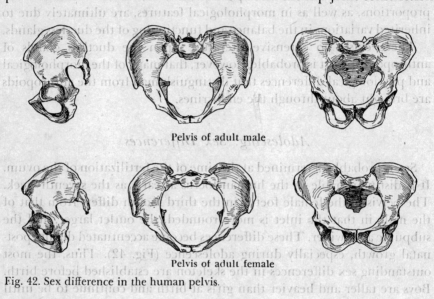

Pelvis of adult male

Pelvis of adult female

Fig. 42. Sex difference in the human pelvis.

begins to disappear. It takes about eighteen months to remodel the girl's pelvis into the typical female form. Since the changes are correlated with breast development, growth of pubic hair, and menarche, they are probably under endocrine control.

In recent years, accurate measurements of the pelvis in the living by X-ray photographs have severely jolted the classic idea that the well developed European woman has a pelvic inlet of a round or fat oval shape, in which the breadth markedly exceeds the diameter from front to back. Dr. Herbert Thoms of Yale University found that only 34 per cent of 334 White mothers had oval or flatly broad pelves.[15] About 45 per cent had round pelvic inlets with the two diameters nearly equal. Nearly 17 per cent had the long, narrow "anthropoid" type of pelvis. Women who have to have Caesarean sections, because their pelves were

15 Thoms, "Newer Aspects of Pelvimetry," pp. 372–378. Greulich and Thoms, "Growth and Development of the Pelvis," pp. 91–97.

too constricted to allow the delivery of their babies, were predominantly those with very broad, short pelves (platypellic). There is reason for suspecting that these short and excessively broad pelvic shapes are the results of rachitis, a deficiency disease. It is rather disillusioning to contemplate the possibility of our having confused ultra-feminity, and presumably "sex appeal," with "rickets."

Because of the great breadth of the pelvis, which must serve both as a support for the viscera and an outlet for the birth of future children, the hip joints of the female are spread apart so that the thighs converge downward, whereas in the boy the narrower pelvic girdle permits the thighs to be more nearly parallel. Hence "knock-knees" are commoner in women than in men. Because the sacrum is tilted upward and backward more strongly in females, the lumbar curve appears more pronounced than in males, and the buttocks are thrown into greater prominence. Add to this the larger accumulation of fat on the thighs and buttocks of the women, and the marked sex differences in bodily proportions of this region are explained.

The pelvis of the female chimpanzee or gorilla differs from that of the male in having a broader inlet and outlet and being lower, as in the case of man. But sex differences are not as clearly defined in anthropoid pelves as in those of human beings.

Before the beginning of the pubertal growth phase, the breasts of girls are as undeveloped as those of boys, only the nipples being elevated above the surrounding tissues. The mammary glands of the female rapidly increase in size during adolescence. First of all, the pigmented circular area around the nipple (the areola) becomes convex, carrying the nipple upward. Then follows the swelling of the gland itself, first to a disk-like eminence, then to a conical shape, and finally to a hemispherical form. This conical or hemispherical elevation is still surmounted by the convex areola with its apical nipple. Conical breasts with convex areolas predominate among Negroid females. The hemispherical type of breast in its final growth phase usually shows a sinking down again of the areola disk, which then conforms to the general curve of the breast without making on its summit an independent hillock. This is the type of breast oftenest found in well-developed European females.

At puberty, the shoulders of the female do not increase in breadth as much as those of the male, and the chest of women is usually less flattened from front to back. The respiration of the female is more pectoral and less abdominal than that of the male, and the rib cage is relatively broader in its lower portion and shorter from top to bottom. Eve was supposed to have been made out of Adam's spare rib, but it happens that women are more likely to "be shy of" their standard number of pairs (12) than men. The latter tend to vary toward the possession of 13 pairs, the ape ancestral quota. The shortening of the female thorax arises from the necessity of increasing the space between the rib cage and the pelvis, which in woman is unduly diminished by the extreme convexity of the lumbar column. Ample room for the expansion of the gravid uterus between the pelvis and thorax is also desirable.

The pelvic and hip region in woman is much broader relative to shoulder width than in man. Associated with this shoulder-hip proportion is an interesting peculiarity of the axis of the female arm. Bend your forearm upward toward the shoulder, and then straighten it out. If you are a man, the axis of the extended forearm will be almost in a straight line with the axis of the upper arm. If you are a woman, your extended forearm will make an angle with the upper arm opening outward. The broad shoulders and narrow hips of the male allow the arms to hang straight downward, with the long axes of upper and lower segments in the same straight line. In the female, the narrow shoulders and broad hips require a splaying out of the forearm axes in order that the hanging arms may clear the hips.

Ranke summarized the sex differences in proportions by saying that women "have shorter arms and forearms, thighs, and legs; relative to their short upper arms still shorter forearms, relative to their short thighs still shorter legs, and relative to the whole upper extremity a shorter lower extremity." [16] Women also have smaller and rounder chests, bigger and more rounded bellies, narrower shoulders and broader hips, smaller hands, feet, and ankles, larger and more conical thighs, and fatter and more protuberant buttocks than men. Women's thighs converge toward the knees and their forearms diverge downward; in men the extremities are more nearly parallel.

A sexual difference that becomes apparent during adolescence is in the growth of body hair. In females, this is largely confined to the pubic and axillary (armpit) regions. The male, arriving at puberty, begins to develop in addition a beard, and the body hair on the abdomen, chest, arms, and legs becomes more and more abundant.

Sex differences in the head and face begin to show before puberty and are pronounced at the end of growth. The male has, on the average, a larger head than the female, and this male superiority is evident in each successive age group. Usually the female has a relatively shorter and broader brain-case than the male of the same group, although in

[16] J. Ranke, *Beiträge zur physischen Anthropologie der Bayern, Beiträge zur Urgeschichte Bayerns*, Bd viii, Fasc. 1 and 2, 1888, quoted by Ellis, *Man and Woman*, p. 46.

some racial groups or nationalities this tendency toward more pronounced long-headedness in males is not present. There is some evidence
that in the later periods of growth increase in head length is greater in
males than in females. This larger male increment may be attributed
in part to the sex differences in the frontal bone. The frontal sinus (a
mucous membrane-lined cavity in the frontal bone just above the nasal
and orbital region) is usually more extensive in males than in females,
and the bony supraorbital ridges are much larger in men, since these
serve, to some extent, the function of resisting the upward stresses exerted in chewing by the more massive jaws of the male. The male face
is both absolutely and relatively longer than that of the female, owing
to the greater depth of the jaws. This latter is especially marked in the
lower jaw, of which the symphysis (the median frontal region) is much
higher in males. The chin eminence is also bigger and juts more strongly
forward in the maculine sex. In harmony with their shorter, broader,
and less projecting faces, women have relatively broader and less receding foreheads, little or no development of brow-ridges, and noses that
are both relatively and absolutely shorter and lower. The height of the
brain-case in woman is lower than in man; the cranial capacity of the
skull averages about 150 cubic centimeters less in European females
than in males, although proportionate to their entire body bulk and
weight women have the larger brains. The contours of the skull are more
rounded and smooth in the weaker sex, and the ridges for the attachment
of muscles and ligaments are less rugged. All of the bones of the female
skeleton are lighter, smoother, and more delicate than the corresponding
male bones, as well as smaller. Women usually average 100 to 120 millimeters shorter in bodily height than males of the same race. Their stature
varies from 92 per cent of the male dimension in tall races, to 94 per cent
in shorter races among which the sex difference is less pronounced.

Fatty deposits in women are more abundant than in men. In the male,
41.8 per cent of the body mass is muscle and 18.2 per cent is fat, while in
the female the proportions are 35.8 per cent of muscle and 28.2 per cent
of fat. (Bischoff.)

Because women carry more blubber and less of the more solid and
weighty body tissues, they float more easily and swim with less effort
than men. This adipose tissue, together with a faster pulse, also permits
them to keep warm in fewer clothes than men need.

In the Peabody Museum of Harvard are two life-sized figures of plaster, one representing the average college woman and the other the average college man (Plate 17). These figures were modelled on the basis of
averages of physical measurements taken by Dr. Dudley Sargent, a pio-

neer in scientific physical education in this country, upon some thousands of students from Radcliffe, Simmons, and other women's colleges, and upon Harvard men. The mean age of these students was 20 years. The plaster figures were made for the World's Fair held in Chicago in 1893. The average Harvard man of 1892 was 5 feet, 8 inches, in height (172.72 cm.) and weighed 138 pounds. The college woman of that day had a mean stature of 5 feet and 3 inches (160.02 cm.) and a weight of 114 pounds. The male figure is well built, with a strong neck, broad shoulders, ample chest, and straight muscular limbs. But the female figure has hips and legs too heavy for her slender chest and narrow shoulders; the lumbar curve is over accentuated, and her appearance as a whole is not one of grace and vigor. Of course, these figures represent the average dimensions of college people of Massachusetts in the "gay nineties." It is hardly probable, however, that the combination of wasp-like waist and swelling hips in the female figure is a result of the constricted waist styles of the period. It would be interesting to compare with these figures similar models of the college men and women of today. Unfortunately, no such models are available. It is certain that the stature of college women in the United States has been increasing. The average height of 1,116 women of Stanford University in the decade from 1891 to 1901 was 63.2 inches (160.53 centimeters). But the mean for 1,707 students between the years 1911 and 1921 was 63.8 inches (162.05 centimeters), an increase of three-fifths of an inch. Similarly, the average stature of 1,600 women students of Oberlin College increased from 62.6 inches in the years 1886–1903 to 63.6 inches in the years 1909–1915. Smith and Vassar women also show increase in recent years. The average of Yale men students in 1909 was 173 centimeters and in 1915, 174.75 centimeters. Dr. Gordon Bowles has investigated the statures of Harvard fathers and sons measured when attending college. The fathers of one large series (1875–1910) averaged 174.37 centimeters, and their sons (1905–1929) 177.76 centimeters. A smaller series of Harvard men yielded the following means of four generations:

Great grandfathers (8), 170.11 centimeters; grandfathers (132), 174.13 centimeters; fathers (132), 175.30 centimeters; sons (153), 177.94 centimeters.[17]

Perhaps this increase of stature in college students is attributable to more healthful conditions of food and housing, a more general participation in athletic sports, and other environmental factors, although no one really knows the cause. Such a tendency toward increased stature has been manifested throughout the civilized populations of Europe and

[17] *New Types of Old Americans*, p. 68.

America during the past five decades. It certainly began in this country before the vogue of spinach, orange juice, vitamins, and pediatricians. I am of the opinion that one contributing factor may have been the tremendous decrease in infant mortality that has been effected by the advance of hygiene and medical science. Such a salvaging of the weaker infants and children who, in earlier days, would have been eliminated, may have increased the proportion of tall, slender, weedy individuals. These would reproduce in their offspring their bodily linearity. However, this theory presupposes that measles, whooping cough, and other diseases that harry the young discriminate lethally against the long and skinny. I know of no evidence to support this hypothesis. Some of the statural increase in this country might reasonably be referred to heterosis or hybrid vigor—an increase in size of offspring that sometimes takes place when diverse races or stocks interbreed. Yet, similar increases have been noted in Japanese and in various European countries that have not received accretions of new stocks by immigration.

If we had a plaster statue of the average dimensions of American college women of today, our modernized college Minerva would be 1⅓ inches taller, with much broader shoulders, a better developed chest, less slender and fragile waist, markedly narrower hips (but larger buttocks), much slimmer and longer legs, and (notably) bigger feet. She would resemble Ginger Rogers rather than Lillian Russell. There is little doubt that the college woman of the nineties was an anemic blue stocking type as compared with the vigorous, athletic female student today, whose intellectual faculties may not be any more acute, but whose legs are certainly more slender, as anyone may observe.

One of the most marked sex differences that appears at puberty is in the quality of the voice. At this time, the boy's larynx increases more than the girl's; his voice "breaks" and becomes deeper in pitch. The female larynx is higher in the neck than that of the male and about one third smaller. It is especially in the antero-posterior diameter and in the external prominence of "Adam's apple" that the larynx of the male exceeds that of the female. The masculine vocal cords are also considerably longer. In correlation with these anatomical differences are the divergences in vocal pitch and quality. The hen, the bitch, the mare, and the she-ass also have weaker and shriller voices than their male counterparts.

The most striking phenomenon of sexual maturation is the beginning of menstruation and ovulation in the female.[18] From puberty to the cessation of sexual life, with intermissions due to pregnancy, women

---

[18] Ellis, *Man and Woman*, pp. 279–298.

are subject to a monthly loss of blood from the uterus, averaging between 100 and 200 grams. As a Frenchman put it, "woman suffers incessantly the eternal wound of love." This flow lasts from three to five days and recurs on the average every twenty-eighth day. This discharge from the uterus is probably subsequent to ovulation—the release of a ripened egg cell from the ovary. The ova develop in the Graafian follicles—round, transparent vesicles in the ovaries. Every month, a follicle containing a matured ovum is ruptured, and the ovum passes into the Fallopian tube, which leads into the uterus. In one of these two places it may be fertilized, otherwise it is discharged from the uterus. When the ovum has burst through the follicle, the lining of the ruptured follicle is thrown into folds, and vascular processes grow inward forming a radial arrangement of yellow cells called the corpus luteum or yellow body, which is supposed to secrete a hormone. The corpus luteum remains in the ovary for about a week but is broken up and absorbed before the maturation of the next ovum. But, if the ovum released is impregnated, the corpus luteum continues to develop for three months and is not discharged until the end of pregnancy. Its hormone may, therefore, be responsible for the changes that take place in the uterus during pregnancy and for the prevention of menstruation and ovulation during this period. It may also stimulate the functioning of the mammary glands after childbirth.

The menstrual blood is discharged from the lining of the uterus. During the period, the whole organ is enlarged, and the mucous membrane of the lining becomes thicker, softer, and of a darker red color. According to the theory of Sir J. Williams, at each recurrence of menstruation there is a complete disintegration and removal of the uterine lining, only the bases of glands imbedded in the muscles being left. When menstruation ceases, a new mucous membrane is formed by the proliferation of the remaining structures. It is the lining membrane of the uterus in which the fertilized ovum becomes imbedded and which is dissolved by the trophoblast, or outer covering of the segmented ovum. The embryonic coverings send out processes that invade the maternal tissues and become bathed in maternal blood. It seems probable that the discharge of menstrual blood that is more or less coincident with ovulation is the sloughing off of a surplus product, which, in the event of impregnation, would serve for the nutrition of the embryo. Earlier data on the onset of menstruation (the menarche) encouraged the theory that girls in the tropics mature earlier than those in the temperate zone and that the age of menarche was some sort of a function of latitude or mean annual temperature. Some students of the subject were inclined to suspect that racial or hereditary differences were also involved in this time variation. Steggerda [19] found that the age of first menstruation in Maya Indian girls of pure stock in Yucatan averaged 12.91 years; Mestizo girls (mixed Maya and Spanish), 12.81 years; and Dutch White girls in Michigan, 13.91 years. The differences are insignificant and neglible as regards the menarche, but the racial differences of the stocks involved are vast and so are also the climatic and nutritional differences, as between the Maya and Mestizo girls, on the one hand, and the Michigan lasses of Dutch descent, on the other. If one scrutinizes an elaborate table of the mean age of first menstruation, involving many thousands of individuals in some of the samples and including many races and nationalities, it becomes apparent that the mean age of menarche in a world wide sample is not far from 15 years. The Maya girls have the lowest average age of menarche, and the highest (16.98) is recorded in a small sample of Spanish girls from Asturia. However, another somewhat larger sample of Spanish girls from Valencia has an average age at menarche of 13.33. There is a considerable difference in mean age of two or more samples drawn from the same nationality or race. It seems necessary to abandon the idea that onset of mestruation is closely related either to climate or to race.

The chimpanzee begins to menstruate, according to 7 observations, at an average age of 8 years, 11 months. A single observation of the menarche in the gorilla places it at approximately 9 years. The age of first menstruation in the orang-utan is not known, but in the gibbon, according to Pocock, it is the seventh year. Carpenter was given an adult gibbon that did not menstruate until the approximate age of 10 years. Menarche takes place in the macaque at $3\frac{1}{2}$ years. Apparently, all Old World monkeys menstruate, and some sort of vaginal bleeding has occasionally been seen in capuchins and marmosets, of the New World monkey group. Tarsius is also said to menstruate, but this phenomenon has not been observed in lemurs. Seemingly, menarche takes place in the anthropoid apes several years earlier than in man, and in monkeys this indication of sexual maturity occurs a great deal earlier than in apes.

The sexual cycle of primates—from one menstruation to the next—varies around 30 days. In women, although individually variable, it averages about 28 days, which is the same as in the macaque. The average in the chimpanzee is 36 days, in the gibbon, a little less than 30 days; in the Hamadryas baboon, 31 days; and in three other kinds of baboons, between 30 and 40 days. All of the Old World apes and monkeys show such monthly cycles, but they have not been accurately observed, with a few exceptions. In the human species, ovulation occurs about midway

[19] Steggerda, *Maya Indians*, pp. 203–207.

in the menstrual cycle, and there are important rhythmical changes in the ovaries and other reproductive organs, involving destruction of the endometrium, or uterine lining, after menstruation; regeneration in the first few days of the cycle; a resting phase or interval; and extensive growth of the endometrium following ovulation. The sexual or menstrual cycle gives way to a reproductive cycle when the mature ovum is fertilized and the woman becomes pregnant.

In many apes and Old World monkeys, swelling and coloration of the skin around the genital organs take place during the sexual cycle and are directly related to maturation and rupture of the ovarian follicles. The reddening and swelling of the sexual skin, which is a specialized area of the body surface, usually in the perineal region, ordinarily comes during the first half of the cycle and subsides after ovulation. These sexual skin changes occur in the chimpanzee in a very marked fashion, much less conspicuously in the gorilla, according to an isolated observation, and are absent in man, gibbon, and orang. Baboons, macaques (but perhaps not all species) show these cyclical changes of the sexual skin. Yet they are lacking in many other genera of Old World monkeys and have not been observed in the New World primates. These phenomena seem to have little phylogenetic significance—they are of no particular value in tracing relationships. When they do occur, since they are so noticable, they can be related to variations in sexual behavior and in temperament. Males of any species experience no such sexual cycle, so far as is known. They ought to be more stable in personality, since they are not subject to these physiological rhythms. However, they are indirectly affected by the cyclical vacillations of the females when these latter manifest themselves in what is called "sexual receptivity" —to say nothing of psychological variations and kaleidoscopic changes of disposition. The old Latin saw, *varium et mutabile semper femina,* is a philosophical reflection based upon a sexual periodicity in females that can be studied in chimpanzees more profitably than, at present, in *Homo sapiens.*

The resemblance of the menstrual interval to the lunar cycle has been made the subject of an ingenious theory by Darwin. He points out that animals living on the seashore must be greatly affected by the tides. Animals living about the mean high water mark or the mean low water mark pass through a complete cycle of tidal changes in a fortnight, and their food supply undergoes marked alterations week by week. The periodicity of certain reproductive functions in the higher vertebrates would be explicable if they were descended from such animals as tidal Ascidians. For, the vital functions of such animals can hardly fail to run their course in weekly periods. A recurrent period when once gained would not be liable to change and might be transmitted through almost any number of generations. If the function changed, the period would be likely to change by abrupt jumps of an entire week or multiples of a week. Darwin cites as examples the fact that the eggs of a pigeon are hatched in two weeks, those of a fowl in three, those of a duck in four, those of a goose in five, and those of an ostrich in seven weeks.[20]

The blood pressure and temperature of women are alleged to rise just before the menstrual flow, and the thyroid and parotid glands, the tonsils, and other organs are actively engorged during this period. It is maintained that in most healthy women sexual emotions are at a maximum before the period and at a lesser maximum after it. The field of vision is said to be narrowed during the flow; the breasts are slightly enlarged; there is a tendency toward increased pigmentation about the nipples, and many other physical signs of a far-reaching organic disturbance are manifest. On the psychic side, there is greater suggestibility, greater impressionability, diminished self-control, and a general irritability and nervous instability, often leading to abnormal behavior.

It has been demonstrated that the secretions of the gonads affect not only the behavior, but also the development, of normal sex differences in proportions and morphological features. The eunuch, whose sex glands have been removed before puberty, fails to develop many of the secondary sexual characters of the male. His beard and body hair grow scantily, if at all; his voice preserves the high-pitched tones of childhood; his pelvis retains the early sex differentiae, but does not show the characteristically narrow subpubic arch, constricted inlet and outlet, and great height development of the normal male. The epiphyses, or caps of the long bones, fail to ossify at the proper times, and there is an abnormal continuance of growth; the thighs converge, and the knees knock together; depositions of fat on the legs, thighs, buttocks, and elsewhere recall the infant. A eunuch is often regarded as a "feminine" male, but, properly, he is infantile. For, the characteristics retained through removal of the gonads are those of childhood.

The female is commonly said to be more infantile than the male. Certainly, man has diverged further from the skeletal and bodily proportions of infancy than has woman. But in so doing he has in most characters departed from the ultra-human type toward lower mammalian prototypes. The hairiness of the adult male body, the relatively great size of face and jaws, the high, narrow, and firmly knit pelvis—all these are adult male characters recalling the apes. The female shows ultra-

[20] Darwin, *Descent of Man*, p. 254 footnote.

human differentiation as regards her broad low pelvis with its generous apertures, although these features are foreshadowed in the infants of both sexes. This specialization for the bearing of large-brained infants is reflected only dimly in the male pelvis, which is better adapted for the support of the body in the erect posture. The breasts of women also show advanced evolution, while those of man are vestigial. Woman is tethered to her reproductive function and varies within the narrow radius prescribed by the necessities of propagating the race. Man's sexual organization is merely auxiliary; his organism is not built around his reproductive system; he ranges in bodily characters within the ample limits of natural selection.

Getting Married and Having a Baby

Beaumarchais said: "That which distinguishes man from the beast is drinking without being thirsty and making love at all seasons." Certainly, most animals bring forth their young at a stated and unvarying period of the year, which is probably determined by climate, seasonal variation, food supply, as well as by the length of gestation, period of infancy, and the general organization of the species. If, as seems probable, the time of birth of offspring is governed by the conditions of the year favorable for survival, the time of mating must be similarly regulated so as to precede the season of advantageous births by an interval equal to the gestation period. Reptiles, birds, and many mammals give birth to their young in the spring or at the commencement of the rainy season when food and water begin to be most abundant and life is most easily sustained. Differences in climate and altitude generally affect the mating seasons of animals of the same genus; species living in different latitudes breed earlier or later according to climate.

In spite of seasonal fluctuations in the number of births recorded among various civilized peoples, there is no real evidence of the existence of a single mating season, either in primitive men or in their ape ancestors. Nor are the anthropoid apes known to confine their breeding to any one period of the year. Carpenter, in northern Siam, during the period between February and June, saw infants and young gibbons in all stages of development. The pregnant uteri of gibbons collected in these same months showed a considerable range of development of foetuses. Chimpanzees mate during a restricted phase of the sexual cycle only, but the sexual cycle recurs every 36 days. In a captive colony of rhesus macaques on an island off the coast of Puerto Rico, Carpenter observed mating in February, March, and April but not in May and

June. There were also modes of birth during August, September, and October. Consequently, these Old World monkeys seem to have a breeding season, but the mating period in Puerto Rico may not be the same as in India, the native habitat of these macaques. However, the American howling monkeys are known to breed all the year round, as are also spider monkeys. There is ample evidence also that the tarsier breeds continuously, but, so far as known, the lemurs are demarcated from the rest of the primates by having a definitely restricted breeding season. Thus, it would appear that Carpenter's observations on the macaque immigrants in Puerto Rico are the only instance in which a breeding season is indicated for higher primates. This case, indeed, may be merely a seasonal fluctuation or a temporary physiological upset in consequence of a radical change in habitat.

Development from the fertilization of the ovum to birth requires about 280 days in man, counting from the beginning of the last menstruation to parturition. In the chimpanzee, this period averages 251 days. Counting from the date of impregnation up to the day of birth, the duration of human pregnancy averages about 266 days, as against 231 days in the chimpanzee and 275 days in the one orang-utan of which there is a record. Pregnancy lasts 163 days in the macaque, usually between 150 and 180 days in other Old World monkeys observed, about 150 days in marmosets, and, according to two estimates, 111 days in one species of lemur and 145 days in another. It is clear that man and the great apes resemble each other in length of foetal development much more closely than the apes resemble lower primates.

Sir Arthur Keith thinks that the period of embryological development of the gibbon may be only 7 months, as against approximately 9 in man, the same in the orang, and a little shorter period in the chimpanzee. If this guess is correct, the increase of the period of gestation to 9 months may have occurred when giant primates developed from the ancestral small ape stock. Although ape mothers have smaller and lighter babies than human mothers, so far as is known the infants of the former are at least as advanced in development as are human babies at birth. In the case of the chimpanzee, at any rate, foetal development must be a little more rapid than in man.

During human pregnancy, the menstrual flow ceases, the mammary glands usually become somewhat enlarged and tender, and there is often a swelling of the thyroid gland. At the beginning of the period and sometimes throughout its whole duration, the mother frequently suffers from nausea, especially in the morning; the blood pressure is lowered, and the bowels are sluggish. The amount of haemoglobin in the blood is asserted by some writers to decrease markedly. Anemias are frequent. It has been suggested that the storage of iron in haemoglobin takes place in the maternal organs before the first conception, in readiness for the supply of the foetus through the maternal circulation. Young animals have a greater content of iron in the blood than adult animals, and human milk contains a small but consistent amount of iron, which is said to be less in the milk of mothers of mature age than in those who are youthful.[21]

Pregnant chimpanzees at Orange Park, Florida, may exhibit periodic genital swellings for two or three months after conception; later these swellings become irregular and unpredictable until, during the latter half of gestation, periodic changes may be only slightly indicated. Menstrual bleeding does not occur after conception. As the pregnancy progresses, the female becomes increasingly cautious and self-protective, avoiding conflict and other risks, including acceptance of the male, except as a measure of self-defense or to guard against injury.[22]

When the foetus is fully developed, the uterus begins a series of rhythmical contractions, whereby the child is forced outward through the vaginal orifice. First the amniotic membrane is ruptured, and the fluid, in which the developing embryo has been enclosed, escapes. By further contractions, the child is forced through the pelvic outlet, usually head first; the bony basin spreads at the symphysial cartilages, and the coccyx and sacrum are pushed upward and backward as the head of the child passes over the pelvic floor. The tissues of the perineum are stretched to allow the egress of the head, which is the largest part of the body. The hole in the pelvis of the female must be large enough to permit the passage of the big-brained child, and the outlet must be especially ample. After the child has been delivered, renewed contractions of the uterus dislodge and eject the placenta. The open vessels of the uterine lining are closed by the continued contraction of that organ, so that haemorrhage is checked. The umbilical cord is tied between the new-born infant and the placenta, and cut. After a few days, the stump of the tied cord atrophies and drops off, leaving the navel scar.

Yerkes reports, on the authority of Madame Abreu, that on the morning of delivery of Monona, a pregnant female chimpanzee of Madame Abreu's primate colony at Havana, the keeper, hearing the prospective mother rattling her chain, loosed the animal and, returning after some time, discovered that a baby chimpanzee had been born but was, apparently, dead. "Presently the mother began to work over it, breathing

---

[21] Ellis, *op. cit.*, pp. 221–222.
[22] Yerkes, *Chimpanzees*, p. 67.

into its mouth and drawing its tongue out with her lips. After a period of this treatment the infant began to breathe. She then cleaned it thoroughly and subsequently chewed at the umbilical cord until it was shortened to about a half yard. Somewhat later she chewed it off close to the body of the infant." An orang-utan mother bit off the cord close to the baby's abdomen about twenty-eight hours after the birth.

The psychobiologists of the Yerkes laboratories at Orange Park have had ample opportunity in recent years to observe chimpanzee pregnancies, births, and the exercise of maternal care. They have never seen a mother attempt to stimulate respiration in a newly born baby. Elder and Yerkes have summarized accounts of 14 single births and one twin birth. Most of the births were normal, and the labor was not difficult. The time of labor varied from 30 minutes to 5 hours. The placenta was usually expelled immediately and was eaten by the mother in 8 of 15 cases. The chimpanzee mother gains on an average of about 12 pounds during pregnancy and loses about the same amount after birth. Worthy of comment is the improvement of the chimpanzee's disposition during pregnancy. I have no data that would permit me to conclude that a comparable amelioration of disposition takes place in expectant human mothers—nor, for that matter, to deny such parallelism.

Since this book is a treatise upon human evolution and not upon chimpanzee obstetrics, I must content myself with one detailed account of a chimpanzee birth and infancy. The event occurred at the Zoological Garden in Berlin, and the mother was Loca, one of Köhler's chimpanzees from the experimental station at Tenerife, arrived with five other chimpanzees on the 17th of October, 1920. Toward the end of the same month, the mother menstruated. The infant was born on the 1st of April, 1921, which, counted from the last observed menstruation, would give a period of gestation of only five months. It is probable that the chimpanzee continued to menstruate for the first few months after pregnancy began. The animal seemed to enjoy the best of health during pregnancy. Soon after the delivery, the mother put the head of the infant in her mouth and appeared to suck; she then licked it dry. The infant was apparently lifeless. About 25 minutes after the delivery, the baby was observed to breathe. The mother kept it in her groin, supporting it against her abdomen with her flexed thigh. The infant clung to the hair of the mother's body with hands and feet. On the morning of the second day, it uttered its first sound, a lusty U-sound of moderate pitch, similar to that customarily emitted by adult chimpanzees. About the middle of this day, the other apes were admitted for a half hour. They were extraordinarily interested in the baby and crowded around the mother, touch-

ing the head and hands of the infant. The mother was not at all anxious.
The baby was about 20 centimeters long from crown to rump, and the
head was relatively much smaller than in human infants. Head, shoulders, and back were covered with long black hair, which lay smooth on
the scalp and showed a clear parting in the middle. The exposed parts of
the skin were a bright rust color (a grayish orange). During the second
and third day, the infant was seen a number of times with its mouth
applied to the mother's nipple, but it was not certain whether it actually nursed. On the fourth day, however, suckling definitely began
and became more energetic thereafter day by day. The infant seemed
wholly unable to find the breast and turned its head aimlessly in all
directions, blindly seeking the source of food. Even when its open mouth
was no more than one centimeter from the nipple, it seemed to have no
sense of direction and was apparently unaided by smell. The mother
seemed to offer little or no assistance to the undirected efforts of the baby
and often, by casual movements of her body, frustrated attempts that
seemed otherwise destined to succeed. Sometimes, however, she lifted the
infant to the breast. There seems to have been a complete lack of precision in the nursing technique of the chimpanzee mother. The mother
would often hold the infant up to her face and regard it long and
earnestly with a most expressive look, interrupting with this sentimental
scrutiny a much desired meal.

Within two or three days of the birth of a human infant, the milk is
established in the mother's breast, and the baby begins to nurse. The
baby chimpanzee begins to take the breast within the space of minutes
to hours after birth. A baby orang-utan born at the Philadelphia
Zoölogical Gardens was put to the breast by its mother and began to nurse
on the second day. During the period in which the human mother is
nursing her infant, the menstrual flow usually does not return, but, when
the baby is weaned and milk production ceases, the monthly period
begins again. There is some disagreement of observers with respect to
the return of menstruation in the chimpanzee. Madame Abreu maintains
that there is no resumption of the menstrual flow until after the infant
is weaned. Professor Yerkes substantiates this statement by his own observation that, during the summer of 1924, when mother and father and
the infant (still nursing, though not entirely dependent upon the breast)
were caged together, the adult female gave no evidence of menstruation.
During this period, the male and female chimpanzee have no sex relations with each other. Generally speaking, primitive man abstains from
intercourse during the pregnancy of his wife and throughout the whole
nursing period, although this is not invariably the case. It is at least usual

among the Negro tribes of Africa living in a state of polygamy. Under conditions of monogamy, however, man relaxes his continence and often has marital relations with his wife both during pregnancy and throughout the period of lactation. In the latter practice, he shows less consideration for the nursing mother than does the chimpanzee, to whom, however, we should be careful not to ascribe any self-denying motives, as his continence under these conditions is due to the fact that the female in this period is neither sexually attractive nor receptive. The baboon, according to Zuckerman, emulates man in copulating with pregnant females. So does the gibbon.

The human mother suckles her infant for a varying period, usually between 6 months and 3 years, and probably for an average period of 18 months. In the cases of two baby chimpanzees born in Cuba, the nursing periods extended for about 18 and 21 months, respectively. A gibbon mother is known to have nursed her offspring for more than 2 years. Yerkes thinks that the orang-utan mother weans her infant during the second year. Among savages, children are usually suckled for 2 to 3 years, but among civilized peoples the nursing period is usually much shorter, either because of failure of the milk supply of the mother or because adequate artificial foods make it possible for her to get rid of this burden.

One may conclude from these descriptions of anthropoid births that in reproductive functions also the great apes closely resemble man. Even among savages, there is usually a midwife on hand to assist the mother in her labor. But the chimpanzee or orang-utan mother has to be her own obstetrician. Nor does she benefit by traditions of infant care and feeding.

Bringing Up a Family

Lower forms of animal life reproduce their kind with great prodigality, and the offspring have to shift for themselves. Many succumb, but the survivors continue the species. Among the invertebrates, sex relations are generally of a most fleeting character, and the females have little or no responsibility for their offspring.

Parental care is almost unknown among the lowest vertebrates, but the male of some fishes makes a nest for the eggs and guards them, and, in one species of Arius, the male carries about the eggs in his pharynx.[23] Reptiles usually lay eggs and depart without further concern. But some snakes lay their eggs in a heap and coil around them. Some crocodiles carry their young with them. There seems to be little evidence of parental

[23] Westermarck, *Human Marriage,* Vol I, p. 20.

care among the amphibians, but birds are vastly in advance of their
reptilian precursors in this respect. The male usually remains with the
female even after the breeding season, helps build the nest, brings food
for the young, and defends mother and offspring against the attacks of
enemies.

Family life is not greatly developed among most mammals. The mother
does her utmost in the care and protection of the offspring, but the male
commonly consorts with the female only during the mating season and
does not concern himself with his progeny. He may even be an enemy
to them. However, there are a few mammals among whom the sexes are
said to remain together until after the birth of the offspring, the male
acting as the protector of the family. Westermarck cites as examples of
such enduring alliance and paternal care: whales, seals, hippopotami,
some deer, antelope and gazelles, squirrels, moles, and a few carnivores
such as cats, martens, and possibly the wolf.

Data on family organization and parental care in the subhuman primates are generally defective and virtually worthless, excepting in the
few groups that have been observed in the wild by modern scientific
students, or, rarely, in zoological gardens under somewhat artificial conditions, and, finally, in the unique chimpanzee laboratory founded by
Professor Robert M. Yerkes of Yale University. Wood Jones (a reliable
authority) states that lemur mothers (of the true genus *Lemur*) do not
nurse or handle their offspring, and their fathers are perfectly indifferent
to them. One lemur baby was observed to suckle for 6 months. Dr.
Florence de L. Lowther, of Barnard College, kept a pair of bush babies,
or galagos, that were obliging enough to produce twins. The babies
were nursed for 3½ months. The female displayed great maternal solici-
tude. She kept her babies clean by licking their fur, carried them round
in her mouth, lifted them back into the nest when they strayed out or
were removed, and summoned them by calls up to the age of 9 months.
The father displayed a certain amount of affection for his offspring and
obeyed the signals of the mother, along with the babies. Wood Jones
reports a disillusioning case of a slow loris mother that escaped from her
cage, leaving her nursing infant to its fate. She hung around in the trees
within ear shot of the squalling infant but never returned. The infant
died. Tarsiers live in pairs. The new born infant clings to the fur of the
mother's belly but is not held by her.

Red spider monkeys have been splendidly studied in their native
haunts by C. R. Carpenter.[24] For a month, the infant clings to its mother's
belly and thereafter rides on her back with its tail coiled around the base

[24] Carpenter, "Behavior of Red Spider Monkeys."

of the mother's. The mothers travel across tree tops to pick up their young when the latter are in difficulties, and they help the semi-dependent young across risky spots in the arboreal pathways. A mother at first controls the movements of her infant by physical force and later by teaching it to respond to certain postural clues, especially movements of her body. In the spider monkey group, one adult male is usually accompanied by more than one female, together with infants and immature animals. The male has protective duties, and arrogates himself the function of leadership. Carpenter does not describe any participation of fathers in the care of their offspring.

The American howling monkeys have also been studied in the wild by Carpenter.[25] These animals travel about in groups averaging more than 17 individuals and including, typically, 3 males; about 7 females with young of various ages, carried or semidependent; sundry immature animals, and occasional bachelor males. Within this group, the females are promiscuous and the males neither jealous nor competitive. The mothers are not over-solicitous toward their young, but help them over difficult crossings and retrieve them when they fall. The newly born infant is cleaned by the mother and at first clings to her belly, then rides on her back. The howler mother gives her youngster very little tuition. She may move away from it a short distance and encourage it to try to walk toward her. She weans her baby by cuffing it away or biting it when it tries to suckle. This weaning probably takes place during the next pregnancy of the mother, when the baby is between one and a half and two years old. Males are usually indifferent to young howlers but may tolerate the attempts of the latter to play with them. They may stop fights between immature animals and may even go so far as to retrieve a youngster that has fallen out of a tree and carry it on the back in the position in which it usually rides upon its mother.

Zuckerman observed the Hamadryas baboon in a captive colony in the London Zoological Garden.[26] The family group seemingly consists of a brutal, dominating overlord, as many adult females as he can acquire and retain, their young, and possibly a bachelor male, hanging about and looking for a chance to commit adultery. Observations on parental care in this colony were limited by the fact that but one baby was born before the colony was broken up as a result of fights between males over possession of the females. The Hamadryas baboon mother nurses her baby for about 5 months, watches it carefully, keeps it in her arms for the first couple of weeks, and gathers it to her bosom in time of danger. It

[25] Carpenter, C. A., *A Field Study of Howling Monkeys.*
[26] Zuckerman, *Social Life.*

first clings to her belly, then rides on her back. She does not play with her baby nor attempt to teach it. Fathers never play with their babies, but they may tease them.

Wild gibbons live in family groups consisting of father, mother, and young. They are definitely monogamous, and it seems probable that the matings endure for a considerable period, perhaps reinforced by the fact that there is no breeding season and copulation takes place all through the year. Carpenter, again, is our authority for the life of the wild gibbon, but his observations on family life and parental care are supplemented by one or two records on captive animals. A gibbon was born in the San Diego zoo, which is under the direction of that very careful observer, Mrs. Belle Benchley, but, unfortunately, the actual event was seen only by a casual visitor. When Mrs. Benchley arrived, the mother had already severed the cord, cared for herself and the baby, and had everything under perfect control. The father huddled nearby, interested, but pursuing a policy of non-interference. Gibbon males do not dominate their wives, as a rule. The mother and father ate the placenta together. The baby began to nurse the second day and seemed to be more precocious in its activity than are chimpanzee babies. The mother did not ordinarily support the infant with her hands as it clung to her; did not instruct it in walking and climbing, as do chimpanzee mothers; and did not hold it away from her when it was urinating or evacuating its bowels, as did a chimpanzee mother in the San Diego zoo. When the baby began to climb about, the mother would reach out a casual arm and gather him in, if he appeared to be in difficulties. The baby was unafraid of the father and pulled at his fur and gnawed him as freely as if he were the mother. The father's attitude toward the infant was one of mild interest or gentle indifference.

Wild gibbon mothers keep their infants astride of their abdomens. The mother's thighs are flexed to provide a seat for the baby, which encircles her body with its long arms. For 6 months the infant rarely if ever leaves this furry nest. When it begins to move away from the mother, she is very solicitous for its welfare and pulls it back to her if it gets too far away. When the mother gets ready to brachiate, she arranges the baby in the proper position as a preliminary. Gibbons handle their babies more than do American monkeys, perhaps because apes lack prehensile tails and hence cannot caudle [27] their offspring. Again, the ape

---

[27] My erudite printer informs me that there is no verb derived from *cauda*, "tail." "Caudle" means "to administer a warm drink" (Webster, Oxford, etc.). Nevertheless, "caudle," as I use it here, means "to palpate, touch, examine, or hold *with the tail*," I reject "to manipulate with the tail," or "to handle with the tail." A primate with a prehensile tail needs a verb for it. So do I.

baby matures more slowly, and its hand grasp is probably initially weaker. A wounded mother gibbon has been known to leave its baby in one tree and attempt to lure away the hunters by going to another tree.

Practically nothing is known of the family life of free-ranging orangutans. Some say that the male is solitary, except in mating seasons, but it seems unlikely that orangs have a single yearly breeding period. Others assert that the orang family consists of a male, a female, and their young. One orang birth occurred in the Philadelphia Zoölogical Garden, but the event itself was unobserved. Incidentally, reports of this mother orang's condition during pregnancy state that she had a poor appetite and was constipated in the earlier part and that, toward the end, she became peevish and irritable. She failed to show the improved disposition characteristic of pregnant chimpanzees. After the baby was born, she licked it and cuddled it but did not attempt to put it to the breast until the second day, at which time she bit off the umbilical cord close to the baby's abdomen and then held the infant to her nipple. Further accounts of her maternal care and tuition are lacking, but two photographs of Maggie and her infant are herewith presented (Plates 18, 19).

Except that the gorilla family consists of an adult male, several wives, and some immature animals, nothing is known of mating, reproduction, and parental care in this animal. However, admirable data are available in the case of the captive chimpanzee. The social life of wild chimpanzees has been observed only by Nissen, and his account is far from complete.[28] In French Guinea, the number of chimpanzees in a group averaged 8.5 and ranged from 4 to 14. Often there was more than one adult male in a group and usually several adult females. There is no evidence here of a monogamous family.

Chimpanzee mothers pick up their newborn infants and handle them gently and often skilfully. They clean them with lips, teeth, fingers, and nails; help them to find the breast and suckle them exclusively for 3 to 6 months. After that time, the baby is encouraged to take supplementary food. The mother chimpanzee begins to play with her baby at an early age, but the extent of such activities depends upon the individual mother. She exercises the infant and teaches it to stand, walk, crawl, and climb. Mothers are of the "progressive" or "conservative" school. The latter variety is very patient, cautious, and painstaking in tuition. The progressive mother pays very little attention to the infant and allows it to "express itself." Yerkes thinks that chimpanzees understand their babies so thoroughly that they are able to forestall their needs and correctly interpret every infantile posture and movement. An experienced chim-

[28] Nissen, *Field Study of the Chimpanzee.*

panzee mother cares for her baby and trains it better than the tyro. Again, some chimpanzee mothers are gifted nurses and teachers, whereas others are awkward and inept.

Of chimpanzee fathers, Yerkes says: "The role of the chimpanzee father in reproduction seems limited to mating. He has no part in the process of birth nor is he permitted to help to care for the infant during its dependent stage of development. Only after it has achieved a considerable measure of freedom from the mother may he become its guardian or playfellow." [29]

The mammalian method of nourishing the young in the uterus of the mother and of suckling them at the breast during a period of helpless infancy restricts the number of offspring produced and necessitates maternal care. With the further prolongation of foetal development, the number of offspring produced at a birth is still further diminished, because the continued intra-uterine growth of the foetus demands more and more space in the maternal womb, the expansion of which is strictly limited. In such mammals as horses and cattle, the usual limitation of offspring to one at a birth is probably determined by the gross bodily size of the foetus, but, in the higher primates, it is due to the precocious growth of the brain during development. Among the primates, only some lemurs and possibly degenerate marmosets habitually produce litters of two or more young. Twins, triplets, and quadruplets, of occasional occurrence in the Anthropoidea, may be regarded as atavistic phenomena—reminiscences of lower mammalian stages of evolution. The long prenatal period and the protracted and helpless infancy of man and the anthropoid apes are prerequisites for the ultimately high development of the nervous system and of the mental powers in these families. Since all of the eggs are put into one basket, or, more accurately, since the basket will hold but one egg at a time, that basket must be watched very carefully, and its contents must be assiduously cherished. At this point logic and sentiment demand that the father's care be added to that of the mother for the perpetuation of the species. However, Nature does not seem to have arranged the evolution of the primate family according to man's ideas of what is fitting and proper. The subhuman father, instead of serving the mother's needs by waiting on her, getting food for her, and tenderly cherishing her, pushes her around and dominates her (at any rate in the case of chimpanzees), so that she has a hard time getting her share of the food except in the short periods when she is sexually attractive, and thereby temporarily gets the upper hand. Probably the ape father may, in a pinch, defend his females and his off-

[29] Yerkes, *Chimpanzees*, p. 68.

spring. But he certainly does not get out and hustle food for them. Of the male orang, it is alleged that he merely procreates and departs, leaving females to consort with their kind and the young, except at certain seasons. Probably this report is incorrect. It is more likely that he hangs around without being of any use to his children and any, other than that of sexual satisfaction, to his mate. Westermarck, one of the past generation of social anthropologists, tried conscientiously to prove that monogamous marriage was a sort of a primate sacrament inherited from ape ancestors. For him, marriage at the minimum was a continuance of conjugal relations up to the birth of offspring. In order to be a real husband and sociological father, you had to stick around during your wife's pregnancy and stand by at the parturition. In the first edition of this book, I suggested that man had acquired a new paternal function, that of rearing as well as procreating offspring, because human childhood is so long, human wits mature so slowly, and human beings are lacking in the offensive and defensive organic equipment of the other giant primates. I made the following pompous pronouncement:

"A mother is a mother in every sense of the word all the way down the mammalian class and even in some lower forms of life. The full dignity and responsibility of paternity was attained only when man became an erect-walking, ground-dwelling animal. Mother's Day can be celebrated by all of the animals down to the reptiles. But Father's Day belongs to us."

The statement about the antiquity of the maternal function is undoubtedly correct, yet I can see no reason for making a sociological virtue out of a biological necessity, and I share with Philip Wylie an impatience with the American "Cult of Mom." [30] The sanctification of the maternal relationship in modern human societies is a feminine achievement that probably should not be grudged. For an interesting series of parallels at the chimpanzee level of intelligence, the reader may be referred to Yerkes' accounts of how the lady ape trades on her sex to get the better of the naturally stronger, dominant, and generally selfish male. The human female more intelligently utilizes and sublimates the mother-child relation in preference to a crude display of sex appeal to her mate. The former method involves or ensnares but one individual and one sex; the latter works both ways, both as to gender and generation. I am far from belittling the reproductive and child-nurturing function of the sex, but why apotheosize woman because she fulfills her biological destiny in accordance with her instincts (if there are such things as instincts)?

As for the human father, the efforts of civilized society to strengthen its

---

[30] Wylie, *Generation of Vipers*.

basic unit, the natural family of parents and children, by harnessing the evasive male progenitor to economic and educational responsibilities, are altogether commendable. However, let us not create for these new paternal functions a wholly specious primate phylogeny. I doubt that it is possible to prove, for a majority of contemporary savage societies, a constancy of paternal affection and an active participation in the care and nurture of offspring. If it can be proved, it is one of man's cultural triumphs over his biological nature.

Getting Old and Dying

The period of physical decline begins in none of us later than the twenty-fifth year. In the ascending period of development, strength and body tissue are added in harmonious proportions and activity increases. In descending development, the proportions of the body in respect to its various requirements are maintained, but strength and activity gradually decrease. By the time a young man has reached the age of twenty-five years, all of the lines of epiphysial growth in the skeleton have closed and the cranial sutures are beginning to ossify. At the age of thirty, the bones of the skull vault show active signs of sutural obliteration, and the brain has ceased to grow. Bodily weight increases. We begin to "settle down." For a decade or two after adult years have been reached, the decline of bodily strength is gradual and almost imperceptible. But the athlete of thirty-five years is considered an aged veteran, because the flood tide of his strength has ebbed some ten years back.

The sex life of the European woman ends between the ages of forty-five and fifty years. This is the climacteric or menopause, commonly known as "change of life." Menstruation and ovulation cease; there is some growth of hair on the body and face; the voice often becomes deeper and the outlines of the skeletal framework are accentuated. The breasts shrivel. This period of readjustment is often accompanied by serious physical and mental disturbances.

In the male the cessation of sex activity is marked by no such well-defined signs. Usually he remains sexually potent until after the age of fifty years.

With the onset of middle age, the skin, which has gradually become coarser in texture since infancy, tends to become sallow and wrinkled or to take on an unhealthy mottled look in corpulent persons. The nose tip grows downward; the ears elongate; the lips appear coarser and fuller; the bony framework of the face stands out, and fat, when present, tends to accumulate in unsightly folds. The sagging of the skin beneath the eyes, under the chin, and in the neck, is especially noticeable. The eyebrows become bushy and hair grows out of the nostrils and ears. The head hair begins to thin and to show graying. The veins on the backs of the hands become enlarged and the body tissues lose their elasticity. Persons who are getting thinner lose the slender grace of youth and appear stringy and scrawny; those who are taking on weight look bloated and unwieldy, when compared with the pleasing chubbiness of childhood.

The changes in the skeleton with increasing years are clear and interesting. The bones, which have been gaining in weight and size up to maturity, now grow lighter; ridges mark the site of the muscular attachments and the margins of the joints often develop bony lips or fringes. Absorption takes place in the interior of the bones, particularly in the vascular and cancellous parts. The spaces and canals in the interior of the bone are enlarged and filled with marrow at the expense of the fine supporting framework that is called cancellous tissue, and of the inner plates of the shaft walls. These latter are thinned from within, but the cancellous ends of the bones are most affected, so that in old age these become liable to fracture. Degenerative or pathological outgrowths from the margins of the bones are common.

The bones of the skull vault have a middle spongy layer of cancellous tissue called the diploë and thinner layers of compact bone outside and inside of this middle stratum. Usually in old age, the diploë becomes thinner and the outside and inside layers tend to come together, the skull walls thus becoming thinner and lighter. Sometimes, however, the senile skull becomes thickened, heavy, and massive.

The teeth begin to wear and usually to decay, early in life. As they die, they blacken, and abscesses tend to form around the lifeless roots. With the loss of teeth, the bony alveolar processes of the jaw that contain the tooth sockets are absorbed and cleared away, leaving only a narrow bar of the lower margin and the chin prominence, which seems to protrude outward and upward toward the pendant nasal tip. The lips lose their fullness and fall in over the toothless jaws. The lower jaw tends to revert to an infantile shape, excepting that bony tissue left in old age includes the lower part of the mandible and chin, whereas in infancy the jaw consists mainly of the tooth-bearing part and the lower portion is almost undeveloped. The resistance of the teeth being removed, the direction of muscle pull upon the jaws is altered so that the ascending branch of the mandible is brought almost into line with its lower margin, the angle between it and the horizontal ramus having opened up.

The vertebrae of the spinal column decrease in height and the cartilaginous disks between them are flattened and often show some calcification.

In general, the cartilaginous portions of the skeleton become thinner in old age. Humphry, who studied 824 octogenarians, regards the calcification of cartilage in old age as a morbid rather than a senile change and not a necessary consequence of advancing years.[31] Similarly, he considers the calcification or "hardening" of the arteries as a pathological process intruding upon, interfering with, and arresting the normal progress of senile development. In 368 returns from persons over the age of eighty years, the arteries were said to be knotty in only 40; to be tortuous in 71; and to be "even" in 257. Similarly, the pulse was compressible in 311 cases and incompressible in 72 cases. Thus, the arterial system seems to be healthy in those who attain a ripe old age. The pulse, which is usually higher in women than in men, does not vary much as age advances, according to the findings of this investigator. Respiration is generally quicker in females than males, at all ages. In the very aged, Humphry found an increased rate of respiration in both sexes.

Only 11 per cent of Humphry's octogenarians were fat; 41 per cent were described as "spare," and 47 per cent as "average." Accounts of their previous conditions as to bodily fullness indicate that the majority were always "spare" or "average."

The men of this aged group averaged 67 inches in height and the women 62 inches. If we allow a liberal estimate for the diminution of stature due to old age—say 2 inches for men and 1½ inches for women— it is evident that these octogenarians were well above the average of Englishmen of the lower classes and equal to the mean of the upper middle classes (69 inches for males, 63.5 inches for females). The lowering of stature is partially a result of increased curvature of the spine and thinning of the intervertebral cartilages; it is also due to inability to maintain the fully erect posture, which requires at all times of life a muscular effort largely exerted by the extensor muscles of the knees and hips. Hence the bent knee gait of the aged. The muscular strength and coordination necessary for easy maintenance of the upright posture have been lost. Yet, of the octogenarians studied by Humphry, 62 per cent were stated to be "erect" and only 28 per cent to be "bent."

The average weight of 227 of these men was somewhat under 144 pounds, and of 114 women, about 126 pounds. The decrease of weight in old age seems not to have been pronounced in this hardy group. About 58 per cent of the octogenarians were "anaemic" and 30 per cent were characterized as "pale," an indication of the comparative atrophy of the spleen, lymphatic glands, and other blood-making organs, in the aged. Sixty-three per cent were noted to be of "average" strength or "strong."

[31] Humphry, *Old Age*, p. 22.

A large number (80 per cent) retained good sight, but the hearing was "indifferent" or bad in more than half of the entire group. The more frequent impairment of the hearing is attributed by Humphry to the liability of injury to the delicate mechanism of the middle ear from colds, shocks, and a variety of other causes.

Seventy-one per cent of this group had good digestion and 62 per cent good appetites, and elimination of the waste products of the body occurred easily and naturally in the majority of cases. Intelligence was stated to be low in only 11 per cent and high in 15 per cent. Fifty-nine per cent of these persons were noted to have good memory for recent events and 78 per cent for past events. Only 9 per cent were bad sleepers.

In 41 per cent, all of the teeth had been lost—in 52 per cent of the women and 30 per cent of the men. Only 37 of the entire number had artificial teeth. About half were reported to be of a "placid" disposition, and 45 per cent were still "energetic" and brisk, while 17 per cent were said to be "irritable." Fifty-four per cent were "active" and took more or less out-of-door exercise; 31 per cent were "sedentary" and 14 per cent confined to bed. Sixty per cent were "moderate" eaters, 30 per cent "small" eaters, and only 9 per cent "large" eaters. Almost half (41 per cent) were in the habit of taking a little alcohol; a smaller proportion were "moderate" drinkers; 36 per cent were total abstainers, and 2.5 per cent are described as "taking too much." The majority of them ate but little meat.

Most of these old people had lived in comfortable circumstances (55 per cent); 35 per cent had been "poor," and 10 per cent "affluent." Ninety per cent had enjoyed good health throughout the most of their lives.

Humphry concluded from the study of the physical condition and life history of this group of aged people that the prime requisite for the faculty of age was inheritance and "temperance in all things."

The same writer reports some interesting results of post-mortem examinations of centenarians, which throw further light upon old age changes. The first and best known of these is that of Thomas Parr, who is said to have died at the age of 152 years and 9 months, and whose body was examined by Dr. William Harvey, the discoverer of the circulation of the blood, by command of Charles I. Harvey seems to have had no doubt as to the accuracy of the age assigned to Parr, but today we are more sceptical. However, he probably was at least 100 years old when he died. The body of Parr was still muscular, with hairy chest and forearms; the genital organs were not atrophied. It was a common report that this old reprobate did "public penance under a conviction for incontinence after he had passed his 100th year; and his wife, whom he had married in his 120th year, did not deny that he had intercourse with her after the manner of other husbands with wives." His chest was broad and ample; his heart was large with considerable fat; rib cartilages were soft and flexible; viscera all sound; spleen very small; brain healthy, firm, and hard to the touch.

A group of eminent authorities has recently collaborated in a volume that discusses the medical and biological problems of ageing.[32] Interest in this subject has been stimulated by the population prospect in the United States. As a result of decrease in the birth rate and the survival of an increased proportion of the population into advanced age through better medical care and adequate nutrition, we are approaching a condition in which more than one third of the population will be over 50 years of age, while it is calculated that in 1980 the number of persons over 65 years will be double that of today.

With advancing age, the valves of the heart gradually lose their softness and pliability and often become deformed. The striated muscle fibres that form the essential bulk of the heart undergo important alterations, including pigmentation, dessication, and loss of elasticity. The coronary arteries undergo changes often leading in certain locations to calcification, constriction, and thrombosis. The rate of the heart beat declines from birth (130 to 140) to about twenty-five years (70) and then increases gradually to reach nearly 80 at ninety-five years.[33] The heart rhythm becomes less regular. The arteries undergo sclerotic changes (hardening), and the rate at which the pulse beat passes along their walls diminishes.

Deaths from disturbances of the digestive organs are more frequently due to disease not directly related to wearing out of the system or ageing *per se*. Josh Billings wrote: "I have finally kum tu the konklusion that a good reliable sett of bowels is worth more tu a man than enny quantity of brains." [34]

In old age, a general atrophy of the brain, visible to the naked eye, is commonly present. Loss of weight accompanies this process, which is more marked in the white matter than in the gray matter. Pigmentary elements are found in excess in the brain cells, and the senile brain shows depositions of various substances, including free iron and complex formations throughout the cortex called "senile plaques." Physiologically, the reflexes become more sluggish and there is diminution of

[32] *Problems of Ageing*, edited by E. V. Cowdry.
[33] Cohn, "Cardiovascular System," p. 130, citing C. Bramwell, 1937.
[34] Quoted by Ivy, "Digestive System," p. 249.

motility. It is difficult, however, to distinguish clinically between changes in the nervous system due to senescence and those caused by cerebral arterio-sclerosis.

Comparison of the expectancy of life with the expectancy of sight shows that the normal life span of the eye as a functioning organ exceeds that of the body as a whole.[35] However, there is a steady fall of visual acuity with advancing old age. The extent of the visual field and the speed of dark adaptation decrease; the minimal threshold of light perception is raised, and there is a greater proportionate loss of visual acuity in dim illumination. The eyelids become thinner and less elastic; the cornea loses some of its luster and transparency; the color of the eyes fades, and the pupil gets smaller and reacts feebly. The pattern of the iris is obscured; the lens accumulates a larger and larger proportion of inert and desiccated tissue in its center, and because of loss of elasticity the range of accommodation is decreased; refractive changes are also involved.

Impaired hearing for high-pitched sounds must be regarded as the normal condition of old age. Average acuity of hearing for tones from *high c* of the musical scale upwards decreases with each decade of life, and hearing for extremely high tones is usually lost entirely. Hearing for low tones is not usually impaired in the elderly, but bone conduction is diminished.[36]

Performance tests of manual motility and reaction time show a gradual rise of speed capacities in childhood and youth and a slow decline from the fifth to the eighth decade. Whereas intelligence-speed tests show a marked decrement in old age, the elimination of the speed factor decreases the correlation of intelligence with age.

In old age, there is no noteworthy alteration of bodily temperature, nor of glucose content and hydrogen-ion concentration in the blood, but there is a progressive impairment of regulatory devices of body temperature, of acid-base balance in vigorous exertion.

The United States Life Tables calculate the number of 100,000 born alive surviving at each age, the rate of mortality per 1,000 at each age, and the average expectancy of life at each age. In the 1929–31 table, the number surviving to the exact age of 100 is 29. However, the proportion of centenarians in the population is probably much smaller than the calculations in such tables show. A painstaking study of the records of nearly a million persons by T. E. Young revealed satisfactory evidence of only 30 persons who had lived 100 years or more. Of these, 21 were women and 9 were men. The oldest person whom Young was able to

[35] Friedenwald, "The Eye," pp. 501–521.
[36] Guild, "The Ear," pp. 523–532.

discover was about a month and a half short of 111 years. It therefore appears that authentic centenarians are very rare indeed, although reputed centenarians are common.[37]

More males are born than females, and the death rate is at all periods of life higher in males than females. Many more females than males survive to advanced ages. Havelock Ellis summarizing data on the mortality of sexes concludes: [38]

The female is the mother of the new generation and has a closer and more permanent connection with the care of the young; she is thus of greater importance than the male from Nature's point of view. We therefore find the female—notwithstanding her greater affectability by minor stimuli—is more resistant to adverse influences and longer lived than the male.

Professor T. Wingate Todd has developed new and accurate methods of determing the age of skeletons and has conducted some illuminating researches upon the ages at death in primitive and ancient populations. The mean age at death of 189 West African Negroes, whose skulls are preserved in the Museum of the Royal College of Surgeons, was 30 years; only 2 of these lived to be more than 60 years of age. Of 32 native Tasmanians, more than half died at the age of 25 years or under; 2 attained 60 years. The mean of death age in an eleventh century fortress community at Scarborough, England, was 39 years. Eight of 143 individuals lived to be more than 60; the oldest was 74. Of 600 Indians who lived at Pecos, New Mexico, between 800 and 1838 A.D., only 60 attained the age of 65 years or more, and but 3 were octogenarians. Todd concludes that the difference between the peaks of mortality in primitive and ancient peoples on the one hand, and of modern civilized humanity on the other, is roughly 30 years; that "this difference does not indicate a prolongation of the potential duration of life which undoubtedly remains stationary through the ages"; and that the absence of the old age peak in the lower strata of modern civilized society is due to the hazards of life to which these unfortunate people are exposed.[39]

Among the White males in the original death registration states of our country, the expectation of life at birth increased from 48.23 years in 1901 to 58.84 years in the period 1929–1931, a gain of 10.61. However, at the age of 40, the corresponding gain was only 0.74 years, and, at higher ages, the gains are negligible. The situation in the case of females is substantially the same. It therefore appears that increased life expectancy in this country is almost entirely due to lowering infant mortality and

[37] Pearl, "Biology of Death," pp. 196–197.
[38] Ellis, *Man and Woman*, pp. 438–439.
[39] Todd, "Skeletal Records of Mortality," pp. 481–496.

eliminating certain diseases of childhood and curtailing conditions once thought typical of adolescence and early maturity.[40] We have not succeeded in stretching the life span.

The life spans of the subhuman primates are unknown. Even in the chimpanzee Yerkes states that there are no adequate descriptions of senility either in structure or in behavior, and the oldest male he has known alive was not beyond his fourth decade.[41] None of the three oldest gorillas in captivity in this country is estimated to be much older than 17 years. Zuckerman has compiled a table of average length of life in captivity and maximum years in captivity of various primates in the London Zoological Garden.[42] These maxima of life in captivity are: chimpanzee 26 years, 2 months; orang 26 years, 6 months; gibbon 24 years; mandrill 46 years, baboon 45 years, macaque 29 years, cebus monkey 25 years, marmosets 16 years, true lemurs 26 years. Todd says that most mammals have a life span of between 15 and 25 years, and the only mammals known to exceed 50 years of age are the Asiatic elephant, the horse, and man.[43]

Raymond Pearl has suggested that life is inherently continuous and that death appears in the course of evolution only in such multicellular organisms as have lost through differentiation the power of reproducing the whole body from a part of it, or have lost the necessary mechanism for separating a part of the body from the rest for such sexless reproduction. Somatic death results from the functional breakdown of an essential part of the organism from external or internal causes. Since life is a mechanism, death must be the result of physico-chemical changes in the cell or organism. The time of death is determined by the combined action of heredity and environment.[44]

The same writer, classifying the deaths in the Registration Area of the United States, in England and Wales, and in the City of São Paulo, Brazil, for a period of 10 years, finds that in all three localities the respiratory and the alimentary tract together account for more than half of the deaths biologically classifiable. These two systems are internal body surfaces, so to speak, and come into contact with food, water, and air, with all their bacterial contamination. The skin is also exposed, but, with its cornified and stratified layers, it is far more resistant than the mucous membrane of the alimentary canal and lungs.

The heart, arteries, and veins are next in importance in the location

40 Dublin, "Longevity," pp. 106–107.
41 Yerkes, *Chimpanzees,* p. 61.
42 Zuckerman, *Functional Affinities,* p. 27.
43 Todd, "Ageing of Vertebrates," p. 80.
44 Pearl, "Biology of Death," p. 214.

of diseases causing death, but, because the blood reacts against invading organisms and is, in a sense, an inner line of defense, it is not usually the first part of the fortress to give way. The nervous system causes more deaths than the excretory system. In the United States, the kidneys and related excretory organs are responsible for mortality to a greater extent than are the sex organs. The reverse is the case in England and Wales and São Paulo; in the former countries, because of premature births and cancer, in the latter, because of premature births and syphilis. But it may be that we are more squeamish about reporting deaths from syphilis than are the people of Brazil. The skeletal and muscular systems, the skin, and the endocrine organs are responsible for so few deaths as to be of little account.

During the first year of life, the alimentary tract is the most fatal system in both sexes. Thereafter, until the fifty-fifth year in males and the fiftieth year in females, the respiratory tract is the principal seat of danger. In the fifty-fifth year in males and the sixtieth year in females, the weakness shifts to the circulatory system and remains there until death, but the females show a temporary recurrence of first rankings for alimentary fatalities in the decade between 50 and 60 years.

Pearl also classifies mortality statistics according to the embryological germ layers from which the organ systems have developed. These germ layers are the entoderm (the primitive inner layer), the mesoderm (middle layer), and the ectoderm (outer layer). In the population areas dealt with, the investigation finds that about 57 per cent of all biologically classifiable deaths result from a breakdown of organs arising from the entoderm. From 8 to 13 per cent of deaths are caused by the ectodermal system, and the remaining 30 to 35 per cent are deaths due to malfunction or breakdown of mesodermal origin. Of course, the deaths arising from the disease of the alimentary and respiratory tract are of entodermal systems, and those charged to the circulatory system are of mesodermal origin. Pearl points out that in the evolutionary history of man and the higher vertebrates, the ectoderm has differentiated farthest from its primitive condition, a fact that is attested by the central nervous system. The entoderm has been least differentiated, and the mesoderm occupies an intermediate position. He therefore regards man's entoderm as his own greatest enemy. "Evolutionally speaking, it is a very old fashioned and out-of-date relic, which causes him an infinity of trouble. Practically all public health activities are directed toward overcoming the difficulties which arise because man carries about this antediluvian sort of endoderm." The strain put upon the excretory organs of the female in child bearing makes death due to breakdown of mesodermal organs almost equal to that caused by entodermal systems.

Usually the heart outwears the lungs, and the brain outlasts both. Professor Pearl explains these facts as the result of the purely mechanistic rather than intelligent nature of the evolutionary process. "It is conceivable that an omnipotent person could have made a much better machine, as a whole, than the human body which evolution has produced. He would presumably have made an endoderm with as good resisting and wearing qualities as the mesoderm or ectoderm. Evolution by the haphazard process of trial and error which we call natural selection, makes each part only just good enough to get by." But we need not agree with Professor Pearl's pessimistic conclusion, since it is evident that the ectodermal organs are much superior to the minimum requirements that he attributes to natural selection. They are more than "just good enough to get by." We have much larger and better brains than we need for the rough and tumble fight of natural selection. If we used our brains as hard as we use our stomach and lungs, the nervous system might not "get by" so easily. If the evolutionary development of various systems were entirely controlled by natural selection, our nervous systems would have reached only the least efficiency and durability compatible with survival, and all organs being reduced to the same level of mediocrity, we should go to pieces all at once like the one-hoss shay.

Natural selection is a restrictive rather than a creative force. It operates to eliminate such animals as possess variations in one system or another that are likely to prevent their living long enough to reproduce their kind in sufficient numbers to insure survival, or that are likely to make them produce progeny of an inferior quality that will in turn succumb before adequately reproducing their kind. Then, so far as biological survival is concerned, the minimum and maximum requirement for any system of an animal is that it be good enough to last the animal until he has fulfilled his reproductive function and exercised whatever parental care may be necessary for the safeguarding of immature offspring. Natural selection does not interfere with the further evolution of certain organs or systems toward a state of perfection that is not essential for biological survival. It merely establishes a lower limit of species or individual viability. Professor Pearl is perhaps right in his judgment that the processes of natural selection are "unintelligent" in that they are uneconomical, when some bodily systems are so durable that they are not yet worn out when death comes from the breakdown of weaker elements or parts.

If the expectation of life at birth is 58.84 years for White males and 62.37 years for White females, it is obvious that the average individual lives long enough to reproduce and rear offspring. A further stretching of the life span by prolonging the existences of those who have passed their reproductive period would hardly affect the survival of the species. The reduction of the mortality of infants, immature individuals, and the part of the population in its reproductive prime is all that matters. Dublin estimates that if there had been no deaths from cardiovascular-renal diseases in the general population as constituted in 1930, 7.2 years would have been added to the expectancy of life for White males and 7.5 years for White females.[45] However, such prolongation of life would affect principally the age groups of 40 years and upward, since this category of diseases as a cause of death is of little importance in the younger groups. The elimination of deaths from influenza and pneumonia in the 0–19 age groups (death rates: males 14.9, females 15.5) would preserve more of the young than would the removal of any other single cause of death. In the 20–39 age groups, the most important large categories of causes of death are tuberculosis (males 17.6 per cent, females 21.1 per cent), and for males accidents (25.0 per cent) and for females infections during child-bearing (15.3 per cent).

It is evident that, in so far as most of the modern prolongation of expectancy of life has been due to the lowering of the death rates in infancy and immaturity, it is a victory of human science over natural selection. For medicine, hygiene, and improved nutrition help the organism to withstand environmental adversities. The last-named may, and probably does, in addition, improve the quality of the stock itself. Yet there is room for doubt that this triumph of man over nature can be regarded as the strengthening of the weak rather than their preservation for the reproductive perpetuation of their infirmities.

In spite of a continually dropping infant mortality, the proportion of the younger age groups in our population is rapidly declining because of diminishing birth rate. The question then arises whether we have really licked natural selection after all, if we have rescued the perishing weaklings in their tender years, only to find that they grow up to be sterile.

[45] Dublin, "Longevity," p. 110.

Part IV. Fossil Ancestors and Collaterals

Why We Hunt for Ancestors

If we are descended from apes, our remote ancestors ought to look their part. We need not expect that men born at the beginning of the Christian era will prove to be any less human than ourselves; 2,000 years is but as a day in evolution. But the men of 100,000 years ago ought to display unmistakable signs of their relationship to giant primate forms. If we were to discover an ancestor removed from us by 30,000 generations or 1,000,000 years, we might reasonably expect him to be scarcely more human than anthropoid. Our forebears of the hundred thousandth generation might be claimed by a chimpanzee with a taste for genealogy as direct ascendants in his own family line.

You may not be willing to admit that you resemble an ape; if your thousandth ancestor is more like an ape than you are, you may, if you wish, call it a coincidence. But if that thousandth ancestor's forebears become progressively more simian as you trace back the genealogical lines, you will have to admit that somewhere in your family tree there squats an ape.

We can be sure that a murder has been committed only when we find the body. On the basis of contemporaneous animal clues, Darwin hypothecated for man an ape ancestor; no one as yet had found the body. Before Darwin died in 1882, skeletons of fossil men of definitely simian affinities had been brought to light. Scarcely a year now passes without the recovery of at least one more specimen of early man that bears witness to the accuracy of Darwin's theory of human descent. The reconstruction of the descent of man from fossil finds is like piecing together a picture puzzle with some parts lost and others in duplicate. We have most of the pieces necessary to make the foreground and a few parts here and there of the background. We cannot complete the foreground satisfactorily until we get more of the background, but we have enough of that to be pretty certain of the main outline of the picture. We are confident of digging up more pieces to fit into the puzzle, but we shall never get them all.

Let us, then, acquaint ourselves with these fragmentary but venerable

277

forebears, beginning with some that are out-and-out apes and perhaps not our ancestors at all but only fossil collaterals.

Toothy Mementos of Fossil Apes

The classic remark of Little Red Riding-hood, "Oh, grandma, what big teeth you have!" very nearly summarizes all of our earlier knowledge of fossil apes that would be of interest to a layman unversed in the intricacies of tooth pattern and unfamiliar with the really horrible jargon of the odontologist (a title obscuring the identity of a mere student of teeth). I have dealt briefly with the forbidding subject of dental evolution on pages 170–174 of this book. Since most finds of fossil apes and monkeys have consisted of nothing more than teeth, occasionally imbedded in fragmentary jaws, deductions about the course of primate evolution were necessarily made from this restricted field of evidence. Unfortunately, recent palaeontological discoveries of both human and ape remains in which teeth are accompanied by skull bones and other skeletal parts indicate that the definition of the zoological status of an animal and inferences concerning his phylogenetic position based upon teeth alone are most precarious. Early human types may have some teeth that are indistinguishable from those of apes and vice versa. Dentitions that would have been assigned confidently to early apelike forms of man have been discovered implanted in crania of veritable apes.

We can deduce from the assemblage of fossil primate remains of the various geological periods the approximate stage of evolution reached; we can observe the extent of specialization revealed by tooth pattern and the degree of resemblance to other forms of apes and men, fossil and contemporary, shown by the dentitions. Also some conception of the diffusion of primate forms throughout the world in ancient geological times can be gained from the distribution of finds, although these latter are limited by the extent to which various areas have been commercially exploited in excavations that reveal fossils by chance, or have been explored by palaeontologists looking for them.

The remains of the earliest anthropoid ape, *Propliopithecus haeckeli*, were found in Lower Oligocene deposits of a dried-up lake bed in Egypt called the Fayum. The Oligocene period may have begun 35 millions of years ago. In the same deposit occurred a mandible and teeth of the earliest known Old World monkey, *Parapithecus fraasi*. Of the latter it need be said only that it was a very tiny animal with small canines and unspecialized teeth suggesting an omnivorous diet. Propliopithecus is represented by a lower jaw, minus the ascending branches that articulate with the skull, but complete with its teeth. The entire tooth row of this first ape was only 30 mm. long, as contrasted with 51 mm. in the gibbon, the small anthropoid ape of today. The lower canines were not much enlarged, and the jaw was relatively shorter, deeper, and more pointed than the jaws of gibbons of today. The face was probably not so projecting.

In the Lower Miocene period, some 19 millions of years ago, there existed an Old World subfamily of giant apes known as the *Dryopithecus* group. The earliest and most primitive of these have been found in Africa, although the Dryopithecus apes were first known from several lower jaws and some teeth in the Upper Miocene and Pliocene deposits of Europe. Later, a much richer assortment of forms was recovered from the deposits of the Siwalik Hills, at the foot of the Himalayas in northern India. The Siwalik fossil apes date from the uppermost Middle Miocene to the Middle Pliocene. All of this family have "the fundamental Dryopithecus" pattern of the lower molar teeth, with three outside cusps and two inside cusps. The middle outside cusp is separated from its neighbors fore-and-aft by grooves that form the V of the letter Y. The lower and vertical part of the Y separates the two inside cusps from each other. Gregory calls this the Y5 pattern. Since this pattern and its derivatives are found in fossil and modern man, Gregory and others believe that the

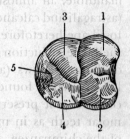

Fig. 43. The Y5 *Dryopithecus* pattern. Lower second left molar of *Dryopithecus frickii*. (After Gregory and Hellman.)

anthropoid apes of today and man had in these Dryopithecids common ancestors. There are, of course, other points of dental resemblance, but this lower molar tooth pattern is the most important. In all males of the Dryopithecus family the canines are tusk-like, but in females they are much smaller. Various evolutionary trends toward the present great apes can be detected in the successive types of Dryopithecus teeth assigned to different geological ages. One form, at least, foreshadows the orang-utan; several others seem to have been evolving in a gorilloid direction, and still others show affinities both with the dentitions of the gorilla and the chimpanzee. All of these fossil apes were much larger than Propliopithecus, and, judging from the teeth, some of them may have been bigger than the present gorilla. According to Gregory, Hellman, and Lewis, these Dryopithecus apes "were on a distinctly infrahuman grade of evolution."

One of the most prolific fossil primate areas has been discovered by Dr. L. S. B. Leakey in Rusinga Island and Songhor, Kenya, East Africa. Leakey and Dr. D. G. MacInnes have exploited these sites since 1932.[1] Here, in addition to sundry remains of fossil lemurs and monkeys, important fossil ape specimens have been discovered, referable, apparently, to the Lower Miocene. *Limnopithecus*, represented by fragments of mandibles and lower teeth, may well have been a development from the Fayum Propliopithecus in a generally gibbonoid direction. *Xenopithecus*, as the name implies, is a stranger, badly preserved and of dubious affinities. It may represent another offshoot of the Propliopithecus stock. *Proconsul africanus* is a big ape, represented by a crushed palate and part of the facial region of an adult with most of the teeth, a juvenile mandible, an almost complete adult mandible, and three tarsal bones (astragali and calcaneum). The adult lower jaw, the best preserved of any fossil ape heretofore found, is remarkable for the absence of the simian shelf, the reduction in size of the premolars, the anterior convergence of the tooth rows (as contrasted with the anterior divergence or parallelism usually found in apes), the humanoid form of the mandibular condyle (not preserved in any other fossil ape), the flat wear of the molar teeth as in man. The tarsal bones, when compared with those of the chimpanzee, also show slight approximations toward the human type.

The upper jaw of Proconsul is crushed and distorted so that it is impossible to determine the amount of its prognathism. The nasal bones are very narrow and long and are parallel as in the orang. The nasal aperture is exceedingly narrow. The canine is massive and projecting, but the reduction in the length of the tooth rows and the excess of breadth over length in premolars and molars do not indicate a very protrusive face. These new specimens of Proconsul agree in general with an earlier Proconsul find of Leakey, which was described by Hopwood, yet they show certain points that require a new estimate of this fossil ape's position. Instead of being ancestral to the chimpanzee, this fossil ape seems to have been nearer to the main ancestral line from which man ultimately was derived. It appears probable that the ancestral chimpanzee diverged from the main giant primate stock before the differentiation of the more specialized Proconsul form in early Miocene times.

We shall see that the fossil apes of South Africa developed in such a way as barely to miss the human mark. Perhaps some of them hit it!

[1] Leakey, "A Miocene Anthropoid Mandible from Rusinga, Kenya," p. 319.
MacInnes, "Notes on the East African Miocene Primates," pp. 141–181.

The South African Man-Apes

In 1925 Professor Raymond A. Dart of Johannesburg, South Africa, gave the name of *Australopithecus africanus* to a fossil brain cast and incomplete skull of a young anthropoid ape found in a limestone fissure deposit, of Pliocene or Lower Pleistocene age, at Taungs, near Kimberley, in the Transvaal. The brain cast has lost its covering bones, except the frontal, which is nearly complete. Most of the face is preserved, with 24 teeth—the 20 milk teeth and the 4 permanent first molars. These molars begin to erupt in man at the begining of the sixth year and in apes somewhat earlier. Probably the Taungs primate was about 5 years old at the time of its death. Dart considered this specimen to be a new type of ape, much closer to man than any fossil form heretofore discovered and possibly in the direct line of human descent. After fifteen years of lively discussion of the status of this fossil by many anthropologists, Professor Dart resurveyed the situation and was able to state: [2]

Thus today practically all competent authorities are agreed that Australopithecus is a genuine and unusual fossil type: that it is ultra-anthropoidal in status; that it is closely related to the living anthropoids but is far more intimately related to a series of extinct humanoid Pleistocene creatures in Southern Africa; and that, where it differs from the living anthropoids, it has made small but absolute advances in the direction of mankind.

The most recent palaeontological and geological evidence suggest that the sandy patches in the limestone breccia that yielded Australopithecus, as well as remains of fossil baboons and other primitive animals, are more likely of Pliocene than of Pleistocene Age. Indeed, Broom attributes this fauna to the Lower Pliocene.

In cranial and facial measurements, Australopithecus most closely resembles the living African apes, especially the chimpanzee, but in some generalized characters recalls the orang. It differs from all living apes in excessive facial shortening; short, wide, unfused nasal bones; high nasal aperture, and robust mandible. In face, prognathism, and head form, there is a similarity to the chimpanzee; in the vault, relatively high in comparison with its breadth, and in many features of the lower jaw, the resemblance is rather to the gorilla. Unlike all contemporary apes except the mountain gorilla, Australopithecus is dolichocephalic and is humanoid in its highly arched forehead and generally expanded cranium, the lateral contraction of the orbits under the forehead, the

[2] Dart, "Status of Australopithecus," p. 176.

rotation of the face downward, and the lowering of the nuchal plane of the occipital bone (the area of the attachment of the neck muscles). The last indicates an improved poise of the head, a slender neck, and (according to Dart) an erect body and the plantigrade habit. However, we must be cautious in allowing for the fact that Australopithecus was a juvenile. Young apes have smaller brow-ridges, higher foreheads, lesser jaw projection, and a more horizontal and forward position of the foramen magnum than do adults of the species. In my opinion, Professor Dart still fails to make sufficient allowance for the immaturity of his specimen.

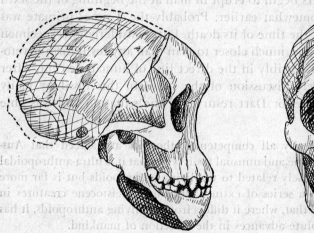 

Fig. 44. *Australopithecus africanus.*

The lower jaw resembles that of chimpanzees and orangs but differs from all apes in the massiveness of its body, the eversion of its hinder angles, in reduced height and the verticality of the symphysis, and in widening of the mandibular arch anteriorly. The canine teeth are small and do not project above the level of the other teeth more than do those of man; the incisors are small and almost vertical, not sloped as in apes. The milk molars are also small, and the permanent molars, although very large, are quite human in pattern.

Keith,[3] in a very elaborate study of Australopithecus, called attention to the scooped-out and orang-like profile of the face, which is inhuman; to the flat nasal bones, which recall those of the chimpanzee, although they are much wider; to the persistence on the face of the lines of the premaxillary sutures, which are visible in apes, but disappear precociously in man; and to the great size of the permanent first molars that

[3] Keith, *New Discoveries,* pp. 37–116.

augurs an adult dentition of a massiveness far exceeding man and the chimpanzee and approximating that of the gorilla. He considered the relation of palatal area to brain volume to be essentially apelike.

The cranial capacity of Australopithecus, according to Dart, was 520 cc., and the range in adult forms is estimated at 518–733 cc. This virtually overlaps the range of Pithecanthropus, the lowest known fossil man. Adult Australopithecids certainly had larger brains than chimpanzees and may have exceeded slightly those of the giant and lumbering gorillas, although the adult Taungs apes were probably agile, lithe, and not excessively large. Dart considers that three areas of the cerebral cortex exhibit expansions that are of special significance in prehuman types. The parietal cortex is greatly enlarged beyond those of living apes, so that the visual area has been thrust back to a humanoid position and the occipital lobes overhang the cerebellum in human fashion. The parieto-occipital association areas are so profoundly different from those of living apes that Dart considers their development explicable only on the supposition that manual and pedal experiences have been differentiated as a result of some revolutionary divergence in the creature's habits affecting the hands and feet, such as the assumption of the erect posture.

The prefrontal cortex shows a well defined, lower motor bulging and precentral depression, as well as a highly convoluted surface. These features connote greater manual dexterity, enhanced control of the orbital muscles, the masticatory muscles, and those of facial and vocal expression. The inferior temporal cortex, though expanded, lags behind the other two. There are some indications of a development indicating improved understanding of sounds and enhanced intellectual control of muscles concerned in maintaining balance during the performance of designed movements. Yet the absence of a widening of the temporal lobe and of localized expansion of the middle temporal gyrus indicate to Dart that Australopithecus had not acquired the power of speech.

These deductions from brain casts are somewhat speculative, but there can be no doubt that the cerebral development of this fossil ape was progressive in a humanoid direction, perhaps particularly in its lateral compression and increased height.

Dart makes the following inferences from the deposit in which the remains of the Taungs ape were found and its associated animal contents and from his consideration of the anatomical features of this fossil:

Australopithecus was terrestrial, troglodytic and predaceous in habit—a cave-dwelling, plains-frequenting, stream-searching, bird-nest-rifling and bone-cracking ape, who employed destructive implements in the chase and preparation of his carnivorous diet. The variety of the dietary: tortoises and lizards, fresh-water crabs, birds' eggs, rock rabbits, rodent moles, spring hares and antelopes, is witness to the ultra-simian agility and cunning of the hunter. . . . Only a methodical exploitation of every accessible source of food could render the existence of an ape in this untoward environment of Bechuanaland possible; it involved resourcefulness, agility and rapacious but social instincts, such as are evidenced in minor degree by living South African baboons.[4]

More temperate in our Australopithecine enthusiasm than Dart, we nevertheless must admit that here was a near-man (although still predominantly an ape) that failed of his destiny, if that was ultimately human. On the basis of teeth alone, it might have been claimed that Australopithecus was human. However, we must now admit that teeth do not make the man, although I am inclined to think that the loss of them may ultimately unmake him.

The tumult and the shouting about Australopithecus had pretty well died in 1936 when Dr. Robert Broom, the eminent South African palae-ontologist, decided that adult specimens of the same ape or an allied type ought to be obtained in order to settle the controversy about the status of this extinct primate, whether an apelike man or a manlike ape. In a couple of months he discovered in a limestone cave deposit at Sterkfontein, about 30 miles northwest of Johannesburg, a fairly complete cranial cast of an adult ape with much of the base of the skull and the face, together with the molars and premolars. Dr. Broom named this new specimen *Plesianthropus transvaalensis* (the Near-man of the Transvaal). Then, at the beginning of 1938, a boy brought Dr. Broom parts of an ape skull broken out of the breccia on the farm Kromdraai, in the same general vicinity, including, again, most of the face and many teeth, with no little of the brain-case. This fossil ape, also an adult, was christened *Paranthropus robustus*. The two new fossil apes have not yet been published completely,[5] but their teeth have been studied in detail, not only by Broom, but also by Doctors Gregory and Hellman of

---

[4] Dart, *op. cit.*, pp. 177–178.

[5] According to the latest Broom publication received by me ("South Africa's Part in the Solution of the Problem of the Origin of Man," pp. 68–80) the following is an inventory of the new ape finds made by him (cf. pp. 77–78):

Sterkfontein: 1936—Brain cast, most of skull of *Plesianthropus transvaalensis*, fragment of basal rim of left side of mandible.

        1937–1938—Maxilla of a female, maxilla of old male; many isolated teeth; parts of two brain casts; few postcranial bones, including distal end of a femur and a carpal bone.

Kromdraai: 1938—Left side of skull of adult *Paranthropus robustus;* mandible; parts of humerus, ulna, finger bones.

      1941—Part of mandible of young child of same species; milk teeth.

New York, who visited South Africa especially to bring their odonto-
logical wisdom to bear both upon these new discoveries and upon the
earlier find, Dr. Dart's Australopithecus. Both of these new fossil apes
are also of Pleistocene age—perhaps as late as the Middle Pleistocene.

The brain cast of Plesianthropus is estimated by Broom to have a
volume of about 440 cc. only, although the specimen is that of an adult
ape, probably a female. It is much shorter and relatively wider than the
brain cast of a large gorilla, especially across the frontal region. The
temporal lobes, as restored in the brain cast, are better developed than
those of the gorilla, but in actual size the brain is much smaller—no

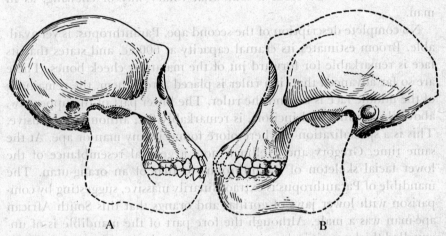

Fig. 45. A, *Plesianthropus transvaalensis*, B, *Paranthropus robustus*. (After Gregory
and Hellman.)

larger than that of an orang-utan. The face of Plesianthropus can be
reconstructed provisionally from the portions present in the type specimen and also from another right upper jaw, with many teeth in place,
that belonged to a second individual. Plesianthropus had moderately
large brow-ridges and a remarkably long nose, concave in profile, with
the nasal bones flaring inferiorly above a quite narrow nasal aperture.
The top of the skull lacked a bony front-to-back crest, such as occurs in
adult male gorillas and orangs; nor were the crests delimiting the attachments of the temporal muscles to the sides of the skull well marked. The
middle face was concave and the upper alveolar border excessively
prognathous and reminiscent of the orang. Most of the lower jaw is
missing, but it must have been massive.

The most recent reconstruction of the skull of Plesianthropus, by
Gregory and Hellman,[6] differs somewhat from the earlier efforts of these

[6] Gregory and Hellman, "Revised Reconstruction of the Skull of Plesianthropus."

students and from the figure used here to illustrate the specimen (Fig. 45). Based upon additional data, the dimensions of this new model lie mostly between the anthropoid and human limits, whereas those of Broom are chiefly in the anthropoid range. The revised model of Gregory and Hellman shows greater width across the parietals and in the minimum frontal diameter, a larger auricular (ear-hole to vertex) height, less protrusion of the face and jaws, a slightly longer face, and a wider nasal aperture. The orbits are somewhat larger than in the earlier Gregory-Hellman reconstruction. The facets of the upper canine and lateral incisor indicate an edge-to-edge bite, and the relatively flat crowns of the molar teeth a somewhat rotary way of chewing, as in man.

No complete description of the second ape, Paranthropus, is yet available. Broom estimates its cranial capacity at 600 cc. and states that its face is remarkable for forward jut of the malars or cheek bones. These are so far advanced that, if a ruler is placed across them, the remainder of the middle face is behind the ruler. The lower part of the upper jaw, above the canines and incisors, is remarkably flat, although protrusive. This is a specialization not heretofore found in any man or ape. At the same time, Gregory and Hellman note a general resemblance of the lower facial skeleton of Paranthropus to that of an orang-utan. The mandible of Paranthropus is extraordinarily massive, suggesting by comparison with lower jaws of gorillas and orangs that this South African ape-man was a male. Although the fore part of the mandible is of unequalled thickness, it is shorter antero-posteriorly than those of any fossil or contemporary apes examined by Gregory and Hellman. The prognathism of this ape was greater than that observed in any fossil man, but evidently less than is typical of apes.

The canine teeth of Plesianthropus are slender and short and not dagger-tipped as in modern female apes. The canines are not preserved in Paranthropus, but the socket and the root of an upper canine show that they were also quite small and un-apelike. The upper premolars of Plesianthropus come nearest in size to those of Sinanthropus, the fossil man of China. They also resemble Sinanthropus premolars in having two roots instead of three as in apes—a step toward the reduction to a single fused root, characteristic of modern man. The pattern of the upper premolars resembles the human condition in that the two cusps are almost equal in height, as contrasted with the ape form in which the outside cusp is much higher than the inside cusp. The lower premolars in both of these apes have two roots and show a stage of development intermediate between Dryopithecus apes and early fossil human types.

The molars of these adult fossil apes from South Africa greatly surpass in size those of the chimpanzee, of Sinanthropus, and of modern man. They are intermediate between those of the fossil Siwalik ape, Sivapithecus, and those of the gorilla, and agree with both of those apes in that the third molars are larger than the first molars, the reverse of which is the case in Sinanthropus and in most fossil and all modern men. The upper molars of the South African fossils have obtusely conical cusps that wear down into gently rounded surfaces as in man, which are unlike the sharply pitted wearing surfaces of these teeth in gorilla and chimpanzee. These latter apes are provided with more pointed molar cusps. The lower molars present typical Dryopithecus patterns, but with 6 cusps, as are found in certain human teeth but rarely in apes. The reconstruction of the palate of Plesianthropus shows that the dental arches diverged somewhat posteriorly, making its shape slightly parabolic as in typical men, and not U-shaped as in apes, with the tooth rows converging posteriorly. Altogether, the dentitions of these apes with reduced canines and lowered cusps of the grinding teeth suggest a change from the frugivorous habits of modern apes to omnivorous diets. The present apes use their tusk-like canines to pierce and hold tough fruits, bamboo shoots, sugar cane, etc. and their sharp-crested molars to chop this tough vegetable food into small bits. Primitive men use their sharp canines and incisors to hold and tear, and their flat-crowned molars to grind up flesh, small bones, and grain. Dart suggested that his Australopithecus killed baboons and broke open the skulls to eat the brains, since many broken skulls of fossil baboons were discovered in caves about Taungs.

Gregory and Hellman conclude that the South African man-apes were derived from the Dryopithecus-Sivapithecus stock of the late Tertiary of Asia and Europe and are both in a structural and a genetic sense the conservative cousins of man. Broom thinks that the Australopithecinae and man both diverged in Pliocene times from a common ancestral ape stock from which previously the Siwalik anthropoids and the ancestors of the gorilla and the chimpanzee had branched off. Gregory and Hellman are much impressed with certain resemblances between man and the orang-utan that also appear in the South African fossil anthropoids. They think that these may well be explained by a rapid and wide divergence of both orang and man from a chimpanzee-like ancestor and the supposition that the Australopithecinae are late Pleistocene survivors of the common stock from which man, chimpanzee, and gorilla were derived and hence retain many of the ancestral characters found in the orang as well as in man. This theory does not seem to me to clarify matters to any appreciable extent.

Although these Pleistocene apes of South Africa are undoubtedly much closer to man than any existing or extinct subhuman forms heretofore discovered, they lacked the brain overgrowth that is specifically human and perhaps should be the ultimate criterion of a direct ancestral relationship to man of a Pliocene precursor. Because they lacked brains, they remained apes, in spite of their humanoid teeth. Since the Australopithecinae died out in Africa, while the gorilla and the chimpanzee survived, it would appear that a thorough-going ape is better than half a man.[7]

Pithecanthropus Erectus: The Low-Brow Who Took a Chance on the Ground

The tropical island of Java is a severed portion of the ancient mainland of Asia. Today it is one of the most densely populated areas of the world, and in geologically ancient times it was the home of some of our hardly human ancestors. The great islands of Sumatra, Java, and Borneo are the remains of a sunken continent called Gondwanaland, the most of which was submerged before the elevation of the great Central Asiatic Plateau. The orang-utan dwells now in Sumatra and Borneo but formerly was at home also in Java. The gibbon is found in all three islands.

In 1890–1891, Dr. Eugene Dubois, later Professor of Geology at the University of Amsterdam, discovered in Java various remains of higher primates which he attributed to a being called *Pithecanthropus erectus* ("the erect ape-man"). No further finds of this type occurred in Java until 1936, when Dr. G. H. R. von Koenigswald, a most able and energetic palaeontologist of the Geological Survey of the Netherlands East Indies, made the first of a series of important discoveries resulting from an intensive search he had begun in the previous year. Subsequent finds have come thick and fast. Before listing and describing the remains now attributed to Pithecanthropus erectus, it is necessary to consider the sequence of geological strata and fauna that recent researches have established in Central Java.

---

[7] Although all and sundry human scientists have expressed themselves upon the relation of the Australopithecinae, no one seems to have thought it worth while to give them a chance to present their own views. Here they are—right off the ouija-board and in poetry (of a subhuman sort):

Cried an angry she-ape from Transvaal,
Though old Doctor Broom had the gall
    To christen me Plesi-
    anthropus, its easy
To see I'm not human at all.

STRATIGRAPHY OF JAVA [8]

Age	Zone	Fauna and Industries
Holocene	Recent	Present day
	Sampoeng	Neolithic, but with extinct mammals
Upper Pleistocene	Ngandong	High level terraces of the river Solo. Highly specialized *Stegodon*, *Elephas*, *Hippopotamus*. Solo man with Upper Palaeolithic industry
Middle Pleistocene	Trinil	Middle Pleistocene fauna: *Hippopotamus* and *Stegodon* highly developed, *Elephas namadicus*(?), fossil monkeys, gibbon, orang, *Pithecanthropus erectus*, crude stone implements
Lower Pleistocene	Djetis	Rich Lower Pleistocene fauna: *Epimachairodus*, *Felis*, *Hyaena*, *Rhinoceros*, *Hippopotamus*, *Homo modjokertensis*
	Kali Glagah	*Merycopotamus* absent; typical fossil, *Mastodon*
	Tji Djoelang	Typical Siwalik fauna: *Merycopotamus*, *Hippopotamus*, first appearance of *Stegodon*, a primitive elephant
	Tji Sande	First land mammals in Western Java; other parts still submerged

As a result of joint studies by Dr. von Koenigswald and Dr. Franz Weidenreich the following finds are now attributed to Pithecanthropus or to allied humanoid forms: [9]

1. Skull cap of Trinil (Dubois, 1891) *Pithecanthropus* I
2. Mandible of Kedung Brubus (Dubois, 1890), *Pithecanthropus*, mandible A
3. Juvenile skull of *Homo modjokertensis*, (Geological Survey, 1936)
4. Mandible of Sangiran (v. Koenigswald, 1936) *Pithecanthropus*, mandible B
5. Skull of Sangiran (von Koenigswald, 1937), *Pithecanthropus*, Skull II
6. Skull fragment of Sangiran, juvenile (von Koenigswald, 1938), *Pithecanthropus*, Skull III
7. Maxilla and skull fragment of Sangiran (von Koenigswald, 1939), *Pithecanthropus*, Skull IV (*Pithecanthropus robustus*, Weidenreich)
8. Mandible of Sangiran (von Koenigswald, 1939), *Meganthropus palaeojavanicus*, female, (possibly ape).
9. Mandible of Sangiran (von Koenigswald, 1941), *Meganthropus palaeojavanicus*, male.

Pithecanthropus I, a skull cap, was found by Dr. Dubois in a bone bed in the east bank of the river Solo, which rises among the volcanic hills of central Java and flows northeasterly toward the sea. The deposit has now been determined to belong to the Trinil zone (cf. outline above), which is Middle Pleistocene. In addition to the top of the skull, Dubois found here three teeth and a left thigh bone. Dr. G. S. Miller, Jr., has re-

[8] Von Koenigswald, "Stratigraphy of Java," pp. 24–32.
[9] Von Koenigswald and Weidenreich, "Pithecanthropus and Sinanthropus"; Weidenreich, *Giant Early Man*.

cently shown that these are the teeth of a fossil orang-utan. The skeletal parts were scattered over a distance of 46 feet and do not represent a burial, but bones washed into the deposit by the river. Dubois considered that teeth, skull cap, and thigh bone were parts of a single individual. The femur is estimated by Dubois to have belonged to an animal that stood 5 feet, 8 inches (1.70 meters), and weighed about 154 pounds. There is nothing simian about this straight and slender thigh bone, which is quite unlike the short and massive femora of the present great apes. A convexity or swelling on the posterior surface just above the knee joint (the popliteal region) is reminiscent of the condition found in the femur of the gibbon but may also be observed occasionally in the thigh bones of modern man. The marked development of the linea aspera (the longitudinal ridge on the back of the femur that affords attachment for the extensor muscle group) indicates an erect posture. Many years after the original discovery, Dubois reported upon portions of five other femora that he had found in his early Java explorations, which he also attributed to Pithecanthropus. Von Koenigswald and Weidenreich doubt the attribution, both of the original Trinil femur and of the subsequent specimens, to Pithecanthropus, principally because they differ from seven femora belonging to Sinanthropus, the closely akin fossil man of China, in lacking platymeria (a front-to-back flattening of the femur just below the lesser trochanter) and a poor development of the pilaster (the median posterior ridge of the bone), both of which features are constantly found in the Sinanthropus femora. The alleged Pithecanthropus femora are in all respects like those of modern man. In any event, these modern students of Pithecanthropus agree that this primate had an erect posture, because the foramen magnum in specimens recovered is in the modern human position, well forward on the skull base. Thus, since the adjective *erectus,* as applied by Dubois, seems to have been justified, it makes little difference whether one or all of the femora found by Dubois actually belonged to Pithecanthropus. My own opinion is that the original Trinil femur probably went with the skull of *Pithecanthropus I.* The differences between the skull and teeth of Pithecanthropus and Sinanthropus are sufficient to permit their femora to exhibit also certain divergences.

The skull cap of *Pithecanthropus I* shows markedly simian features. It is 184 mm. long, and the maximum breadth has to be estimated, since this diameter would occur low down, in a position below the part of the skull cap preserved. Keith thinks the maximum breadth was at least 135 mm., and von Koenigwald estimates it at 145 mm. If we accept the latter figure, the length-breadth index is 78.80—intermediate between the long-narrow and short-broad cranial categories. The actual length of the brain cavity in the interior of the skull cap is about 154 mm., so that 30 mm. of the total skull length is bone. The brain space is then 84 per cent of the length, as against 92 per cent in modern man and 73 per cent in adult male gorillas, according to Keith.

The vault of the skull is remarkably low and apelike. Keith orientated it on a horizontal plane running from the juncture of the external portion of the brow-ridge and outside orbital rim (the fronto-malar articulation) to the lower and hinder corner of the parietal bone (the main portion of the side wall of the skull). Above this line, the vaults of the anthropoids rise from 50 mm. to 60 mm. In *Pithecanthropus I*, the height above this plane is 74 mm., but in average skulls of modern man the elevation is about 100 mm. In all human skulls, the highest point of the skull vault varies from 1.5 to 2.5 inches behind bregma (the point where the transverse and longitudinal sutures meet in the top of the skull vault). But Pithecanthropus shares with the anthropoid apes the peculiarity of having the highest point of the skull just at bregma. The elevation of the post-bregmatic region is caused by the enlargement of the parietal lobes of the brain, which are association areas and centers controlling voluntary movements. It appears that these areas were poorly developed in the Java fossil.

The forehead of Pithecanthropus has little elevation and the supra-orbital ridges extend straight across the frontal bone in a simian bar or torus. The temporal crests of modern man diverge as they pass upwards; those of anthropoids converge at the vault, while those of Pithecanthropus are nearly parallel, as in young apes. The minimum width of the forehead is only 84 mm., which is much below the average of modern men's crania.

In this Java specimen, the attachments of the muscles that haft the skull to the neck rise high up on the occipital bone, nearly reaching its apex, which is called lambda. In anthropoid apes, these attachments rise above lambda, but in modern man they fall far below it. The head of Pithecanthropus was thus set upon his neck in a very apelike manner, such as has not been observed in any human type. The cubic contents of the skull have been calculated at 914 cc. Keith says that the brain capacity of orangs, gorillas, and chimpanzees ranges from 290 to 610 cc. Human racial means of cranial capacity vary between about 1200 and 1500 cc. A very small-brained man of pygmy stature may have a skull not much more than 900 cc. in contents. But the brain size of Pithecanthropus falls below the limit of normal individual human variation. It is intermediate in size between human and anthropoid ranges.

A rough idea of the characteristics of a fossil brain may be gained from the plaster cast of the interior of the skull. Such an endo-cranial cast bears upon its surface impressions of bony ridges on the inner walls of the skull, which are guides to the topography of the brain. The convolutions of the cerebrum do not come into contact with the skull walls, since the brain coverings, and, to some extent, the cerebrospinal fluid, interpose. However, a number of ridges and depressions of the skull walls do correspond to and define brain areas, so that the cast not only outlines the general shape and proportions of the brain, but even permits the anatomist to distinguish some few blurred details of pattern.

The frontal lobes are the latest acquisition of human brain specialization. In Pithecanthropus they are much smaller than in man, but larger than in the gorilla. The inferior convolution, identified as the area of speech, is distinguishable. The left frontal lobe of the brain is somewhat larger than the right, indicating that the Java primate was probably right-handed. The parietal lobes are emphatically expanded in comparison with those of the gorilla but distinctly inferior to human development; the occipital lobes also show an intermediate status. Tilney deduces from a study of the endo-cranial cast that the following advances from a lower primate stage are found in Pithecanthropus: [10]

1. The development of more extensive kinesthetic and motor capacity
2. The assumption of the erect posture
3. The freeing of the hand for manual performances and the inception of unidexterity
4. The expansion of visual and auditory sensibility
5. The development of speech
6. The establishment of human personality and the higher psychic faculties.

The skull of *Pithecanthropus II*, together with a part of a lower jaw, was found in the deepest part of the Trinil stratum at Sangiran, somewhat north of the Solo river, in 1937. Van Koenigswald had shrewdly established a fixed price for each fossil brought in to him by natives, but in this case the defect of the policy was revealed. The finder of the skull broke it up, either through ignorance or through guile, and brought von Koenigswald only one fragment. Subsequent pieces were brought in, one by one, later, and each was paid for separately, but important portions of the skull may have been lost in the process. Altogether some 30 fragments were recovered. Most of the skull vault is present, except the right side of the frontal bone, but the face and a large part of the base are missing. All of the sutures of the skull vault are obliterated, so

[10] Tilney, *The Brain*, Vol. II, pp. 883–884.

that the specimen must be judged to have been fully adult. This skull is slightly smaller than that of *Pithecanthropus I,* but otherwise the specimens are as nearly alike as two peas. The postorbital notching or constriction, the apex of the vault at bregma, and the other typical features of this early fossil man are all present. The second specimen is only about 180 mm. long (according to Weidenreich, 176.5 mm.) and about 140 mm. wide, but the bones are extraordinarily thick. The inner length of the brain case is 82.22 per cent of the outer length, and the external length-breadth index is 77.78.

The temporal bone, missing in the type specimen, is well preserved in this second example. The glenoid fossa (the socket in the temporal

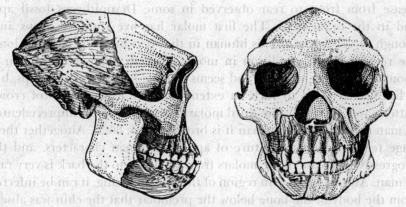

Fig. 46. *Pithecanthropus erectus* male. (After Weidenreich's reconstruction.)

bone that lodges the condyle of the lower jaw) is excavated as in man, not flat as in apes. In *Pithecanthropus II,* the mastoid processes, to which are attached the muscles that turn the head, are worn off. Weidenreich states that they were undoubtedly present, though small, as is usual in females.[11]

The cranial capacity of this skull is only 750 cc., as contrasted with about 900–914 cc. in the first Pithecanthropus. Both specimens were probably females, and it seems likely that a male skull would be somewhat larger.

The lower jaw fragment from Sangiran (*Pithecanthropus,* Mandible B) was collected in the absence of Dr. von Koenigswald but appears to have come from the Trinil zone that yielded Pithecanthropus. It consists of the greater part of the right half, minus the ascending ramus (the vertical branch behind the dental row). The second premolar and

---

[11] Weidenreich, *Skull of Sinanthropus,* p. 63.

all three molars are preserved in their sockets. The jaw had been embedded in conglomerate and was thoroughly fossilized. The alveoli, or sockets, of the first premolar and canine are present, although filled with a rock-like deposit, and it may be deduced that the canine was neither unusually large nor projecting to any great extent. The second premolar is a very large and apelike tooth but closely comparable with second premolars found in Sinanthropus, the fossil man of China. The combined length of the three molars is about 40 mm.—considerably greater than that found in any other fossil man and almost as great as the length given by Gregory for orang molars (42.4 mm.). The molars increase in size from the first to the third—contrary to the case in modern and most other fossil men and in accord with the increase from front to rear observed in some Dryopithecus·fossil apes and in the orang-utan. The first molar has five rounded cusps and, though of very great size, is human in that it is broader than it is long, the reverse of the condition in most ape teeth. The second molar is about as broad as it is long and seems to have had five or six cusps, but it has been eroded to such an extent that the exact details of crown pattern are obscured. The third molar is of a size almost unprecedented in man and much longer than it is broad (index 86.2). Altogether these huge teeth present a mixture of ape and human characters, and the progressive increase of the molars from the front to the back is very rare in man. Although the chin region of the jaw is missing, it can be inferred from the body of the bone below the premolar that the chin was absent and the symphysis sloped sharply backward. But there was no simian shelf (cf. p. 167). The small fragment of a Pithecanthropus mandible discovered by Dubois at Kedung Brubus, 32 miles from Trinil, includes a bit of the rim, the first premolar, and the socket of the canine. It agrees in character with the larger fragment found by von Koenigswald and adds little to our knowledge of Pithecanthropus lower jaws. Since the mandibular fragment from Kedung Brubus is a part of a much shallower jaw than the Sangiran fragment, it is probable that the former lower jaw belonged to a female and the latter to a male. On the whole, the characteristics of these jawbones are primitively human rather than apelike.

The skull fragment of *Pithecanthropus III* was also found in the vicinity of Sangiran. It has not been fully described but seems to consist of the larger part of the right parietal bone and about half of the left parietal of an immature individual. Along the middle line of the skull, where the two parietal bones meet in the sagittal suture, there is an elevation like the ridge-pole of a roof. This sagittal elevation appears in other Sinanthropus and Pithecanthropus specimens and is common enough in modern skulls of small cranial capacity. It is not a simian feature.

Pithecanthropus IV consists of most of the posterior half of a skull (the most massive prehominid skull ever found, according to Weidenreich), including the hinder part of the base, and an upper jaw (maxilla) with all of the teeth in place except the incisors and the last two molars on the left side. This upper jaw is very large but not so prognathous as might be expected. The lower part of the nasal aperture is preserved and seems to be of a primitive human type—broad with poorly defined lower borders and a rudimentary nasal spine. The roof of the palate is smooth, as in the apes. The teeth are huge, and the molars increase in size from front to back, as in the lower jaw. Here, for the first time in fossil man, the upper canines of both sides are separated from the lateral incisors by a broad diastema, or gap, the width of which on

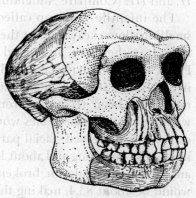

Fig. 47. *Pithecanthropus erectus* male. (After Weidenreich's reconstruction.)

the right side is about 6.2 mm. (as against 6.8 mm. and 6.2 mm. in male orangs). This gap in apes ordinarily permits the interlocking of the canines, since it receives the point of the lower canine. The canine preserved is much worn, but it must have protruded to a moderate extent. The first upper premolar has three roots as in apes, and the second is larger than the first—another simian feature. The upper dental arch was comparatively long and narrow, but the tooth rows diverged backward as in man. The patterns of the upper molars are obscured by wear and no detailed description of them is available. The single lateral upper incisor present is shovel-shaped (the back is hollowed out), a feature common in modern man, especially in Mongoloids. The back of the head of *Pithecanthropus IV* had been caved in by a blow with a club or stone weapon, when the bone was fresh. The individual, who from the size and thickness of the skull must have been an adult male, thus came to a violent, but possibly not untimely, end. No full description of this hinder portion of skull vault and base is available, but it is stated that the occipital torus is pronounced. There is a keel-like saggital crest composed of more or less isolated knobs. From published drawings it appears that the glenoid fossae were human and bounded anteriorly by well

developed articular eminences; the tympanic plates were also human in
conformation, the mastoid processes quite well developed, and the foramen magnum in a modern position—well forward on the skull base and
not sloped from before upward and backward as in apes. An erect posture
is again indicated by the occiput and skull base of this specimen. Because
of its giant size, diastema, and smooth apelike palate, Weidenreich has
some doubt that *Pithecanthropus IV* belongs to the same group as *I,
II,* and *III.* (Compare Addendum, pp. 414–421, for new data.)

The infantile skull cap called *Homo modjokertensis* was found in a
small, shallow excavation in the Djetis zone, which underlies the Trinil
zone. It is, therefore, attributed to the Lower Pleistocene, whereas other
Pithecanthropus material is Middle Pleistocene. The skull was imbedded
in sandstone and thoroughly fossilized. The bones are so thin that it
must have been recovered from the place where its owner died; any
washing about of the bones would have disarticulated them. The skull
cap only is preserved; facial parts and teeth are missing. The brain-case
is only 138 mm. long and about 115 mm. in its greatest width, when allowance has been made for broken parts. Thus, the length-breadth index
would be about 83.4, making the skull brachycephalic or round-headed.
The height of the skull cap from the ear holes is 62 mm.—exactly the
same as that of the adult female, *Pithecanthropus I.* In this infant specimen, guessed to be about 18 months old, the forehead appears to be
steep, not sloping, and the brow-ridges are undeveloped. Yet measurement of the angle of the frontal bone reveals that the forehead has less
of frontal elevation and more slope than is found in modern men of
such tender age. Again, although the brow-ridges are undeveloped, there
is a marked notching of the region behind the outside of the orbital
rim (a so-called postorbital constriction), which is completely lacking in
modern infantile skulls and gives sure promise of the sharp narrowing
of the forehead behind the supraorbital bar, or torus, that would have
developed during the later phases of growth, had these occurred. In
the cranial vault, where the corners of the frontal halves and the parietals
meet, and in similar positions in the temporal and occipital regions, there
are always to be observed in infants the so-called fontanelles. These are
irregular gaps covered with membrane where the corners of the bones
have not yet ossified. In this infant specimen from Java, the fontanelles
are much smaller than would be expected in a skull of such tiny size and
tender age, and furthermore, the sutures are more advanced in their
development and state of ossification than is typical of an infant under
two years. In the modern baby, when the fontanelles have closed during
the course of the second year, the size of the brain is such as to make

the skull much larger than that of this little fossil Javanese. The glenoid fossa in the temporal bone, which lodges the condyle of the lower jaw, is quite human in form, but further advanced in ossification than would be expected in so young a subject. Altogether, the small size, precocious ossification, incipient postorbital constriction, and other features of this infant skull seem to justify von Koenigswald's conclusion that it is, in fact, an infant Pithecanthropus.[12]

In the many years when Pithecanthropus was represented only by the original finds of Dubois at Trinil, there was no little controversy about the status of this apelike and, at the same time, humanoid primate. Dubois at first considered it truly intermediate between man and the apes. Strangely enough, in his old age, when the important subsequent discoveries of von Koenigswald had conclusively established the primitive human status of Pithecanthropus, Dubois, the original finder, swung over to a view earlier favored by a number of anthropologists; that the Java fossil was only a gigantic ape allied to the gibbon. This position is now completely untenable. Pithecanthropus seems to have been an erect-walking primate with a brain that in size and conformation had far surpassed that of any known fossil ape and was more human than simian. Although the dentition and morphology of the skull show a mixture of anthropoid ape and humanoid characteristics, the scales are tipped strongly toward the human side. The face was projecting and chinless, the nose broad and probably low-bridged, but quite unlike that of an ape; the jaws were massive and equipped with formidable teeth, but not tusk-like canines. Above the orbits was a massive transverse bar of bone,

[12] The janitor of the Peabody Museum has passed on to me a crumpled bit of paper that he picked up from the floor in front of the case in which the cast of the baby Pithecanthropus is on exhibition. He says that he noticed a frustrated-looking Radcliffe student gazing wistfully and prolongedly at this case and he thinks she may have written this pitiable effort:

ODE TO HOMO SOME-JERKTENSIS

Young Pithy from your Djetis bed
You raise a scarcely human head,
With all its soft spots ossified
And sutures closed that should gape wide.
Your marked postorbital constriction
Would clearly justify prediction
That had you lived to breed your kind,
They would have had the childish mind
That feeds upon the comic strips
And reads with movements of the lips.
They would have had no need for braces
To warp their teeth into their places—
Equipped for general mastication
And not progressive education,
In place of brows a bony torus,
And no ideals with which to bore us.

behind which sloped the exiguous forehead to a very low-crowned, gable-shaped vault. The upper part of the brain-case was narrower than the base—a very apelike feature. The back of the head, with the lower portion shelving sharply downward and forward, was buried in the neck muscles attached very high up along another tranverse crest or bar. The archaeological evidence shows that primitive stone implements occur in the same geological strata in Java that have yielded the ape man. It seems highly probable that Pithecanthropus was already a tool-user. It also seems probable that the Javanese specimens of Pithecanthropus represent the late survival into the Pleistocene of an archaic type that must have come into being at least in the Middle or Upper Pliocene. Java was a refuge area where out-moded fauna lasted for a longer time than in continental centers, since, by their isolation, they escaped competition with more progressive and more highly evolved forms. An anatomically advanced and virtually modern form of man may well have existed in Europe when the apish Pithecanthropus still reigned in Java.

As yet undescribed, except a few casual references to it by Weidenreich,[13] is the fragment of a human mandible with three teeth *in situ*, discovered in 1939 in the Sangiran district of Central Java, from which the more recent Pithecanthropus finds have come. It is much larger than that of any ape or fossil man heretofore recovered. Yet it is distinctly human in character, and von Koenigswald has proposed for it the name *Meganthropus palaeojavanicus* (which is certainly big enough for a giant). Weidenreich says that the mandible and teeth are much too large to belong to *Pithecanthropus IV*, and their presence proves that several types of early hominids lived in the Far East, some of which exceeded in size and massiveness of their cranial bones all forms hitherto known. The chin region has a humanoid cross-section and the first indication of a mental spine; the enormous teeth are unquestionably human. Weidenreich thinks that this new Java discovery makes it probable that the huge *Gigantopithecus* lower molar found by von Koenigswald in South China, which is even larger than the new Java Sangiran teeth, should be assigned to a human, rather than an anthropoid, owner. (Cf. Addendum, pp. 414–421.)

Sinanthropus: The Earliest Connoisseur of Human Brains

In the middle twenties there was a great ballyhoo sent out from certain scientific quarters about Central Asia as the birthplace of man. Explorers penetrated the Gobi desert with the avowed intention of

13 Weidenreich, *op. cit.*, pp. 216, 224, 229.

finding man's earliest ancestor and returned in triumph with the eggs of dinosaurs. They promised men but delivered eggs. However, the great American public was satisfied, although some anthropologists became skeptical of the reality of this central Asiatic cradle of mankind. Nevertheless, from 1927 onward, until the Japanese occupation of Peiping arrested archaeological excavations, a succession of discoveries of one of the most ancient types of man took place in the neighborhood of China's ancient capital. In the history of human evolution, these finds are of the very first order of importance.

Choukoutien is a town about 37 miles southwest of Peiping, China. It lies at the foot of the western hills of the Chili plain, where the Ordovician limestone has been quarried in large masses to supply numerous lime kilns. In the limestone, fossil beds have been discovered, mostly in the periphery of a small hill, 60 meters high, where clefts or caves have been filled up with deposits of red clay and angular pieces of the rock. These deposits have become so hardened by calcareous infiltrations that they usually remain in place as solid dykes after the surrounding limestone has been quarried away.

The first finds of fossil "hominid" teeth in these deposits occurred as early as 1922, and in 1927 Professor Davidson Black, of Peking Union Medical College, recognized the importance of the features of a lower molar tooth discovered *in situ*, and announced the establishment of a new genus of man, *Sinanthropus pekinensis*. Intensive excavations of the various sites were begun, and 1929 revealed the first, almost complete, brain-case of Sinanthropus.

The age of the deposits in the caves or fissures is largely determined by the fauna. The strata that have yielded Sinanthropus skeletal remains and tools are apparently Middle Pleistocene to Lower Pleistocene. The animals in the cleft deposits seem to be the same from top to bottom and include a big beaver, a primitive water buffalo, a deer with thickened jaws and short, flattened antlers, as well as rhinoceroses, hyaenas, bears, rodents, and other mammals. This fauna is quite distinct from the later fauna of the so-called Loessic period, which is characterized by the woolly rhinoceros, the spotted hyaena, the bison, the mammoth, and other animals. The Loessic fauna is Middle and Upper Pleistocene, while the Choukoutien cave fauna is identical with that elsewhere in North China assigned to the Lower Pleistocene and the Upper Pliocene, although the most archaic forms are not found at Choukoutien.

The earlier Sinanthropus finds were competently described by Professor Davidson Black, whose lamentable death occurred in his early middle age in 1934. Fortunately, he was succeeded by Professor Franz

Weidenreich, an experienced and distinguished physical anthropologist, who has studied the later Sinanthropus material most exhaustively and quite admirably.

In 1938 the number of individuals in the Sinanthropus collection was approximately 38, most of them represented by teeth, jaw fragments, and odd bits of skulls. Six skulls have the vaults more or less preserved. About 40 per cent of the individuals represented were children up to the age of 14 years. Three skulls may have belonged to persons under 30 years, three within the age range of 40 to 50 years; one fragmentary skull may have been that of a really old woman.

The Sinanthropus skulls are somewhat larger than those of the Pithe-

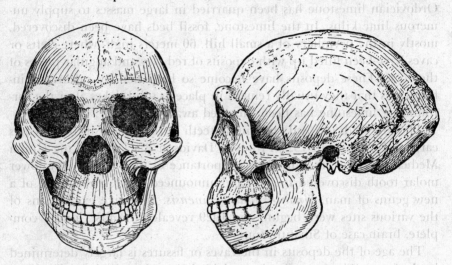

Fig. 48. *Sinanthropus pekinensis* female. (After Weidenreich's reconstruction.)

canthropus people, but much the same in form. Weidenreich calculates the range of cranial capacity in Sinanthropus from 850 cc. to 1300 cc., with an average of 1075 cc. The cranial capacity of three Pithecanthropus skulls, according to the same author, averages 860 cc. The maximum lengths of Sinanthropus skulls range from 165 mm. to 205 mm., with an average of 194 mm., which is probably considerably above the Pithecanthropus mean. The average maximum breadths of Sinanthropus skulls apparently vary from about 137 mm. to 143 mm., and these again exceed those of the two Pithecanthropus specimens. The greatest breadth of the skull vault in Sinanthropus is low down on the side walls of the skulls, just above the ears—an apelike feature. Total height of Sinanthropus vaults is about 115 mm., against about 105 mm. in Pithecanthropus. The length-breadth index of Sinanthropus skulls averages

72.2, which is very long-headed, as are also the majority of fossil and modern human skulls.

The Sinanthropus forehead is receding, but there is a distinct bump on the frontal of most specimens that is missing in Pithecanthropus. The heavy, projecting frontal torus is separated from the forehead by a distinct furrow, also lacking in Pithecanthropus. A prominent ridge or sagittal crest runs down the middle of the skull from front to back, and on either side the parietals are flattened, giving a gable-shape to the vault. This same feature occurs in Pithecanthropus and in some modern skulls, notably those of Eskimo and Australians. There is also a well developed occipital crest or torus, which not only extends across the entire occipital bone, but also is prolonged into the lateral mastoid region and is continued in a supramastoid crest. The frontal and occipital tori and the sagittal crest are a part of a reinforcement system that forms the architectural framework of the skull. Nothing of this sort is found in the apes. In Sinanthropus, and even to a greater extent in Pithecanthropus, the cranial bones are extremely thick and massive, much more so than in any ape.

The frontal sinus (an air space in the thickness of the frontal bone above the root of the nose) is very small in Sinanthropus, in contrast with its large size in Pithecanthropus.

The face of Sinanthropus is relatively small but projecting. It is extremely broad in comparison with its length—a feature that contrasts with the relatively very long faces of the great apes. The nasal bones are much broader than those of modern man, and the nasal bridge is broad and relatively high. The nasal index (relation of breadth of nasal aperture to height of nose) averages 57.2, which is excessively broad and comparable with the values in modern Negroes. However, the nasal floor is separated from the alveolar process of the upper jaw by a low ridge. There is no nasal spine. The upper jaw is not sunken or hollowed out below the orbits, as in modern man. The palatal arch is relatively wider than that of the apes, but narrower than that of modern man. The surface of the palate is rough, traversed by crests and ridges, as in modern man. Pithecanthropus, like the anthropoid apes, has a smooth palate. The Sinanthropus malar (cheek bone) is very high and juts forward as in modern Mongoloids. The orbits are capacious, but they may be relatively high or relatively low.

The cranial sutures of the Sinanthropus skull appear to close at an earlier age than in modern man—an apelike character that is even more pronounced in Pithecanthropus.

Weidenreich has also studied exhaustively the fragmentary lower jaws of 11 Sinanthropus individuals. The male mandible is much larger and bulkier than that of recent man, but the female lower jaws, though large, do not fall outside of the range of modern Mongolians. The index of robustness is obtained by taking the thickness of the jaw at the level of the mental foramen and dividing it by the height of the body of the jaw at this point. This index amounts to 48.3 in the male Sinanthropus jaw, as against 38.9 in recent Mongolian man. However, the Sangiran jaw of Pithecanthropus is considerably thicker at that point than is any Sinanthropus mandible. The chin region slopes backward more sharply in Sinanthropi than in any human jaw measured except the Heidelberg jaw. While there is no proper mental eminence or bony projection forward in the chin region, there is an incipient triangular elevation of this region and a very slight indentation of the profile of the jaw just below the incisor tooth roots. The roots of the anterior teeth in the lower jaws are so deeply implanted that a strong concavity just above the bony chin eminence, such as is found in modern man, would be impossible. The interior of the backward sloping symphysis of the mandible shows no simian fossa and simian shelf. There is a real mental spine for the attachment of the genio-glossal muscles (cf. p. 167). The shape of the lower dental arch is a long and relatively narrow curve, with its frontal part rounded and not flattened as in recent man. The hinder ends of the arch approach each other (converge), in spite of the great breadth of the ascending branches and condyles. On the whole, the jaws show more primitive human than simian features.

Many Sinanthropus teeth have been found, the lower molars all with five or six cusps and variations of the Dryopithecus pattern. The molars often have complicated wrinkles of the enamel on their crowns, recalling the teeth of orang-utans. The premolars are apelike in their oblique oval shape and in the development of a heel or talonid. The upper canines in the males are larger than the lowers and rather projecting, the upper incisors shovel-shaped.

Pithecanthropus molars are much bigger than those of Sinanthropus, and the simian increase in size from the first to the third molar found in the Java man is missing in Sinanthropus. Apparently, however, the lower canines and incisors of Sinanthropus are larger than those of Pithecanthropus. Yet, thus far, there has been found in Sinanthropus no apish diastema or gap between upper canines and lateral incisors, such as occurs in the *Pithecanthropus IV* upper dental arch.

Apart from teeth and pieces of the skull, only a very few skeletal fragments of Sinanthropus have been discovered. There are seven pieces of femora, two of humeri, one broken clavicle, and an isolated wrist bone (the right lunate). Yet the Sinanthropus deposits abound in animal bones.

The thigh bones are human in every particular, but possess some peculiarities. They are short and slightly bent, with the apex of the bend below the middle of the shaft at the place of smallest circumference. They also show marked front-to-back flattening in the subtrochanteric region (upper fifth of the shaft) and in the popliteal region (just above the condyles). The linea aspera, indicative of the erect posture, is present, but the strongly marked ridging of the middle of the posterior surface of the shaft (the pilaster), usually found in the femora of modern peoples that walk with a bent-knee gait, is little developed. This pilaster, when present, is surmounted by the linea aspera (the rough line to which the extensor muscles of the thigh are attached) and is supposed to buttress the shaft of bowed bones. In the subtrochanteric region, the medial and lateral borders are developed crest-like—a common enough feature of platymeric femora. A marked convexity of the medial border in the upper half of the shaft is reminiscent of chimpanzee thigh bones. The cross sections of the femora show that the central or medullary canal is very narrow and the walls correspondingly thick, with their thickness extending up to the very head end of the shaft—much farther than in modern man. The internal structure of the upper part of the human femur, where the head and neck are joined to the shaft, is marked by an elaboration of spongy or cancellous tissue, beautifully arranged in delicate trabeculae ("little beams") in such a way as to combine maximum strength and resistance to stresses with minimum weight. These so-called "trajectorial systems" are much less differentiated in the femora of Sinanthropus than in modern man, and still less so in the apes. The thigh bones of Sinanthropus are less stout, less bowed, and (in my opinion) less apelike, than those of Neanderthal man, whose femora also lack extensive trajectorial development and a few other advanced features that are absent in the early Chinese type.

The Trinil femora, associated by Dubois with Pithecanthropus, are even more modern in their features than those of Sinanthropus. It is for this reason that Weidenreich rejects the association.[14] As far as Weidenreich can estimate by attempting to complete the missing ends of femora, one of the male Sinanthropi (Femur IV) stood about

[14] It affords the present writer some amusement to note that discoverers of fossil man rarely seem to doubt the validity of attributing a mess of scattered bones to one individual, or at least to one species, when the discoveries are their own, but when someone else discovers a skull in one part of a bone bed and a femur or a jaw in the same deposit but separated, these students lose their credulity and are likely to become extremely skeptical. This psychological idiosyncrasy is by no means limited to Professor Weidenreich.

156 cm. (5 feet, 1½ inches). This makes the fossil man of China about as short as Eskimos, Ainu, and Japanese. If the women bore the modern relation of their stature to that of the males, the average height of the Sinanthropus women would be 144 cm. (4 feet, 8½ inches). However, this possibility brings up a point that Weidenreich emphasizes—hitherto neglected in this discussion. The Sinanthropus jaws and teeth and skull bits are divided into two groups—one of which is marked by very large size and the other by great inferiority in this respect. Weidenreich thinks that the big teeth, heavy jaws, and very thick skull parts belong to males, and the thinner, more fragile bones and small teeth to females. He is probably right. Recall that there is an enormous size discrepancy between the males and females of gorillas and orang-utans—a difference reduced in the chimpanzee and virtually absent in the gibbon. However, if Sinanthropus males are as short as calculated, one might expect the females, in view of the above argument, to fall considerably below the ordinary ratio of female-male stature.

The collar bone and the humeri and wrist bone of Sinanthropus show no unhuman or remarkable features—at least none worth discussing in this elementary volume.

One tidbit of Sinanthropiana has been reserved for the closing paragraphs of this abbreviated description. For the most part, only the skulls of Sinanthropus seem to have been brought into the caves at Choukoutien and, with the exception of the few fragmentary postcranial parts mentioned above, there are simply no long bones, vertebrae, etc. in the deposits. It appears that these skulls were trophies of head hunters, and, furthermore, that said hunters usually bashed in the bases of the skulls when fresh, presumably to eat the brains therein contained. Many crania also show that their owners met their deaths as a result of skull fractures induced by heavy blows.

The question naturally arises: "Who dunnit?" Professor Weidenreich argues powerfully that, since the Sinanthropus deposits yield remains of no other kind of man save Sinanthropus himself, it follows that this amiable precursor of modern Mongoloids (Weidenreich's genealogy, not mine) must have been addicted to cannibalism. I see no reason why this revelation should be inordinately shocking, in view of the fact that *Homo sapiens* has frequently been a cannibal, not only in remote times and among savages, but recently (only rarely, one hopes), when cast away in small boats, on rafts, and on desert islands.

Weidenreich's theory that Sinanthropus is the ancestor of the modern Mongoloid division of mankind rests upon some 12 peculiar features of skull and teeth and limb-bones. The first of these is the possession of scoop shovel-shaped upper incisor teeth, which are inordinately common among Mongoloids but by no means absent in other racial types. The second is a thickening of the bony alveolar processes on the inner side of the lower jaws, commonly known as the mandibular torus. This feature occurs at a maximum in modern Eskimo, but is by no means confined to them. Most of us attribute it to excessive strains put upon the teeth in chewing and regard it as physiological, functional, and not hereditary. Sometimes these bony lumps on the inside of the mandible are clearly pathological—tumors of a sort. The third alleged Mongoloid feature is the keeling of the top of the skull in the middle line—the sagittal elevation. So far as I know, this feature is commonest in the native Australian and occurs sporadically in all races. I doubt that it is as common in Mongoloids as in Negroids and Whites. Other allegedly Mongoloid features found in Sinanthropus include: the Inca bone (a transverse suture cutting off the upper part of the occipital bone so that the latter forms a separate triangular bone); broad nasal bones with little difference between upper and middle breadths; supposedly Mongoloid resemblance of the profile of the nasal bridge; sharply angled, frontally oriented malars; bony growths (exostoses) on the outside of the palate, and thickening and bony growths in the auditory meatus; platymeria (the flattening front-to-back of the upper part of the shaft of the femur). Most of these features do appear oftenest in Mongoloid skeletons, but none of them is limited to that division of mankind. Some of them are generally considered functional or adaptive rather than hereditary, and the bony growths on palate, mandible, and tympanic plate are frequently regarded as pathological.

Weidenreich was able to check 74 of 121 cranial characters of Sinanthropus (excluding the teeth and the lower jaw) upon the Pithecanthropus material. In 57 of the 74 characters the two types agreed; 8 were doubtful and 5 accidental. The 4 exceptional characters are: size of the brain-case, in which Pithecanthropus is definitely inferior; absence of a bump on the frontal bone and larger frontal sinus in Pithecanthropus; the more primitive smooth form of the palate in Pithecanthropus; the apelike gap between the canine and the lateral incisor in Pithecanthropus (diastema). If the mandible and teeth are included, further more primitive features of Pithecanthropus are to be noted: the greater robustness of the frontal part of the mandible, the increase in the size of the molars from front to back. On the other hand, Weidenreich points out some dental features of Sinanthropus that are more apelike than the conditions found in Pithecanthropus.

Weidenreich concludes that, on the whole, Pithecanthropus and

Sinanthropus represent about the same level of human evolution but two different regional or racial variations of that stage.[15] He is unwilling to admit that Pithecanthropus is the more primitive type, although practically all differences—and some are important—point to such a conclusion. That the types are closely akin is, however, incontestable. Weidenreich also maintains that modern man descends directly from the Sinanthropus-Pithecanthropus stage through the intermediate fossil type of Neanderthal man. We may defer this problem for later discussion.

Dame Eoanthropus: The First Female Intellectual

England and France produce great amateurs of science. An English parson or a French priest is more than likely to be an authority on local antiquities or upon butterflies or moths; the town clerk may have an international reputation as a folklorist. Nor are these interests confined to the educated and well-to-do classes. The pioneer student of the earliest implements of man was a petty customs house official in France, and the discoverer of the most ancient human artifacts in England was a grocer.

Mr. Charles Dawson was a lawyer who lived in the historic town of Lewes, Sussex, where the river Ouse flows through a gap in the South Downs to empty its waters into the English Channel at Newhaven. For more than twenty years, Dawson employed his leisure time in searching the strata of the Weald for finds of interest to natural science. About eight miles to the north of Lewes is a fertile wooded land with quaint villages and comfortable farms. In this charming Sussex country is Piltdown Common, a moorland tract lying 120 feet above the sea.

In 1908, Mr. Dawson was walking near Piltdown Common along a road that had been mended with some peculiar brown flints, unusual in the district. He learned that these flints were dug from a gravel bed in a nearby farm and shortly afterward visited the place. There he inquired for bones and fossils and urged the workmen to keep a lookout for such finds. Sometime later, one of the laborers handed Mr. Dawson an unusually thick piece of a human parietal bone, but many searches failed to reveal any further animal remains. Mr. Dawson, with true British perseverance, continued at intervals to visit the pit and, in the autumn of 1911, picked up, on one of the rain-washed dumps, another and larger piece of the same skull, including a part of the left brow-ridge. He then enlisted the cooperation of Sir Arthur Smith-Woodward, the great palaeontologist of the British Museum, and together they made a

15 Ibid., p. 274.

systematic search among the spoil heaps of the gravel, to be rewarded in the spring of 1912 by the finding of the larger portion of a fossil human skull.

The gravel pit lies by the side of the road in the lane leading up to Barkham Manor, an English farmhouse. The gravel has been laid down in strata by running water; its sand and stones are cemented together by iron oxide, and everything in it is stained a deep brown. Underneath the gravel deposit is a thin layer of yellow clay and, below that, the Hastings Beds, ancient rock deposits of the Weald. The human remains came from the lower and darker layer of the gravel just above the clay. Here were also found dark brown eoliths—crudely worked implements that had been washed into the ancient bed of the Ouse—some of them with rolled and abraded edges and some with the cutting edges still sharp. Battered fragments of the teeth of Miocene and Pliocene forms of elephant, of the hippopotamus, and of a beaver came out of the same fossil bed. The upper stratum of the gravel, which is lighter in color, yielded up some flint implements that were not stained as dark as the eoliths and the animal remains. These upper implements are better chipped and shaped than the eoliths and have been attributed to the pre-Chellean industry, a vaguely characterized class of flint work that occurs in the early Pleistocene period, succeeding the formless eoliths.

The gravel deposit on Piltdown Common was laid down when the river Ouse was meandering over the plateau that is now 120 feet above sea level. Since then it has cut its valley down 80 feet, and the great expanse of gravel, almost 100 square miles, has been elevated. When the Ouse flowed over the Piltdown plateau, the English Channel was the bed of a great river that drained the southern area of the Weald and of which the Somme and Seine were probably tributaries. There is little reason for doubting that the Piltdown man lived near the beginning of the glacial period. His age is estimated from 200,000 years to 1,000,000 years. For the moment we need concern ourselves no further with the prodigal drafts upon time made by geologists.

The fragments of the Piltdown skull recovered include the larger part of the left side of the frontal bone with the outer portion of the orbit, almost the whole of the left parietal bone and about two thirds of the right, most of the lower part of the occipital bone including the hinder margin of the foramen magnum, almost the entire left temporal bone, the nasal bones, the right half of the mandible, and a lower canine tooth. Since one half of the skull is almost an exact duplicate of the other half, it is possible to reconstruct the missing side from the corresponding parts of the side found. All of the skull bones are very thick,

averaging from 8 to 12 mm. as against a modern range of 4 to 8 mm.
There is no question of a pathological thickening.

Each half of a lower jaw or mandible consists of the horizontal tooth-bearing part—the body—and the portion that extends up to the temporal bone and articulates with it, called the ascending ramus. The latter terminates in a knob or condyle that fits into the articular socket of the skull base. In the half of the Piltdown jaw recovered, the condyle and a portion of the chin region are missing. The rest of the jaw

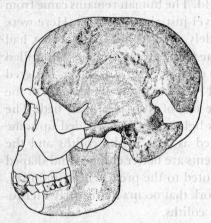

with the second and third molar teeth is intact. It is almost indistinguishable from that of a chimpanzee. The chin region does not jut out in human style but falls away as in apes. We have discussed the evolution of the human jaw in a previous section (pages 162–169), and the reader will do well to refresh his memory on these points. In the Piltdown mandible, the origins of the genio-glossal muscles which work the tongue are in a pit, behind which there projects a simian plate or shelf.

Fig. 49. Restoration of the Piltdown skull (Eoanthropus dawsoni). (Drawn with a camera lucida from the British Museum cast.)

The canine tooth, found some time after the rest of the mandible, is a massive projecting tusk much like that of a female chimpanzee. The molar teeth are, however, within the human range, and the jaw, while large, is not enormous. Keith estimates the area of the palate constructed to fit this jaw at 53.2 cm., as contrasted with 26.6 cm., the average of twenty-two British medical students, 36.5 cm. in a female chimpanzee, and about 70 cm. in male orangs and gorillas.

When compared with the completely apelike jaw, the brain-case of the Piltdown specimen is not obviously simian. In the fitting together of the fragments and the parts restored from the opposite side, there developed a notable controversy between Sir Arthur Keith and other anatomists. The original reconstruction of Sir Arthur Smith-Woodward had a contracted and apelike forehead and an ill-filled and roof-shaped cranial vault with enormously projecting face and jaws. The brain-case was also markedly lopsided. Dr. Smith-Woodward called the new specimen Eoanthropus dawsoni ("Dawson's Dawn Man"). Because of the small brow-ridges and mastoid processes, the skull was thought to be that of a female.

Keith objected to the Smith-Woodward reconstruction of Eoan-thropus on the ground that the right side was markedly smaller than the left, whereas we expect primitive men and apes to have notably symmetrical skulls. He maintained that the middle line of the skull vault had been incorrectly identified, in that a portion of the left parietal had been pushed over the median line to the right side so as to thrust both of the lateral skull walls inward toward the center line, thus reducing the height and breadth of the vault. Keith re-identified the center line, pulling both parietals outward. The resulting restoration yielded a much more capacious brain-case with a cubical content of 1500 cc. as against the 1070 cc. of the original Smith-Woodward restoration.

In the course of further reconstructions, Keith admitted the asymmetry of the Eoanthropus brain-case, and Smith-Woodward placed the right and left parietal fragments farther apart, so that the two main disputants converged in their opinions to the extent of agreeing that the cranial capacity of Eoanthropus was 1358 ± 1 cc. This figure is about the average generally given for adult European females, but Sir Arthur Keith (1938) has now changed his mind about the sex of the specimen and thinks that it may have been male. He undertook a complete re-survey of the whole Eoanthropus reconstruction problem (having written nearly an entire volume about it in 1913) as a result of the find of the Swanscombe skull, which he considers to represent a later Pleistocene descendant in the Piltdown line. We shall discuss the Swanscombe find in later pages of this book, but here it is desirable only to summarize Keith's new findings on Eoanthropus, the brain-case of which he has re-reconstructed.[16] Meanwhile Smith-Woodward also did a new reconstruction of the skull, and other versions were produced by Elliot Smith, Friedrichs, Weinert, et cetera.

Keith's new reconstruction gives Eoanthropus a maximum cranial length of 195 mm., which is only 1 mm. more than that of his earlier edition. However, he has now modelled the frontal bone upon a frontal fragment of Piltdown II, discovered by Mr. Dawson in 1915. This makes the lower part of the forehead almost vertical and the upper part of the frontal nearly horizontal. He points out that the frontal region and brow-ridges of Eoanthropus seem to have differed from those of other fossil men in resembling the conformation of those areas in a young orang rather than a chimpanzee or a gorilla. In the orang, the brow-ridges are raised bands moulded to the curved upper rims of the orbits, as if the upper one third of the rims of tortoise-shell spectacles were pasted to the top edges of the orbits. There is no continuous bony bar, and the

16 Keith, "A Resurvey."

supraorbital ridges do not unite in the center to form an elevated glabella region. Keith says that the Piltdown frontal fragment recovered in 1915 shows this peculiar separation of the rim-like brow-ridges in the middle. Keith states also that it is possible to discern the orang-like beginning of the supraorbital rim or band in the fragmentary left external angular process of the original Eoanthropus, but it seems to have escaped him in his earlier work, and the present writer must admit that he never has noticed this feature on the cast. This frontal bone, according to Keith's latest ideas, is elevated in the middle like that of an orang, and he states that, from the frontal markings alone, he would say the Eoanthropus belongs to an entirely different phylum of ancient man than Sinanthropus and Pithecanthropus.[17]

Other features of Keith's new reconstruction of Eoanthropus include a slight lowering of the vault, a pronounced occipital asymmetry whereby the left occipital lobe of the cerebrum deviates far to the right of the center line of the skull, and, conversely, the right lobe of the cerebellum extends over to left of the center line; a downward bulge of the entire basal or cerebellar part of the occiput, which is modernistic and in-

[17] Here I wish to relegate to a footnote several very technical points of resemblance of Eoanthropus to anthropoid forms that are hardly comprehensible to the elementary student. The first is that Keith now says that he read the asterionic region of Piltdown incorrectly and that he is convinced that it resembles the Swanscombe skull and those of anthropoid apes in that the lateral sinus passes directly from the occipital to the temporal bone, instead of crossing over and grooving a hinder and lower angle of the parietal. This mistake was made because a missing part in the asterionic region of the original was credited to the parietal instead of to the temporal.

Keith now thinks that the pterion region of the Piltdown skull had a fronto-temporal articulation as in gorillas and chimpanzees, instead of the spheno-parietal contact usual in man. This condition also exists in Swanscombe. Associated with this *pterion retourné* is an unusually extensive squamosal articulation on the lower border of the parietal, and it is the anterior part of the temporal squama that makes contact with the frontal by a very shallow dovetail process. Incidentally, Keith's reconstruction gives the squamous suture an extraordinarily high arch.

The interior of the skull in the pterion region also shows an unusual feature, according to Keith, where the Sylvian fissure divides the frontal from the temporal lobe of the brain. Keith asserts that the Sylvian margin of the frontal bone, instead of ending in a sharp Sylvian falx (a sickle-shaped ridge), forms a wide, curved, elevated surface as in the anthropoid apes, which is hitherto unknown in human skulls. In conformity with this peculiarity, the brain cast shows that the third frontal convolution is more anthropoidal than in any other fossil man, because the area of the orbital and triangular opercula, instead of rising into a bulging convexity, is cylindrical and low. Keith thinks that the entire pattern of the frontal lobe was primitive and simple.

Weidenreich (*Skull of Sinanthropus*, p. 2 and passim) contests Keith's opinion as to the significance of the Sylvian falx or crest. He considers it not a progressive feature but rather a structural reinforcement of the skull and notes that it is extremely well developed in Sinanthropus, Pithecanthropus, and in some Neanderthal skulls, and frequently present in the orang. He thinks that it was present in a common ancestral form and lost independently by modern man and the gorillas and chimpanzees. Weidenreich, who firmly disbelieves in the antiquity of Eoanthropus, regards the absence of a Sylvian crest in that form as an evidence of modernity.

fantile as contrasted with the flat, upward-shelving nuchal or inferior occipital plane observed in apes and in fossil forms that show a high attachment of the neck muscles.

This latest Keith reconstruction gives the Piltdown brain-case a length of 194 mm., a parietal breadth of 150 mm., an auricular height of 110 mm., and a capacity of 1358 cc. The cranial index is 79.4—on the verge of round-headedness. The foramen magnum is sloped slightly upward and forward; the attachments of the neck muscles are low on the occiput; the poise of the head on the spinal column must have been ultra-human and the posture of Eoanthropus erect.

Although the present writer is not wholly convinced of the correctness of some of Sir Arthur Keith's latest revisions of the Piltdown brain-case, there can be no doubt of the essential humanity of this portion of the Eoanthropus anatomy. But we are now confronted with the difficulty of being asked to believe that with this capacious and noble-browed skull there went an almost completely apelike jaw. Some students have attempted to resolve this difficulty by assigning the jaw to a chimpanzee or an orang-utan and the brain-case to a man. Such attempts to reconstruct two animals of widely different types out of complementary parts from the same deposit, and presumably belonging to one individual, are the result of a misconception of human evolution. Evolution is not a harmonious progression of all parts of the organism; it is a jerky and asymmetrical transformation. Some parts of the body, such as the upper limb, remain much as they are in primitive reptiles; others, such as the foot and lower limb, evolve rapidly to adapt themselves to a new function. The human body is like an old house that has been modernized only where modernization is necessary. It has a new foundation and the topmost story is greatly enlarged, but the wings are old. Only a few readjustments have been made in the plumbing, wiring, and lighting.

It is quite wrong to expect all forms of fossil man to display the same balance in the development of their bodily parts. If the brain of your great-grandfather is 15 per cent smaller than yours, you must not conclude that his jaws should be 15 per cent larger, his arms 15 per cent longer, and his legs 15 per cent shorter. Human stocks did not evolve along the lines of one fixed and immutable pattern any more than have the anthropoid apes. The association of a simian jaw with a human brain-case need not disturb us more than the association of a human thigh bone with an apish skull cap in the Sinanthropus fossils.

The lower jaw articulates with the skull base in the temporal region. In modern mandibles, the condyles or knobs of the ascending branches of the jaw fit into deep hollows in the temporal bones, called the glenoid fossae. In front of these fossae are rounded elevations, the articular eminences. The hind walls of the glenoid fossae are formed mainly by the tympanic plates, which encircle the entrances into the bony ear. When you move your jaw in opening your mouth or in chewing, the condyles slip forward onto the summits of the articular eminences. In the lateral movements of chewing, one condyle is somewhat in advance of the other and slips back into its socket before the other comes to rest. The pulling forward of the mandible in opening the jaws is accomplished by the action of the pterygoid muscles, which have their origin in bony plates running upward behind the hard palate and are inserted inside the angles of the ascending branches of the jaw. The closing movements are accomplished by the temporal and masseter muscles, which originate on the sides of the skull vault and the lower borders of the zygomatic arches and are also attached to the ascending branches, the temporals along the internal and anterior face, and the masseters on the outside. The rotary chewing movements are directed toward the center line—that is, in masticating food on the left side, the lower jaw grinds toward the right, and vice versa. These inward grinding movements tend to wear the crowns of the teeth in a slope toward the center line of the palate, so that the crowns of the lower left molars slope upward and inward when deeply worn; and those of the left upper molars have a corresponding inclination. On the right side, the slopes are reversed. The "tripping" of the condylar knobs against the articular eminences accelerates the opening of the jaws. The condyles of the jaws slipping forward upon the articular eminences give more room between the molar teeth for the grinding of food.

In anthropoid apes, the condyle of the jaw does not fit into a deep glenoid depression but moves on a slightly convex articular plateau. The back wall of the temporo-mandibular joint is not formed as in man by the tympanic plate, but by a bony ridge called the postglenoid process, running inward in front of the auditory opening. The jaw of the ape does not rotate laterally in the movements of chewing because the interlocking canines do not permit such movements. The ape chews straight up and down. Hence, the wear on the crowns of the teeth tends to cause blunting of the cusps and pitting of the indentations between the cusps as the upper and lower teeth interlock. For, each conical cusp fits into an inter-cusp depression in the opposing tooth above or below. Thus, the teeth of an old gorilla show wear on the molar crowns in the form of hills and hollows. The crowns are not worn flat or sloping as in man.

Now, the temporo-mandibular joint in Eoanthropus is a deeply excavated glenoid cavity with a high articular eminence before it, as in modern man. Condyles of the human shape are required to fit into the glenoid fossae. Unfortunately, the condyle is missing from the half of the mandible recovered. So it cannot be proved that the jaw belongs with the skull by fitting it to the temporo-mandibular joint. This absence of the condyle has afforded yet another opportunity for the separatists to affirm the lack of kinship between mandible and brain-case. They allege that the lower jaw, being almost wholly simian in shape, should be equipped with an apelike condyle that would not fit the modern type of glenoid fossa in the temporal bone. A further difficulty lies in the fact that a long projecting canine tooth, evidently a lower canine, has been recovered, and we should expect jaws with protruding apelike canines to be fitted to the shallow articular plateaus of the anthropoid rather than to the deeply excavated glenoid fossae of modern man. In order to fit the simian jaw to the human socket, we must model upon the mandible a humanly shaped condyle that is incongruous with the rest of the bone. This little difficulty need not, however, embarrass us. If nature puts conjoined human and anthropoid parts into the same organism, some compromise has to be made at the junctures.

Because the skull base of Eoanthropus, as reconstructed by Keith, is of considerable breadth and the sockets of the mandibular condyles are far apart, the two halves of the lower jaw must be spread posteriorly in order to articulate the jaw to the skull. This necessitates a departure from anthropoid jaw proportions. The great apes have long narrow jaws in which the molar tooth rows converge toward the rear so that the space between the molars is actually less than between the canines. In conformity with this narrow, U-shaped dental arcade, the ascending rami of the anthropoid jaws are moderately close together. The narrow skull base makes the distance between the glenoid fossae relatively small. Thus, the Piltdown jaw cannot be fitted to the skull without modelling the missing side and the symphysis in such a way as to cause the tooth rows to diverge posteriorly and the condyles to be spread far apart, thus imparting to the whole jaw approximately human shape and proportions in bicondylar breadth and hinder spread of the dental arch. Such a restoration increases the tongue space and provides for its movements in speech.

The association of the long canine tooth with a deep glenoid fossa and a pronounced articular eminence creates, as we have said, a dilemma. The crown of the tooth in question rises about 14 mm. above the neck and is pointed. In female anthropoids, whose canines are much smaller than those of males, the canine crowns rise from 16 to 20 mm. above the necks. In human races of today, this elevation is rarely more than 12 or

13 mm. (Keith). The greatest diameter of the crown of the Piltdown canine also exceeds that found in modern man, and the broken root was probably of more than human length. The crown of the tooth is hollowed by the grinding on it of an opposed tooth of the upper series, but the way in which it is worn differs from that found either in anthropoid apes or in man. In anthropoid apes the canine teeth are in the lateral or side series, but, in man, they have become reduced in size and are rather a part of the front or incisor series. In the chimpanzee, the lower canine crown fits into a V-shaped gap between the upper lateral incisor and the upper canine, which latter tooth is farther back in the upper jaw than the opposing mandibular canine. Thus, in the chimpanzee, the canines act as shears, the point of the lower one impinging against the outer edge of the upper lateral incisor and the anterior edge of the upper canine, while the upper canine fits into the gap between the lower canine and the first premolar and grinds against both of their edges. Since the lower canine of a chimpanzee is worn both anteriorly by the upper lateral incisor and posteriorly by the upper canine, its inner or lingual aspect presents two worn surfaces separated by a ridge, showing the areas abraded by the opposing upper teeth. In the Piltdown tooth, there is no ridge delimiting the areas of incisor and canine wear, but the whole inner surface is deeply excavated. Keith thinks that this wear is due to the upper lateral incisor alone, and that the missing upper canine ground only against the lower first premolar. He explains this condition by the inference that, in Piltdown man, the lower canines had already been displaced from the lateral series to the front series and that by their approximation the chief tooth opposing the lower canine became the upper lateral incisor instead of the upper canine.

In modern man, the blunt conical canines are, as stated, in the front series and are used for biting in exactly the same way as are the incisors. The lower jaw has receded so that the incisors no longer meet edge-to-edge as in primitive man and the anthropoid apes, but the lower ones bite behind the uppers, making what is known as an "over-bite." In Keith's opinion, the canine of Eoanthropus represents a transitional stage in the conversion of a projecting, shearing canine of the lateral series to a short, blunt-cusped canine of incisor function in the front series.

The molar teeth of Eoanthropus are longer from back to front than from side to side—an anthropoidal characteristic. Instead of the molars decreasing in size from the first to the third, the second molar is larger than the first and the third as large as the first. In modern man, the third molar is the smallest and the first the largest of the series. In the gorilla, the molar teeth increase in size from front to back. Thus, as regards molar tooth size, Eoanthropus is in a class midway between modern man and the apes. The lower molar teeth of modern man often have but four cusps. The fifth hinder cusp belongs to the ancestral Dryopithecus pattern and is preserved in many modern savages. This fifth cusp is well developed in the surviving molars of the Piltdown specimen. Since the molars of Eoanthropus are ground flat, rotary chewing movements must have taken place, as suggested by the character of the glenoid fossae. The canines could not then have interlocked.

The face of the Eoanthropus must be reconstructed from forehead and brow-ridges, the nasal bones, and the lower jaw. Fortunately, in 1915, Mr. Dawson found three fragments of a second Piltdown skull on the surface of the plateau two miles distant from the site of the first discovery. These were a portion of the frontal carrying the inner side of the right orbit, a portion of the middle of the occipital bone, and a left lower molar. These new finds ought to settle the case of the association of the original jaw with the skull, since the second specimen shows the same broad and high vaulted forehead, and the molar tooth is declared to be identical with those found implanted in the original jaw. The new fragments could not, however, have belonged to the first skull, since they were found at too great a distance from the site of its discovery.

The nasal bones are flat and broad, much like those of modern Negroids or Australians. The external angle of the brow-ridge, together with the root of the zygomatic arch attached to the temporal bone and the articulated lower jaw, give some idea of the width of the face. This was moderate. When the jaw is articulated to the skull base and the coronoid process put at the correct level with reference to the zygomatic arch, it is seen that the face was not overlong nor remarkably projecting. Details of the nasal aperture are of course impossible of restoration. It seems clear, however, that the nasal bridge was low and broad and the aperture wide. From the heavy, but not greatly prognathous, jaws the mandible dropped away in chinless fashion.

Keith's recent recognition of the orang-like brow-ridges and frontal region of Eoanthropus recall the fact that Friedrichs in 1932 argued that the lower jaw and molars of the Piltdown find were in fact those of an orang-utan, and he and Weidenreich proposed to dissociate this mandible from the skull and give the former the name and status of a new fossil ape—"*Boreopithecus.*" To the present writer it is inconceivable that a fossil orang should have roamed England in Lower Pleistocene times, since no remains of fossil great apes have ever been discovered in England and none in the whole European continent later

than Miocene times. There is, however, the supplementary evidence of
the orang-like character of the original teeth associated by Dubois with
Pithecanthropus I, which von Koenigswald has dismissed as those of a
fossil orang and quite alien to Pithecanthropus. It is one thing to attribute teeth to a fossil orang in Java, where the animal doubtless dwelt
in the late Pliocene, and quite another to hypothecate an ape of this
kind in England in the Pleistocene. Finally, we have the opinion of
Gregory and Hellman to the effect that the South African fossil man
apes show marked resemblances in some ways to orangs and their suggestion that the convergence of human and orang characters may be
due to a common and rapid separation of both of these animals from a
prototypical, chimpanzee-like precursor. Putting together all of these
disjointed opinions and scraps of evidence, there emerges the probability
that some nearly human and fully human types of early man paralleled
the orang in teeth, brow-ridges, forehead conformation, and concavity
of the middle face, whereas others resembled rather the chimpanzee-
gorilla line with surpraorbital tori, fleeting frontal regions, and mid-
facial prognathism.

Herr von Heidelberg: His Bark Was Worse than His Bite

Six miles to the southeast of the university town of Heidelberg is a
huge sandpit, close by the little village of Mauer. This pit has been dug
through the valley deposits of a stream that flows into the Neckar river,
itself a tributary of the Rhine. The pit has been worked down almost
to the valley bottom, which is about 440 feet above sea level and 260
miles from the mouth of the Rhine. Because of the clear stratification of
its glacial deposits and the remains of fossil animals found in its bed,
the Mauer sandpit has long been a favorite place for explorations of
geologists and palaeontologists. Dr. Otto Schoetensack, lecturer on geology at the University of Heidelberg, made almost daily visits to this
pit for a period of 20 years, hoping that it would yield the remains of
an early form of man. In 1907, his patience was rewarded, when the
owner wrote him that a primitive human jaw had been found at a depth
of 82 feet. In his subsequent monograph upon this important discovery,
Dr. Schoetensack described 24 strata overlying the resting place of the
mandible.

The uppermost layers are known as the "recent loess," a fine mixture
of sand and clay laid down by floods and blown in during the droughts
of the last 10,000 or so years. This deposit is more than 18 feet in depth.
Below are 17 feet of "ancient loess"—also a sandy loam, but laid down

in the glacial epoch. Then follow a series of stratified sands in the middle of which are beds of clay and sandy clay almost 13 feet in thickness. Ten feet below this clay bed the Mauer jaw was found. The animal remains recovered from the pit include *Elephas antiquus,* the Etruscan rhinoceros, a type of horse transitional between the Pliocene horse and the modern kind, bison, two types of bears, a dog, a lion, wildcat, beaver, et cetera. These animals lived in a warm climate and suggest the Pliocene age, which precedes the glacial epoch. However, geologists are of the opinion that the Mauer jaw belongs to the Pleistocene. It will be recalled that the glacial epoch consisted of four advances of the ice sheet, separated by periods of considerable duration in which the climate became warmer. Geologists have usually attributed the Heidelberg jaw to the first or second interglacial period, with the probabilities favoring the former. Now Zeuner, who has resurveyed the stratigraphic evidence, assigns it to the interval between the first and second phases of the Mindel glaciation, the second great glacial advance.[18] One wonders whether the stratigraphic and palaeontological evidence justifies such a precise dating (Mindel I, 476,000 years ago; Mindel II, 435,000 years).

The Heidelberg man may have been a geological contemporary of the Piltdown Lady, but he was no near relation of that early English intellectual. Had they met, they would scarcely have been on speaking terms. They were no more alike than are the orang-utan and the chimpanzee.

The Heidelberg man is represented only by his well preserved lower jaw with all of its teeth in place. But what a jaw it is! It considerably exceeds in size even the prodigious chimpanzee-like chewing apparatus of the Dawn Lady. The body is thick, deep, and chinless; the ascending ramus is of enormous breadth (60 mm. as compared with 37 mm. in moderns). The chin region falls away as in apes, without any vestige of a forward jutting mental process. The genio-glossal muscles take their origin from a simian pit or fossa, instead of from the tubercles characteristic of man. But there is no simian shelf strapping together the two halves of the jaw at the symphysial region, such as regularly occurs in apes and is a feature of the Piltdown mandible. The lower border of the body of the mandible is concave as in baboons, contrary to the condition found in anthropoid apes and man.

Perhaps the most astonishing feature of the Heidelberg find is the discrepancy in size between the teeth and huge mandible in which they are implanted. Actually, the teeth are of quite ordinary size. A hasty search through any large collection of modern crania that included

[18] Zeuner, "Age of Neanderthal Man," pp. 1–20.

aboriginal Australians, Negroes, and American Indians would probably bring to light several mandibles of lesser bulk but with larger teeth. The dental arch is short, wide, and evenly rounded in front, and the teeth are set in continuous series without gaps. The small and non-projecting canines have passed into the frontal part of the tooth arcade and somewhat resemble incisors; the incisors do not lean forward as in apes and some more primitive human types, but are erect, and the premolars are small and modern in conformation. The lower first molars are five-cusped, with broad, rounded, and rather flat-topped crowns. The conservative first molar preserves fairly well the old Dryopithecus pattern, but the second molar shows widening of the posterior pair of cusps and reduction of the hinder middle fifth cusp, so that it approaches the plus pattern of modern lower molars. The third molars show definite shortening and rounding of their crowns. The dental arch is adapted for typically human, rotary grinding movements. Some years ago, Keith and other students laid great emphasis upon molar "taurodontism"—the vertical deepening of the pulp cavities at the expense of the roots—which is markedly present in the Heidelberg teeth, even more pronounced in some of the Neanderthal fossil men, and shown to some extent in the molars of Sinanthropus. It was argued that these enlarged pulp cavities are an extreme specialization away from the condition found in the present great apes and in recent man. They were alleged to resemble the condition found in cud-chewing animals—hence the term "taurodontism"—and were adduced as evidence that Heidelberg man, together with the Neanderthal race, his later Pleistocene descendants, could not be the ancestor of *Homo sapiens*. The Heidelberg-Neanderthal line thus represented an early and divergent human offshoot. This theory now has to be abandoned, since Dr. Muzaffer Senyürek, my former student, has shown that taurodontism or enlargement of the molar pulp cavities is regularly present in certain American monkeys, is extremely common in the gibbon, not infrequent in the orang-utan, and of sporadic occurrence in many modern human groups.[19] It

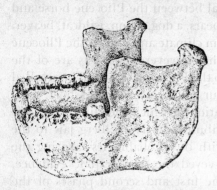

Fig. 50. The Heidelberg jaw. (Drawn with a camera lucida from a cast and photographs.)

[19] Senyürek, "Pulp Cavities," pp. 119–130. Dr. Middleton Shaw has also shown that taurodontism often occurs in the teeth of South African Banto Negroids.

has no phylogenetic significance whatsoever. These new findings and the discoveries of Sinanthropus, the new Pithecanthropus specimens, and the South African fossil man-apes have tended to divest the Heidelberg jaw of much of its importance. A few peculiarities of the very bulky mandible—the enormous breadth of the ascending ramus, the very shallow sigmoid notch, and the concavity of the basal rim—are of interest as primitive human specializations but of no particular evolutionary significance. Gregory remarked as long ago as 1916 that, in spite of the huge size of the jaw, the teeth are identical generically with those of *Homo sapiens.* Heidelberg man probably represented a crude, pre-Neanderthal who had a massive head, with low brow and heavy supraorbital torus, projecting jaws, and a chinless mandible. His teeth were hardly up to his bony specifications.

Neanderthal Man: Darwin's First Witness

The first apelike fossil man to attest the correctness of Darwin's theory of human evolution was discovered in 1856 in a cave of the Neanderthal, the valley of a small stream near Düsseldorf, Germany. Since that time, discoveries of the skeletal remains of this early race—mostly burials in cave deposits in Europe—have been many. Before describing the Neanderthal men, we may outline their position in the geological and archaeological sequences established by the study of Pleistocene deposits in Europe.

In the high plateau gravel deposits of southern England and northern France, which belong to the Pliocene period before the onset of the glaciations, battered, formless, chipped stones have been discovered which are claimed by many archaeologists to have been shaped or used by early man. These chipped flints are called eoliths, "stones of the dawn," and some of them look like crude scrapers, borers, choppers, and other tools known to have been fabricated and used by man at later periods. No human bones of Pliocene date have been discovered up to now, and many cautious students of man's early attempts at stone-working refuse to accept these eoliths as genuine tools or artifacts, since it is clear enough that they may have been shaped by earth pressure, stream battering, frost action, or other natural agencies.

In the later gravel deposits of the Pleistocene, mostly laid down on terraces of the river valleys of western Europe in interglacial phases, unmistakable stone axes appear. There were four major advances of the ice sheet in Europe and North America, separated by long interglacial periods in which the climate was temperate to tropical. The rivers just outside of the glaciated areas usually narrowed and excavated their beds during a glaciation and deposited thick layers of sand, clay, and gravel in those beds during the warm interglacial periods. Thus, they began as new streams in the warm Pliocene period, flowing through wide and very shallow valleys, and, in successive phases of the Pleistocene, narrowed and scoured out their beds, leaving a succession of steps or terraces, each covered with layers of gravel and other deposits. The highest terraces have the oldest gravels, containing the remains of the most archaic fauna and the crudest and earliest stone tools chipped by man. Successively lower terraces often yield up later animal forms and more highly evolved stone tools.

The first chipped flints universally admitted to be of human origin are crude hand-axes, made by knocking coarse trimming flakes from a flint pebble, discarding these flakes, and keeping the core, or residue, as a tool. Sometimes, the butt end, to be held in the hand, is left unworked and still shows the crust of the original flint pebble, while the business end of the tool has two very sinuous edges converging to a point, produced by striking large chips alternately from both faces of the pebble. The resulting implement is roughly pear-shaped and can be used as an axe or a pick. In another type the edge is carried clear round the butt, so that both sides of the tool are chipped all over and an almond shape is produced. These hand-axes of the earliest and crudest forms have often been rolled about in the gravels until the edges and the sharp ridges of the scars made by the removal of trimming flakes are worn and battered. Also, the surfaces of the tool, where the crust or cortex has been removed, may be stained or patinated to a yellow, dark brown, or china white color, according to the length of time that the implement has been exposed on the surface, the character of the original flint, and the amount of iron and various other materials carried in the water and in the soils in which it has been embedded.

The crudest hand-axes, recognizable by their irregularly wavy edges, belong to an industry named Abbevillian or Chellean, from typical sites, and seem to date back at least to the first of the three interglacial periods and to the second glaciation that followed. In the second interglacial period, which was of enormous duration the hand-axes are much better worked, with straighter edges and more regular shapes. They are thinner and have been produced by detaching finer trimming flakes by the use of a wooden billet for a chipping tool rather than a stone pebble. These tools belong to the Acheulean industry. They go through a long course of evolution in which they become smaller, better chipped, and more triangular. They occur in the river drift gravels from the second interglacial period through the next glaciation and the third or last genial interglacial period. With the Abbevillian and Acheulean hand-axes are found various scrapers, knives, and borers made of flint flakes, but the majority of these are of the same types and workmanship throughout, so that they cannot be identified with any particular industry except by their association in the gravels with the stereotyped and classifiable hand-axes. Up to now, the skeletons of Neanderthal man have not been found in the gravels of river terraces in association with Abbevillian or Acheulean axes. The majority of the finds of this archaic type of man have been cave burials, dated from the first half of the fourth or last glaciation. A few Neanderthal skeletons in Germany have been recovered from limestone quarries or other river deposits that date back at least to the last interglacial period (which may have begun 175,000 to 150,000 years ago) and perhaps even to the third glaciation, but in such deposits the stone tools are not hand-axes but crude and amorphous flake implements.

In the caves of western Europe and Palestine, the stone tools that were used by Neanderthal man belong to an industry called Mousterian, from the type site at Le Moustier, Dordogne, France, where the culture was first identified. Ordinarily, the implements are made of flakes rather than cores, and one side is left unworked, showing a smooth, conchoidal surface where it has been detached from the original block or core. Characteristically, this unworked surface in a flint flake implement shows at the top, where it has been detached from the core by a sharp blow, a so-called "bulb of percussion" which merges into the thinned-out extremity of the flake. The outside of the flake tool of Mousterian technique usually shows some scars left by detaching large trimming flakes, but the business edges are carefully retouched by the removal of tiny flakes by pressure rather than by percussion. The maker pressed up against the edges of the unfinished flake tool with a piece of bone, horn, or wood, or perhaps even a pebble, thereby detaching minute and almost vertical flakes, which by the confluence of their scars produced a very regular and sharp edge. Three principal types of Mousterian flake tools are easily recognizable. The first of these is roughly triangular with a thick butt, showing the striking platform where the flake was struck off the original flint core. Below this butt, both edges are carefully retouched in convex edges converging to a sharp point. This tool is the Mousterian point. The second Mousterian implement is a side-scraper, the retouched working edge of which is parallel with the long axis of the flake and opposite the thickened butt, which is held in the hand. These side-scrapers are often shaped something like a section of an orange. They can be used either for scraping or for cutting. The third type is an end-scraper, with its retouched surface ordinarily at the butt end of an elongated flake. The business end is steeply flaked to a convex edge. These end-scrapers can be used as planes and in other ways. The Mousterian industry has no bone tools, but the oblong toe bones of bisons were often used as flaking anvils and show the marks of flints rested on them in the process of manufacture. Some bones are also cut and scratched.

Most of the Mousterian points and scrapers are found in limestone caves containing evidence of human occupation in the form of hearths and the remains of animals devoured by the cave-dwellers. These animals are usually species that flourish under Arctic conditions, such as the woolly elephant or mammoth, the woolly rhinoceros, and the cave bear. All of these are extinct mammals which were clothed with heavy coats of wool or fur to enable them to withstand the rigors of a glacial climate. The human skeletons found in the caves of Western Europe with these Mousterian implements are without exception those of the Neanderthal race. By the beginning of the second advance of the last great glaciation (Würm II, c. 72,000 years ago), the Neanderthal men had disappeared, and the caves they occupied had been taken over by men of modern types (*Homo sapiens*) with different stone industries and a rudimentary graphic and plastic art.

Neanderthal man certainly flourished on the European continent as late as the end of Würm I, which began about 115,000 years ago according to Zeuner. This authority tentatively refers most of the western European cave finds to this glacial phase, but is inclined to ascribe a number of the remains of Neanderthal man discovered in Central Europe and in the Near East to the last interglacial (which may have begun more than 150,000 years ago).[20]

Remains of Neanderthal man have been found in Jersey, France, Belgium, Germany, Czecho-Slovakia, Yugo-Slavia, in Spain and on the Rock of Gibraltar, in Italy, and Russia. Outside of Europe, important finds have been made in Palestine and in the Soviet Republic of Uzbek, east of the Caspian Sea and south of Lake Aral. Fragments of a maxilla and

[20] Zeuner's attributions are specifically ("Age of Neanderthal Man," p. 18):
Würm I (115,000 years):
Gibraltar II, Jersey, La Quina, La Ferrassie, Pech de l'Azè, La Chapelle-aux-Saints, Spy, La Naulette, Monte Circeo (?), Mount Carmel (in part), Sipka, Le Moustier (?)
Interglacial Riss-Würm or Last Interglacial:
Monte Circeo (?), Mount Carmel (in part), Galilee (?), Krapina, Saccopastore, Steinheim (?), Taubach, Ehringsdorf
Riss II (187,000 years):
Interstadial RI/RII:
Steinheim (?)
Riss I (230,000 years).

a couple of teeth have also been found in a cave near Tangiers, Morocco. Some other archaic forms of fossil man with big brow-ridges in Africa and in Java have been assigned to the Neanderthaloid group, incorrectly in my opinion. These other palaeoanthropic types, as some scientists addicted to big words call them, will be treated in their proper places. Since all of the Neanderthal finds cannot be described individually, I have prepared for this section a check list of the more important and better authenticated discoveries, with a few facts about each.

In the last few years, it has become apparent that there are at least two distinct types of Neanderthal man, a conservative type and a progressive type. The conservative type has a flattened-down brain-case, a bun-shaped protuberant occiput, marked projection of the jaws, and practically no chin. The bones of the postcranial skeleton show many apelike features. The progressive type has a laterally compressed and higher cranial vault, lower attachments of the neck muscles, submedium to fair development of the bony chin, and features of the rest of the skeleton that approximate those of primitive but anatomically modern forms of man. These types must be described separately and in more detail before we can discuss their significance and their relationships to Homo sapiens.

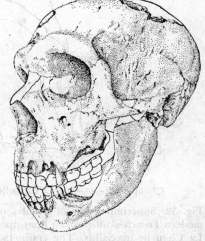

Fig. 51. The skull of the Neanderthal man of La Chapelle-aux-Saints. The restored parts unshaded. (Drawn with a camera lucida from a cast and photographs.)

Perhaps the best preserved of all the Neanderthal skeletons of the classic, conservative type is that of the old man of La Chapelle-aux-Saints, found in 1908 in a small cave in the department of Corrèze, France. This skeleton was made the subject of a masterly monograph by Professor Marcellin Boule, which describes in detail the characteristics of the conservative Neanderthaloid type and which we may follow in our general summary.

The skull of the old man of La Chapelle-aux-Saints is very large and of a bestial aspect. The brain-case is very elongated and low, the supraorbital ridges immense, and the forehead low and retreating; the occiput is protuberant and bun-shaped; the whole brain-case gives the impression of having been flattened down. The face is long and projecting; the orbits are very large; the nose is long and very broad, the upper jaw strongly prognathous and the mandible powerful, but with only a rudimentary chin. Since both face and brain-case are nearly intact, we are able to compare the development of the one with the other. Remembering that the anthropoid apes differ from man particularly in that their faces are very large and their brain-cases very small, let us examine the superimposition of the profile of the Neanderthal skull of La Chapelle-aux-Saints upon those of a chimpanzee and of a modern

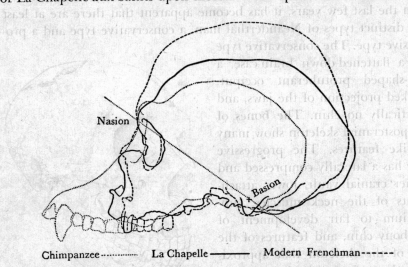

Nasion

Basion

Chimpanzee ·············· La Chapelle ——— Modern Frenchman ------

Fig. 52. Superimposition of profiles of a chimpanzee skull (dotted line), and a modern French skull (broken line) upon the profile of the Neanderthaloid skull of La Chapelle-aux-Saints. The cranio-facial axes (Nasion-Basion) are drawn to the same length. (After Boule, *Les hommes fossiles,* Fig. 119, by permission of Masson et Cie.)

Frenchman (Fig. 52). The face of the chimpanzee is by far the most projecting and the outline of his cranial vault is much smaller both in length and in height than either of the human outlines. The modern man has the straightest and least projecting face and the loftiest skull with the highest forehead region. Neanderthal man falls between modern man and the chimpanzee both in facial projection and in height of the cranial vault, but the fossil human skull in both parts is much nearer to the modern human type than to the chimpanzee.

The crania of the conservative type of Neanderthal man are longheaded, the width varying from 70 to 76 per cent of the length. They are all low-vaulted, being in the characters of the brain-case far inferior to the type of the Piltdown Dawn Lady. The temporal crests, which outline on each of the lateral skull walls the area of attachment of the temporal muscle that works the jaw, are not especially strongly marked, nor do they rise high up toward the middle line of the skull roof. The zygomatic arches, which enclose the temporal fossae, are stouter and much less curved than in modern man, thus approaching the anthropoid condition. In apes, the hind wall of the glenoid fossa, which receives the mandibular condyle, is formed by a transverse bony ridge called the postglenoid process. In modern man, the postglenoid process is usually vestigial, since the tympanic ring which encloses the auditory opening has grown downward into a plate that serves as the back wall of the jaw joint. In Neanderthal man, the postglenoid process is large and keeps the mandibular condyle from butting against the still ring-like tympanic bone. The glenoid fossae are very shallow and resemble the articular plateaus of chimpanzees.

The mastoid processes, those conical bony protuberances that project downward from the temporal bones just behind the ear opening and to which are attached the muscles that turn the head from side to side, are practically absent in anthropoid apes and best developed in modern man. In the conservative type of Neanderthal man they are small and almost rudimentary. The bun-shaped and protruding occiput is traversed from side to side by a swollen ridge or torus to which the neck muscles are attached and which is homologous with the transverse occipital crest in anthropoid apes. The neck muscles and ligaments are hafted much higher up on the back of the skull than in modern man— again an ape feature. The base of the skull presents many primitive features. We remember that in lower mammals the occipital foramen (the great hole in the skull base through which the spinal cord passes to the brain) is situated at the back of the skull rather than beneath it; that with the gradual assumption of an upright sitting posture this foramen moves forward beneath the skull, so that in the entirely upright human being it is well underneath the skull vault and the skull is poised upon the spinal column. The foramen magnum of Neanderthal man is situated farther back in the skull base than in modern man, thus approaching the ape condition.

The face is of great size. Below the huge brow-ridges the root of the nose is deeply depressed, somewhat as in modern Australians. This is the opposite of the anthropoid condition. The form of the nasal bones is ultra-human, being very broad. The nasal aperture is very wide, as in the dark races of today. The lower borders and the nasal spine present a development comparable with that of modern savages. The slope of the alveolar process does not merge with the nasal floor as in apes. On the contrary, there is a distinct nasal sill (cf. pages 181–182). The cheek bones are not at all prominent. The upper jaw is large and strongly prognathous. Instead of the face being hollowed out beneath the orbits as in modern man, this area is almost flat as in apes. This lack of suborbital hollows is the result of the greatly expanded air chambers or sinuses in the interior of the bone. The superior alveolar border is very deep and strong, but does not bulge as in Negroes and Australians. In anatomical language, there is no alveolar prognathism.

The skulls of children of the Neanderthal race are also long-headed and show the same low and retreating foreheads. Although in modern man the brow-ridges are not usually developed until almost the end of adolescence, the Neanderthaloid children show early in life the beginning of the great supraorbital crests that are such a striking feature of the adults of the race.

A considerable number of lower jaws of Neanderthal man have come to light. They are all massive affairs, but by no means as large as the ponderous Heidelberg mandible. There is the merest beginning of a chin, which, we recall, is altogether absent in the Heidelberg and Piltdown forms. The symphysis slopes backward and inward as in apes, but there is no simian shelf. There is a trace of the ape fossa from which the tongue muscles take their origin in anthropoids, but in Neanderthal man the little spicules of bone, called the genial tubercles, are already developed as in modern human races.

The teeth of Neanderthal man are arranged in a very broad U-shaped arch with the canines set in the curve rather than on the sides of the arch. The canines are not projecting. The enlargement of the pulp cavities of the teeth in this race has been mentioned in connection with Heidelberg man. Boule denies this feature in the teeth of his La Chapelle-aux-Saints specimen, but in much worn teeth of elderly individuals the cavities are largely eliminated, since secondary dentin forms to take the place of the crown surfaces worn down by grinding. Boule mentions that the wear of the teeth in Neanderthal man indicates that the lower jaw in chewing was thrust forward and retracted in a manner not observed in modern man. This perhaps explains the shallow and almost flat glenoid fossae and the great apelike condyles.

The bones of the trunk and limbs are well preserved in the conservative Neanderthal skeletons from La Chapelle-aux-Saints and La Ferrassie and give a fairly clear idea of the build and posture of this archaic type of man. The spine is short and massive. The vertebrae of the neck have long, almost horizontal, spinous processes, hardly distinguishable from those of the chimpanzee and radically different from the bent down and degenerate cervical spines of modern man. These long cervical spines in Neanderthal man provide, as in the apes, attachments for the muscles and ligaments that support the overbalanced jaws. Because Neanderthal man's face was not bent down beneath the brain-case but extended, and because of the great depth of his jaws, the head had to be tilted backward and the occiput buried in the neck, in order to provide room for the easy opening of the jaws. These arrangements also necessitated the great backward projection of the spines of the neck vertebrae.

The dorsal and lumbar vertebrae of Neanderthal man are poorly preserved. Apparently his lumbar curve was feeble and the sacrum was straight instead of being anteriorly concave as in modern man. Here again is an apelike feature. The pelvic basins are fragmentary, but some simian features may be observed even here. The pelvis of the La Chapelle-aux-Saints man was very high relative to its breadth; the iliac blades were much flattened, and the tuberosities of the haunch bones, or ischia, very prominent as in anthropoid apes. The general features of the pelvis are, however, human.

The collar bones are long and arched, and the shoulder blades present some characters peculiar to the race. The arms were not long but extremely massive, with very large joints. Both in the bones of the upper arm and of the forearm there occur apelike details of morphology. Notable is the strong curvature of the radius, the outside bone of the forearm. Nevertheless, the proportions of the limb are ultra-human, the forearm being very short relative to the upper arm and not enormously elongated as in the brachiating anthropoids. The hand is quite human. The thumb is rather short, as are all the other digits. Altogether, Neanderthal man's upper extremity does not suggest arboreal life much more forcibly than does the arm of modern man.

Naturally, we are interested in Neanderthal man's legs. We recall that the leg is a much more human member than the arm. Perhaps this is why legs have always commanded a disproportionate share of popular interest, as compared with other parts of the anatomy. The thigh bones of Neanderthal man are strongly bowed forward as in apes. They are short and massive with great articular heads. In their stumpy, curved form they recall the gorilla and the chimpanzee, while the straight femora of modern man rather resemble the form of the gibbon's thigh bones. The femoral shafts are rounded and do not show the sharp development of the rough line along the posterior surface (the linea aspera) that is characteristic of modern man. This line, absent in apes, shows the attachments of the extensor muscles concerned in maintaining the erect posture (cf. page 122). In Neanderthal man, it is sufficiently marked to indicate an upright carriage but is inferior in its development to that of modern man. The tibiae or shin bones are short and strong. The upper surfaces of their articular heads, forming the lower part of the knee joint, are sloped backward, indicating perhaps that the Neanderthal man walked with his knees bent. The shape of the tibial shaft in Neanderthal man is also reminiscent of apes in that the sharp S-shaped shin crest of modern human bones is but slightly developed, and the cross section of the shaft is oval instead of prismatic.

The skeleton of the Neanderthaloid foot is of especial interest because of its human adaptations. It was a supporting rather than a prehensile organ, but it retains some of the characteristics of the grasping foot that have been lost in modern human types. The head of the ankle bone, which is in direct continuation with the axis of the great toe, is skewed sharply inward, indicating that the great toe was widely separated from the other digits. The vault of the foot was low and the heel bone small. We recall that the anthropoid foot has a very short and undeveloped heel bone, which is tipped toward the outside so that the animal rests its weight on the outer border of the sole of the foot. In modern man, the base of the heel bone is flattened instead of curved, so that the bone stands upright on a plane surface and does not roll over on its outer side. The heel bone carries the ankle joint, and in man the great extension backward of the bone affords leverage for the powerful calf muscles that are attached to the hinder surface by the tendon of Achilles. These muscles lift the heel in walking (cf. page 120). The heel bone or calcaneum of Neanderthal man is smaller than that of modern man, and its hinder tuberosity is less developed. It is inclined over toward the outside, so that the weight must have been borne principally on the outer side of the foot. The toe bones are not extraordinarily long, their only ape-like features being the retention of the interval between the great toe and the other digits. Generally speaking, the foot of the Neanderthal man is not more simian than the other parts of his extremities. Such a foot could probably be fitted in a modern shoe shop.

The approximate stature of a person in life may be estimated from the measurements of the long bones of the skeleton. The classic Neanderthal men were of low stature, varying from 5 feet, 1 inch, to 5 feet, 5 inches. Boule calculates the height of the old man of La Chapelle-aux-Saints at 5 feet, 1 inch (1.55 meters). We must, then, picture him as a short, bull-necked individual with massive head and heavy projecting jaws. The head was carried thrust forward. The chest was deep and round, the arms of moderate length, the legs very short. The gait may have been a shuffling, bent-knee walk, in which the legs were not completely extended upon the thighs. On the whole, Neanderthal man must have been a rather gorilla-like type.

Some anatomists model reconstructions of fossil skulls by building up the soft parts of the head and face upon a skull cast and thus produce a bust purporting to represent the appearance of the fossil man in life. When, however, we recall the fragmentary condition of most of the skulls, the faces usually being missing, we can readily see that even the reconstruction of the facial *skeleton*, leaves room for a good deal of doubt as to details. To attempt to restore the soft parts is an even more hazardous undertaking. The lips, the eyes, the ears, and the nasal tip leave no clues on the underlying bony parts. You can, with equal facility, model on a Neanderthaloid skull the features of a chimpanzee or the lineaments of a philosopher. These alleged restorations of ancient types of man have very little, if any, scientific value and are likely only to mislead the public.

The cranial capacities of the conservative Neanderthalers are not very small. The skull found on the Rock of Gibraltar is that of a woman, and the cubical contents are estimated at 1300 cc. by Boule. The La Quina female skull is reckoned at 1367 cc. by the same authority, and the type male skull from Neanderthal itself at 1408 cc. The old man of La Chapelle-aux-Saints had a cranial capacity of about 1600 cc., which is far above the average of male Europeans today. In the gross size of the brain, the Neanderthal ancients were quite up to the level of modern man.

The endocranial casts of Neanderthal skulls reveal some features of importance. The La Chapelle-aux-Saints specimen had a long, broad, and low brain, with the left side somewhat larger than the right, indicating, perhaps, right-handedness. The cast gives evidence of a crudity and simplicity of the pattern of the convolutions far different from the complicated markings found on modern endocranial casts. Boule compares his specimen in this respect with the brains of microcephalic idiots and of anthropoid apes.

In anthropoid apes, the frontal lobes constitute about 32 per cent of the cerebral surface, in modern man about 43 per cent, and in the Neanderthaloid man of La Chapelle-aux-Saints only 36 per cent. Tilney regards the brain casts of Neanderthal man as demonstrating an expansion of all the lobes in comparison with those of Pithecanthropus and of the Dawn Lady. But the frontal lobe is proportionately less expanded than the other parts of the cerebrum. Its outstanding feature is the prominence of the inferior frontal convolution (the speech area),

TABLE 3. CHECK LIST OF PRINCIPAL NEANDERTHAL FINDS

Place	Name	Date	Site	Industry	Content	Remarks
Europe						
Belgium						
Dinant	La Naulette	1865	Cave	?	Toothless mandible, canines, tarsals, young adult female	
Namur	Spy	1886	Cave terrace	End of Mousterian	2 skulls, frag. skeletons, adult males	#1 Conservative #2 Progressive
Channel Isles						
Jersey	St. Brelade	1910	Cave	Mousterian	13 teeth (taurodont) frag. of tibia	
Czecho-Slovakia						
Moravia	Šipka	1880	Cave	?	Frag. mandible, child	
France						
Ariège	Malarnaud	1888	Cave	Mousterian (?)	Mandible, 1 tooth	
Corrèze	La Chapelle-au-Saints	1908	Cave	Mousterian	Skeleton, middle-aged male	Conservative
Dordogne	Le Moustier	1908	Cave	Type Mousterian	Skeleton, adolescent male	Conservative
Charente	La Quina	1908–21	Rock shelter	Upper Mousterian	Skeleton, adult female, skull of child, fragments of other skeletons	Conservative
Dordogne	La Ferrassie	1909–21	Rock shelter	Mousterian	2 adult skeletons, 4 children	
Germany						
Düsseldorf	Neanderthal	1856	Cave	?	Fragmentary skeleton, adult male	Type specimen, Conservative
Weimar	Ehringsdorf I	1914–16	Limestone quarry	"Pre-Mousterian"	2 mandibles, remains of a child's skeleton, other fragments	
"	Ehringsdorf II	1925	"	"	Fragmentary skull	Progressive
Würtemberg	Steinheim	1933	Alluvial gravels	?	Skull, male, minus lower jaw	Progressive

CHECK LIST OF PRINCIPAL NEANDERTHAL FINDS (continued)

Place	Name	Date	Site	Industry	Content	Remarks
Gibraltar	Gibraltar I	1848	Quarry	Mousterian	Complete skull minus lower jaw	Conservative
	Gibraltar II	1926	Cave	?	Fragmentary skull, 5 year child	Conservative?
Italy						
Rome	Saccopastore I, II, III	1929 1935 1935	Quarry " Cave	Mousterian (?) " Mousterian	Skull without lower jaw, female 2 incomplete skulls Complete skull minus lower jaw, male	Conservative?
"	Monte Circeo	1935	Cave	Mousterian		
Jugo-Slavia						
Croatia	Krapina	1899–1905	Rock shelter	"Pre-Mousterian"	Parts of 20 individuals, various ages, many teeth	Progressive
Spain						
Gerona	Bañolas	1887	Quarry	?	Lower jaw	
Africa						
Morocco	Tangiers	1939	Cave	Mousterian (?)	Upper jaw of child (?) adult molar	Progressive
Asia						
Palestine	Galilee	1925	Cave	Mousterian	Frontal, r. sphenoid, frag. upper jaw, nasals	Progressive
"	Mt. Carmel	1931–32	Caves.	Levalloiso-Mousterian	Incomplete skeletons of 12 individuals of various ages, many isolated fragments	Conservative and Progressive
Uzbekistan	Baisun	1938	Cave	Mousterian	Skull and lower jaw of 8–9 year old child	Progressive

which is more developed than in either of the fossil types just mentioned. Tilney regards this frontal development as indicative of psychic powers in advance of the more primitive types and of a capacity for speech approaching modern standards. The parietal lobes are greatly expanded, according to this authority, and the prominence of the parietal eminence reflects a greater sensory development and a more complete mastery over manual movements than is found in earlier forms of man.

The temporal lobe is also well developed and displays a large auditory eminence, which is generally accepted as a part of the speech mechanism. In the occipital lobe, the visual and visuopsychic areas show important increments.

The brain stem in the conservative type of Neanderthal man, in conformity with the position of the occipital foramen and the poise of the head, was directed more obliquely than in modern man, sloping downward and backward.

Altogether, Neanderthal man's brain was a massive and primitive affair but distinctly human. The intelligence of this type of man may have been but little lower than that of some primitive men of today.

PROGRESSIVE NEANDERTHALERS

Two of the oldest Neanderthal skulls that have been discovered in Europe differ surprisingly from the classic and conservative Neanderthal type as exemplified by La Chapelle, the Neanderthal specimen itself, and the Gibraltar woman. The Ehringsdorf skull was disinterred from a travertine quarry near Weimar, Germany, in 1925, under geological and palaeontological associations which indicate that it dates back to the third or last interglacial period (c. 130,000 years?). The Steinheim skull came out of a gravel pit, in 1933, near Marbach, Würtemberg, the birthplace of Schiller. It is stated to belong to a genial interval between the first and second phases of the Riss glaciation, which is the third of the four great glacial advances of the Pleistocene (according to Zeuner's chronology between 230,000 and 187,000 years ago). It will be remembered that most of the western European Neanderthaloids date from the first stage of the fourth glacial advance, the Würm glaciation (beginning about 115,000 years ago, according to Zeuner).

The Ehringsdorf skull, represented by a fragmentary brain-case, was that of an adult female according to Weidenreich, who described it, but, in the opinion of Keith, belonged to a youth of about 18 years. Whoever owned it seems to have met a violent death or at least an unseemly burial, since there are evidences of no less than five wounds on the frontal bone, one delivered by the blunt implement of detective stories and the others by some sharp-edged weapon, probably of flint. The skull had been fractured when the bone was green and no other bones of the skeleton were at hand. It seems probable that here, as in the lair of Sinanthropus, somebody had been eating brains. The bones of this skull are thin, and the vault is high and gable-roof-shaped, instead of flattened down as in the conservative Neanderthal type. The forehead is also moderately high, although the brow-ridges are massive. This supraorbital shelf is more clearly separated from the forehead curve than in ordinary Neanderthal skulls. The skull is 196 mm. long and 145 mm. wide. Its cranial index is 74—dolichocephalic. The interior brain space takes up 87.7 per cent of the skull length, the rest being in the bony walls. Keith says that the bony walls of classic, conservative Neanderthaloids usually make up 16 per cent of skull length, as against 12.3 per cent in this specimen and 8 to 10 per cent in modern man. The cranial capacity was approximately 1480 cc., about the average for modern adult male Europeans. The other features of the skull are mostly classic Neanderthaloid, including the temporal bone and the bun-shaped occiput with high rising nuchal attachments and occipital torus.

The Steinheim skull has the right side of the skull vault and face beautifully preserved. It is a small affair—only 182 mm. long and also narrow. Its cranial index is 70. The supraorbital torus is huge, but the forehead is not so low as in conservative Neanderthaloids. The vault rises to a moderate height and is laterally compressed rather than squashed down vertically. The occiput is mediumly convex instead of bun-shaped, and the wisdom teeth, which are still in place in the upper jaw, are definitely smaller than the second molars.

These very early German Neanderthaloids are progressive in their high pitched vaults and in certain other features. They approximate *Homo sapiens*. We need not elaborate upon them further, because the Mount Carmel Neanderthaloids of Palestine, exhaustively studied by Sir Arthur Keith and Theodore McCown, present an entire series of more nearly complete skeletal material ranging from an almost classic and conservative Neanderthal type through progressive forms to some that are nearly *Homo sapiens*. A summary of this material will be the best presentation of the important problem of the possibility of a progressive Neanderthal type's having evolved into anatomically modern man.[21]

The Mount Carmel skeletons were buried in two adjoining caves, each of which yielded a Levalloiso-Mousterian culture, probably covering a considerable part of the third interglacial period and the beginning of

[21] McCown and Keith, *Stone Age of Mount Carmel*, Vol. II.

the last glaciation. The finds were made in 1931–1932 in the course of excavations of a joint expedition of the American School of Prehistoric Research and the British School of Archaeology in Jerusalem. The work was under the direction of Miss Dorothy Garrod, but the skeletons were disinterred, for the most part, in her absence by Theodore D. McCown and Hallam L. Movius, Jr. The first cave, Skūhl, produced more or less fragmentary remains of 10 individuals, in addition to a considerable number of isolated specimens. The second cave, Tabūn, contained the skeleton of an adult female, the mandible of an adult male, and sundry odd bones and teeth. The progressive Neanderthaloids come out of the Skūhl cave and the conservatives from Tabūn. The stone tool industries are the same in both caves, but the fauna of the Tabūn cave is perhaps slightly more archaic.

Our interest is primarily in the progressive people of Skūhl, who first may be compared with the conservative Neanderthal type, as described by Boule in his study of the man of Chapelle-aux-Saints. The latter was short and stocky, while the men of Mount Carmel are tall and the women short or medium. Both have massive heads, but the conservative type has a relatively large face, whereas this portion of the skull is not excessively developed in the progressive Mount Carmelites. In contrast to the classic type, the progressive Neanderthaloids have vaults that are of medium height or even above medium; their foreheads are moderately full instead of receding; their occiputs are not compressed vertically but project slightly beyond the attachment of the neck. The eyebrow ridges in both types are very large, but in the Palestinians they show a tendency to separate into medial and lateral parts instead of forming a continuous torus. The faces of the conservative Neanderthal men are long and prognathous, but in the progressive forms they are usually of moderate length and orthognathous. Both tend to have flat, apelike malar bones, but in some Mount Carmel individuals a tendency toward the jutting cheekbones of neanthropic man may be discerned. In both, the upper jaws are devoid of suborbital or canine fossae, but, in the conservatives, they are snouted, whereas they usually are not so in the progressives. The high, cavernous orbits of the classic type are replaced, in the progressives, by wide and not particularly high forms. The nose is more variable in its proportions in the Mount Carmel people, and the lateral margins of the nose are demarcated from the face, in contradistinction to the condition found in the conservatives. The latter have much deeper jaws in the subnasal region, and the chin eminences are absent or rudimentary, whereas the progressive type usually has jaws of moderate depth, and the chin, though variable, is sometimes fairly well developed. Again, the mandible in the classic Neanderthal type has a very broad ascending ramus, and the hinder angle is planed off or truncated, whereas the breadth of the ascending branch of the jaw is variable in the more advanced type, and the hinder or gonial angle is fairly well developed. Teeth in the progressives are not always large as in the conservatives, although the molars of both types show certain primitive features. The mean cranial capacity of the conventional type of Neanderthal man, according to Keith and Boule, is about 1400 cc.; in the Mount Carmel skulls it ranges in three adult males from 1518 cc. to 1587 cc., while the Tabūn woman had only 1271 cc. and a Skūhl woman (II) between 1300 and 1350 cc. As far as the evidence of the endocranial casts permits the comparison of the brains of the two types, it is concluded that the size and form of the brain in the Mount Carmel people lacked the primitive and simian features of the conservative type. Again, instead of short legs and a somewhat imperfect adaptation to the human erect posture, the Palestinians are altogether modern.[22]

Altogether, McCown and Keith discuss 111 skeletal characters in which the Mount Carmel people are compared not only with the classic, conservative Neanderthal type, but also with the anatomically modern (neanthropic) type of the Cro Magnon men who lived in the caves at the end of the glacial period after Neanderthal man had disappeared. Of this list, the count of resemblances in the Mount Carmel people is as follows: Neanderthal, 16 (14.4 per cent); neanthropic, 32 (28.8 per cent); intermediate, 46 (41.4 per cent); indeterminate, 13 (11.7 per cent); peculiar, 4 (3.6 per cent). According to this crude census, the Mount Carmel skeletal series is closer to modern man than to Neanderthal man. However, the authors point out that all of these characters are not of equal diagnostic value, and that the larger proportion of advanced, modernistic characters in the Mount Carmel skeletons have to do with the conformation of their limb bones. Since these are liable to functional alteration, the characters of skull and teeth weigh more heavily. On the basis of these later, McCown and Keith place the Palestinians in the palaeoanthropic (anatomically ancient) rather than neanthropic group.

---

[22] Here is a selected list of more technical characters in which the Mount Carmel people diverge from the conservative Neanderthal type: in the plane of the foramen magnum which slopes from behind slightly upward and forward as in modern man; in the squamous suture of the temporal bone which is more arched than in classic Neanderthal skulls, but less than in modern men; in the occasionally large mastoid processes; in the convexity of the occiput, the lesser development of the torus, the lower hafting of neck muscles and occasional development of an external occipital protuberance; in the prevalently neanthropic character of the tympanic plate and the glenoid fossa; in the intermediate stage of the differentiation of the zygomatic arch and malar from the maxillary portion of the face; in the absence of taurodontism of the molar teeth and in the moderate size of the teeth.

So far, the present writer follows the detailed analyses of Sir Arthur Keith and his young collaborator with deep admiration of their skill and complete confidence in the validity of their conclusions. However, we now approach the crucial question of the significance of the so-called Neanthropic traits in these otherwise Neanderthaloid human fossils. There are two straightforward opinions as to the phylogenetic implications of this approximation of certain Neanderthaloid specimens to the anatomical status of modern man. The first is that these progressive Neanderthaloids represent the conservative type in process of evolving into *Homo sapiens*. The second is that the Palestinians are hybrids between Neanderthal man and some variety of *Homo sapiens*.

There are two principal objections to the view that Neanderthal man is our direct ancestor: (1) that he shows specialized traits that indicate an early and wide divergence from the main road of human evolution that leads to modern man; (2) that completely evolved modernistic types of fossil man were the contemporaries or predecessors of Neanderthal man in western Europe and hence could not be his descendants. The first of these objections has been invalidated in recent years by a whole series of fossil finds of human beings showing in their teeth and their skeletal characters the piecemeal replacements of Neanderthaloid "specializations" by modern morphology. One of the strongest reliances of Sir Arthur Keith and other adherents of the theory of Neanderthal specialization was the "taurodont" molars found in Heidelberg, most Neanderthaloids, and, to some extent, in Sinanthropus. This enlargement of the pulp cavities was supposed to be a ruminative specialization quite out of line with the cynodont molars (having small pulp cavities) alleged to be characteristic of all anthropoid apes and modern men. But Dr. Senyürek has shown that molar teeth with enlarged pulp cavities are sporadically distributed throughout the human and infrahuman primates, fossil and modern. They may be a primitive, generalized feature rather than a specialization. In any event, they are no Neanderthaloid monopoly.

The objection to an Neanderthaloid ancestry of modern man based upon the prior or simultaneous occurrence of *Homo sapiens* forms in the geological strata that have yielded Neanderthal man could be dismissed as long as the evidence of such a precociously modern type of man could be questioned. Bevies of allegedly Middle Pleistocene, Early Pleistocene, and even Pliocene finds of *Homo sapiens* have been acclaimed and ultimately discredited. A geological bar sinister has defaced their scutcheons, and they have been refused admission to the human palaeontological society. However, there has finally appeared a

candidate so fully equipped with geological, archaeological, and anatomical qualifications that it seems impossible to refuse her admission
to the Daughters of the Revolution. I refer to the Swanscombe skull,
which will be discussed in due course. By the same token, it is hard to
deny the authenticity of the Piltdown Lady as a non-Neanderthaloid
human being with a *Homo sapiens* brain-case and a geological pedigree
longer than that of any Neanderthal man, save only the gentleman from
Heidelberg, whether you leave her her lower jaw or take it away and
give it to an ape.

The question of the possible hybridity of the ancient Mount Carmelites
bears upon the main problem of a "Neanderthaloid stage" in modern
man's ancestry, in that there is an inherent improbability that the complete range of human evolution from conservative Neanderthal man to
out-and-out *Homo sapiens* would be manifested in such a short series,
in so brief a space of time, and in such a constricted locality. Some years
ago, I commented upon this situation as follows: "That Neanderthal
man should have changed thus rapidly into modern man within the
space of two caves and a city lot would seem to me to be a less credible
miracle than the changing of water into wine at Cana in Galilee, which
was reported perhaps 50,000 years later." On the other hand, the results
of a radical race mixture within a small group, as observed in modern
studies, are exactly the sort of phenomena that are shown in the skeletal
series from the caves of Skūhl and Tabūn in Palestine. Some individuals,
and particularly the females, tend to reproduce almost in entirety the
conservative parental type, while the males usually vary more widely
toward the progressive parental stock. The one almost typical, classic
Neanderthaloid in the Mount Carmel assortment is the woman from
Tabūn, but the females of the other cave also apparently show more
Neanderthaloid features than do the males.

The conclusion reached by Keith and McCown with respect to the
two contrasted interpretations of the Palestinian series—whether hybrids or Neanderthaloids on their way to becoming *Homo sapiens*—is
both ambivalent and ambiguous. In the first place, they reject the hybridization explanation on the ground that to win support for such a
theory it would be necessary to produce from a Palestinian level as old
as, or older than, the Levalloiso-Mousterian of Mount Carmel a fossil
form of *Homo sapiens* that could serve as one of the principals of such
a hybrid mating. To my mind, this viewpoint is analogous to that of
the doubting Thomas who would insist that a White father be produced
in persona viva before he would admit that a Negress, with a bevy of
children ranging from very light mulatto to almost fully Negroid, had

indulged in a little miscegenation. For, in the next breath, or at any rate in a few pages, McCown and Keith commit themselves to the view that Palestine was a transitional zone between an area farther to the east in which neanthropic man was evolving and one in the west that witnessed the evolution of palaeoanthropic man.

Yet these authors also reject the explanation that their Mount Carmel people are Neanderthaloids in transition to modern man. They do not believe, apparently, that *Homo sapiens* evolved through a Neanderthaloid stage. They regard the Mount Carmel people as "Neanderthaloid collateral or cousins of the ancestors" of the Cro Magnon type but not their direct ancestors. Seemingly, they think that their "transitional zone" between palaeoanthropic and neanthropic cradles of man produced by evolution a transitional type that was neither flesh nor fowl, but some kind of a red herring. In this argument, Sir Arthur Keith seems entirely to have overlooked his view that a western European neanthropic type may well have evolved through the Piltdown-Swanscombe succession before most of the Neanderthaloids occupied the caves of that area.

My own opinion, which I do not guarantee to be either correct or immutable, is that the Neanderthal genus included both a conservative type, which became set in the classic mould of the man of La Chapelle, and a progressive, continually evolving type, exemplified by Steinheim, Ehringsdorf, etc., which may well have produced, all by itself, some such archaic form of *Homo sapiens* as the Australian aboriginal (minus his Negrito or Tasmanoid infusion). However, I do not think that this Neanderthaloid stock was the sole source of modern human types. Other varieties of *Homo sapiens* may well have developed and evolved through protohuman types that never carried the chimpanzee-gorilloid supraorbital torus found in the Pithecanthropus-Sinanthropus-Heidelberg-Neanderthal succession or lineage. Further, if there were transitional zones between the evolutionary areas of contrasted human types, I should regard these as zones of intermixture and hybridization, rather than a sort of evolutionary no-man's-land in which the genes and characters of one form and the other vacillated in the germ plasm and skeletal structure of the individuals therein resident. Perhaps the Neanderthaloids became extinct because, somewhat in the manner of the inhabitants of the Scilly Islands, they made their livings by eating each other's brains. But I think that they were absorbed and swamped by admixtures with progressive and genetically dominant types of *Homo sapiens*. When Cro Magnon met Neanderthal, one or the other may occasionally have bled, but I think that they surely bred (if the sexes were properly assorted). That is what has happened everywhere in historical times when one type of man has encountered another.

The Man from Rhodesia Who Needed a Dentist

Broken Hill is in the country drained by the northern tributaries of the Zambesi River, about 14 degrees south of the equator. Here a limestone hill or kopje rises 50 feet above a swampy flat. At its southwestern base was the entrance to a cave famous for its immense yield of fossil bones. The splintered remains of elephants, hippopotami, rhinoceroses, zebra, and many other animals had literally choked the cave, which sloped sharply downward under the hill. The limestone, of which the kopje is an outcrop, is rich in the ores of lead, zinc, and vanadium. Mining operations began here in 1905 or earlier and were carried deep into the side of the kopje, eventually cutting through the lower part of the cave. The hundreds of tons of bones filling the deeper levels of the cave were accumulated during alternate periods of occupation by animals and by human beings. At some intervening periods the cave was untenanted, probably because of flooding. Throughout the bone deposit were found rude implements of quartz and chert. Most of the bones identified are those of animals that still inhabit Africa south of the equator. There is, however, no reason for supposing that the fauna of Central Africa has been changed since Pleistocene times, since there were no glaciations here and no alternations of heat and cold that would cause a replacement of the animal occupants of the region. Since the bones were impregnated with the metals, they were, as a rule, thrown with the limestone into the smelting furnace. Many a fossil man may have gone down the maw of modern industry.

In the summer of 1921, the miners had reached a depth of about 110 feet below the summit of the kopje and 60 feet below ground level. Here they reached the cave bottom, 30 feet below water level. Mr. T. Zwigelaar, a miner, uncovered a human skull while working with a black boy in the ore at the 60 foot level and about 10 feet above the floor of the bone cave. No other bones were with the skull, but "the leg bone of a man" was found about 3 feet away. The human skull, with some other human bones found in the cave, somewhere or other, was sent to the British Museum. In addition to the skull, minus its lower jaw, there were included a left tibia, parts of the left femur, a sacrum, portions of two pelves, and part of the upper jaw of another individual.

The sacrum, pelves, and leg bones recovered are in no way remarkable. They belonged to a man about 5 feet, 10 inches in height (1.78 meters). Keith, in restoring the bones of the lower extremity, came to the conclusion that the tibia was not long relative to the femur, as in Negroids or Australoids, but somewhat short as in Neanderthal man, in Mongolian races, and in some Europeans. There are no markedly anthropoidal features in these limb bones. There are large and very robust, with massive joints. The femur is straight as in modern man, not bowed as in the Neanderthal race and in anthropoid apes. It has not the front-to-back flattening (platymeria) of the upper portion of the shaft that is found in some primitive men and in savage peoples of today.

The associated lateral flattening of the tibia (platycnemia) is not pronounced. It may be mentioned that these modifications in the femur and tibia have been attributed to the bent-knee gait. Keith infers that the Rhodesian man was a heavy and powerful fellow, weighing at least 208 pounds. His gait was as erect as ours, and he extended the leg fully upon the thigh in walking.[23] He could have done the "goose step" of the German army with perfect ease. The sacrum is narrow and straight but otherwise unremarkable. The size and muscular markings, as well as other features of the bones, indicate that we are dealing with a male individual. If only the limb bones had been found, they would have been referred to an entirely modern type of man. But the skull is extraordinarily apelike. Dr. Aleš Hrdlička, who made a pilgrimage to Broken Hill and carefully examined the site of the find, is of the opinion that the modern-looking limb bones do not belong to the owner of the skull. They were found several feet away from the skull and represent the remains of at least two individuals, one a male and the other a female.

Whether or not the leg bones belong with the skull is a matter of minor importance. One may dismiss it with the remark that the skull calls for leg bones of an upright walking human being of good size, and that the specimens sent with the skull fulfill these requirements.

No definite conclusion can be reached as to the geological antiquity of the Rhodesian find from the evidence available. From an evolutionary point of view, it ought to be early Pleistocene or late Pliocene, but it is possible that an ancient and primitive type of man may have survived to comparatively recent times in this out-of-the-way spot in south central Africa. The skull is so remarkable that it would be an anthropological

[23] Mr. W. P. Pycraft, in the British Museum report on the remains of Rhodesian man, infers from certain features of the pelvic fragments that this individual walked in a stooping posture. The argument offered is ingenious, but unconvincing. (Pycraft, *Description of Human Remains*, p. 35.)

discovery of the highest importance even if it had been found in an ash can in a city alley.

The first glance at this skull shocks even the hardened anthropologist. The truly enormous brow-ridges and the bestially low forehead are really gorilline rather than human. No anthropoid ape, save only the male gorilla, can equal in size the great supraorbital bar which in this skull extends straight across the brow region from the outside angle of one orbit to that of the other. Chimpan-zees have brow-ridges in the form of flattened arches over the orbits. These arches thin out toward the ex-ternal angles and above the root of the nose. The most massive brow-ridges in Neanderthal man also have the form of an eyebrow curve with a depression above the nose and thinned external edges. In the male gorilla, the brow-ridges are thickest at the external corners of the orbits and extend straight across the fron-tal region with a central eminence rather than a depression above the root of the nose. Rhodesian man has the chimpanzee form of brow-ridges, but they approach the gorilloid con-dition in their lateral extension and

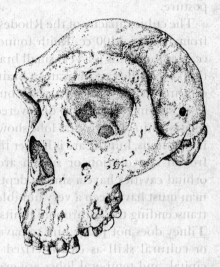

Fig. 53. The skull of Rhodesian man. (Drawn with a camera lucida from a cast and photographs.)

median development, and they are much larger than those of any other fossil man. The forehead of the Rhodesian skull is much lower and narrower than in any Neanderthal form and displays little more vault-ing than that of Pithecanthropus.

In other respects, the brain-case is of primitive but human shape, being very long (208–210 mm.) and relatively narrow (145–148 mm.). The ratio of breadth to length is 69 to 71 per cent. The great length of the skull is partially due to the projection forward of the brow-ridges and backward of the occipital crest. The actual length of the brain cavity, according to Keith, is only 171 mm., or 81.4 per cent of the total skull length. In Europeans, brain cavity length is 92 per cent of skull length, in Australian aborigines 88.5 per cent, in Neanderthal man 86 per cent, in Pithecanthropus 84 per cent, in the chimpanzee 81 per cent, and in the gorilla 75 per cent. Thus, in this relation Rhodesian man falls within the range of the apes, being inferior even to Pithecanthropus erectus.

The Rhodesian skull is low-roofed relative to its great length, but it shows the human expansion of the parietal region, with the highest point of the skull vault about one third of the way back of the coronal suture. Keith points out that this elevation overlies the part of the brain controlling the movements of the limbs that have to do with the upright posture.

The cubic capacity of the Rhodesian skull has been estimated variously from 1280 to 1400 cc. Keith found the endocranial cast displaced 1305 cc. of water. This is a very small brain capacity for so large a skull. Tilney thinks that the cast indicates a brain much superior to those of the Pithecanthropus or Piltdown types, but it is too different from any of the fossil specimens hitherto discovered to permit any assumption of a close relationship. The frontal lobe shows a marked absence of convolutionary impressions, but the arc is higher than in Neanderthal man. The inferior frontal convolution or speech area is, however, well developed. The orbital cavities have a simian depth. From the frontal lobes, Rhodesian man must have been a very humble sort of human being, with capacities transcending the anthropoid limits but far below those of *Homo sapiens*. Tilney does not judge him to have been capable of any such handicraft or cultural skill as characterized Neanderthal man. The parietal, occipital, and temporal lobes are exceedingly primitive. The sensory and kinaesthetic areas are so poorly developed as to suggest that their possessor was not an efficient artisan and did not possess as wide a range of motor adaptability as did Neanderthal man.

The inferiority of the temporal lobe is so insistent as to suggest pathological retardation in growth. It is remarkably small, and the auditory eminence is greatly limited in its development. The temporal lobes are deflected inward in a simian fashion. Because of the smallness of the auditory region, Tilney thinks that the language of this individual must have been very rudimentary. The portion of the occipital lobe representing the visuo-psychic functions is well developed, and, in general, the lobe indicates a marked advance toward the human status as compared with other parts of the brain. Tilney agrees with Elliot Smith that Rhodesian man occupies a far inferior rank in the human family to the Neanderthal type.

The face of Rhodesian man lacks the lower jaw but is otherwise complete. The distance of the front part of the jaws from the ear hole is very great, 24 mm. more than in the average Englishman, 50 mm. less than in the male gorilla, and exactly the same as in the Neanderthal man of La

Chapelle-aux-Saints (Keith). The forward projection of the jaws is, however, masked by the great projection of the brow-ridges. Anthropoid apes are notable because of their great facial length from the root of the nose to the point on the jaw between the upper incisor teeth. Whereas an average dimension in Englishmen is about 70 mm., this facial length in Rhodesian man is 95 mm. (Hrdlička), as contrasted with 87 mm. in the long-faced Neanderthal man of La Chapelle-aux-Saints. Keith states that the male gorilla approaches 110 in this measurement. The total facial length, including the lower jaw, must have been similarly intermediate between modern man and the gorilla.

The facial breadth of Rhodesian man, according to Hrdlička, was about 148 mm., an ample but by no means unusual dimension. An enormously elongated but relatively narrow face is also characteristic of the great apes and especially of the chimpanzee and the gorilla. The great size of the brow-ridges is perhaps the most notable feature of the entire skull. Keith asserts that the thickness over the middle of the orbit (21 mm.) exceeds that of any known skull, anthropoid or human. In the male gorilla and in the biggest Neanderthal skull this thickness is only 14 mm. It is hardly explicable by the projection of the jaws and the upward stress exerted in chewing, since the gorilla with less massive brow-ridges has much larger facial projection and is equipped in addition with enormous and projecting canine teeth which the Rhodesian man lacked. The distinguished English anthropologist is inclined to regard this development as in part a secondary sexual character, although doubtless to some extent functional.

The orbits, which lodge the eyes, are of great size in Rhodesian man and relatively very high. Here again is a definitely anthropoid characteristic, although it is sometimes found in modern man. The nasal bones are extremely long and broad, but the bridge of the nose was not high. Great length of the nasal bones is a feature of the gorilla face, but, as we have seen, these beasts have nasal bridges greatly constricted and almost flat. In gorillas, the nasal root begins high up in the glabella region between the supraorbital crests; but, in man, there is characteristically a depression below the glabella eminence, which marks the root of the nose. In some types, such as Australians, the nasal root is greatly depressed. This depression of the nasal root is of moderate depth in the Rhodesian man and asserts his humanity. We recall also that in the gorilla the side walls of the nasal aperture merge into the slope of the jaw without being continued round the bottom of the nasal opening to form a nasal sill, whereas, in well-developed human types, the recession of the part of the upper jaw lodging the incisor and canine teeth has caused the formation of a sharp ridge delimiting the nasal floor (cf. page 181). In Rhodesian man, the side walls of the aperture are lost in the alveolar slope, but back of their terminations is the transverse ridge that, in modern types, fuses with the side walls to form the nasal sills. A small nasal spine is also present. The nasal aperture, in the formation of its lower borders, is, then, of a very primitive but human type. More apelike configuration of this region may sometimes be observed in the skulls of modern man belonging to the less civilized races. The nasal opening of the Rhodesian man was relatively and absolutely very wide. In this respect he resembles Neanderthal man and the modern Negroids and Australoids. Anthropoid apes show absolutely wide nasal apertures, which are, nevertheless, narrow in relation to the great length of the whole nasal skeleton. In general, it cannot be said that the nose of Rhodesian man was markedly simian.

The fullness of the upper jaws in the suborbital region is, however, an apelike condition that we have previously met in Neanderthal man. To a lesser degree, it may be observed among certain modern Mongoloids, notably the Eskimo. The prodigious depth of the upper jaw is beyond anything previously observed in a human being. The palate, of which this maxilla forms the supporting structure, is enormous. Keith gives as its area 41 cm., as contrasted with 39 cm. in the La Chapelle-aux-Saints skull, an estimated area of a little less than 39 cm. in Heidelberg man, 34.6 cm. in a large-jawed Australian, and 25 cm. in the average Englishman of today. According to the same author, the ratio of palate area to cranial capacity in the Rhodesian skull is 1:37.1 (reckoning the brain volume at 1300 cc.), in the La Chapelle-aux-Saints man 1:41, in modern Europeans 1:55, and in the chimpanzee 1:8.7. In spite of the huge size of the palate, its shape is essentially modern and human. It is its breadth rather than its length that is excessive. Instead of being relatively long and narrow and U-shaped, it is horseshoe-shaped or elliptical. The breadth is 120 per cent of the length, a very common ratio in modern man. The vault of the palate is not only long and exceptionally broad, but also high, and the alveolar borders in which the teeth are implanted are of great thickness and strength. The distance between the canine teeth, according to Keith, is 53 mm., as against an average bicanine breadth of 39 mm. in modern Englishmen.

The teeth themselves are of notable size but of modern human proportions. The canine teeth are reduced to the level of the other teeth; the molars are remarkable for their width rather than for their length. The third molars are very much reduced in size and degenerate, a condition met with in civilized man and sometimes in modern savages but quite unexpected in this apelike brute. According to Keith, however, the wisdom teeth of the chimpanzee also show reduction. The pulp cavities of the teeth of the Rhodesian man are not enlarged.

The most remarkable fact about these teeth, however, is their rottenness. Ten of the 15 teeth preserved in the upper jaw have been affected by decay or caries. Alveolar abscesses have formed at the roots of the molars and other teeth. Rheumatic changes have taken place at the knee joint, which (if the limb bones belong with the skull) may have been caused by the infection of the mouth. There is also a peculiar perforation about a quarter of an inch in diameter in front of the left ear hole and a larger eroded hole behind the ear passage. These two perforations are connected by a curved tract of roughened and pitted bone. It was originally suggested by Yearsley that these lesions might be explained by the hypothesis that the chronic septic condition of the mouth led to suppurative middle ear disease, complicated with mastoid abscess; that this abscess broke through the cortex at the base of the process and tracked upward into the temporal fossa along the lines of least resistance. He assumed that the hole in front of the ear was due to a wound inflicted by some sharp implement during life and was not the cause of death.[24] Mollison has recently made a minute study of these perforations and of a still larger hole in the skull base, together with certain fractures and marks on the associated limb bones.[25] He contended that the holes were made by the canine teeth of a large carnivore. Weidenreich, however, has pointed out that the two lesions are only 18 mm. apart at their closest point and are almost circular. Therefore, only a very small carnivore could have been the offender, because even a medium-sized dog has its canines set much farther apart. Further, there are no marks of the opposing teeth and such a small carnivore would not have the strength to perforate the bones of this skull, anyway.[26] The mastoid abscess theory seems more plausible, but it is hardly probable that the hole in the temporal bone was caused by an agency independent of the eroded hole behind the ear.

The prevalence of decayed teeth and other pathological affections of the mouth among civilized peoples has often been ascribed to the degeneration of the jaws and teeth caused by the use of soft, cooked foods. Dental caries may perhaps be related to functional atrophy of the entire

[24] Yearsley, *Rhodesian Man*, pp. 59–63.
[25] Mollison, "Die Verletzungen am Schädel," pp. 229–234.
[26] Weidenreich, *op. cit.*, p. 189.

masticatory system. Here, however, we have a human type with tremendous masticatory musculature, and with large teeth showing the marks of very hard usage, but nevertheless diseased.

The skull base of the Rhodesian man shows a combination of primitive and relatively advanced features. It is wide relative to the breadth of the vault—an inferior feature—and the mastoid processes are small as in Neanderthal man, whereas in modern races they are large. The occipital foramen shows a small displacement backward but not as marked as in the Neanderthal type. The attachments of the neck muscles to the occiput are higher than in modern man, but the occiput was not buried in the neck as in the Neanderthal type. We may infer that the poise of the head was intermediate between the almost balanced condition found in modern man and the apelike hafting of the Mousterian cave-dwellers.

Keith calls attention to the fact that acromegaly, a disease associated with an unbalanced or pathological state of the pituitary gland, produces in its victims an elongation of the face and jaws and an enlargement of the brow-ridges and increase in the forehead slope somewhat similar to that displayed by the Rhodesian man. In acromegalics, the attachments of the neck muscles are increased in area, in conformity with the enlarged face and jaws. In the Rhodesian skull the bony socket of the pituitary gland, the sella turcica, shows no distortion such as usually accompanies that disease, and all of the parts of the skull have developed normally and harmoniously. Nevertheless, it is possible that the great brow-ridges, deep jaws, and other features common to this and to the Neanderthal type have been developed through some hyper-functioning of the pituitary, not as a pathological condition but as a hereditary racial complex of physical features.

Thus the importance of Rhodesian man consists in his wholly simian brow-ridges and frontal region and in his great face and jaws with human-shaped palate and degenerate teeth, his small brain of inferior human pattern, a poise of the head approaching the modern and, so far as can be gathered from the limb bones, a completely upright posture. Again we may point out the essential asymmetry of the type that he represents—the combination of simian with human features—that recurs in every fossil type, although the combinations are always varied.

Some authorities regard the Rhodesian man as a variant of the Neanderthal race. To my mind, there is no real basis for such a view. Except in the size of the brow-ridges and the lowness of the forehead, the two types have little in common. Rhodesian man is in some respects inferior to the Neanderthaloids and even to Pithecanthropus—especially in conformation of the forehead and brow-ridges.

Africanthropus njarasensis: a Candidate for African Primacy

In 1935, Dr. Ludwig Kohl-Larsen found a large number of human skull fragments partly on the surface and partly embedded in the sand on the northeastern shore of Lake Eyasi (Najarasa), in Tanganyika Territory, East Africa. The site also was strewn with the bones of fossil animals and with crude stone implements. The study of the human bones was entrusted to Dr. Hans Weinert, Germany's foremost authority on fossil man.[27] Somewhat later Weinert also received some additional finds of human bones from the same region made by Kohl-Larsen in 1938. The late African explorer, Dr. Hans Reck, and Dr. L. S. B. Leakey made a quick resurvey of the same area in 1937. Leakey and Reck referred the remains to the Upper Pleistocene, since they were certain that the deposit was more recent than the Middle Pleistocene strata that yielded Oldoway Man. All of the bones were fossilized and much rolled. They included parts of the three-toed Hipparion as well as remains of recent animals. The stone implements were partly crude hand-axes of Chellean type and some of the finer Acheulean types. Kohl-Larsen's original finds seem to have been embedded in an ancient bed of the lake and subsequently eroded out in part by wind action. The human bones were smashed into small pieces and included only skull fragments. The first find in 1935 included about 200 small bits of skull; and the 1938 resurvey yielded some 20 more fragments recovered from similar deposits some 430 to 450 meters east of the original site. These three collections of fragments represent at least three skulls, of which only the first has been restored. Since the nearly 200 small fragments of this skull have been worn along the edges and often split horizontally so that the outer and inner tables of the bone are separated, the restoration achieved is highly speculative and dubious. The parts found usually do not make contact with each other. They include a fragment of the right brow-ridge (apparently somewhat imaginatively restored), portions of the hinder part of the left side of the frontal, about half of the left parietal, the greater part of the occipital, and a piece of the left maxilla that includes a part of the lower border of the nasal aperture and lodges the left canine and first premolar. There is also a loose molar tooth, probably the upper left. All of the teeth are greatly worn and they are not unusual in size. The temporal bone has a very small mastoid process, but Weinert gives no precise description of its morphology, nor, for that matter, of the morphology of any of the other skull fragments. Instead, he bases his conclusions as to the nature of the find mostly upon a comparison of the

---

[27] Weinert, "Africanthropus njarasensis," pp. 252–308.

curves, outlines, and measurements of the restoration. The present writer has no faith in the accuracy of the restoration and consequently cannot accept the measurements and the conclusions from contours. Weinert wishes to ascribe this so-called *Africanthropus* to the Pithecanthropus-Sinanthropus group with closer affinities to the more advanced Chinese form.

Even if serious consideration be given the Africanthropus reconstruction, its resemblance to the Sinanthropus type is not impressive. In the occipital, or rear view, Africanthropus does not show its greatest breadth just above the level of the ear-holes, the most primitive condition, but higher up. Its rounded, but somewhat flattened-down, contour, from this aspect, is more like that of the classic Neanderthaloids. Weidenreich [28] remarks that the occipital portions of the Africanthropus skulls preserved (there are two incomplete occipital bones), clearly show the disintegration of the occipital torus and also of the frontal torus. He rejects Weinert's contention of Sinanthropus or Pithecanthropus affinities for this new fossil and regards its primitiveness as not beyond that of the European Neanderthaloids or of Rhodesian man.

It seems to the present writer that Weinert has built up his Africanthropus in much the same way that the traditional German scientist evolved a camel from his inner consciousness and that German anthropologists have built up their ideal and largely supposititious Nordic race.[29]

The Men of Solo: Scions of Pithecanthropus

After the find of *Pithecanthropus I* and a sterile expedition in 1909–10, which undertook new excavations at Trinil but discovered nothing of great consequence, the focus of interest in human phylogeny shifted to Europe, where fossil men were coming thick and fast out of cave deposits and quarries. After the discovery of Sinanthropus in China, the scientists of the Geological Survey of the Netherlands East Indies began to pay more attention to Pleistocene formations and Java re-emerged as an area of first importance for the study of human evolution.

In 1931, a member of the Geological Survey mapped the high level river terraces along the Solo River in central Java. Trinil, the first Pithecanthropus site, as well as the places of subsequent finds, is in this

---

28 Weidenreich, *op. cit.*, p. 221.

29 From *Das deutsches anthropologisches Kuchenbuch:*

"Recipe for Palaeoanthropic Goulash: Take 1 quart Plaster of Paris and mix with 1 pint water. Stir to a doughy consistency. Now add 3 cups assorted chopped skull bones and allow to harden in cool place. Serve with deutsche technische anthropologische Sauce (to Aryans only)."

same river valley. At Ngandong, excavations were begun on a 20-meter terrace rich in fossil bones. The fauna here included *Stegodon, Elephas, Hippopotamus* (highly specialized), and recent species of rhinoceros, cattle, and deer. These beds gave their name to the Ngandong Zone (cf. p. 289), which overlies the Trinil Zone and is Upper Pleistocene. In Ngandong, there were found parts of eleven fossil skulls and two tibiae. Whereas all of the skeletal parts of associated animals were found in the deposit, the human remains consisted of skulls only, with the exception of the tibial fragments. Further, all of the skulls had their bases smashed in, quite in the same fashion that may be observed in trophy skulls among the Dyak of central Borneo, head-hunters who open the skulls in order to eat the brains. As we have seen, this brain-eating seems to have been almost a standard practice among the human low-brows of the Pleistocene. The best preserved of the Ngandong skulls include most of the vault and some of the base; there are no faces and no lower jaws or teeth. The remains of this cannibalistic barbecue seem to have been dumped in one spot. Implements associated with the Solo men have also been found. These include primitive stone tools and some well-worked bone implements—a sort of axe made of deer antlers, a barbed spear head of Upper Palaeolithic type.

Some of the skulls of the Solo men have been described in a preliminary way by W. F. F. Oppenoorth,[30] a former member of the staff of the Geological Survey. They are all of the same type—with heavy supraorbital tori, forming a nearly straight, continuous ridge and merging into the very low and receding forehead imperceptibly, as in Pithecanthropus, and contrary to the groove or *fossa supraglabellaris* that demarcates the brow-ridges from the frontal curve in Sinanthropus and in most Neanderthaloids. Although the faces are missing, Oppenoorth thinks that the shape of the upper orbital rims suggests a wide and not very high orbital form in place of the rounded, deep orbits that are usual in the conservative Neanderthal type. The frontal bone has a slight median ridge, so that the vault is moderately roof-shaped rather than flattened anteriorly. The occiput is not flattened down as in classic Neanderthaloids, but the nuchal part, to which the neck muscles are hafted, is an almost flat plane shelving toward the foramen magnum at an angle of about 100° with the upper or occipital plane of the bone. At the top of the nuchal plane, a very prominent and sharp transverse crest delimits the two areas of the occiput and forms the uppermost attachment of the neck muscles. This crested form of torus is different from the swollen, rounded ridge form usually observed in Neanderthal

30 Oppenoorth, "Ein neuer diluvialer Urmensch," and "Place of Homo Soloensis,"

man and is more apelike. However, both types of occipital tori—crest
and ridge—may be observed in skulls of recent man. The Ngandong
skulls are all low-vaulted but exceed those of Pithecanthropus and Sinanthropus in height. Oppenoorth has attempted to calculate or to estimate
the cranial capacities of some of the better preserved specimens and
finds for two supposedly female skulls (Ngandong I and VI) 1160 cc. and
1190 cc., respectively. Ngandong V, a huge skull, is presumably that of a
male and yields a calculated capacity of 1316 cc. These figures are, on the
whole, below the average of Neanderthaloid cranial capacities, though
considerably above those of Pithecanthropus. Ariëns Kapper, a noted
authority on the brain, studied the endocranial casts of Ngandong I,
IV, and V and came to the conclusion that the general shape of the brain
of Solo man was more primitive than that of Neanderthal man and
approached in some respects that of Sinanthropus.

The temporal bone of the Solo man is much more modern in conformation than that of the conservative Neanderthaloids. The glenoid
fossa is very deep and has a well-marked articular eminence in front of
it; the tympanic plate is crested, and the mastoid process well-developed.
The position of the foramen magnum in the base of the skull is described
as well forward. Oppenoorth gives the approximate length of the large
male skull (Ngandong V) as 221 mm. and its breadth as about 144 mm.
The height of the calvaria or skull cap may have been about 87 mm. The
inner length of the skull cap is about 178 mm., so that the index of inner
to outer length would be about 84. However, these figures must be taken
as merely approximate. Ngandong I, probably a female, has a maximum
skull length of about 196 mm., a maximum breadth of approximately
144 mm., a skull-cap height of about 85 mm., and a cranial index of about
72.3. Ngandong VI (according to Weidenreich another probable female)
has the following dimensions and indices: length (maximum), 192 mm.;
breadth, 142 mm.; height from ear-holes, 102 mm.; calvarial height,
81 mm.; and cranial index, 74.2. These are, then, low-vaulted long-
heads of small capacity.

Oppenoorth says that the only postcranial bone found in four excavations on the Ngandong terrace is a right tibia, the upper part of which
is badly damaged. It is not short and robust, as are those of Neanderthal
man, but slender and straight, with the head probably retroverted, or
tipped back, as in bent-knee–gaited persons. The shape of the shaft in
the middle is primitive and perhaps apelike. The sharp shin crest of
modern man (absent in Neanderthaloids) is undeveloped. If this bone
belonged to a male, the stature may have been about 166 cm., and if
to a female, 161 cm. Judged by the length of this single bone, Solo man

was not tall. It may be mentioned that Weidenreich and Koenigswald think it possible that some of the femora attributed by Dubois to Pithecanthropus may belong to the later Ngandong man.

Weidenreich, in sore need of a full and detailed study of the imperfectly published Ngandong skulls for comparison with Sinanthropus, undertook his own investigation of the material from casts.[31] He found that in his comparison of 121 cranial characters only 69 features of Homo soloensis (as this type has been named) were available, since there are no teeth and no facial bones among the finds. Excluding 5 characters that seem to be merely individual or racial variations and 6 that are dubious, there remain 58 features in which *Homo soloensis* can be compared with Sinanthropus and Pithecanthropus. In these, there is almost complete agreement, with two exceptions: the size of the calvaria and the cranial capacity. Maximum lengths of the Ngandong skulls, according to Weidenreich's measurements on the casts, range from 193 mm. to 219 mm., as against 188 mm. to 199 mm. in Sinanthropus, and 176.5 mm. and 183 mm. in the two Pithecanthropus skulls available for measurement. Average maximum breadth in the Solo men is 146 mm., as against 141 mm. in Sinanthropus and 135 mm. in *Pithecanthropus II.* Differences in auricular height of the skulls are even greater: Soloensis 107.4 mm., Sinanthropus 98.4 mm., and *Pithecanthropus II* 89 mm. The capacity average of the Solo type is not correspondingly increased. According to Weidenreich's calculations, it ranges from 1035 cc. to 1255 cc., with an average of 1100 cc. (These estimates are considerably smaller than those made by Oppenoorth.) In any event, they fall perceptibly below the level of Neanderthal average cranial capacities. The cranial diagrams and tracings suggest that the Soloensis type is a little higher than the Sinanthropus—Pithecanthropus stage. The occipital torus, though large, is beginning to disintegrate. Characters of the frontal torus and the frontal sinus resemble Pithecanthropus rather than Sinanthropus. Although the Ngandong skulls still show the maximum breadth low down toward the skull bases—an apelike feature notable in Sinanthropus and Pithecanthropus—there is a tendency for this greatest breadth to shift upward to the parietals.

Weidenreich concludes that the Ngandong skulls resemble Pithecanthropus more closely than Sinanthropus, that they represent the next stage in evolution above Pithecanthropus and are probably his descendants, and that they are more primitive than the Neanderthaloids. With this conclusion the present writer agrees.

31 Weidenreich, *op. cit.*, pp. 229–232 and passim.

THE WADJAK SKULLS

Professor Dubois, the discoverer of *Pithecanthropus I,* had a habit of digging out of his fossil closet, after the lapse of many years, sundry skeletal specimens that had been brought back from his early expeditions. In 1920, he produced a couple of allegedly fossil skulls that had been dug up in 1889–1890 at a place called Wadjak, on the southern seaboard of central Java, about 60 miles southeast of Trinil. These skulls came out of the conglomerate of terraces supposed to mark the former levels of a dried-up, freshwater lake. Dubois considered them of Pleistocene age, but von Koenigswald states that this dating cannot be confirmed and that a similar population inhabited Java (in the Sampoeng cave) during the Neolithic cultural stage, which is geologically recent. These Wadjak skulls had big brow-ridges and receding foreheads but were less primitive in this respect than the Solo men. They were long-headed and had big brains. Wadjak I, thought to have been a female, had a cranial capacity reckoned by Dubois at 1550 cc. and Wadjak II, a male, no less than 1650 cc. These capacities are far above the level of modern Europeans.

The palate of Wadjak II, according to Keith, equals in its area (41 cm.) the record-breaking size of the Rhodesian palate. The width between the second molars is 3 mm. greater than in the Rhodesian skull, but the incisor, canine, and premolar teeth are smaller in the Wadjak specimen, and the portion of palatal arch that lodges them is more constricted. In Wadjak I, the palatal area is 35 sq. cm.—4 cm. more than in modern Australian males and 10 cm. greater than average dimensions of Englishmen (Keith). The breadth of the ascending branch of the mandible of Wadjak II falls only 5 mm. short of the unsurpassed Heidelberg jaw. The chin region is the weak, receding affair found in modern Australians—primitive but human. The teeth of the Wadjak skulls are much like those of the Rhodesian skull, large but of modern proportions, especially in the canine reduction and in the great transverse breadth of the molar crowns.

The faces of the Wadjak crania, according to the incomplete descriptions available, show features much like those of the Australian aborigines of today. Below the pronounced brow-ridges are low and broad orbits; the nasal root is depressed below the overhanging glabella; the nasal bones are small, narrow, and very flat, but the nasal apertures are wide. The alveolar portions of the jaws are thrust forward as in modern Negroids.

So far as can be deduced from the meager account of these Javan skulls given by their secretive discoverer, they were allied to the modern Australian aborigines. But their brain-cases were much larger and more capacious than those of that most primitive of present-day races. The average cranial capacity of the male Australian is only 1287 cc., which is about 300 cc. less than the contents of the Wadjak crania.

These Wadjak people, if they were Neolithic, almost certainly lived too late to be, as Dubois thought, progenitors of the Australian aborigines.

The Antecedents of the Australian Aborigines

Most of Australia remained submerged during Primary and Secondary times. It was, first of all, part of a huge Antarctic continent called Gondwanaland, which included India and the Indo-Malayan islands, Madagascar, and a part of South Africa. This continent broke up, and parts of it were submerged in the Indian Ocean; Australia was separated from Madagascar and South Africa, but maintained a connection with the Asiatic land mass until some time toward the end of the Secondary Era. During this period of Asiatic connection, Australia received its floral and faunal population. The animal and plant life cut off on this great island seems to have remained almost stationary and to have preserved a great deal of its Secondary character. However, the marsupials diversified most astoundingly. Neither man nor any placental mammal originated in Australia. Man must have reached Australia by way of the Malay Peninsula, Sumatra, Java, and New Guinea, probably well along in the Pleistocene Period, during one of the glacial phases when the sea level fell and only a short stretch of sea had to be crossed. Tindale suggests that this immigration took place when the old continental shelfs of Sunda and Sahul, now at the 40-fathom level, were above the sea. Even then the use of sea-going rafts or bark canoes would have been required in order to bridge gaps of 30 or 40 miles between islands.[32]

In Australia, the correlation of Pleistocene glacial deposits, river terraces, raised beaches, submerged strandlines, sand dunes, and alluvial deposits has not yet been completed. However, at least three glaciations have been recognized: the Margaret, the latest mountain tarn stage; the Yolande, the most obvious, cirque-cutting stage; and the Malanna, the oldest and most extensive, an ice-cap stage.[33] The Margaret glaciation is tentatively correlated with the Alpine Würm glaciation, the last of the four major glaciations of the Pleistocene, the Yolande with the European Riss (the third), and the Malanna with the Mindel (the second). A series of Australian raised beaches are thought to correspond to interglacial phases during which the sea level rose because of the melting ice.

---

[32] Tindale, "Antiquity of Man in Australia," pp. 144–147.
[33] Mahony, "Antiquity of Man in Australia," p. 18,

Among the finds of fossil or subfossil human bones found in Australia and New Guinea, the recently discovered Keilor skull is most important because its Pleistocene age appears to be irrefutable. Actually, two Keilor skulls have been found, but only one has been described up to now. The specimens were encountered with some other bones in undisturbed ground at a depth of 19 feet in a terrace adjoining the Maribyrnong River, and 45 feet above the river level. The sand pit that yielded them is a mile north of Keilor village, which lies 10 miles northwest of Melbourne. The discovery took place in October 1940. The Keilor terrace, in which the skulls were found, is the uppermost of three terraces of the Maribyrnong River which Mahony regards as representatives of

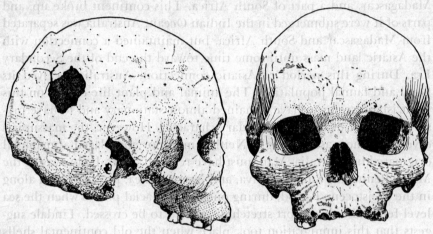

Fig. 54. The Keilor skull.

the eustatic rise of sea level that occurred during the Riss Würm interglacial period.[34]

A quartzite flake, evidently an artifact, was found protruding from the undisturbed sand of the pit close to the spot where the skull was unearthed. No bones of fossil animals were found in the Keilor terrace, but, in any event, since the order in which extinct marsupials died out is not known, their fossil remains cannot be used at present to date deposits.

The Keilor skull, when found, was almost completely covered with a mineral incrustation. The mandible is missing but otherwise the specimen is nearly complete.[35] The skull is 197 mm. long, 143 mm. wide; the cranial index (72.6) is dolichocephalic. The basion-bregma height (143 mm.) is distinctly high. The cranial capacity is calculated from

34 Mahony, *The Keilor Fossil Skull*, p. 80.
35 Wunderly. "The Keilor Fossil Skull: Anatomical Description," pp. 57–65.

formulae to be 1593 cc., a figure far above the averages of modern Australian skulls (1294 cc.) and of Tasmanian skulls (1247–1264 cc.). This figure, if accurate, indicates also a capacity nearly 150 cc. higher than that usually given for modern adult male European skulls. The brow-ridges and glabella are only moderately developed; the root of the nose is not deeply depressed. The orbits are low; the suborbital or canine fossae deep; the nasal bones are short, broad, and concave and the nasal aperture broad and low, but without distinctively primitive features of its lower border. The nasal index (54) is chamaerrhine. The short, broad face of the Keilor skull is only moderately protruding (gnathic index 99.1)—less so than the average of Tasmanian skulls (101.4) and considerably below the Australian mean (104.5).[36] The gnathic index expresses the diameter from the point on the upper alveolar border between the central incisors to the middle point on the anterior border of the foramen magnum as a percentage of the length of the cranio-facial base (root of the nose to middle of anterior border of foramen magnum—"basion-nasion"). Skulls with indices below 98 are orthognathous or straight-jawed; indices of 103 or more are prognathous; the intermediate category is mesognathous. It is here that the Keilor skull falls. However, this index is not too useful a measure of jaw protrusion because it disregards the height of the face.

The palate of the Keilor skull is horseshoe-shaped and very broad relative to its length. The third molars are reduced in size and turned inwards. The external palatal index, which expressed the maximum outside breadth of the palate as a percentage of the external length, is 116.6, which puts it in the evolutionarily advanced groups with relatively broad palates. Tasmanian crania average 111.9 in this index and Australian crania 107.7. Both Australian and Tasmanian skulls have palates more primitive in form and approximating the U-shape seen in most ancient types of man and in apes. The broad Keilor palate has a longitudinal bony swelling along the center line of its roof. This feature is known as the palatine torus. It is commonest among Eskimo. Many consider this torus a reinforcement against the stresses exerted toward the middle line in vigorous mastication. It is not an apelike feature. The teeth of the Keilor skull are so badly worn that the details of their cusp pattern cannot be studied, but they fall well within the size range of modern Tasmanian and Australian teeth. The studies of Wunderly and Adams on the Keilor skull lead them to conclude that the specimen shows characters intermediate between modern Australian and Tasmanian skulls.

[36] The teeth and palate of the Keilor skull have been described by Adam, "The Keilor Fossil Skull: Palate and Upper Dental Arch," pp. 71–77.

The Keilor skull has not the gable-roof shape of Australian vaults and lacks their massive brow-ridges and rough areas of muscular attachment. Its parietal bosses are more pronounced than those of Australian skulls but less than those of typical Tasmanian crania. Incidentally, the cranial sutures are of a simple pattern, and the suture between the two halves of the frontal bone, the metopic suture, which ordinarily closes in the second year of life, has remained open—a progressive feature often seen in European skulls but rather uncommon in primitive skulls.

The combination of Australian and Tasmanian cranial features in this specimen accords well with opinion that the modern Australian native has sprung from an archaic White stock that has absorbed a certain amount of Negrito blood through mixture with the Tasmanians who preceded the Australoids in the continent. The great cranial capacity of the specimen agrees with the superior measurements of volume found in the Wadjak skulls of Java, which are certainly Australoid, even if their geological date is too late, as von Koenigswald now thinks, to permit us to regard them as ancestors of the Australians.

Here, as in the South African Boskopoid types (cf. pp. 394–395), we encounter the phenomenon of palaeolithic precursors who seem to have had much larger brains than their putative modern descendants. Dr. Carleton S. Coon thinks that reduction in cranial size is a fairly constant phenomenon in the transition from *Homo sapiens* men of the Upper Palaeolithic to recent races. Our brains may have shrunken since the close of glacial times.

Among the other supposedly geologically ancient human remains found in Australia, the Talgai skull, according to Mahony, has the best claim to authenticity.[37] It was found in 1884, at Talgai Station, Queensland, in Northern Australia, but did not come to scientific notice until 1914. The locus of the find depends upon the memory of the original discoverer, an untrained observer, who pointed out to Professor Edgeworth David a spot in the bank of a gully within a few yards of which he said he had found the skull 30 years previously. The specimen was stated to have protruded from the bank about 3 feet above the bottom of the gully. The skull was embedded in the upper part of a clay layer, overlaid here by 6 or 7 feet of black soil. No bones of extinct marsupials were found here, but they do occur in similar clay at various places in the vicinity. The skull is mineralized to a degree similar to that exhibited by the bones of the extinct marsupials found in this red-brown clay of the Darling Downs. Mahony thinks the age is probably Pleistocene.

The face and lower portion of the frontal bone of the Talgai skull

---

[37] Mahony, "Antiquity of Man in Australia," pp. 26–28.

are in a fair state of preservation, but the vault is nothing more than a mosaic of fragments, which have been pieced together by Dr. A. Stewart Smith. Its exact dimensions cannot be recovered, but Dr. Smith estimated the length at 192 mm. and the breadth at 141 mm., the height of the vault above the ear holes as 105 mm., and the cranial capacity about 1300 cc. The skull is that of a boy 14 or 15 years of age. It has a very thick glabella region (the prominence above the root of the nose) for so young a subject, and the forehead recedes sharply as in modern Australians. The face is extremely prognathous—much more so than in modern natives. However, the conformation of both brain-case and face is typically Australian.

As originally reconstructed, the palate of the Talgai boy was the most simian ever found in a human being and had enormous, projecting canine teeth. However, further studies by Dr. Milo Hellman revealed that the canines, although large, were not unduly projecting, and that the palate, in spite of its great size, was quite human in shape.

Another famous Australian skull is the Cohuna specimen, which is that of a very primitive-appearing, adult male with exaggeratedly Australoid characters. This skull was publicized by Sir Colin Mackenzie and Sir Arthur Keith,[38] the latter of whom considered it a representative of the stock of the Talgai boy and described several of its features as the most primitive heretofore observed in man. However, Mahony and other competent Australian authorities state that there is no evidence whatsoever of the geological antiquity of this Cohuna specimen, which falls within the range of modern aboriginal Australian skulls in all respects.[39]

It is unnecessary to enumerate and describe here sundry other mineralized human remains found in various parts of Australia and of dubious antiquity. All seem to represent types closely similar to those to be observed in the present Australian aboriginals, with some individual variations, often in the direction of larger teeth, or greater prognathism than the run-of-the-mill modern Australian shows. The most significant fact is that the Keilor skull, which apparently stands alone as authentically Pleistocene, presents a combination of Australian and Tasmanian features that accords with the best modern analysis of the affinities of the present Australians.

In the Aitape District of New Guinea, an area in which a large Japanese army was surrounded and liquidated toward the end of World War II, a fragmentary skull of possible geological antiquity has been discovered. It was found in 1929 by a member of the Northern Aus-

[38] Keith, *New Discoveries*, p. 307.
[39] Mahony, "Antiquity of Man in Australia," pp. 34–35.

tralian Geological Survey.[40] The skull fragments were *in situ* in a bed of littoral marine clay outcropping in the bank of a creek near Barida Village, Aitape, 10 miles from the coast and about 300 feet above sea level. Over the skull were 4 feet of undisturbed littoral deposit containing marine molluscs, and above this, 6 feet of gravel surmounted by top soil. The marine littoral deposit forms a part of the Upper Wanimo series, regarded by the Survey authorities as of Pleistocene age.

The Aitape skull fragments include the larger part of the frontal bone and portions of both parietals. Fenner, who studied the skull, regards it as that of a female, about 45 years of age, who did not differ in any important respect from the Southern type of the modern Australian aboriginal. Modern Australoid-looking skulls sometimes occur in New Guinea. This specimen shows no Tasmanian affinities. When we discuss Birdsell's still unpublished analysis of the tri-hybrid origin of the Australian race (pp. 610–612), we shall see that considerable segments of the aboriginal Australian population show little evidence of admixture with the Negritoid Tasmanians.

Precocious Advent of Homo Sapiens in England

One could fill a fat book with elaborate accounts of anatomically modern skeletal finds that are dubiously attributed to the Middle Pleistocene, the Lower Pleistocene, and even to the Pliocene and earlier geological periods. Because the earliest finds of Neanderthal man were referable to the first part of the fourth glacial advance (Upper Pleistocene), and because Neanderthal man was, on the whole, rather apelike, it was inconceivable to most anthropologists that a physically modernistic and unsimian human type could have preceded him. Sir Arthur Keith was perhaps the only distinguished student of fossil man who steadfastly adhered to the belief that the Mousterian Neanderthal men, who buried their dead in the caves of Western Europe, were palaeontological hang-overs, outmoded survivors of an earlier stage of human evolution who persisted in some places long after *Homo sapiens* in all of his cerebral glory, with reduced teeth and jutting chin, had emerged from the concourse of our ape ancestors.

It is very difficult to establish the geological age of chance finds of human remains that come out of gravel pits, railway cuttings, and other commercial excavations, particularly because the bones are usually removed before they have been seen in position by qualified archaeologists and geologists who can judge whether they have been introduced into

[40] *Ibid.*, pp. 32–33.

the deposit after it was laid down or are contemporaneous with the stratum (*in situ*). Even when there is no question of a burial or any other intrusive agency, the exact geological age of the layer in which the bones occur is often arguable or indeterminate, so that the discounter of high antiquity always has an advantage. Thus, case after case of finds of *Homo sapiens* in apparently mid-Pleistocene deposits has had to be relegated to the "not proven" category. Now at last, however, the persistent searches of archaeologists among the glacial gravels have been rewarded by one cast-iron, irrefragable case that serves not only to establish the main point of contention, but also to validate or, at any rate, to strengthen numerous other claims previously dismissed.

THE SWANSCOMBE SKULL

In early Pleistocene times, the Thames river laid down a sheet of gravel that is now 100 feet above its present bed. Later it eroded its valley, depositing subsequent layers of gravels at the 50 foot level and below. At the beginning of the Neolithic period, about 8000 years ago, the southern part of England stood about 100 feet above its present level; the English Channel was a river valley and the Dogger Bank, now covered by 60 feet of water at low tide, was a marsh through which the Thames wound its way into the North Sea. These old land surfaces of the Neolithic times, now buried, are called the "submerged forests," for stumps and trunks of trees are often dredged up. And both Neolithic skeletons and characteristic stone implements of the New Stone Age have been recovered from these deposits. By a gradual and long-continued subsidence, these old land surfaces were invaded by the sea; the lower part of the Thames valley became an estuary. Toward the present mouth of the Thames the old Neolithic floors now lie more than 30 feet below the level of the river.

At Swanscombe, on the south side of the Thames, between Dartford and Gravesend, there are several big gravel pits that expose the deposits of the 100-foot high terrace. Among these, the Barnfield pit has been for many years a classic site for the succession of human cultures of the Lower Palaeolithic, as well as for remains of Pleistocene mammals. It was opened more than 60 years ago and has yielded many thousands of flint implements and countless fossil animal bones, but never a scrap of human bone until 1935.

The main working-face of the pit, overlooking a deep excavation in the chalk, is about 40 feet high and exposes a series of sands, gravels, and loams of the 100-foot terrace. The sequence of strata from the top downward is: (1) Upper Gravel and Hill-wash, (2) Upper Loam, (3) Middle

Gravels and Sands, (4) Lower Loam, (5) Lower Gravel. On June 29th, 1935, Dr. A. T. Marston of Clapham, who had visited the pit at regular intervals to collect palaeolithic implements, found a fossil human occipital bone in the Middle Gravels, at a depth of 24 feet from the surface. He kept a constant lookout as the face of the pit was worked back, and nine months later found a left parietal bone in the same seam of gravel and at the same depth from the surface, but 8 yards farther back. The two bones articulate and undoubtedly belonged to the same individual. A considerable number of well-recognized types of Lower Palaeolithic implements were found in the same stratum as the skull, one no farther than a foot from the occipital bone and another at a distance of 6 feet. A committee of the Royal Anthropological Institute, consisting of the best qualified geologists, archaeologists, and physical anthropologists available, examined the site, made additional excavations, studied the implement series and the bones, and concluded that the Swanscombe skull is an indigenous fossil of the 100-foot terrace of the lower Thames; that the industry in the skull layer is Middle Acheulean; that the associated fauna is Middle Pleistocene of an interglacial type, testifying a climate probably warmer than the present; that the interglacial phase represented was probably the second or Mindel-Riss, the Great Interglacial; that only the breadth of the occipital bone and the great thickness of both bones are peculiar in comparison with modern remains of *Homo sapiens*.[41]

The Acheulean hand-axe industries, primarily characterized by lanceolate, disk-shaped, or pear-shaped axes, made of a flint core or a large flake and worked on both sides, are stratigraphically preceded by a cruder hand-axe industry known as Abbevillian (formerly Chellean). The Abbevillian industry seems to have begun during the first glaciation or the first interglacial, and the Acheulean succeeded it about the earlier part of the second or Great Interglacial. Acheulean types of implements went on evolving through the rest of the Pleistocene up to the end of the last or third interglacial. In the caves of the last glaciation—Würm— Neanderthal man succeeds with his quite different Mousterian industry, while, at Steinheim and Ehringsdorf, Neanderthal man occurs with an earlier "pre-Mousterian" industry, at the former site probably in a Riss horizon (third glaciation), and at the latter in an early phase of the last interglacial. The Swanscombe skull is, then, older than any other European skulls except Heidelberg and Eoanthropus, both of which may possibly be second interglacial, but are more probably first interglacial.

41 Clark and Morant, "Report on Swanscombe Skull," pp. 97–98.

Professor W. E. Le Gros Clark and Dr. G. M. Morant reported on the skull for the Committee and found it to be, probably, that of a female who died in her early twenties, who had a well-convoluted cerebral hemisphere, with a cranial capacity of about 1325 cc. and a cranial index of about 78. They felt that by the characters of the occipital bone the Swanscombe skull could be distinguished from Spy II (Neanderthaloid), from Pithecanthropus, and probably from all other Lower Palaeolithic skulls except the Steinheim skull, and that the only remarkable features of the specimen were the thickness of both bones and the great breadth of the occipital, neither of which are sufficient to throw Swanscombe out of the range of *Homo sapiens*.

Sir Arthur Keith, however, undertook a detailed study of the Swans-

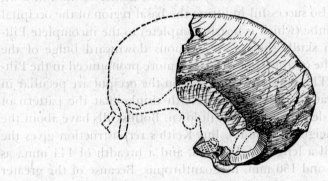

Fig. 55. The Swanscombe skull.

combe specimen and at the same time a revision of Eoanthropus, which led him to some interesting inferences as to their relationship that must be summarized here. Firstly, in both skulls, the lateral sinus (a venous channel on the interior of the skull) passes directly from the occipital to the temporal bone over a special process of the occipital bone that may be named the asterionic angle. This direct transmission is regular in apes and occurs rarely in human crania. Ordinarily, the transition is effected by the sinus cutting across the hinder inferior angle of the parietal. Next, the squamous border of the temporal in each of these skulls is extraordinarily arched and extremely extensive in its long, dovetailed flanging. These peculiarities may be due either to the unusual extent to which the temporals are bent inward (as demonstrable upon the Piltdown specimen only), or to the inward pressure of the temporal muscle that exerts its strength against the squamosal suture as it ascends the side of the cranial vault in growth. Again, it is apparent that in both skulls the temporal extended far enough forward to make contact with the frontal at pterion (a form of pterionic articulation customary in apes but rare in man. The interior of the parietal bone in this same region indicates that a sharp Sylvian falx, as seen in modern skulls, was missing both in Piltdown and Swanscombe (cf. footnote, p. 310). From the endocranial casts, it may be concluded that the temporal and temporo-occipital regions were more extensive in Swanscombe than in Piltdown. However, in both casts there are indications of a simplicity beyond what is usual in modern crania. The brain casts show that both of these skulls were characterized by a high degree of asymmetry of the occipital lobes, but in Piltdown the left lobe is larger, in Swanscombe the right. The occipital lobes of the latter skull are the more richly convoluted. Keith found that the Swanscombe parietal and occipital could be fitted very well to a slightly narrowed model of the Piltdown frontal. He was also successful in fitting the basal region of the occipital bone of Swanscombe (which is nearly complete) to the incomplete Piltdown base. Both skulls show a conspicuous downward bulge of the nuchal plane of the occiput, but this is the more pronounced in the Piltdown specimen. The muscular markings on the occiput are peculiar in each skull and rather different, but Keith thinks that the pattern of Swanscombe is a derivative of the Piltdown. Both skulls have about the same auricular height (110 mm.), but Keith's reconstruction gives the Swanscombe skull a length of 185 mm. and a breadth of 144 mm., as against 194 mm. and 150 mm. in Eoanthropus. Because of the greater thickness of the bones, the capacities are not dissimilar: Swanscombe about 1350 cc. and Piltdown about 1358 cc.[42] In neither skull does the occiput resemble the Neanderthaloid shape found in the progressive Steinheim skull, and Keith does not think that the Steinheim Neanderthaloid forehead could be fitted to the Swanscombe parietal and occipital. He concludes that the Swanscombe man is a later member of the Piltdown phylum—the Swanscombe skull is second interglacial and the Piltdown probably first—and regards the London skull and the Bury St. Edmunds fragments (which will be described later) as still more recent members of the group. Keith does not commit himself definitely to the opinion that this Piltdown phylum is that of *Homo sapiens* but notes that it was a strange mixture of neanthropic and simian features. Incidentally, he considers the Swanscombe individual to have been a male under 25 years and the Piltdown to have been a probable male over 30 years.

These identifications and deduced relationships of the Swanscombe to the Piltdown are those of perhaps the greatest authority on fossil man.

[42] Keith, "A Resurvey," p. 252.

They may not be in all respects correct. However, there is no denying the conclusion that Swanscombe is either mid-Pleistocene *Homo sapiens* or something so close to it that the differences are zoologically inconsiderable.

GALLEY HILL MAN

The most notorious of the anachronistic and questionable finds of *Homo sapiens* in the mid-Pleistocene is Galley Hill man, stoutly defended by Sir Arthur Keith but usually disregarded by other students of human palaeontology. The authenticated find of the Swanscombe skull, some 47 years after the Galley Hill discovery, comes very close to validating the antiquity of the earlier specimen.

The schoolhouse at Galley Hill stands on the brow of the 100-foot terrace overlooking the Thames valley some miles below London. In 1888, workmen were removing the gravels to get at the underlying chalk, which is used in the making of cement. The Galley Hill skeleton was found by one of these workmen, apparently about 8 feet down in the gravel and 2 feet above the chalk. Unfortunately, no geologist observed the find *in situ*, but two amateur archaeologists, the schoolmaster and a printer, examined the bones before their removal, and both have given Sir Arthur Keith very clear testimony as to the undisturbed condition of the strata above the bones.[43] In 1894, Mr. E. T. Newton, a geologist, went carefully into all of the evidence and satisfied himself that the skeleton was actually found at a depth of 8 feet in the gravel of the 100-foot terrace.

Since the Galley Hill gravel pit is only a few hundred yards from the Barnsfield pit and the stratification is stated to be the same and the implements found in the various layers are of the same types, it is difficult to evade the conclusion that the Galley Hill skeleton is roughly contemporaneous with the Swanscombe skull—namely a Middle Acheulean man, probably belonging to the second or Great Interglacial period. However, since most parts of the Galley Hill skeleton are represented, and the various bones were found close together, they must represent a burial. Sir Arthur Keith thinks that this burial was made on a former land surface, and it is clearly stated that the skeleton was embedded in the loam below the gravels and just above the chalk. Keith identifies the stratum as the Lower Loam, which in the Barnsfield pit overlies the Lower Gravels. These latter gravels contain a Clactonian flake industry and are just below the Middle Gravels, which yield Acheulean hand-axes. In the Barnsfield pit, the Lower Loam has its surface weathered

---

[43] Keith, *Antiquity of Man*, I, 252, ff.

as if it were an ancient land surface, but no implements are found in it. The Swanscombe skull lay somewhat higher, in the Middle Gravels.

The Galley Hill bones themselves are not extraordinary in a morphological sense. They include a skull cap, most of the left half of the lower jaw, and fragmentary limb bones. Galley Hill man was a male of 50 years or more. His stature was short, not more than 5 feet, 3 inches, (160 cm.). There is nothing anthropoid or even Negroid about the limb proportions. The shin bone is not long relative to the thigh as in Negroids, nor yet very short as in Neanderthal man. The collar bone and humerus show, according to Keith, remarkable development of the large pectoral muscle.

The skull has been warped, so that its width is somewhat diminished and its length increased. It seems to have been very long, about 204 mm., and narrow (width 140 mm.). The cephalic index (ratio of breadth to length) is about 69. The vault is relatively low (height above ear-holes 120 mm.). The cubic contents seem to have been between 1350 cc. and 1400 cc.—not below the average of many men of today. The brain cast shows modern development of the convolutionary patterns and presence of all of the areas connected with sight, hearing, touch, speech, movements, et cetera. The fossilization of the bones is pronounced, not necessarily an indication of great age but yet one of its prerequisites. The skull is exceptionally thick, 10 to 12 mm. in the vault, and the brow-ridges, though of the modern divided type, are pronounced. The mandible shows some primitive features, although the chin is well developed. The ascending branch has a very shallow depression or sigmoid notch, in front of the condyle. This is not a simian feature, but occurs in Neanderthal man and occasionally in some modern peoples, notably the Eskimo. The glenoid fossa, which receives the condyle of the jaw, is of a form seen in primitive races of today. The area of the temporal muscle is exceptionally large, and the mastoids are small. The five teeth left in the jaw are not large, but the crowns of the molars are greater in length than in breadth, and the third molar is slightly longer than the second. The pulp cavities of the molars are not enlarged as in Neanderthal man, and the roots are of modern shape and proportions. Keith calculates the area of the palate at 29 to 30 sq. cm., a figure by no means extraordinary in primitive peoples of today.

Galley Hill man had a good forehead and a satisfactory chin, a normal amount of brains, and other skeletal features quite in harmony with the development of a modern individual of the less civilized human races.

In view of the authentically Middle Pleistocene age of the neighboring Swanscombe specimen, I am puzzled to note that Sir Arthur Keith in studying it makes no mention whatsoever of the Galley Hill skeleton, but concerns himself principally with a comparison of Piltdown and Swanscombe. This omission suggests that he has recently lost faith in the antiquity of Galley Hill man, although a better case for it can now be advanced than ever in the past.

THE LONDON SKULL

Sir Arthur Keith has assigned two other Pleistocene English skulls to the Piltdown-Swanscombe lineage. The London skull, discovered in 1925 in excavating for the foundations of new buildings for Lloyds, is of doubtful age. It may belong to the 20-foot terrace of the Thames and be post-Mousterian—subsequent to the disappearance of Neanderthal man. It may belong to the 50-foot terrace and be Middle Pleistocene. Most of the parietals and the occipital were found. Keith has restored the specimen and notes the following resemblances to the Piltdown skull: open angle of the nuchal plane of the occipital bone (in contrast to the flat, sharply shelving Neanderthal nuchal plane), marked asymmetry of the occipital lobes; long, gently curved contour of the occipital above the attachments for neck muscles; general similarities in shape and muscular markings of the bones.

THE BURY ST. EDMUNDS SKULL

The Bury St. Edmunds skull, found in 1882 in West Suffolk, comes from a pocket in the chalk filled with brick earth. Similar pockets have yielded Acheulean implements, and the fossilized skull may have been washed into the depression when the river Lark was flowing 100 feet above its present bed. The fragments consist of the upper part of the frontal and anterior portions of the parietals. The forehead is bulging, and the bones are thin. The skull, probably that of a woman, was certainly not Neanderthaloid. The vault was flattened and broad, probably brachycephalic.

Neither of these cases is convincing, nor do they add to the already established case of the existence of Middle Pleistocene *Homo sapiens* in England.

The Cave Artists: Art for Meat's Sake

In the caves of France and in strata overlying those that have yielded the implements of the Mousterian industry and the remains of Neanderthal man, are found the artifacts belonging to the Aurignacian culture.

The flint tools and weapons of this industry are smaller and more diversified in form than those made by Neanderthal man. The use of bone for
tools becomes very common. The beginnings of graphic and plastic art
date from this period. The tenants of the caves who succeeded Neanderthal man scratched on bones, on pebbles, and on the walls of the
caves, drawings of the animals they hunted, at first crude outline sketches,
but from the very beginning done with a certain boldness and realism.
Before the end of the last glacial retreat, these engravings had reached
a pitch of excellence in delineation of animal forms that was not afterward equalled until the Minoans of Crete produced their masterpieces.
On the walls of the caves the men of the Aurignacian period also painted
pictures of animals, at first in flat tints, then shaded. In the latest phase
of the palaeolithic culture, these paintings were elaborated into poly-
chrome efforts of considerable merit. The Aurignacians also carved
statuettes in ivory and stone, usually representations of the female figure
with swelling breasts, greatly protuberant buttocks, and sex organs
strongly accentuated. Such female figurines probably had a magical
significance and symbolized the reproductive force in nature.

The bones of the animals found in these deposits of the Upper Palaeolithic period still indicate a glacial climate. The woolly rhinoceros,
the mammoth, the cave bear, the arctic fox, and the glutton occurred in
abundance. Gradually, however, the climate seems to have become
dryer, and a fauna like that of the Siberian tundra began to dominate
the scene. The reindeer became increasingly abundant, and with him
the musk ox and the horse. A cold, dry, steppe climate succeeded the
damp cold of the glacial maximum.

One of the best preserved skeletons of the Aurignacian periods is
that discovered at Combe-Capelle in the Périgord region of France in
1900. It was found in a cave with typical implements and animal remains of the Aurignacian period. The skull is long (202 mm.) and very
narrow (breadth 134 mm.), the cranial index or breadth-length ratio
being 66.3. It is high-vaulted, the diameter from the anterior edge of
the occipital foramen to the top of the frontal bone being 139 mm. The
brow-ridges are strongly developed, although much smaller than those
of Neanderthal type, and the forehead is high and rather steep. The
face is of moderate breadth and length and no more projecting than
that of modern big-jawed men of the less prognathous races. The jaws
are, however, very strong. The orbits are low and broad; the roof of the
nose is not high, and the nasal aperture is rather broad. All of the teeth
are present in a large U-shaped palate such as is sometimes seen in modern Australians; the lower jaw is very large and heavy, but the chin is

fairly well developed, and the attachments of the tongue muscles are as they should be in an entirely human jaw. The teeth are large, but the pulp cavities are small as in modern man. There is nothing remarkable about the other bones of the skeleton; they belonged to a short man (161 cm.), of robust build and upright carriage. Aurignacian man was somewhat crude and brutal in appearance but showed none of the gorilla-like features observed in Neanderthal man.

The first well-preserved skeletons of the Aurignacian period were discovered in 1868 in the little village of Les Eyzies, which lies in the valley of the Vézère river. The Vézère is a northern tributary of the Dordogne, in the Périgord, one of the most charming and picturesque parts of south central France. Here have been found the richest and most varied remains of Pleistocene man encountered anywhere. In caves and rock-shelters the Mousterian Neanderthaloids lived, and in the same dwelling places their successors—the men of the Aurignacian, Solutrian, and Magdalenian periods—evolved their industries and developed their arts of realistic painting, sculpture, and engraving on stone and bone. The type sites of two of these periods, the Mousterian and the Magdalenian, are in this valley.

The small rock-shelter of Cro Magnon is at the foot of the cliffs within the village of Les Eyzies. When I visited it some years ago, the site of the famous discovery had been converted into a hen coop, but even then I picked up a flint flake, perhaps struck off by one of the palaeolithic hunters and artists. When M. Louis Lartet excavated this rock shelter in 1868, he found it to contain hearths and strata yielding implements of the Aurignacian culture. The human remains occurred in the highest strata of the deposit, far back underneath the overhanging wall of the cliff. They consisted of a skull and some other bones of an old man and, a short distance away, parts of the skeletons of four other individuals. The type of man here discovered is one that seems to have inhabited various places in western Europe throughout the three Upper Palaeolithic periods.

We may take as typical of the group the "Old Man of Cro Magnon" himself. His stature was 168.4 cm., or 5 feet, 6¼ inches, according to the conventional estimates. His forearms were rather long when compared with his upper arms, and his shins were long relative to his thighs. Most writers refer persistently to these as Negroid proportions, and they are *not* usual in modern Europeans, but they occur frequently in the taller groups of American Indians and in other races that are not ordinarily considered Negroid.

It is, however, the skull of the Cro Magnon man that is supposed to define the type. It is a massive skull, large in every dimension. The length is 203 mm., the breadth 150 mm., and the height above the ear-holes 132 mm. The brain-case of this old man is estimated to have contained 1660 cc.,[44] which is roughly 150 cc. above the modern European average. The brain-case is dolichocephalic, and of a pentagonal or coffin shape when looked at from above, since the bosses on the sides of the parietal bones are strongly projecting. The forehead is broad and of moderate height, the brow-ridges of ordinary size. The occiput bulges behind and displays a marked flattening in the lambdoid region, right at the crown of the head where the hair whorl ordinarily is observed in the living. Although the skull is relatively narrow compared with its length, it is absolutely broad across the middle of the parietals where the lateral bosses protrude. Hafted to this long brain-case is a broad and very short face. This combination of a short, broad face with a long, narrow head is known as cranial disharmony. The orbits of the eyes are extremely broad and, because of the shortness of the face, very low. The cheek bones are large and protruding ("high"), although not nearly so prominent as in most American Indians. The nose is narrow and high, or leptorrhine; the alveolar borders, which lodge the teeth, are prognathous. The palatine arch is of medium size and somewhat narrow; the teeth are not extraordinary. The lower jaw is robust, of an entirely modern conformation with the chin jutting forward strongly.

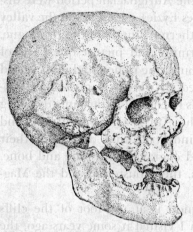

Fig. 56. The skull of the Old Man of Cro Magnon. (Drawn with a camera lucida from a cast.)

A fairly constant feature in this type is the flattening of the thigh bones, called platymeria, and the side-to-side flattening of the shin bones, called platycnemia, which have been attributed to the habit of walking with the knees bent on unlevel ground. The femora are also strongly bowed and have marked pilasters on their posterior surfaces (cf. pp. 121–122).

Thus we are shown the picture of a powerful man with relatively long forearms and shins, who perhaps did not extend the leg completely in walking. This man had a massive brain-case and a fine brow; the back of his head protruded, and above the bulging occiput was a flattened

[44] These are Keith's figures; Boule gives the capacity as 1590 cc.

area. His face was very broad and short; his eyes long and with narrow openings, his nose high and narrow, and his chin thrust forward in a pugnacious manner.

From the original Old Man of Cro Magnon, the French anthropologists have evolved a race. Like Procrustes, they have attempted to fit into the Cro Magnon bed almost all finds of modernistic man belonging to the late Palaeolithic, ruthlessly stretching them out or lopping them off. Collignon saw in a certain long-headed, but broad-faced type of man still resident in the Dordogne a direct lineal descendant of the ancient Cro Magnon cave-dwellers. This opinion is in spite of the fact that the type referred to is very short in stature, whereas an outstanding feature of the Palaeolithic "race" was its supposedly great height. Verneau thought that the Guanches of the Canary Islands, a cave-dwelling people who were conquered and either exterminated or absorbed by the Spanish during the fifteenth century, were a Cro Magnon group that emigrated to these islands off the coast of North Africa at the end of the glacial period. He even saw cultural parallels between the two groups, although the Canary Islanders were a Neolithic people who kept domesticated animals, raised barley, made pottery, and possessed a stone-chipping industry far inferior even to that of the Mousterians. The Canary Islanders had no arts of painting or engraving; apart from their cave-dwelling habits they had scarcely one cultural trait in common with the Cro Magnons. There did occur in the Canary Islands a type of man with a long skull and a short face, sometimes of elevated stature, but oftener short. Such types of cranial disharmony may be seen in many peoples all over the world and belonging to various racial stocks.

One also reads in many books on prehistoric archaeology the statement that the Cro Magnons had larger brains than modern man, and it is implied that these great brains indicated a more powerful intelligence than men of today possess, and that there is some connection between the size of the Cro Magnon skulls and their owners' proficiency in drawing and painting animals. This is nonsense. In the first place, the French method of measuring cranial capacity with lead shot yields much higher capacities than are correct. Secondly, people who are tall have absolutely bigger heads and larger cranial capacities than small people, simply because their body masses are larger. But this does not mean that they are more intelligent than the smaller people. As a matter of fact, small people usually have *relatively* larger brains and heads than tall people. Finally, there is no reason for believing that a trick of accurate observation and skillful delineation of animals necessarily implies any high mental powers in the artist.

I am so unregenerate as to be sceptical of the reality of the Cro Magnon "race," if the term "race" be used in its proper anthropological connotation. A race is a great body of mankind having a majority of identical physical characters inherited from its common ancestors. The criteria
by which race should be determined are heritable features. In order to
establish a type of any racial significance, it is absolutely essential that
the individuals attributed to it show a certain homogeneity in the crucial
physical features. They must vary less in their bodily characters than
do random individuals collected from assorted racial groups. This is not
true of the so-called Cro Magnon "race." Not a single feature by which
this "race" is distinguished shows any reasonable constancy in its members. The Cro Magnons are supposed to have been of almost gigantic
stature. Some of them have been considerably stretched, and others are
of medium height or even short. Cro Magnons are credited with dolichocephalic skulls, flattened on the crown, and with short, broad faces
hafted to these skulls. But some of them have round heads; others exhibit
no lambdoid flattening; quite a few of them have very long faces, and
some have narrow, compressed facial skeletons. They are also distinguished by the possession of broad and low orbital openings, but this
feature is lacking in some of the specimens. The condition of leptorrhiny, or a relatively narrow and long nose, is also asserted to be a feature
of the Cro Magnons. Here, again, the skeletons assigned to the type exhibit a high degree of inconstancy.

Platymeria, the front-to-back flattening of the femur in the upper
part of its shaft, and platycnemia, the associated lateral flattening of
the shin bone, are other Cro Magnon features. These seem to be almost
exclusively adaptive characters and are so widely distributed among
modern primitive peoples, as well as among ancient races, that they have
absolutely no diagnostic value from a racial standpoint. Again, the
elongation of the forearm relative to the arm and of the leg relative to
the thigh is so common among all tall peoples and not a few short peoples
that it has no racial significance whatsoever. In short, there is not a single
feature found in Cro Magnon man that has not a wide inter-racial distribution, and most of the physical features whereby the race has been
defined are of little or no value as racial criteria.

At Solutré, the type site for the Solutrian period of the Palaeolithic
Age, other skeletons attributed to the Cro Magnon race have been uncovered. Solutré is four miles west of Mâcon, on the right bank of the
Saône, in east central France. Above the village a limestone bluff rises
to a height of 300 feet. Sloping away from the base of the rock are de-

posits covering the hearths of ancient man. At the bottom level, averaging about 10 feet in depth, is a layer 15 to 20 inches in thickness, made up of charred, broken, and split horse bones, mixed up with fireplaces and yielding implements and carved bones typical of the Aurignacian culture. The remains of 100,000 horses are estimated to lie here. The Aurignacians were great horsemen, or rather great eaters of horse flesh. Above the so-called "equine" layers are strata containing objects of the later Solutrian culture, characterized by finely worked, laurel leaf-shaped blades of flint, beautifully chipped with ripple flaking on both sides. The Solutrian period coincided with a climatic change marked by an increase in the number of reindeer and a decrease in the number of horses. During the succeeding Magdalenian period, the climate became so cold that this open air site was no longer inhabited. The uppermost layers at Solutré yielded Neolithic burials. During the last century, round-headed skeletons were found in this field; these have generally been referred to the New Stone Age or Neolithic period, since all palaeolithic men were formerly supposed to have had long and narrow heads. In 1923, Professors Dépéret, Arcelin, and Mayet undertook to clear up some of the problems of this site. Underneath the layer of horse bones, deep in the Aurignacian stratum, they found the skeletons of three adults and two babies. These people were buried with tombstones at their heads and at their feet.

In 1924, the excavations were continued, and two more skeletons of Aurignacian age were discovered close to those previously disinterred. No. 4 is an adult male and No. 5 an adult female. In 1925, Dr. G. M. Morant, a most careful and accurate craniometrist, was permitted to make measurements of the original Solutré specimens, and his data will be utilized here. Morant noted that skulls No. 2, male, and No. 3, also male, had been badly warped and distorted posthumously, so that they could not be restored satisfactorily, and measurements taken from them are of doubtful value. He thinks that the height, breadth, and cephalic index of No. 2 have been markedly increased by this post-mortem distortion. The point is of importance, because these crania are perhaps the first *Homo sapiens* brachycephals to be found. No. 2 has an approximate cranial length of only 182.5 mm. and a breadth of about 155.5 mm. yielding a length-breadth index of 85.2. Morant's excellent photographs of this skull suggest that the brachycephaly has been exaggerated by warping, but that the undeformed specimen may well have been round-headed in life. Keith estimates the cranial capacity of this man, who was a young adult, at about 1550 cc., and his stature at about 1.80 meters

(5 feet, 10.8 inches). No. 3, also distorted, seems to have had a skull of about the same length, but narrower, giving a cranial index of 79.3—on the verge of brachycephaly. From the photographs, the warping of this skull seems not to have increased the breadth and the cephalic index, but rather to have diminished them. Keith reckons the cranial capacity of this second adult male at 1472 cc., and his stature at about 1.75 meters (5 feet, 9 inches). No. 4 is the undeformed skull of a somewhat older adult male, with a length of 194 mm., a maximum breadth of 147.5 mm. and a cranial index of 76, which is mesocephalic. The skull of the first female, No. 1, has a cephalic index of about 78.7, and that of the other, No. 5, is frankly round-headed, cephalic index, 81.0. The faces of these Solutré skulls are, on the whole, short and broad. From the photographs, I receive the distinct impression that these people represent a blend of round-headed and long-headed strains, with the brachycephaly in ascendancy, except in No. 4. Keith states that the height of female No. 1 was about 1.55 meters (5 feet, 1 inch) and that the limb bones of the Solutrians were robust, but showed no flattening of the upper shafts of the thigh bones (platymeria) and no lateral flattening of the shin bones (platycnemia), no bony pilaster of the femora (a ridge on the back of the bone buttressing the shaft at the region of greatest bowing), and no undue lengths of the forearms and the shins.

The provincial museum of Périgueux contains one of the most famous skeletons of the Magdalenian period, the last cultural phase of the Palaeolithic Age. Périgueux lies in the center of the Dordogne region of south central France. The skeleton was discovered in 1888 in a rock-shelter near the village of Chancelade, four miles from Périgueux. The deposits on the floor of the rock shelter were 5 feet, 4 inches, in depth and yielded the typical fauna and implements of the Magdalenian period. The skeleton lay on its left side in the deepest stratum, with its arms folded on its breast and its knees doubled up against the body. It had been powdered with red ochre. It was that of a man between 55 and 65 years of age and of short stature (about 5 feet, 2 inches, according to Keith). The limb bones were fragmentary, but very robust.

Special attention has been paid to this skull of the Chancelade man because of its resemblance to the crania of modern Eskimos. It is long and narrow (length 194 mm., breadth 137.5 mm.), with a cranial index of 70.9. The vault rises high above the ear-holes (124 mm.), and its extreme height from basion to bregma is 149 mm. Keith estimates its cubical contents at 1530 cc. The brow-ridges are slightly developed; the forehead rises almost vertically; the occiput is steep behind, as in brachycephals. The face is long and of moderate breadth. The malars, or cheek bones, jut forward strongly, giving the face a flat appearance, reminiscent of Mongoloids. The nose is long and narrow, but the nasal bridge is broken, so that its elevation cannot be estimated accurately. However, Sir Arthur Keith has found a photograph of the Chancelade skull taken before the nasal bones were broken off and lost. They are high and long, springing from the nasal root at an angle never seen in Eskimo crania or in any typically Mongoloid faces. The Chancelade fellow may have had the high, beaky nose often seen in North American Indians, but such a narrow, convex nose is far commoner in Whites.

The lower jaw is deep and has a well-developed chin eminence; the ascending branches are very broad, but the angles of the jaws do not flare outward as in Eskimos. Most of the upper teeth have been lost from wear and disease; the lower teeth are not especially large, but show the peculiarity of having the molars increase in size from the first to the third, whereas in modern man the third molar is usually smaller than the first or second.

The resemblance of the man of Chancelade to the modern Eskimo lies in the combination of short stature with a capacious, dolichocephalic skull, a fairly broad and long face, a narrow nasal aperture, strongly developed masticatory apparatus, a flatness of the face imparted by the squared cheek bones, and the presence of a ridge-like elevation along the middle line of the skull roof. On the basis of a fancied cultural resemblance between the Eskimo of today and the ancient Magdalenians, certain writers have argued that at the close of the glacial age the Magdalenians followed the retreat of the ice sheet northward, eventually reaching North America and becoming the ancestors of the Eskimo. The cultural similarities include the extensive use of bone tools: needles, polishers, harpoons, et cetera, and the habit of engraving pictures on bone. The physical likeness of the man of Chancelade to the Eskimo affords anatomical support for this theory. That such a resemblance exists is incontestable, but it is no more marked than are many of the Eskimoid features that I have observed in a large series of skulls of twelfth century Icelanders now preserved in the Peabody Museum of Harvard University. These Icelanders are of Norwegian and Irish origin, but show, perhaps because of the diet of tough fish upon which they subsisted, masticatory development and other skeletal approximations to the type so strongly marked in the modern Eskimo. While the possibility of a Mongoloid admixture in the man of Chancelade is not to be dismissed lightly, I do not believe that this ancient inhabitant of the Périgord was an Eskimo or a proto-Eskimo.

The Grimaldi Widow and Her Son: Who Were Not as Black as They Have Been Painted

Near Mentone in the Italian Riviera, just across the French frontier, the red rocks of Grimaldi rise from the sea above the coastal road. In these cliffs are many caves where Upper Palaeolithic man lived. The Prince of Monaco financed their excavation by French scientists between 1895 and 1902.

In one of the caves of Grimaldi, the Grotte des Enfants, two skeletons were buried which are said by Professor Verneau to be of a Negroid type. The cave was so named because the skeletons of two children were found in its upper strata. It was choked with layers of débris almost 33 feet thick. Ten habitation floors were discovered, marked by hearths, implements, and other signs of human occupation. All of the remains were of Pleistocene age, since reindeer bones occurred in the uppermost deposits. In the lowest stratum were found bones of the *Rhinoceros mercki* and of the *Elephas antiquus,* animals characteristic of the warm interglacial climate. Above them was the fauna of the last glacial advance. At the level of the second hearth from the top was found the skeleton of an old woman, and at a depth of 9 feet the skeletons of the two children. Twenty-three feet below the surface was the skeleton of a tall man. Verneau assigns him to the Cro Magnon race and credits him with a stature of 6 feet, 2½ inches, but this is an exaggeration. If the Lee-Pearson formulae, the most accurate known for the reconstruction of stature, are applied to his bones, his total height is no more than 5 feet, 11¾ inches. This man lay on his back with a slab of red clay under his head and large stones around his feet. Associated objects were of the Aurignacian culture. Almost 29 feet deep in the cave deposits and at the level of the oldest hearth was found a grave containing two skeletons, those of an old woman and of a boy 15 or 16 years of age. The old woman was buried with her arms doubled up under her chin and her knees flexed against her abdomen. She was lying on her right side. The boy was interred a little above and to one side of her, also on his right side, but in a loosely flexed posture with arms half bent and doubled-up legs at right angles to the axis of the spine. His skeleton was stained with red ochre. Objects of Aurignacian manufacture were found with the burials. Evidently, they dated from the very beginning of the glacial retreat, when the Mousterian culture was first replaced by the industry of the Aurignacians.

The woman was not particularly short—5 feet, 2¾ inches (1.60

meters). The adolescent boy was about 5 feet, 1½ inches, in height. I have mentioned in connection with the Cro Magnon type the alleged Negroid proportions of the arms and legs. Both the boy and the woman show exaggeratedly long forearms and long shins, as do the "tall" people of that much discussed "race." Professor Verneau thinks that the pelvis of the woman also recalls that of a Negroid in the vertical projection of the iliac bones, in the strong curvature of the iliac crest, and in the narrowness of the sacrosciatic notch. He finds in the limb bones a pronounced curvature of the femur, a tipping backward or retroversion of the tibial head, and a projection of the heel bone that again suggests the Negro race.

But it is in the skulls of these subjects that the most markedly Negroid features have been observed. Both of them are long, narrow, and high. The maximum length of the female skull is 191 mm., its breadth 131 mm., and its height above the ear holes 115 mm. The length-breadth index is only 68.5. The boy had a cranium of similar proportions with an index of 69.2. Both skulls lack the flattening of the crown region seen in the Cro Magnons; they also show the bulging foreheads and the feeble development of the brow-ridges often observed in Negro crania. The cranial capacities are estimated by Dr. Verneau to have been 1375 cc. in the case of the woman and 1580 cc. in the boy. These are again rather exaggerated estimates. Keith, using Lee-Pearson formulae, calculates them at 1265 and 1454 cc., respectively. The mastoid processes are small as they naturally would be in a female and an adolescent.

The faces of both mother and son were rather narrow and decidedly short, but we must recall that the boy was an adolescent with incompletely developed jaws and the old woman had lost most of her teeth. The orbits are very low relative to their breadth, as in the Cro Magnon type. The root of the nose is rather depressed in both subjects; the bridge is low and broad. The nasal aperture in both is extremely wide, yielding a platyrrhine nasal index in the female (63.6) and an approximation to it in the boy (54.3). (A nasal skeleton in which the breadth of the aperture is 55 per cent or more of the total nasal height is said to be platyrrhine or broad-nosed.) Moreover, the lower borders or sills of the nasal aperture are not sharp but grooved or guttered, as in primitive and pigmented races. The suborbital or canine fossae (hollows below the eyes), are very deep, another Negroid characteristic. Both skulls have very much swollen and prognathous alveolar margins. The chins are poorly developed and the tooth-bearing margin of the lower jaw also projects forward, imparting the muzzle-like appearance so notable in Australians and in Negroes.

The old woman has lost most of her teeth, but those of the boy are well preserved. His palate is long, narrow, high, and U-shaped as in modern Australian natives. It is 65 mm. long, 15 mm. more than in modern Europeans, but only 65 mm. wide, or 2 to 3 mm. more than average. This long U-shaped palate is anthropoidal, Negroid, or Australoid. Keith calculates the palatal area at 39 cm., as compared with an average of less than 25 cm. in modern Englishmen. The same writer finds that the relation of palatal area to cerebral capacity in the Grimaldi lad is as 1:37; in modern British it is as 1:59, and in the chimpanzee 1:9.2. The teeth are large also, and, in the retention of four cusps on each of the upper molars and five on the lowers, recall those of Australians.

Morant, an altogether dependable craniometrist, has examined and remeasured the Grimaldi skulls. He reports that post-mortem lateral flattening of the brain-cases and twisting of the facial parts have probably exaggerated the prognathism and some other "Negroid" features of the Grimaldi specimens. Certainly the palate of the boy has been diminished in breadth (thus creating a more "Australoid" shape) and has been increased in height. The boy's nose has been narrowed. Morant's measurements upon the original specimen yield a nasal index of approximately 46.8, instead of the 54.3 reported by Verneau, evidently based upon a reconstruction. Although I am of the opinion that it is necessary to discount Verneau's estimates of the extent to which these Grimaldi specimens show Negroid affinities, the latter cannot be dismissed as entirely non-existent. I agree with Verneau that there is enough evidence to suggest very strongly some Negroid admixture and dissent from Keith's conclusion that the allegedly Negroidal features merely constitute a part of a primitive complex of the so-called Cro Magnon race.

The efforts of Sollas, Boule, and others to identify these Grimaldi "Negroids" with the little, yellow-skinned, woolly-haired, prognathous Bushmen of South Africa, or with the allied Hottentots, are interesting but not altogether convincing. The Bushmen made cave paintings and engravings delineating men and animals, and their women are remarkable for steatopygia—an enormous accumulation of gluteal fat. Some of the Aurignacian women were also steatopygous—a fact unmistakably shown in figurines made by Aurignacian artists—and, of course, the Aurignacians painted and engraved. These and the common possession of a few Negroid characters of the skeleton, together with a similarity between the Aurignacian stone industry and that of the Bushmen, are the points upon which rests the romantic theory that the Bushmen are descendants of the Upper Palaeolithic artists of Europe.

It is unfortunate that the French anthropologists should have started the entire study of Upper Palaeolithic man off on the wrong foot by establishing from the defective remains of two or three skeletons each a trinity of so-called "races"—the race of Cro-Magnon, the race of Grimaldi, the race of Chancelade. Attempts to fit all subsequent finds of Late Pleistocene men into one or other of these ill-considered "races" and efforts to trace their lineage into modern populations have resulted in little more than error and confusion. It was, therefore, an excellent corrective procedure for Dr. G. M. Morant, the English anthropologist, to gather together, remeasure, and analyze statistically all of the Upper Palaeolithic crania accessible for study in 1930.[45] Morant managed to secure a measurable series of 27 skulls which he compared with four modern cranial series, each supposed to be more or less homogeneous from a racial viewpoint. These series were the Farrington St. English series (all from a single London cemetery that was used only from 1610 to 1722); a Greenland Eskimo series, studied by Fürst and Hansen; an Egyptian series from a single cemetery south of Gizeh that was used from the 26th to the 30th Dynasties—a period of some 400 years; a series of skulls exhumed from a charnel house in Carinthia, measured by Shapiro. The first surprising result of these comparisons was the fact that the Upper Palaeolithic population proved to be, on the whole, somewhat less variable than the Egyptian and Eskimo series, about equal in variability to the Carinthian series, and considerably more variable than the London series. This is remarkable in view of the fact that the Upper Palaeolithic series represents—from the Aurignacian through the Magdalenian period—a span of time which, according to Zeuner's chronology, extends from Würm II (c. 72,000 years ago) through Würm III (c. 22,000 years). The Upper Palaeolithic series is appreciably larger than the modern races with which it is compared in head length, head circumference, sagittal arc, bizygomatic diameter (face breadth), and distance between the eyes. It is smaller than any of the modern races in height of the orbits only. This last-named inferiority leads to a mean orbital index (height of orbit expressed as a percentage of its breadth) that is lower than any of the racial series compared. These differences may be summarized in the statement that the *Homo sapiens* types of the Upper Palaeolithic are remarkable for their very long (and generally oversized) brain-cases and for their low broad orbits and relatively short, broad faces. Most of the crania are pronouncedly long-headed (dolichocephalic), but a few verge upon or attain the lower range of round-headedness (brachycephaly). Incidentally, in the features

---

[45] Morant, "Studies of Palaeolithic Man, IV," pp. 109–214.

in which the Upper Palaeolithic series diverges from modern racial types, they do not resemble Neanderthaloid man or Rhodesian man, nor do they, for that matter, display any other close metric similarities of importance to either of these two archaic types.

Von Bonin has supplemented Morant's study of the crania of Upper Palaeolithic males by a similar investigation of the female skulls of that period and also by a study of the long bones of the skeletons of this period.[46]

The few crania of Upper Palaeolithic females are no more distinguishable from females of modern races compared than are the males—in fact, they seem to be in no way extraordinary. They probably lack the excessive skull length, face breadth, and lowness of the orbits that characterize the Upper Palaeolithic males.

Von Bonin has recalculated by the best formulae available for the reconstruction of stature from long bones the individual heights of some 11 Upper Palaeolithic males and 5 females. The males average about 173 cm. (68.1 inches) and the females 155 cm. (61 inches). This is a very much larger sex difference in stature than ordinarily occurs within a racial group. I think it probable that the discrepancy is due in part to the inclusion in the very short male series of two or three individuals credited with statures of 178 cm. to 181.8 cm., which have been exaggerated by over-liberal reconstructions of the length of defective long bones.

From these biometric analyses there issue as residual peculiarities of the Upper Palaeolithic population (as regards males only) their very long heads, very broad and relatively low faces, in which are naturally implanted low, broad eye-sockets. If the faces are broad and low, the orbits are necessarily of similar proportions. This facial shortening is a specialization in the opposite direction of that displayed by the anthropoid apes, Neanderthal man, and Rhodesian man, in all of whom great height of the face results from the deep alveolar processes in which the teeth are implanted. The orbits are correspondingly high. (However, if Weidenreich's reconstructions are trustworthy, Pithecanthropus and Sinanthropus had short faces and low orbits.) These very short, broad faces hafted to long, narrow skulls occur sporadically in many European populations of the present day, but they are almost regularly characteristic of Australians, Ainu, and West African Negroes. Broad faces with long heads are very frequently observed among Eskimo, American Indians, and some of the Asiatic Mongoloids, but, in my experience,

46 Von Bonin, "European Races," pp. 196–221.

Mongoloid faces are usually not short and broad, but both long and broad. Among the ancient Guanches of the Canary Islands (a White stock), the combination of low, broad face and long, narrow head seems quite clearly to have resulted, among other combinations, from crossings of a low, broad-faced, short- and broad-headed stock with a long-headed, long- and narrow-faced stock. The hybrid type thus inherits the cranial shape of one stock and the facial shape of the other. In the European Mesolithic period the skulls from the cave of Ofnet show the extreme types and the intermediates displaying this so-called disharmonic combination. However, it now seems to me that the increase in breadth of the face and compensatory diminution in its height can occur in either a long-headed or a round-headed stock, and the association of the broad, low face with the long, narrow skull is not always due to hybridization and should not be called "cranial disharmony." The splaying out of the malars and zygomatic arches and general broadening of the face are likely to take place in connection with strong lateral and rotary grinding movements of the jaws as typically exemplified in modern men of carnivorous habits. I am not aware that such lateral increase of facial diameters through masticatory hypertrophy is necessarily accompanied by a compensatory shortening of the face. On the other hand, there is no doubt that both narrowing and degenerative elongation of the whole face in modern stocks is directly consequent upon masticatory atrophy in peoples who live upon soft, cooked foods and suffer vitamin deficiencies from the processing of such foods or from ill-balanced diets.

At present, then, the persistent manifestation of facial shortening in long-headed Upper Palaeolithic men of Europe is not clearly understood by me, but it seems to reflect a probably hereditary tendency within the restricted racial complex from which Europeans of the Upper Palaeolithic have been derived. These short, broad faces are by no means universally present in *Homo sapiens* of the Late Pleistocene, as we shall see from the African data.

There can be no question of the continuity of the Upper Palaeolithic strains down to modern times in Europe. Yet it seems probable that the majority of the ancestors of modern Europeans reached the continent in later times, as a result of new immigrations from Asia and from Africa. It seems to me unprofitable and precarious to attempt to identify this or that modern European "race" with some one or other of the Palaeolithic strains, since all of the Palaeolithic types may well have been introduced repeatedly in subsequent migrations.

TABLE 4. CHECK LIST OF THE MORE IMPORTANT AND BEST AUTHENTICATED FINDS OF FOSSIL HOMO SAPIENS IN EUROPE

Country	Place	Date	Associated Industry	Content	Remarks
Czecho-Slovakia	Brünn I	1891	Aurignacian	Adult male skull and some other skeletal parts	Dolichocephalic, about 1600 cc., Combe Capelle type
	Brünn III	1927	Aurignacian	Poorly preserved female	Narrow-faced, long-nosed dolicho, Combe Capelle type
	Lautsch I	1881–1882	Aurignacian	Three skulls, 3 skull caps, other bones	No. 1 strikingly recalls the Old Man of Cro Magnon
	Predmost	1880–1928	Aurignacian	Skeletons of at least 40 persons, various ages	Dolichos, long-faced, robust, short-statured, Combe Capelle type
England	Halling	1912	Upper Palaeolithic (?)	Fragmentary skull and skeleton, adult male	Galley Hill = Combe Capelle Type
Wales	Galley Hill	1888	Acheulean (?)	Incomplete skeleton of adult male	Piltdown affinities (?)
	Swanscombe	1935	Acheulean	Occipital and left parietal	" " "
	London	1925	?	Occipital and parietals	
	Paviland	1822	Aurignacian	Parts of male skeleton minus skull	Dolicho, 5 ft., 4 in.
	Cheddar I	1903	Aurignacian	Skeleton of adult male	Galley Hill-Combe Capelle type
	Cheddar II	1928	Magdalenian(?)	Parts of 5 persons	
France	Cap Blanc I	1912	Magdalenian	Incomplete skeleton	"Eskimoid" (?)
	Chancelade	1888	Magdalenian	Skeleton, adult male	Type short-statured dolichocephal of the Upper Palaeolithic
	Combe Capelle	1909	Aurignacian	Skeleton, male	Type "Old Man of Cro Magnon"
	Cro Magnon	1868	Aurignacian	Three skulls and skeletal remains of at least 5 persons	
	Solutre II	1923–1924	Aurignacian	Skeletons of 3 adult males, 2 females, 2 children, 1 foetus	Brachycephalic trend; tall males
	Cap Blanc II	1910	Magdalenian (?)	Skeleton of 20 year female	
Germany	Obercassel	1914	Magdalenian	Adult male and female skeletons	Short, dolichocephals
Italy	Grotte des Enfants	1900–1901	Aurignacian	Adult male and female skeletons	Cro Magnon type
	Grotte du Cavillon	1872	Upper Palaeolithic	Adolescent male and adult female	"Negroid" type
	Barma Grande	1884–1894	Upper Palaeolithic	Skeleton and fragmentary skull of adult male; Some 6 fragmentary skeletons	Tall Cro Magnons

More Early Dwellers in the Dark Continent

We think of Africa today as a vast continent with the decayed remnant of an ancient and precocious civilization in the northeast corner and retarded cultures and primitive men elsewhere, isolated in various refuge areas by rocky deserts or impenetrable jungles. The gorilla and the chimpanzee, most nearly human of the anthropoid apes, still survive in the Congo forests, cheek by jowl with the pygmy Negrito—an early but apparently specialized human type—and the full-grown Forest type of Negro, certainly a form stringently adapted to an extreme environment. Tucked away in the Kalahari Desert, away down in the southwestern part of the continent, are a few survivors of the Bushman-Hottentot stock, assuredly the greatest of all contemporary puzzles to the student of racial evolution. Africa is cut up by natural geographic and climatic boundaries into a considerable number of areas large enough to permit evolution to work out local types and sufficiently isolated to prevent half-completed experiments from being wrecked by repeated arrivals of new tenants of the evolutionary laboratory.

GAP-TOOTHED ORANIANS

However, the Mediterranean strip of Africa is more accessible for cultural diffusion and for human migration, although west of the Nile it seems to have been a sort of back pasture on the human farm, somewhat neglected and never brought into intensive cultivation. In Morocco, Algeria, and Tunisia, and in the desert south of the Atlas range, archaeological excavations have uncovered Palaeolithic cultures, including typological equivalents of the European Chellean (Abbevillian), Acheulean, and Mousterian, and substitutes for the Upper Palaeolithic cultures. In southern Tunisia and southeastern Algeria, the Upper Palaeolithic industry is called the Capsian, whereas in the rest of Tunisia, Algeria, and Morocco it goes under the name of Oranian. In a general sort of way, both of these cultures are very similar to an Aurignacian, prolonged down to recent geological times and at no time characterized by technological progressiveness and achievements in graphic and plastic art such as manifested themselves in the Aurignacian, Solutrean, and Magdalenian periods in Europe.

No Lower Palaeolithic skeletal finds have been made in northwestern Africa, with the exception of fragments of a human skull blasted out of a quarry in Rabat in 1934 and, apparently, not yet described. The pieces recovered included the anterior part of the lower jaw, part of the left

half of the upper jaw, a canine tooth, an imprint of the palate in sandstone, and a few miscellaneous bits of the brain-case. This specimen
is said to represent a young adult male, with large teeth, rudimentary
chin, and primitive features of the nasal aperture.[47] The stratum from
which these skull fragments were recovered is a sandstone formation
considered by geologists to be of approximately Chellean Age.

There is, in addition, the isolated find of part of the left half of a
maxilla and a couple of teeth, in a cave near Tangier, presumably
attributable to Neanderthal man and the Mousterian culture. Upper
Pleistocene skeletal finds, or, at any rate, finds of *Homo sapiens* associated
with Upper Palaeolithic industries, have been plentiful enough in the
Province of Constantine in Algeria, which has been exploited archae-
ologically, but most of the material has been fragmentary, incompletely
documented, or inadequately studied. The exceptions are two good
series, one from Mechta el Arbi, of Capsian association, and the other
of Oranian provenience, from the rock-shelter of Alfalou Bou Rhummel,
on the Mediterranean coast, 30 kilometers east of Bougie, Algeria.[48] This
rock-shelter opens half way up the face of a high cliff and is about 20
meters wide and 10 meters deep. At the back of it, a chimney opens to
the surface of the plateau. In the shelter are 15 to 16 meters of fill, made
up of several layers of clay, rocks, sand, ashes, bones, and tools. The bulk
of the skeletal material came from the topmost archaeological layer,
which included a huge pile of human bones lying in disorder directly
underneath the chimney. About 48 individuals of both sexes and all ages
were represented, from whose scattered remains 6 fairly complete skeletons could be reconstructed. It seems probable that this skeletal series
consisted of the victims of a massacre, whose bodies were thrown down
the chimney. In a lower archaeological stratum, called Level III, were
found the full length burial of an adult male and the skull of a child.
The industry throughout the cave is Oranian, the tools consisting of
75 per cent to 80 per cent of small, backed flint blades, with a considerable number of polished bone tools. The occupants of the cave
seem to have lived principally upon shell fish, although there are a
few bones of the mouflon and other game animals.

The lower level skeleton of the adult male is that of a robust individual only 161.5 cm. tall (5 feet, 3½ inches). The skull differs widely
from those of the upper level in being excessively dolichocephalic
(length-breadth index 65.1), ovoid in shape instead of pentagonal, and
in having relatively high orbits, a U-shaped instead of a V-shaped palate,

[47] Marcais, "Decouverte de restes humains fossiles," p. 579.
[48] Arambourg, Boule, Vallois, Verneau, *Les Grottes Paleolithiques.*

less massive face, and root of the nose less depressed. It resembles the upper level skulls in having large brow-ridges, large mastoid processes, pronounced occipital torus, high nasal bones, and no prognathism. The nasal aperture is short and broad and yields a platyrrhine or chamaerrhine index. This individual was shorter than the males of the upper series, had relatively longer arms, but forearms and legs less elongated with reference to the upper segments of the respective members than occur in the taller, high level skeletons. The skeletal type of this male is quite clearly that of the Aurignacian man of Combe Capelle, which is the same as that of the fundamental Galley Hill type of long-headed European.

From the upper level, some 40 odd crania are available for study, including 21 measurable adult male skulls and 10 female skulls. The bones are in general those of muscular individuals of tall stature. Five male skeletons yielded reconstructed heights varying from 172 to 180 cm. (67.7 inches to 70.9 inches), according to the French method of reckoning stature from the tables of Manouvrier. However, these tables yield exaggerated statures. Three female skeletons are supposed to have had statures ranging between 169 and 175 centimeters (66.5 inches to 68.9 inches). Since the sex differentiation is admitted to have been difficult, it seems probable that the disproportionately high female stature may be due to erroneous sexing. These skeletons represent individuals with broad shoulders, forearms elongated in comparison with the upper arms, and shins correspondingly long relative to the length of the thighs. The scapulae are said to show Negroid characteristics. The bones of the leg show some of the modifications associated with a bent knee gait, and the feet and hands are massive.

The skulls are heavy, brutal, thick-walled affairs, with muscular markings so prominent that it is difficult to distinguish males from females by the ordinary criteria. The mean cranial capacity of 14 male skulls is 1622 cc. and of 9 female skulls 1456 cc. (Probably these capacities are too high). The cranial indices of males range from 70 to 80 with a mean of 74.8, while the corresponding ranges and mean of the females are 70 to 84, and 75.7. The vaults of the skulls are slightly keeled, the brow-ridges excessively jutting, and the foreheads receding and low. The mastoid processes, supramastoid ridges, and transverse occipital tori, are all very large. The faces are very broad with massive malars, jutting anteriorly and flaring laterally. The upper faces are short, with low broad orbits, deep nasion depressions, high beaky nasal bones, but with either broad, guttered, or sharp-silled nasal apertures. The jaws are straight (orthognathous), not projecting or prognathous. The palates are relatively short and broad; the mandibles massive, with prominent chins and flaring hinder angles. The teeth are worn and of ordinary modern dimensions. Invariably, some of the upper incisor teeth, usually the middle pair, have been knocked out, presumably in childhood—a habit widely prevalent among Negroes and Negroids in Africa.

Dr. C. S. Coon, in summarizing this series, has undertaken certain further analyses that clarify considerably the affinities of the Alfalou men.[49] He points out that the Alfalou noses are perfectly European in conformation, with high and mostly convex bridges, and strongly developed, jutting nasal spines. However, the Alfalou nasal index (mean for 21 males 53.1) is chamaerrhine or platyrrhine (broad-nosed) and furnishes a real metrical difference between this North African type and that of Cro Magnon. This feature, together with the great brow-ridges and sloping foreheads, differentiates the two types. Again, although the French anthropologists who have described the Alfalou crania insist upon calling them "disharmonic," with the implication that short, broad, low-orbited faces are hafted to long and narrow brain-cases, actually the broad, short faces occur with only 4 of 9 dolichocephalic skulls, whereas 14 out of 18 crania that have this facial form are either round-headed or verging upon brachycephaly. Thus the low, broad faces are predominantly associated with rounder types of head. Again, the very low, broad (chamaeconch) orbits occur in only 3 of 11 dolichocephalic or long-headed skulls, but in 14 of 18 of the more nearly round-headed skulls. These observations made upon an ample series serve to confirm in some measure the opinion long ago expressed by the present writer that the Cro Magnon association of short, broad face and low orbits with long, narrow skulls may have resulted from a hybridization of medium-faced dolichocephals with short, broad-faced, chamaeconch brachycephals, in which the face of the latter type has been hafted to the brain-case of the former. This phenomenon has undoubtedly occurred independently in many places and at different times. It does not constitute evidence of any close relationship between the Cro Magnons and the men of Alfalou. Dr. Coon considers that both Alfalou and Cro Magnon types are the result of a cross between the Galley Hill–Combe Capelle form and a Neanderthal type. Certainly, some of the western European Neanderthaloids (notably Spy II and probably some of the Krapina specimens) show a marked tendency toward brachycephaly, and the heaviness of the brow-ridges in the Alfalou men, which is paralleled in some of the Predmost specimens, might easily be attributed to Neanderthaloid admixture. I agree with Dr. Coon that Neanderthaloid strains were prob-

[49] Coon, *The Races of Europe*, pp. 40–44.

ably infused into *Homo sapiens* men of the Upper Palaeolithic and later times, but I am not certain that this strain is the basic ingredient that entered into the blend with the Galley Hill–Combe Capelle type to produce the Cro Magnons and other related forms of the Late Pleistocene in Europe and North Africa. There may have been a massive, brachycephalic *Homo sapiens* type as a principal ingredient of the cross. Low orbits and short wide faces, to say nothing of mandibles with jutting chins and flaring hinder angles, are characters antithetic to those ordinarily observed in Neanderthaloid forms.

I am unimpressed with the supposedly "Negroidal" features of the Alfalou men, because these consist almost exclusively of relative elongation of fore arms and shins with reference to the upper segments of the limbs. Since Professors Boule, Vallois, and Verneau identify the Mechta el Arbi skull type with that of Alfalou, it is unnecessary to discuss the former separately.

THE NEGROID WHO WAS DROWNED IN THE SAHARA

In 1927, a French scientific expedition discovered a fossilized human skeleton in the middle of the Sahara Desert, about 400 kilometers northeast of Timbuctu, not far from the dry valley of the Tilemsi, a former tributary of the Niger. This skeleton, known as the Asselar man from the name of a neighboring French garrison post, was accompanied by no finds of implements or of animal bones. However, the skeleton came from a deposit of fluvial origin, probably laid down by a Pleistocene tributary of the vanished Tilemsi river. Close-by sands from the same formation yield numerous fossilized bones of very large fishes, crocodiles, antelope, gazelles, and other mammals, as well as fresh-water shells. These fossil animal bones present the same aspect and are mineralized to the same extent as those of the human skeleton. Surface finds of archaeological specimens include both Upper Palaeolithic and Neolithic types. Taking all of the evidence into account, it appears reasonably probable that the Asselar man dates back to the Upper Pleistocene.

The skeleton seems to have been embedded in the river sands shortly after the death of its owner, who may have been drowned. These sands have consolidated into stone, from which it is most difficult to disengage the bones. The owner of the bones was a tall, slender individual, probably more than 170 cm. in height, and certainly of the male sex.[50] The limbs were long relative to the trunk, and the shin and forearm were especially elongate. The skull was pronouncedly dolichocephalic (index 70.9), rather high, and slightly keeled or scaphoid. It was 193 mm. long

[50] Boule and Vallois, *L'Homme fossile d'Asselar.*

and 137 mm. in breadth, and 136 mm. in basion-bregma height. The cranial capacity was 1507 cc. according to calculations made by the Lee-Pearson formulae. The face was moderately broad and of medium length, although Boule and Vallois call it short and "disharmonic." The frontal region is rather bulbous; the brow-ridges are only moderately developed; the malars jut laterally and frontally; the orbits are tilted and rather low; the root of the nose shows slight elevation, and the bridge is concave.

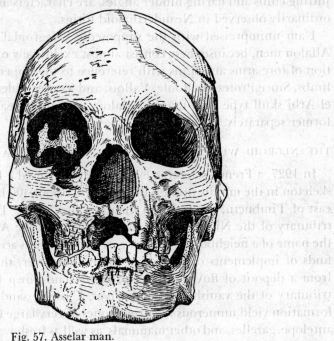

Fig. 57. Asselar man.

The nasal bones are fused together throughout their length—a rare feature in man, but observed most commonly in Negroids. The nasal bones are, on the whole, narrow, but the nasal aperture is broad with poorly defined sills and small development of the spine. The nasal index is chamaerrhine (54.9). There seems to be little prognathism of the middle face, and the alveolar prognathism cannot be observed because the upper middle incisors had been removed in the youth of the individual. Probably a good deal of alveolar prognathism of the upper jaw would have been manifested, were it not for this mutilation. The lower jaw is notable for the great breadth of its ascending rami and for its strong alveolar prognathism; the chin eminence is developed, but is retracted behind the alveolar projection. The teeth are of a good size, but not remarkable; the palate was broad and parabolic in shape.

This Asselar skeleton is that of an indubitable Negroid of the elongated, gracile type frequently seen in the Nilotic area and in East Africa. Full Negro characters are hardly developed, but in contrast with the Cro Magnons, the Alfalou men, and even with the alleged Grimaldi "Negroids," the evidences of such affinities are much clearer. Boule and Vallois consider that the Asselar Negroid is more nearly akin to the Bushmen-Hottentots and to the Southern Bantu than to the full Sudanese Negro type or to the Hamitic Negroids of East Africa and the Nilotic region. They regard the slender Asselar Negroid as a prototype of the later, more fully developed Negroids, such as the Sudanese Forest Negroes and the Bushmen-Hottentots. They offer the suggestion that contemporary types ordinarily described as of mixed Negroid and White origin are, in fact, undifferentiated rather than hybridized, and that the full Negroid characters that we ordinarily consider the marks of racial purity are merely end products of specialization. This theory of imperfectly developed Negroid characteristics in Late Pleistocene Whites as a part of a residuum of tendencies common to all early forms of *Homo sapiens,* will have to receive our serious consideration at a later stage of our racial discussion. For the moment, we may dismiss it with the remark that the fag end of the Pleistocene seems to be too late a time to make probable the survival of protypical *Homo sapiens* still carrying a mélange of Negroid, Mongoloid, and White features. I believe that further explorations in Africa and Asia will reveal the Late Pleistocene antiquity of fully differentiated Negroids and Mongoloids.

PLEISTOCENE SUSPECTS IN EAST AFRICA

British East Africa—Kenya, Tanganyika, and Uganda—have been sedulously exploited by students of early man during the past 15 years and have yielded sequences of Palaeolithic industries beginning with crude "pebble cultures," continuing through Chellean (Abbevillian) and Acheulean hand-axe industries with Levalloisian influences, Middle Stone Age types roughly equivalent to the European Mousterian, Aurignacian and later Upper Palaeolithic types of tools approximating the Smithfield and Wilton industries of South Africa. All of these industries lie stratigraphically below the full-blown Neolithic. The problem of dating the East African Palaeolithic cultures geologically presents many difficulties. Most students support a theory that recognizes long periods of heavy rainfall—pluvial periods—as the equivalents of the glaciations that took place farther north. These pluvial periods are based upon studies of former high level shore-lines of some of the smaller East African lakes and upon certain glacial deposits high up on the slopes of the lofty peaks, such as Kenya, Elgon,. and Kilimanjaro. In Kenya, there are stated to have been two great Pleistocene pluvial periods separated by a long, dry interpluvial and also subdivided by drier intervals. There are also a number of post-Pleistocene or recent pluvial phases. The identification of various geological deposits with these several pluvial and interpluvial periods is complicated, however, by the possibility of earth-tilting in this volcanic region, where the great Rift Valleys have created tremendous chasms running north and south and now forming the valleys of rivers and the beds of lakes. In Kenya, the first great Pleistocene pluvial period is called the Kamasian and is equated with the first two European glaciations and the interglacial period that separates them. The great interpluvial is supposed to be equivalent to the long Mindel-Riss interglacial. The second or Gamblian pluvial is matched with the Riss and Würm glacial advances and the third interglacial; the Malkalian and Nakuran pluvials are post-Pleistocene. However, these correlations seem to be highly speculative. The sequences of Palaeolithic industries are, on the contrary, well established, with the exception of some of the earliest "pebble" cultures, which consist of alleged tools fashioned from river pebbles. The recognition of some of these pebble implements as human artifacts requires no little faith and optimism on the part of the archaeologist.

The first find of human skeletal remains from this region was made by Dr. Hans Reck of the University of Berlin in 1913. In the Oldoway gorge in Tanganyika are rich fossil remains of a Pleistocene fauna, including many extinct mammals, but also half or more of forms still living in Africa. The human skeleton was alleged to have lain below 10 feet of undisturbed strata; it was fossilized and was thought by Dr. Reck to have represented a drowning or submersion when Oldoway was a marsh or a lake. The body lay on its right side with the thighs flexed and the arms folded—a posture commonly found in deliberate burials. The stratum from which it came is supposed to have yielded bones of an extinct form of elephant, of the *Hipparion,* and implements of an advanced Chellean or Abbevillian type. Thus the find was attributed to the Lower Pleistocene, and it occasioned a good deal of scepticism, partly because the posture of the skeleton indicated a burial, partly because Dr. Reck asserted that the lower incisor teeth of the skull had been chipped or filed, a custom of many contemporary Africans, and finally because the skeleton is undoubtedly that of a *Homo sapiens.* Not very much attention was paid to this discovery until 1926–27, when Dr. L. S. B. Leakey, who had made important finds of Palaeolithic cultures and human remains in Kenya in the interim, reopened the subject and satisfied himself that the Oldoway skeleton was actually of the great antiquity claimed for it by Reck and that it conformed in type to the skeletal remains he himself had found under similar geological circumstances.

The Oldoway skeleton is that of an adult male, over 180 cm. tall (5 feet, 10½ inches), with a very long and narrow head (length 203 mm., breadth 133 mm., cranial index 66). The vault of the skull is well developed with a rounded forehead, and to it is hafted an exceptionally long and narrow face (total height from the root of the nose to the lower border of the chin 132 mm., total facial index 102). The orbits are extremely high, the nasal skeleton long (51 mm.) and moderately wide (26 mm.), yielding an index of 51, which is mesorrhine or medium. The palate is also long and narrow. The jaws show a moderate amount of alveolar prognathism, but the very deep lower jaw is equipped with a well-developed chin eminence. The teeth are perfectly modern. The limb bones offer nothing of particular interest.

This Oldoway skeleton is not that of a Negro, but is referred to the tall, slender Hamitic White race of East Africa, by Mollison and Gieseler, who studied it.[51] To the present writer, the representatives of the Oldoway skull give a somewhat Negroid impression, although it is by no means as clear as that created by the skull of Asselar man. A subsequent laboratory examination of samples from the different strata of the Oldoway site forced a revision of the earlier dating of the skeleton and reduced it to Upper Pleistocene. It was then regarded as an intrusive burial, probably of Aurignacian age.

In the meantime, in 1932, Dr. Leakey made excavations in supposedly Lower Pleistocene deposits exposed on the southern shores of the Kavirondo Gulf of Victoria Nyanza at a place called West Kanam, and discovered a large fragment of the symphysis of a human mandible which he attributed to the early part of the Kamasian pluvial—that is, Lower Pleistocene. The mandibular fragment included roots of the anterior teeth and parts of the crowns of the left premolars, together with the upper part of the chin eminence. The study of the specimen revealed nothing incompatible with the conclusion that it belonged to *Homo sapiens,* and it was heralded by Dr. Leakey, with the full endorsement of an impressive committee of English scientists, as the long awaited proof that *Homo sapiens* existed in the Early Pleistocene.

In the same expedition, fragments of four other morphologically

51 Mollison and Gieseler, "Untersuchungen über den Oldoway Fund," p. 50.

modern skulls and a bit of femur were recovered from a neighboring site, Kanjera, apparently in association with remains of *Elephas antiquus* and from a stratum that yielded Chellean tools. These remains were referred to the Middle Pleistocene. Unfortunately, the information given by Dr. Leakey on these important discoveries lacked the wealth of detail and the documentation in the way of measured sections, photographs, etc., that science demands before it is willing finally to accept a revolutionary find, such as that of *Homo sapiens* in the Lower or Middle Pleistocene.[52] Professor Boswell, a veteran in the study of the geology of the Rift Valleys of East Africa, dissatisfied with the evidence presented by Leakey, led an expedition to Tanganyika for the purposes of a reinvestigation of the sites. His report failed to corroborate Dr. Leakey's findings and thus relegated Kanam and Kanjera man to the large company of discredited *Homo sapiens* claimants to high geological antiquity. This fiasco was particularly regrettable because it involved the ill-considered underwriting of an improperly attested discovery by a large committee of highly qualified British scientists. It in no way impaired the probability that *Homo sapiens* was a mid-Pleistocene dweller in East Africa, but it discredited, perhaps unduly, a great deal of important archaeological work accomplished by Dr. Leakey elsewhere in East Africa. The present writer is strongly of the opinion that further research in this area will re-establish Leakey's contentions and prove that he was right.

In the years 1926–29, Leakey excavated rock shelters at Elmenteita, Kenya Colony, and discovered in Gamble's Cave II some five damaged skeletons, which he associated with an Upper Aurignacian culture. Curiously, the Aurignacian strata in this cave underlie layers that yield a Still Bay (Mousterian) culture. Leakey thinks that the Mousterian and Aurignacian cultures in Kenya were contemporaneous but produced by different races. No Mousterian men have been discovered.

Two of the "Aurignacian" skeletons, No. 4 and No. 5, have been partially described by Leakey. Both are considered to have belonged to adult males. They have large and markedly dolichocephalic crania, with small brow-ridges and poor development of the muscular attachments and mastoids. The foreheads are rounded and rather submedium in height; the orbits are very high and the faces long and of more than average breadth. The noses are long and only moderately wide; the jaws not projecting, although a slight amount of alveolar prognathism is evident. The mandibles have chins of medium development and rather broad ascending rami. Leakey, however, says that they are not massive.

52 Leakey, *Stone Age Races of Kenya*, pp. 9–36.

The teeth and palates seem to present no features out of the ordinary. Sir Arthur Keith reckoned the stature of one of these skeletons at 180 cm. or more, and it is certain that both belonged to very tall individuals. These smooth-skulled, gracile, long-faced dolichocephals of apparently high stature and slender build present no obviously Negroid features, so far as one can judge from the photographs and drawings of the reconstructed skulls and from the somewhat inadequate descriptive and metric data that accompany them. The conclusion that they belong to Hamitic Whites, such as some of the purer strain Galla of Abyssinia, or even some of the Bahima aristocrats among the Eastern Bantu, whose slight Negroid admixture is not apparent in the skeletal structure of the face, would seem justified, and, so far as I can gather, that is the judgment of Sir Arthur Keith and of Dr. Leakey. These "Aurignacian" skulls certainly are not obviously Negroid.

From a burial site at Elmenteita, where the bones of many individuals had been stuffed into different rock crevices and subsequently covered by the waters of a rising lake, Dr. Leakey recovered remains representing at least 28 persons. He ascribes these burials to a Mesolithic culture that flourished during the Makalian wet phase, a post-Pleistocene pluvial. These skeletons, again, seem to have belonged to tall dolichocephalic individuals, with a few exceptions. Several of the better preserved crania are shown in excellent half-tone reproduction, and from these illustrations, as well as from Dr. Leakey's description, it may be deduced that the Elmenteitan people were in many respects similar to the Gamble's Cave Aurignacians who, presumably, preceded them. They have the same very long faces, projecting occiputs, strongly developed malars. The noses are long, and in some instances the nasal bones are strongly concavo-convex. Alveolar prognathism in the skulls figured is more pronounced, and the nasal apertures, as well as the general configuration of face and skull, appear to me distinctly more Negroid than do the corresponding features of the Aurignacian skulls. In fact, I should not hesitate to diagnose these crania as Negroidal.

A still later series of skeletons, recovered by Leakey from burial mounds and shell mounds and definitely associated with Neolithic cultures called Gumban A and Gumban B, seem to me to be so strongly Negroid in their characters that one might almost pronounce them out-and-out Negroes. They lack the gracility of the earlier crania; the relief of the skulls is rugged, and the faces are massive. Prognathism is still mainly alveolar rather than affecting the entire face. The limb bones of these Neolithic skeletons are declared by Dr. Leakey to be very robust.

Altogether, the status of knowledge of the antiquity of man in East

Africa is most unsatisfactory, not because of a paucity of finds, but because of the clouds of doubt that shroud the geological age, the archaeological associations, and the very anthropological features of these finds. The whole elaborate scheme of pluvial periods and their supposed correlation with European glaciations has not yet been accepted by all climatologists and geologists, and, granting its validity, there remains the difficulty of dating strata and archaeological deposits accurately to one or another of the multiple Pleistocene and recent phases it postulates. I have a very strong impression that much of the correlating of finds of ancient man in East Africa with pluvial periods depends upon tenuous or questionable evidence. Even the archaeological sequences postulated by Dr. Leakey and his associates seem very peculiar. Aurignacian is contemporaneous with Mousterian, according to his findings, and Aurignacian includes pottery—never found in Europe or Asia before Neolithic times.

If we dismiss all of our uncomfortable feelings about exact dating and sequence of these East Africa finds and assume that they are, in fact, geologically ancient (as I am most desirous of doing), we are still faced with the puzzling fact that any one of the skeletons found (with the possible exception of the very fragmentary and questionable Africanthropus) could easily be duplicated in the contemporary native population of that very region. The whole area is still peopled with tall, slender Hamites and Hamito-Negroids with exactly the same skeletal anthropology as Leakey's Aurignacians, Elmenteitans, etc. Either East Africa has been peopled with virtually exactly the same types of hybrids between Mediterranean Hamitic Whites and Negroes ever since Middle and Upper Pleistocene times, or, alternatively, if these *Homo sapiens* types are the common ancestors of both Whites and Negroes, as yet undifferentiated and carrying in solution all of the gene potentialities of both stocks, then no further evolution has taken place in East Africa. Accordingly, we must regard the Masai, the Galla, the Kavirondo, the Watussi, the Bahima, and all the rest of them as prototypical *Homines sapientes*, stuck in a Pleistocene stage of evolution. Such a view seems ridiculous to an anthropologist who has studied the results of race mixture between Whites and Negroes in the United States and has observed the production *passim* of these so-called Hamito-Negroids in contemporary miscegenation.

If we close our eyes, gulp hard, and swallow the whole unmasticable mass of dubious stratigraphy, bizarre archaeological typology, and incomplete anthropometric and morphological analysis of specimens, we may conclude that the Middle and Upper Pleistocene inhabitants of

East Africa were perfectly modern Hamito-Mediterranean, tall, slender brunet Whites, and it was not until Mesolithic times that they became perceptibly adulterated with, or differentiated into, Negroids, and that, finally, nothing approaching a full Negro type is to be found until late Neolithic times in that area, if then.

DEVOLUTION IN SOUTH AFRICA

South Africa is a vast evolutionary cul-de-sac in which, apparently, men and apes have worked out their evolutionary destinies according to their hereditary potentialities and environmental opportunities, leaving in their skeletal remains a magnificent record which "he who runs may read." South of the mouth of the Congo, Africa is a lofty plateau, in most places 3,000 feet or higher, that has been warped along a series of parallel corrugations which have given rise to alternations of lake-like expanses and raised water gaps.[53] The rivers flow in arcs on an east-west axis in the downfolds and cut deep gorges through the continental scarp to the sea. The plateau has been in course of desiccation and draining, probably since the end of the Pleistocene. The dolomitic and limestone formations of South Africa, as Dart has pointed out, have provided innumerable abodes, refuges, and burying places of ancient man, which, as they are carefully exploited by scientists, are sure to yield an almost unbroken sequence of evolutionary stages in the development of ape and human types. In recent years, it has been possible to correlate the remains of extinct animals in South Africa with archaeological successions and some human types, so that the lack of Pleistocene glaciations and of the alternation of fauna involved in glacial advances and retreats has been compensated, to some extent, by careful stratigraphic work.

It is fortunate for the science of anthropology that such a promising area for exploitation as South Africa should be the home of a brilliant, energetic, and competent group of physical anthropologists, palaeontologists, geologists, and archaeologists that would adorn any country of Europe and would be hard to match in most of them.

In the study of fossil primates and fossil man, the names of Broom, Dart, Drennan, Dryer, and Shaw represent outstandingly important contributors, and their younger associates—Galloway, Gear, Gillman, Schepers, Shore, Slome, and Wells—are all enriching our knowledge of present and past races in South Africa by sound and definitive researches. In the prehistory of the area, order has been brought out of a former chaos by such distinguished archaeologists as Goodwin and van Riet Lowe, and the geologists of the South African universities have done

[53] Taylor, *Environment, Race, and Migration,* pp. 108–119.

their part admirably both in dating artifacts and skeletal remains. There
is no real doubt that the South African Palaeolithic industries are
roughly contemporaneous with those of the continent to the north. The
former are divided into the Older, Middle, and Later Stone Ages. The
Older Stone Age includes the Stellenbosch and Victoria West industries
with crudely chipped hand-axes and other implements of lydianite, and
the Fauresmith industry with better worked tools of the same material.
These correspond more or less to the Chellean and Acheulean cultures of
Europe. The Middle Stone Age comprises the Still Bay and other industries, mostly characterized by flake implements with the edges retouched. It is roughly analogous to the Mousterian of Europe. The
Later Stone Age consists of the Smithfield and Wilton industries. These
latter show transitions from an Upper Palaeolithic type of work like the
Capsian to a full Neolithic industry with pottery and some polished stone
implements.[54]

No human remains have been found in South Africa definitely associated with implements of the Older Stone Age. But it is almost certain that a large-brained, modern type of man inhabited South Africa
during the Middle Stone Age. The first discovery of fossil man occurred
in 1913, near Boskop in the Transvaal. Workmen digging a ditch came
across mineralized bones in the subsoil about 4½ feet below the surface.
A few rudely worked stones occurred in the burial. Only a few fragments
of the skull and the long bones were found. The most remarkable feature
of the Boskop man was the great size of his brain-case. According to Keith,
the reconstructed skull measures 205 mm. in length and 154 mm. in
breadth, and its calculated capacity is 1630 cc.—150 mm. above that of
modern Englishmen. The cranial index is about 75, indicating that the
skull was long relative to its breadth. The brow-ridges are not large; the
forehead is swollen and bulbous, as in certain modern Negroid types; the
mastoid processes are small. A fragment of the lower jaw tells us something about the face. There seems to have been little protrusion of the
jaws, and the teeth and mandible are much like those of the modern
Bushmen—little yellow-skinned Negroids of South Africa. The limb-
bone fragments indicate a stature of about 5 feet, 6 inches.

Most of the South African anthropologists seem to agree that the
Boskop type represents the principal *Homo sapiens* ancestral stock of
present South African races. The latter have been modified, however, by
admixture with some other racial elements, both in the Bushman-
Hottentot group and in the Bantu. Fossil skulls of the Boskopoid type
include not only the original specimen but, according to general agree-

[54] Goodwin and Lowe, *Stone Age Cultures.*

ment, those from the Zitzikama caves, from the Matjes River, and from Fish Hoek. Certain other fossil crania included in the range of the Boskop type by some students are referred to an "Australoid" type by others. Galloway has given a general description of the Boskop type, compiled from a survey of all of its known representatives.[55] It is invariably of massive construction and great dimensions (length exceeding 190 mm. and capacity over 1500 cc.). It is dolichocephalic, somewhat low-vaulted, and coffin-shaped (or pentagonoid) when viewed from above. The narrow frontal region shows a median ridge, and the glabella (the eminence over the root of the nose) and brow-ridges are usually prominent and emphasized by a groove that separates them from the forehead. The latter is low but almost vertical and curves into a flattened or slightly arched vault that has its highest point just behind a vertical drawn through the ear-holes. The occipital region of the skull is broadly wedge-shaped, with its upper portion describing a flat slope, the occipital protuberance prominent, and the area for the attachment of the neck muscles flat and almost horizontal. The mastoid process is usually diminutive and nipple-shaped, and the groove for the attachment of the digastric muscle, just inside of it on the skull base, is very deep and extends far back of the mastoid process, irrespective of its size. Above the mastoid process is a well defined supramastoid groove and a definite and often massive supramastoid crest. These details of the mastoid region of the temporal bone are important because they are characteristically reproduced in Bushmen skulls. The glenoid fossa is shallow, with a flattened articular eminence. The external angular process (the outward extension of the brow-ridge and upper rim of the orbit on the frontal bone) is triangular and projects so markedly that the minimum breadth of the frontal bone just above it (where the crests or lines of the temporal muscles are closest together) is usually 90 per cent or less of the bi-orbital diameter. Grooves on the lateral parts of the frontal bone for branches of the supraorbital nerves are common. The face is short, broad, and massive, with an index of about 50. It is not usually prognathous; the orbits are low and rectangular with their axes tilted downward, outward, and backward, their margins massive. The region between the orbits includes flat or only slightly arched nasal bones, a low, broad nasal aperture, a short alveolar border in the subnasal region that is not excessively projecting. The surface of the upper jaw below the middle of the orbits is not markedly depressed into a canine fossa; the malars or cheek bones are sharply angular, with the body of the bone facing laterally and tilted upward, and the portion forming the lower

[55] Galloway, "Characteristics of the Skull," pp. 31–46.

rim of the orbit bent to face forward. The palate is broad and shallow
and either horseshoe-shaped or V-shaped. The teeth (not included in
Galloway's description of the type) are small, as in the modern Bushman, and their pulp cavities, according to Middleton Shaw, are enlarged (taurodont). This taurodontism is an infantile or primitive feature and not a herbivorous specialization. In general, the outstanding
characteristics of the Boskopoid skull type are very large brain-case and
relatively very small and short face, with reduction in the size of the
teeth. These are foetal or infantile characters, and the phenomenon of
their retention in adult years is called pedomorphism.

A second Homo sapiens strain of Pleistocene antiquity in South Africa
shows certain "Australoid" features, stressed by Broom, Drennan, and
Keith but regarded as Boskopoid variants by Galloway. In order to understand the Australoid problem in South Africa, we must consider the
Florisbad skull, which ranks in importance with Rhodesian man and
Weinert's new Africanthropus but is here discussed with Homo sapiens
because its total characteristics seem to place it in that category. This
cranium was discovered in 1933 by Professor T. F. Dreyer while excavating a site at Florisbad, a warm lithium spring about 25 miles north of
Bloemfontein. It lay amid the accumulated débris that had choked one
outlet or "eye" of the spring, in association with two extinct forms of
horse, the extinct giant buffalo (Bubalus antiquus), and other fauna no
longer extant. Stone points of Mousterio-Levalloisian affinity, also found
in the débris, are assigned by Mr. A. J. H. Goodwin to the Hagenstad
variation of the Middle Stone Age, and Professor Dreyer considers the
oldest deposits of the spring to be Middle Pleistocene, if not earlier.

The portion of the Florisbad skull recovered includes the frontal
region except the left supraorbital portion, the top of the left parietal,
and enough of the left side of the face and the nose to permit certain
restoration of all of the face except the palate and alveolar border. The
outstanding feature of the frontal region is its flat, receding character
and the forward and lateral projection of the supraorbital torus. The
frontal curve is as low as that of Neanderthaloids, and the breadth of
the supraorbital torus (136 mm.) considerably exceeds the Neanderthal
maximum and is inferior only to that of the Rhodesian man (139 mm.) [56]
The constriction of the frontal bone behind the torus is about equal to
the amount found in the original Neanderthal specimen and in the
La Chapelle-aux-Saints cranium, relatively much less than that of the
Rhodesian man, and far more pronounced than in modern man. However, the minimum and maximum widths of the frontal bone (120 mm.

[56] Drennan, "Florisbad Skull," pp. 103–114.

and 136 mm., respectively) are far greater than those of the Neanderthaloids or of most specimens of *Homo sapiens*. Galloway particularly
stresses the fact that the supraorbital torus in the Florisbad man is not a
continuous bar, as in Neanderthal and the other more primitive human
forms, but consists of a central glabellar eminence separated from the
lateral swellings on the outer halves of the orbital rims by a well defined
sulcus, running upward from the supraorbital notch. This is a *Homo
sapiens* type of supraorbital region and not palaeoanthropic.[57] Instead
of the high Neanderthaloid orbits and flat, stream-lined malars, curving
back from the face without sharp angulation, the Florisbad skull has
broad, low, tilted orbits with the infero-lateral angles bevelled and the
malars or cheek bones breaking from the frontal surface of the maxilla
at almost a right angle. Again, the face of the maxilla in Florisbad man is
very deeply excavated below the orbits, whereas in Neanderthal man
this suborbital region is flat or even puffy. The root of the nose is deeply
recessed under an overhanging glabella, an Australoid feature quite
alien to Neanderthal man; the nasal bones are ridged rather than flattened. A feature of the Florisbad reconstructions figured by Drenann and
Galloway is a very slight mid-facial prognathism combined with excessive alveolar prognathism, which imparts a decidedly Negroid contour
to the facial profile. Only one tooth, a much worn and very long-rooted
upper third molar, is available. It has fused roots—a character common
enough in recent man. No dimensions of the fragmentary vault are available, except those pertaining to the frontal bone. The length of the skull
is thought to have been at least 200 mm.; the width must have been
ample, and the cranial capacity could not have been small. A great deal
of discussion about the brain cast, which includes only the frontal and
parietal regions, does not, in my opinion, lead to any very specific conclusions. Generally speaking, I should say that the interpretation of
endocranial casts of fossil skulls is a very precarious business.[58] The brain
coverings and the cerebrospinal fluid interpose between the brain itself
and the inner skull walls, and the relief of convolutions on the latter is
usually faint. However, the general size and development of the brain is
undoubtedly determinable by a careful study of the cast as a whole. In
the Florisbad case, all students agree that a primitive and inferior status
of the frontal and parietal lobes is indicated by the proportions, regional
development, and convolutional pattern of the cast, but those who think
that Florisbad should be classified with *Homo sapiens* believe that the

[57] Galloway, "Nature and Status of the Florisbad Skull," pp. 1–16.
[58] Le Gros Clark, Cooper, and Zuckerman found that little information about the sulcal
pattern of the brains of chimpanzees could be gained from a study of these casts. Le Gros
Clark, Cooper, and Zuckerman, "Endocranial Cast of the Chimpanzee," pp. 249–269.

TABLE 5. PRINCIPAL FINDS OF FOSSIL *HOMO SAPIENS* IN SOUTH AFRICA

Place	Date	Archaeological Association	Content	Sex	Cranial Length	Cranial Breadth	C.I.	N.I.	Capacity
Boskop, Transvaal	1914	Middle Stone Age?	Skull cap, right temporal, part of lower jaw, parts of limb bones	m.	205	154?	75.1	?	1600–1700 cc.?
Zitzikama	1923	Upper layer—Late Stone Lower, Middle Stone?	Upper—23 Bush; lower 3 fragmentary Boskopoid	f.	210	150	71.4	?	1600–1750 cc.?
Fish Hoek	1928	Still Bay (Upper Palaeolithic)	Skeleton, primitive Bushman, 5 ft., 2 in.	m.	200	151	76	60	1500–1631 cc.?
Matjes River	1929–34	Lower cave level, Late Middle Stone Age, underlying Bush skeletons with Late Stone Age industry	Boskopoid I skeletons IV V		193 203 201	131 149 135	70.0 73.4 67.1	? ? ?	1377–1400 cc. 1660–1664 cc. 1475–1490 cc.
Springbok Flats	1929	In limestone with advanced Middle Stone Age implements	Buried skeleton, fragmentary	m.	196	148	75.5	?	1500 cc.
Cape Flats	1929	In sand pit, from old land surface. Wilton, Still Bay (Late and Middle Stone)	Fragments of Bush skull; "Australoid" skull		191	132	69.1	?	1230 cc.
Florisbad	1932	Closed-up eye of ancient spring. Early Middle Stone (Hagenstad Variation)	Frontal calavaria and most of face Australoid? Neanderthaloid?	m.	200?	150?	75?	48?	
Ingwavuma	1940	Middle Stone Age? (Pietersburg Culture)	Adult skull, mandible, femora, tibiae; infant skeleton	?	195–200	140–42	71–71.8	?	1450 cc.?

generalized characters of the cast support their position, whereas those who would put the specimen into the Neanderthal category consider that the lowness and flatness of the cast is enough to rule Florisbad out of the anatomically modern species.

Professor Drennan stresses the resemblance of the Florisbad frontal region and brain cast to Neanderthal man, and Professor Dreyer, the discoverer, is much impressed with the similarities between Florisbad and the Steinheim skull, a progressive Neanderthaloid form, of allegedly third glaciation (Rissian) age. Galloway is of the opinion that Florisbad has a Boskopoid vault and face but an Australoid supraorbital region. Actually, the Boskopoid face, so far as known, is not unlike the Australoid face but very dissimilar to the faces of Rhodesian and Neanderthal man. Galloway calls attention also to the close likeness between Florisbad and the Wadjak skulls (Neolithic or Mesolithic large-brained crania that seem to be intermediate between the Solo men and the modern smaller-brained Australians). Galloway thinks that Florisbad may well be ancestral both to the infantile Boskop type and to the gerontomorphic (adultiform or senilized) Australoid type. In his view Florisbad is allied in endocranial characters also to the more primitive Rhodesian man.

The Cape Flats skull, well described by Professor Drennan,[59] certainly presents features of the supraorbital region and face that ally it to Florisbad, and its mastoid processes are large, not small as in the Boskop-Bush type. Moreover, its teeth are large, like those of Australians and Negroes and in contrast with the dental reduction in the Bush line. Professor Dart, in an admirable survey of the relationships of fossil to recent man in South Africa,[60] expresses himself as unsatisfied with the theory of the derivation of either Bush or Negro types from any known ancestral form. He says "Both the Bush and Negro types differ from the Rhodesian and Florisbad types in lacking projecting eyebrow ridges; they differ from the Boskop type sufficiently to hybridize with it. If Florisbad man is indeed the ancestor of Boskop man, we may expect to find the contemporary smooth-browed ancestors of the Bush and Negro types further northward in this continent in comparably ancient strata." With this view I am inclined to agree.

The enormous reduction in skull size and cranial capacity that marks the Bushman-Hottentot types when compared with the Boskop type, to say nothing of a diminution from average to pygmoid stature, would have to be interpreted as a phenomenon of degradation if the Bushmen and Hottentots are directly descended from the Boskop stock. A similar

[59] Drennan, "An Australoid Skull," pp. 417–427.
[60] Dart, "Recent Discoveries," pp. 13–27. Cf. especially p. 18.

phenomenon would be manifested in the dental reduction. It seems to me probable that this size diminution may have been caused by hybridization of the large-brained, normal-statured Boskopoid type with Congo Negrillos, or pygmies, to bring about the Bush type. Similarly, in Australia, a marked decrease in cranial capacity from the Wadjak type (actually found in Java) and the Talgai type to contemporary Australian aborigines may have been effected by a hybridization of proto-Australoids with the pygmoid Tasmanians. However, these relationships of modern races to fossil forms will have to await further discussion in the section of this book dealing with contemporary racial stocks.

The most recent addition to the South African series of fossil man comes from the Border Cave, near the boundary between Zululand and Swaziland, just below the crest of the western scarp of the Lebombo range.[61] The cave yielded implements of a rich industry of Middle Stone Age times (Pietersburg Culture), with a majority of the remains of modern low-veld animals, an extinct species of equine larger than a zebra, and also an extinct bovine. Human remains included fragmentary parts of the skull vault ascribed to an adult of thirty years, an adult mandible, portions of adult femora and tibiae, and parts of the skeleton of an infant of three months. The skeletons were probably associated with the Middle Stone Age industry.

The adult skull is estimated to have been 195 to 200 mm. in length, 140 to 142 mm. in breadth, with a height from the ear-holes of at least 115 mm. Its minimum estimated capacity is 1450 cc. (well up to the average of modern adult male Europeans). The brain-case was long-headed, with an ovid outline, small broad mastoids with well-marked supramastoid grooves, and no occipital torus. The forehead was of moderate height and curvature, but very broad (minimum frontal diameter, 108 mm.) The brow-ridges form a continuous transverse bony torus, but they do not project greatly. The frontal sinuses are small. Portions of the mandible minus all teeth indicate a shallow symphysis and a lack of alveolar prognathism that distinguishes it sharply from characteristic Negroid forms. The brow-ridges are much larger than are usually found in collections of South African Negro, Bushman, and Hottentot crania. Fragments of femora indicate longer bones than the average of Negro skeletons, markedly flattened below the level of the lesser trochanter)platymeric index 77.4), and strongly pilastered at the mid-shaft (index, 128.0). The tibiae are transversely flattened to some extent. These features of the lower limb are also unusual in Negroes.

[61] Cooke, Malan, and Wells, "Fossil Man in the Lebombo Mountains," pp. 6–13.

Cook, Malan, and Wells state that this Ingwavuma skull occupies an intermediate position between the Florisbad specimen and those of Fish Hoek and Springbok Flats. It may represent an intermediate evolutionary stage, a reversion of the Springbok Flats type to a Florisbad ancestor, a hybrid between Florisbad and Springbok forms, or a more generalized type from which the Floribad skull, with its fantastically broad and flat frontal bone, developed. It is in the broad and massive frontal that the skull departs from Springbok and approaches Florisbad.

The Old Man of China Who Married
an Eskimo and a Melanesian

Choukoutien, the apparently inexhaustible mine of human palaeontology near Peiping, China, has yielded the most bizarre polygynous family on record, according to the conclusions of that masterly student of ancient man, Professor Franz Weidenreich. In 1933, Mr. W. C. Pei, of the Geological Survey of China, began to excavate a cave discovered under the soil of the hilltop over Choukoutien, Locality I, in 1930, in the course of tracing the southern extension of the Sinanthropus sediments. This Upper Cave was filled with gray, slightly consolidated, fossiliferous breccia. It represents a "dissolution cavity" in the original limestone, and the deposit in it is quite different from the Sinanthropus strata and much later. The cave was apparently not accessible in Sinanthropus times, but was reopened in the Late Pleistocene. Its contents included the bones of literally thousands of animals—among them extinct forms of hyaena, bear, and ostrich, as well as the tiger and the cheetah, which have disappeared from this part of Asia. This cave fauna is closely linked with the Loessic fauna of China (Late Pleistocene). The human industries include implements of bone and stone, a variety of ornaments such as perforated teeth and shells, beads—of a generally Upper Palaeolithic character but not assignable to any of the European cultures of this period. On the whole, the artifacts are much inferior to those of the Aurignacian, Solutrean, Magdalenian, or Capsian. The bones of at least seven persons were in this cave, under earth upon which red ochre or hematite had been scattered—a common custom in Upper Palaeolithic burials of Europe and in prehistoric Chinese sepultures. However, this funeral site had been disturbed; the skeletons were scattered and many bones missing. All four of the skull caps preserved have fractures, dents, and perforations caused by heavy blows with sharp or blunt instruments, evidently inflicted when the scalp tissues still covered the skull vaults, because the fragments and splinters of the broken vaults are still in their proper anatomical relations. Perhaps the people whose remains were found in the cave were dismembered and some of their parts were thrown into the cave, then afterwards covered with hematite as a sort of an excuse for a proper funeral.[62] Those were rough times. Of the seven individuals thus summarily dismissed to the Palaeolithic Happy Hunting Grounds, four were adult, one adolescent, one a child of five years, and the other a newborn baby or perhaps even a foetus. One of the males seemed to be over sixty years, the other relatively young, as were also the adult females. The tools and ornaments found in the cave were not more than enough to be carried on the persons of the unfortunate family (if it was a family; on this point Weidenreich speculates interestingly and romantically).

The best preserved of the skulls is that of the old man, which is intact, lower jaw and all, except the left temporal region, which has a small depressed fracture with radiating cracks—probably the result of a blow delivered with a pointed weapon. It is strongly reminiscent of the Old Man of Cro Magnon and the male Obercassel skull, but it has bigger brow-ridges, which fuse more gradually with the frontal curve; the forehead is lower and more receding; the entire vault relatively lower. This old man of Choukoutien had a cranial length of 204 mm., maximum breadth 143 mm., basion-bregma height 136 mm., cranial capacity about 1500 cc. and cranial index 70.2. His orbits were relatively low, his malars laterally flaring, frontally jutting, and strongly angled; his nasal aperture wide, in spite of nasal bones pinched at the root (nasal index 55.2). The lower border of the nasal aperture is guttered, and there is a medium alveolar prognathism. Professor Weidenreich has not yet described the mandible, palate, and dentition of this skull. But it is clear enough that the lower jaw is massive, with a well-developed chin eminence and a broad ascending ramus. Weidenreich thinks that the type represented is somewhat more primitive than that of comparable European crania of the Upper Palaeolithic; that it does not particularly resemble Australian crania or proto-Australian crania, such as the Wadjak skulls, nor is it an Ainu type. He thinks that it ought to be classified as a primitive Mongoloid. My own opinion is that this old man looks like a primitive European White, with more than a dash of the archaic Australoid features and can be duplicated almost exactly in the skulls of modern Ainu. Incidentally, this fellow was fairly tall—174 cm. (5 feet, 8½ inches).

The second skull, which Weidenreich considers female, is also com-

---

[62] Weidenreich, "On the Earliest Representatives," pp. 161–174.
Pei, "A Preliminary Report," pp. 327–350.
Pei, "On the Upper Cave Industry," pp. 175–179.

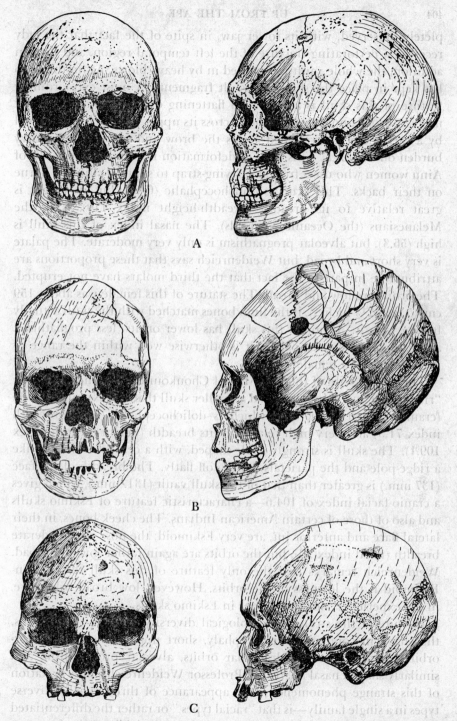

Fig. 58. A. Old Man of Choukoutien. B, Melanesoid lady (?). C, Eskimoid lady (?).

pletely preserved, with its lower jaw, in spite of the fact that the lady received a perforating fracture of the left temporal region, and that, in addition, the whole vault was bashed in by heavy blows. Again the scalp has kept in place the shattered vault fragments. A most extraordinary feature of this skull is an artificial flattening of the frontal bone that makes a broad annular depression across its upper part such as is caused by a carrying strap stretched across the brow and supporting a heavy burden on the back. This kind of deformation is found in the skulls of Ainu women who use a frontal carrying-strap to support children borne on their backs. This skull is dolichocephalic (69.3), but its height is great relative to its breadth (breadth-height index 110) as in the Melanesians (the Oceanic Negroids). The nasal index of this skull is high (56.3), but alveolar prognathism is only very moderate. The palate is very short and broad, but Weidenreich says that these proportions are attributable in part to the fact that the third molars have not erupted. The orbits are low and broad. The stature of this female was about 159 cm. (5 feet, 2½ inches), if the limb bones matched with the skull actually belong with it. Although this skull has lower orbits, less prognathism, and a broader, shorter palate, it is otherwise well within the range of New Caledonian female skulls.

The second wife of the Old Man of Choukoutien was undoubtedly a "ringer" for an Eskimo. She had a smaller skull than the Number 1 wife (cranial capacity 1300 cc.), which is dolichocephalic (length-breadth index 71.3) and very high relative to its breadth (height-breadth index 109.1). The skull is strongly gable-shaped, with a central elevation like a ridge-pole and the parietals sloping off flatly. The breadth of the face (137 mm.) is greater than that of the skull vault (131. mm.), which gives a cranio-facial index of 104.6—a characteristic feature of Eskimo skulls and also of those of certain American Indians. The cheek bones, in their lateral flare and anterior jut, are very Eskimoid; the nose is of moderate breadth (nasal index 50), but the orbits are again rather low and broad. Weidenreich remarks that the only feature of this skull that is non-Eskimoid is the lowness of the orbits. However, low broad orbits are, in my experience, not infrequent in Eskimo skulls.

In spite of the strong morphological diversity of these three skulls, they have in common dolichocephaly, short upper faces, great inter-orbital breadth, low quadrangular orbits, alveolar prognathism, and similarly shaped nasal apertures. Professor Weidenreich's interpretation of this strange phenomenon—the appearance of three racially diverse types in a single family—is that "racial types," or rather the differentiated types that we are accustomed to regard as "racial," are in fact very ancient in both palaeoanthropic and neanthropic man and may co-exist within very small groups, or even in single families, and that the tendency to "breed and cultivate complete unitary groups, corresponding to the suggestion of 'pure races,' does not represent primary conditions, but must be considered as a later acquisition." [63]

I should incline rather to the view that race mixture is a very ancient phenomenon, and that to find the isolated, inbred types of restricted variability, we shall have to go back still farther than the Upper Palae-olithic. We may then expect to encounter these relatively homogenous groups only in their own respective areas of concentration and char-acterization.

The Minnesota Girl Who Fell into the Lake

Skeletal finds of man in the New World of supposedly Pleistocene antiquity are "reckoned by the dozens." The late Dr. Aleš Hrdlička, dean of American physical anthropologists, devoted two sizeable volumes to the demolition of the claims made on behalf of these discoveries and, before he died, had written enough destructive criticisms of subsequent finds to fill still a third volume.[64] None of these "fossil" Americans showed craniological or metric features that could not be duplicated in the skeletons of recent Indians, and in no single case were the geological, palaeontological, and stratigraphic associations such as establish in-dubitably the Pleistocene age of the finds. Many of them were obviously and palpably modern; some were archaic in appearance but in no case Neanderthaloid or definitely palaeoanthropic. It may be presumed that some of these finds were, in fact, geologically ancient, but, as in the case of *Homo sapiens* in Mid-Pleistocene Europe, an irrefragable case is required to establish the truth. To my satisfaction, at any rate, the reality of Late Pleistocene man in North America is attested by the find of Minnesota Man.

On June 18, 1931, men working on the highway at Pelican Rapids, Otter Tail County, Minnesota, were ripping up the road with a grader, because the surface had become roughened from "frost boils." They were ploughing a V-shaped cut in the middle of the road when the grader brought to light a bone dagger and a skeleton in the silt underneath the road. They stopped work and dug out the skeleton, which lay 10 inches below the blade of the grader and 3.3 feet below the road bed. On the

---

[63] Weidenreich, "On the Earliest Representatives," pp. 172–173.
[64] Hrdlička, *Skeletal Remains.*
   Hrdlička, *Early Man in South America,* and many short articles.

20th of June, Dr. Clinton Stauffer, of the geological staff of the University
of Minnesota, visited the site, reported the circumstances of the find,
and brought the bones to the laboratory of Professor A. E. Jenks, head of
the Department of Anthropology. In May of 1932, Dr. Jenks and assist-
ants redug the site of the discovery and again excavated the whole area
thoroughly in August of the same year, recovering additional parts of
the skeleton and ample stratigraphic evidence as to its position. The road
bed lay in a cutting and the skeleton was in varved silt about 10 feet
below original ground level. The geological studies and resulting reports
show that the skeleton lay in the undisturbed silts of the glacial Lake
Pelican, formed at the edge of the last glacier, the Wisconsin glacier, in
its retreat northward. The age of this lake is estimated at 20,000 years—
Late Pleistocene. Most of the competent geological experts that have
visited and examined this site concur in this estimate of the age of the
deposit and in the conclusion that the skeleton was undisturbed and
in situ.[65]

The bones are mineralized and represent the almost complete skeleton of a young woman of about fifteen years. The clay varves or bands
near the skeleton were undisturbed. Since the skeleton rested on the left
shoulder with the legs highest in the silt, there is no likelihood of its
representing a modern burial. Probably the young lady fell into the lake
(or was pushed in), off a boat or through the ice.

There is nothing remarkable about the skull measurements, which
are those of a female of average cranial capacity (1345 cc.), mesocephalic
(length-breadth index 77.1), high orbits, and a nose of medium breadth
(nasal index 44.7). There are some unusual U-shaped grooves on the
occiput, doubtless marking the course of blood vessels, and some anomalous arrangements of the internal features of the occipital bone, but
these have no evolutionary significance and are undoubtedly individual
variations. In the face, the features worthy of remark are the primitive,
guttered lower borders of the nasal aperture, the very small development of the nasal spine, and the excessive alveolar prognathism. The
malars jut forward but are not unduly large. The suborbital fossae
are shallow, as in many Mongoloids. All of the teeth are in place, except
one incisor (lost post-mortem). They constitute the really distinctive
feature of the skull in their very large size. The molars are individually
much larger than those of Piltdown, Heidelberg, Ehringsdorf, Spy I
and II, Krapina (Neanderthaloids), and the Aurignacian man of Combe

[65] Jenks, *Pleistocene Man in Minnesota.* This volume contains the fullest possible information upon the circumstances of the find, together with a report on the geology of the region
in Pleistocene times. The study of the skeleton by Professor Jenks is a model of complete and
competent description and analysis.

Capelle. The third molars are larger than the seconds, and the molar patterns are somewhat primitive and marked by extensive wrinkling of the crown enamel surfaces, such as frequently may be observed in the molars of orangs and, rarely, in those of man. The upper middle incisors are shovel-shaped—a very common feature among Mongoloids and also observed in the incisors of Sinanthropus and of some Neanderthal specimens. The postcranial bones present no very remarkable features but are those of an immature, non-muscular female with somewhat slender

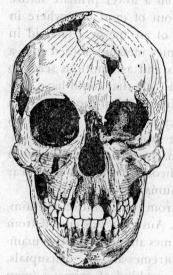
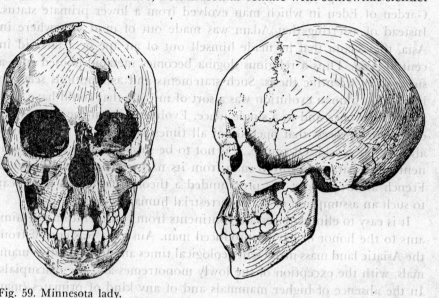

Fig. 59. Minnesota lady.

frame and relatively long forearms. The shaft flattenings of the femora and tibia (platymeria and platycnemia) usual in Mongoloids are not present. Stature was about 155 cm. (5 feet, 1 inch).

Artifacts with the Minnesota girl included a bone dagger, some fragments of clam shell, a conch shell pendant, pieces of turtle carapace, a wolf's tooth, bird bones, and bits of antler. They look like the contents of a primitive "medicine kit."

Professor Jenks concluded that the Minnesota girl was a primitive form of *Homo sapiens* of an early type of evolving Mongoloid with closer affinities with Eskimos than with most Asiatic Mongoloids or with American Indians in general. I am not impressed with the particularity of Eskimo resemblances as contrasted with generalized Mongoloid characters. Features of the Minnesota lady that recall Australoid or Negroid races are pronounced alveolar prognathism and, especially, the indices and morphological characters of the long bones.

The Garden of Eden

Pedants of bygone generations were fond of using up reams of paper in learned arguments about the geographical situation of the Garden of Eden. I remember reading one such effort that purported to prove that the birthplace of man was either in Washington or Oregon. Some scientists of the present day are naïvely interested in locating a zoological Garden of Eden in which man evolved from a lower primate status. Instead of asserting that Adam was made out of mud somewhere in Asia, they claim that he made himself out of an ape or a tarsioid in central Asia. Thus a religious dogma becomes metamorphosed into a supposedly scientific thesis. Such statements and assumptions seem to imply that human evolution was a sort of miracle that could have happened only once and in a single place. Evolution is, on the contrary, a continuous process that operates at all times upon plants and animals all over the world. Of course, it is not to be supposed that every continent has separately evolved man from its native primates, although a French anthropologist has propounded a theory that comes very near to such an assumption of an all-terrestrial human evolution.

It is easy to eliminate certain continents from consideration as claimants to the honor of having produced man. Australia was cut off from the Asiatic land mass in ancient geological times and has no native mammals, with the exception of the lowly monotremes and the marsupials. In the absence of higher mammals and of any kind of primates (man being a fairly recent immigrant), Australia could hardly have been an area in which the process of human evolution was effected. The same is true of the neighboring great island of New Guinea.

North and South America were probably not occupied by man before the end of the glacial period or the beginning of the recent period. Although North America in Eocene times was the home of some of the earliest fossil lemuroids and tarsioids, the subsequent evolution of primates seems not to have proceeded beyond the Cebidae or American monkeys, unless one is gullible enough to accept the tale of excremental anthropoids of Venezuela (cf. pp. 20–21). Lacking such credulity, we may dismiss the New World from serious consideration.

Europe was an Old World seat of fossil lemuroids and tarsioids in Eocene times. In the Miocene period, the Dryopithecus family of great anthropoids inhabited the southern zone of the continent, and fossil monkeys lived cheek by jowl with their primate relatives of loftier status. In the Pleistocene period, we are confronted by the Dawn Lady of

Piltdown, the Heidelberg man, the whole assemblage of Neanderthalers, as well as the more modern types of fossil human beings. In short, Europe seems to bulk as large in primate evolution and in prehistory as in cultural evolution and history.

But we must not forget that objects dug up in our own backyard do not prove that the unexcavated gardens of our neighbors are sterile or even less treasure-laden. The soil of Europe has been turned over by the hand of man more thoroughly than that of any other continent. Furthermore, there are probably ten archaeologically-instructed or scientifically-minded persons sitting on the edge of every promising gravel pit in Europe for one such competent observer in the Americas, and a thousand for each discerning scrutinizer of Asiatic or African fossil beds. Mute, inglorious Pithecanthropi are far less likely to blush unseen in Europe than anywhere else, and Dawn Ladies do not waste their sweetness on the desert air of England, France, or any other of the great centers of European science and culture. European scientists, like vultures, poise aloft ready to drop upon any carcass of ancient man discernible to their far-sighted vision. When one is found, they certainly "perch upon his bare back-bone and pick his eyes out one by one."

Africa and Asia have scarcely begun to yield up the fossil prehuman and human remains that must lie concealed in their geological deposits. Both of these continents hold out richer promises than Europe for the student of primate evolution. This is principally because most of the primates, from the lowest to the highest, are at home today in Asia or Africa. Man presumably evolved, like the rest of the primates, in a tropical forest area, unless we suppose that he was forced to the ground by having the trees die under him.

In the Lower and Middle Miocene periods, generalized forms of anthropoid apes of the Dryopithecus family extended from southeastern Asia westward along the Mediterranean zone as far as France, and in North Africa probably south to the farther margin of the present tropical forest area. During the Upper Miocene period, there is some evidence that temperature dropped and more or less desert conditions prevailed over the Iranian plateau and possibly over a part of North Africa. The African anthropoids were cut off from their oriental relatives. It seems probable that at this time some of the more progressive apes took to the ground in Africa, others in southeastern Asia, possibly still others in Europe. In short, the probable cradle of humanity, the site of our prehuman ancestors' first ventures on the ground, is not some single hallowed spot or limited Garden of Eden, but the whole broad area through which the progressive great apes ranged. A terrestrial habitat and an upright biped gait were not God-given attributes of a single Adam and Eve among the great anthropoids. It is difficult to avoid the conclusion that, of the diverse families and genera of giant anthropoids developed in the Miocene period, several may have taken to the ground in different areas and at various times. Some of these attained a semi-human status, and some achieved complete humanity; some have survived to the present day, and some have fallen by the wayside. Evolution operates not upon one single line and one single species, but upon multiple lines, some converging and some diverging, and upon large groups of animals. Nor is this process restricted to a single continent.

If the finds of fossil man hitherto brought to light mean anything at all, they mean that nature has conducted many and varied experiments upon the higher primates, resulting in several lines of human descent, all of which probably issued from a generalized and progressive family of giant anthropoids not earlier than the Miocene period.

Making a Family Tree

Figure 60 is my present idea of the family tree of man and the primates. It does not resemble very closely any tree one sees out-of-doors, perhaps because it is not a botanical tree but a zoological tree. It shows the primate trunk rising from the Cretaceous zone. Alongside, and obviously springing from the same roots, is the trunk of the Insectivora. During the Eocene period, we see the limb giving rise to the modern lemurs—the lorises, galagos, and true lemurs—springing off from the lemuroid trunk. The Eocene family of the Adapidae may have been ancestral to the living lemurs. The extinct American family, the Notharctidae, is represented by the broken stump of a branch. A similar lopped-off branch represents the extinct American tarsioids. Here also diverges the limb leading to the modern Tarsius. From this tarsioid-lemuroid Eocene trunk, and possibly from a family closely allied to the Eocene Notharctidae, the New World platyrrhine monkeys diverged but perhaps reached the monkey status only in the Oligocene period. In the Upper Eocene or Lower Oligocene, the ancestors of the modern Old World monkey diverged from the tarsioid stem, and, in the Lower Oligocene, we find the first small anthropoid, Propliopithecus, standing very close to the branch leading to the modern gibbons and, perhaps, at the very base of that branch. In the Miocene period the giant anthropoid stock, common ancestors of the existing great apes and man, came into being. From this Dryopithecus trunk there diverged, in the Miocene period, first, the branch that leads to the modern great apes. The orang

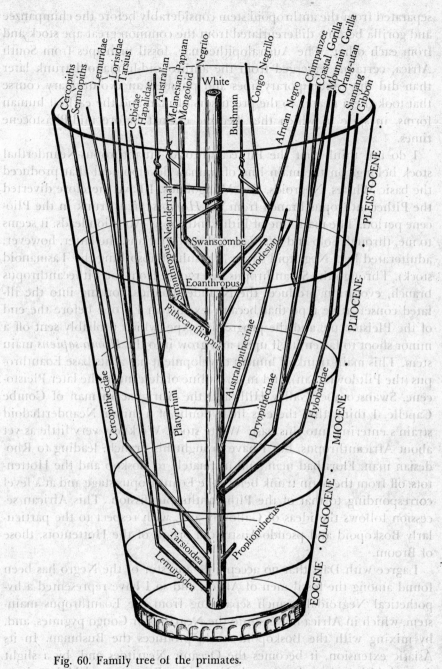

Fig. 60. Family tree of the primates.

411

separated from the anthropoid stem considerably before the chimpanzee and gorilla became differentiated from the common great ape stock and from each other. The Australopithecinae, fossil man-apes from South Africa, certainly emerged from the anthropoid-humanoid trunk later than did the contemporary apes and pursued an evolutionary course that took them nearer to the precursors of man and the earliest human forms, in spite of which they became extinct before mid-Pleistocene times.

I do not think that the Pithecanthropus-Sinanthropus-Neanderthal stock belongs on the main line of human development that produced the basic Whites, Negroids, and Mongoloids. I have therefore diverted the Pithecanthropus branch from the *Homo sapiens* trunk in the Pliocene period. The main line of Pithecanthropus evolution leads, it seems to me, through Solo and Wadjak to the Australians, the latter, however, adulterated by a Negritoid strain (a result of absorbing the Tasmanoid stock). Through the Sinanthropus divergence from the Pithecanthropus branch, evolution produces the Neanderthaloids, forking into the ill-fated conservative type that became extinct in Europe before the end of the Pleistocene, and the progressive type, which probably sent off a minor shoot to fasten itself upon and grow into the *Homo sapiens* main stem. This main trunk of human development has at its base Eoanthropus (the Piltdown man), and in direct line of descent in the later Pleistocene, Swanscombe, Galley Hill, and the Aurignacian man of Combe Capelle. I think that there is little doubt of a minor Neanderthaloid strain's entering into this basic White stock. We know very little as yet about Africanthropus, but I have brought his branch, leading to Rhodesian man, Florisbad man, and ultimately to Boskop and the Hottentots, off from the main trunk before the Eoanthropus stage and at a level corresponding to that of the Pithecanthropus fission. This African secession follows the ideas of Galloway and, with respect to the particularly Boskopoid and pseudo-Australoid origin of the Hottentots, those of Broom.

I agree with Dart that no acceptable ancestor of the Negro has been found among the fossil men of Africa, and so I have represented a hypothetical Negroidal branch separating from the Eoanthropus mainstem, which in Africa flowers into the Negrillos or Congo pygmies, and, by mixing with the Boskopoid stock, produces the Bushman. In its Asiatic extension, it becomes the Oceanic Negritoes and, by a slight Australoid infusion, the Oceanic Negroids—Papuans and Melanesians. Since I am also unable to derive the Mongoloids from any known fossil strain (Weidenreich to the contrary, notwithstanding), I have repre-

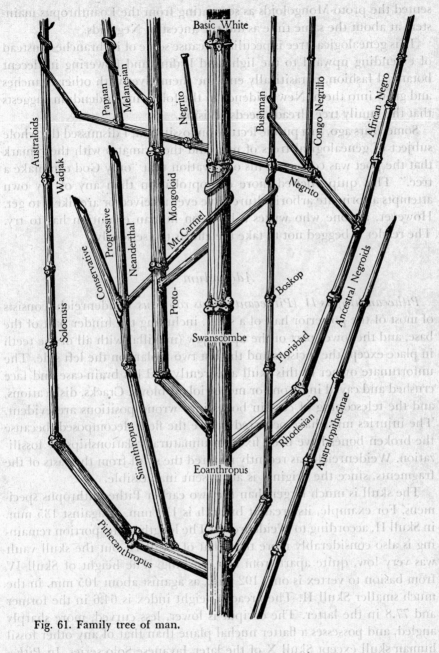

Fig. 61. Family tree of man,

sented the proto-Mongoloids as separating from the Eoanthropus main-stem at about the same time as did the ancestral Negroids.

This genealogical tree is peculiar because some of its branches, instead of extending upward to the light and leafing and flowering in decent botanical fashion, parasitically entwine themselves with other branches and grow into them. New evidence in the following addendum suggests that the family tree already needs revision.

Some years ago, in a public lecture on fossil man, I dismissed the whole subject of genealogical trees of man and the primates with the remark that the poet was correct in his observation that "only God can make a tree." This quip elicited more of approbation than any of my own attempts at primate arboriculture have ever received or are likely to get. However, anyone who writes a book on human evolution has to try. The reader is begged not to take the efforts too seriously.

Addendum

Pithecanthropus IV (*Pithecanthropus robustus* Weidenreich) consists of most of the posterior half of a skull, including the hinder part of the base, and the lower part of the upper jaw (maxilla) with all of the teeth in place except the incisors and the last two molars on the left side. The unfortunate owner of this skull apparently had his brain-case and face crushed and caved in by one or more violent blows. Cracks, dislocations, and the telescoping of certain bones into wrong positions are evident. The injuries must have occurred before the flesh decomposed, because the broken bones have been fixed in unnatural relationships by fossilization. Weidenreich has recently restored the skull from the casts of the fragments, since the original is at present inaccessible.

The skull is much larger than the two earlier Pithecanthropus specimens. For example, its greatest breadth is 158 mm. as against 135 mm. in Skull II, according to Weidenreich. The length of the portion remaining is also considerably more than that of Skull II, but the skull vault was very low, quite apart from any crushing. The height of Skull IV from basion to vertex is only 102 mm., as against about 105 mm. in the much smaller Skull II. The breadth-height index is 64.6 in the former and 77.8 in the latter. The occiput is lower, less curved, more sharply angled, and possesses a flatter nuchal plane than that of any other fossil human skull except Skull X of the later Javanese Solo series. In *Pithecanthropus IV* the predominance of the breadth of the skull across the base over its breadth higher up in the parietal region is greater than in any other Pithecanthropus or Sinanthropus specimen and gives the skull an almost triangular appearance when viewed from the rear. This is an excessively apelike feature.

Running from front to back in the parietal region (the frontal bone is missing) is a continuous keel-like sagittal crest, accentuated by a depression on each side and by a chain of knob-like thickened areas which comprise its hinder portion. This sagittal crest is unlike that of the great apes because it does not serve for the attachment of the temporal muscles. These chewing muscles do not reach the mid line of the skull. Weidenreich states that this knobby sagittal crest is quite unlike that found in other Pithecanthropus or Sinanthropus skulls. The occipital torus is an enormous bulge that encircles the occipital bone from one supramastoid area to the other, separated from the upper plane of the occipital bone by a deep sulcus or furrow and from the nuchal plane (where the neck muscles are attached) by a sharp line (linea nuchae superior). The muscular impressions of the nuchal plane are well marked. These features are far more prominent than the corresponding parts of *Pithecanthropus II*. The mastoid process is very large as in modern man, but is bent so that the tip turns sharply inward—a primitive feature. The auditory meatus is a vertically directed oval as in modern man, not rounded as in most Pithecanthropus and Sinanthropus specimens and in apes. The glenoid fossa (which receives the condyle of the jaw) is deep and narrow with no indication of the articular eminence found in modern man, but no postglenoid process as in apes. There is, rather, a well-developed postglenoid crest as in modern man.

The palate is somewhat reduced in size by crushing, but it is by far the largest ever found in man. It has a smooth roof, as contrasted with the ridges and furrows found in other fossil and recent men. The height of the alveolar borders which lodge the teeth is excessive; this upper jaw was deep and protrusive. The lower border of the nasal aperture is primitive and there is no well-developed nasal spine. The width of the nasal aperture (reconstructed) is 36 mm., a dimension exceeding that of all other fossil skulls and approaching the maximum found in modern broad-nosed men.

The teeth of *Pithecanthropus IV* are much worn but show human characteristics. The canine is one of the two or three largest ever found in fossil men, but is small in comparison with anthropoid teeth. It projects downward beyond the level of the premolar and is separated from the lateral incisor (or rather its socket) by a diastema or gap that is so far unique in man, but characteristic of apes whose canines interlock. This diastema measures 6.2 mm. on the left side and exceeds the average width of the similar gap found in anthropoid apes.

Weidenreich made a provisional reconstruction of this *Pithecan-thropus IV* skull which gives it a length-breadth index of 79.3—almost brachycephalic. Because of the missing anterior parts, this reconstruction is provisional and speculative. The occipital foramen, or foramen magnum, occupies the same central position in the skull base as in modern man; it is not far back as in apes. The restored maxillo-alveolar length (external length of palate) is 81 mm.; unrestored it is 75 mm. Even this latter dimension exceeds all previous records for man—fossil or recent. The restored breadth is 94 mm., that of the compressed bone 78 mm. Any conservative estimate of the actual breadth (say 89 mm.) would still establish a new high for man. This palate is much larger than that of the Rhodesian man, the previous record-holder. It was long relative to its breadth (dolichuranic). A peculiarly anthropoid feature of the temporal bone of this specimen is that its squama (the shell-like upper part that articulates with the parietal) does not extend straight fore-and-aft as in all other men; its anterior end is turned inward as in apes, thus accentuating the postorbital constriction or pinching of the skull in the temporal area. If this feature is rightly constructed, it is unique in fossil man.

Weidenreich now believes that the differences between *Pithecan-thropus IV* and previously found Pithecanthropus specimens are greater than can be explained on the assumption that Skulls I and II are female and Skull IV is male. As a result of further new discoveries that indicate a gigantic strain of ancient man, this eminent authority proposes to assign to Skull IV the name *Pithecanthropus robustus*. He considers it a somewhat more primitive though closely allied form to the Pithecanthropus specimens previously found.

GIGANTIC-JAWED JAVANESE

In 1939 von Koenigswald obtained the fragment of a lower jaw with two molars from the "lower Pleistocene" of Sangiran, near Solo, Central Java, and in 1941 another fragment of an extremely heavy lower jaw with the first molar and both premolars. He considered them as probably female and male specimens, respectively, of a new type of fossil man (*Meganthropus palaeojavanicus*). Weidenreich has now described and discussed these specimens from casts sent to him, since von Koenigswald in Java has been unable to publish the new finds.[66]

We may deal first with the heavier 1941 mandible, since Weidenreich is doubtful whether to refer the 1939 mandible to man or to ape. The

---

[66] Weidenreich, *Giant Early Man*, pp. 15–16, 34–124. This monograph includes also the description and discussion of the Gigantopithecus teeth.

1941 specimen consists of a fragment of the right side of the body, with the two premolars and the first molar in place and with the socket of the canine present in part. The base of the mandible is preserved on the right side from about the symphysis to the level of the first molar. The alveolar portion is mostly broken away. The mandible is huge and of an unbelievable thickness. It shows an average thickness of 26.6 mm., which surpasses that of all known men and apes. Weidenreich explains that large male gorillas surpass the thickness of the Meganthropus mandible at the level of the symphysis (the front of the jaw where the two halves are joined together) and at the level just below the molar teeth. However, the gorilla mandibles thin to much lesser dimensions toward the lower rim of the jaw, whereas the mandible of Meganthropus is almost uniformly thick. Sinanthropus mandibles are only 59 per cent of the thickness of the Meganthropus specimens. Neanderthal mandibles about the same, and the Heidelberg jaw, thickest human mandible heretofore known, attains 69.6 per cent of the thickness of the Javanese specimen.

In spite of its vast size and thickness, the jaw has certain typically human characteristics. The canine (as shown from its socket) was small, with a narrow, compressed root; the premolars are bicuspid; the dental arch shows a widely curved parabola with divergent side rows and no sharp angle at the canines; prognathism is only moderate; the inside of the symphysis shows a shallow genioglossal fossa, the beginning of a mental spine, and a flattened basal plate (instead of the simian shelf). Simian peculiarities include complete absence of the chin, arrangement of the premolars and molars in a straight row, and a peculiar position of the digastric fossa paralleled so far in but one specimen of a fossil ape (*Dryopithecus fontani*). In the symphysial region the lower rim of the mandible is markedly arched—a feature called the incisura submentalis, slightly indicated in Sinanthropus jaws and more clearly in the Heidelberg or Mauer mandible.

Both the premolar and molar teeth of this Meganthropus specimen are considerably larger than those of any human fossil heretofore known, but they are definitely human in conformation. Weidenreich has examined and rejected the suggestion that this jaw is pathologically thickened. The size of the teeth and the symmetrical development of the bone probably rule out the possibility of acromegaly or any other diseased condition.

Meganthropus is the name tacked on this jaw by von Koenigswald, and Weidenreich retains it (although he rightly remarks that *Megalanthropus* would be etymologically more correct).

The 1939 Sangiran mandible, considered by von Koenigswald to belong to a female Meganthropus, will have to go back into the fossil cupboard until the original can be examined because of its incompleteness (particularly in the premolar and canine region) and because of the uncertainty of judgments based only on a cast. The bone and teeth are larger than those of Pithecanthropus, Mandible B, but much smaller than those of Meganthropus—even smaller than would be expected of a female of this type. As far as can be seen, the jaw combines human and simian peculiarities; there is but slight prognathism, moderate angling of the dental arch at the canine, high horizontal mental foramen. However, the defective symphysis recalls that of an ape and it cannot be ascertained from the cast whether the canine and incisor teeth were simian or humanoid.

Let us defer the discussion of the status of Meganthropus until we have dealt with the giant teeth that von Koenigswald bought in a South Chinese drugstore.

GIGANTOPITHECUS, THE HONG KONG DRUGSTORE GIANT

Between 1935 and 1939, von Koenigswald bought various fossils in Chinese apothecary shops, among them three teeth from a Hong Kong establishment. From the associated fossils bought at the same time (molars of *Stegodon,* tapir, and orang-utan) and from the fact that the roots are broken off and the pulp cavities show traces of a yellow matrix; these *Gigantopithecus* teeth are thought to have originated in the "yellow deposits" of the caves of South China, which may belong to the Middle Pleistocene or possibly to the Lower Pleistocene. Von Koenigswald identified some of the drugstore specimens as teeth of a large orang, but one of them, a right lower third molar, could not be assigned to any primate known to him. Hence he named it *Gigantopithecus blacki* (after Davidson Black, the discoverer of Sinanthropus, the fossil man of China). In addition to the original specimen (the holotype), there is a left lower third molar and an upper molar, all attributable to the same form of animal, a giant hominid (according to Weidenreich).

The three Gigantopithecus teeth exceed all known anthropoid and human teeth in length, breadth, and height. For example, the lengths of the crowns of the right and left third lower molars of Gigantopithecus are 22 mm. and 22.3 mm., respectively. The maximum value for apes occurs in *Dryopithecus giganticus* with 19.2 mm., and in fossil man in *Pithecanthropus,* Mandible B, with 14.5 mm. Recent man averages in this dimension (crown length of lower third molars) 10.7 mm., and the chimpanzee 12.3 mm. Even the great fossil South African apes fail to approach Gigantopithecus: *Paranthropus robustus,* 16.2 mm.; *Plesian-thropus transvaalensis,* 16.6 mm. If the mass of the crown of the upper molar of Gigantopithecus be calculated by multiplying height by length by breadth, it is about 4170 cu. mm., as against 926 cu. mm., the average for modern man, and 1526 cu. mm. the maximum. The third lower molars of Gigantopithecus have a mass almost six times larger than those of average modern man and three times larger than the biggest teeth of anthropoids or fossil man.

Only one of the third lower molars of Gigantopithecus is sufficiently unworn to permit a study of the details of cusp pattern. It has the Dryopithecus pattern common to anthropoids and primitive men: three main cusps on the outside (buccal) and two main cusps on the inside (lingual), with a small sixth cusp jammed in at the back. However, there is an additional small cusp between the two main lingual or inside cusps. This additional middle inner cusp is present in both lower molars of Gigantopithecus and is said to be relatively frequent in the orang-utan. The cusps differ from those of the gorilla in having neither high nor steep cones, and in not being isolated and separated from each other by wide interstices. They differ similarly from the molar cusps of the chimpanzee, and diverge from those of the orang in not fusing into one shallow basin with their tips reduced to slightly elevated points at the margins. The Gigantopithecus cusps rather conform to the hominid type of Sinanthropus and of certain Neanderthal molars in appearing as broad-based tubercles with gently declining slopes, separated at their bases by deep narrow grooves. The wrinkles of the cusps are typically human, fewer than in the orang, but individually larger.

Another peculiarity of the Gigantopithecus lower molars is that the anterior breadth of the crown (trigonid) is much greater than the posterior breadth (talonid). This excess of anterior breadth occurs in all the anthropoid apes, but in man the breadth of the talonid is usually only a little less than that of the trigonid.

Although the absolute height of Gigantopithecus lower molar crowns exceeds that of all living or fossil men and apes, the height relative to length is less than that found in modern man and only slightly greater than in anthropoid apes.

Weidenreich discusses in great detail the relationship of all features of the Gigantopithecus teeth to those of anthropoid apes and man, fossil and living. He concludes that, apart from size, the Hong Kong drugstore teeth show a striking combination of primitive and advanced characters. The most remarkable feature is the great length of the third lower molars and the pronounced preponderance of trigonid breadth over talonid breadth. In all other hominids with the exception of *Pithecanthropus,* Mandible B (he says), the third lower molar is reduced, especially in length, and chiefly at the expense of the talonid. Weidenreich thinks that the teeth indicate a closer relationship of Gigantopithecus to Pithecanthropus than to Sinanthropus.

One must admire the courage of Professor Weidenreich in his essay to reconstruct the size of all the teeth, of the mandible, of the whole face, and even of the brain-case of *Gigantopithecus.* He has but three straws with which to make all of the bricks of this gigantic edifice. Based upon the absolute size of the three Gigantopithecus molars and the ratios observed in other forms of apes and fossil men, the results indicate a mandible about double the size of that of modern man—about 180 mm. long, 55 mm. high at the molar level and 34 mm. thick at the same level. This would be about 75 per cent higher and 100 per cent thicker than the average mandible of modern man. The bicondylar breadth of the Gigantopithecus, however, could hardly have been more than 170 mm., as against 150 mm. for Meganthropus and 120 mm. for the average of modern man. Weidenreich thinks that Gigantopithecus may have had a total facial height of about 225 mm., as against about 175 mm. for Meganthropus. The former figure is almost twice the average of modern man. Nevertheless, Weidenreich thinks that the capacity of the Gigantopithecus brain-case could not have been more than 800 to 900 cc., if it reached that figure. The walls of the skull must have been very thick, since *Pithecanthropus robustus* with a much smaller skull has about twice the thickness of modern man. There must have been enormous frontal and occipital tori, but probably no sagittal crest for the attachment of the temporal muscles, such as is found in male gorillas and orangs. However, the sort of sagittal elevation found in *Pithecanthropus robustus* may have been present. Anyhow, Weidenreich thinks that Gigantopithecus certainly had a skull far exceeding in size that of the largest male gorilla ever recorded.

Even he quails at an attempt to estimate the stature of this giant "hominid" from three odd teeth. On the basis of the position of the foramen magnum in *Pithecanthropus robustus* and in Sinanthropus specimens, together with the features of the Sinanthropus femur, he thinks that Gigantopithecus probably was erect in posture. One of the femora attributed to Pithecanthropus by Dubois belongs to an individual about 178 cm. in height (5 feet, 10⅛ inches). The original Trinil femur corresponds to a stature of 168 cm. (5 feet, 6⅛ inches) or thereabouts. Sinanthropus was shorter, 156 cm. (5 feet, 1½ inches.) On the basis of the relationship in size of a giant fossil lemur (*Megaladapis*) to a living dwarf lemur with the same locomotor habits (*Nycticebus*), it would appear that teeth double the size of those of modern man would not necessarily imply legs twice as long. Gigantopithecus may have had only slightly longer and stronger leg bones than occur in modern man.

Weidenreich's tentative phylogenetic suggestion is that the giant ancestral hominids may have been located in South China, or, earlier, in India. He thinks that a straight line development may have taken place from Gigantopithecus to Meganthropus, to Pithecanthropus robustus, to Pithecanthropus erectus, to Homo soloensis, to Wadjak Man, to the modern Australian. He also thinks it possible that some gigantic ancestral form may connect Sinanthropus with Gigantopithecus, although none has been discovered up to now.

The present writer, although profoundly impressed by Weidenreich's skill, erudition, and painstaking methods of research, is not convinced that the present state of the knowledge of odontology enables anyone to assign the molars of Gigantopithecus either to an ape or to a man with absolute certainty. The criteria of differentiation are not well enough established. On the whole, it seems more likely that Weidenreich is right than wrong, especially in view of the Meganthropus teeth and mandible, which are almost unquestionably human. I am disposed to accept Meganthropus according to Weidenreich's specifications, but to keep the matter of Gigantopithecus in suspense until further finds confirm the Weidenreich hypothesis of his humanity or refute it.

In the succeeding portions of this book dealing with various types of fossil men and with the general question of man's ancestry, the Meganthropus-Gigantopithecus question will receive no further discussion. The reason for this is that Weidenreich's monograph (*Giant Early Man from Java and South China*) has been published too late to permit its utilization *passim* in a work already set by the printer. The reader should bear in mind, however, that in the family tree of man (Fig. 61, p. 413) the common trunk of Pithecanthropus-Sinanthropus may well be represented by giant fossil hominids of whom Meganthropus is a more advanced representative and Gigantopithecus a putatively earlier ancestral form.

dwarf femur with the same locomotor habits (Osteoborus). It would appear that teeth double the size of those of modern man would not necessarily imply legs twice as long. Gigantopithecus may have had only slightly longer and stronger leg bones than occur in modern man. Weidenreich's tentative phylogenetic suggestion is that the giant ancestral hominids may have been located in South China, or, earlier, in India. He thinks that a straight line development may have taken place from Gigantopithecus to Meganthropus, to Pithecanthropus robustus, to Pithecanthropus erectus, to Homo soloensis, to Wadjak Man, to the modern Australian. He also thinks it possible that some gigantic ancestral form may connect Sinanthropus with Gigantopithecus, although none has been discovered up to now.

The present writer, although profoundly impressed by Weidenreich's skill, erudition, and painstaking methods of research, is not convinced that the present state of the knowledge of odontology enables anyone to assign the molars of Gigantopithecus either to an ape or to a man with absolute certainty. The criteria of differentiation are not well enough established. On the whole, it seems more likely that Weidenreich is right than wrong, especially in view of the Meganthropus teeth and mandible, which are almost unquestionably human. I am disposed to accept Meganthropus according to Weidenreich's specifications but to keep the matter of Gigantopithecus in suspense until further finds confirm the Weidenreich hypothesis of his humanity or refute it.

In the succeeding portions of this book dealing with various types of fossil men and with the general question of man's ancestry, the Meganthropus-Gigantopithecus question will receive no further discussion. The reason for this is that Weidenreich's monograph (Giant Early Man from Java and South China) has been published too late to permit its utilization passim in a work already set by the printer. The reader should bear in mind, however, that in the family tree of man (Fig. 8, p. 413) the common trunk of Pithecanthropus-Sinanthropus may well be represented by giant fossil hominids of whom Meganthropus is a more advanced representative and Gigantopithecus a putatively earlier ancestral form.

your hair would depend upon the prevailing of one kind of gene over its alternate, or allele. That is called dominance.
The growth of body cells occurs by division or mitosis. Within each cell is a more or less spherical nucleus. Inside the nucleus are masses of long coiled threads which cannot ordinarily be seen because it can be colored or stained by certain dyes. When the cell is going to start the process of division, these coiled threads become thicker and it can be seen that each is really double, having been split longitudinally. They thicken and shorten, becoming sausage-shaped, V-shaped, or rod-like.

cell bodies, divide. Thus tw

Part V. Heredity and Race

The Fundamentals of Genetics

You are an animal, a vertebrate, a mammal, a primate, and a man because of your individual heredity—and for no other reason, whether you like it or not. Furthermore, the peculiar combination of physical features that makes you recognizable to your acquaintances is largely the result of the particular and probably unique assortment of hereditary factors that came together in the fertilized cell from which you developed. Half of these hereditary characters came from the germ cells of your father and half from those of your mother. These units of inheritance are called genes. Many thousands of them are involved in the determination of the gross and fine variations of your external and internal anatomy, your physiological capabilities and disabilities, your mental equipment, and nearly everything else that goes into the make-up of your corporeal and spiritual personality.

The genes, so small as to be invisible under the most powerful microscope, are not the characters themselves, but only the determiners of their earlier or later development and their ultimate form and nature. These genes are found in the nuclei of the germ cells, apparently arranged in stated order on thread-like chromosomes, which can be seen under the microscope. The chromosomes occur in pairs, the number of which is ordinarily fixed for every animal and plant species. Human beings have 24 pairs of chromosomes or 48 in all. Each pair of chromosomes, with the genes strung on it like beads, presents alternate possibilities of the ultimate form determined by the inheritance units. Thus, if the third couple of beads on a pair of these strings determines whether your hair is straight or wavy, the gene on one chromosome might be that for one type of hair and its mate on the other string that for the other hair form. Actually, the situation is more complicated than that, because it is probable that more than two factors or genes are involved in the determination of hair form. In any event, whether your hair is straight or curly depends upon what genes for hair form you have had in your chromosomes. All of your genes might be "curly," or all might be "straight," or you might have some of each, in which case the form of your hair would depend upon the prevailing of one kind of gene over its alternate, or allele. That is called dominance.

The growth of body cells occurs by division or mitosis. Within each cell is a more or less spherical nucleus. Inside the nucleus are masses of long coiled threads, made of stuff called chromatin, because it can be colored or stained by certain dyes. When the cell is going to start the process of division, these coiled threads become thicker and it can be seen that each is really double, having been split longitudinally. They thicken and shorten, becoming sausage-shaped, V-shaped, or rod-like. They are now called chromosomes and are arranged in pairs on the equatorial disk of the global nucleus. In the meantime, at each pole of this hollow globe there is a small body called a centrosome, having migrated thither after the division of a parent centrosome that was at one side of the nucleus during the resting phase of the cell. Between these polar centrosomes radiate very fine fibres, so that the whole arrangement is spindle-shaped or like two cones with their apices at the poles and their bases meeting at the equatorial disk. These spindle fibres now, in a manner of speaking, go fishing; for they draw to themselves half of each longitudinally divided chromosome, one of the identical halves going to one end, the other to the other. When the two halves have nearly reached their respective poles, the entire nuclei and the outer cell bodies divide. Thus two cells have grown out of one, and in each cell the nucleus contains the same number of pairs of chromosomes as in the original, because every original chromosome has been split longitudinally, half going to each daughter nucleus.

Since every animal begins by the union of an egg cell of the mother and a sperm cell of the father, it is evident that there must be some way of reducing the number of chromosomes in both egg cells and sperm cells to one half before fertilization. Otherwise, a fertilized egg cell would contain 48 pairs of chromosomes instead of the 24 pairs found in body cells. Actually, the germ cells mature by going through a reduction process. In the first phases of egg or sperm cell production, growth takes place by ordinary mitosis. However, in the later stage, when penultimate nuclear division takes place, each new cell gets only one of each chromosome pair (instead of a longitudinal half of each chromosome that becomes a complete replica of the original). Consequently, the sperm cell that penetrates the egg cell has only one of each of the 24 pairs of chromosomes and, similarly, the egg cell has only one of each pair. However, this is not generally a simple separation of whole chromosomes, as will be seen below. Upon fertilization the corresponding single chromosomes from each parent match up.

After multiplications of the potential germ cell by ordinary mitosis, the chromosomes appear as slender coiled threads, and then the two chromosomes belonging to a pair become closely applied to each other —practically glued together throughout their lengths. This is called "synapsis"—a Greek word that simply means "joining together." After this intimate association the members of a chromosome pair pull apart again, but in so doing they may get one of their two pairs of wires crossed (for each chromosome consists of two longitudinal strands— chromatids). Thus, when they separate, the end of one chromatid has become hitched to the end of a chromatid from the other chromosome, so that one of the two pairs of strands has swapped sections. The places where the strands of the two chromosomes have crossed are called "chiasmata"; singular, "chiasma" ("a crossing"). These crossings may affect only one of the two pairs of wires (chromatids) involved in the synapsis of the two chromosomes, or may involve both pairs. It is after this separation, when the crossings are still stuck together, that the fibre fishing-lines from the respective poles (centrosomes) hook one chromosome apiece and pull them in to the opposite ends of the cells. As a matter of fact, the nature of the spindle fibres is still uncertain, and it seems probable that the chromosomes are separated in three stages by different forces. After this reduction division in germ cell maturation, another ordinary mitosis takes place, so that the unmatched ends of the two strands of each chromosome resulting from a chiasma split away from the matched half of the chromosome. Thus, from the synapsis and a single chiasma in the reduction division with a single subsequent mitosis, there are found in 4 mature germ cells 4 chromosomes, 2 with crossovers and 2 without. Many cytologists, however, consider that the number of strands involved in a crossover is 8, 4 in each chromosome.

The laws of inheritance, discovered by Mendel, postulate pairs of unit factors (genes) that determine the ultimate development of any bodily character. If a character is determined by a single pair of factors, the germ cells of the father contribute one factor of the pair of "alleles" and those of the mother the other. The factor from the paternal germ cell may be identical with that contributed by the maternal cell, in which case the offspring has a double dose. If the parents produce in their germ cells only contrasted factors of a pair, since each parent must contribute one of whatever kind he has, the offspring gets one of each kind. If one of the contrasted factors of a pair prevails over the other and causes the development of its variation—say brown in eye color—at the expense of the variation carried by its mate—say blue in eye color—the winning factor is said to be dominant (D), the losing, recessive (R). The opposing factors are carried distinct in the germ plasm and do not blend. Such a person is of the genetic composition DR (heterozygous) for that character, since he is the result of the union of opposing factors. He produces in his own germ cells both D and R units in approximately equal numbers, but only one or the other in a single germ cell. If a person's germ cells produce only D factors or R factors, he is DD or RR—homozygous.

When persons producing, respectively, only D's and R's in their own germ cells mate, all of their offspring must be DR. When DR's mate, their factors recombine according to the laws of chance, so that the F2 (second filial) generation consists of the proportions 1 DD, 2 DR, 1 RR. This is segregation in the F2 generation and is Mendel's first law of heredity for characters controlled by a single pair of factors.

By similar chance combinations, the offspring of parents who are, respectively, DD and DR are expected to be 50 per cent DD and 50 per cent DR, whereas matings DR x RR give 50 per cent DR and 50 per cent RR. These formulae are useful in testing the results of back crosses of the F1 (first filial) generation with pure (homozygous) parental stocks. Dominance is not necessarily present in characters determined by a single pair of factors (alleles). For example, in shorthorn cattle, red crossed with white gives all roan in F1, and in the F2 generation the offspring are in the ratio of 1 red, 2 roan, 1 white. Thus the heterozygote in the F2 generation shows no dominance, but a blend. In roan, hairs of both colors are interspersed. If the two factors or alleles are represented by RR and rr and neither is dominant, evidently RR = red, Rr = roan, and rr = white.[1]

In crosses in which the character combination is determined by two pairs of factors that assort at random, the proportions obtained by segregation in the F2 generation are 9:3:3:1 when there is dominance. That means that 9 offspring out of 16 will show both dominant features, 3 the combination of one dominant with the recessive, 3 the other dominant with the recessive, and one both recessive features. Thus, if the dominants were straight and coarse hair and the recessives wavy and fine hair (a purely hypothetical example), the F2 generation should yield 9 straight, coarse; 3 straight, fine; 3 wavy, coarse; 1 wavy, fine. It is easy enough to work out this kind of formula by symbols and a checker board. Thus, if SS = homozygous straight and CC = homozygous coarse, ss = homozygous wavy, and cc = homozygous fine, and if the parents are SSCC x sscc, the F1 possibilities would be SC, Sc, sC, and sc, providing that either of the factors for hair form could be contained in the same gamete (germ cell) with either of the factors for hair texture. In the F2

[1] Snyder, *Principles of Heredity*, p. 17.

generation, the result is obtained by totting up all of the possible combinations of the meetings of these pairs of factors in the zygote (fertilized ovum).

	SC	Sc	sC	sc
SC	str.-co. SSCC	str.-co. SSCc	str.-co. SsCC	str.-co. SsCc
Sc	str.-co. SSCc	str.-f. SScc	str.-co. SsCc	str.-f. Sscc
sC	str.-co. SsCC	str.-co. SsCc	wav.-co. ssCC	wav.-co. ssCc
sc	str.-co. SsCc	str.-f. Sscc	wav.-co. ssCc	wav.-f. sscc

Similarly, the F2 ratio in a cross involving three independent pairs of factors is 27:9:9:9:3:3:3:1. The expectation for any number of pairs of independent factors can be worked out in the same way.

The character combination in an animal that is the visible result of its genetic composition is called a phenotype. The gene combination that causes the visible character combination is the genotype. In crosses involving two independent pairs of factors with dominance, as in the hypothetical case given above, there are 4 phenotypes (in this case straight-coarse, straight-fine, wavy-coarse, wavy-fine). However, the number of phenotypes in a two-factor cross may be increased to 9 when dominance is lacking in both pairs, or to 6 when dominance is lacking in one pair. Again, the number of phenotypes may be reduced to 3 or 2 because of dominance and various types of what the geneticists call epistasis. This Greek word means a "stopping" or "stoppage," and it implies that a factor of one pair stops or masks the expression of factors of another pair. Such a dominating factor is said to be epistatic to the factor it masks. But it may be recessive to its own allele. Thus, we have dominant and recessive epistasis and also duplicate dominant and recessive epistasis—all of which furnish severe headaches to the geneticist attempting to make an analysis of the results of a cross when he has the phenotypes but does not actually know the genotypes.

If we examine the germ cells of Drosophila, a kind of fruit fly that is the favorite laboratory material for the experimental geneticist, we find that the males can be distinguished from the females by the fourth pair of chromosomes (there are 4 pairs of chromosomes in Drosophila). In the females, both members of each pair of chromosomes look alike, but in the males, one of the fourth pair looks like the corresponding female pair, but the other has a hook on the end. This latter is the Y chromosome, and the other is the X chromosome. The females have two X chromosomes and the males an X and a Y. These are the sex chromosomes, and they are found also in man. In the reduction division during the maturation of the sperm cells, some sperms get an X chromosome and others a Y. When the Y cell fertilizes an ovum, it unites with the female X chromosome to make a male (XY), but when the X sperm cell fertilizes, the resulting XX combination produces a female. It has been proved that some bodily characters, known as sex-linked, are carried on the X sex chromosome (and are absent from the Y chromosome). Such characters usually appear only in the male and are recessive, for, if they were dominant, they would express themselves whether one or two doses were present, but the male has only one X chromosome, so that any recessive gene on it may show itself, whereas the female with the two X chromosomes normally has the dominant character in one of them to offset the recessive in the other. Usually, in the sex-linked features, a male who shows the condition will not transmit it to his sons or his daughters, but the latter will pass it on to about half of their sons. (Any textbook of genetics will show diagrams explaining this process. If the Y chromosome be designated as O, because it does not carry the character, and the X chromosomes as X dominant, and x recessive alleles of the character, the only individual normally showing it will be Ox—half of the males—since the other half will be OX and will have the dominant allele from their X chromosomes.)

More than 20 sex-linked characters are known in man—most of them pathological or defective conditions, such as hemophilia and red-green color blindness. Unpleasant genes to have in one's germ plasm are those known as "lethal," because when they appear in a homozygous condition (a double dose), they cause the death of the individual, usually at an early stage of development. In a heterozygous condition, they sometimes produce known abnormalities without killing. When lethals are sex-linked, they are easy to spot, even when death occurs at an early stage, since only males fall victims, because they get the sex-linked recessive. Certain defects in man are suspected of being lethals when homozygous, as, for example, a shortening of the fingers called brachyphalangy.

Instead of a single pair of genes, one on each chromosome, there may be 3 or 4, or a whole set, up to 11 or 12, that influence the development of a character one way or another. These multiple genes are probably located at one place on the chromosomes. But no single gamete (germ cell) can have more than one of these multiple alleles and no fertilized ovum (zygote) more than a pair (one on each chromosome). In this case, whichever pair of the alleles is present determines the development of the character. In such cases, one allele may be dominant over all or some of the others. This dominant allele is symbolized by a capital letter. One allele is likely to be recessive to all the others, and that is noted by a small letter in italics; the rest in the series, which may be dominant over some, recessive to others, or even blending, receive the same small letter with an appropriate superscript.

One of the most important examples of heredity controlled by three alleles is the human blood groups. There are two antigens that may be present in human blood cells. These protein substances cause clotting or agglutination when they come into contact with the antibodies in the sera of bloods that do not possess them. If you have antigen A in your red cells, however, there is no antibody against A in your serum, but rather one against B, the second antigen. There are four blood groups: O,A,B, and AB. Group O has neither antigen, and group AB has both. The blood groups are also found among the anthropoid apes and the monkeys (cf. page 46). Let A represent the gene that produces antibody A, a^B the gene that produces B, and a the gene that produces no antibody at all. A and a^B are both dominant over a, but neither over the other. The inheritance of the blood groups is then as follows, since no person has in his body cells more than a single pair of the three alleles: aa = Group O; AA and Aa = Group A; $a^B a^B$ and $a^B a$ = Group B; Aa^B = Group AB. From these possible combinations of alleles in parents, the blood groups of the children may be worked out and are of use in determining questions of paternity and in unscrambling babies whose identities have become mixed.

Sex-influenced factors are those in which the dominance of one or another allele depends upon the sex of the individual in which the character is found. They are not common in animals, and none has been found in plants. A probable example of such sex-influenced characters is ordinary pattern baldness in man. From family histories, it appears probable that BB, the double dominant, causes baldness in both sexes, but Bb makes the male bald but not the female, and bb causes baldness in neither sex. Snyder states that in human beings any character that is much commoner in men than in women and is transmitted from a father to about half of his sons is likely to be dependent upon sex-influenced factors.

Sex-limited factors are those which are capable of expression in one sex only. They are probably controlled by the sex hormones—secretions of the testis and the ovary. Secondary sexual characters are of this nature. Recent studies, especially of Drosophila, seem to show that the determination of sex itself is not a simple matter of XX chromosomes for a female and XY for a male. There seem to be practically no genes on the Y chromosome except one for fertility, but the X chromosome of Drosophila has a small region that contains a gene or genes that set sex development going. This discovery was made by breaking up the X chromosome with X-rays and studying the breeding of Drosophila in whom only fragments of one of the X chromosomes are present. Thus the locus or position of the genes for sex was determined. Furthermore, it appears that the balance of the autosomes (chromosomes other than X and Y) and the sex chromosomes is also concerned in sex determination. It is thought that there are genes in all the chromosomes that make for masculinity or femininity. A Drosophila with the two ordinary X chromosomes, but with some extra autosomes (three of each set instead of two) is not a female but an intersex—a mixture of male and female parts. Given the ordinary combinations of the sex chromosomes for male or female, an intersex or a supersex can be produced by overbalancing to a greater or less degree with an excess or deficiency of autosomes, or even of sex chromosomes. Apparently, the chromosomal balance initiates the development of the primary gonads, which then produce the sex hormones. These latter take care of sex determination from that point on. Since both birds and mammals show higher metabolic rates for the male than for the female, it is possible that environmental changes affecting the metabolic rate may upset the genic balance and condition sex determination. This seems to be fairly easy to accomplish in plants, but very difficult in vertebrates. In general, then, it appears that sex is determined by Mendelian factors that are, however, conditioned in their operation by an environmental complex.

Characters that vary continuously, such as size, weight, and skin color, were formerly considered blending and not subject to Mendelian laws of inheritance. In such features, the Fl generation shows offspring intermediate between the two parents and the F2 generation gradations from one parental extreme to the other. Such inheritance is now adequately explained by the multiple factor hypothesis, which assumes a large number of pairs of factors that are cumulative and more or less equal in their effects. By testing the F2 generation, it is possible to find out how many pairs of factors are concerned, if there are enough offspring available. If one out of 16 of this generation is like each of the original parents, the number of pairs of factors involved is 2; if one of 64, the pairs are 3; if one of 256, the number of pairs is 4; if one of 1,024, there are 5 pairs of factors. If there are 10 pairs of factors, only one of 1,048,576 individuals may be expected to reach the parental extreme, and from there on, the

chances of getting individuals attaining the parental types are practically infinitesimal. When F2 individuals go beyond the extremes of the
original parental types, it is concluded that the parental types do not
represent the full expression of the cumulative multiple factors. For example, they might be AaBBCCDd and aabBccdd, instead of AABB-
CDD and aabbccdd.

Since it is now believed that many, if not most, human characters of
the more fundamental nature are inherited through multiple factors,
the prospect of complete genetic analysis is not very favorable because
of the impossibility of experimentation and the inadequate numbers
of subjects of known genetic composition.

One of the most important principles of Mendelian inheritance is
the random assortment of factors. Such assortment can easily be tested
by back-crossing an individual heterozygous for all of the factors concerned with a pure recessive, when the heterozygotes differ from both
the pure dominants and the pure recessives of the parental generation in
the appearance of the characters concerned. Thus, if a heterozygous fruit
fly with gray body and red eyes is crossed with a recessive parent with
black body and sepia eyes, the offspring are of four types—all of the
possible combinations of body color and eye color, and all in equal proportions. This is a proof of random assortment. It is also an indication
that the genes for body color and eye color must be on different chromosomes; otherwise they would stick together—wherever the chromosome
went, each pair on it would go. If a heterozygous fruit fly with gray body
and long wings is crossed with a recessive with black body and vestigial
wings, instead of all four possible combinations there appear only black-
bodied flies with long wings and gray-bodied flies with vestigial wings.
Such factors are linked, and it is inferred that linked pairs of factors are
on the same chromosome and that each chromosome includes a linkage
group. However, when linked factors are crossed, they do not stay completely linked; a minor percentage crosses over. The implication is that
one of the two pairs of strands of homologous chromosomes has exchanged
parts for a certain portion of their lengths. Between any two pairs of factors the percentage of crossovers always remains constant and is different
from the crossover percentage for any other two pairs of factors. This circumstance permits geneticists to map the position of genes or factors on
the chromosomes of animals that lend themselves to rapid and mass breeding experiments, such as Drosophila. Theoretically, a crossover may occur
at any point in two synapsing chromosomes. If two factors on the same
chromosome are far apart, breaks or crossovers between them would
naturally occur oftener than if they are close together. Thus, on the

same chromosome, differences in the percentages of crossovers between different pairs of factors may be taken as a measure of their distance apart on the chromosome. If, in three linked genes, A,B, and C, A crosses over from B with a certain percentage, and B crosses over from C with another percentage, the crossover percentage between A and C is either the sum or the difference of these two percentages. The relative positions of A and B can then be tested experimentally. In this way, the linear relationship of genes on the chromosome is established. However, when genes are far apart on the chromosome, and a relatively large amount of crossovers between them takes place, it is always somewhat less than the sum of the percentages of intervening crossovers. The reason for this deficiency is probably the occurrence of a double crossover, or perhaps a certain rigidity of the chromosome interferes with twisting and breaking at too close intervals.

Unfortunately, all of this beautiful testing of linkages and mapping of chromosomes is up to now impracticable in man, even though a number of linkages are now known, notably those sex-linked, such as hemophilia and red-green color blindness. Since these are sex-linked, they must be carried on the sex chromosome.

Sometimes the chromosomes misbehave. Extra pairs or extra single chromosomes may occur, and these produce exceptional offspring, often supermales, superfemales, or intersexes. A piece of a chromosome may be broken off and become attached to another chromosome, sometimes of an entirely different pair. Occasionally a broken-off piece remains free and may be lost without lethal effects upon the individual, if the fragment is not too large. These are deletions, and some recessive mutations are of this nature. A broken-off end may be re-hitched to its own chromosome, but upside down, so that the order of the genes is inverted. The multiplication of the normal number of chromosome pairs may get as high as twelve or fifteen times in some plants. All of these genetic variations caused by aberrations of the chromosomes are likely to produce new types and new species and are thus important in evolution.

A chemical or physical change in the locus of a gene, potentially capable of being transmitted, is called a mutation. In order to be handed down to the next generation, the mutation has to occur in the germinal tissue rather than the somatic tissue. Most mutations are recessive to wild types, and hence a recessive mutation cannot show up in the offspring unless it has been doubled by coming through both parents. Experiments show that most genes have a low mutation rate; they are relatively stable. It is estimated that the mean life of an unchanged gene in Drosophila is something approximating 100,000 years. Two genes in man, that for hemophilia and that for epiloia (a type of mental deficiency associated with tumors of the brain and skin), are calculated to show a mutation rate of about 1 in 100,000—ten times the Drosophila frequency.

However, different genes have different mutation rates, and gene mutations may take place at any time during the life of an organism, either in somatic or germinal tissue. Apparently mutation takes place oftenest just before or during the maturation of germ cells. Loss of a gene may occur through chromosomal deletion, or breaking away, and Gates states that some recessive mutations are of this nature. Possibly a certain environmental condition is necessary in order to bring about the chemical or physical change in a gene that is a mutation, but since mutations do not usually take place in more than one gene at a time, the cause is not grossly environmental. Most mutations seem to be recessive, more or less harmful to the organism, and to produce slight visible effects or none at all. Attempts to cause mutations by variations of food, temperature, humidity, and other environmental factors have been generally unsuccessful, but, in 1927, it was discovered that the use of X-rays and other types of irradiation may greatly increase mutation rates.

It is possible that a gene is a large and complex organic molecule occupying a specific place in a group arranged in a string. If this is true, a mutation may be a rearrangement of the atoms of a molecule. Fairly recently it has been found that the salivary gland cells of the larvae of Drosophila and certain other larval tissues of two-winged flies have giant chromosomes, from 100 to 200 times longer than the ordinary chromosomes of plants and animals, which usually measure only a few micra in length (a micron is 1/1,000th of a millimeter). The study of these giant chromosomes, which appear banded under the microscope, has greatly increased knowledge of the nature of chromosomal construction, variation, and gene location. The X chromosome of the Drosophila, mapped by Bridges, shows 1,024 bands, but it is not known whether the bands, or points on them, or the non-chromatic region between the bands represent genes.

Breeds of domesticated animals are developed by the selection of a comparatively few distinguishing qualitative characters based upon gene combinations (such as coat color, coat length, etc.) and, in addition, a definite degree of development of one or more quantitative characters (such as size, and, in cattle, milk production). Quantitative characters generally depend upon large series of multiple factors. The same principles of genetics apply to plants, of which the linkage relations of many genes are known. In either plants or animals, the breeder has to get rid of deleterious mutations and combine desirable characters in the most efficient form.

Control of heredity and direction of evolution are most easily effected by selection. Natural selection picks out for survival those animals or plants that possess favorable variations which give them advantages in the struggle for existence. Artificial selection of domesticated plants or animals usually preserves certain combinations of genetic factors because they happen to suit the fancies of breeders or because they possess certain qualities of superior usefulness. The selection has to be applied to heterozygous factors that can be reassorted. When homozygous or pure lines are developed, there can be no further genetic selection, except in so far as new types may arise through mutations or chromosomal aberrations. However, wild organisms are rarely homozygous, so that most of them lend themselves to selective breeding. Selection has to be made of individuals rather than groups, and it must be made on the basis of the genotype rather than the phenotype—in the sense that it is not the appearance or qualities of the parents that count, but rather the kind of qualities and appearance that interbreeding proves them capable of transmitting to their offspring. A vigorous, homozygous type is the object of selection. Inbreeding rapidly brings about homozygosity and uncovers recessive and undesirable traits by isolating them in pure lines. These lines may then be eliminated (in subhuman animals and in plants) and the desirable, homozygous strains perpetuated. Selection creates nothing new at all; it merely effects new combinations of weakness or strength. To make selection effective, it has to be accompanied by destruction of the stocks in which undesirable characters have been genetically isolated.

Sometimes, in the first generations resulting from hybridization, the offspring are bigger and stronger than their parents. This phenomenon, known as hybrid vigor or heterosis, is possibly due to genes for growth and vigor, each dominant to its own allele for lack of such qualities. These genes are scattered on various chromosomes in linkage groups, and crosses between inbred lines may bring all the dominant genes together in a hybrid, if one strain has the vigor factors that the other lacks. Apparently, it is impossible to keep this hybrid vigor in subsequent inbred generations of the crossed lines, because the vigor factors are reassorted among the chromosomes, and recessive features are likely to crop out in the recombinations.

The fundamental characters of animal species are probably genetically homozygous, since any deviation from them would be likely to be lethal.

Normal development seemingly demands that a group receive at least one of each type of chromosome, and so it can be inferred that the genes are also necessary for development. How they effect their end products is a matter of speculation. It is probable that they provide the stimuli whereby the egg and the embryo are enabled to respond properly to various environmental conditions. It has been suggested that the genes begin to operate at the time when the ratio of cytoplasm (the material in the cell outside of the nucleus) to the nucleus in each cell is reduced to that characteristic of the species. Prior to this time, the egg, because of the inclusion of the yolk, is larger than other body cells, and it may be postulated that development up to this stage is largely dependent upon environmental factors acting upon the vegetative pole or the yolk, as contrasted with the animal or protoplasmic pole. It is further possible that the genes act as enzymes or catalysts that produce various trends or gradients in differentiation, or they may control the presence or absence and relative potency of such enzymes. Such catalytic action of enzymes in the nucleus apparently brings about the formation in the cytoplasm of pigment from a colorless amino acid by oxidation. The genes also may control the productions of the hormones that regulate growth. The analysis of relative growth rates of breadth and length by Sinnott and Durham in elongate, spherical, and disk-shaped gourds suggests that shape is also under genic control.

In short, the genetic process seems to be of the following order: (1) a normal complement of chromosomes in a normal environment; (2) an early stage of differentiation primarily imposed by the environment upon the cytoplasm (already under genic control); (3) a later and continuous process of differentiation through the action of gene substances upon the cytoplam in various trends or gradients; (4) a final assumption of the genes of the function of enzyme production, elaborating chemical substance, establishing specific metabolic rates, and modifying the rate of cell division or growth in localized areas in different directions.

Man has achieved sufficient control of his environment to modify considerably the expression of certain of his inherited characters and potentialities, although such interference with the effects of heredity in no way changes the transmission of the characters. It must be assumed also that there is an extreme range of variation of environmental modifiability in hereditarily transmitted characters. Some may be easily and profoundly changed in their expression by environmental stimuli, whereas others are little affected. The bulk of human characters of which the heredity has been studied are pathological conditions and physical abnormalities that are presumably caused by deleterious mutations. Most of these seem to be determined by single pairs of factors. In many of them, hereditary transmission is demonstrated by pedigrees, but the exact genetic analysis is lacking because of paucity of cases, ignorance of the genetic composition of lineages, and impossibility of experimentation. Even the linkages of human characters are, for the most part, only suspected and not definitely established. Such impalpable qualities as "intelligence," "temperament," and "artistic ability" are known to have a mainly hereditary basis, but their expression and degree of development obviously depends in large measure upon environment. A science of eugenics can hardly develop until far more is known of human heredity. The physical variations of hereditary origin that are used for the classification of mankind into physical groups will be discussed in succeeding sections.

Some of the difficulties of the study of human heredity arising from the impossibility of experimentation and ignorance of the genetic composition of subjects have been resolved by the application of new statistical methods to the problem. The frequencies of observed inherited traits in samples of the population are checked against the theoretical expectations based upon various postulates as to the type of inheritance, the number of factors involved, and the recessive or dominant character of this or that expression of the feature. It must be understood that under a system of random assortment, and excluding any kind of selection, a dominant gene does not increase at the expense of its recessive allele. The frequencies of the two are constant from generation to generation. Under such circumstances, the population is said to be in equilibrium with respect to two such alleles. This equilibrium can be tested by the use of the binomial expansion. If three kinds of offspring in the F2 generation conform to expectation, the homozygotes for one allele, the heterozygotes, and the homozygotes for the other allele will be in the proportion of p^2, $2pq$, and q^2 when $p + q = 1$. To put it another way, the population is in equilibrium when the proportion of heterozygotes is twice the square root of the product of the proportions of the two homozygotes. With this beginning, it is possible to proceed to test assumptions of manner of inheritance by various formulae based upon probability.

Modern students of heredity are careful to distinguish between the genetics of the individuals and the genetics of populations. The former has to do with the physico-chemical factors and the various mechanisms that give rise to hereditary variations in the individual organism. The latter deals with the effects of hereditary variations when produced and injected into populations.[2] Artificial and natural selection, various kinds

[2] Dobzhansky, *Genetics*, pp. 152 ff.

of environmental pressures, and even sociological and historical factors have a great deal to do with the survival of such hereditary variations and their effect upon the population. In other words, the genetics of populations are concerned with more than chromosomes, genes, and mutations. Environment, of one sort or another, gets into the saddle and sits there holding the reins of heredity (although the latter sometimes gets the bit in its teeth and bolts).

Population dynamics can be explored by statistical methods. We have already referred to the basic finding that the genetic equilibrium in a sexually reproducing, random breeding population where none of the three genotypes has any selectional advantage is expressed by the formula 1 AA: 2 Aa: 1 aa (or for the genes p^2, $2pq$, q^2). However, such a static condition is hardly likely to be maintained under the impact of evolutionary forces such as the selection of one genotype over another for breeding and survival, and the production of mutations.

In order to evolve, a population has to maintain its variability— either through chromosomal change or through mutation. Since most mutations are more or less harmful, natural selection tends to suppress them, but does not manage to do so entirely. A mutation disadvantageous in the environment of its origin may acquire survival value by a change of that environment; animals with deleterious variations may "get by" in spite of natural selection.

In addition to the adverse pressure of natural selection against variation, there are important chance factors that militate against the survival of mutations. If gene A mutates to a and produces one Aa individual, this mutant must mate with a normal AA and produce, according to expectation, offspring in the proportion of 1 AA: 1 Aa. However, if but two offspring are produced, in 25 per cent of cases both will be AA, in 25 per cent of cases both will be Aa and in 50 per cent of cases one AA and one Aa. Thus there is by chance a loss of 25 per cent of the mutant gene in the first generation, and the same risk is run in each succeeding generation. By the same chance, another mutation may be doubled. Therefore it is apparent that in a small population a single mutation with no selectional advantage is unlikely to establish itself. The chances of survival and extinction have been calculated by Fisher and Sewall Wright.[3] Fisher shows that if a mutation confers no advantage upon its carrier and appears in but a single individual, only 153 out of 10,000 mutants avoid extinction after 127 generations of breeding. If the mutation has a 1 per cent selective advantage, 271 of 10,000 will be retained. Wright demonstrates that, in a population of N breeding individuals, ½ N

[3] *Ibid.*, pp. 161–165.

genes either reach fixation or are lost in each generation. The smaller the size of the population, the quicker is the dispersion of variability and the attainment of genetic uniformity. Thus, in small populations, genetic homogeneity may be attained quickly by chance, and the ultimate fixation of genes and their resulting characters may be independent of any selectional advantage they confer. However, this random course of evolution would hardly be pursued in a population of breeding individuals so numerous as to discount the scattering of variation.

Since effective breeding populations in primitive human societies were probably very small, the differentiation of local physical types must have been promoted to a considerable extent by "genetic drift"—an expression covering the chance fixation or loss of genes and consequent loss of variability.

It is also possible to calculate the number of generations required for stated percentage increases of a gene that has a certain percentage of selectional advantage, whether that gene is dominant or recessive. These calculations assume that mutations do not occur; but if they do, selection takes place much more rapidly or more slowly, according to the direction of mutations—whether away from the allele favored by selection or toward it. If a dominant gene has a selectional advantage of 0.01, it requires 230 generations for its increase in the population from a frequency of 0.01 to 0.1, but only 559 generations for an increase from 1.0 to 50.0. However, it takes 90,231 generations for a dominant gene to increase from 99.0 to 99.9 per cent. It is thus apparent that, if the gene frequency is very small or very large, the rate of its increase is remarkably slow, whereas the intermediate frequencies increase rapidly. It is also possible to calculate equilibrium values for a population under varying conflicting influences of mutational rates and selectional rates.[4]

Isolating mechanisms are those that prevent the interbreeding of two populations. They play a seemingly contradictory role in evolution. Isolation is a conservative agent in that it represses variation, but, on the other hand, formation of species cannot occur without the inbreeding and the fixation of genes that isolation necessitates. This paradox can be resolved, in part, by the reservation that isolation encourages evolution only when it is not experienced so early as to cause too narrow specializations of organisms to localized environmental requirements, and when its operation is not so tardy as to permit the proliferation of many discordant gene combinations that have to be eliminated by natural selection and represent a total loss to the species.

4 *Ibid.*, pp. 218–221.

Isolating mechanisms may be either geographical or physiological. In the former case, which is apposite in the formation of human races, interbreeding is prevented solely by lack of contact. In the latter case, which would be operative, presumably, between any human group and most, if not all, ape species, the populations do not interbreed because they are confined to different ecological habitats, or have different breeding seasons, or lack mutual sexual attraction, or are prevented from mating by physical incompatibilities of their reproductive organs, or because their germ cells do not fertilize each other, or because the hybrids produced are not viable. Both of these types of isolating mechanisms have probably been of great importance in the divergence of proto-humanoid stocks from ancestral ape forms and from those leading to the present apes. Only the geographical isolating mechanism was probably operative in the differentiation of modern races within the species *Homo sapiens,* and probably between palaeoanthropic and neanthropic types of man.

Genetics and Racial Classification

Experimental geneticists have to depend upon visual observation and verbal description of plants and animals in their recording of the facts of heredity. Their inferences and deductions with respect to genes, chromosomes, and the processes of heredity are based partly upon the study of cells under the microscope (cytology) but more largely upon the gross manifestations of hereditary factors seen in the variations of organisms. These observable variations are principally those of form (morphology) and of size. Impalpable or invisible variations presumably of hereditary origin include those that may be classified broadly as physiological and psychological. The genetics of such variations are harder to study.

In their breeding experiments with plants and animals, geneticists insist upon the distinction between the phenotype (which is all that can be seen and recorded in the living organism) and the genotype (which is the sum total of hereditary factors received by the organism from its ancestors).[5] However, a geneticist can merely deduce the properties of a genotype from an analysis of the pedigree of a phenotype, or a study of its ancestors, its siblings, and its offspring. No one has ever seen a genotype, whether he be a geneticist, an anthropologist, or a mere man in the streets. The classification of organisms has to begin with phenotypes, because the nature of an animal or plant is manifest primarily through sensory perception and not through inference. When Mendel began to

[5] *Ibid.,* p. 16

experiment with garden peas, and Morgan began to breed fruit flies, these pioneers had to depend upon old-fashioned methods of taxonomy (the classification of organisms by the sum total of their morphological resemblances and differences) in order to select their experimental material. You have to be able to tell a fruit fly from a horse fly or a garden pea from a sweet pea before you can get to work upon the genetics of *Drosophila* or *Pisum sativum*. It was not until many generations of the same animals and plants had been bred and observed in the laboratories that it was possible to work with material of known genetic composition, and even now "genotypes" are known only imperfectly and with respect to a limited number from an enormous aggregate of character-producing factors. Even in the case of those Drosophila, or fruit flies, whose genetics probably occupy the attention of one hundred biologists for every one who studies human inheritance, the mapping of genes on the 4 pairs of chromosomes (as against 24 pairs in man) is far from complete.

Geneticists have neglected the study of human heredity because of the impossibility of controlled breeding experiments in such a slowly reproducing and refractory animal as man, and also because of the vast complexity of human inheritance as compared with that of simpler organisms. This situation is understandable and perhaps excusable, but it hardly justifies the supercilious attitude of the maize, rabbit, and fruit fly specialists toward the attempts at physical classification of man by the handful of physical anthropologists who work with this immensely more important subject and, at the same time, have to be responsible for the cultivation of the vast fields of human palaeontology and the comparative anatomy of man and the rest of the primate order. In my opinion, the ultimate aim and principal justification of genetic studies is their application to man, and if the geneticists are unable or unwilling to tackle this subject, they ought, at any rate, to refrain from carping at the efforts of more courageous though possibly less competent scientists to do for them the job that has to be done.

Actually, science is forced to recognize the differences in physical characteristics between the great divisions of mankind, to analyze those differences, and to elucidate their significance and their potentialities for good or for evil. For, the ordinary layman—the plain, untutored *Homo sapiens*—today and for past thousands of years has observed these gross anatomical differences between the principal groups of his kind, has drawn the generally correct inference that they are transmitted from parents to children, and has attributed to them enormous political, sociological, psychological, and biological significance, rightly or wrongly. It is obviously up to science to replace rule-of-thumb, super-ficial, and often erroneous "racial" classifications by refined and accurate categories and to substitute for the prejudices and superstitions about racial behavior and the significance of physical differences some sound body of knowledge that can be utilized for human betterment. Man is an inveterate amateur of the taxonomy of his own kind. He cannot be argued out of the habit of connecting the physical differences he sees in individuals or groups with their equally obvious variations in behavior by any set of "social scientists," however loudly and persistently they tell him that there is no difference between black and white skins apart from exposure to the sun, and no difference between the psychology of a Mongolian and a White, apart from their having grown up in the Rice Bowl and the Dust Bowl, respectively. Probably taxonomic errors and misapprehensions of the relationship of human anatomy to behavior are not ineradicable, but they cannot be corrected or removed by the mere mouthing of idealistic dogmas about human equality and of un-substantiated claims of environmental omnipotence.

Racial classifications, in so far as they are to be employed by scientists or by anybody for human betterment and the alleviation of human struggles, must conform to the ancient, natural, and, on the whole, correct procedure of taxonomy. They must be based upon observable characters of human phenotypes. Yet these classifications, if they are to be valid and meaningful, must be brought into line with the discoveries of modern genetics. If the physical groupings of mankind are assumed to be based upon combinations of inherited rather than acquired characters, it is necessary to demonstrate that the phenotypes involved do, in all probability, represent the visible manifestations of genetic factors—that behind these phenotypes are inferential genotypes which are responsible for them, in conjunction with the inevitable modifying effects of en-vironment.

The first task of the taxonomist working with man is to establish classifications that are valid phenotypically—he must devise a set of criteria that distinguish human groups, each composed of individuals who present mutual resemblances sufficiently numerous and close enough to create the impression of unity or homogeneity of type. Each of these groups must also differ from every other group in enough easily ob-servable characters to make it collectively and also individually dis-tinguishable, not by the use of intricate techniques of measurement and of statistical or biochemical analysis, but by obvious differences that strike the eye of the ordinary observer and in combination delimit separate and easily discernible types.   (A type consists of forms so nearly alike that they seem to have been struck out by the same die or cast from the same mould.)

The extent of resemblances between individuals of the same group and the breadth of difference between separate groups depend upon the number of characters used to establish group classifications. Suppose that we divide mankind into groups according to the three conventional categories of the length-breadth index of the head (long headed—below 77, medium-headed—77 to 82, round-headed—82 and above), we are likely to emerge with three groups of men, each almost completely heterogeneous except in this single criterion of head-form. Suppose, on the other hand, that we utilize five separate criteria of classification, each of which can present three distinct variations. Then the number of separate groups or the different combinations of the variations in question will be theoretically 3^5 or 243. The individuals within each of these 243 groups will not only resemble each other in distinct combinations of the variations of five characters, but will probably show numerous other similarities as a result of the linkages between the complex of identical variations selected and other physical features that have not been used in the classificatory process. Further, it is almost certain that a considerable number of the 243 mathematically possible combinations will not occur in nature, because they consist of incompatible morphological variations that cannot co-exist in an individual by any conjunction of hereditary and environmental factors. For example, it is improbable that one could find anywhere in the world an individual with a combination of black skin, blue eyes, straight hair, red hair, and a complete Mongoloid eye-fold.

It is evident, further, that by the simple process of increasing the number of physical criteria required in an identical combination in individuals, it is possible to subdivide the human population so finely as ultimately to select identical twins or even single persons with unique and exclusive combinations of physical variations.

When we have divided mankind into a smaller or greater number of physically homogeneous groups, according to the extent of the mutual resemblance that we demand of individuals constituting each single group, and under the limitations of the existence of these groups in nature, we have next to inquire into the significance of the groupings established. Theoretically, similarities or identities of phenotypes may be due to any one of three causes, or to any two of them, or to all three in combination. These causes are: (1) chance, (2) heredity, (3) environment.

If the several distinct variants of a morphological feature occur at random or as independent events, either singly or in their combinations with variants of other morphological features, the resulting type combinations may be considered to be the result of chance and to be governed by the laws of probability. In inheritance, Mendelian factors segregate and combine in accordance with the laws of chance. At fertilization, the chances are even that the sex of the embryo will be male or female, because the sperm has one X chromosome and one Y chromosome, while the egg has two X chromosomes. It is to be expected that, in one half of cases, a female X chromosome will unite with a male Y chromosome to make a male, and, in the other half, a female X chromosome will unite with a male X chromosome to make a female. However, the greater the number of variants involved in a combination, the larger will be the possible number of distinct combinations and the smaller the probability that any specific combination will be formed. The odds against chance occurrence rise with increasing complexity of the combination. An elaborate combination of specific morphological variants may occur in a few individuals by chance, but identical occurrences of such elaborate combinations in large segments of a population are very unlikely to be due to the effect of chance alone. Thus, in selecting the physical combinations to be used for classifying mankind, we diminish the probability that our subclasses are the random assortments of chance by increasing the number of criteria employed in combination to distinguish a class.

The essential characters of any animal, morphological or physiological, may safely be assumed to be due to hereditary factors. For example, man inherits a spinal column from his vertebrate ancestry, flat nails and stereoscopic vision from his primate ancestry, non-opposable great toes from his human ancestry, etc. Ordinarily, however remote may be the ancestral derivation of a character that occurs in man, the range of its variation is limited by the nature of the genes that are peculiar to the human species. Within that range of specific variation, the ultimate differences in phenotypes are, to some extent, genetically determined but subject to modification by the impact of environment upon the individual animal.

Hereditary factors—the genes—endow the individual animal with restricted potentialities of development, and the full realization of these potentialities, or the prevention of their fullest expression, must often depend upon the environment to which the animal is subjected. Thus, hereditary factors probably set limits of body size, beyond which the animal is not viable, but it is clear enough that any animal can be dwarfed by a radical undernourishment. Bodily weight relative to stature is probably controlled by inherited factors when adequate nutrition and sufficient muscular activity have established functional equilibrium approaching an optimum. However, no hereditary tendency to obesity can be realized on a semi-starvation diet. Whereas gross size and weight are perhaps the most obvious examples of characters that are strongly affected in their phenotypical expression by environment, it seems improbable that any hereditary character is completely emancipated from environmental interference.

Although it is impossible to disentangle the interlocking hereditary and environmental forces that have produced the phenotype, it is both desirable and feasible to base physical classifications of man upon features that are not subject to radical change during the lifetime of the individual as a result of environmental fluctuations. Since the theory of evolution postulates that new species have developed from older species by the selection of inherited variations, physical classifications of animals ought to delimit groups of individuals having features that indicate a common descent. Characters that are easily modifiable during the life of the individual by changes of diet, climate, and of bodily activity tend to confuse the relationships that we seek to trace. However, if we should attempt to classify man physically by using characters conceived to be controlled mainly by environment rather than by heredity, we should be hard put to it to find enough of such characters to establish any sort of meaningful groupings. Ordinarily, environment only restricts or modifies the expression of characters derived through heredity; if it creates new characters, it probably does so only by bringing about chemical changes in genes that result in mutations. In other words, as a creative force environment operates exclusively through the mechanisms of heredity, whether in stimulating genic change or in selecting for survival. The mechanisms of heredity are a sort of biological constant; the influences of environment upon them are a biological variable.

It is easy enough to describe in general terms the conditions that make for physical differentiation in man and ultimately may result in the evolution of new species. They are the isolation of populations and the intercommunication of populations, in the order named. A human or protohuman group wanders into some geographical area where it is cut off by distance or by some physical barrier from other such groups. There follows genetic isolation or inbreeding. If the isolated population is small, a certain proportion of genetic variations will be lost by chance. Hereditary variability will be reduced and genes fixed by chance in such a small inbred population. Whether the isolated population is small or large, natural selection is likely to operate constantly to insure the survival of certain variations or types particularly adapted for the physical environment of that circumscribed habitat and to eliminate those least fitted for it. Possibly, the peculiar conditions of certain physical environments may bring about the chemical changes in genes that originate and control the direction of mutations.

Obviously, the longer the geographical and genetic isolation, and the more specialized the physical environment, the more homogeneous and physically peculiar the evolving group will become. There are also certain social anthropological factors that must make for the restriction of variability in small and isolated human populations. In some primitive tribes, female infanticide is rather extensively practiced, presumably as a measure to restrict the size of the group in an area that cannot support a population increase. Such a measure is sometimes accompanied by polyandry—a form of marriage in which one woman is married to several men—often brothers. It is clear that such an institution would restrict physical variability in the group to an inordinate degree. The same effect is produced by the much commoner practise of polygyny—a type of marriage in which a man has more than one wife, usually resulting in a certain proportion of unmated males. Other primitive marriage institutions that similarly restrict variability and hence tend to produce homogenous and physically peculiar groups are the sororate and the levirate. In the former, a husband successively marries sisters, and, in the latter, the widow is married by a surviving brother.

We may assume then that the initial differentiation of mankind into distinctive physical groups has been brought about by the interaction of hereditary and environmental factors operating under conditions of isolation over protracted periods. Such groups may be called, for the moment, primary races.

The secondary differentiation of races is brought about by renewed communication of populations following upon the periods of isolation that have resulted in the fixation of various primary races. Owing to population pressure within original geographic areas of physical differentiation, or because of unfavorable changes in the local environment, or through improved methods of transportation, or for a variety of other reasons that need not be enumerated, one genetically specialized and more or less fixed population impinges upon the territory of another, and intermixture or hybridization takes place. The range of genetic variability is at once extended, and a whole assortment of new physical types arises, most of them intermediate between the types of the parental stocks, but in general presenting new mosaics of features inherited from one or the other. If there follows upon these primary intermixtures another period of isolation and inbreeding, there is ultimately formed a stabilized blend of characters that is distinct from that of either of the primary races contributing to the initial admixture. Such a blend is a secondary race. It may simulate or reproduce in many of its combinations types that occur much earlier in undifferentiated human stocks. In the study of the remains of fossil man, particularly, this similarity of early undifferentiated types to the recombinations effected later by the hybridization of primary races gives rise to many disagreements as to interpretation, depending upon different opinions as to the antiquity of the formation of primary races by isolation. In this process of the formation of secondary races through intermixture, individual offspring within a single family may show quite different racial resemblances. These replicas of earlier racial strains that have arisen by recombination of characters out of the ancestral pool of variations also occasion many problems of interpretation. They will have to be discussed at a later stage of our presentation.

At this point, having recognized primary and secondary races, it is high time to come to grips with the question of the terminology of our physical classifications of varying fineness.[6]

Zoologists, in classifying animals, fling about families, genera, and species like drunken sailors scattering their wages. These terms connote little more than relationship based upon morphological features. Families are groups of animals of common descent, the members of which bear to each other fundamental structural resemblances. Genera are smaller groups within the families, and the members of a genus are more like and more closely related to each other than they are to animals belonging to any different genus. The species is merely another splitting up of the genus into still smaller, more similar, and more nearly related groups. Varieties or races constitute a still further subdivision. Linnaeus gave to the term "species" a definite conception of fixity when he formulated the aphorism *species tot sunt diversae, quot diversae formae ab initio sunt creatae*—"just so many species are to be reckoned as there were forms created at the beginning." According to him a species was a sort of eternal biological verity—immutable, objective, requiring only to be discovered and named. Darwin in *The Origin of Species* rejected the objective concept of species, not only because he did not believe in special creations, but also because he

[6] The larger part of this section has been extracted from a vice-presidential address of the author to Section H of the American Association for the Advancement of Science, "Methods of Racial Analysis," 1926.

could not satisfy himself as to the existence of any dependable criteria whereby a group of animals could be ranked as a genus, given the less important classification of a species, or degraded into a variety. An attempt to distinguish as a physiological criterion of species the ability to interbreed without loss of fertility is futile, since many forms universally recognized as species produce fertile hybrids with other species. So the term "species" is little more than an artificial rank in classification, a label for a pigeonhole of a certain size into which may be thrust conveniently subjects closely related to each other in form and by origin. Hence, the modern systematist has no qualms about the recognition of a new species, providing it is sufficiently distinct from those already known; he does not feel as if he were interfering with the works of the Creator in so doing.

In dealing with man, however, anthropologists have usually been very chary in their use of zoological terms of classification. Usually all human types, extinct and recent, except, perhaps, Pithecanthropus erectus, have been included in the family Hominidae. In the matter of species subdivision, such archaic and apelike forms as Neanderthal man, Heidelberg man, Sinanthropus, and Eoanthropus have usually been assigned separate specific rank and have sometimes been elevated to the grade of a genus. Everything seems to depend upon the systematist's idea as to the distinctness of the form he describes and its nearness or remoteness of relationship to other human types. Obviously, this is a very subjective and arbitrary procedure. All existing forms of man are usually included in one species, *Homo sapiens,* although the differences between the several races are quite as marked as usually serve to distinguish species in other animals. The purely academic nature of any discussion as to the unity or diversity of species in modern groups of men makes it a sheer waste of time. We avoid difficulties by talking about "races."

Even the term "race" as applied to man is commonly employed with no accurate and well defined meaning. One often sees references to the "White race," the "Jewish race," the "Latin race," the "Irish race." Such indiscriminate use of the word "race" implies a confusion of criteria. To speak of the "White" race is to assume that race is a matter of skin pigmentation; to refer to the "Jewish race" is to differentiate race on a basis of religion; a "Latin race" implies a linguistic criterion, and finally any reference to an "Irish race" must mean a race characterized either by geographical position or, failing that, by temperament. Such confusions of usage are usually confined to the non-anthropological writing public. All anthropologists agree that the criteria of race are physical characters.

Years ago I formulated the following definitions of race, which seem to me to require but one important revision as a result of subsequent studies either in human taxonomy or in genetics.

A race is a great division of mankind, the members of which, though individually varying, are characterized as a group by a certain combination of morphological and metrical features, principally non-adaptive, which have been derived from their common descent.

A primary race is one which has been modified only by the operation of evolutionary factors, including the selection of its own intrinsic variations and of the modifications, adaptive or non-adaptive, possibly caused by environmental stimuli.

A secondary or composite race is one in which a characteristic and stabilized combination of morphological and metrical features has been effected by a long-continued intermixture of two or more primary races within an area of relative isolation.

However, some amplification of the above definitions is desirable in order to provide names for smaller physical groupings within secondary and primary races. The processes of physical differentiation do not stop with the formation of great groups of mankind such as Negroid, Mongoloid, and White, nor yet with the secondary races derived by the stabilization of their intermixtures. A great primary race, even without modification by intermixture with other primary races, may go on differentiating by precisely the same processes of isolation, inbreeding, and subsequent resumption of communication and interbreeding. Thus new types are formed, which, when they occur in substantial numbers and localized within certain areas, are really incipient races and may conveniently be called subraces. The crossing of subraces within the same primary racial grouping results in new composite subraces or reversions to the parental, more generalized primary racial type. A secondary subrace may also be formed by the same methods. Finally, a subrace may be modified by admixture with another subrace which has been derived from quite a different primary grouping. So the process goes on and on. Thus we have the following terminological outline:

Primary Races (Differentiated by early geographical and genetic isolation, by the loss of some genes and fixation of others, by mutations, by inbreeding, and by selection)
    (a) Primary Subraces—formed by precisely the same processes within the breeding populations of primary races; individually, breeds.
    (b) Composite Primary Subraces—formed by the intermixture of primary subraces: individually, interbreeds
Secondary Races (formed by the stabilization of blends of two or more primary races)

(a) Second Subraces—formed by evolutionary processes operating within a secondary race
(b) Composite Secondary Subraces

When specialized phenotypes of a primary race occur in very small groups or in sporadic individuals, I propose to call them breeds, reserving the term "primary subrace" for a stabilized and geographically extensive phenotypical group. Similarly, for small groups or individual types deriving from the intermixtures of two separate subraces within the same primary or secondary racial population, I suggest the term "interbreeds." The term "hybrid" would then be restricted to types of individuals or groups arising from the crosses (unstabilized) between primary races (or their more differentiated derivative groups) or between primary and secondary races. In the latter case, such hybrids may represent back crosses, if the secondary race contributing to the mixture already carries a strain of the primary race with which it remixes.

This terminology, which may seem regrettably complicated, is not derived from theory, but merely from the necessity of assigning distinctive names to the various phenotypical groups of man that occur in nature, with such names suited to their presumptive genetic origins. The use of terms here proposed differs from that previously employed by me principally in that I have formerly recognized three principal divisions of modern mankind—White, Negroid, and Mongoloid—as groupings of a higher taxonomic or zoological order than races, without designating these great groupings as subspecies or species. Since we know that all of these great subdivisions interbreed without diminution of fertility, and since, indeed, there are no such profound morphological and physiological differences between Mongoloids, Negroids, and Whites, as would seem to justify the implication of any very great and geologically ancient genetic discontinuity between these three groups, it would seem preferable to recognize them simply as different races. Then, because the differences between the various subgroupings within the three great or primary races are obviously more recent and quantitatively and qualitatively less than exist between the primary races respectively, it becomes necessary to relegate them to the subrace category. This terminological degradation of human physical groups in no wise changes the groups themselves. I think it clarifies and even simplifies matters by assigning to each successively smaller and more nearly related group a name more fitted to what we know of its genetic and generally evolutionary origin. It also has the advantage of agreeing with the universal non-anthropological use of the term race as applied to White, Negroid, and Mongoloid divisions of mankind, and avoids the confusion of using the same term to designate lesser and more restricted subdivisions such as Alpine, Nordic, and Mediterranean. It reduces the latter terminologically to a status that is more appropriate to their biological importance and taxonomic rank.

The characters that may be used for the establishment of physical groupings of mankind are either morphological (anatomical), or physiological, or both. Nearly all of the characters at present available for classificatory purposes are in the morphological category. They may be subdivided, according to methods that have to be used in studying them, into attributes and variables. Attributes are characters that appear to vary discontinuously so that they fall into distinct descriptive categories, such as presence and absence, in the case of eye-folds, and, in the same character, median, external, or internal, or all three together, according to position and extent. Similarly, eye color may be described by shades: black, dark brown, blue-brown, gray, blue, etc. In some cases, the descriptive categories connote form—as in the case of the nasal profile: straight, concave, convex, etc. These morphological attributes are ordinarily incapable of metric expression in our present state of knowledge. They may be observed and classified, often with comparative ease, but they are hard and sometimes impossible to measure. As contrasted with these attributes, we have the continuously varying features—variables—such as dimensions and indices (the expressions of one dimension in percentage of another). One of the principal advantages of the use of attributes, or discontinuous morphological variants, is that they spring to the eye; they are obvious. They lend themselves easily to description for the purpose of taxonomy or genetic analysis. In their inheritance according to Mendelian laws, dominance is often manifested; sometimes only one or two pairs of factors or alleles are responsible for the different variations. It is this sort of characters that has been used so successfully in exploring the genetics of fruit-flies and of many attributes of domesticated animals. However, there are certain difficulties in the use of such morphological attributes for classificatory purposes. The mathematics of attributes is difficult and tricky, as soon as one goes beyond simple counting of noses and reckoning of percentages. Again, many apparent morphological attributes that seem to fall easily into neat and separate categories are really only superficially discontinuous in their variation. Actually, they may shade into each other by almost imperceptible gradations, so that the verbal pigeonholing of them is often an artificial and precarious process. Descriptive classification is often subjective and unprecise. It is likely to be a crude substitute for measurements that cannot be made through lack of knowledge and proper techniques.

On the other hand, straightforward dimensions and calculations of indices appeal to the technician because they are capable of precise numerical expression and of easy mathematical elaboration. The main difficulty with them lies in the fact that most crude dimensions seem to be controlled genetically by multiple factors, often without dominance, so that in inheritance they give the specious effect of being blended rather than the result of particulate, Mendelian heredity. It is easy enough to calculate the arithmetical mean of a measurement and to express it in millimeters, but it is extraordinarily hard to ascertain the genetic significance of different values of such means. Again, measurements of gross size are probably much more strongly affected by purely environmental factors than are the most of qualititative attributes. This, at least, is true of such measurements as stature, weight, length of bodily segments, etc.

Indices, the tabulation of one measurement in terms of another, give some indication of form. Thus, if the maximum breadth of the head is less than 77 per cent of its length, we describe the head as dolichocephalic (long-headed) etc. However, an index is an extremely crude and imperfect expression of form, and its genetic significance is even more difficult to ascertain than is that of a simple dimension. Because measurements are easy to make and there is no end of the indices that may be derived from them, and because it is possible to play all sorts of mathematical games with them, anthropometrists, and particularly those who work with skulls and bones, have often formed the habit of depending almost exclusively upon arrays of averages of measurements and the calculation of statistical constants in their attempts to describe human groups and to find out how they differ. But these differences in arrays of means do not usually lend themselves to any precise genetic interpretation.

In human taxonomy it is, therefore, best to depend primarily upon combinations of qualitative attributes, which have easily observable variations that are obviously inherited, with only secondary reliance upon such variables as size and the percentage relation of one dimension to another.

An ancient and persistent fault in methods of the study of the physical characteristics of human groups has been the habit of hypothecating "types" or "races" from isolated means of measurements and indices, together with the modes (or most frequent occurrences) of such attributes as hair color, eye color, skin color, etc. For example, we measure a population and reckon that the average stature is 172 cm. (which is tall), and the average cephalic index at 75 (which is dolichocephalic). Suppose, then, that 75 per cent of this population have dark hair (medium brown to black) and 60 per cent have dark eyes (brown to black). According to this method, which ought to be obsolete, but is not entirely so, it would be concluded that the population in question consists principally of a racial type that is tall, long-headed, dark-haired, and dark-eyed. The assumption that the average metric characters and modal morphological features of a population are associated in the majority of the individuals constituting the population ought to be verified or refuted by the actual counting of occurrences of combinations in individuals. The sorting out of such individual combinations, previously an almost hopeless task, has now been rendered easy by the use of punch cards and mechanical sorting and tabulating apparatus. We cannot be sure of the phenotypic composition of a population until the type combinations have been observed and tabulated in individuals as combinations and not as isolated traits.

In the earlier edition of this work, I made the following statement:

If race implies the common possession of certain variations as a result of the same ancestry, significant racial criteria should be based principally upon non-adaptive bodily characters. No bodily characters are absolutely unmodifiable, but certain organs are more or less stabilized in their functions, and the less important these functions are, the greater is the probability of hereditary variations manifesting themselves unimpeded and unmodified in such organs. Heredity runs riot in indifferent variations and atrophied organs. The very insignificance of certain features, such as the form of the hair or the thickness of the lips, insures their hereditary transmission in the absence of adaptive modifications that have survival value. The human foot, on the contrary, is rigorously adapted and modified for support and locomotion in all varieties of man, and the practically identical requirements tend to obscure and obliterate any racial variations that may have existed, or to subordinate them to such variations as may be due to the habits of going barefoot or shod.

I then proceeded to list three classes of morphological and metrical variations in man: (1) traits that are apparently "non-adaptive" and can be used safely in racial classification; (2) traits that are inherited but subject to considerable environmental modification, which may be used with caution; (3) traits so radically affected by environmental factors that they ought not to be used as racial criteria.

This insistence upon the use of "non-adaptive" characters in human taxonomy now seems to me to be impractical and erroneous. In the first place, we cannot legislate environmental forces out of participation in the formation of human groups merely because similar adaptations occurring in different stocks tend to confuse our reckonings of descents. One of the most potent factors in human differentiation is natural selection, which is simply the environmental sifting of hereditary variations or acquired modifications so as to permit the survival of individuals with characteristics that have adaptive value. There are doubtless many human traits of taxonomic value that are indifferent, "non-adaptive," and without survival value, but these cannot be employed exclusively in classifying human groups, if we want natural groups that are objective and utilizable and phenotypically recognizable. We cannot, for example, disregard skin color, which can hardly be claimed as a "non-adaptive" character. Again, mutations are most important in human differentiation and, although these originate presumably through environmental stimuli of the germ plasm and are not ordinarily of adaptive value, it is clear enough that such mutations as happen to have some survival or adaptive value are more likely to be perpetuated than those that are either disadvantageous or indifferent.

Actually, we have very little knowledge of the "adaptive" or "non-adaptive" value of most hereditary physical variations and are hardly in a position to place them finally in one category or the other. Further, it is wholly possible that certain hereditary variations, as, for example, head form, that seem to us to have no adaptive value, may be genetically linked with constitutional, physiological characters that have definite survival value and may consequently share in their preferential selection. All that we can do is to avoid, as far as possible, the use of acquired modifications in establishing racial or other taxonomic groups that are supposed to indicate community of descent. An acquired modification is a change in the form of an organ or a variation that is directly due to function as exercised during the life of the individual, or to atrophy of function, or to pathology. Acquired modifications are not supposed to be heritable. We can go a little farther and exclude from any but very subsidiary use, in the classification of human groups for purposes of tracing ancestry, characters that may be primarily controlled by hereditary factors, but are subject to obvious and extensive interference by environment, such as stature, weight, and other variables involving proportions and size.

It would be pleasantly satisfactory to state that we shall employ as taxonomic criteria only such characters as are known to be rigidly controlled by heredity, and, further, of which the method of inheritance is so far established that we know the number of genes involved and the exact method of their operation, and hence may talk about genotypes. Such knowledge is not available for man with respect to any but a few and, for the most part, taxonomically unutilizable characters.

Before we can establish a classification of racial groupings, the several characters or criteria that are used for this purpose must be discussed critically. Their different variations must be described and the extent to which they are affected by certain factors that are irrelevant to taxonomy must be examined. Many hereditary anatomical features are profoundly altered during the growth of the individual from birth to maturity and in the process of aging, and so are also body proportions and body size. For this reason, the anthropological taxonomist often prefers to utilize only mature, but not yet senile, individuals as the standard subjects from whom to establish characteristic racial differences. Many very notable racial features do not express themselves fully until adult years are reached and tend to become blurred or even obliterated in old age. Sexual differences in racial features also have to be taken carefully into consideration. For example, the amount of beard and body hair (as contrasted with head hair) is quite important in racial classification but cannot be used in classifying females, because they normally have no beards, whatever their race, and very scanty body hair. Generally speaking, males appear to exhibit a fuller development of features useful for racial classification than females, because the latter are less variable and usually retain more infantile characters. However, some few racial characters are better developed in females than in males, or even limited to the fair sex. For example, the shape of the breast in fully mature females whose breasts have not fallen or shrivelled as a result of prolonged suckling of infants or old age, or both, is of some utility in racial classification. Naturally, we cannot utilize this feature if we confine our survey of racial characters to males. Steatopygia, an enormous accumulation of fat on the buttocks and the sides of the thighs, which is racially characteristic of the Bushmen-Hottentots, is alleged to occur sporadically in the Negritos or pygmies and seems to have been prevalent among some of the peoples who inhabited the caves of Europe in the Upper Palaeolithic period. However, this feature is hardly perceptible in the males of the races that possess it. It is really an especial hereditary variation of a secondary sexual character.

In the case of each physical variation that we intend to use for racial classification, we have to consider also the evidence as to the extent it may be modified in the lifetime of the individual by sundry non-hereditary agencies such as use and disuse (leading to hypertrophy and atrophy), state of nutrition and often nature of diet, exposure to sunlight, and changes in temperature and humidity. The more easily anatomical characters fluctuate as a result of these generally environmental and functional influences, the less reliable they are for taxonomic use.

Finally, it is necessary to survey the evidence as to the heritability of any feature used in the classification of man into human groups. Of course, we start off with the utilization of characters that, as a matter of common observation, are known to pass along from parents to offspring and that exhibit easily discernible variations, such as thickness of the lips; color of the skin, the hair, and the eyes; form of the hair. In the past, most anthropological workers on race classification were forced to content themselves with the general conclusion that this or that racial criterion seems to be utilizable because, in the main, its several variations are determined by heredity and not by environment. They could not go any farther than this because studies of the inheritance of the features in question had not been made. The science of genetics practically came into being with the rediscovery, in 1900, of Mendel's forgotten work on garden peas, which established the laws of heredity. However, it is hardly possible to assert that a science of human genetics yet exists. There have been made, to be sure, many studies of the inheritance of various diseases and malformations and not a few efforts at ascertaining the genetics of the ordinary anatomical characters that are used for racial classification. Unfortunately, very few of these latter studies are conclusive, apparently because of the multiple factors usually concerned, in addition to the difficulty of experimentation. All that the anthropologist can do, even now, is to summarize what little is known of the genetics of the racial criteria he employs.

The Physical Tests of Race

SKIN COLOR

The layman has always used skin color as the main basis of his classification of man into races. He talks about "the White race," "the Yellow race," and "the Black race." The anthropologist employs many more criteria of race, but he also uses skin color as one of the most important distinguishing characteristics and has a great deal of difficulty in trying to deal with it scientifically. First, he must ascertain the sources of skin color and the distribution of various pigments in different parts of the body. Then it is essential to know something of the biochemistry of skin pigmentation, to what extent and how it is inherited and acquired in the lifetime of the individual. Further, there is a need for an appraisal of the variation of intensity of pigmentation in different human groups.

Recently, spectrophotometry has been made the basis of an objective and accurate measurement of the color of the living human skin.[7] Colori-

[7] Edwards and Duntley, "Pigments and Color," pp. 1–33.

metric values can be computed from the spectrophotometric curves and the analysis by wave length permits identification of the substances that give rise to skin color and some estimate of their quantity. The sources of skin color are five pigments and an additional optical effect. The pigments are melanin; an allied, diffuse substance, melanoid; carotene; reduced hemoglobin; and oxyhemoglobin. The optical effect is known

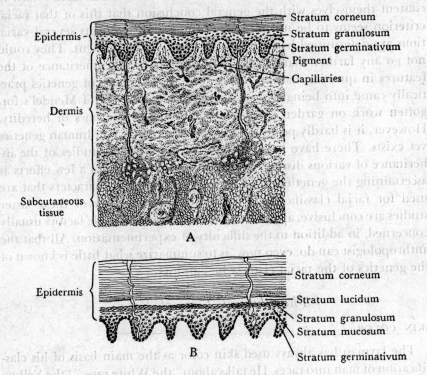

Fig. 62. A, diagrammatic microscopic section through the skin of a heavily pigmented person. B, enlargement of the epidermal layers of same. (Modified from Martin and other sources by permission of Gustav Fischer.)

as "scattering." In order to understand these sources and their combined effect, we must know something about the structure of the skin and the underlying tissues.

The skin is composed of two main layers, the outer cuticle or epidermis, and the true skin (dermis or corium) (Fig. 62). There is no blood supply to the epidermis. It varies in thickness in different parts of the body, reaching its maximum on the palms of the hands and the soles of the feet. The outermost stratum of the epidermis is called the horny layer (stratum corneum). It is transparent and scaly. Below the stratum corneum is a clear layer of closely packed cells (the stratum lucidum). Next comes the granular layer (stratum granulosum), composed of two or three layers of flattened cells, perhaps in a transitional stage between the protoplasmic cells of the layer below and the horny cells of the superficial layers. Then follows the mucous layer (stratum mucosum), consisting of rounded or polyhedral cells, which are soft, opaque, and granular. Fine fibrils connect these cells, and between them the lymph flows. In the intercellular spaces may be found pigment granules. At the base of the mucous stratum are columnar cells, constituting the germinative layer (stratum germinativum). These are attached to the basal membrane which is moulded into the papillae, minute conical eminences of the true skin or dermis. Most of the pigment that gives to the skin its color is in the cells of this stratum and of the mucous layer just above it.

The true skin (corium or dermis) includes two main layers of connective tissue with elastic fibres, blood-vessels, lymphatics, and nerves. The superficial or papillary layer consists of numerous minute, conical, sensitive, and highly vascular eminences received into pits in the under surface of the epidermis. The papillae are few in the least sensitive parts of the body, but in the palms and soles they are large and numerous, and are arranged in parallel curved lines, forming the ridges seen on the free surface of the skin. Each ridge consists of two rows of papillae between which the sweat glands pass to open on the summit of the ridge. Within each papilla is a capillary loop furnishing the blood supply, and in some cases tactile corpuscles. The lower or reticular layer of the dermis consists of interlacing bands of fibrous and elastic tissue and connective tissue corpuscles. Between the bands are fat globules and the sweat glands. Below the reticular layer is the subcutaneous connective tissue containing fat.

The most important skin pigment is called melanin ("black substance") and consists of very dark brown or black granules closely packed together within the cells, but not involving the nuclei. Since most of the pigment is in the deeper layers of the epidermis, the blood supply of the dermis beneath cannot show through and impart a ruddy color to the skin unless the pigment of the epidermis is sparse. If there is very little pigment in the mucous layer and the germinative layer, the skin appears white, or, if the blood supply is abundant, ruddy. When the pigment is thicker, the skin appears yellowish, brown, or black, according to the amount present. In heavily pigmented peoples, the granules lie mostly within the cells, but in newly born infants and in the lightest colored parts of the body in adults, pigment granules are found more commonly between the cells. In weakly pigmented Europeans, there are only a few granules of melanin in the cells, but in very dark races, the cells of the deepest portion of the stratum germinativum are stuffed with granular pigment. In the darkest parts of the body in the White race and in most parts of the body in Negroes, pigment is also found in the cells of the horny layer.

The pigment granules individually vary in color from yellow to black, but, in the main, skin color is determined by the amount rather than by this variation in color of the granules. Nor is the pigment evenly distributed—light and dark spaces occur even in the blackest races. It is found not only in the epidermis or cuticle but also in the underlying true skin. Here it occurs mostly within the cells, and its amount is proportionate to that in the epidermis, although much less abundant and more sporadic. In the darkest parts of the body of brunet Europeans, pigment may usually be found in the dermis, but it is often absent in the lightest colored individuals. In any case, it usually does not affect skin color.

The blue birth-marks often seen on the skin of the sacral region in Mongoloids and similar blue birth-marks found in various parts of the bodies of Europeans are usually caused by large pigmented cells in the lower part of the true skin (dermis). The blue tinge is imparted by the brown pigment granules showing through the imperfectly transparent, superficial layers of the skin.

Melanotic pigment is not confined to the skin. It is found in the pia mater (the inner covering of the brain), in the eye, in the inner ear, in the suprarenal glands, and in the mucous membranes.

Melanin occurs in the skin in discrete granules, and the darker the race the more numerous are the particles through which the light passes, thus producing the same effect as if the melanin were in solutions of increasing concentrations. In primary or native pigmentation, the normal deposition of melanin is controlled by constitutional and racial factors and is largely responsible for the differences between blond and brunet Whites, between Whites and Negroes, and regional variations in pigmentation as exemplified in the melanization of eyelids, nipples, and scrotum. Secondary or acquired pigmentation forms in response to exposure to light and gradually disappears after the stimulus is removed. Its deposition depends upon the ease with which the light can penetrate the epidermis and also upon the ability of the individual to react to the light stimulus. In very dark-skinned persons, the primary melanin layer is so heavy that it requires strong exposure to bring about the reaction, and in very blond Whites the light penetrates with ease, but the reactive ability is minimal. Brunet Whites, who tan easily, are in an intermediate position. Freckling is merely tanning in spots.

The skin of women is usually poorer in melanin than that of men, but in both sexes the regional differences are similar. They are, in decreasing order of intensity: nipples and areolas, external genitals and perinaeum, axillae, eyelids, back of the neck, front of the neck and face, back, thorax and abdomen, extensor surfaces of the limbs, flexor surfaces of the limbs, palms, soles. Melanin is responsible not only for yellow, brown, and black skin color, but also for bluish effects when heavy masses of melanin underlie a layer highly diffusible to light but of a neutral color. This last phenomenon is observable in shaven-haired regions, sometimes in the eyelids, the axilla, and the sacral patch or so-called "Mongoloid spot."

Edwards and Duntley found that the spectrophotometer revealed a diffuse pigment in the epidermis arising from the disintegration of melanin particles. They called this derivative "melanoid." Its absorption characteristics in the spectrophotometric curve indicate that it makes the skin a yellow of higher purity than that produced by melanin. Its amount in any region depends upon the concentration of melanin and the thickness of the epidermis in which the derived melanoid is stored, especially the stratum corneum, which is wholly made up of stored dead epithelium. Melanoid is not found in appreciable quantities in regions where the stratum mucosum is heavy and the stratum corneum thin. The most important blood pigment is hemoglobin, and in arterial blood its characteristic absorption bands and transmission peaks are manifested in the curves as oxyhemoglobin. Venous blood shows the presence of reduced hemoglobin, imparting a bluish rather than a reddish tinge. The body areas rich in arterial blood are the red parts of the head and neck, nipples, palms, soles, parts of the buttocks, and the extensor surfaces of the joints. Reduced hemoglobin is particularly marked where the veins are dilated and the blood flow is sluggish—the dorsum of the foot (instep), lower parts of the trunk, scrotum, loins, and buttocks (especially in males).

Another skin pigment is carotene, which is a coppery lipochrome particularly noticeable in female subjects and found in the dermal and subcutaneous fat, and also in places where the stratum corneum of the epidermis is especially thick. Bodily carotene is derived from ingested food, and, therefore, individual variations may be due to dietary habits.

"Scattering" is an optical effect produced by the turbidity or cloudiness of both layers of the epidermis but especially the mucosum. It tends to raise the blue end of the reflected spectrum and to lessen redness of the skin. It accounts in large part for bluish effects in certain areas, because light transmitted through a turbid or scattering medium involves the longer wave-lengths (red), while that which is reflected or scattered back is of the shorter wave-lengths (blue). This phenomenon accounts for the blue Mongoloid spot, the blue of the shaven male cheek, and (probably) for the blue of eyes. It occurs in regions where melanin is clumped in the dermis or subcutaneous tissue, because the pigment masses absorb most of the impinging light and prevent ordinary transmission to, and reflection from, the deep dermis and the subcutaneous tissue.

The lighter color of the female skin is due to its containing less blood and melanin than that of the male. Carotene is also present in much larger amounts in the female. However, racial variations are said to be caused entirely by differences in the amount of melanin and derivative melanoid. The darker subjects studied by Edwards and Duntley showed no increase in carotene. In increasing order of melanin content, the Japanese came first, then Hindus, mulattos, and finally Negroes. In all of these dark-colored peoples, melanin was so abundant as to make it increasingly difficult to study the other pigments present. The Japanese diet is very rich in carotene, and it may be taken for granted that Japanese store more carotene than do Whites. However, the Japanese skin is so heavily melanotic that the increase in carotene is probably completely screened by melanin.

On the basis of a number of analyses, it may be concluded that melanin is made up approximately of 55 per cent carbon, 6 per cent hydrogen, 12 per cent nitrogen, 2 per cent sulphur, and the remaining 25 per cent, oxygen. There is probably no difference between the chemical composition of normal and of pathological melanin. The belief that melanin is derived from hemoglobin is now abandoned. The important chromogen from which it is formed is a simple amino acid called tyrosine. Tyrosine goes through a process of oxidation in the presence of the enzyme, tyrosinase. It is converted in five stages to what R. S. Raper called "Red Substance," the exact structure of which is in doubt. This "Red Substance" then undergoes an intramolecular change and is converted to a colorless compound by spontaneous action, which may be hastened by the application of heat. The colorless compound is then oxidized to melanin spontaneously, an alkaline medium speeding up the reaction and an acid medium retarding it.

Bruno Bloch and other German workers, in their attempts to ferret out the processes of melanogenesis as it occurs in the body, concentrated upon the second stage of the oxidation of tyrosine—into dihydroxyphenylalanine, which Bloch mercifully abbreviated to "dopa." A series of reactions were formulated, not too dissimilar from those postulated by Raper, but with the most important phase centered around the oxidizing enzyme, dopa-oxidase—an organic catalyst similar to tyrosinase but not identical with it. Both tyrosinase and dopa-oxidase seem to be important in the synthesizing of melanin. Iron, phosphorus, and sulphur crop up in analyses of melanin, and of these elements sulphur is most consistently present and in the largest amounts, but it may not be an intrinsic part of the melanin molecule. The melanin isolation and purification process is far from perfected.

Experiments with the chemistry of melanin have been carried on in test tubes, but something is also known of the process of melanogenesis within the body. There are two types of body cells involved: the melanoblast, which produces the pigment, and the chromatophore, which merely stores it. It seems probable that melanin is formed by the extrusion of chromatin particles (probably tyrosine) into the cytoplasm, which must then contain the oxidases, since the melanin is formed in the cytoplasm, and not, under normal conditions, in the nucleus. With the appearance of the melanin, the cytoplasm takes on a violet hue (the tyrosine element) because of the presence of many chromatin granules. Ultimately, the cytoplasm is almost filled with melanin granules, and nuclear extrusion ceases. These melanoblasts are strictly limited to the epidermis and are especially abundant in the strata germinativum and mucosum. They have never been found in the corium. The pigment cells in this deep layer are carriers—chromatophores—and not producers of pigment. They are phagocytes—cells that feed on foreign particles and can alter or digest them. Epidermal cells, on the contrary, cannot absorb melanin. The melanin granule is probably not pure melanin but fixed in some sort of a carrier or matrix. Diffuse melanin (melanoid?) may be merely a mass of very minute granules, or it may be pigment freed from its matrix, or it may be disintegrated chemically.

It is probable that melanoblasts originally developed around the neural tube to protect the central nervous system from the ill effects of radiation. As the nervous system branched out, the pigment cells made their way toward the body surfaces, where their function is now to protect the blood and the tissues from injury by exposure to radiant energy. Because of his relatively hairless condition, man needs this protection more than most mammals. Measurement of the transmission of light through the various skin layers shows that no ultraviolet light reaches the subcutaneous layers. The non-pigmented stratum corneum takes care of all rays with a wave length less than about 220 mu and the melanoblast- and chromatophore-carrying strata germinativum and

corium absorb the rays that reach them in the 250 *mu,* 280 *mu,* and
(practically) the 400 *mu* zones. In addition to protecting the deeper parts
of the body against ultraviolet rays that the corneum fails to absorb or
reflect, Bloch suggests that melanin protects the deeper parts of the body
from excessive warming by yellow-red rays, thus acting as a regulator of
body temperature.[8]

It is generally supposed that light is definitely not the activating agency
in the formation of primary or native melanin. However, light stimulates
the production of melanin, as is indicated by tanning. The wave-lengths
that produce this effect are from a restricted part of the spectrum—the
ultraviolet end. Two workers have discovered that ultraviolet light
injures both the enzymes tyrosinase and dopa-oxidase, which are concerned in the formation of pigment. Hence, by a process of elimination,
it seems probable that this light source must increase the amount of
tyrosine produced in the exposed melanoblasts or bring the cell environment nearer to an optimum.

Edwards and Duntley, by means of the spectrophotometer, measured
the pigmentary changes in the skin after a single hour of exposure to
the mid-day August sun. The sacral region of one subject was used,
which had not previously been exposed to direct sunlight for two years,
and was kept from further exposure after the experiment.[9] Readings
were made with diminishing frequency for nine and one half months.
First, hyperemia caused the skin to be much darker and noticeably more
red, because of increased arterial blood flow (oxyhemoglobin). Then
there was a shift from oxyhemoglobin to reduced hemoglobin, indicating
blood stagnation. An increase in melanin was apparent in two days,
reaching a maximum on the nineteenth day. The increase then slowed
down, and in one month its total quantity began to diminish. At nine
and one half months, the curve showed the melanin to have returned to
approximately the same level as before exposure. The spectrophotometric curve also showed melanoid at nineteen days, increasing to a
maximum at four months, but not discernible at the final reading. It
thus seems that the initial appearance of melanoid depends upon considerable melanin formation and that the former increases after the
production of new melanin ceases, but ultimately disappears with the
failure of the mother substance.

Copper probably plays a catalytic role in the formation of melanin.
The copper content of pigmented hair is significantly higher than that of

[8] The foregoing account of melanogenesis has been summarized from Glodt, *Melanogenesis: A Review.*
[9] Edwards and Duntley, "An Analysis of Skin Pigment Changes," pp. 235–237.

unpigmented hair, and a lesser tendency in the same direction is found in white skin, brown skin, and black skin. It has been ascertained that copper accelerates the oxidation of a dopa solution with dopa-oxidase.

Possibly copper may be a factor in the production of postnatal "darkening" or increase of pigmentation. The copper content of the foetus is relatively much higher than that of the adult, but this metal is mostly in the liver, where it is connected with the blood-forming function of that organ at this stage of life, since copper is a catalyst in hemoglobin formation. During uterine life and infancy, none of the mineral gets a chance to work out toward the skin and hair. Later on, hemoglobin production merely functions to replace that excreted in the urine after the breakdown of red corpuscles. Then the copper may find its way to the pigment-producing regions.

Pregnant women often show an increased pigmentation of certain skin areas, including the areola of the breast. Their blood analyses show an excess of copper associated with its transport to the foetus. Under these circumstances, with the blood overloaded with copper, some of the melanoblasts in the areas where overpigmentation occurs may get an overdose of copper and hence produce excessive melanin. Finally, unhealthy organs often show a higher than normal copper content, and it is said that the copper content of the tissues is increased in all degenerating tumors. Possibly, then, increased copper may explain pathological pigmentation. A good deal of the foregoing is, however, speculative.

Lewis summarizes a curious industrial depigmentation occurring in Negroes who used rubber gloves continually in their work.[10] They gradually lost the pigment of the skin covered by the gloves, but the color of the skin returned when the gloves were discarded. The active agent of this depigmentation was agreed to be an anti-oxidant containing monobenzyl ether of hydroquinone and free hydroquinone. Experimentally, temporary depigmentation of the skin was obtained by the application of monobenzyl ether, but formaldehyde, which is a decomposition product of hydroquinone, produced negative results.

Lewis notes that evidence of the relation of vitamin C to pigmentation is furnished by the fact that certain Europeans are known to consume large quantities of lemon juice in order to maintain pallor. Under certain conditions Lewis states that vitamin C will inhibit the *in vitro* formation of melanin from dopa-oxidase. However, attempts to change Negro skin color by feeding large amounts of ascorbic acid have failed.

[10] Lewis, *Biology of the Negro*, p. 387, citing Schwartz, Oliver, and Warren, Pub. Health Rep., 55: 1111, 1940; and the same authors in *J.A.M.A.*, 113: 927, 1937. Also McNally, *Indust. Med.*, 8: 405, 1939.

The details of the inheritance of skin color in man have not been worked out satisfactorily, but something is known about the process. In the first place, multiple factors are involved. It is clear enough that there are in man the following potentialities for pigment production, all of which or some of which may be absent: (1) basic factors for the pigmentation of the retina of the eye and probably pigment around the neural tube, present in all except albinos; (2) various "racial" factors for producing pigment in the skin, the hair, and the stroma of the iris and conjunctiva of the eye, probably cumulative and resulting in successively intensified pigmentation; (3) factors for tanning or the production of additional skin pigment under the stimulus of light. There can be little doubt that all of these pigment-making potentialities are under hereditary or genic control. If the foregoing postulates are correct, there should be genotypes and phenotypes as follows: (1) individuals lacking any capacity for pigment production—complete albinos with pink eyes and unpigmented skin and hair; (2) those who can produce only retinal pigment and a minimal amount of skin and hair pigment, with no tanning potentiality—pure blonds with blue eyes; (3) brunet Whites with more factors for producing natural or racial pigment and a capacity for acquiring pigment or tanning; (4) several classes of genotypes with progressively more pigment-producing factors plus the tanning potentiality, grading phenotypically through Mongoloids to Negroids.

C. B. Davenport, studying the differences between Whites, Negroes, and mulattoes, thought that two pairs of genes were responsible for the various grades of color between white and black skin.[11] If S and s, T and t represent the genes for pigment control, with the capital letters standing for the gene-producing alleles, the following scheme results:

SSTT = black; SSTt and SsTT = dark brown; SsTt, SStt, and ssTT = medium brown; Sstt and ssTt = light brown; sstt = white.

This genetic outline seems inadequate, because it includes no provision for the basic factors that permit the development of retinal and neural pigment, in the absence of which albinism results. Again, it seems necessary to postulate factors to take care of the acquisition of temporary pigment through light stimulation—tanning. These are not present in many pure blonds, who, nevertheless, are not albinos.

It has been suggested that the genes controlling pigmentation operate through the provision or suppression of the enzymes that act upon tyrosine to synthesize melanin through its various stages. Perhaps another pair of genes determines the reaction of the melanoblasts to light stimu-

---

[11] Davenport, and Danielson, *Heredity of Skin Color.*

lus by controlling their tyrosine content, producing tanning or failing to do so.

It is perhaps safe to assume that early generalized human and proto-human types may have been of intermediate skin pigmentation—neither white-skinned nor black-skinned, but of some medium brown or yellow-brown shade. Mutations may then have taken place in both direction, on the one hand, toward the suppression of the tanning capacity, the in-hibiting of natural pigment-formation, and ultimately to the complete prevention of melanogenesis, even in the retina and the nervous system. On the other hand, or in the opposite direction, mutations toward pig-ment intensification may have taken place. These various mutations would be selected for survival or extinction according to the environ-mental requirements. Mutations toward blondness and albinism would be discriminated against least in cool, temperate regions, where the actinic rays of the sun are less direct. Mutations in the direction of in-creased pigmentation would be advantageous in the tropics.

The cross of a White with a Negro results in Fl offspring called mulat-toes, somewhat variable, but generally of a medium brown color. The offspring of mulattoes, the F2 generation, range in color from very dark to very light; some mulattoes are able to pass for brunet Whites. There is thus segregation, but the multiplicity of the factors in most cases prevents the extremes of the parental skin colors from being attained. The phenomenon known as progressive pigmentation generally operates in these hybrids so that their skin color darkens steadily with age. In infancy, their skins are often extremely light. It seems probable that this progres-sive pigmentation may be of the same nature as tanning, but I am not aware that it affects only those portions of the body habitually exposed to sunlight.

One of the great difficulties in the utilization of skin pigmentation for scientific racial classification is the lack hitherto of any suitable scale for measuring quality and intensity of pigmentation. The Hardy spectro-photometer provides an accurate instrument for this purpose, but, at present, it is a cumbersome and expensive apparatus that is not available for field use. The overlap between the apparent skin color of natural origin and of medium intensity in Mongoloids unexposed to tropical light and mixed Negroids and that of brunet Whites who have acquired a deep coat of tan is such as to confuse greatly the extremes of the racial variations in the three primary groups.

The pigmentation of the apes and monkeys has not been thoroughly studied. Martin says that the chimpanzee and the American cebus mon-key approach closest to man in having a combination of a pigmented epidermis with a sparsely pigmented corium. The gibbon, the sem-nopithecus monkey, the spider monkey, and the howler monkey have a profuse epidermal pigment but no pigment in the underlying dermis. In the orang-utan, both layers are heavily pigmented, whereas in baboons, macaques, cercopithecus monkeys, and the squirrel monkey of South America, the dermis is rich in pigment, but there is very little in the epidermis. The marmosets and the lemurs have little pigment in either part of the skin.[12]

Pathological pigmentation of the skin may occur from various causes. Certain degenerative changes in the suprarenal bodies may lead to Ad-dison's disease in which, often, the skin and mucous membrane becomes bronze-colored, yellow, brown, or even black. Melanin is also found in pigmented moles of the skin and in certain tumors, especially melanotic sarcomata or cancers. So far as is known, the pigment thus produced is indistinguishable from the ordinary melanin found in the skin.

Pathological loss of pigment, such as leukoderma or vitiligo, seeems to occur particularly in the tropics as a result of obscure nutritive and nervous conditions. These causes do not ordinarily bring about com-plete albinism or generalized partial albinism but produce localized depigmented patches in which the color seems to be washed out from certain centers and concentrated around the borders of the symmetrical pigmentless patches. Such depigmented patches may often be seen on the skins of aged White persons, especially on the neck and on the backs of the hands. They probably have no more relation to the action of light than has the production of pigment in moles and certain cancers, or the loss of it in scars.

Negro children are not black at birth but of a dusky or brick red color. They do not attain their definitive skin pigmentation for a few days or weeks. As a matter of fact, almost all individuals of whatever race gradually become darker in skin color as they advance in years. The aging skin becomes coarser, tougher, thicker, and more heavily pig-mented. The formation of pigment seems to begin in Negro foetuses as early as the fifth month and is then noted in the parts of the skin that are ultimately the darkest.

Important contributions to the knowledge of pigmentation have been made by the study of albinism. The term "albinos" ("whites") was origi-nally applied by the Portuguese to the white Negroes whom they met on the west coast of Africa. An albino is an unpigmented individual of a normally pigmented race. A complete albino is altogether devoid of pigment, not only in the skin and hair, but also in the eyes and in the

12 Martin, Lehrbuch, Vol. I, pp. 452 ff.

deeper organs. Albinism is a definitely pathological condition usually correlated with specific defects. In man as well as in the other vertebrates, the complete albino has pink eyes, since the cornea, iris, and retina are transparent and thus show the red blood in the capillaries unmasked by opaque pigment. This condition usually brings about a nearly closed position of the eyelids, accompanied by blinking and a wrinkling of the skin about the eyes. In normal eyeballs, the light is adequately diminished by the absorptive power of the pigment of the retina, but in albinos the intensity of light is so great as to effect this partial closure and blinking. It has been suggested also that the flickering and rolling of the eyeballs (nystagmus) usually observed in albinos is correlated with the absence of pigment in the central nervous system. The skin of albinos is said to be characteristically rough in texture.

Partial albinism occurs both in man and in lower animal forms. In the former, pigment may be entirely absent from the skin, but the eyes may be blue and the hair straw-colored, or a piebald condition of the skin may exist, unpigmented patches occurring on various portions of the body. Some animals are wholly pigmented during the summer and autumn but become partial or almost complete albinos during the winter and spring. Among these are the Scotch blue hare, the Norway hare, the North American hare, the arctic fox, the stoat, the ermine, and some birds. It does not seem to be clear whether the change in coat is due to a loss of pigmentation or to an entirely new moult in which pigmented hairs are replaced by others that lack pigment. In any case, the pigment of the eyes is not lost. Among some of the invertebrates, fishes, and other lower animal forms, partial albinism sometimes occurs, especially in such species as live in caves and lack the stimulus of light. Complete albinos certainly appear in birds and mammals.

Because of the concentration of dark-skinned races in the tropics and of light-skinned groups in the temperate zones, and because of the supposed function of melanin in the skin, it has often been concluded that the racial variation in the skin pigment is principally an effect of environment and especially of light. Furthermore, it has been thought that the lightly pigmented condition known as "blondism" is closely related to albinism, or, at any rate, to partial albinism.

The distribution of albinism among human races does not lend much support to such theories. Albinism is not more common among the blonds of Scandinavia than in the darker peoples further to the south, although, indeed, A. R. Gunn found cases of partial albinism among the Scotch and was of the opinion that the piebald condition that is so marked in many Negroes would be equally manifest in Europeans were

it not for the lack of contrast between the lightly pigmented and pigmentless areas of their skins. Albinism is frequent among heavily pigmented races and especially among Negroes. As these heavily pigmented
Negroid races ordinarily inhabit the tropical regions, the incidence of
albinism in no way corresponds with the absence of a need for protective
pigmentation. Further, there is no evidence of frequent albinism or
any tendency toward depigmentation among the Eskimo and other pigmented Mongoloids inhabiting the far north.

Some years ago, a good deal of interest was aroused by the report of
the existence of a colony of "White Indians" in Panama on the St. Blas
Coast. Three of these "White Indians" with some pigmented individuals
were brought to the United States by their discoverer, as evidence of the
reality of their existence. As early as 1691, Lionel Wafer, an English
sailor, visited Darien and subsequently published what seems to be a
fairly accurate account of the existence of complete albinos among the
Indians there. Many subsequent references to Indian albinos appear in
literature pertaining to this region. An investigation of these San Blas
albinos in their homes, by Reginald G. Harris, indicates that they are
found, contrary to report, in villages of ordinary pigmented Indians and
are never segregated. The males are not allowed to marry, but the females
sometimes cross with pigmented males. It is estimated that the entire
San Blas population of 20,000 includes some 138 "White Indians," or
0.69 per cent. This occurrence of albinism is about 50 to 100 times as
numerous as would be expected.

The "White Indians" of Panama are, according to modern observations, partial albinos. Many, if not all, have copper-colored freckle spots.
The hair shows traces of brown and is in some cases auburn. The eyes
are blue with brown spots or dark blue. These individuals are rather
smaller than the ordinary Indians but exhibit unmistakably Indian
features of head, face, and body build. They seem to be more susceptible
to disorders of the skin and eyes than the normal Indians. Family data
indicate that albinism here was due originally to a mutation (the appearance of a new hereditary character that breeds true) and that it appears
individually as the expression of a recessive condition. The "White
Indians" are clearly Indian and could not have sprung from the
crossings of Indians and Whites. The large number of albinos among
the San Blas Indians is ascribed to frequent matings of related brown
individuals who carry recessive albino factors. Were it not for the limitation of marriage to the females, possibly a white race might be established.

This case is of particular interest in its bearing upon the origin and nature of human skin pigmentation. It is obvious that the depigmentation of these Panama Indians cannot have been due to the absence of any need of protective pigmentation, since the Isthmus of Panama is in the tropics where the ultra-violet rays of the sun are most powerful. It seems possible to exclude lack of light as a factor in the depigmentation process.

Since partially depigmented types have arisen and have continued to survive in an area, which, from the standpoint of light, is least favorable to unpigmented animals and most conducive to pigment production, it can hardly be argued that the sparsity of pigment found in North Europeans must be ascribed to the sunless, foggy area in which the race differentiated. None the less, it would appear that such an area as the Baltic lands would furnish a far more favorable environment for the fostering and propagation of depigmented types than any tropical region in which the rays of the sun are vertical.

HAIR COLOR

Hair color is the result of the amount and quality of pigment in the hair, the extent of the unpigmented spaces in it that reflect the light, and the variations in the quality of the outer hair covering. The commonest hair pigment is granular, brown or black pigment identical with that in the skin. This is found both in the hair cells and between them. It will be remembered that a hair shaft consists of the thin, unpigmented, outer layer or cuticle made of overlapping scales, the cortex of horny cells in which is commonly found both diffuse, non-granular pigment and the granular melanin, and innermost, the medulla or pith of fewer and looser cells, which are often discontinuous and separated from each other by light spaces. In blond Northern Europeans, the pigment is usually confined to the cortex, but in Negro hair the medulla is stuffed with melanin. Black-haired Europeans have much less pigment in the pith than have Negroes, Chinese, or Indians.

In addition to the brown or black pigment, a diffuse and soluble red-gold pigment is sometimes present in the hair. The reflection of light from the unpigmented cortex and medullary spaces of the hair shafts gives the gray or white appearance to hair, while the combination of this reflected light with the varying quantities and qualities of the pigment in the hair accounts for the different shades and colors. The old-age graying of hair is caused by the increase in the empty spaces in the medulla and by the absorption of the other pigment in the shaft. Although some writers have argued in favor of certain cells absorbing or destroying pigment in the hair, it seems more probable that, in the case of gray or white hairs, these do not become depigmented but drop out and are replaced by hairs lacking the substance. The life span of human hair is not known. It seems probable that a hair grows from eight to eleven weeks, then remains stationary for an equal or longer period and is shed. A new papilla forms and the old hair is crowded out. No one has ever explained satisfactorily why the pigment of the hair disappears with advancing age while that of the skin persists or even increases. All races grow gray or white in old age, but this condition seems to develop earliest in European races. Anthropoid apes, monkeys, and lower mammals show this old age depigmentation of the hair to a varying extent. Graying usually affects the head hair first, then the beard, and finally the hair of the body. Some of the instances of sudden graying or whitening of the hair connected with nervous shocks are apparently well authenticated, but the cause of this is quite unknown. Danforth, one of our best authorities on hair, doubts that abrupt whitening occurs.

Very little seems to be known about the nature of the diffuse red-gold pigment in hair, although its existence has long been recognized. One observer, Klinke,[13] found that the melanin molecule in the hair had more tendency to hold the sulphur atom than the melanin of the skin and the eye, but he managed to free all hair melanin from its sulphur except red-hair melanin. This suggested that red-hair melanin may represent an incomplete phase of the tyrosine-to-melanin oxidation process, with activity ceasing at the "Red Substance" phase.

Recently it has been discovered that the pigment in red hair is soluble in a weak acid solution that precipitates melanin.[14] The spectroscopic analysis of this solution seemed to indicate that the red pigment was identical with an ordinary oxidation product of melanin. It is possible, then, that red coloring in dark hair may be either the incompleted synthesis of melanin, as suggested in the previous paragraph, or an actual decomposition product of melanin. Bleached or faded brown hair often shows rusty tints that may be due either to the showing up of red pigment originally in the hair or the break down chemically of melanin in the hair. Thus it seems probable that there is original red pigment in which the tyrosine-melanin oxidation process is incomplete and secondary red pigment that may be due to the chemical decomposition of original melanin.

Pipkin and Pipkin succeeded in bleaching the yellowish hair of light albino Negroes, together with the normal hair of a dark Negro and

---

13 Glodt, *Melanogenesis: A Review*, p. 39, citing K. Klinke, 1925, *Biochem. Zeitschr.*, 160, 28.
14 Brues, *Sibling Resemblances*, p. 99, citing Arnow, L., "The acid-soluble pigment of red human hair," *Biochem. J.*, Vol. 32, 1938, pp. 1281–1284.

samples of the hair of Whites, light brown, red, and blond, by using a 3 per cent solution of hydrogen peroxide (H_2O_2). This bleaching of hair pigment with an oxidizing agent is nothing new. However, these experimenters also succeeded in darkening albino Negro hair and light brown, red, blond, and gray hair of Whites by the use of a reducing agent, stannous chloride ($SnCl_2$). The reduction produced reddish yellow diffuse pigment, reddish brown, and black granular pigment. Their results support previous experimental work of Saller and Maroske indicating that black granular pigment may be oxidized to a reddish yellow diffuse pigment, between which reddish granular pigment may be an intermediate stage.[15]

Gardner and MacAdam carried out a pioneer colorimetric analysis of hair color, using the Hardy recording spectrophotometer, the instrument later employed by Edwards and Duntley in their study of skin pigmentation.[16] A series of 53 hair samples, ranging in color from black to very blond and including a wide selection of reds was analyzed. The curves of the black, browns, and blonds are almost straight lines, but the reds show a decided upward curvature in the region of the green. The difference between brown and red is not due to disparity in the reflectance of the red bands of the spectrum as much as to difference in the green and blue bands, the reds showing much less reflectance in this region of the spectrum. When hair reflects less than 47 per cent as much light at 546 *mu* wave-length as it does at 700 *mu* wave-length, the eye distinguishes the color as red or reddish, but, when the reflectance at the two wave-lengths is greater than 47 per cent, the resulting impression is brown. A separation between red and reddish brown occurs when the reflectance at 546 *mu* is less than 40 per cent of that at 700 *mu*.

All of this seems to mean that there are two quite distinct series of hair color—a brown series and a red series, in addition to a series in which the two are mixed. The brown series ranges from black through dark brown, medium brown, and light brown to the lightest blond. In this series the dominant wave-length ranges from 580 *mu* to 583 *mu* with uniform increase in relative brightness and colorimetric purity. The brightness relative to a perfect reflector ranges from a little more than 2 per cent (2.2) in black to nearly 21 per cent in light blond. Purity, which indicates the degree of similarity between the color of the sample and the color of pure spectrum light with a wave-length equal to the dominant wave-length of the sample, ranges from 25 per cent up to

[15] Pipkin and Pipkin, "Albino Hair," pp. 203–205.
[16] Gardner and MacAdam, "Colorimetric Analysis of Hair Color," pp. 187–201.

about 43 per cent in this black-to-blond series. The pure red series is characterized by high purity (50 per cent to 60 per cent), together with low relative brightness (3.2 per cent to 8.6 per cent), and a longer dominant wave-length (585 *mu* to 593 *mu*). The red-brown series, with a dominant wave-length of 583 *mu,* is higher in purity but lower in relative brightness than the blond series and falls in general between the red and the black-blond series.

These colorimetric studies confirm the supposition that there are really three series of hair color: the pure melanotic series ranging from black through the flat browns and light ash browns to almost colorless ash blond; a red series ranging from very intense red to very light red and red-golden; a mixed series in which melanotic pigment is found with the red pigment. This last series may range again from black (the red pigment present being perfectly masked) through darker to lighter red-browns. If red hair is bleached with peroxide, lighter reds of higher purity and brightness are produced, but the dominant wave-length is not changed, and the spectrophotometric curve shows the same bend upward in the red. It is still red hair.

Red heads are not as common in Sweden, the greatest center of blondness, as in Scotland where many of the people have dark hair. Martin states that the percentage of red-haired individuals in Holland (2.5) is the same in the predominatingly blond districts as in the brunet districts. The canton of Schaffhausen in Switzerland, which contains 68.9 per cent of blonds, has only 1 per cent of red heads. Beddoe gives the percentage of red hair in the highlands of Scotland as 11.2, and in all Scotland, 5.4 per cent. This is the highest known frequency of red hair.

It seems very probable that red-haired individuals often result from the crossings of a black-haired parent in whom there is a good deal of recessive red-gold pigment, with a blond mate in whose hair is little pigment of any kind, and some of that little the red-gold pigment. Thus, by a process of segregating out recessive red-gold pigment, pure red-haired individuals result. This supposition becomes more plausible when we consider the usual combination of red hair with a milky white skin that freckles. The freckles represent the tanning capabilities of the brunet stock irregularly distributed in the epithelial cells. The milky white background on which the freckles form represents the inheritance from the blond stock which is incapable of acquiring a protective pigmentation under the stimulus of solar rays.

The reddish tinge of the hair is oftener seen in the beard and in the axillary and pubic hair than in that of the head. Sweat, light, and seawater seem to have the effect of bleaching the melanotic pigment in people who have both pigment components, and of accentuating the red tones of the hair.

Among the children of light-haired races, the blond or light hair of infancy often becomes darker year by year until the full pigmentation is reached at varying ages, sometimes as late as 30 years. In Denmark, for example, the percentage of light-haired boys decreases from 52.1 in the sixth year to 33 per cent in the fourteenth year, according to Hansen. European pigmentation of the hair is said to be completed more rapidly in boys than in girls. Similarly, the light red hair of the young is often replaced by brown hair in adult years. But most black-haired peoples, such as Negroes and Mongoloids, have black hair from earliest infancy. Brues, in an analysis of published data on hair color of children at different ages, found that there was a continuous increase of the darker shades, with especially rapid rate from 7 to 10 years in girls and from 10 to 14 years in boys. In her own material, which consisted of siblings of European stocks 18 years of age and older, the same observer noted that the percentage of light brown and fair hair together increases to the age of 25 years and then is slowly reduced until it again reaches the sub-adult level at the age of 40 years. The percentage of dark brown and black hair increases steadily throughout the period covered. Post-adolescent increase of light hair lasts about three years longer in men.

Babies of mixed European ancestry are often born with a fairly thick head-covering of dark brown or black hair. In a few days or weeks, this hair rubs off, and a new growth of very light hair erupts. This gradually darkens to a medium or dark brown shade. This prenatal crop of dark hair must represent some ancestral brunet strain which asserts itself temporarily during infancy and is replaced ultimately by hair of an intermediate but lighter shade. Pure blond children usually have little or no hair on the head at birth; when the hair grows, it is very light in color, and it stays light. Children of pure brunet stocks similarly grow one crop of dark hair that stays dark.

Hair color does not seem to be affected by physical environment to any appreciable extent. Blondness is almost confined to the peoples around the Baltic area of Europe and to their kin who have migrated to other parts of the world. Dark hair is everywhere much commoner, and the Mongoloids of the far north have just as black hair as those dwelling in the tropics. Yellow-haired Negroes have been reported from Africa and Melanesia. These are probably either partial albinos or have bleached their hair with lime, urine, or some other artificial agency, like the peroxide blonds of civilized society. Dark red hair certainly is found occasionally in the Oceanic Negroids, probably more commonly in children and adolescents than in adults. Among the native Australians, a gingery or foxy reddish hair frequently occurs in children of full-blooded ancestry. This reddish hair is always replaced by dark brown hair at maturity, and, as far as I am aware, is never associated with light eyes. This phenomenon apparently has no relation to blondism in the melanotic series but pertains exclusively to rufosity.

The genetics of hair color is not simple. Alice Brues, in an important unpublished study which she has kindly permitted me to summarize, states that dominance is unclear in the series of sibs of mixed European ethnic origin upon which her observations were made. Dark brown is not purely dominant over medium brown or light brown because its frequency of repetition in families is low, and there are few in which it occurs to the complete exclusion of medium brown. Again, medium brown can hardly be a true heterozygous intermediate because it is a shade that shows little tendency to pile up in families. It seems very unstable. Brues points out that the color value, which corresponds approximately to the amount of light reflected, does not bear a simple relationship to the amount of pigment present. If a certain quantity of pigment absorbs half of the incident light and reflects the rest, the addition of a second dose of pigment equal to the first will result in the absorption of not all of the remaining light, but only half of it. Thus two dark hues may appear closely alike and may yet differ markedly in amount of pigment present. Successive increments produce diminishing effects, and the second of two dominant genes in a factor pair may produce no visible change in the phenotype because the first has already brought about the maximum apparent change in the trait. European "black" hair is probably far less heavily pigmented than the black hair of Negroids and Mongoloids. This fact may explain the apparent dominance of dark hair over blond, when the dark hair is that of Negroids or Mongoloids, and the apparent blending of dark hair with lighter shades in crosses between the European stocks. In the former case, the number of pigment factors in black hair may be large enough so that even when halved in a cross with blonds it is still sufficient to produce a dark shade. On the other hand, in crosses within the White race, the "black" hair may not have much pigment to spare and, when halved in unions with blonds, the effect is immediately evident.

It seems to me probable that at least two (and more probably three) pairs of cumulative factors for the production of melanin in the hair must be postulated to account for Negro black, Mongoloid black, White black, dark brown, medium brown, light brown, and blond. In addition, there must be at least a pair of factors tending to check the melanin synthesis at the red stage and producing red-gold pigment that is hypostatic to the melanotic pigment. The factors for red hair seemingly occur most commonly mixed up with the melanotic series but may be segregated out into pure red series varying from intense red through light red to golden blond.

Further discussion of hair pigmentation must be deferred until it can be dealt with in correlation with eye color.

EYE STRUCTURE AND EYE COLOR

The bulb of the eye is composed of segments of two spheres, a smaller anterior sphere which is transparent and forms about one sixth of the bulb, and a posterior segment of a larger sphere which is opaque (Fig. 63). The conjunctiva is the mucous membrane of the eye and not properly a portion of the bulb. It lines the inner surface of the eyelids and is reflected over the fore part of the sclera and cornea. The coverings of the eye include a fibrous tunic, a vascular pigmented tunic, and a nervous tunic. The fibrous tunic consists of a transparent portion, the cornea, which forms the anterior sixth of the eye, and an opaque, pigmented portion, the sclera, which constitutes the posterior five sixths. The cornea bulges out in front; the sclera is white outside and brown inside. The vascular tunic consists of the iris in front, the ciliary body in the middle, and the choroid innermost. The iris is a circular diaphragm behind the cornea, with a rounded aperture, the pupil, near its center. It is suspended in the aqueous humor between the cornea and the lens, and is a thin, circular, and contractile disk. The ciliary body is continuous with the periphery of the iris and consists of a ridged zone about 4 mm. in width, the ciliary processes forming a sort of fringe behind the iris and around the margin of the lens, and a circular band of muscle, the ciliaris muscle. The choroid is a thin, highly vascular membrane of a dark brown color, which invests the posterior part of the globe and adheres to the sclera. It is pierced behind by the optic nerve. The retina is the delicate nervous membrane upon which images of objects are received. It is the inner tunic of the eye and is in contact outside with the choroid; it continues forward nearly as far as the ciliary body where it ends in jagged edges. The retina is of a purple tint when in a fresh state, owing to a coloring matter named visual purple. Behind, it is continuous with the optic nerve. The retina consists of an outer pigmented layer and an inner nervous layer.

In the interior of the eyeball are the refracting media: the aqueous humor, consisting mainly of water; the vitreous body, a jelly-like transparent substance filling four fifths of the bulb of the eye; and the crystalline lens in front of it and immediately behind the iris. The lens is a transparent, biconvex body retained in position between the iris and

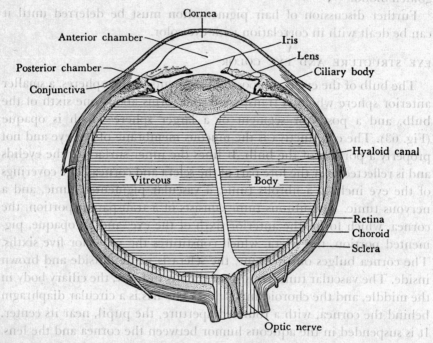

Fig. 63. Horizontal section of the human eyeball, showing pigmentation of the iris.

the vitreous body by a suspensory ligament and enclosed in a capsule. A varying amount of light is admitted through the pupil according to the contraction or dilation of the iris; the rays of light are focused through the lens and the image is cast upon the opaque and sensitive retina at the back of the eye.

The pigment of the eye is found in the conjunctiva, the sclera, the iris, the choroid, and the retina. There is no pigment in the cornea, the aqueous humor, or lens. But some is found in the ciliary processes. The retinal pigment consists of a single stratum of black pigment-filled cells. The black color of the pupil is due to the fact that the pigmented layer of the retina reflects back no light to the eye of the observer. Retinal pigment does not enter into eye color unless there is no pigment in the iris. In complete albinos, the retina has no pigment, and the red color of the pupil is imparted by the rays of light reflected back and showing the color of the blood of the choroid layer. The pigment in the retinal layer is denser in Negroids and Mongoloids than in Whites.

There is a variable amount of pigment in the choroid and in the ciliary body, more, of course, in the dark-skinned races than in Whites, but this has little effect upon eye color. It is the pigment in the diaphragm or iris of the eye that is mainly responsible for eye color. In the front of the iris is a layer of flattened cells which may be heavily pigmented in Negroes and also contains some pigmented cells in the dark, colored irides of Europeans. Behind this is a network of cells and fibres called the stroma, which contains pigment in dark-eyed races, but is pigmentless in blue-eyed persons and albinos. Behind the stroma, is a layer of circular and radiating muscular fibres. The back of the iris is of a deep purple tint, being covered with two layers of heavily pigmented cells, and is continuous with the ciliary part of the retina at its periphery. The color of the iris is produced by the reflection of the light from the pigmented cells. In purely blue-eyed persons, there is no pigment in the superficial layers of the iris, and the pigmented epithelium of the posterior or retinal surface shows through the translucent overlying layers, imparting a blue tone. If there is also pigment in the middle and the outer layers of the iris, the eye color is gray, yellow, brown, or black, according to the quality, amount, and position of the pigmented cells. If there are only a few pigmented cells in the stroma (the middle layer) and these, as is often the case, are concentrated around the pupillary zone, the background of the iris is gray or "hazel," and brown color radiates from or is ringed around the pupil, the brown being the pigment in the stroma and the lighter background the retinal pigment somewhat obscured by scattered pigment in the intermediate zone. If the stroma is very heavily pigmented, the iris color will be some shade of brown throughout, though usually not homogeneous. If, as in Negroes and other dark-skinned races, the outermost layer of the eye is very heavily pigmented, neither the pigment of the stroma nor that of the posterior portion of the iris affects the eye color, which is very dark brown or almost black because of the pigment in the outermost layer.

The dark brown or black color of the Negro eye is, therefore, due to the density of the melanotic pigment in the outer layer, while the brown eye color of lighter races is largely the effect of the deeper pigment in the stroma showing through the unpigmented or scantily pigmented outer layer. The stroma of the Negro eye is not as heavily pigmented as the external layer, and the boundaries between the layers are more distinct than in the White. In Mongoloids and Indians, the pigment in the eye is not as dense as in Negroes, and the color of the pigment tends to be yellowish brown instead of black. In Europeans it is yellowish brown, yellow, or red-brown. Nevertheless, eye color seems to be the result more of quantitative than of qualitative differences in pigment, the same melanin showing different shades according to its density and the translucent layers through which it is reflected.

The outermost layer of the iris in most mammals is complete and pigmented and presents a smooth brown surface. It is thus in nearly all races of man. However, in the groups that have partially or wholly depigmented irides, this outer membrane tends to atrophy and to be eroded away to a greater or lesser degree. The most noticeable phase of this detrition of the outer layer results in "crypts"—more or less elliptical gaps that reveal a lower layer of the iris differing in hue from the outer membrane. The cryptose eye is intermediate structurally between the smooth brown eye with the outer membrane intact and the light eye in which the latter has wholly disappeared. In a "ridged" eye, the crypts have so expanded that the anterior layer is represented solely by more or less radial ridges. Finally, a "scalloped" eye shows the last vestige of the anterior layer in an irregular circle around the pupil—representing the region where the widened bases of former ridges come together. This scallop is very persistent in light eyes.

A blue eye can hardly occur without the destruction of the outer layer, since the retinal pigment has to show through an unpigmented fibrous layer which must be very thin to give the optical effect of blue. Possibly a pure, homogeneous brown cannot occur unless the outer layer is complete.

In mixed Europeans, the eyes become darker during growth just as the hair darkens. New-born infants show a blue or violet colored background, but during growth the area around the pupil becomes pigmented so that the eye changes from blue to "mixed," i.e. a brown areola with a lighter background. In pure blonds, the eye color remains blue but often fades somewhat in old age. Certain pathological conditions also tend to change the iridical blue to a grayish color. In some few instances, notably among the Kaffirs and certain of the North American Indians, it has been observed that the dark brown or mixed brown color of youth and maturity sometimes becomes lighter in old age and may even turn to gray or blue. Whether or not this is a pathological condition has not been determined.

The conjunctiva, which is reflected across the eyeball, also contains some melanotic pigment. In blond Europeans, there is very little of this conjunctival pigment, and the sclerotic or "white of the eye" is a clear white. In more heavily pigmented races, it may be yellowish, spotted, or a dirty brown color.

The pigment of the iris and of the other portions of the eye probably has the same protective function as the pigment of the skin. The eyes of lightly pigmented Europeans are then least protected from the destructive ultra-violet solar rays.

The eye of the gibbon is said to approach closest to man in the distribution of its pigment in the iris and ciliary body. Both men and apes show strong conjunctival pigment as a compensation for the heavy pigment of the sclera found in other mammals.

It was suggested in early studies of the inheritance of eye color that pure blue eyes are recessive to heavily pigmented dark eyes, that "mixed" eyes (with a light background and a pigmented area around the pupil) are heterozygous—that they contain both dominant and recessive factors. As usual, such a simple scheme has proved to be inadequate. In the first place, it seems probable that the far more heavily pigmented dark brown or black eyes of Mongoloids and Negroids are genetically distinct from the dark brown eyes of Europeans. In a general way, it still seems to be likely that such heavily pigmented dark eyes are dominant in most cases over the mixed eyes and light eyes of Europeans, although perhaps incompletely so. Similarly, it would appear that blue eyes are usually recessive but not invariably so. Gates has observed deep blue eyes in a native of Ceylon with full dark skin color and jet black, wavy hair. This man was of putatively pure Singhalese descent and several of his relatives had this same pure blue shade of eye color associated with dark skin and black hair. Gates secured a pedigree and came to the conclusion that blue eyes had arisen in this population as a dominant mutation independent of factors for skin color.[17]

There is little doubt that blue eyes have originated as a mutation from brown and often independently of depigmentation of the hair, if not of the skin. There is no other adequate explanation for the enormous prevalence of the combination of blue eyes and dark hair in Ireland in the so-called Keltic type. We shall have to discuss this matter in more detail in our consideration of European morphological types.

[17] Gates, "Blue Eyes in Natives of Ceylon," p. 921.

The principal types of eye color may be classified according to primary, or background, color, in combination with secondary, or superficial and detailed, hue. Thus, "light" eyes have blue or gray background with unpigmented (white or gray) detail markings; "pale mixed" have blue, green, or gray backgrounds with yellow or orange detail; "mixed" have similar backgrounds, but with brown or red-brown detail; whereas "dark" eyes have dark green or brown backgrounds and distinguishable detail is always brown. Alice Brues, using this classification in a study of eye colors of White siblings, found that light eyes were commoner in males than females and produced evidence that light eyes in males are a sex-linked recessive. Pure light eyes and light eyes having specks or a slightly darkened scallop line seemed to be distinguished from each other by one or more hereditary modifying factors added to their general basis. However, Brues could find no genotypic difference between mixed eyes with a small amount of brown and those much darker. She postulated a sex linkage of eye color involving a recessive light, a dominant intermediate, and probably another independent, non-sex-linked factor producing the larger class of the dark eyes. A further correlation of eye color with eye structure by this same observer indicated that the eye with a complete, smooth anterior layer, always pigmented, is controlled by one dominant, non-sex-linked factor. There also seems to be a common determiner for degeneration of the anterior layer involved in both partially and fully atrophied irides (the cryptose-eroded and scalloped types). This latter is a dominant sex-linked factor (hypostatic to the smooth, pigmented determiner) which advances structural excavation of the iris.

ASSOCIATION OF HAIR COLOR AND EYE COLOR

In the dark-colored races, there is usually a proportionate intensity of pigmentation in hair, skin, and eyes. The melanin-stuffed hair of the Negro goes with dark brown or nearly black skin and a dark brown iridical hue which sometimes attains a black that makes the iris indistinguishable from the pupil. It is to be doubted that the blue-black hair and yellow-brown skin of the Mongoloid are ever accompanied by eyes that are so black. The prevalent Mongoloid eye color is dark brown or medium brown. In Whites, irides that can properly be called black are very rare, perhaps non-existent. For that matter, really black hair (which shows no brown tints in transmitted light) is found in large proportions only among the very swarthy Whites. Pittard recorded a maximum occurrence among the Balkan peoples of 75.7 per cent of black hair in Gypsy men, the Greeks ranking a very poor second with 36.9 per cent. It is to be doubted that the strict criterion of blackness mentioned above was applied in these observations. Most of the hair that laymen describe as "black" in Europeans is really dark brown.

In the relatively depigmented White race, the darkest mean hair color is found with smooth pigmented eyes (eyes in which the anterior layer of the iris is uneroded and brown in color), according to the observations of Brues. Amount of brown pigment by area in mixed eyes also correlates definitely with hair color. Pale mixed eyes go with lighter hair than mixed eyes. Finally, the lighter shades of blue eyes are more likely to accompany very light shades of hair than are medium or deep blue eyes. Red pigment in the hair in Alice Brues' series showed no correlation with the three shades of blue background color, but rather was associated with green and brown background colors. Redness of hair was more strongly correlated with detail or superficial coloring of the iris than was brown hair. Pale mixed eyes are more likely to go with red in the hair than are light eyes, and the association of red pigment in hair with dark eyes, as contrasted with mixed eyes, is stronger than the association of brown pigment in hair with these darker eye colors.

There is a difference in hair-color and eye-color associations between the sexes. Fair and light brown hair are commonest with light eyes in men but frequently occur in the women with intermediate eye colors. Brues thinks that the evidence in siblings indicates that this sex difference is due to the ineffectiveness or possibly the recessive character of the sex-linked, intermediate eye-color factor in respect of hair pigmentation.

MacConaill and Ralphs, in an investigation of age-changes in hair color and eye color in a large series of English males, found that brown eyes with blond hair are commonest in the second quarter of the period from birth to maturity.[18] This combination during growth appears to be due to the fact that progressive pigmentation in blond-brunet mixtures affects the eyes earlier than the hair. It is extremely rare in adults. On the other hand, blue eyes and dark hair are very common in certain White stocks, probably most notably in Ireland. MacConaill and Ralphs postulate three pigmentation phases during development and nine developmental combinations of hair color and eye color. The phases are: Fast (full pigmentation immediately after birth), Medium (full

[18] MacConaill, and Ralphs, "Post-Natal Development," pp. 218–225.
   MacConaill, "Stature of Male School Children," pp. 117–125; "Classification of Hair and Eye Colour," pp. 173–178.

pigmentation at puberty), Slow (full pigmentation of hair and eyes at 20 years). Persons with blond hair and brown eyes are called "cyanopes," those with blue eyes and blond hair "glaucopes." Assuming a pair of factors for blue or non-blue eyes (EE,Ee,ee) and another pair for blond or dark hair (HH,Hh,hh), they propose the following genetic scheme: EEHH = Fast Dark; EEHh = Medium Dark with cyanopic stage; EeHH = Medium Dark with glaucopic stage; EeHh = Slow with intermediate stage variable; EEhh = Fast Cyanope; E$e$$hh$ = Slow Cyanope; eeHH = Fast Glaucope; eeHh = Slow Glaucope; $eehh$ = Blond (blue eyes and fair hair). The developmental phases and the included eye- and hair-color combinations are plausible, but certainly the genetic scheme seems oversimplified. This study led the authors to interesting and probably valid conclusions as to the sequence of mutations that has produced partial or full depigmentation of hair and eyes in combination. It is assumed that from the original condition (EEHH) of dark hair and eyes, E first mutated to e, resulting in the glaucopic combination (blue eyes and dark hair). This suggestion is rendered plausible not only by the large numbers of blue-eyed, dark-haired adults in the British Isles and elsewhere in Europe, but also by Gates' independent observation of a blue-eyed, mutant Singhalese. The further assumption of MacConaill is that the mutation of H to h, of dark hair to blond hair, came separately and later, and that such light-eyed, light-haired stocks as the Nordic and East Baltic are recombinations into a double recessive. Gates suggests that if e and h occurred as separate mutations, crossing over must have taken place in order to stabilize the double recessive blond type $eehh$.[19] However, there exists among adult Whites no sufficient reservoir of cyanopes of adult years (brown-eyed, blond-haired) as would afford credibility for the hypothesis that pure blonds have come about by a recombination of light eyes from a dark-haired stock and light hair from a dark-eyed stock. Rather it would seem reasonable that in a stock or stocks that had already undergone the initial step toward depigmentation—the blue eyed mutation—a second mutation or series of mutations occurred in which the hair color was reduced to blond.

It would appear probable also that the repeated mutations that establish blue eyes in a dark-haired race are accompanied by decrease in skin pigmentation, since in such "glaucopes" the complexion is usually pale white or ruddy, not swarthy. Yet the possibility of blue eyes appearing in a heavily pigmented stock without concomitant lightening of skin color is established by Gates' Singhalese example.

[19] Gates, ms.

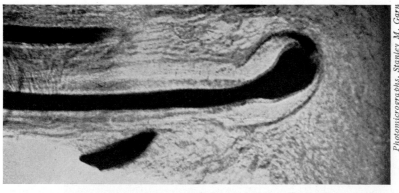

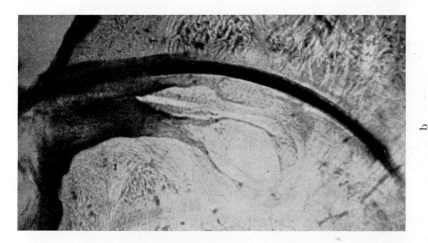

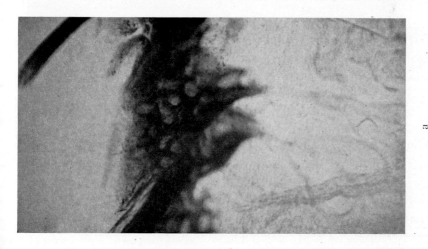

Photomicrographs, Stanley M. Garn

c

b

a

a. Section of Negro scalp showing pigmented *stratum germinativum* and underlying dermis
b. Section of Negro scalp showing sebaceous glands opening into neck of hair follicle and curvature of follicle
c. Section of Negro scalp showing hair follicle and hair root at base of follicle

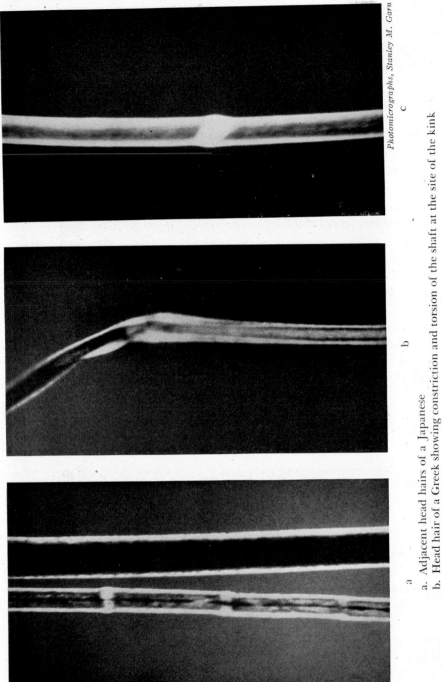

Photomicrographs, Stanley M. Garn

a. Adjacent head hairs of a Japanese
b. Head hair of a Greek showing constriction and torsion of the shaft at the site of the kink
c. Head hair of an Old American

HAIR

The form of the hair affords the most used basis for a primary classification of present day human groups. But, among civilized peoples nowadays, one has to be very wary in employing hair form as a racial criterion, since many White persons have their hair "permanently" waved and many colored individuals artificially straighten it. Mongoloid races are remarkable for their straight, coarse, blue-black hair, and Negroes are equally notable for short, matted, wiry hair which grows in tiny spirals and is rather inappropriately called "woolly." Between these extreme and characteristic gradations are several varieties of more or less curved hair. So-called "frizzly" hair is longer than the "woolly" hair with its tightly coiled spirals. "Kinky" is a better term than frizzly, for this form of hair usually does not grow in spirals but in short, deep, U-shaped waves. People whose hair is kinky or frizzly generally have small spirals or tight curls on some part of the head. It is certain that kinky or frizzly hair ordinarily occurs in racial types in which there is at least a generous admixture of the Negro or the Negrito. Kinky hair, according to the unpublished research of Stanley M. Garn, shows, under the microscope, a pinching or constriction at the site of the kink and also a twisting of the hair shaft. Below the waist, or place of greatest constriction, the hair shaft seems to have been given a half-turn in one direction, and above it a half-turn in the opposite direction (Photomicrograph 2). Woolly or tightly curled spiral hair apparently has the twisting of the hair shaft in one direction only, but shows the same constrictions at very frequent intervals along the hair shaft.

Garn has studied numerous examples of kinky or frizzly hair from the heads and bodies of Europeans who presumably do not carry any strain of Negro blood. There are at least two well-attested examples in the literature of hair form in which definitely kinky or apparently woolly hair appears in the families of blond North Europeans and seems to behave as a dominant mutation. In these families, one Norwegian, the other Dutch, the supposition of Negroid admixture is thought to be quite untenable.[20] It seems clear enough, then, that mutations of straight or wavy hair to frizzly or even woolly may occasionally take place in the White race, but it is interesting to note that such frizzly or woolly White hair seems not to have established itself as a characteristic feature of any White subrace. It is a sporadic familial inheritance. Garn states that kinky hairs occur, here and there, on the head and body of most Whites.

[20] Mohr, "Woolly Hair," pp. 345–352.
    Schokking, "Another Woolly Hair Mutation," pp. 337–340.

The hair simply called "curly" is also spiral hair, but the spirals are large instead of small and are loose. Tightly curled hair, in which the spirals are small but not minute as in Negroes, occurs in many peoples who may and probably do have minor Negroid strains in their composition, as, for example, Australians, East Indians, and some Polynesians. It may be seen not infrequently among the White races, and in my opinion here too it usually points toward the expression of a latent Negroid strain. It is possible, however, that the lesser degrees of curly hair may have arisen as spontaneous variations in some White stocks.

Wavy hair is properly so called when the strands of hair are curved in such an equal and symmetrical way as to produce regular undulations, either long and shallow or short and deep. There is no doubt that these wavy varieties of hair are genetically as well as morphologically intermediate between the extreme grades of straightness and curvature, as exemplified in Mongoloids and Negroes. Such wavy hair is known in some cases to result from crosses of straight-haired and curly-haired parents. Wavy hair is widely distributed among most of the secondary or composite races and is particularly common among Polynesians and Europeans.

The fine, straight hair of Europeans differs considerably in texture and cross-section from the coarse, straight Mongoloid hair and does not stand up against woolly hair in crosses as does Mongoloid straight hair. It is not improbable that straight, coarse Mongoloid hair is dominant over woolly hair, but fine, straight European hair is certainly recessive to all degrees of curved hair. Curvature of the follicle accompanies curly hair (Photomicrograph 1).

Brues, in studying the hair form of siblings of European ancestry, found some evidence that, in sib pairs, straight hair is a sex-linked recessive, but dominance is certainly incomplete, if not lacking. If males have only a single determining gene for hair form (that on the X-chromosome), whereas females, in addition to the doubled genotypes corresponding to the two types of hair form found in males, have also a considerable heterozygous class, there ought to be a considerable piling-up of females in the intermediate classes of hair form. In four classic studies of radical race mixtures [American-Negroid (Day), Dutch-Hottentot (Fischer), Spanish-Maya (Williams), and English-Tahitian (Shapiro)], this tendency of females to exhibit excesses in the middle classes (low waves, deep waves, and curly) as contrasted with the male tendency toward extremes (straight and frizzly) is plainly exhibited. Testing the putative sex-linkage in hair form with the known sex-linkage in eye color, Brues found that, in pairs of the same sex, the excess of likeness in hair form with likeness in eye color is a 99 per cent certainty, whereas similarity in hair form with siblings of different eye color is virtually that which might be expected through chance alone.

In Brues' series, straight hair tended to be excessively associated with pale mixed and dark eyes, low-waved hair with light and mixed eyes. Higher grades of hair curvature (deep waves and curly) show no such association with eye color. In the dark (smooth-pigmented) eyes and also in the pale mixed class, there appears to be some factor suppressing a low wave of the hair, but it does not affect deep waves or curly hair. Brues found no clear association of hair color with hair form in her European siblings.

On the whole, it would appear that the very straight and coarse Mongoloid hair form, the markedly curved, woolly, frizzly Negroid types, and a third category of more or less intermediate forms (fine or smooth, straight hair, low waves, deep waves, and curly) constitute the main varieties that are useful for racial classification. The intermediate forms occur in secondary races (of hybridized origin) and in the different morphological types of the White primary race. In this last-named race, the association of the variations of intermediate hair form with such subraces as Nordic, Alpine, Mediterranean, etc., seems to have little taxonomic value. Familial rather than broader racial genetic factors seem to be principally responsible for variations within European and other White stocks, with the exception of certain specialized inbred types and others in which some minor admixture of a racially extraneous strain may tend to express itself in a predominant hair form. Thus inbreeding in Jewish peoples may account in part for the high incidence of deep-waved hair, particularly if some selectional factor operates in favor of that variation within the stock involved. Again, the prevalence of straight and somewhat coarser hair in Eastern and Central Europe than is commonly found farther to the north, south, and west may well be caused by infusions of Mongoloid strains.

It was formerly believed that the shape of the cross-section of the hair shaft as expressed by an index was an exact indicator of the form of the hair. Thus an index of the hair cross-section in which the lesser diameter exceeds 80 per cent of the greater was thought to be virtual proof that the hair in question was straight, whereas an index below 60 per cent was the invariable mark of a strongly curved hair. It is now known that there is a considerable overlapping of hair-form indices between races and no little variation in the hairs of the same individual. All of the hairs of Chinese are not circular, nor are all of the Negro hairs flattened oval in cross-section. It is unsafe to predict the form of the hair from indices of cross-sections, unless one uses a whole series of cross-sections (30 to 100) from each individual and strikes an average. These averages are still valid for primary racial groups. Thus, average indices in excess of 80 in whole groups of people may be presumed to indicate straight Mongoloid hair (Jakuts 80.2, Ancient Peruvians 84.1, Paraguay Indians 86.4), while low average indices, such as 50.7 in the Gallas and 55.4 in the Kru of Liberia, do mean Negroid curved hair. Yet Trotter, in a short series of 340 Whites, found indices ranging in individual head hairs from 47 to 90 in females and from 57 to 92 in males, with mean indices of 74.2 in males and 74.7 in females.[21]

It is to be doubted that hair form is modifiable by environment. "Naturally curly" hair becomes more curly in damp weather, but artificially curved hair straightens out when exposed to moisture. "Permanent waving" of the hair is accomplished by twisting the hair and applying to it intense heat, while keeping the hair moist. Straightening of the hair is effected by ironing it out under moist heat. Apparently hair that is "permanently waved" is little affected by subsequent damp weather, but the wave is gradually lost as the hair grows out and is cut. Straightened hair becomes curved, however, as soon as the atmosphere gets humid. These considerations make it probable that there is some relationship between heat and moisture and curvature of the hair. It should be recalled, however, that very curly hair is flattened oval in cross-section, whereas very straight hair is almost round, and curly hair intermediate in form. The circular cross-section makes for greater rigidity and straightness. I should doubt that it would be possible to put a "permanent wave" into really straight, coarse Mongoloid hair, or to make permanently straight the flattened oval, twisted Negroid hair.

It may be that Negroid hair is an adaptation to the moist tropics, but Mongoloids dwelling in the tropics have just as straight hair as those under Arctic conditions. Nor does straight European hair become curved under tropical conditions. Negroes living in temperate zones seem to show no diminution in the curvature of the hair. Changes in hair form during the lifetime of the individual, such as are observed in many Europeans who have wavy or curly hair in infancy which gradually straightens out, are perhaps due to temporary dominance of an ancestral strain producing curly hair, which is afterwards swamped by a new growth of straight hair. At any rate, this seems to be the most plausible explanation of such cases, and it may indicate that curved forms of hair are not perfectly dominant over the coarse, straight forms. Straight Mongoloid hair is almost twice as heavy as a like amount of Negro hair,

[21] Trotter, "Form, Size, and Color of Head Hair," p. 436.

and the hair of Whites is intermediate in weight. Of the White stocks, Nordics have the lightest hair; that of Alpines is heavier, and Mediter-.raneans have the heaviest.[22] Head hair is longest in Mongoloids, shortest in Negroids, and intermediate in length in Whites and composite races.

Beard and body hair are very sparse in Negroids and Mongoloids and thicker in the White race. Probably the most abundant beard and body hair is found in the aborigines of Japan, the Ainu, who seem to be the remnant of an ancient stock that may have extended across northern Asia in early times (Plate 23). The Ainu, when unmixed with Mongoloid strains, have wavy black hair or slightly curly hair and are neither Negroid nor Mongoloid but should be classed among the light brown or brunet White subraces. The native Australians, although showing a distinct Negroid strain and very dark skinned, often have abundant body hair and well-developed beards (Plate 26). The head hair varies from wavy to moderately curly. There is, in this race, in all probability, a strain of the same stock that has given rise to the Ainu. Other hirsute stocks are the Central European Alpines and the allied Armenoids. Especially in the former group the body hair is abundant and the beard and moustache long and thick. Both the blond North European subrace and the brunet Southern or Mediterranean subrace have less abundant body hair than the other White stocks but much more than Negroes or Mongoloids. Most of the composite or secondary races in which predominant Mongoloid or Negroid strains may be detected have scanty beards and little body hair. Where, however, Negro strains have been mixed with those of the various White subraces, the hybrids show an intermediate degree of hairiness.

Cutting the hair does not make it grow thicker or faster, nor does shaving make the beard thicker or coarser. Dr. Mildred Trotter of Washington University, St. Louis, persuaded three women to shave one leg from knee to ankle twice a week for eight months. No change in hair growth was effected. Similar experiments, carefully controlled, have been made by both sexes on various parts of the body with identical results. External applications of cold cream, liquid petrolatum, and other agencies have no effect upon hair growth. Exposure to sun as contrasted with protection by clothing seems to make little or no difference to growth of hair. X-rays discourage hair from growing by destroying the follicle. State of nutrition is probably immaterial as a factor in the production of body hair. On the whole, it seems probable that the secretions of the ductless glands are the most important agents in promoting or inhibiting the growth of hair. According to Leopold Levi, the secre-

---

[22] Bernstein and Robertson, "Racial and Sexual Differences in Hair Weight," pp. 379–385.

tion of the thyroid affects the hair of the scalp, the eyebrows, and the lashes; that of the ovaries and testes, the body hair and beard. The pituitary and the suprarenal secretions, through their influence on. the testes, operate on the hair in general except the head hair, eyebrows, and lashes. But all of this is rather speculative. It does seem to point toward a conclusion that the quantity of the hair in all parts of the body is governed in individuals and in races by the endocrine balance. But men who are bald and women who have "superfluous" hair are not advised to resort to gland quacks nor to expose themselves to X-rays. The safest course is to "grin and bear it."

HEAD FORM

Any man or woman who has ever tried on a stiff straw hat, a bowler, or a silk "topper" knows that heads differ in shape and do not fit all hats. The only people who seem to be ignorant of this fact are those who make the hats. Skulls or heads when looked at from above show much variety in their contours. Almost all heads are longer than they are broad, but the vertical view may show a long narrow ellipse, a fat oval, a coffin-shaped pentagonoid form, a somewhat wedge-shaped ellipse with the hinder breadth much greater than the frontal breadth, and other forms. The great Italian anthropologist Sergi devised an elaborate scheme of classification for head contours. It bristles with appalling terms such as "Pentagonoides acutus" and "Ellipsoides embolicus" which are hard to pronounce and almost impossible to apply, except as opprobrious epithets. Moreover, this descriptive classification of head form does not lend itself readily to statistical analysis and elaboration. Consequently, anthropologists have usually adhered to another method of classifying head form from the vertical aspect—the ratio of the maximum breadth to the maximum length. Any skull viewed from above must be either narrow relative to its length, or broad, or medium. To put it another way, a skull may be long, short, or medium with reference to its breadth.

When the maximum breadth of a skull is less than 75 per cent of its greatest length, the skull is said to be long-headed or dolichocephalic. When the breadth is 80 per cent or more of the length, the skull is called brachycephalic or short-headed, and when the ratio of breadth to length is between 75 and 80 per cent the skull is called mesocephalic. On the head of the living, the thickness of the temporal muscles on both sides of the vault increases disproportionately the breadth diameter, so that this ratio, called the cephalic index, ranges about two units higher on the head of the living than on the dry skull. Colloquially we refer to dolichocephals as long-heads, and brachycephals are often called round-heads. There are no "square-heads," at least to the anthropologist. It is clear that the ratio of the maximum breadth to the greatest length of the skull or head is a very imperfect expression of the head contour. It does not take into account the breadth of the forehead, which is always less than the breadth over the ears; it makes no allowance for the variation in position of the maximum breadth, which may be far back on the side walls of the vault (the parietals) or nearer to the middle points of the bones, and either low down just over the ear holes or high up on the parietal bosses or bumps; it disregards also the shape of the occiput or back of the head. Nevertheless, this cranial or cephalic index has the merit of expressing a proportion and being capable of mathematical treatment.

What determines the extreme variations of this cranial or cephalic index? We recall that to be of use for purposes of racial classification a feature must be hereditarily transmitted and should not be subject to obvious environmental adaptations. Does the length-breadth index of the skull fulfill these prerequisites?

The horizontal contour and every other contour of the head are determined primarily by the shape of the brain. The form of the nutshell depends upon the shape of the kernel, or, at any rate, the shell grows to cover the nut. The bones of the skull vault are laid down in membrane in the embryo and those of the skull base in cartilage. The membranous and cartilaginous plates ossify into bone from centers of ossification, a certain number in each bone. The bones of the skull meet each other at their edges, forming cranial sutures which remain open until the growth of the brain has ceased. So, to cover the expanding brain, the cranial bones enlarge, growth taking place particularly along the sutural lines. After maturity has been attained and the brain has ceased to grow, these cranial sutures become obliterated, until, in aged persons, the skull vault is often a single shell of bone. Thus, the skull vault is a plastic covering moulded roughly to the shape of the brain and serving to protect whatever of brain is present. But the brain-case has other functions.

To the cranio-facial base is hafted the skeleton of the face; the sides of the vault afford attachment for the great temporal muscles of mastication; the supraorbital region may develop brow-ridges which serve both to protect the eyes and to resist the upward stresses of chewing. The hinder part of the brain-case also provides attachments for the muscles and ligaments that support the slightly overbalanced jaws. How much do these mechanical functions affect the form of the brain-case? Evidently, the larger and more projecting the face, the stronger must be the scaffolding that provides for masticatory attachments and for jaw support. In such snouty forms as the Rhodesian man, Neanderthal man, the gorilla, and chimpanzee, the brow-ridges protrude far forward of the frontal lobes of the brain, forming pent-houses over the eyes. The skull is much longer than the brain on account of this frontal buttress. Similarly, the projection backward of the occipital region and a bony transverse ridge or torus afford firmer purchase for the neck musculature, which must be adequate for jaw support. Further, the fan-shaped areas of attachment of the temporal muscles on the sides of the brain-case increase in size with greater massiveness of the jaws. Some anthropologists think that these temporal attachments restrict the transverse growth of the brain and of the brain-case by the compression they exert upon the skull walls. When you chew, you squeeze your skull, if not your brain.

It is apparent, therefore, that men with big faces and protruding jaws are likely to have longer and relatively narrower skulls than those with recessed jaws and smaller faces, especially if the face and jaws have increased disproportionately to the growth of the brain. But how do individuals acquire large and protruding faces and jaws? Apart from some special cases, individual men do not *acquire* big jaws at all; they inherit them. Negroes and Australians put upon their chewing apparatus no special strain that causes them to develop protruding jaws. The functional utility of a protruding snout vanished in the prehuman stage of evolution. Even in such fossil forms as Neanderthal man and Rhodesian man, massive jaws and prognathism must be mere survivals of a lower primate condition, since the diet of these races could scarcely have made any greater demands upon their jaws than do the foods masticated by many primitive and straight-faced men of today. Modern civilized races, which live for the most part upon diets of soft, cooked food requiring little chewing, have small and non-protrusive jaws hung to long and narrow skulls or to short and broad skulls, quite indiscriminately.

Only one group of modern men affords any plausible support for the theory of skull modification through the masticatory function. This is the Eskimo.

The skull of the Eskimo is the most easily recognizable of all cranial types (Fig. 64). Characteristically, it is very long, narrow, and high, with a ridge-pole-like elevation running down the middle line of the roof from front to back. The temporal muscle attachments are very extensive; the temporal crests or ridges bounding the upper parts of these areas rise high up on the vault and often approach close to the middle line. The face of the Eskimo is long and extremely broad. The cheek bones or malars, prominent in all Mongoloids, project outward to an exaggerated degree and are also pushed forward. The hinder angles of the jaws are everted and flaring so that the face looks very square. The forehead is narrow but usually of fair height and rather steep. Brow-ridges are feebly developed. The nasal aperture is very narrow and the bridge of the nose is also narrow and shows but little elevation. The face is flat. The palate is very broad and shallow and of a parabolic or hyperbolic form. The lower jaw is shallow, with the chin eminence poorly developed, but it is very thick in the body and enormously strong in the ascending branch. The teeth are large and in adults show the marks of extraordinary usage. Yet the entire face and jaws protrude very little.

It is commonly supposed that the great development of the chewing muscles in the Eskimo has modified the form of the brain-case. The

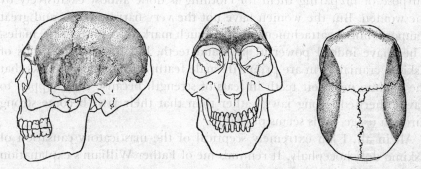

Fig. 64. Side, front, and top views of the skull of a male Eskimo, with areas of temporal muscle attachment and relief of brow ridges indicated by stippling.

tremendous attachments of the temporal muscles to the side walls of the skull are supposed to have restricted the lateral growth of the brain, compensation taking place by increase in length, thus rendering the Eskimo head excessively dolichocephalic and relatively high or hypsicephalic. The reason for the great masticatory development is supposed to be the tough fish and flesh diet upon which the Eskimo principally subsist. In addition to consuming large quantities of whale, seal, walrus, and other tough meat, the Eskimo are reputed to use their teeth for untieing frozen knots and lashings and for various feats of strength. Furthermore, they are reported to soften up leather and prepare it for use in clothing by chewing it. In the evening, Eskimo ladies chew up their husbands' frozen boots so that the latter may have nice, soft footwear ready for the next morning. All of these facts are correct. The Eskimo have, of all living men, the most powerfully developed chewing apparatus. To the anatomist, most Eskimo crania give plain evidence of dental and masticatory hypertrophy.

But there are grave objections to attributing their excessive dolichocephaly to squeezing of the skull walls by the powerful temporal muscles.

In the first place, it is questionable whether the temporal muscles actually exert any great inward pressure upon the skull walls, as their pull is almost straight up and down. The masseters and pterygoids, which also function in chewing, could have no such effect, since they are attached solely to the facial skeleton. Again, the food of the Eskimo is probably not as tough as it is reputed to be.

Mr. Vilhjalmur Stefansson, who has lived ten years with the Eskimo and for long periods exclusively upon their food, informs me that frozen fish is about of the consistency of ice cream. Freezing breaks up the fibres of the flesh. The chewing of sealskin and other kinds of hides for the purpose of preparing them for clothing is done almost exclusively by the women. But the women have not the very narrow skulls and great temporal muscle attachments that are such marked features of the males. They have indeed powerful jaws and teeth, but the exaggerations of Eskimo cranial form are primarily male features. Stefansson thinks that the Eskimo use their teeth in feats of strength because they happen to have inherited strong jaws, rather than that their jaws become strong through usage. This seems plausible.

All in all, I am extremely sceptical of the masticatory causation of Eskimo dolichocephaly. It reminds me of Father William's explanation of his mandibular prowess:

"You are old," said the youth, "and your jaws are too weak for anything tougher than suet;
  Yet you finished the goose, with the bones and the beak—pray, how did you manage to do it?"
"In my youth," said his father, "I took to the law and argued each case with my wife,
  And the muscular strength which it gave to my jaws has lasted the rest of my life."

It is much more probable that the strength of the chewing apparatus and its vigorous use in the Eskimo have caused his face and palate to increase in breadth than that they have squeezed out his skull to an excessive dolichocephaly.

Even if we admit that the Eskimo skull may have become constricted in breadth and increased in length through temporal muscle pressure, we cannot suppose that such external mechanical factors are generally operative in mankind or have been important factors in producing long-headedness. Professor Arthur Thomson of Oxford University long ago showed that there is a close relation between the shape of the skull and the mass of the brain therein contained. Since the skull base is laid down in cartilage and the vault in membrane, the latter is more plastic than the former. Professor Thomson illustrated the conditions of human brain and skull growth by taking a skull from which the vault had been sawn off and placing therein a rubber bladder. He then pumped air into the bladder as a substitute for brains. As the bladder expanded, it first took on the long, narrow egg-shape into which it was moulded by the rigid base and lower portions of the skull walls. When, however, more and more air was pumped into the bladder, it swelled above and beyond the edges of the base and gradually became nearly spherical. Successive increments of air increased the breadth more than the length.

Evidently a sphere is the most economical shape of container. Given two persons of the same stature and of markedly different cranial capacity, the one with the larger brain is likely to have the rounder skull. Or, if we take two men with identical cranial capacities, one of whom is short and the other tall, the taller individual is almost certain to have the longer head. For, the length of the skull base and the length of the head are related to the stature of the individual more closely than the breadth of the skull to body breadth or to stature. Of course, some short individuals have long heads, and other tall persons have short heads, but in general the length of the head and the height of the entire body are correlated. It seems, therefore, that an increase of stature without a corresponding increase of cranial capacity is likely to reduce the relative breadth of the skull, whereas an increase in brain size without an addition to stature tends to increase the relative breadth of the skull, making it more brachycephalic.

Since stature fluctuates markedly in offspring of the same parents, it seems probable that this fluctuation affects the cephalic index, since brain size appears to be more stable than stature. But such variations of the cephalic index with stature are probably slight and scarcely affect the mean cranial index of a population, unless some very untoward environmental condition operates constantly to depress stature through malnutrition.

Many years ago, Professor Franz Boas offered evidence that the children born in this country of foreign parentage differ in cranial index from their parents. Round-headed Eastern European Jews produced offspring in this country whose heads were absolutely longer and relatively narrower. On the other hand, children of dolichocephalic Italian immigrants showed an increase in the relation of the breadth to the length of the head. The accuracy of these findings has been attested by at least two later and independent investigations.

How are these changes to be explained? Many have leaped to the conclusion that something in the American environment moulds diverse head forms into a uniform type approaching that of the American Indian. This idea is not supported by results of studies of Americans of European origin whose ancestors have been residents of the United States for several generations. Dr. Aleš Hrdlička found that these "Old Americans" resembled closely the European stocks from which their ancestors had sprung.

Professor Boas examined and rejected the hypothesis that the alteration in head form in children of foreign parents in this country was due to abandonment of the habits of cradling which, practised in the home countries, tended to deform the skulls of infants. In some European countries, the infants are tightly swaddled, and their heads rest upon pillows that are alleged to flatten the back of the head. But there is satisfactory evidence neither that the heads are actually deformed by this practice nor that such methods of cradling are abandoned immediately upon arrival in the United States. Boas himself was inclined to think that the variation of the head form in the children of immigrant parentage may be explained by the greater diversity of strains involved in marriages of Europeans contracted in the United States. In Europe, an Italian is likely to marry a girl of his own home village where most families have been more or less inbred for centuries. In New York, an Italian may mate with a girl of his own nationality from *any* part of Italy. Such an increased diversity in family lines would be likely to cause fluctuations in the physical characteristics of the offspring.

Formerly, it seemed to me that the explanation of this change in head form might lie, in part, in another set of factors. Russian Jews coming to this country beget children here who are taller and less brachycephalic than themselves. Many of these Eastern immigrants come from crowded city ghettos where they have been badly nourished and subjected to such unfavorable living conditions that their stature has been depressed. Such immigrants usually settle in some congested urban district in the United States. But they earn more money and get more and better food than in their native lands. Their children attain to their full hereditary measure of stature. In conformity with the increase of stature, their skull bases become elongated, but, since the brain mass does not increase proportionately, the skull becomes relatively narrower and longer.

Unfortunately, this neat little theory does not work in some other cases. For example, Dr. Harry L. Shapiro found that the Hawaiian-born children of Japanese-born immigrants are substantially taller than their parents, but their heads are significantly shorter and broader, so that they combine greater stature with more pronounced brachycephaly.[23] Experience has taught me to beware of simple and seductive explanations of bodily changes.

Professor Boas himself did not argue for an unlimited plasticity of head form. He merely pointed out the changes in people of the same stock in two different environments. It should be noted that Boas found that children born in the old countries, however young at the time of their arrival here, retain the head form of the parental stock, and that in some cases the second generation born in this country seem to show an increased deviation from the parental type as compared with the first. One wonders what happens to the head form of an immigrant child born during the voyage over from the old country.

Professor Alexis Ivanovsky [24] investigated a large sample of the population of Southern Russia just before the onset of a famine and at intervals of six months during the three years of its duration. All bodily measurements were diminished by the starvation diet to which these people were reduced. Weight and stature were especially lowered. All head and face measurements decreased, but the head breadth decreased more than the head length, so that in most of the groups studied the cranial index was lowered, and brachycephaly was diminished. The number of long-heads in the population increased. Only in the case of the male Armenians, the male Gruzins, and the male Tartars of Crimea, the brachycephaly was increased. Apparently not even starvation can modify some types. The females of these groups, like the majority of all the peoples studied, showed increased dolichocephaly. In conformity with the decrease in head breadth, face breadth also decreased more than face length, so that the subjects suffering from undernourishment became relatively longer and narrower in their facial proportions—more hatchet-faced and lantern-jawed. Four months after the famine ended, most of the subjects studied had practically regained their normal size and proportions.

The decrease in cephalic index among the famine stricken population of Russia amounted to an average of about two index units, or 2 per cent of the ratio of head breadth to head length. Professor Boas' studies of the head form of children of European immigrants showed changes in the cephalic index of about the same average quantity. One may perhaps conclude that radical environmental disturbances, especially those affecting growth and nutrition, may alter the length-breadth index of the head 2 or 3 per cent. A five unit change is necessary to shift a head from dolicho-

---

[23] Shapiro, *Migration and Environment,* pp. 29–49.
[24] Ivanovsky, "Physical modifications," pp. 331–353.

cephaly to brachycephaly or the reverse, according to conventional sub-divisions of the index. It seems probable that the effect of such environmental disturbances is insufficient to shift the head index from one extreme category to another unless it can be shown to be cumulative for several generations. We do not know whether or not this ever happens, but to me it seems improbable. It is more likely that an adjustment of the organism to the new environment takes place so that succeeding generations tend to revert to the parental mean or to fluctuate about it.

But, if we grant that head form as expressed by the cephalic index is, in the main, a heritable and non-adaptive feature, though subject to some environmental fluctuation, we have, nevertheless, to explain in what way head form is inherited. During early prehistoric times, the prevalent head form in most parts of Europe was dolichocephalic.

The first brachycephals appear late in the Upper Palaeolithic Age or in the succeeding Mesolithic. During the Neolithic period, dolichocephals are in the majority in most parts of Europe, but the round-headed element seems to increase in strength. The Bronze Age shows a further reinforcement of the brachycephalic strain. In Great Britain during this period the predominantly long-headed population of Neolithic times is almost entirely replaced by round-heads. The spread of cremation makes it difficult to judge the relative proportions of dolichocephaly and brachycephaly during the latter part of the Bronze Age and the Early Iron Age. Bone ash yields no cranial index. But there seems to have been a recrudescence of long-headedness during the Early Iron Age and the Roman period. Sometime after the tenth century A.D., the tide of brachycephaly suddenly rose and has continued at its flood down to the present time. In Central and Eastern Europe, the long-headedness of early times has disappeared, and brachycephaly is generally prevalent. Round-heads also predominate in the western part of the continent, but centers of long-headedness still exist in Spain, Southern Italy, Scandinavia, the British Isles, and other isolated, but not necessarily benighted, regions.

Various explanations have been offered for this change of head form in Europe during the last ten centuries. Some have supposed that the long-heads have been weeded out by a process of natural selection or perhaps exterminated by too free indulgence of their war-like propensities. No valid evidence has been adduced in support of the theory that dolichocephals are constitutionally inferior to brachycephals, nor has it ever been shown that the death rates in long-headed stocks are higher than in round-headed stocks. There is, however, some truth in the argument that the dying out of the North European long-heads is partially the result of their dispersion throughout the world in colonizing and military attempts. It is hardly possible to evaluate the importance of this factor, however lachrymose we become over the "Passing of the Great Race."

The brachycephalization of Europe finds a rough parallel in the New World. The American Indian population seems to have consisted of an earlier dolichocephalic stratum which, in later times, was supplemented by a brachycephalic element. Here, as in Europe, round-headedness increased until the long-headed populations survived only as remnants in isolated areas. My late colleague, Professor R. B. Dixon, accumulated evidence that long-headed primitive stocks have been replaced by round-heads in so many parts of the world that brachycephalization may almost be claimed as an universal phenomenon.

In the effort to explain why their early prehistoric or historic predecessors were long-heads, whereas they themselves are round-heads, some central and eastern European anthropologists have argued that their lack of resemblance to their supposed ancestors is due to an evolution of dolichocephalic types into brachycephalic types. Both the ancient Slavs and the ancient Germans seem to have been dolichocephalic, while the opposite head form now prevails in that area. A comforting suggestion is that the increase in the size of the brain in recent centuries is responsible for the greater relative and absolute head breadths of today. We have noted that an increase in cranial capacity with constant stature is likely to increase the cephalic index. But the theory that our head shapes differ from those of our ancestors because our brains are larger and therefore rounder is not supported by evidence of an increase of cranial capacity or of brain mass during the period of brachycephalization. It cannot be shown that wherever brachycephals have succeeded dolichocephals the cubical contents of the brain-case display increments proportional to the rise of the cephalic index. Our brains simply have *not* grown.

Probably the most important single factor in the brachycephalization of Europe in historic times has been the continuous infiltration of Asiatic round-heads, their intermixture with the earlier European dolichocephals, and the actual replacement of these latter by brachycephals. This obvious cause has been consistently neglected or minimized by Central European anthropologists. The Huns were out-and-out Mongoloids, consisting of long-headed and round-headed types, with the former probably in the majority.[25] The Avars were also Mongoloid and pre-

25 Coon, *Races of Europe*, pp. 226–240.

dominantly brachycephalic. The Magyars were probably only partially Mongoloid and mesocephalic, with a strong tendency toward increasing brachycephaly. The Turks were and are non-Mongoloid but markedly brachycephalic, and the Mongols themselves who entered Europe were presumably largely of the brachycephalic variety. There seems to be some evidence that the Finno-Ugrians and Bulgars may have been long-heads originally. All in all, the bulk of the populations entering Europe from Asia in the historical migration period seems to have been round-headed.

Anyone who thinks that Europe could have been overrun for centuries by these Asiatic hordes without undergoing a profound modification of the genetic and phenotypic constitution of its population is either ignorant of modern studies of race mixture or unwilling to face facts. A probably minor brachycephalic element already widespread in Europe was tremendously reinforced by these repeated immigrations. It is probable that many of the older dolichocephalic stocks were driven out, absorbed, or exterminated. It is pertinent to note that those areas of Europe that were relatively immune from these historical invasions of Asiatic brachycephals—Scandinavia, the British Isles, the Spanish peninsula, and Southern Italy—are precisely the places in which modern brachycephalization is least evident. The invasions of Moors and Berbers into Spain brought principally dolichocephals. The New World was colonized at first largely by the English, Spanish, Portuguese, and French—all predominantly long-headed or mesocephalic, with the possible exception of the French. I am unaware of any evidence of progressive brachycephalization of these stocks in North America, Central America, and South America.

The European swing toward brachycephaly in mediaeval and modern times naturally involves also the inheritance of head form. If the cephalic index were inherited by the operation of a single pair of factors with brachycephaly completely dominant, and if the original populations of long-heads and round-heads mixed in equal proportions and without subsequent selection, we might expect three out of four Europeans to be brachycephalic and the rest dolichocephalic. Obviously, neither of these conditions has been fulfilled. In the first place, whether the average of a European population is brachycephalic or dolichocephalic, that population is sure to include large proportions of persons with indices that are mesocephalic (77 to 81 on the living, 75 to 79 on the skull). If we assume that pure homozygotes in head form are either pronouncedly dolichocephalic or markedly brachycephalic, then it is clear that these mesocephals must be heterozygous and that multiple factors are concerned in the inheritance of the cephalic index. Yet it is barely possible that mesocephaly may have been the original head form of early and undifferentiated hominids, and that many modern mesocephals are of pure mesocephalic lineage. In such an event, we should have to postulate repeated mutations in both directions from the intermediate head form. On the whole, such a theory has little support in human palaeontology, since most forms of fossil men, whether anatomically archaic or of the modernized *sapiens* types, seem to have been long-headed. A safer assumption from the evidence in hand seems to be that early man was usually long-headed and that most mutations have been toward brachycephaly.

In all of the three primary races of modern man—White, Negroid, and Mongoloid—head form ranges from extreme dolichocephaly through mesocephaly to brachycephaly. Therefore mutations toward brachycephaly (or possibly in the opposite direction) must have taken place in all three of them. Yet brachycephaly is comparatively rare in Negroids, and dolichocephaly in Mongoloids. Only in the White race does there seem to be no strong numerical predominance of one or the other form.

An elementary work such as this has no space for a full discussion of schemes of the inheritance of head form. It seems necessary to assume that more than one inheritance factor or unit is involved in the determination of head length, and a number of factors also in head breadth. Further than this, in order to account for the excess of brachycephals, one must suppose that in some way great head breadths dominate over the lesser breadths, or that short head lengths assert themselves at the expense of hereditary factors making for great head length. In no other way does it seem possible to explain the fact that studies of family inheritance show an excess of brachycephalic children in families whose parents are diverse in head form. Dr. Frets, a Dutch anthropologist, has investigated some thousands of families in which it is apparent that this is the case. But no satisfactory scheme of expressing these observations by a Mendelian formula has yet been devised.

We do know that when brachycephals and dolichocephals interbreed, the resulting offspring may be dolichocephalic, mesocephalic, or brachycephalic, and that of such offspring few are likely to be long-heads, and many more either mesocephalic or brachycephalic. All evidence seems to indicate that the intermediate head breadth-length indices are usually, if not always, the result of crossing the extreme types. But there are also data that show that parents of the same head form but of radically different size may produce offspring with head form different from themselves. If, for example, both parents are dolichocephalic, but the father has a very large head and the mother a very small one, a child may inherit the absolutely small head length of the mother with the absolutely large but relatively small paternal head breadth, and thus be mesocephalic or even brachycephalic. Instances of this kind, which may be observed in Fret's tables of head dimensions of parents and children, show that offspring may inherit the exact or approximate dimensions of the head from their parents, usually both diameters from the same parent, but sometimes one measurement from one parent and the other from the other. However, head form differing radically from that of either parent is likely to occur in children only occasionally, and especially when the parents manifest wide differences in head size. Generally speaking, long-headed parents have long-headed children and round-headed parents round-headed children. Parents differing widely in head form have children of all categories but are likely to produce an excess of brachycephals.

More recent studies of Frets and others suggest that, in addition to several pairs of factors determining head breadth and others determining head length, there may be shape factors involved in the inheritance of head form. Sinnott and Durham found that elongate, spherical, and disk shapes in gourds depended upon simple factors which could be analyzed only when relative growth rates in length and breadth were studied rather than absolute or separate growth rates.[26] In these gourds the genes seemed to operate in two ways: (1) to control the plane of cell division in growing tissues, so that division is more frequent in one plane than the other; (2) to localize or restrict growth to particular parts. Anyone who has studied the growth of the head in children knows that in successive months there are alternate and variable increases in the two different dimensions involved in the cephalic index. Sometimes head length grows more rapidly than breadth, and vice versa. This alternation causes an oscillation of the index during growth. However, as far as I am aware, there is usually no consistent change in head form from fairly early infancy to adult years. The first few weeks or even months after birth have to be ruled out because of possible deformation of the head incident to passing through the birth canal. Steggerda has measured the same 50 individuals of each of four races or stocks annually from the age of 6 to the age of 18 years.[27] In Maya Indians, Navajo Indians, Negroes, and Dutch Whites from Michigan, the cephalic indices seemed to be

[26] Snyder, *Principles of Heredity,* p. 364, quoting E. W. Sinnott, and G. B. Durham, *Botanical Gazette,* 1929, 87: 411. Cf. also Gates, ms.
[27] Steggerda, *Maya Indians,* p. 184.

established at the earliest age measured and to show no consistent or uniform change thereafter.

The properties of the cephalic index may then be summarized as follows:

(1) It is inherited, but the multiple factors involved relating probably to length of the head, breadth of the head, and shape, have, up to now, prevented the genetics of the index from being worked out. In Europe, there is evidence that brachycephaly is to some extent dominant, meso-cephaly heterozygous, and dolichocephaly recessive, but multiple alleles are unquestionably concerned, and the genetic composition can hardly be predicted from the phenotype. There is considerable doubt that dolichocephaly is recessive in Africa among the Negroes or in Oceania among the Melanesians and Papuans.

(2) There is no consistent postnatal change in the cephalic index of the individual, which seems to be established at birth or shortly after birth. This index is likely to run one or two units higher in females than in males of the same stock, presumably because of the greater de-velopment of glabella and brow-ridges in the male sex, which increases the length disproportionately. But in some stocks, especially mixed stocks, females tend to be somewhat more dolichocephalic than males.

(3) The cephalic index is apparently subject to modification, within limits, by radical environmental changes. A starvation diet seems to reduce the index, apparently because the thickness of the temporal muscles on the sides of the head decreases. Increased stature in the chil-dren of European immigrants to the United States seemingly lowers the index because the length of the head is more closely correlated with stature than is head breadth. However, increased stature in the Hawaiian born offspring of Japanese immigrants is accompanied by shortening and broadening of the head. The cephalic index may also be modified by artificial deformation of the head, brought about by pressure on the occiput during infancy, or other pressures. It seems improbable that masticatory function affects head shape, even in the case of the Eskimo.

(4) While there is no direct evidence that either dolichocephaly or brachycephaly confers upon its possessor an advantage in the struggle for existence, it seems probable that in Central and Eastern Europe, and possibly in Polynesia, round-headedness is associated with certain con-stitutional or other qualities in some body types and stocks that have conferred upon it survival value. Otherwise, it is almost impossible to explain the brachycephalization of certain areas in Europe and else-where during modern times.

(5) Evidence thus far available suggests that early man was generally dolichocephalic and that there have been in different regions and different races independent and repeated mutations toward brachycephaly.

The vagaries and vacillations of head form, as expressed by the cephalic index, relegate it to a position of secondary importance as a taxonomic character in man, or as a criterion of race. Although it seems to be, in the main, a feature that is hereditarily determined, more or less stable during the life of the individual, and, so far as is known, non-adaptive, it lacks reliability as an indicator of ancestry. We cannot be sure, for example, that a brachycephalic person has descended from unbroken lines of mainly brachycephalic ancestors, nor even that his parents are brachycephalic, although the latter is a strong probability. The situation in the case of dolichocephaly—which seems to be more or less recessive in Whites—is not quite so bad, but here again the clear evidence of certain abrupt swings toward long-headedness that can be related to stature increase, on the one hand, and starvation diets, on the other, bids us pause before placing all of our taxonomic trust in this variant of head form.

This degradation of the cephalic index is regrettable, because it has been so widely used as the primary basis of classification, especially in skulls, which naturally afford no reliable clues as to the hair form and pigmentation of their possessors in life. The craniologist is only too well aware that he cannot ordinarily use the cranial index as a means of distinguishing Negroes, Mongoloids, and Whites from each other; he employs rather combinations of morphological features that have little or nothing to do with the shape of the skull viewed from above. It is only when the classificationist is called upon to subdivide one or more of the primary races, that he has recourse to the cephalic index with any justifiable confidence, and even here such confidence is not always well placed. Now I do not propose to abandon completely the use of the cephalic index in racial classification but only to recognize its obvious limitations and to restrict its use accordingly. It may be properly used, in my opinion, only when it is associated with several other more reliable racial criteria of a metric or morphological character in a hereditary combination that is apparently stabilized and representative of a sizeable and relatively homogeneous breeding population. Such a population usually has a certain geographical continuity—i.e., tends to be localized within certain areas—and may correspond roughly to the zoologist's concept of a geographical race. Thus, if a Negroid population is characterized by pygmy size, a shield-shaped forehead, an exaggerated bulbousness of the nasal tip and excessive alar flare, a convex and long upper integumental lip with little membranous eversion, *and a long head,* and if, further, that Negroid population is restricted to the Congo basin, it seems legitimate to regard the dolichocephaly as an element of the racial complex, although by no means the most distinctive.

Actually, virtually any hereditary physical character that is used for taxonomic purposes, must, in any event, be combined with other characters in order to attain any large measure of validity as a racial criterion. The cephalic index is not peculiar in this inability to stand alone, but it must not be regarded, as it sometimes has been regarded, as any sort of an eternal racial verity. It is far from immutable.

The height of the head relative to its length and breadth is also expressed in the height-length and height-breadth indices. The height indices have not been employed as often as the length-breadth index because of the great difficulty of getting an accurate head height measurement on the living. Height, length, and breadth of the head are doubtless interdependent. There may be a wider range of individual variation in height than in length. It has been suggested that skull length and breadth are primarily inherited characters, but that the height varies with development of the individual brain. Really, our knowledge of the distribution and significance of height indices is so defective that it is hardly practicable to employ them as racial criteria.

FACE FORM

We recognize our acquaintances by looking at their faces rather than at the shape of their heads. Individual variations express themselves here more plainly than in any other part of the body. Racial differences too are much more marked in the countenance than elsewhere. If you are called upon to describe a Negro, you define the type by the color of the skin, the form of the hair, the projection of the jaws, the shape of the nose, and the thickness of the lips. Unless you are an anthropologist, you say nothing about the head. The distinguishing marks of race to the layman and to the anthropologist alike are mostly facial features.

We may attempt to describe the shape of the face as oval, round, or square, but these terms cannot be applied with any accuracy to most individuals. The somewhat vulgar terms—"hatchet-faced," "horse-faced," "moon-faced," and even "pie-faced" and "lantern-jawed"—are much more useful, if less polite. It is even more satisfactory to classify the relation of the breadth of the face to its length, so that one recognizes long-narrow, short-broad, and medium subdivisions of the index. Further, the size may be taken into consideration, so that to the classification may be added long-broad, short-narrow, and other combinations. The facial index is the length of the face from the root of the nose to the bottom of the chin expressed as a percentage of the greatest breadth across the cheek bones. Facial indices, when subdivided conventionally, furnish us with a means of physical classification similar to the length-breadth index of the skull and much more noticeable than the latter. But the facial index is inferior to the cranial index as a test of race because it is much more affected by function, age, and sex.

The use of the teeth in chewing may modify the proportions of the face. Strong-jawed people are likely to have broad faces. It is quite possible that the rotary movements of the jaw observed in gum-chewing stenographers and tobacco-chewing rustics may stimulate the transverse growth of the dental arches and of the whole face. In early finds of "modern" types of Europeans, facial breadth is often or usually greater than in people of today. Stone Age inhabitants of Great Britain, for example, usually have broader and somewhat shorter faces than the present inhabitants of that island. It may be that the modern dietary of soft, cooked food has brought about a partial atrophy of the chewing muscles affixed to the sides of the face and the brain-case, thus diminishing face breadth. By way of compensation, the face may elongate or grow downward along the line of least resistance. This tendency toward lengthening and narrowing of the facial skeleton is certainly pronounced in northwestern Europeans and in many of their American relatives, but it is by no means as widespread in modern groups as the broadening and relative shortening of the brain-case.

One has only to go back to such fossil types as the Rhodesian and Neanderthal men to realize that great length of the face in primitive man is due to deep jaws. Every great ape also has a very long and relatively narrow face. Neanderthal man has a longer and relatively narrower face than most Nordics but shows no signs of masticatory degeneration. However, if Weidenreich's reconstructions of Sinanthropus and Pithecanthropus are correct, these very archaic human types had relatively short faces, although prognathous.

Persons who have broad skulls usually have broad faces, because, after all, the face is fitted to the brain-case. Most individuals with narrow brain boxes have narrow faces for the same reason. But strong-jawed persons are likely to have rather broad faces, regardless of the great or small breadth of their skull vaults. The length of the face is largely dependent upon the depth of the jaws as gauged by the distance from the sill of the nasal opening to the bottom of the chin. But some types owe the great length of the face more to the height of the mid-facial or nasal region than to the depth of the jaws. Males almost invariably have longer and relatively narrower faces than females of the same race, because the masculine jaws are heavier and deeper, and the upper lip and chin are longer. There is no close relationship between the length of the face from the root of the nose to the chin and the length of the head from the glabella (just above the nasal root) to the mid-occipital point. People with relatively short and broad faces often have long and narrow skulls, but, in such cases, the breadth of the face, though great relative to its length, is usually absolutely small or medium. Again, persons with relatively long and narrow faces may have relatively short and broad skulls, but, under these circumstances, the appearance of narrow face breadth is often due to the great length of the face rather than to its diminished breadth.

Many of the types showing disharmony of face form with head form are racially mixed, but we are by no means certain that such is always the case. It seems probable, for example, that most pure Negro types have relatively short and rather broad faces hafted to narrow and long brain-cases. Armenoids almost always have long and relatively narrow faces, but their brain-cases are absolutely short and relatively broad.

There is some connection between the proportions and diameters of face and the secretions of the ductless glands. Individuals afflicted with acromegaly, which involves an enlargement of the anterior lobe of the pituitary body at the base of the skull, have enormously elongated faces, especially deep jaws. Probably most very long-faced persons have over-active pituitary glands. Cretins, Mongolian idiots, and other pathological types in which there is deficiency of the thyroid gland in the neck, invariably have very short and relatively broad faces, usually attached to broad, short skulls.

The protrusion of the jaws that is called prognathism is clearly a reminiscence of the mammalian snout. None of the modern races that exhibit this feature has any more use for a snout than have the Europeans with the most receding faces. The most marked forward protrusion of the jaws in modern groups is found among the dark-skinned Negroes and Australians. Among these races, the whole face juts out so that the tangent to the root of the nose and the most projecting part of the jaws forms an acute angle with the forward prolongation of the horizontal from the ear-hole to the lower border of the eye-socket. In Europeans, this angle is almost a right angle or slightly more, so that the facial axis is nearly perpendicular to the eye-ear horizontal. This straight-faced condition is called orthognathism. Such markedly prognathous groups as the Negroes and Australians usually show also a bulging of the alveolar regions of the upper and lower jaws which lodge the front teeth. This is called alveolar prognathism. All apes and monkeys show both facial and alveolar prognathism. Most Mongoloids and some White groups show a moderate alveolar prognathism but little or no facial prognathism. Studies of racial mixtures seem to show that when prognathous types are crossed with orthognathous types, as for example Negroes and Whites, facial protrusion tends to disappear or to be "recessive." It is for this reason that the majority of our mixed Negroids in the United States show little prognathism.

Facial projection or prognathism is not very useful as a criterion of race because it is a recessive and easily suppressed feature. Since most races are mixed, prognathism is only sporadically distributed, even in those dark-skinned groups of whom theoretically it should be a distinguishing feature.

The chin projects forward most strongly, as a rule, in people whose faces are straight rather than prognathous. Extreme alveolar protrusion masks the chin prominence and seems to be developed at the expense of the latter. On the other hand, many European types with degenerate masticatory apparatus show great nasal projection with weak, receding lower jaws and poorly developed chin eminences. There is some reason in the physiognomic classification of profiles as convex or concave. The convex type is a nasal type and the concave type a mandibular type. The former is ultra-modern, often degenerate; the latter is primitive and sometimes bestial. But if your nose points the way, and your chin lags behind, it does not mean that you have natural qualifications for scientific investigation. Nor does a jutting ram of a chin imply either force of character or pugilistic aptitude. You may demonstrate the two extreme types of faces by manipulating one of those old rubber dolls in which the features are moulded on a flexible, air-filled, rubber sphere. If you push in the root of the nose, the sides of the face and the front parts of the jaws bulge out, making a prognathous, broad-faced, concave type. If you squeeze the sides of the face, the breadth is diminished, the middle or nasal portion is thrust out into prominence, and the face is elongated. Some such compensating interdependence of facial breadth, facial length, and facial projection is evident in different racial and individual types. Thrust-out jaws go with a pushed-in mid-facial region and expanded breadth. A protruded nasal region is usually associated with an elongated and narrow face and recessed jaws. These variations and correlations of facial form are, in some cases, intimately bound up with function, but in modern races they may result primarily from evolutionary tendencies inherent in different stocks which have little or nothing to do with use.

In the facial index, the length is expressed as a percentage of the breadth. If this percentage or index is less than 84, the person or group falling within this range is called euryprosopic, or broad-faced. If the index ranges between 85 and 88, it is called mesoprosopic or medium-faced, if 88 or above, leptoprosopic or narrow-faced. On dry skulls, the mesoprosopic range is from 85 to 89.9; otherwise the indices are altogether comparable.

Several difficulties prevent an extensive utilization of the facial index for purposes of racial classification. The first of these is its change during growth when the teeth are erupting and the jaws are elongating. During all these years, the facial index usually increases; i.e., the face becomes longer and relatively narrower. Then, in middle life, there is presumably a resting period during which the facial index does not change, except in so far as the crowns of the teeth wear down, involving some slight shortening of the face length. However, in-old age, with multiple loss of teeth, the alveolar borders that previously lodged them shrink and are absorbed, so that pronounced diminution of face length takes place and the index decreases again. There are also the functional complications already discussed, which suggest that continual and vigorous use of the masticatory apparatus from infancy onward tends to broaden the jaws and the whole face, whereas jaws and teeth that have no hard work to do may become attenuated and long.

Finally, we know little or nothing about the inheritance of face form and the facial index except that, apart from these functional and age interferences, inheritance does seem to manifest itself as a generally controlling factor. We do not know that short, broad faces are dominant over long, narrow faces, or how many pairs of factors control face length and face breadth respectively, or whether, in addition, shape factors are involved. In such a state of ignorance, about all that we can do with the facial index in racial classification is to make some vague statement about this or that type to the effect that "the associated face form is usually long and narrow"—or whatever it happens to be, according to the metrical data available on samples of the type or according to one's personal morphological impression. Facial proportions are probably related to types of body build, as well as to racial inheritance.

EYES

Poets and novelists rhapsodize about the color and expression of eyes, the arch of the eyebrows, and the length of eyelashes, but the form of the eye opening and the variations of the soft parts are left to the anthropologist for accurate description. If you really want to know how to describe a pair of eyes with precision, consult the French anthropologist Bertillon in his instructions for policemen. There is nothing of beauty or romance in a French detective's description of a criminal's eyes; it does not grip the imagination, but it does catch the criminal.

We all recognize that the eye of the Mongolian differs markedly from that of the European because of its slant and its narrow opening. There are, perhaps, only two sharply contrasted varieties of the eye in modern man—the Mongoloid eye and the non-Mongoloid eye. The non-Mongoloid eye tends to be more or less deeply recessed in its orbit or socket and, in the male, is usually overhung by the brow-ridges and the eyebrows. The Mongoloid eye characteristically fills the orbit and protrudes slightly, but the lack of development of brow-ridges and the scanty eyebrows of the Mongoloid contribute to this appearance. Often, in the Mongolian eye, the outer half of the eyeball or that portion of it covered by the upper lid seems to be in the same vertical plane as the forehead immediately above it. Another reason why the Mongoloid eye seems to fill the orbit is that it is extremely fatty with very thick lids. The lower rim of the Mongoloid orbit juts forward, and the entire cheek-bone or malar is not only large and laterally projecting, but also sharply angled at the outside corner. This part of the face in the Mongoloid is usually covered with a pad of fat. All of these features, together with the low-bridged nose, contribute to the flat-faced appearance of this race. We usually think of slanting eyes as having the outer corners higher than the inner. Actually, the transverse axis of the eye opening, from the inner to the outer corner, may slope upward and outward, downward and outward, or may be horizontal. Mongoloid eyes, it is true, usually have the external corners elevated, and a similar slant of the eye, but not so marked, may often be observed in Europeans. Most eyes that are not slanted upward are horizontal, but not a few narrow-faced people show a slight downward and outward inclination of the axes of the eyes. Incidentally, eyes slanted upward are not usually observed in narrow-faced persons; the horizontal position of the eye opening is very common in broad-faced people, and is characteristic of most who have broad faces but lack the Mongoloid eye.

Complete Mongoloid

No fold

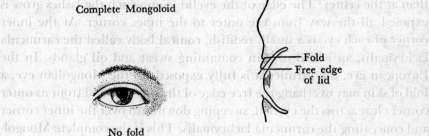

Fold
Free edge of lid

Internal epicanthus

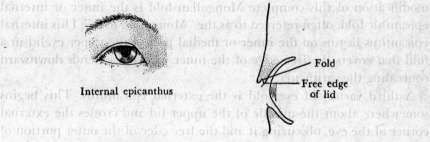

Fold
Free edge of lid

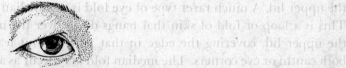

External epicanthus

Median fold

Fig. 65. Human eye folds. (In each case the right eye is represented.)

Another feature of the Mongoloid eye is the small vertical opening that gives it a slit-like appearance. This is due in a measure to the thick and overhanging upper lid, which often has a fold of skin that drops down over the free edge of the eyelid, partially obscuring the eyelashes.

Indeed the principal mark of the Mongoloid is the arrangement of these upper lid folds (Fig. 65). When the typical European eye is wide open, the upper lid shows a sulcus or wrinkle running almost parallel to the free edge of the eyelid, but approaching it more closely at the corners than at the center. The edge of the eyelid from which the lashes grow is exposed all the way from the outer to the inner corner. At the inner corner of each eye is a small, reddish, conical body called the caruncula lachrymalis, an island of skin containing sweat and oil glands. In the European eye, the caruncula is fully exposed. In the Mongolian eye, a fold of skin may overhang the free edge of the upper eyelid from its outer corner clear across the eyeball, sweeping downward over the inner corner and concealing the caruncula lachrymalis. This is the complete Mongoloid fold. Often it is not recognized as a fold, since it traverses the entire upper eyelid, obscuring the edge but showing no wrinkle. A common modification of this complete Mongolian fold is the inner or internal epicanthic fold, often referred to as the "Mongoloid fold." This internal epicanthus begins on the inner or medial part of the upper eyelid in a fold that covers the free edge of the inner part and extends downward concealing the caruncula.

A third variety of eye fold is the external epicanthus. This begins somewhere about the middle of the upper lid and crosses the external corner of the eye, obscuring it and the free edge of the outer portion of the upper lid. A much rarer type of eye fold is the median or cover fold. This is a loop or fold of skin that hangs down over the middle part of the upper lid, covering the edge in that portion, but leaving exposed both canthi or eye corners. The median fold may occur as a continuation of either the internal or external epicanthic folds.

The relationship between skin tension and eye folds is not simple. Certainly the disappearance of an inner epicanthic fold in the course of growth seems usually to be related to elevation of the nasal bridge and taking up of slack in the skin. Again, the external epicanthic fold develops most commonly in middle-aged and elderly adult males, the skin of whose upper lids has begun to bag over the outer corner of their recessed eyeballs, probably because of the loss of elasticity and the absorption of subcutaneous fat. However, the external fold as an old-age manifestation can hardly be due to the same causes as produce the external part of a complete Mongoloid fold that runs from one corner of the eye to the other. This complete Mongoloid fold is present in the young, the middle-aged, and the old alike, so far as I am aware. One would expect that the laterally and frontally jutting Mongoloid malar would stretch the skin at the outer corner of the eye to such an extent that no slack for an outer fold would be available. Obviously this is not the case. In spite of the prominence of the Mongoloid cheek bone, it is overlaid with an exuberance of fatty padding and loose, thick skin tissue. It is in precisely this setting that the complete, corner-to-corner fold occurs.

I have observed that the median fold seems commonest in young adult males with low eye openings and recessed eyeballs, and there is little doubt that with the attainment of maturity and the loss of skin elasticity such a median fold tends to merge with a developing external fold. Flat temples (small cheek bones that do not produce skin tension), deeply recessed eyeballs, and overhanging brow-ridges favor the development of the external fold in Europeans. This fold rarely, if ever, appears in young subjects. The inner epicanthus or "Mongoloid fold" is commonest in infants and children because lack of height development of the nasal root is an infantile feature. Further, because females are more infantile than males both in nasal height and in absence or small size of brow-ridges, the inner epicanthus is observed more frequently in the frail sex and, conversely, the outer epicanthus in the males.

However, a low nasal root in itself does not necessarily cause a fold over the inner corner of the eye. The internal epicanthus is not particularly common in Negroes, whose nasal roots are often low, although not so low as those of Mongoloids. Curiously enough, the great Asiatic anthropoid—the orang-utan—sometimes shows an inner epicanthus, while the African apes never have it, although they also have flat nasal roots.

The Mongoloid eye, with its inner epicanthus or complete Mongoloid fold, is found in varying degrees of development in most races of Mongoloid stock or Mongoloid intermixture. When it occurs in non-Mongoloid peoples, it is probably due to the appearance of a Mongoloid strain latent in the ancestry, unless it be a pathological feature as in cretins and so-called "Mongolian idiots." Ancestral exuberance, not thyroid deficiency, is the normal cause.

On the other hand, it seems doubtful that the median and external folds have any Mongoloid significance; they appear rather to be age features. Of course, it is also possible that some inner epicanthic folds may carry with them no implication of Mongoloid admixture. It should be noted that the internal epicanthus is stated to be normally present in the foetuses of all races.

The details of the inheritance of the various eye folds are as yet imperfectly known. Dunn and Tozzer found evidence that the "Mongoloid fold" (by which the internal epicanthus was probably meant) behaved as a dominant in crosses between Hawaiians and South Chinese, and was possibly controlled by a single pair of factors. However, their data were insufficient for a conclusion other than tentative. There are also indications that the internal epicanthus is dominant in crosses between Europeans and Chinese, according to Tao. A couple of pedigrees in Europeans in which internal epicanthus is combined with ptosis (drooping of the eyelid) also suggest that the internal fold is dominant, but, in this case, since it is associated with an abnormal condition, the data are not very useful.

On the whole, the various characteristics of the Mongoloid eye are of great utility in racial classification when composite races of partially Mongoloid origin or White stocks with the possibility of Mongoloid admixture are being observed. The occasional occurrence of Mongoloid or pseudo-Mongoloid eyefolds in some African Negroes and particularly in the little, yellow Bushmen and Hottentots is a puzzle. I shall postpone consideration of it until the general position and affinities of the Bushmen are up for discussion.

NOSE

An inquisitive and curious person is called "nosey," but intellectual curiosity to a great extent accounts for man's material and mental progress. Anatomically, the more highly evolved man is, the "nosier" he looks. I have discussed in a previous section (pages 180–183) the evolution of the human nose from the anthropoid and lower primate type, a process marked by the elevation of the bridge, the retention of a broad nasal root, and the development of nasal sills and spine, as well as by the downward growth of the tip and the differentiation of the lateral wings bounding the nostrils (the alae). No modern human type displays markedly anthropoidal characteristics of the soft parts of the nose nor, indeed, of the nasal skeleton. To have a nose like an ape, you would have to be one.

Here we are concerned with racial differences in nasal form. Let us first examine the proportions of the nose, especially its breadth relative to its length. On the skull, the length of the nasal skeleton is measured from the juncture of the middle point of the nasal bones and the frontal bone above, to the inferior border of the aperture below. The greatest breadth of the aperture is also measured with calipers and expressed as a percentage of the length. If this index falls under 47, the nasal aperture is said to be leptorrhine or "narrow-nosed"; if between 47 and 51, mesorrhine; if over 51, platyrrhine, "broad-nosed." The nose length of the living person is measured from the same superior point to the juncture of the septum with the upper lip, and the breadth is measured between the alae or wings. Thus, the nasal index on the living does not correspond closely to that on the skull, since the soft parts of the nasal wings extend beyond the sides of the bony aperture, and the tip and septum are below the nasal sills and spine. The range of the nasal index on the living subject is higher than on the skull; leptorrhine indices are those below 70 and chamaerrhine or platyrrhine indices those of 84 and over.

The nasal index has long been considered a significant measure of racial difference. The Negro is notoriously broad- and short-nosed; the Mongoloid usually has a short and moderately broad nose, though the width is not exaggerated as in the Negro. Mongoloid nasal indices are prevailingly mesorrhine. The native Australian, a very clearly marked racial type, is excessively platyrrhine, and the narrow-nosed groups are, for the most part, the Whites of Europe, Asia, and North Africa. There is, however, a wide age and sex variation in the nasal index. Almost all children and infants are platyrrhine, because the greater part of the nasal breadth is developed early in life, while as yet the jaws are small and the face and nose short. Because of the lesser depth of the jaws of the female, the nose in this sex tends to be relatively broader and shorter than in the male. Further, there is no doubt that from middle life to old age the nasal tip tends to increase in length and often to become somewhat depressed. The nose sags toward the chin, thus contributing to the nut-cracker effect created by Mr. Punch and the witches of fairy lore. The nasal index then decreases considerably from infancy to old age.

A current anthropological view is that the form of the nose is affected by the temperature of the air habitually breathed. Broad-nosed races with wide nostrils usually live in hot climates and can snuff up great draughts of the warm air without cooling the linings of the respiratory organs. On the other hand, the very cold air of far northern lands must be breathed in smaller quantities to prevent the lowering of the body temperature. A narrower nasal aperture reduces the volume of cold air admitted to the lungs. The high, narrow nose of the North European, lined with thin mucous membrane charged with blood, warms the air as it goes through the nasal passages, much as in our modern heating systems we place radiators in front of the windows so that the air admitted to the room may be warmed as it enters. Here again, the Eskimo is invoked to furnish evidence of environmental modifications. For the Eskimo shows the narrowest nasal aperture and the most leptorrhine nasal skeleton of all recent human groups with the exception of some North Europeans.

Thomson and Buxton were the first to show that the average nasal index of groups is closely correlated with the average temperatures and average relative humidities of the areas they inhabit—the higher the temperature, the broader the nose and the higher the nasal index. They found that they could predict with fair accuracy the average nasal index of groups from these climatic conditions.[28] Later, A. Davies resurveyed the problem and, in the main, confirmed their conclusions. However, Davies discovered that the closest relationship lay between the maximum mean monthly temperature and the maximum mean monthly relative humidity. The breadth of the nose seemed little affected by the cold of winter and mostly by the greatest heat of summer.[29] In plotting the world distribution of averages of the nasal index against predictions based upon the climate, it was found that a fair agreement was obtained in most areas, but, in some regions, the populations had much narrower or much wider noses than climatic expectation. The discrepancies seemed to occur particularly in regions that have been subjected to immigration and change of population in the past two or three millennia, such as India (which was invaded by narrow-nosed Aryan-speakers about 2000 B.C.) and the Americas, which the correlators of nose breadth and climate have assumed (probably erroneously) to have been peopled within that space of time. These recent immigrants are supposed not to have had time to adapt to their new climate as respects the nasal index. Davies argues very reasonably that the modification of the nasal index in response to environmental requirements is neither so rapid nor so radical as to invalidate its use as an ethnic or racial criterion. A sceptic might assert that the correlations between the nasal index and climate amount to little more than this: broad-nosed or platyrrhine Negroids are the indigenous inhabitants of most of the tropics of the Old World, whereas narrow-nosed Whites and mesorrhine Mongoloids are found prevailingly in the temperate zones. Wherever Whites or Mongoloids have impinged upon or entered Negroid areas, intermixture with Negroids has taken place, giving rise to intermediate indices of the nose in intermediate geographical zones. Thus, most of the gradations in average index that seem to be in step with climate would be nothing more than group averages resulting from intermixture of broad-nosed and narrow-nosed elements in different proportions together with their hybrids. Actually, I am not inclined to dismiss the correlation in this contemptuous

28 Thomson and Buxton, "Man's Nasal Index," pp. 92–122.
29 Davies, "A Re-survey of the Morphology of the Nose," pp. 337–359.

manner. Selection of nasal breadths suitable for various climatic conditions may well have taken place, in addition to the race mixtures or mixtures of nasal forms which indubitably have taken place. However, there are some glaring examples of stocks long resident in areas to which their nasal indices are not climatically adapted. Notable are the excessively platyrrhine Bushmen and Hottentots of South Africa and the now extinct platyrrhine Tasmanians. Evidently climatic selection of nose form has not taken place in these stocks. If it has taken place anywhere, it must be a very slow process, in contrast with the rapid oscillations that have been observed in the cephalic index.

It is difficult to measure accurately the length of the nose in the living, principally because the finding of the point called nasion (the middle of the juncture of the nasal bones with the frontal bone) is often uncertain on account of the overlying soft parts. Since the nasal diameters are very small, a deviation of a millimeter or two in measuring the length or breadth of the nose causes the nasal index to fluctuate over a wide range. Further, as I have said, the nasal index on the living is only roughly comparable with that taken on the skull. Because of these technical difficulties and because of the possibility of adaptive alterations in the form of the nose, the nasal index has a limited value as a racial criterion, its significance being restricted to such groups as show extreme variations of platyrrhiny or leptorrhiny.

The shape of the nose is much more important than its absolute or relative dimensions. Unfortunately, however, there is no practicable method of measuring nasal form. It must be described. The nasal root is that portion of the nose between the eyes and at the juncture of the nasal skeleton with the middle part of the forehead. It may be depressed below the level of the glabella or median frontal eminence, or it may be at the same level. It may be high and narrow, low and broad, or of medium proportions. The height and breadth of the bridge of the nose vary similarly but not always in the same direction as the nasal root. A nasal root of medium height and breadth may flare out into a broad and high bridge, for example. The profile of the nose includes the lateral view of the root, the bridge, the tip, and the septum, which separates the nostrils. Usually, the root of the nose dips downward just below the nasion region, and the nasion point itself may be deeply depressed if the glabella region of the forehead (just above the nose and between the eyes) is prominent or swollen. If glabella is, on the contrary, flat, no nasion depression is observable, although the dip below nasion is usually present. "Straight" noses are those that exhibit no concavity of the bridge in profile below the subnasion dip. Concave noses are saddle-shaped; the deepest portion of the concavity is usually in the middle of the bridge. Convex noses are of varied profiles. Below the subnasion dip, the bridge rises into an elevation which may be high up on the bridge, in the middle of it, or at its lower end. Below the elevation, there may be a straight slope leading to the tip, or a slight dip may intervene between the bridge elevation and the convexity of the tip. Concavo-convex noses are transitional between concave and convex forms and hard to distinguish. The subnasion dip in this form of nose is deep, and below it the bridge rises to a convexity at its inferior extremity. The tip and the septum of the nose are built upon cartilages. The tip may be thick or thin, bluntly rounded or sharply pointed; it may be snubbed or pushed upward, "retroussé"; it may be horizontal, depressed, or "hooked." Again, the septum that forms the juncture of the nose with the lip may be horizontal in profile, inclined upward from the lip, or downward; it may be straight, concave, or convex.

The wings of the nostrils (alae) may be thin and compressed, broad and flaring, or intermediate. They may be on a level with the nasal septum, or they may be attached to the cheeks farther back so that the nasal profile reveals the septum and a portion of inner wall of the nostril. The nostrils themselves may be almost round, broad oval, or narrow oval, and, when observed from below, their long axes may form an acute angle with the nasal tip above, an obtuse angle, or, in some very platyrrhine forms, the direction of the long axes of the nostrils may be nearly transverse so that they form almost two right angles.

It is evident that the nose in the living is an organ extremely complicated in form. This complexity is further increased by the fact that all of the different parts may be combined in most of their possible variations with the variations of every other part.

The nose is also liable to change of form caused by accident or disease. A broken bridge makes a hump on the nose; a deflected septum skews the nose and causes asymmetry of the nostrils and wings; alcoholism sometimes produces a proboscis-like enlargement of the nasal tip that is called "brandy nose" (acne rosacea).

In spite of the intricacy of combination in different parts of the nose, certain general types of nasal form are racially typical. The Negro nose *par excellence* has a slightly depressed root which is low and broad; the concave or straight bridge is of great breadth and low or of medium height; the tip is thick and bulbous and usually turned upward; the wings are very thick and flaring, the nostrils round or with their long axes directed transversely and frontally visible. The septum is thick and inclined upward, although viewed from the side it is convex. The whole nose is short and very broad at the tip and wings (Plate 28). Nevertheless, many Negroes do not show all of the features of the Negro nose in their typical development, and when there is a slight admixture of non-Negro blood, as is frequently the case even in Africa, the nose shows some refinement of form and proportions. The Australian nose is much like that of the Negro, but the root is more deeply depressed, the tip even larger, and the wings more exaggerated in their spread. The nose of the Oceanic Negrito sometimes shows a faintly anthropoidal feature. The bridge and root are not so broad as in the true Negro, but the tip is poorly developed, the round nostrils directed forward instead of downward, and the thick semicircular alae surrounding them recall the circular and swollen alae of the gorilla. Oceanic Negroes (Melanesians and Papuans) do not show the exaggerated form of the Negro nose but tend to have high and often convex bridges and depressed tips (Plate 30).

The Mongoloid nose differs from that of the Negro in that its root is much lower and not so broad and is almost never depressed at nasion (Plate 31). Often the Mongoloid nose shows practically no elevation of the root. The bridge is also much lower than that of the Negro and much narrower. The tip is not swollen, and the wings are much thinner and less flaring. The nostrils are round or broadly oval and directed forward, the tip and septum elevated. The septum is thinner than that of the Negro and does not usually show a convexity. In profile, the Mongoloid nose is strongly concave, whereas some Negro noses are slightly convex and many straight. The Mongoloid nose is more infantile than that of the Negro. Of course, Mongoloid peoples display a wide range of nasal variation. I have described what I believe to be the typical and characteristic development of the nose in this great human stock.

Nose form among the Whites usually differs from both Negroid and Mongoloid types in the greater height development of root and bridge and in their diminished breadth, in the elongation of the tip, and in the compression of the nasal wings. The least characteristic nasal form found among Whites is that of the round-headed, round-faced, brunet, and thickset Central Europeans, often called the "Alpine race." In this group, the nose is likely to be somewhat short and broad without the excessive narrowness and elevation of root and bridge characteristic of Nordics and Mediterraneans. Its profile is seldom convex, oftenest straight, and occasionally concave. The tip is of medium thickness and elevated, the alae are of moderate lateral extension; and the nostrils are partly visible from the front, since the septum is inclined upward. The wings are attached at the septum level so that there is little lateral visibility of the nostrils. This is an infantile and "blobby" form of nose and differs from the

Mongoloid form principally in its much greater height development of root, bridge, and tip.

The characteristic nasal form of the long-headed, oval-faced, brunet Mediterranean subrace is leptorrhine and straight-bridged. Root and bridge are rather narrow and of medium height or higher; the tip is usually prolonged downward to the horizontal septum but is not depressed. The wings are compressed or of medium spread and often are sufficiently recessed to show in profile part of the inner wall of the nostril (Plate 23).

The Nordic nose differs from that of the Mediterranean in its greater height, diminished width, increased length, and extremely "pinched" wings (Plate 24). The bridge is oftener convex in Nordics, and the tip is sharper and sometimes slightly depressed. The convexity of the Nordic bridge is likely to be high up on the nasal bones, making an "aquiline" or "Roman" form of nose. This long, thin, convex type of nose is frequently seen also among Semites of Mediterranean subrace, especially in hawk-visaged Arabs, who often show marked depression of tip and downward slope of the septum, without, however, the tip thickening and alar flare characteristic of Armenoids.

Certainly the most distinctive form of the nose in the White race is that often described by anthropologists as "Armenoid" and known to lay Americans and Western Europeans as "Jewish" (Plate 25). This nose is remarkable for its great length, great height, convexity, and depression of its thick tip. It is not a narrow nose, especially at its lower end, which shows heavy wings curving back so as to expose a large part of the inner wall of the nostrils. Very often this kind of nose has no depression either at nasion or below it but continues the forehead slope without a dip, ending in a thick, rounded, and depressed tip with a concave and downward sloping septum. The eminence or hump in the bridge may be very marked or hardly perceptible, but the tip is almost invariably thickened and depressed and the wings coarse and recurved. This nose was found among the ancient Sumerians, Babylonians, Assyrians, Hittites, and Persians, and it is an inescapable feature of many Syrians, Armenians, Jews, Greeks, Turks, and other Levantine peoples of today. A modified form of this nose with a considerable refinement of the tip and wings occurs in the tall, brachycephalic Balkan group called the Dinaric subrace (Plate 25). In its more pronounced development, the Armenoid nose usually occurs in a brachycephalic physical type with a very high, "sugar-loaf" head which slopes steeply up from the eyebrow region to a peak far back on the parietals and is then cut down almost vertically

so that the occiput appears flat. The face is long with somewhat prominent malars, but the chin and jaws are not heavy.

A remarkable caricature of the Armenoid nose may often be observed
among Melanesians, Papuans (Oceanic Negroids), and occasionally elsewhere. This has been called the "pseudo-Semitic" nose or the "hybrid nose." The nasal root is of moderate height and breadth or
even high and narrow; at the bridge, the breadth and height are very
great, and the profile of the nose in this region is strongly convex; the
tip is tremendously thickened, elongated, and depressed; the wings are
as flaring and thick as in the ordinary Negro nose, and the septum is
strongly convex downward. Why this exaggerated imitation of an Armenoid nose should appear in New Guinea is a mystery. A similar nose
appears, equally mysteriously, in two or three individuals of the fifth
generation hybrids resulting from the cross of the English mutineers of
the Bounty with the Polynesian natives of Tahiti. Here, as often elsewhere, it goes with curly hair.

Probably neither the "Armenoid" nose nor the pseudo-Armenoid or
"hybrid" nose represents a pure racial nasal type. They are rather combinations of dominant nasal features emerging from extensive racial
crossings. There is reason for believing that a high and narrow nasal
root is a dominant feature, as is also a high and convex nasal bridge. But
great breadth of the bridge also appears to be dominant. Similarly, thickness and depression of the tip and lateral flaring of the wings, with downward convexity of the septum, may be features that persist in race mixtures at the expense of recessive developments of the same parts. Thus it
is possible to regard the Papuan nose as the combination resulting from
the mixture of a Negroid type of nose, having a broad bridge, thick tip,
and flaring wings, with a non-Negroid type, in which the root is high
and narrow, the bridge convex, and the tip elongated and depressed.

The recent anthropometric studies of Dr. Henry Field in Iran indicate that the basic type there is a massive-headed, brunet dolichocephal,
with a very long, heavy face and a correspondingly long, very high, and
rather wide nose. This nose is usually slightly to markedly convex, but
may be straight. It now seems probable to me that Mediterranean Semitic
and Armenoid noses may be a legacy from this stock in admixture with
more gracile Mediterraneans or round-headed Alpines. The huge nose
of the Iranian plateau type is in harmony with the general size and massive bony structure of the elongated face. It is possible that this dominant
nose form has been grafted upon Mediterranean and Alpine faces, for
which it is really *too large*, involving in the process elongation of the tip

and exaggerated buckling or bowing of the bridge. This may seem a fantastic idea, but disharmonic proportions frequently are inherited. Many persons inherit teeth that are too large to be accommodated properly in their constricted alveolar arches. The maxilla and the mandible in some civilized stocks are undergoing rapid atrophic reduction, but the nose continues its exuberant evolutionary growth or, at any rate, more than holds its own.

The American Indian shows a hybridized nose form (Plates 33 and 34). The nasal root is usually narrow but rather low and without a nasion depression. The subnasion dip is pronounced, and the bridge rises into a convex eminence. Often this convex bridge is rather broad. The tip is prolonged and often bent downward or depressed, but it is not thick or coarse. The lateral flare of the wings is very pronounced, and these are strongly recurved, laying bare the inner nostril walls, but the wings themselves are not thick. The resulting combination is a high concavo-convex nose with a long and depressed tip and considerable breadth across the wings. This nose seems to be the result of the superimposition of a dominant, aquiline nasal form upon the low, concave Mongoloid form.

Beyond those that have been described, there are probably no types of noses that are racially distinctive, with the possible exception of the Bushman-Hottentot nose which looks like a Mongoloid-Negroid hybrid nose (Plate 30). It combines the exaggerated interorbital width and broad nasal root of the Negro with the lack of height development of root and bridge and the deeply concave profile of the Mongoloid. The tip shows the swollen bulbous character of the Negro; the nostrils are round and frontally visible as in both parental types, and the wings have the excessive spread commonly seen in Negroids.

Space forbids a full discussion here of the somewhat inconclusive and inadequate data available on the inheritance of nose form. I propose to state merely my impressions, based upon a consideration of the behavior of nasal features in crosses between Whites and Negroes, between Whites and Polynesians, Whites and Mongoloids, and in different stocks within the White race. High nasal roots, bridges, and tips are probably dominant, as are also convex bridges and depressed tips. It seems probable, however, that broad roots and broad bridges are also dominant, but the dominance of broad nasal roots seems to apply rather to the interorbital space (especially the frontal processes of the maxillae) rather than to the upper portions of the nasal bones themselves, in which progressive narrowing may be noted, often even in the skulls of Mongoloids who appear to have very broad roots. I am inclined to think that flaring alae or wings of the nostrils are recessive but not bulbous tips. The breadth of the nose measured on the living across the alae usually shows average intermediate values in crosses between broad-nosed and narrow-nosed stocks, with a mean approaching closer to that of the parental strain with the wider nose. Probably more than a single pair of inheritance factors is involved.

The nasal index is a ratio based on the effect of too many factors to be of much use in genetic analysis.

EARS

Ears escape notice unless they are outstanding and obtrusive. Yet they are individually characteristic—so much so that criminologists measure, classify, and describe them in minute detail. Mozart had a peculiar anomaly of the pavilion of the ear, but it probably had nothing to do with his musical genius. When I travel in the subway, I often look at ears. Most of them are mediocre, and those that are interesting are usually ugly. I once knew a girl who was very beautiful excepting her ears, but I always had to look at those ears. They were long, flaccid, fish-belly white appendages, which looked more like bleached oysters than shells. If that girl has any children, I hope they have not inherited her ears. The external ear has been put by man to uses other than that of catching sound waves. The upper part of the ear may serve as a rest for spectacle bows, pens, pencils. The lobe is pierced by women and savages to receive ornaments and by doctors to extract blood to find out whether the owner of the ear is anemic. Yet this useful organ is little known in its racial variations.

Negroes and Negritos have short, wide ears; Whites have longer and narrower ears; the longest and relatively the narrowest ears seem to occur in Australians, Mongoloids, and some Whites (e.g., Ainu). Professor R. B. Bean distinguished among the natives of the Philippine Islands at least eight types of ears, each of which he thought was associated with a definite cranial, facial, and bodily morphology. Most of these ear types also occur in Europeans. Bean's observations require confirmatory studies.

The only distinctive racial type of ear known to me is that of the Bushmen and Hottentots of South Africa (Fig. 66). This is a short, broad ear, with a very deep roll or infolding of the helix (rim). The upper border lies very close to the head and is sometimes attached to it. This superior border runs back almost horizontally, making an approximate right angle with the hinder border. The lobe is very small or absent, and there is no "Darwin's point." This Bushman ear seems to be a variant of the Negro ear, which is usually small and round with little or no lobe. The lobe is most developed in Europeans and Mongoloids, but these stocks oftener show a comparatively unrolled helix and more frequently have the cartilaginous knob or point on the edge of the helix where the upper and hinder borders join (Fig. 66). This "Darwin's point" is, of course, the vestige of the free tip of the mammalian ear (Fig. 33).

The attached or "soldered" ear lobe is a more primitive feature than the free lobe and probably occurs oftener in Whites than in Negroids,

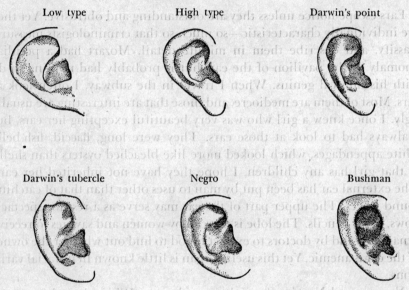

Low type   High type   Darwin's point

Darwin's tubercle   Negro   Bushman

Fig. 66. Some of the variations of the human ear.

who frequently have no lobes at all. But it is scarcely possible to assert that the ear of the White is more highly evolved than that of the Negro or *vice-versa*. The small Negro ear, with its narrowly rolled helix, is certainly not primitive. A primitive ear should be large, with an unrolled helix. The chimpanzee is the only anthropoid with an ear unreduced in size, and even among chimpanzees, the bald-headed variety is said to display this "stigma of degeneracy." European ears are more chimpanzee-like than those of Negroes because they are larger and oftener have unrolled helices. The lobe of the ear, which is well developed in Europeans and Mongoloids, is thought by some to be a progressive feature. Yet it sometimes occurs in the small and otherwise degenerate ear of the gorilla. I am inclined to regard the lobe as the useless, fatty excrescence of a vestigial organ.

The ear is relatively shorter and broader in infancy and during immaturity than subsequently. In middle-aged and elderly persons, this organ has a recrudescence of growth and becomes much larger and more elongate. Particularly the lobe (when present) increases in length. These age changes render ear measurements and indices of small use for purposes of racial classifications. Observations on the minutiae of ear form clearly indicate that they are inherited, but the details seem to be familial variations rather than racially significant features.

LIPS

The Negro has the only form of lip that is racially distinctive. The thick, puffy, and everted Negro lip represents a highly evolved form, which, nevertheless, does not seem to dominate completely over the lips of lesser thickness that are more anthropoidal. Non-Negroid races show a diminished lip thickness, which probably reaches its minimum among certain European stocks. For practical purposes of racial distinction, the lips are of little value unless there is a Negroid strain in the race under consideration, when it is often betrayed by eversion or thickness of membranous lips. The integumental lips are thicker in all non-European stocks than in Whites. Here again the Negroids seem to stand at the farthest remove from the European races, while Mongoloids are in an intermediate position.

Marking the boundaries between the lips proper, or membranous lips, and the integumental lips (upon which, in males, the moustache and the goatee may grow) there is often a "lip seam." In Whites, this is a white line usually more distinct on the upper than on the lower lip. In Negroes and other heavily pigmented groups, the lip seam often takes the form of a prominent ridge lighter than the skin in color (Plate 28).

FINGER, PALM, AND SOLE PRINTS AS RACIAL CRITERIA

Everyone knows that the variations of finger prints are used for individual identification because it is easy to select, in any set of prints, a combination of pattern and peculiarity of ridge detail that is unique. There are also some racial differences in finger prints. The ordinary patterns of the finger prints include the arch, the loop (which may open inward—ulnar—or outward—radial), and the whorl, or spiral. Ulnar loops are commonest in man and occur in between 45 and 65 per cent of all prints examined. The radial loop seems to vary between 2 per cent and 6 per cent.[30] One of the most convenient, quick methods of com-

[30] Dankmeijer, "Some Anthropological Data on Finger Prints," pp. 377–388.

parison is to tabulate the percentage of arches against the percentages of whorls, counting all digits together. Arches generally diminish in frequency as whorls increase. The following table gives roughly the range of human racial variation and includes also data from 26 sets of chimpanzee finger prints.[31]

TABLE 6. PERCENTAGE FREQUENCIES OF ARCHES AND WHORLS IN THE FINGER PRINTS OF MAN AND CHIMPANZEE

Race, People	Investigator	Number	Whorls	Arches
Americans				
Greenland Eskimo	Abel	68	72.2	0.8
Maya, Tarahumara	Leche	50	51.6	4.5
Arapahoes	Downey	50	47.6	4.6
Comanches	Cummins, Goldstein	67	43.3	6.3
Mayas	Cummins, Steggerda	127	33.2	7.6
Mongoloids				
Chinese	Kubo	300	50.7	1.4
Koreans	Kubo	700	45.2	2.6
Indonesian-Malays				
Japanese	Hirano	12,940	50.1	1.2
Menangkabau Malays	Kleiweg de Zwaan	500	45.1	1.7
Niassians	" "	1,300	34.7	2.4
Javanese, males	Dankmeijer	1,000	35.9	2.7
Javanese, females	"	1,000	32.7	3.3
Whites				
Ainu	Hasebe	55	31.8	2.9
Jews	Cummins, Midlo	200	42.7	4.2
Italians	Falco	1,579	36.9	4.7
French	Bayle	15,000	29.3	4.2
Germans	Heindl	99,400	30.8	4.9
Hungarians	Bonnevie	833	32.3	5.0
Portuguese	Lopes	1,000	29.8	5.5
Danes, males	Bugge	86,654	29.8	5.4
English	Collins	5,000	20.2	5.0
Russians, males	Semenovsky	11,000	32.1	6.2
Russians, females	"	11,000	27.3	8.4
Spaniards	Oloriz	10,000	30.3	6.5
Norwegians	Bonnevie	24,518	25.7	7.4
Dutch, males	Dankmeijer	2,222	26.2	7.7
Negroids				
Negroes, Sierra Leone	"	343	28.5	6.4
Mulattoes, Jamaica	Davenport, Steggerda	213	24.7	9.5
Efe Pygmies, Congo	Dankmeijer	207	19.6	16.2
Chimpanzees	Cummins, Spragg	26	49.6	1.5

Racial differences discernible from the above table are not impressive. The Greenland Eskimo and the Congo Pygmies stand at opposite ends of the series, the former with the highest percentage of whorls and the lowest of arches, the latter vice versa. Both of these isolated and primitive groups, which are also racially far apart, are separated from the con-

[31] Cummins and Spragg, "Dermatoglyphics in the Chimpanzee," pp. 457–510.

tinuous array of the human series by large gaps. On the other hand, the chimpanzee is nicely ensconced inside of the human range with whorl and arch percentages virtually indistinguishable from those of the Japanese and Chinese. The data suggest that Mongoloids and composite races with a strong Mongoloid element in their make-up, such as American Indians and Indonesians, tend to have high proportions of whorls (considered by experts the most primitive of apical skin patterns) and low proportions of arches, whereas Whites tend to have many more arches and correspondingly fewer whorls. The few Negroes studied seem to fall within the White range, except the little Congo Negritos, who, incidentally, are farther removed from their geographical neighbors, the chimpanzees, than is any other recorded human group.

The proportions of arches to whorls are higher in females than in males in every group investigated except the Congo Pygmies, and the arch whorl index in peoples hitherto studied is lower in the right hand than in the left hand (i.e., the left hand shows more arches). Apparently, differences connected with handedness and with sex are more consistent than racial differences. A stable human feature is the predominance of certain patterns on specific finger tips. Whorls are commonest in digits I and IV, arches on II and III; radial loops are almost confined to the index finger. The chimpanzee differs from man in that arches are commoner in this

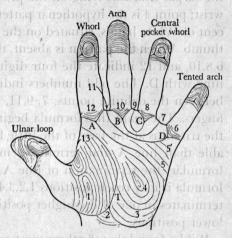

Fig. 67. Various types of finger prints, palmar areas (1–13), the main lines (A–D), and the axial triradius (T). The main line formula shown is 11.9.7.5.

animal on digits IV and V, and radial loops are found chiefly on the thumb rather than the index finger.

The classification and study of palm and sole prints were initiated by the late H. H. Wilder and seem to offer some significant racial variations. On the palms at the bases of the fingers, elevated tactile pads, or walking pads, develop in foetal mammals. These elevations in pentadactyle mammals are consistent in number and position. In the lower primates, the pads are better developed than in the chimpanzee and man. In the human foetus, the pads, initially developed, undergo involution, and some pads regress more rapidly than others. Apparently, this early history is paralleled in the case of the chimpanzee.[32] The pads determine the development of ridge pattern and alignment. There are four triradii (Y's with long tails), one at the base of each finger, and designated by letters A to D, beginning with the index finger. The short arms of the Y's define small areas at the bases of the fingers, but the tails of the Y's describe longer and quite variable courses across the palm. These are the four main lines, designated by the letters A to D. When their courses and their terminations (points at which they issue from the margin of the friction-skin area) are traced, these main lines can be described and located by simple formulae. The regions or points along the margins of the palm are given a series of numbers from 1 to 13. The triradii or pattern cores, which are more definite points, are designated by even numbers and the intervals between them by odd numbers. Point 2 is the carpal triardius lying on the proximal margin at the middle of the wrist; point 4 is the hypothenar pattern, a conspicuous feature on 20 per cent of White hands, situated on the eminence opposite the base of the thumb. When the pattern is absent, the number 4 is not used. Numbers 6,8,10, and 12 indicate the four digital triradii in reverse order, beginning with D. The odd numbers indicate the entire lengths of margins between the definite points; 7, 9,11, and 13 are the spaces between the fingers. The main line formula begins with the termination of line D, the triradius at the base of the little finger, because line D is more variable than line A and terminates more precisely.[33] In the main line formulae, the termination of line A is usually omitted because in any formula it may reach positions 1,2,3,4, or 5. Typically, in right hands, it terminates in one of the higher positions and, in the lefts, in one of the lower positions.

Wilder found that the three most common main line formulae in every race were 11.9.7.–, 9.7.5.–, and 7.5.5.–. He came to the conclusion that the 11.9.7.– type is essentially the European formula and the 7.5.5.– type the Negro formula.

An inspection of Table 7, selected from data compiled by Steggerda, Steggerda, and Lane [34] may or may not convince the sceptical reader of the validity of these claims.

In addition to the formulae of the main lines, the palms of individuals and groups differ in the presence or absence and variations in the pattern of the axial or carpal triradius, of the patterns on the hypothenar,

[32] *Ibid.*, p. 501.
[33] Cummins, "Methodology in Palmar Dermatoglyphics," pp. 30–33, quoting H. H. Wilder, "Palm and Sole Studies," *Biol. Bull.*, Vol. XXX (1916). Some slight modifications of the Wilder termination numbers have been made.
[34] Steggerda, Steggerda, and Lane, "A Racial Study," pp. 133–194.

TABLE 7. PERCENTAGE FREQUENCIES OF THREE PRINCIPAL MAIN LINE FORMULAE [35]

Race, People	Number	11.9.7.–	9.7.5.–	7.5.5.–
Whites				
European Americans	200	27.7	16.8	9.0
European Americans	300	31.0	26.2	10.2
Jews	200	37.5	21.7	8.7
Ainu	55	30.9	33.6	20.9
Mongoloids				
Chinese	100	9.0	23.5	27.5
Koreans	134	22.7	32.0	35.5
Indonesian-Malays				
Japanese (Wilder)	195	16.6	19.2	24.3
Japanese (Hasebe)	276	23.0	30.2	34.6
Japanese (Keith)	100	20.5	25.5	24.0
Americans				
Eskimo	64	34.3	29.6	11.7
Comanches	77–79	21.9	37.7	17.2
Tarahumara	26	21.2	13.5	32.7
Maya	224	20.5	33.7	22.2
Mexican Indians	33–36	7.2	49.2	29.0
Negroids				
Jamaica Negroes	64	13.3	16.4	35.3
West African Negroes	52–80	9.9	21.7	44.8

thenar (thumb), first interdigital, and the other interdigital areas. For example, in the hypothenar area, a pattern is present in between about 33 and 45 per cent of Whites and is much less common in other races examined, whereas in the thenar/first digital area, the American Indians show a much higher frequency of patterns than other stocks examined.

Steggerda, Steggerda, and Lane have summarized these racial differences.[36] The Maya Indians of Yucatan (and probably all other American Indians) have a high frequency of the 9.7.5.– formula with unusually vertical configuration of palm lines indicated by termination of line A; frequent reduction or absence of line C; occurrence of a single low axial triradius; rare incidence of hypothenar pattern and second and third interdigital patterns, and very high incidence of the thenar/first interdigital pattern.

In contrast, Whites show characteristically the 11.9.7– main line formula; tendency toward transversality of palm ridges; less frequent absence or rudimentary condition of line C; high percentage of hypothenar and third interdigital patterns, and low incidence of a pattern in the thenar/first interdigital area.

Negroes have a preponderance of the 7.5.5.–type of main line formula; diagonal direction of palm lines, but with tendency toward transversality;

[35] Under each formula are included variants in which line C is absent or indeterminate. (Data from Steggerda, Steggerda, and Lane. "A Racial Study," pp. 168–169.)
[36] Ibid., pp. 187–189.

frequent occurrence of second interdigital pattern, and unusually high incidence of fourth interdigital pattern.

Racial differences in sole prints have not been extensively investigated. Wilder found that Chinese and Japanese differ from Europeans in that the former show an extreme degree of effacement of patterns and consequently a monotony of sole prints. The simplest types are the most human, and these occur in 86.2 per cent of Chinese, 83.8 per cent of Japanese, and 55 per cent of Europeans.[37]

The interpretation both of evolutionary status and of racial difference in dermatoglyphics is fraught with difficulties and dangers, as Cummins and Midlo recognize in their admirable discussion of the subject.[38] In finger prints, the whorl-loop-arch sequence seems to represent successive departures from the primitive. But some human populations in this respect are more primitive than chimpanzee, and, indeed, other dermatoglyphic areas suggest that man stemmed from a stock with dermatoglyphic characters more like those of monkeys. Also different dermatoglyphic areas in various stocks are not in accord in their evolutionary status. On the whole, high pattern intensity (predominance of whorls) seems to indicate primitiveness in palm and sole configurations as well as in fingers and toes. Difficulties arise in that certain populations, the Chinese, for instance, combine primitive high pattern intensity in fingers with advanced low intensity in palmar and plantar features. Trends toward longitudinal alignment (in reduced frequency of type 11.9.7.- and reduced values of the main line index) may also be regarded as derived, in contrast with the tendency toward transversality, which is primitive. But here again, races with high finger pattern intensity apparently tend toward the longitudinal or specialized trend in palmar main lines.

Cummins and Midlo are of the opinion that finger prints may possibly be more reliable for tracing racial affinities than other dermatoglyphic areas. On this basis, the Yellow-browns (Mongoloids, Americans, Indonesian-Malays) embrace the most primitive stocks, whereas the most specialized include certain Blacks and, among Whites, "Nordics." (These authors assume that Northwestern Europeans represent the "Nordic" race.) However, Whites in general and typical Negroes show intermediate degrees of pattern intensity, being neither greatly specialized nor particularly primitive. In other words, they seem highly variable and erratic.

It is also noted by Cummins and Midlo that there are geographic trends of pattern intensity (perhaps like the distribution of the blood groups).

37 Wilder, op. cit., p. 199.
38 Cummins and Midlo, Finger Prints, pp. 264–268.

In Asia, the postulated center of distribution of human stocks, the recent populations are characterized by high pattern intensity, which diminishes in passing northward to Europe and southward in Africa and the Americas. The reduction of pattern intensity reaches its culmination in the Bushmen and pygmies of Africa and is next most marked in the Scandinavian countries. Although the New World shows reduction of pattern intensity from north to south, the level of intensity remains relatively high, suggesting that the migrations to these continents were relatively late.

This distribution raises a difficulty in that Congo pygmies and Bushmen, usually considered among the most primitive stocks of mankind and exhibiting also in their peripheral location evidence of early migration from evolutionary centers, are, according to pattern intensity, the most highly evolved of all peoples dermatoglyphically. Mongoloids, according to all evidence most recently evolved and in many respects highly specialized, are, on the contrary, dermatoglyphically primitive (but only in fingers—not in palms and soles). One suspects that the phenomenon of foetalization may have jumbled up dermatoglyphic status in Mongoloids and possibly also in Negroids.

In Germany and Japan, local variations of finger prints have been studied. In the former country, populations of the north and west have relatively many arches and fewer whorls, whereas the conditions are reversed in the south and east, and the middle sections show intermediate trends. Cummins and Midlo think that this difference corresponds to a racial separation between Nordics and Alpines. However, racial composition in Germany is not so simple as they assume.

Although dermatoglyphics are "age-stable" and "environment stable" and consequently seem admirably adapted for genetic studies, the manner of their inheritance is by no means clear. Pattern type, pattern size (by ridge counts), and pattern proportions seem dependent upon genetic foundations more basic than those that give rise to individual variations. There are also trends of unlikeness between the two sides of the bodies, between different digits, and between the sexes, as well as those that pertain to family, ethnic stock, and race. Moreover, there is extensive individual variation, since the genes that determine the capacity of forming ridges operate independently of the factors that condition specific configurational character, or influence the latter only indirectly. Thus stress and tension in growth of parts, thickness of the embryonic epidermis, and distribution of cushioned areas (thickened by increased fluid content of the epidermis) importantly affect ridge alignment.

Although substantial progress has been made in the very complicated subject of the inheritance of dermatoglyphics, results are too contradictory and inconclusive to be discussed here.

Cummins and Midlo take a most reasonable and cautious position upon the utility of dermatoglyphics as racial criteria. They say:

The factors underlying racial divergence are complex, and it is impossible to assign shares to ancientness, degree of isolation and other factors which render the history of races so involved. The student of dermatoglyphics will not fall into the error of presuming that dermatoglyphic features now provide ready answers for refractory questions in the history of races, particularly when he sees that attacks from many quarters have failed to yield a completely knit scheme of the affinities of races.[39]

SWEAT GLANDS

Sweat glands are an important heat-regulating mechanism of the body, since they secrete water that cools the body by evaporation. Whether as an environmental adaptation or a hereditary difference, stocks resident in the tropics seem to have more sweat glands and perhaps larger glands. Clark and Lhamon counted the average number of sweat gland openings per square centimeter on the palms and soles of 200 American Negroes, 300 American Whites, 150 Filipinos, and series of Moros, Negritos, and Hindus.[40] In the various stocks examined, the average number of glands per square centimeter ranges from 558 in American Whites to 738 in Hindus. Taking American Whites as 100, the relative numbers are: American Negroes 107, Filipinos 117, Moros 122, Negritos 127, Hindus 170. These figures seem to show no racial consistency, since the Moros and Filipinos, who belong to the Indonesian-Malay composite race of partially Mongoloid origin, intervene between the American Negros and the Negritos; and the Hindus (presumably of principally White origin with minor elements of Negrito and Australoid admixture) are at the top of the list. Lewis quotes Freer to the effect that adult Negritos of the Philippines have 26.82 per cent more sweat glands than Whites, and Negrito youths 67.54 per cent more. This finding may indicate that age and body size influence the relative number of sweat glands. Aron claimed that the Negritos of the Philippines have a superior manner of sweating in that small beads are secreted over the entire body, forming a thin film that gives the maximum cooling effect from evaporation, whereas, in Whites, sweating is practically

[39] *Ibid.*, p. 264.
[40] Lewis, *Biology of the Negro*, pp. 57–60, quoting Clark and Lhamon, *Anat. Rec.*, 12: 139, 1917.

limited to certain body areas, and most of the secretion drops off. Glaser counted the sweat glands per square centimeter in 29 selected areas of the skin of a Bantu Negro and compared 8 regions of excised skin of a Bantu and a European.[41] The regional distribution in the Negro agreed closely with that of the White, but, in the majority of areas compared, the number of the glands of the Negro exceeded that of the White. The Negro excess was most marked in the upper eyelid (66 as against 37 in the White), whereas the single region in which more sweat glands occurred in the Whites was the third intercostal, midclavicular (Negro 35, White 43).

Sweat glands are of two kinds; the exocrine glands, scattered all over the body and secreting most of the sweat; apocrine glands, which take their origin from a hair follicle and are found only where hair is present at some time of life. The apocrine glands in man occur in such places as the axilla, the external ear duct, and around the nipples and the anus. In contrast with the exocrine type, the apocrine sweat glands lose a part of their cell substance in secretion and exude more solid substances. They are larger than ordinary glands, frequently contain iron, and may be responsible for body odors specific for individuals, races, and sexes. Homma found that these apocrine glands occur in 38.5 per cent of Negroes but in only 11.5 per cent of Whites, in four regions studied.[42] Women have 75 per cent more of apocrine glands than men.

STATURE

Some of us who belong to tall races seem to labor under the delusion that we have added a cubit or two to our stature "by taking thought." We feel superior to those who are shorter; we "look down upon them." In my student days before the First World War, I spent some weeks in the garrison city of Tours. When I first saw the French infantry marching along the streets, I despised them as an insignificant and stunted lot. This disdain remained with me until one day I attempted to keep pace with some marching *poilus*. Within two minutes and two blocks I literally "could not see them for dust." I lost my breath and my contempt for small men simultaneously.

Pithecanthropus erectus, the first humanoid being whom we know, walked erect among the Javan forests and stood about 5 feet, 6 inches, from crown to heel. This is about the average stature of adult male human beings of today, if all races be taken together. Since the time of

[41] Glaser, "Sweat Glands," pp. 371–375.
[42] Lewis, *op. cit.*, pp. 59–60, citing Homma, *Bull. Johns Hopkins Hosp.*, 38: 365, 1926.

Pithecanthropus, there has been no consistent evolutionary trend toward increased stature and body size in mankind at large, although some human stocks have grown larger, and others probably have shrunk.

There are two tales respecting alleged increases in stature during historical times that are always being dinned into the ears of anthropologists. One is that of the tourist who attempts to seat himself in one of the seats in the Colosseum where the sporting populace of the ancient Romans used to be entertained by watching lions lunching upon obstinate Christians. This tourist invariably reports that the seats are scarcely large enough to accommodate a single modern buttock. My reply to this is: firstly, that Italians are still small people, used to living in cramped quarters; secondly, that one has only to arrive late at a football game to discover that modern builders of concrete stadia are none too liberal in allotting space where pinched posteriors mean extra dollars. The seat of the late comer has to be discovered by a process of long division, and he then has to be driven into it like a wedge.

The other tale, involving a supposition that our forebears were smaller men, is also purveyed by tourists who gape at empty suits of armor and simply cannot understand how a normal-sized man could be fitted into one. To these, I would point out that a metal suit standing alone in the middle of the floor is necessarily somewhat telescoped and does not attain the altitude of the person it was supposed to fit. Again I would suggest that these extant suits may have survived because they were outgrown by their owners, like the dress suits of our youth. Odd sizes are generally numerous in bargain basements. And, finally, our own ancestors may have been big even in those days, but perhaps they were churls and thralls and varlets and knaves who could not afford or did not rate suits of mail.

Probably the only substantial increment to human stature since the evolution of the giant anthropoid stage came in connection with the increased use of the legs in biped progression. Walking on the hind legs seems to have elongated them greatly and to have given man a substantial advantage in stature over all anthropoid apes save only the bulkiest and largest gorillas. The latter, in spite of their very short legs, often attain average human stature and sometimes exceed 6 feet in height.

The stature of the adult male is usually taken as the measure of the race. Males under 150 cm. (59 inches) and females under 140 cm. (55 inches) are very small. Males between 150 cm. and 160 cm. (59 inches to 63 inches) and females between 140 cm. and 150 cm. (55 inches to 59 inches) are simply undersize. For males, 160 to 170 cm. (63 to

67 inches) is medium stature, and for the smaller sex corresponding figures are 150 to 159 cm. (59 to 62.6 inches). Males with statures above 170 cm. and females taller than 159 cm. may be accounted tall. Males who attain a height of 180 cm. (70.9 inches) and females 168 cm. (66.1 inches) and more in height are very tall.

The normal range of human stature for males is from about 130 cm. (51 inches) to 200 cm. (78.7 inches) and for females between 120 cm. (47.2 inches) and 187 cm. (73.6 inches). Below and above these limits, we encounter the pathological variations of giants and dwarfs. This enormous range of normal variation is not found among many other species or genera of mammals, unless we include the wide size differences brought about in domesticated animals by selective breeding.

Since stature is the largest bodily measurement and is a composite of many body segments, it naturally varies widely, in fact over a wider range than any other bodily measurement with the exception of weight. Is this variation caused by environment, or is it merely the expression of diverse hereditary tendencies? If the great differences in bodily size are due to factors of nutrition or are brought about by climatic causes, we must reject stature as a criterion of race, since race must be established on the basis of physical characters that are inherited with little if any environmental modification. We may first attack this problem by investigating the effect of malnutrition upon stature. Children who are consistently underfed do not attain their full measure of growth but remain stunted. Studies of the Russian population before and during a three year period of famine demonstrate that starvation decreases stature. Ivanovsky [43] found that Great Russian males suffered an average diminution of 4.7 cm. during the period of hunger and females of the same group 3.5 cm. Other peoples in Russia incurred losses averaging from 3.8 cm. to 6.1 cm. in males, and from 3.6 cm. to 4.8 cm. in females. The Tatars of the Crimea had an average loss of 6.1 cm. (2.4 inches). In both sexes, individuals of high stature suffered more than those of low stature, and among intellectuals the decrease was more than in the laboring class. The winter loss was greater than the summer loss, and persons of more than 40 years of age lost height less rapidly than younger individuals. However, during the three years of famine, the older group suffered a total loss exceeding that of the younger group. Stature decreased considerably during the first year of the famine, but the decrease became slower and slower until, after the end of the first year, no further changes took place. When diet improved, stature was rapidly restored to its former level. The return to normal height extended over a period

43 Ivanovsky, "Physical Modifications," pp. 331-353.

of a month to six weeks. Individuals under 40 years of age showed some tendency to exceed the prefamine level. Fair people decreased in stature more than dark people and long-heads more than round-heads.

It seems impossible from these facts to avoid the conclusion that chronic malnutrition may decrease greatly the stature of a population until a certain irreducible minimum is reached. The Great Russian males decreased during the famine 2.8 per cent of their original stature, the Ukranians 2.5 per cent, the Tatars of the Crimea 3.7 per cent. Under starvation conditions it is, therefore, apparent that the average stature of groups may decrease from 2.5 to almost 4 per cent. This nutritional fluctuation is sufficient to change group averages from tall to medium, or from medium to short, but only if the groups suffering loss of height are below the middle of their original stature classes. In no case is the loss sufficient to shift a group from average tall stature to average short stature.

There are no researches that demonstrate with the same clarity the extent to which stature may be increased under unusually favorable conditions of diet. There is every reason for believing, however, that such increase would be strictly limited in its extent. It is generally supposed that children who have suffered from malnutrition during the growth period never attain their hereditary measure of stature even under corrected nutritional conditions. The evidence of Ivanovsky, however, indicates that the hereditary measure of stature is regained in a very short time after proper diet is resumed and that young subjects tend to exceed their pre-famine stature.

Many studies have yielded results seeming to indicate that differences in occupation, social class, hygienic conditions, and other environmental factors condition differences in stature. Martin quotes figures which show that students in Italy, France, England, Spain, Germany, and Iceland are taller than laborers in the same countries. While such differences may be attributed to the less favorable conditions under which the laboring classes are born, grow up, and exist during maturity, it should be remembered that in every part of Europe the socially superior and economically elevated classes show a disproportionately large number of persons of hereditarily tall subracial stocks. The same holds true, to a great extent, in this country. If the stature and weight of children from public schools in a good urban residential district be compared with those of children of the same grade attending a school in a congested tenement district, it is usually evident that the children of the favorable environment are taller and heavier than those of the same age from the poorer district. But here, again, it cannot be maintained that these differences are necessarily due to environmental factors. The children in the better residential district may be principally of tall North European parentage, while those from the tenement districts may be of Southern and Eastern European parentage and consequently of racial stock that is much lower in stature. The geographical distribution of stature groups is not at all in accordance with the supposition that climate and altitude have anything to do with bodily height. Among the very shortest peoples in the New World are the Yahgan and Alakaluf of the bleak coasts and islands of Tierra del Fuego at the southernmost tip of South America. The mean stature of 67 adult male Yahgans is 158.1 cm. (62.2 inches). Adjacent to the Yahgan live the Ona, 25 adult males of whom yielded the prodigious average stature of 175.44 cm. (69 inches.) Both of these Indian tribes subsist largely by hunting and fishing. The Yahgan are canoe Indians, and the Ona are inland hunters, but they also come down to the shores to fish. Both live upon flesh diets. The principal difference in their food is that the main article of the Yahgan diet is mussels and that of the Ona the camel-like guanaco. The gigantic Ona are said to have a somewhat less abundant food supply than the stunted Yahgan.[44] Neither has the resources to overeat.

Here, I may quote from my own discussion of the theory that the Yahgan have become short through generations of squatting in canoes:

. . . We must, however, consider the possibility that the canoe life of the Yahgan has tended to exercise a selective influence upon their stature. Small men are less likely to fall out of small and primitive canoes than are large and unwieldy men. Great length of legs (which always distinguishes tall persons) is a great disadvantage in such craft. We are given to understand that the Yahgan women swim well and the men not at all. If this is true, it is conceivable that the shorter elements in this population have survived because the larger men proved to be too awkward for canoeing and were consequently eliminated by drowning. But this would necessitate the assumption that the large women were also eliminated or that they failed to transmit their large stature. While it is perfectly true that a large woman and a small canoe make a bad combination, it is equally true that a large woman makes as good a floater or swimmer as a small woman, and even a better.

However, there is another possibility that is worthy at least of mention. The legs of the Yahgan may have been shortened as a result of their boating habits. It is perfectly easy to suppose that a man who spends most of his time

---

[44] Lothrop, *Indians of Tierra del Fuego*, pp. 24 ff. Hooton, "Note on the Anthropometric Characters," in Lothrop, *op. cit.*, pp. 41–47.

sitting in a canoe will have poorly developed legs, as have the Yahgan. It is not at all certain, however, that disuse of the legs for purposes of locomotion would necessarily decrease their length. And it is altogether improbable that such a decrease in leg length would establish itself as a hereditary characteristic. Moreover, the Yahgan are not merely "sawed-off" counterparts of the Ona. Not only are their legs shorter, but they are smaller in every way than their neighbors.

In the arid southwestern United States and northern Mexico, stature varies from 159.3 cm. among the Otomi to 174.9 cm. among the Maricopa. Nor are there any environmental factors which may be invoked to explain these differences. In equatorial Africa, the Akka pygmies, who average according to Deniker 138 cm., live cheek by jowl with the tallest people in the world. In this general region, stature averages range from the above-mentioned figure of 138 cm. (54.3 inches) to 181.7 cm. in the Sara (71.5 inches).

In many European countries, in the United States, and in Japan, it has been shown that stature has increased somewhat in the last half century. In Norway, e.g., according to Arbo, the average stature of males rose from 168.6 cm. in 1850 to 170.7 cm. in 1905. Such increments are usually attributed to improved hygienic conditions, better medical care, dietary improvement, reduction of infant mortality, and such environmental ameliorations. The depressing environmental weight carried on the head is gradually lightened or perhaps cast off entirely. Of course, in accepting such increases as evidence of environmental effects upon stature, we neglect the possibility that the natural selection may operate to eliminate some of the shorter strains, or that the racial character of the population may have been modified.

The pygmies are the most skillful huntsmen and woodsmen of the African forests. There is no evidence that their tiny size is in any way connected with an insufficient diet. Years ago, Kollmann evolved a theory that the pygmies represent an early stage in human evolution prior to the development of normal-sized human beings. Thus they might be compared with the gibbon, the small ape that seems to have differentiated before the giant anthropoids. However, the pygmies present no features of morphological inferiority which justify the assumption that they belong to a lower evolutionary grade than other men. Although somewhat infantile in build and appearance in some groups, they are obviously Negroes, hardly distinguished from other Negroes except by their body size.

Some observers attribute the small size of the Negritos or pygmies to their dwelling in dark, sunless forests. Torday noticed that Negritos (usually called Negrillos in Africa) were taller where they lived in the more open spaces. Yet it does not seem possible that their stunted stature can be due to lack of sunlight or food, since many normal-sized peoples live under similar conditions.

In the north of the Scandinavian peninsula are the Lapps with average stature varying from 152.3 cm. to 160.9 cm. Just to the south of them are the Finns, Norwegians, and Swedes, many groups of whom show mean statures from 170 cm. to 174 cm. Instances of very tall and very short peoples living in the same regions and under substantially similar conditions of dietary might be multiplied. I know of no example of such juxtaposition of very short and very tall peoples in which the differences in size can be explained by invoking any environmental factor.

Many of the very tall peoples of the world live in regions where food is scarce and malnutrition is common. The measurement of recruits for the First World War revealed the fact that the tallest stature group of the United States is found in the sparsely populated mountain region of North Carolina, where the mean stature of males of military age is 68.67 inches (174.42 cm.). In the mountainous area of New York, the average stature is only 67.06 inches and, in the mountainous area of Massachusetts, 66.85 inches. The southern mountaineers are notoriously backward in manner of living and are usually undernourished, but they belong to the tall Scotch stock or to Scotch-Irish and English stocks. In the mountainous sections of New England and New York, a large part of the population consists of short French Canadians.

Martin lists 14 African groups or tribes in which mean stature ranges from 170 cm. to 181.7 cm. Not one of these groups lives in a country notable either because of fertility or abundant food supply. The very tallest groups are usually exceedingly thin, and probably most of them are undernourished. The tallest groups in Europe are the Scotch, the Norwegians, the Icelanders, the Swedes, the Irish, the English, and some Jugo-Slavs. With the exception of England and Ireland, all of these countries are barren rather than fertile, and food is distinctly scarce. The tallest Indians of the New World are found in the arid Southwest and in Patagonia and Tierra del Fuego—notably hungry places. The shortest peoples, except the Eskimos, inhabit the same regions.

Studies of the inheritance of stature show very clearly that tallness and shortness run in families. Davenport has accumulated evidence that tall stature is recessive, and that in short families there are certain growth-repressing factors which are dominant over their absence.

One of the phenomena of hybridization is called by zoologists heterosis, or hybrid vigor. This means an increase in size and strength in the first few generations of offspring following the primary racial cross. This hybrid vigor often tends to disappear in succeeding generations but is sometimes maintained. Hybrid vigor as evidenced by increase in stature does not invariably occur as a result of race mixtures in man. Nevertheless, it can be shown that most of the tallest human groups are of mixed racial origin. Among these may be mentioned the Nilotic Negroes, the gigantic Hamitic Negroids of East and Central Africa, the tall Polynesians, Indian-White hybrids, Polynesian-White hybrids in Hawaii and Norfolk Island.

Thurston tells of a British commandant in the Madras presidency who conceived the brilliant idea that the native troops could be improved in physique and military efficiency by breeding and recruiting hybrids between British soldiers and Indians. He, therefore, encouraged his Scottish garrison to take "nights out." After many years, the "Madras Highlanders," mixed bloods, resulted from this eugenic plan. They are said to be distinguished by their tall stature.

We may then conclude that stature, although doubtless fluctuating somewhat in individuals and groups through environmental causes, is in the main a hereditary character. Variations in the stature of groups are no doubt brought about to some extent by artificial and natural selection. Extreme individual variations in stature are often pathological. No one has been able convincingly to explain tall or short stature in any human group on the ground of adaptation, climate, altitude, or even food supply. Variations in the functioning of the ductless glands doubtless affect stature and growth, but these cannot be brought into any direct relationship with physical environment.

In spite of the mainly hereditary character of stature, its utility as a criterion of race is distinctly limited by the wide individual variations found in every group. Some very short men occur even in exceedingly tall groups, but very tall men are much rarer in extremely short peoples. This fact favors Davenport's conclusion as to the dominance of growth-repressing factors. Hrdlička found that the Otomi of northern Mexico, with an average stature of 159.3 cm., showed an individual range of 21.1 cm. (from 148.6 cm. to 169.7 cm.). The Yuma, averaging 172.2 cm., ranged individually from 159.9 cm. to 184.8 cm. (range 24.9 cm.). The Maricopa, with a mean of 174.8 cm., varied between 162.5 cm. and 185.1 cm. (range 22.6 cm.). However, the widest ranges of statural variation occur in peoples of a medium average stature. For example,

Hrdlička states that Pueblo Indians, with an average stature of 164.5 cm., range individually from 148.2 cm. to 182.3 cm. (34.1 cm.).

Tables of distribution of average statures, such as those compiled by Martin [45] and Deniker [46] yield the following general facts as to racial and ethnic distribution of this bodily character.

The shortest groups of mankind are the Negrito pygmies of Asia and Africa with average statures between 138 and 152 cm. (about 54 to 60 inches). These pygmies of the Congo forest, the Malay peninsula, the Andaman Islands, New Guinea, and the Philippines, are distinguished not only by their small stature, but by a combination of Negroid physical features that justifies, to a great extent, their separate subracial classification. Many of the Mongoloid peoples of southeastern Asia and the Malay archipelago also fall into the stature grouping below 160 cm., but the majority of the northern Mongoloids belong in the medium stature class. In Europe, the Lapps of partly Mongoloid descent, are also very short, but almost all European peoples attain a mean stature of 160 cm. or more. A number of the groups of Oceanic Negroids that may not be classified as pygmies, but probably have pygmy blood, also fall into the low stature group. Among the American Indians, at least 10 groups, including Eskimo, Yahgans of Tierra del Fuego, South American Caribs, and some tribes of northern Mexico and the southwestern United States, are below 160 cm. in average height.

The Bushmen-Hottentots, a Negroid racial remnant in South Africa, are almost, if not quite, as short as the pygmies and by most students are thought to be allied to them.

Taking this short group as a whole, stature is racially characteristic in the cases of the African pygmies and of the Bushmen-Hottentot stock. Between the averages of these groups and 160 cm., the lower limit of the medium stature group, are a great number of southern Mongoloid peoples. Short stature cannot perhaps be distinguished as a characteristic feature of Mongoloids, but they tend to be, at any rate, predominatingly short or of medium stature.

The non-Mongoloid Ainu of northern Japan, another remnant of an aboriginal race, also fall into the lowest stature group and as a stock are distinguished by this bodily character.

The medium group, averaging between 160 cm. and 169.9 cm., includes the bulk of mankind. In it are found most of the White subraces, including Southern Europeans of Mediterranean race such as Spanish,

---

[45] Martin, *Lehrbuch*, Vol. 1. pp. 251–255.
[46] Deniker. *The Races of Man*, Appendix I, pp. 577–593.

Portuguese, Italians, and, on the African side, most of the Berbers and Arabs. In Europe, the Alpines of the western, central, and eastern parts of the continent and the Armenoids of the east and in Asia Minor are of medium stature. Not a few Scandinavian groups are within this range. In Asia, a great number of Mongoloid groups, most Indians, and such Armenoids as the Armenians themselves, the Kurds, Persians, and Syrians, have mean statures less than 170 cm. At least a score of African groups range between 160 and 170 cm. These are Negroes and Negroids, mostly from the lowlands of the west coast, but including also some in the Congo forest, in South Africa, and in the Lake Region. In Oceania, the medium groups include the native Australian race and some few of the Negroids of New Guinea and the neighboring islands, many of whom may have pygmy blood. American Indians of medium stature include most of those along the northwest coast, in southwestern United States, in Mexico, and in the cordillera and Amazon basin of South America.

Medium stature may, then, be said to be characteristic of Mediterraneans, Alpines, Armenoids, and Australians. It is also the mode among many of the mixed Mongoloids, including the bulk of the Indians along the Pacific coast of the Americas.

Tall stature (more than 170 cm.) is especially characteristic of the northwestern Europeans and their kin in other countries. It is also found in Europe among the so-called Dinarics, including many Albanians, Bosnians, Serbs, Dalmatians, et cetera. Some Russians also fall into this category. In Asia, great stature is characteristic of Sikhs and Rajputs of India and is found to some extent among the Northern Chinese.

In Africa, great bodily height is commoner than in any other continent. It occurs especially in the head waters of the Nile, in the eastern Lake Region, and among the Bantu of South Africa, but not a few of the western Sudanic groups are also tall. Among the American Indians, bodily heights in excess of 170 cm. are found particularly among the Plains and Eastern Woodland Indians of Canada and of the United States, also in some southwestern United States groups and among the Patagonians and the Ona at the southernmost extremity of South America.

In Oceania, great stature is almost universal among the Polynesians and occurs in some few groups of the Oceanic Negroids (Melanesians and Papuans).

On the whole, stature or gross bodily size is of little use as a racial criterion. One may judge race by body height with about as much accuracy as one can determine the merit of a book by its length.

The Physiological Tests of Race

Do racial physical differences in man correspond to any marked variations in bodily functioning? Frankly, we do not know. Up to the present, physiologists, biochemists, and physicians have been preoccupied with the working of the individual human organism and with groups undifferentiated as to racial physical type. What has been found to be sauce for the goose has been assumed to be sauce, not only for the gander, but also for the duck and the drake. The conductors and the subjects of physiological research alike have been mainly of European racial antecedents. Experimentation upon the so-called White races has yielded results and methods which, as a rule, have been applied to other physical groups without serious impairment of their efficacy. Nevertheless, it seems probable that there are racial physiological differences at least as marked as those morphological features that distinguish the outward appearance of diverse races.

Some racial differences of a physiological character do not lend themselves to accurate measurement. Bodily odor, for example, may be racially characteristic, apart from dietary peculiarities which undoubtedly influence it. Here we are in the difficulty of not being able to smell our own kind and being at a loss to classify the effluvia of other races. I once took occasion to ask a brilliant Japanese student of anthropology whether he detected any odor as a distinguishing feature of Whites. He said that he did most decidedly, and that he found it very unpleasant. Then he went on to say that it particularly assailed his nostrils whenever he entered the Harvard gymnasium. I gave up at once, because I had to admit that his experience coincided with mine. That gymnasium, now happily replaced, was one of the oldest in the country and its entire structure seemed to be permeated by the perspiration of many generations of students. I doubt if the questionnaire method of eliciting information on racial odors will yield satisfactory scientific results.

BASAL METABOLISM, PULSE, TEMPERATURE, ETC.

Basal metabolism involves the measuring of the oxygen consumption of the individual and the calculation therefrom of the heat production per minute. It is one of the best indices of level of nutrition and vital activity and is especially used in the diagnosis of endocrine disease. There are indications of racial differences in this important physiological characteristic. It was first discovered that Chinese and Japanese women living under the environmental conditions of American life have a basal metabolism distinctly lower than the standards for American women of like age, weight, and height. Then G. D. Williams, and after him Morris Steggerda, ascertained that the Maya Indians of Yucatan have a considerably higher metabolic rate than prediction for American Whites and a lower pulse rate. It is not certain whether the metabolism differences are related to food habits, but, in the case of the Mayas, high metabolism cannot be ascribed to an increased specific dynamic action of protein, because Steggerda ascertained that the average protein intake of his Maya subjects was only 74 gm. per day. This is less than the amount consumed by North American Whites.[47]

Steggerda and Benedict also studied the basal metabolism of a group of Negroes and another group of "Browns" (persons of mixed Negro and White blood). The male Browns fell below the standards for Whites of corresponding age, weight, and height, but this result was not confirmed by the female series nor by the full Negroes ("Blacks"). Further investigations of racial differences in basal metabolism are desirable, since important findings may be anticipated from the little now known.

Information on racial differences in pulse, temperature, and respiration is unfortunately scanty. Hrdlička, in his excellent study of the Indians of the southwestern United States and northern Mexico,[48] found that the pulse rate in all tribes and in both sexes of Indians was lower than in Whites. The average pulse rate in healthy adult Indians, in the sitting position, averages in different tribes from 57 to 67 in males as against 70 to 72 in White males. Indian females average between 62 and 73 as against 75 to 80 in White women. V. Suk found the average pulse rate in 55 adult male South African Negroes 72.1, and in 43 females 76.5.[49] The Negro, therefore, stands close to the White in rate of heart beat. The respiration of Indians is about the same as Whites, 16 to 19 per minute in healthy adults, with a slightly higher average in females than in males. In the South African Negroes, on the contrary, the respiration seems to be distinctly higher, averaging, according to V. Suk, 20.5 in adult males and 25.9 in adult females. Temperature under the tongue in healthy adult male Whites averages between 98.6° Fahrenheit, and 99°. In Indians, it is appreciably less, ranging in males from 98.1° to 98.8° Fahrenheit. The temperature in Negroes also seems to be lower than in Whites, averaging in South African males 98.2° and in females 98.3°.

47 Williams, *Maya-Spanish Crosses in Yucatan*, pp. 94–98.
  Steggerda, *Maya Indians*, pp. 160–162.
  Benedict, "Basal Metabolism," pp. 281–292.
48 Hrdlička, *Physiological and Medical Observations*.
49 Suk, "Anthropological and Physiological Observations," pp. 31–70.

GROWTH

Schultz has demonstrated that differences between Negroes and Whites in bodily proportions are already established in foetal life. Such differences are usually similar to those shown between adults.

In early foetal life, the length of the arms exceeds that of the legs, although in the course of development this superiority in arm length is rapidly reduced. The relatively great length of the upper extremity and especially of the forearm in adult Negroes is one of the distinguishing features of the race. Schultz was able to show that in early foetal life the ratio of arm length to leg length in the Negro is consistently higher than in the White. Similarly, he discovered that the excessive length of the forearm relative to the upper arm is a Negro feature already marked in foetal life, as is also the elongation of the Negro shank relative to the length of the thigh. The same author found that the breadth of the hips relative to the shoulder breadth, which is smaller in adult Negroes than in Whites, is already manifest in foetal life. Other differences in bodily proportions that express themselves in the prenatal period are the shorter thumb length and greater length of the second and third fingers in Negroes, as well as the relatively longer and narrower hand; a longer and narrower foot in the Negro with a shorter great toe, longer first and second toes and a more projecting heel; a relatively smaller head in the Negro, and a relatively wider nose. These differences are not, of course, primarily physiological, except insofar as the modifications of bodily proportions are brought about by growth which is a physiological process.

Reference has already been made (p. 236) to Steggerda's remarkable findings that Maya Indian, Navajo Indian, American Negro, and American White children of Dutch descent have virtually identical growth rhythms in spite of their racial diversity and the great differences of climate, altitude, and nature of food supply under which they nature. In Steggerda's series, racial differences in size and proportions are established firmly at the first age measured (6 years). The Maya are about 10 cm. shorter for each age than the Navajo, who, in turn, are consistently shorter than the Dutch-Americans. The Negroes surpass the Dutch in stature at all ages up to 14 years, when the latter pass them and continue taller into adult years.

In all of the four stocks, the girls are taller than the boys for a short period. This period of female superiority in stature begins in the Mayas and Negroes at about 9 years, in the Navajo at 10 years, and in the Dutch at 10.5 years. All of the boys regain their statural lead over the girls of the same race at 14–15 years. The growth curves show that the short Maya boys are growing at relatively the same rate at 15, 16, and 17 years as the boys of the taller races. The average age at first menstruation for Maya girls is 12.9 years and for Dutch White girls 13.2 years.

The remarkable growth similarity in the diverse races coexists with pronounced differences in ultimate body build. The Maya are short, thickset, heavy; the Negroes consistently tall and slender. Chest girth relative to stature is different for each group at every age, and the growth curves remain distinct throughout. I interpret these data to mean that racial anthropometric differences are primarily hereditary rather than environmental, but that the fundamental identity of growth processes bespeaks the specific unity of the races of *Homo sapiens.*

COLOR-BLINDNESS

Congenital color-blindness may be total, in which all colors are confused; the common form, in which red and green are confused; and a very rare form, in which blue is confused with yellow. Total color-blindness occurs in only about one in 300,000 persons and is almost as frequent in females as in males.[50] Racial differences are indicated in red-green color-blindness, which is sex-linked and, therefore, much commoner in males than in females. Early tests of color-blindness, employing colored yarns that have to be matched, are unsatisfactory and have been superseded by tests that require the reading of colored numbers presented against a colored background. The best known is the Ishihara test. By its use, Clements found red-green color-blindness in 3.7 per cent of American Negro males, and 1.9 per cent in 624 American Indian males, as against approximately 8 per cent in White males and 0.43 per cent in White females. Earlier, but apparently trustworthy, work, compiled by Clements from various sources, give the following figures for males: Melanesians (Torres Straits) 0.76, Chukchis (Mongoloid) 3.0, Eskimo 0.8, Chinese 3.17, Japanese 3.4, Egyptians 5.0, Lapps 6.3, Todas (Dravidians) 12.8.[51]

THE BLOOD GROUPS

The human blood groups depend upon the absence in the red blood cells of two chemical structures, A and B, and active substances in the blood serum, called agglutinins, which may affect the receptors in the blood cells so that they stick together or agglutinate. If a patient receives

---

[50] Clements, "Racial Differences in Color Blindness," pp. 417–432.

[51] The high incidence in the Todas may be connected with inbreeding and polyandry (more than one husband to a wife), notorious in this isolated East Indian group.

a transfusion of blood from a donor who belongs to an incompatible blood group, the blood introduced is clotted by agglutinin in the serum of the recipient. This is bad business. Since 1919, serologists have been typing the blood of large samples of every human population that can be reached, to say nothing of the infrahuman primates. This serological activity has produced a new set of anthropological criteria, in addition to serving the practical purposes of preventing harmful transfusions in case of injury or disease and of helping to settle cases of disputed paternity. The latter medico-legal application arises from the known inheritance of the blood groups that permits the prediction of the possible blood groups of offspring of various matings.

Nomenclature	Structure in Cells (agglutinogen)	Substance in Serum (agglutinin)	Genetic Composition (genotype)
O	—	anti-A + anti-B	OO
A	A	anti-B	AA or AO
B	B	anti-A	BB or BO
AB	A + B	—	AB

The three genes that determine O (the absence of A and B), A, and B are triple allelomorphs, and there are only four blood phenotypes because the AO individual is routinely indistinguishable from the AA individual, in spite of the fact that the former has in his blood cells only a single dose of A, as contrasted with the double dose in the AA person. Similarly, BB and BO constitute but one phenotype. Group O (the absence of A and B) is recessive to both A and B, but between these two latter there is no definite dominance. Here we are not interested in the applications of blood group inheritance to paternity cases, although, clearly, when the groups of the parents are known, it is possible to predict what blood groups can occur legitimately in the offspring and what groups cannot. Thus, if you and your wife are both O, and she produces a B baby or an A baby, you have been cuckolded. If you and she are both O, and she has an AB child, she has achieved the genetically impossible, whatever her morals.

In addition, four subgroups of A—A_1, A_2, A_3, A_4—have been distinguished. These subgroups show successively weaker agglutination by B sera. A_3 occurs in only one of about 2000 persons and A_4 in one of 60,000. A_1 is about five or six times as common as A_2, and the inheritance scheme is four multiple allelomorphs—O, A_1 A_2, and B—with A_1 dominant and A_2 recessive.

The A and B structures are not the only agglutinable substances in the red blood cells. In 1927, Landsteiner and Levine discovered two other agglutinogens, M and N, inherited as a simple Mendelian pair of genes and not carried on the same chromosome as the A,B, and O genes. They are thus inherited quite independently of the ordinary blood groups in three different types—M,N, and MN. These M and N types are not important in blood transfusions, since the agglutinins that would clot them do not normally occur in human sera. However, their distribution is anthropologically interesting. In addition to those already mentioned, some eight other agglutinable factors in human red blood cells have been reported. The most important of these are P and Rh. The former, reported by Landsteiner and Levine in 1928 and demonstrated with immune rabbit serum, yields graded reactions, which are more frequent in Negroes than in Whites. Rh is a substance common to human blood and the blood of the rhesus monkey, a macaque, and is more frequently present than absent.

Properties related to A and B are found not only among the primates, but widely distributed through the animal kingdom, perhaps because these antigens belong, at least in part, to carbohydrate series in which the chemical variety is more restricted than in protein series.[52]

We shall first consider the main facts of the distribution of the regular blood groups, A, B, AB, and O, in the many peoples and diverse geographical areas of the world. Our interest is concentrated upon the significance of the blood groups in taxonomy, including racial classification, and the extent to which these serological data throw light upon human evolution and the early migrations of peoples. The discussion of the ultimate utility of this technique to the physical anthropologist must be deferred until a survey of the distribution has been made.

Table 8 is a selection from the vast compilation of data made by Boyd (1939),[53] rearranged so that the various peoples are grouped under the main conventional racial classifications used in this work. Conclusions about the blood group distributions are based not solely upon our abbreviated table, but also upon Boyd's full assemblage of data. In the table, the percentages of the various four blood groups are first given and then the decimal frequencies of p (the gene for A), q (the gene for B), and r (the gene for O).[54]

The lack of conformity of blood group frequencies to conventional racial classifications may be noted from an inspection of Table 8.

The frequency of the gene r is derived from the blood group O (which

[52] Schiff and Boyd, *Blood Grouping Technic*, p. 191.
[53] Boyd, "Blood Groups," pp. 155–225.
[54] For the various methods of calculating the gene frequencies, cf. Boyd, *op. cit.*, p. 148. Briefly, the formulae Boyd used in the tables from which our material has been taken are:
$$r = \sqrt{O} \qquad p = \sqrt{O + A} - \sqrt{O} \qquad q = \sqrt{O + B} - \sqrt{O}.$$
Theoretically, apart from chance deviation, $p + q + r = 1$.

contains neither the A nor the B agglutinogen). In general, throughout the world, r amounts to more than .500. Often it approaches or exceeds .700, and it rarely falls below .400. This recessive gene is then characteristic of the majority of mankind. For example, in a considerable number of series of Whites in the United States, the modal, or most frequent, value of r seems to be about .670. However, it is in the aboriginal (Eskimo and Indian) population of the New World that the highest general frequencies of r are to be observed, usually between .900 and 1.000. In fact, until recently, it was believed that the American race was pure r (O), when not modified by admixture of Negroes and Whites. Leaving out of consideration the immigration of Whites and Negroes in historical times, it is obvious that the New World has been, from the point of view of human populations, an area of isolation.

In Europe, the highest values of r (from .700 to .750) occur in the remoter western and northwestern islands (Iceland .747, Ireland .744, Scotland .704). They tend to diminish from west to east but do not often fall below .500. Around the southern and western fringes of Africa, we encounter further high values of r, diminishing toward the center and northeastern part of the continent. The same phenomenon is discernible in the Arabian peninsula, an isolated region with generally high values of r. Similarly, high values of r seem to occur in the islands of Indonesia more remote from the Asiatic mainland, in Melanesia, Micronesia, and Polynesia, with occasional exceptions. In Australia, prevailingly high proportions of r are found except in the southern portion, where there is an exceptionally high frequency of A. There is a suggestion that the extreme northeastern part of Asia may also be high in r.

In general, then, high values of r, even overwhelming proportions, seem to occur in areas that are isolated or peripheral with reference both to central and southeastern Asia, and (curiously) to central and northeastern Africa.

The gene p (A) has a peculiarly spotty distribution. It has its highest frequency in certain North American Indian tribes (Blackfeet .526, Bloods .583) in the state of Montana and near Alberta, Canada, and among the South Australians (.413 to .437). It is high also in some of the outlying corners of Europe (Norway, Sweden, Spain), but occasional equally high values crop out also in more central areas such as Belgium, Switzerland, Bulgaria, and Armenia (.334). It is virtually absent among the South American Indians. In most places of the world it seems to range from about .150 to .250. Boyd regards it as "centrifugal" and concentrated in "refuge" areas, but it is not so markedly marginal as are the extremely high values of r. Gene p (A) is usually high when q (B)

TABLE 8. THE BLOOD GROUPS (Data mainly from W. C. Boyd, 1939)

Race, Country	Investigator	Place	Number	O	A	B	AB	p	q	r
White										
Europe										
Iceland	Jonsson		800	55.7	32.1	9.6	2.6	.190	.062	.747
Ireland	Boyd, Boyd	Dublin	399	55.2	31.1	12.0	1.7	.186	.076	.744
Scotland	Matta	Glasgow	746	49.6	36.6	9.5	4.3	.224	.065	.704
England	Taylor	South	106,477	45.2	43.2	8.5	3.1	.268	.061	.672
Wales	Boyd, Boyd	Bangor	192	47.9	32.8	16.2	3.1	.206	.108	.692
Norway	Høst	N. of Oslo	615	37.9	46.8	10.9	4.4	.304	.083	.616
Sweden	Hesser	Stockholm	633	37.9	46.1	9.5	6.5	.301	.073	.616
Denmark	Thomsen	Copenhagen	7,488	43.0	43.0	10.5	3.5	.272	.076	.656
France	Rivière, Kossovitch	Paris	1,265	39.8	42.3	11.8	6.1	.276	.088	.632
Belgium	Moureau	Liège	3,500	46.7	41.9	8.3	3.1	.257	.058	.684
Holland Students	Herwerden, Boele-Nijland		3,085	45.7	41.2	9.6	3.5	.256	.068	.677
"	"		705	42.6	39.4	13.4	4.5	.253	.096	.653
Spain	Hoyos Sainz	Madrid?	1,035	43.6	51.2	4.0	1.1	.312	.030	.661
Italy	Cuboni	Milan	1,500	45.6	40.5	10.6	3.3	.253	.074	.676
Switzerland	Liengme, Goudet	Geneva	1,000	40.2	48.9	7.9	3.0	.309	.059	.634
Germany	Schiff	Berlin	39,174	36.5	42.5	14.5	6.5	.285	.110	.604
Czecho-Slovakia	Suk	Brno	3,010	28.8	44.0	18.2	9.0	.317	.149	.537
Poland	Halber, Mydlarski	Polesia	3,389	30.6	36.2	23.6	9.5	.264	.182	.553
Latvia	Weidemann		1,160	32.2	36.6	24.2	6.9	.262	.183	.568
Lithuania	Zilinskas, Masalskis	Kaunas	2,452	40.1	34.1	20.0	5.8	.228	.143	.634
Esthonia	Rooks		1,844	32.3	36.6	22.4	8.7	.261	.170	.589
Finland		Hollola	3,361	37.5	39.2	17.0	6.3	.263	.126	.612
Hungary	Weitzner	Budapest	1,000	35.7	43.3	15.7	5.3	.292	.119	.598
Gypsies	Gärtner		925	28.5	26.6	35.3	9.6	.208	.265	.534
Roumania	Jonescu, Jonescu	Jassy	2,470	41.4	39.5	13.9	5.2	.256	.100	.644
"	"	"	1,135	38.2	39.0	17.5	5.3	.260	.128	.618
Jews										
Bulgaria	Ganev	Sofia	6,060	32.1	44.4	15.4	8.1	.308	.123	.567
Yugo-Slavia	Schmidt	Stapar	408	34.1	40.9	19.9	5.1	.282	.151	.584
Greece	Diamantoupolos	Athens	1,200	42.0	39.6	14.2	3.7	.254	.102	.648
Russia	Chominski, Shustova	Kiev	4,340	33.1	38.7	19.3	8.9	.272	.149	.575
"	Melkikh, Gringot	Irkutsk	4,043	34.8	34.2	22.4	8.6	.239	.166	.591

Race Country	Place	Investigator	Number	O	A	B	AB	p	q	r
Russia Jews	Penza	Zabezhinski	4,802	33.7	37.0	21.4	7.9	.260	.161	.582
" Jews	Kharkov	Rubashkin, Derman	383	28.0	42.3	23.5	6.2	.309	.188	.529
United States	N. Carolina?	Snyder	20,000	45.0	41.0	10.0	4.0	.257	.071	.672
" " Jews	Brooklyn	Wiener, Lederer, Polayes	500	37.4	40.0	16.8	5.8	.268	.125	.612
White Africa										
Egypt	Cairo	Boyd, Boyd	502	27.3	38.4	25.5	8.8	.288	.203	.523
" Copts		Moharram	1,476	31.2	33.9	24.7	10.3	.247	.188	.559
Morocco Rif Berbers		Coon	196	50.0	18.3	28.6	3.1	.119	.179	.707
Shluh' Atlas Mts.			123	61.8	22.0	15.4	0.8	.129	.094	.786
Tunisia Jews		Kossovitch	730	36.8	36.2	19.9	7.1	.247	.147	.607
Berbers		Caillon, Disdier	500	46.4	32.4	15.8	5.4	.206	.106	.682
White Asia										
Armenians	Tiflis	Semenskayar	3,816	31.2	48.5	13.8	6.5	.334	.112	.559
Turkey	Istamboul	Babacan	500	33.8	42.6	14.8	8.8	.293	.116	.581
Syria, Arabs	Aleppo	Altounyan	933	35.7	37.0	20.8	6.5	.255	.157	.598
Arabia	Yemen	Moshkovski	158	55.7	32.3	10.7	1.3	.192	.068	.746
" Jews		Younovitch	1,000	56.0	26.1	16.1	1.8	.157	.101	.748
Iran	N. Samarkand	Libman	500	30.6	31.8	31.6	6.0	.237	.235	.553
Japan Ainu	Saghalien	Furuhata, Kishi	1,141	25.7	28.0	34.8	11.5	.226	.271	.507
Negroid										
Negritos										
Efe-speaking	Belgian Congo	Jadin	1,032	30.6	30.3	29.1	10.0	.227	.219	.554
"	Belgian Congo	"	1,013	27.1	35.9	28.1	8.9	.273	.222	.521
Philippines		Grove	297	48.5	33.4	14.1	4.0	.208	.095	.697
Negroes—Africa										
Balese	Belgian Congo	Jadin	507	48.5	30.8	16.4	4.3	.194	.109	.697
Alur	"	"	512	40.6	38.5	17.0	3.9	.252	.122	.638
Zulu	S. Africa	Pijper	880	53.2	25.3	19.2	2.3	.157	.122	.730
Senegalese	Sierra Leone	Julier	635	47.4	25.0	24.1	3.5	.163	.157	.689
Negroes—United States										
	N. Carolina?	Snyder	500	47.0	28.0	20.0	5.0	.181	.133	.686
Negroids—Melanesia										
	New Guinea	Haydon, Murphy	753	53.7	26.8	16.3	3.2	.164	.104	.733

THE BLOOD GROUPS (Continued)

Race Country	Place	Investigator	Number	O	A	B	AB	p	q	r
	New Guinea	Bijlmer	500	37.6	44.4	13.2	4.8	.293	.099	.613
Papuans	Schouten Is.	Bos	748	62.7	18.5	16.7	2.1	.109	.099	.792
	Solomons	Howells, Moss	107	49.5	31.8	16.8	1.9	.198	.110	.704
Bushman-Hottentot—Africa										
Bushmen (Kung)		Pijper	268	60.4	28.0	7.8	3.8	.163	.049	.777
Hottentots	Pretoria	"	506	34.8	30.6	29.2	5.3	.220	.210	.590
Mongoloid *Asia*										
Buriats "western"		Melkikh	1,602	33.3	20.9	37.5	8.3	.158	.264	.578
Goldi	N.E. Manchuria	Jettmar	196	39.3	18.9	36.2	5.6	.136	.242	.628
Tungus	"	Kunitusa, Makino	813	28.2	29.1	33.1	9.6	.227	.254	.530
Mongols	Urga	Jettmar	114	28.6	23.2	31.3	16.9	.185	.239	.535
Kazaks	Ksyl-Orda	Grubina	1,172	23.7	29.3	31.5	15.5	.241	.256	.487
Kirgiz	army	Askmarin	500	31.6	27.4	32.2	8.8	.206	.236	.563
Tatars	Kazan	Schwarz, Nimtsovitskaya	500	27.8	30.0	28.8	13.4	.233	.225	.527
Chinese	Canton	Dormanns	992	45.9	22.8	25.2	6.1	.152	.166	.676
	Hoang-Ho	Yang-Fung-Min	2,127	34.2	30.8	27.7	7.3	.220	.201	.587
	Peking	Huie	1,296	28.6	26.6	32.0	12.8	.208	.244	.535
Composite Races										
East Indian-Dravidian										
Plainsmen	Assam	Mitra	2,000	33.7	24.6	32.5	9.2	.183	.233	.582
Hindus	United Provinces	Malone, Lahiri	2,357	30.2	24.5	37.2	8.1	.190	.272	.550
Dravidians	Ranchi Chota-Nagpur	"	589	24.3	27.5	36.8	11.4	.227	.289	.493
Todas	Nilgiri Hills	Pandit	200	29.5	19.5	38.0	13.0	.157	.278	.545
Tamils	Ceylon, S. India	Bais, Verhoef	348	37.9	23.0	31.6	7.5	.155	.218	.616
Australian										
Aborigines	Queensland	Cleland, Johnston	1,176	52.6	36.9	8.5	2.0	.221	.051	.725
	South, Musgrave Mts.	Lee	377	60.3	31.7	6.4	1.6	.182	.040	.778
	South & Central	Cleland	149	32.2	67.7	0	0	.433	0	.567
		Cleland, Johnston	842	38.7	61.3	0	0	.378	0	.622
Indonesian-Malay										
Japanese	Tokyo	Biljmer	29,799	30.1	38.4	21.9	9.7	.279	.172	.549
Tobelo	Moluccas		450	51.0	27.0	18.7	3.5	.169	.121	.714
Sundanese	Java	Buining	1,126	37.2	24.4	32.0	6.4	.175	.222	.610

550

THE BLOOD GROUPS (Continued)

Race Country	Place	Investigator	Number	O	A	B	AB	p	q	r
Sumatrans	E. Sumatra	Bais, Verhoef	546	43.7	23.0	29.0	4.3	.155	.191	.662
Bogobo	Davao, Philippines	Grove	302	53.6	16.9	26.5	3.0	.107	.163	.732
Igorotes	Baguio, "	"	214	50.5	21.9	21.9	5.6	.140	.140	.711
Moros	Siasi Is., "	"	501	25.7	18.2	44.9	11.2	.156	.333	.507
Micronesians	Palau	Takasaki	545	58.9	26.4	12.3	2.4	.157	.077	.768
	Truk	"	485	28.6	32.0	33.0	6.4	.244	.250	.535
	Yap	"	213	57.7	20.3	17.8	4.2	.124	.109	.760
Polynesian										
	Easter Is.	Rahm	63	25.4	69.8	3.1	1.6	.472	.030	.504
	Hawaii, Maui, Oahu	Nigg	413	36.5	60.8	2.2	0.5	.382	.018	.604
	Marshall Is.	Takasaki	343	52.2	28.0	16.9	2.9	.173	.108	.723
	New Zealand	Phillips	127	38.6	41.7	0.8	18.9	.275	.006	.622
	Am. Samoa	Stephenson	500	58.6	17.0	19.4	5.0	.103	.118	.766
American										
North America										
Eskimo	Greenland	Bay-Schmith	607	54.2	38.5	4.8	2.0	.228	.033	.735
	Baffin Land, Lab.	Sewall	143	55.6	44.0	0	0	.253	0	.752
Kwakiutl	Br. Col.	Gates, Darby, Ride, Furuhata	123	85.4	12.2	2.4	0.9	.063	.013	.926
Blackfeet	Montana	Levine, Matson, Schrader	107	22.4	76.7	0	0.2	.526	0	.474
Navajo	Arizona	Nigg	457	72.9	26.9	0.2	0.2	.145	.001	.854
Pueblo	Cochiti, N.M.	Allen, Schaefer	353	88.0	11.7	0	0.3	.061	0	.939
Sioux	Crow Creek, S.D.	Snyder	100	91.0	7.0	2.0	0	.035	.010	.955
Maya	Yucatan	Goodner	223	97.7	1.3	0.5	0.5	.006	.001	.988
South America										
Mapuche	Chile	Rahm	382	75.6	17.2	6.2	0.6	.094	.035	.870
	Peru	Arce Larreta	200	100.0	0	0	0	0	0	1.000
Ona	Tierra del Fuego	Rahm	18	94.4	5.6	0	0	.028	0	.972
Yalghan	Navarino Is., T.F.		33	9.0	0	91.0	0	0	.700	.300
Toba	Argentina	Mazza et al.	194	98.5	1.5	0.2	0	.007	0	.993
Caraja	Araguaya R. Brazil	Golden	61	39	5	51	5	.039	.324	.624

is low or lacking and r (O) is also above average. To some degree, high A seems to go with high O.

The gene q (B) seems definitely concentrated in the central Asiatic plateau and in eastern and southeastern Asia. Eastward it fades away in the Pacific islands and is virtually absent from Australia (except the northern fringe) and from the New World (although dubiously present in .700 of a handful of Fuegians—33 of them—and in one or two other South American tribes). From central Asia westward to the Atlantic fringes of Europe it again diminishes to almost nothing, but it is curiously high in the Whites of northeastern Africa and the Pygmies of the Congo forest.

The simplest explanation of the present distribution of p, q, and r is an application of the well-known principles of dispersion of evolving animal types. The most primitive types spread out from the evolutionary center of development and are forced by successively higher evolved types into marginal and refuge areas. On this basis alone, it might be guessed that man was originally all group O (r) and that, since A (p) is spotty and submarginal in its distribution, a first series of mutations produced and disseminated agglutinogen A, whereas a second series of mutations resulted in B, which still preserves its central Asiatic distribution. This was, indeed, an early explanation of the blood group distributions rather widely accepted. Further, since in the nineteen twenties it was commonly thought that the aboriginal inhabitants of the New World lacked both A and B, it followed that A and B were mutations of comparatively recent date, subsequent to the peopling of America, which could scarcely have begun more than 25,000 years ago. However, this simple explanation has now fallen into disfavor.

In the first place, the gorilla, the orang-utan, and the gibbon all have both A and B (probably indistinguishable from the corresponding human antigens) and the chimpanzee has A and O. Since somewhat similar structures are found in the blood of the lower primates also, it is hard to evade the conclusion that the human blood groups must have been inherited from prehuman ancestors. It is rather improbable that the present anthropoid apes and man have developed the same agglutinogens independently, subsequent to our ancestors' attainment of a human status. Again, Boyd and Boyd, as well as other serologists, have been able to ascertain the probable blood groups from ancient mummified tissues and have tested in this way specimens from more than 300 mummies. From their results on Egyptian material, A and B seem to be present as far back as the predynastic period, which came to an end about

3400 B.C. Thus, both A and B are apparently at least 5,000 years old and probably much older.

Boyd explains the present distribution of the blood groups on the assumption that they are "non-adaptive" (i.e., none of them affords any advantage in natural selection) and subject to accidental loss through isolation. He assumes that earliest man probably had a blood group distribution "not far different from that of present day Asiatics or Negroes, say $p = 0.25$, $q = 0.15$, $r = 0.60$," but that isolation early produced groups devoid of gene q.[55] After a small dribble into the New World of people with some B (evidenced in the presence of B in prehistoric American mummies), subsequent groups who had lost B through isolation entered the Americas in successive waves. These groups probably had A and O, but the former through isolation was lost in some places and concentrated in others, whereas the little B present in prehistoric times was usually lost.

Candela has recently shown very convincingly that the gradient, or shading off of B from central Asia into eastern and central Europe, is related to the repeated historical invasions of Mongoloid peoples, beginning with the Huns, although B is not necessarily associated with Mongoloid physical characteristics and may be inherited quite independently of them.[56] Boyd thinks that to some extent the A possessors retreated before the advance of the B group people, who may have been superior in the arts of war, hunting, and agriculture, but that the latter never penetrated in this last advance to the New World and Australia.

Unfortunately, there are also certain difficulties in the way of acceptance of Boyd's explanation. The supposition that earliest man had a blood group distribution of $p = 0.25$, $q = 0.15$, $r = 0.60$ does not account for the origins of the serological differences. If A and B are not the result of mutations from an originally universal O condition, is O, on the contrary, a mutation from A and/or B? The gene r (O) is found among the apes only in the chimpanzee, which has a blood group distribution of about 91 per cent A and 9 per cent O. Some way or other, the recessive O became established early and predominantly in the human stock, and it is hard to see how this state of affairs could have transpired if the blood groups have no selective value, unless O was the original specifically human condition. And if that was the case, and the p and q genes are mutations, how did they establish themselves without any selective advantage, especially if, as Boyd asserts, it is necessary to assume

---

[55] Schiff and Boyd, *op. cit.*, pp. 210 ff.
[56] Candela, "The Introduction of Blood-Group B Into Europe," pp. 413–444.

improbably high mutation rates in order to explain the present distributions of A and B on the basis of mutations? If minority genes and single or rare mutations have little or no chance of survival, but are lost by accident, how did B attain its present predominance in central Asia? If B was lost by isolation in Northern Asia and in the New World, why has it maintained itself at a level of approximately .222 in the Congo pygmies, almost certainly the earliest Negroid population of Africa and without question one of the most isolated peoples of the world? And how has chance operated to produce the following results in the isolated but adjacent tribes of Tierra del Fuego? The answer is, of course, that practically anything *can* happen by the operation of chance, if that is the sole factor to be considered, however great may be the betting odds

Group	Investigator	Number	O	A	B	AB	p	q	r
Ona	Rahm	18	94.4	5.6	0	0	.028	0	.972
Yahgan	"	33	9.0	0	91.0	0	0	.700	.300

against such happening. However, it would seem that the present distribution of the blood groups does not greatly illuminate the prehistoric migrations of man, if it is necessary to start with a wholly gratuitous assumption of the blood group composition of earliest man and then to throw the onus of subsequent changes almost entirely upon hypothetical isolations of small groups and the vagaries of chance.

Gates accounts for the present racial distribution of the blood groups by a theory of parallel and repeated mutations.[57] He bases his contention upon the observation of similar mutations in different plants and animals and upon the possibility of change of mutation rates from time to time within a species. Using a method devised by Fisher, he calculates the time that might be required for A in any race to increase to 40 per cent from an original 100 per cent O, if A was a mutation from O. Assuming a mutation frequency of 1 in 100,000, by these calculations it would require a million years for the Australians, the Polynesians, the Bushmen, or the Basques to build up 40 per cent of A. Since this is much too long a time, Gates concludes that primitive men already had A, derived from anthropoid ancestors. It may have begun with much less than 40 per cent and increased slowly through persistent mutations. It seems certain that A_2, A_3, etc. are secondary mutations from the older A_1. The mutation rate of these subgroups is not known, but there is one definite case on record of A_2 mutating to A_1.

Gates thinks that the human B may be a much later mutation than A and one that occurred in man independently of, and parallel with, the

[57] Gates, ms.

anthropoid ape B. Haldane calculated that the 10 per cent to 15 per cent of B in the European population could not have been acquired in the last 20,000 years through mutation alone, and there is good evidence that the European B is due to infiltration from the east. B may well have increased in repeated mutations in different areas.

A somewhat different interpretation of the blood group distribution assumes that in the early history of man isolated races developed, some exclusively or predominantly group O, some A, and some B, and that subsequently these races mixed and interchanged in part their serological characters. The process of race-making must indeed have proceeded through the isolation and selection of the mutations of our earliest human, or perhaps even anthropoid ancestors, but there is no particular reason for supposing that the gradual differentiation of a specialized Mongoloid type necessarily carried with it a loss of A and O so that the pure Mongoloids were at the same time purely group B. Yet it is wholly possible that the same isolation and selective process that resulted in Mongoloid morphological traits might have piled up B in that stock, fortuitously or through selectional advantages yet unknown.

The fact that O is so rare in monkeys and apes, whereas it predominates in man, has suggested to some serologists that A and B came first, and the gene O arose later by mutation. Then, according to Wiener, it would be more likely that O arose from A than from B, since the chimpanzee has A and O together, but no B, as is also the case in certain human groups.[58] However, it is hard to see how the recessive O could have established itself so strongly in all subsequently mixed races, even granting that it had some selective advantage (which is not known to exist). It would seem more probable that A arose from a primitive and generally established O. Yet A and B must have originated as mutations, or at any rate two of the three genes must have so originated, either in the human or the prehuman stage, unless one believes in separate and original serological creations.

To me, an anthropologist and no serologist, the following explanation seems most nearly satisfactory. Substances that were precursors of O, A, and B must have existed in the blood of our anthropoid ape ancestors, with the O-like substance predominating, the A-like substance next in strength, and the B prototype as yet little differentiated. In very early human times, at least with the first dispersion of *Homo sapiens,* primitive Whites carrying a preponderance of the fully developed human gene O and a possibly new mutation A (the latter in the minority) began to spread over the world. These migrations preceded the complete dif-

[58] Wiener, "Evolution of the Human Blood Group Factors," p. 203.

ferentiation of the mutation B in the human stock. The agglutinogen B either originated or began to proliferate through some selective advantage in central and southeastern Asia at the later period when the common Negroid-Mongoloid branch was separating itself from the trunk of *Homo sapiens* somewhere in Asia. Thus the Congo pygmies, probably the most archaic Negroid stock, carried with them into the isolated equatorial forest region of their habitat high proportions of both A and B. The evolution of the full-sized African Negro type on the periphery of the Congo forest and from these pygmies, involved, possibly fortuitously, but probably through selective disadvantages as yet unknown, a reduction of both A and B in the specialized Negro race. Much the same process may have taken place in Melanesia. In the slightly later development of the specialized Mongoloid race, B increased at the expense of A and O, possibly through selective advantages appertaining not to the agglutinogen itself but to other qualities inherent in the Mongoloid stock associated with B by chance. America must have been peopled by Northern Asiatic, non-Mongoloid or potentially Mongoloid stocks who had not received the excessive infusion of B that accompanied the full development of the specialized Mongoloid type. The peopling of America may well have preceded the great proliferation of B in Central Asia. Boyd's theory of loss and spotty distribution of A and B in the New World through chance and isolation, assuming very little of either of these agglutinogens in the aboriginal immigrants, seems to hold water (with occasional leaks), and Candela's exposition of a late spread of B into Europe by historical Mongoloid migrations quite satisfies me. It is hard to get away from the temporal priority of O and A over B, as carried by the Mongoloids, almost certainly the last of the primary races to be developed.

The serologists insist that, in spite of all sorts of testing correlations of the blood groups with various pathological susceptibilities and immunities, there is no good evidence that significant relationships exist or that any of the serological types give their possessors advantage or disadvantage in the biological struggle for survival. Undoubtedly this contention is correct on the basis of present evidence, but it results in a virtual paradox. Boyd attempts to demonstrate that A and B could not establish themselves from single mutations or repeated mutations because they would have been lost by chance in the absence of their having selectional advantages. He denies that they have such selectional advantages, but nevertheless A and B *have* survived, and in some cases they are predominant within groups.

So far, we have not considered the extent to which A, B, and O are linked or associated with the conventional combinations of hair form, pigmentation, and the other morphological features that are used by anthropologists (and by everyone else) for human classification into racial or other taxonomic groups. The plain facts of the matter are that such correlations are so tenuous as to be virtually non-existent. The following data show the situation:

TABLE 9. SIMILAR BLOOD GROUP FREQUENCIES IN PHYSICALLY
DIVERSE PEOPLES

People	Place	Gene Frequency *		
		p	q	r
Eskimo	Labrador, Baffin Land	.318	0	.682
Aborigines	W. Australia	.306	0	.694
Pygmies	Ituri River, Belgian Congo	.227	.219	.554
Russians	Perm	.231	.203	.573
Iranians	Persia	.237	.235	.553
Zulu	South Africa	.157	.122	.730
Berbers	Tunis	.159	.127	.707
Whites	Agnew, Cal.	.172	.105	.733
Melanesians	N. E. Pantari Is.	.173	.108	.723
Buriats	Mongolia	.158	.264	.578
Bambarra	W. Sudan	.180	.225	.598
Hindus	United Provinces	.190	.272	.550
Manchu	Mukden	.198	.249	.556
Orochi	Saghalien, Japan	.190	.270	.552
Gypsies	Puspokladany, Hungary	.178	.265	.573
Armenians	Tiflis	.334	.112	.559
Micronesians	Kusaie, Carolines	.300	.125	.585
Egyptians	Alexandria	.338	.116	.553

* These series are not always the same as those listed in Table 8. They are samples selected to show similarities of gene frequency.

The table above groups peoples that are physically and racially about as unlike as they could possibly be and are yet nearly identical in blood group distribution: Eskimo and Australian aborigines; Negrito pygmies, Russians and Iranians; South African and Melanesian Negroids, California and Tunisian Whites; ultra-Mongoloid Buriats and Negro Bambarra, etc. It would be quite easy also to compile from Boyd's tables different samples drawn from the same ethnic or racial population with widely dissimilar blood group gene frequencies. Evidently, the blood groups are inherited independently of racial characteristics.

The world distribution of the M and N types in man is by no means completely plotted. Neither type is dominant over the other; there are no agglutinins in the sera to clot these structures, and the inheritance is controlled by a single pair of genes. If M and N were present in nearly equal proportions, it might be expected that the world distribution would approximate M = .25, MN = .50, N = .25. Boyd's table shows that the expectation is roughly fulfilled in the case of MN, but that M usually is found in somewhat higher proportions than N. The largest series tabulated by Boyd (10,894 Germans from the Tyrol) yields a gene frequency of m = .574, n = .448, and the bulk of the Europeans series appear to have m in proportions ranging from about .540 to .590. Boyd and Boyd have found some unusually high values of m in the Ukraine and in the Caucasus (approximating m = .63), and the Finnish and Swedish data show m frequently in excess of .60. Very few Negroes have been typed for M and N and those tabulated present nothing extraordinary, nor do the considerable numbers of Japanese.

The outstanding peculiarities of M and N distribution, as at present known, are found in south Australian aborigines (m = .171, n = .735) and in several small samples of North American Indians in which m ranges from .738 to .794. However, the few Eskimo tested show only the ordinary predominance of m (.559 and .572). Boyd again wishes to explain the irregularities by accidental gene loss due to small numbers in isolation. The substance M was presumably commoner in primitive man than N and thus was less likely to be lost in the manner assumed.

Landsteiner and Wiener used a variety of anti-M sera on a number of species of apes and monkeys and found that they could be graded according to their resemblances to human M blood. The anthropoid apes, of course, were closest to man, with the chimpanzee most nearly human. M agglutinogens were found regularly in the Old World monkeys, but in only one species of New World monkeys (and this involved a blood reaction to a single special serum). Anti-N sera have given positive reactions thus far only with chimpanzees, suggesting that the N factor in ape blood (like the M) is related to the human substance but not identical with it.[59]

Landsteiner and Wiener by immunizing rabbits with the blood of the rhesus monkey succeeded in obtaining anti-rhesus immune sera that reacted with about 85 per cent of the blood of White individuals. The factor in the human blood that reacts positively with such sera is called Rh. Its first importance is due to the fact that it is the first of the agglutinogens to which physiological function (and hence selectional value) can be ascribed. The critical case occurs when a father is Rh-positive and the mother Rh-negative and a foetus *in utero* inherits the Rh-positive from the father. Because of some defect in the placenta, some of the foetal blood may pass into the circulation of the mother and set up the production of anti-Rh isoantibodies. These then filter back through

[59] *Ibid.*, pp. 205–206.

the placenta and destroy the blood of the foetus either *in utero* or after birth giving rise to the disease known as erythroblastosis foetalis.[60] This disease destroys the red blood corpuscles of the foetus and may be lethal or may cause anemia and various other pathological and defective conditions.

The mating and foetal inheritance combination that can produce this disease occurs in about one out of 10 to 12 cases, whereas the actual disease has a frequency of about one in 400, thus indicating that only about one of 40 women is capable of being sensitized. Hence the selective effect is small.

More recently it has been suggested that Rh incompatibility may also be important as a cause of undifferentiated feeble-mindedness. Cook reports the preliminary findings of Yannet and Lieberman on 109 visiting mothers of the same number of feeble-minded children in a Connecticut institution.[61] About half of the children (53 of 109) showed specific types of feeble-mindedness, and the mothers of these showed about the average of Rh-positive and Rh-negative for the White population. Of 56 children classified as "undifferentiated mental deficients," the mothers were Rh-negative in 14 cases—more than twice the average for the general population. Further, of the 14 negative mothers, 11 had Rh-positive children—the situation in which erythroblastosis foetalis sometimes develops. It is thus possible that the Rh incompatibility that destroys foetal blood cells in erythroblastosis may retard brain development in some cases. Snyder and associates have confirmed the results of Yanett and Lieberman (as reported by Cook) in further investigation of 66 mothers and their 68 feeble-minded children.[62] Of the 66 mothers, 17 are Rh— (nearly twice the expected frequency) and of the 68 feeble-minded children, 11 were Rh+ from Rh— mothers (more than double the expected frequency). According to these same authors, the proportion of Rh+ children from Rh— mothers should be about 8 per cent, but since first born children are seldom, if ever, affected, the expected proportion showing the effects of immunization of the mother by the Rh factor is reduced to about 6 per cent.

The Rh gene of human blood, discovered as recently as 1940, is turning out to have so many astounding ramifications that it is very difficult to keep abreast of them. Wiener has found that the Rh agglutinogen is not a single entity but has at least five variants determined by corresponding allelic genes and giving rise to eight types of blood. These types

---

[60] This discovery was made by P. Levine and associates.
[61] Cook, "The Rh Gene," pp. 133–134.
[62] Snyder, Schonfeld, and Offerman, "The RH Factor and Feeblemindedness," pp. 9–10.

correspond to the reactions to three kinds of antisera: Anti-Rh_0, Anti-Rh′, and Anti-Rh″. The first of these antisera corresponds to the original anti-rhesus serum of Landsteiner and Wiener and gives about 85 per cent positive reactions on Whites; the second about 70 per cent, and the third approximately 30 per cent. The types are now designated thus: Rh-negative, Rh′, Rh″, Rh′Rh″, Rh_0, Rh_1, Rh_2, Rh_1Rh_2.[63] Wiener has found very marked differences between Negroes and Whites in New York city in the distribution of these eight Rh types. His Negro Series (a) consisted of a heterogeneous group of outpatients and numbered 93 individuals. Series (b), consisting of 138 persons, included only such as gave no obvious indication of White admixture. The outstanding difference between Negroes and Whites is in the frequency of type Rh_0, which includes 24.5 per cent of the mixed Negroes of series (a), 41.6 per cent of the more or less unmixed Negroes of series (b), and only 3.0 per cent and 2.2 per cent of the White series consisting of 263 and 359 persons, respectively.[64] Thus type Rh_0 seems to be 10 to 20 times as common in Negroes as in Whites, even when the former are considerably mixed. Presumably, tests on really full-blood Negroes would yield even more striking results, and it is suggested that the Rh tests might be used upon Negroid groups as an index of purity. Further, type Rh_1 is more than twice as frequent in Whites as in Negroes, whereas Rh_2 shows an excess in the colored series.

The incidence of negative reactions with both standard anti-Rh_0 and with anti-Rh′ sera is much lower in Chinese than in Whites (with the former serum 1.5 per cent negative in Chinese, 13 per cent in Whites; with the latter 5.1 per cent in Chinese, 29.6 per cent in Whites).[65] The bloods of American Indians, like those of Chinese, give very few negative reactions with standard anti-Rh_0 serum (0.8 per cent), but many more negative reactions with anti-Rh′ than either Whites or Chinese (42 per cent). In this respect the Indians resemble Negroes.

Thus it appears that the Rh serological substance, which, as Cook says, was first regarded as a mere "immunological oddity," turns out to be the gene complex with the most important selective value hitherto known, as well as most promising serological criterion of race. It seems wholly possible that the Rh types are destined to furnish us with the high positive correlations with anatomical racial types that are so disappointingly absent in the case of the standard blood groups. Inciden-

[63] Wiener, "Nomenclature of the Rh Blood Types," pp. 532–533.

[64] Wiener, Belkin, and Sonn, "Distribution of the A_1-A_2-B-O, M-N, and Rh Blood Factors," pp. 187–194.

[65] Wiener and others, "Blood Factors among Chinese," p. 271.

tally, all of the 15 chimpanzees that have been tested so far for the Rh factor have turned out Rh-negative.[66]

If the distinctive agglutinogen combinations in the subhuman primates and in lower mammals generally coincide with the morphological complexes whereby taxonomists identify species, there is here an evident linkage of serological and anatomical characteristics that is not obvious in man. In human serology, as far as present data serve us, there is not even any consistent mutual association of the various antigen series that have been discovered; the O,A, and B groups; the M and N types; the Rh-positive and Rh-negative systems; the P-positive and P-negative systems seem to be inherited independently. Thus, if one assumes that the present mixed distributions of any one system are due to the hybridization of original pure races, such as M races and N races, one is confronted with the necessity of postulating theoretical primitive "pure" blood group races that combine the various serological systems. For example, Boyd and Schiff show that the A,B system, the M,N system, the P system, and the Rh system together make possible the distinguishing of 160 kinds of human blood (not including subdivisions of Rh).[67] If we exclude the subgroups and the mixtures in the respective A,B and M,N series, we still have 24 putative original serological races in terms of combinations of the basic genes of the four systems. And we have absolutely no clue as to their relationship with taxonomic morphological races in primitive human times, nor, for that matter, any indication that the mathematically possible serological combinations ever existed as "pure" serological races.

In spite of the accurate knowledge we possess of the genetics of various blood group substances, their control by very few genes, their allegedly "non-adaptive" character, their permanence in the individual, and their supposed independence of environment, we can hardly discard the ordinary anthropological criteria of race in favor of serology. The reconstructions of primitive races and prehistoric migrations that are based upon serology (at least as respects the standard blood groups) are even more speculative and implausible than those that result from the study of skulls and bones. And, as regards contemporary man, I am afraid that scientists, together with the entire lay population of *Homo sapiens,* will persist in distinguishing Negroes, Mongoloids, and Whites by observing their visible and distinctive morphological combinations rather than by depending upon serological tests. We shall continue to call a gorilla

[66] Wiener and Wade, "The Rh and Hr Factors in Chimpanzees."
[67] Schiff and Boyd, *Blood Grouping Technic,* p. 14.

a gorilla and a chimpanzee a chimpanzee, even if they belong to the same blood group.

At the same time, these serological studies of modern man and their extension to mummified tissues and dry bones open up a field of anthropological investigation that is at least of equal importance with that of morphology and biometry. Physiological tests of human heredity may even be asserted to be potentially more significant than those of anatomy. No physical anthropologist can afford to dismiss the data of serology as irrelevant, merely because it does not jibe with conventional anthropometric techniques. Serology enables us to take a new bearing upon human origins and migrations from an entirely different viewpoint. The separate observations from the widely removed morphological and serological positions ought to facilitate the determination of human and prehuman conditions in the past, as it were, by a method of triangulation.

Some individuals have the substances that characterize their blood groups present in their saliva, their gastric juice, and other body fluids. Such persons are called "secretors," in contrast to those whose fluids are free from the blood group substances. The ability to secrete group specific substances is determined by a gene dominant over the gene for non-secretion. Persons belonging to groups A,B, or AB are easily tested for this secreting ability, but the testing of O group individuals is difficult and has been omitted from the following data. Schiff found that, in a series of 363 Whites studied in Berlin, the percentage of secretors was 78.0; in a series of 74 New York Whites, mostly Jews, 82.4 per cent; but in a series of 178 Harlem Negroes, only 61.2 per cent. Here, then, is promise of another criterion of racial difference of which the heredity is simple and definitely known.[68]

RACIAL DIFFERENCES IN RESPONSE TO DRUGS

There seems to be very little reliable evidence concerning differences in racial response to varied drugs, although many superstitions existed in slavery days with regard to the Negro, who was often considered a separate species and was supposed to require a peculiar and special pharmacopeia. Lewis has recently summarized the finding of various investigators with respect to this subject.[69] The Negro appears to be less susceptible to the central action of atropine than does the White. He also displays more resistance to cathartics but possibly is more susceptible to the actions of anodynes, sedatives, and hypnotics.

[68] Schiff, "Racial Differences," pp. 255–262.
[69] Lewis, Biology of the Negro, pp. 97–98.

Chen and Poth have discovered that the pupil-dilating or mydriatic action of cocaine, euphthalmine, and ephedrine upon the eyes of Whites is very much greater than upon the eyes of Chinese and Negroes. The pupils of Whites were dilated by these drugs more than three times as much as those of Chinese, and the dilation in the case of Chinese was more than twice as much as in Negroes.[70]

Racial Pathology

Differences in racial pathology are complicated by the fact that many diseases to which Whites have been exposed for thousands of years and to which they have developed relative immunities have been diffused by Europeans to Negroes and other races which have never experienced them before European contact. Consequently, these latter peoples have not developed resistance against such infections and are decimated by them. A further difficulty in interpreting differences in the incidence of diseases, the gravity of their effects, and the death rates resulting from them lies in the environments of the races compared. In this country, for example, the conditions of sanitation, housing, nutrition, and almost every other environmental factor that might influence the infection by diseases and recovery from them are greatly inferior for Negroes to those enjoyed by Whites.[71]

Whether in Africa or in the United States, tuberculosis is a much more serious disease among Negroes than among Whites. In the United States, the mortality from this disease is five times as high in Negroes; it begins actively at an earlier age; the annual decline of the tuberculosis mortality is slower than among Whites.[72] Among the causes of death, tuberculosis is second in Negroes of this country, seventh in Whites.

In the United States, syphilis is also far more prevalent among Negroes than among Whites, and the Negro seems to be especially liable to syphilitic lesions of the cardio-vascular system. Another venereal disease much more prevalent among Negroes than among Whites in the United States is lymphogranuloma venereum. This affliction results from the introduction of a filterable virus, usually at the genitalia. It often blocks the lymphatic drainage and causes elephantiasis of the genitalia and stricture of the rectum, as well as buboes.

A supposed immunity to malaria among African Negroes is probably acquired by repeated infections from birth and is not racial. In the

70 Chen and Poth, "Racial Differences in Mydriatic Action of Cocaine," pp. 91–93.
71 The following summary of differences in pathology between Negroes and Whites is based upon Lewis, *Biology of the Negro.*
72 Lewis, *op. cit.*, p. 153.

United States, Negroes suffer more from malaria than do Whites, but they are more concentrated in the malarial districts. The Negro, whether in this country or in Africa, is definitely less susceptible to diphtheria than is the White. He is more susceptible to lobar pneumonia, but, if he contracts it, his chances of recovery are about the same as those of Whites. There seems to be no doubt that the Negro resists yellow fever better than any other race. It seems probable that measles affects Negroes less than Whites. On the other hand, the Negro is the more susceptible to whooping-cough. The evidence is that poliomyelitis (infantile paralysis) attacks Negroes less often than Whites, but infected Negroes are more likely to die of the disease. Fatal termination of typhoid fever seems commoner in Negroes than in Whites.

Probably the clearest example of a nearly complete racial segregation in disease is sickle cell anemia, to which Negroes are especially liable and to which Whites are immune. Lewis states that it is doubtful there is a single genuine instance of sickle cell anemia among Whites, if those are excluded in whom there is a probability of a recent or remote infusion of Negro blood.[73] This disease is secondary to a congenital anomaly known as sicklemia, which is inherited as a Mendelian dominant and occurs in the Negro population in 4 to 15 per cent. Hemophilia is very rare among Negroes. In the hookworm area of the United States, Negroes are much less subject to this infestation than Whites. In Africa, in regions heavily infested with hookworm, the Negro suffers little from the disease.

No safe conclusion can be drawn from the conflicting reports upon the comparative susceptibility of Negroes and Whites to mental diseases because of dubious diagnoses and regional variation of conditions having to do with the recognition of diseases and the admission of mental patients into public institutions. The data on diseases of the heart and blood vessels are similarly unreliable. Many investigators think that the Negro is especially prone to hypertension but less susceptible to coronary disease and to rheumatic heart disease than the White. Mortality statistics clearly indicate an excessive death rate of Negroes from nephritis, both chronic and acute.

The Negro, as a surgical patient, is outstanding in his resistance to infection by suppurative cocci. The incidence of peptic ulcer is extremely low in this race, and the formation of gall-stones is far less frequent than in Whites. The same holds for urinary calculi. Among the benign tumors, uterine fibroids are far commoner in Negroes than in Whites. Keloids are large hypertrophic scars produced by skin injuries, often

[73] *Ibid.*, p. 249.

of an insignificant nature. The Negro is notoriously predisposed to this sort of connective tissue overgrowth. This skin peculiarity is utilized for the production of raised ornamental scars in Africa. It is worthy of note that the Australian, who is not a Negro but probably has an infusion of Negrito blood as a result of crossing with Tasmanians, has also this predisposition to keloid formation and makes similar use of it.

In the United States, the Negro is definitely less susceptible to cancer than is the White, except cancer of the female genitalia. The Negro is relatively immune to cancer of the skin. Cancer is not uncommon in the African Negro. The outstanding features of African cancer are stated by Lewis to include prevalence of primary carcinoma of the liver and of melanoma (excessively rare in U.S. Negroes), unusual occurrence of carcinoma of the stomach, and frequency of skin cancer. These reports seem to indicate that cancer in the African Negro is very different from the forms commonly found in the same race in this country. Appendicitis and acute empyema are also rarer in the Negro than in the White.

The supposition that African Negro women invariably have healthy pregnancies and easy, normal deliveries is now known to be incorrect. In African hospitals, Negro mothers have much the same parturitional difficulties as Whites. Their pelves are smaller. In the United States, abnormally contracted pelves resulting from rickets or other causes are far commoner in Negroes than in Whites. With normal pelves, Negro women have shorter labors than Whites, but considerably longer than White women when both have contracted pelves.[74] However, an analysis of 13,658 consecutive deliveries at or near full term in the Johns Hopkins Hospital made by Peckham, irrespective of age and type of pelvis, showed consistently longer labors for the Negroes. The prevalence of syphilis complicates obstetrics in Negroes, and the outstanding features of Negro gynecology are fibroids and suppurative infections of the generative tract.

There are some differences in the incidence of skin diseases between Negroes and Whites that are probably racial rather than environmental. Psoriasis, which constitutes about 2.7 per cent of all skin diseases in Whites, is rare in Negroes. Ainhum is a very uncommon disease almost completely confined to Negroes. It involves a skin constriction of the little toe with eventual gangrene and spontaneous amputation. Its cause is unknown. Keratoses and precancerous skin lesions are rare in Negroes. The skin of the Negro is remarkable for its resistance to external irritants —both the toxic action of chemicals, and heat and light injuries. Pathological depigmentations such as albinism vitiligo, and leukoderma prob-

[74] *Ibid.*, pp. 362–368

ably occur no oftener in Negroes than in Whites but are much more conspicuous in the colored race.

The amount of infestation of head and body by lice seems to be much
less in Negroes than in Whites, granted equally unclean habits in both
races. Diseases of the skin produced by fungi are in some cases commoner
in Negroes than in Whites and sometimes rarer.

Few comparative studies of the eyesight of Negroes and Whites have
been made in this country. Lewis says that there is a prevalent impression
that the Negro has somewhat better eyesight but inferior to that of his
African cousins, probably because the American Negro has deteriorated
by contact with European civilization. The outstanding difference in
the pathology of the eyes of the two races is the virtual immunity of the
Negro to trachoma. Color-blindness among Negroes averages about
3.75 per cent, as against 8.22 per cent for combined series of Whites.

Little is known of the comparative pathology of Negroes and Whites
in respect to diseases of the ear, nose, and throat. Most of the data on this
subject are not recent, but they suggest that Negroes suffer far less from
these diseases than do Whites. For example, post-nasal catarrh is about
nine times as frequent in Whites as in Negroes and chronic aural diseases
from four to six times.

The incidence of dental disease seems to depend largely upon food
habits. Studies of African natives show that caries and other pathological
conditions of the teeth are very rare in Negroes until they come into
contact with White civilization, but the relative immunity seems to depend largely upon diet. Although the food habits of Negroes and Whites
in the United States are not markedly different, various surveys all point
to the conclusion that the incidence of caries is uniformly lower in the
Negroes. However, gingivitis is more common among colored children,
and there seems to be no particular difference in the frequency of mal-
occlusions.

Data on the comparative pathology of races other than Negroes and
Whites are so scattered that they cannot be reviewed here, apart from
some limited observations upon American Indians. In 1931, Forrest
Clements supplemented earlier observations of Hrdlička on the Indians
of the southwestern United States with new data on the Chemehuevi and
Mohave Indians of western Arizona, together with a comparison of
annual mortality reports of the United States Census Bureau pertaining
to native born Whites, Indians, and Negroes.[75] The proportion of Indian deaths from tuberculosis of the respiratory system is more than

75 Clements, "Racial Differences in Mortality and Morbidity," pp. 397–419.

four times the White rate and about twice the Negro rate. The same relative differences hold for other forms of tuberculosis. In the registration area as a whole, the incidence of deaths due to syphilis is only slightly greater than that of Whites, in strong contrast to the importance of this mortality factor in Negroes. Deaths from diabetes mellitus and cerebral hemorrhage are proportionately far fewer in Indians than in Whites, with the Negroes clearly intermediate in the case of the latter cause of death. Cancer is a much less important cause of death in Indians than in Negroes, who, in turn, suffer from this fatal ailment far less frequently than do Whites. The White mortality rate from this cause is about three and one half times that of Indians and over twice the Negro rate. Similarly, the death rate from heart disease is least in Indians, with the Negroes intermediate. However, since cerebral hemorrhage, heart disease, and cancer are all afflictions particularly characteristic of old age, it seems probable that the excess rates in Whites are due in part to the greater proportion of this race that survives into old age.

The Indian rate of mortality from nephritis and other non-venereal, genito-urinary diseases is less than half of that of either of the other two races. However, mortality among Indian females from puerperal causes is much higher in Indians than in Whites and probably about the same as the Negro mortality rate from this set of causes. Yet a study of 1,815 pregnancies in full-blood and mixed-blood Indian women, the deliveries of which took place in Indian Service hospitals, indicated that labor is no more difficult for Indian mothers than for Whites.[76] High maternal mortality among the Pueblo Indians is probably due to their lack of knowledge of proper conduct of deliveries, according to Aberle.

The infant mortality among Indians, that in childhood, adolescence, and the reproductive period, are all much higher than in Whites. From birth through early youth, according to Clements, out of the number of deaths per 1,000 of both sexes at all ages, the Indian rate (1924–1926) was 492, as against 320 in Negroes and 280 in Whites. The greatest excess of Indian deaths occurs in the first year of life. According to census figures for 1924, the infant deaths per 1,000 live births of children of native White mothers was 63.2, for Negroes 114.1, and for Indians 190.7. The figure for Indians is probably too low. Aberle, in a careful study of five Pueblo Indian villages, found the death rate per 1,000 live births to be 231.[77]

76 Aberle, "Maternal Mortality among the Pueblos," 431–457, quoting E. Blanche Sterling, *Maternal, Fetal, and Neonatal Mortality among 1815 Hospitalized American Indians,* Public Health Reports, 1933, XLVIII, No. 20, 522–535.
77 Quoted by Clements, "Racial Differences in Mortality and Morbidity," p. 408.

The Technique of Racial Classification

A human group may be classified as a "race" only if its members
present, individually, identical combinations of specific physical characters which they owe to their common descent. Once the several criteria
that define any race have been decided, the only valid method of finding
the distribution of that race in the human population is to sort out the
individuals who possess that particular racial physical combination. The
existence of any race is postulated in the first instance by the rough
observation that the bulk of the individuals in the population of some
area look alike because they have similar or identical skin color, hair
color, eye color, hair form, and other definite physical variations which
in combination are peculiar to them as a group. The next step requires
individual measurement and observation of the frequencies of the
critical racial features, taken singly and in combination. Thus, if woolly
or frizzly hair and dark brown to black skin are putative criteria of the
race, it must be determined by counting that these requirements are
actually fulfilled in a vast majority of the individuals of that population.
The minority of non-conformers is assumed to owe its divergence to
mixture with other strains or to individual variation away from the
mode or the average of the race. If we have observed that a Mongoloid
is ordinarily a person with straight, coarse, black hair, yellow-brown skin,
brown eyes, some degree of development of an internal epicanthic fold,
laterally and frontally jutting malars, et cetera, we have to make up our
minds which of these variations and how many of them in combination
are critical for the definition of the race and for the admission thereunto
of any specific individual.

For the demarcation of the three major or primary races of mankind,
simple combinations of only a few characters may be used. More intricate
combinations cut inside of broad racial groupings and define successively
subraces, or local breeds. Elaborate combinations of features, some
derived from the characteristic variations of one primary race and others
from those of another primary race, define secondary or composite races.
In the outline that follows, the irreducible minimum of racially diagnostic combinations for each subdivision will be printed in bold face
type, to which will be added a variable number of other characters of
usual if not universal occurrence in the racial or subracial group. These
accessory features may be used in the combinations diagnostic of subraces or other smaller groups, but are not required as qualifications for
admission to the race as a larger entity.

The racial classification in outline form will be followed by a section that discusses the taxonomic validity of each racial, subracial, or local type defined, together with a summary of what is known of the history of the type.

It may be well here to recapitulate and explain precisely the use of terminology in the racial classification that follows.

PRIMARY RACES

These are the three main physical groups of modern man: WHITE, NEGROID, MONGOLOID. Individuals belonging to any of these three races can easily be distinguished by fairly simple sorting combinations.

Primary Subraces. The major physical subgroups of the main races. A subrace has to have a fairly definite territorial distribution and concentration within the area of the main race, or in some discrete area. The formation of a subrace within a primary race is due to an intensification, localization, and further operation of the same factors that produced the primary race of which it is a subdivision. These factors are, of course: mutation, inbreeding, selection, environmental adaptation, if any, operating upon more restricted groups (i.e. fewer family lines with resulting emphasis upon the individual and familial variations or idiosyncrasies carried in these lines). Primary subraces can be distinguished, as a rule, by the use of supplementary sorting criteria.

Morphological Types. Still smaller and usually more localized physical subdivisions of subraces in which differentiation by the operation of the same processes has been carried yet farther. Usually these morphological types can be observed and classified visually, but they are not easy to sort out by metric criteria because they involve the blending of many subtle anatomical features. This term is also used for types that may really merit subracial classification, when their numbers and distribution are insufficiently known.

Composite Primary Subraces. Stabilized blends due to the interbreeding of primary subraces within a single main race. Rather intricate sorting combinations are necessary for the selection of composite subraces.

Residual Mixed Types. Sortings used, in the case of Whites only, to catch the individual, mixed, and unstabilized types not included in the subraces. These residual mixed types aggregate very high proportions of the population but tend to occur sporadically in families where primary subraces have amalgamated.

Similar residual mixed types naturally occur in the Negroid and Mongoloid races, but present knowledge does not permit us to specify their sorting criteria.

Composite Races. Races representing stabilized blends of two or more primary races. They present mosaics of features from the different racial stocks involved and usually occupy definite geographical areas where the blend has been stabilized in isolation. Often they cannot be selected individually by any simple combination of sorting criteria because the range of variation in individuals is too wide.

Sorting Criteria. Metric or morphological features that may be used in combination to select from a series the persons belonging to a race or subrace. Sorting criteria cannot be specified unless large series have actually been subjected to typological analysis by combinations and the statistical validity of the combinations so distinguished has been established. This device, if pushed too far or elaborated incautiously, is likely to prove something of a statistical Procrustean bed.

Characters. When knowledge is insufficient for the establishment of definite sorting criteria, it is necessary to depend for the definition of a racial, subracial, or smaller group upon generally descriptive characters, averages, etc. Lists of characters have to be used in describing some composite races because the range of individual variation is so wide that rigid sorting criteria cannot be used (i.e., they do not select individuals of the required type).

The foregoing may seem unnecessarily tedious, technical, and terminological. However, something has to be done to bring order into the chaos of racial classificatory schemes. Many of them seem to have been drawn up rather irresponsibly by arm-chair anthropologists who have listed as characters of this or that race whole arrays of subjectively established variations or supposititious metric features for which there is very little scientific basis. Frequently these racial classificationists, immured in their imitation ivory towers, establish wholly new and purely hypothetical racial types or subtypes without bothering to find out whether they exist, and where, and in what numbers. Of course, the whole subject of zoological taxonomy suffers from the same complaint.

Yet I have no patience with those anthropologists (usually social anthropologists who know very little about the biological side of their subject) who are incessantly trumpeting to the world that "there is really no such thing as race, because anthropologists themselves do not agree in defining race and differ also in their schemes of racial classification." This is ridiculous. There are very few, if any, fields of science in which all competent specialists agree upon definition, classification, and interpretation of the phenomena they are studying. Biology is not an exact science, but, for that matter, neither are the so-called exact sciences. Witness recent revolutions in physics and the constant lability

of definitions, principles, and even "laws." It ill befits social anthropologists, who cannot agree upon a definition of society, or cultural
anthropologists, who are in constant dispute about the concept of culture, to deny the existence of race (which has more objective reality
than either "society" or "culture") merely because students of race fail
to display a unanimity that they themselves, in their own specialties, are
even farther from attaining.

There is no radical disagreement among physical anthropologists in
the actual recognition of contemporary human types, because these are
natural, observable combinations in individuals and groups of anatomical features, whether of exclusively hereditary or of partially environmental origin. When any single observer picks out a group of persons who look alike because they present closely similar or identical
combinations of physical features, there is no argument as to whether
or not a physical type has been distinguished, but only as to the
significance of the type from a genetic standpoint, its distribution, and
its proper classificatory status in the array of mankind. A type is literally
an impression—something struck out by a die. Successive impressions
are nearly or quite identical. Of course, mechanical identity does not
occur in living organisms; there are always minute or gross differences
between individuals whom we assign to the same type. Presumably, the
most restricted repetition of nearly identical physical combinations
occurs in the case of identical twins. One would hardly assign to a pair
of twins the designation "a type"; but there are certainly fraternal types
or sibling types restricted to offspring of a single pair of parents; beyond
these, there are assuredly somewhat larger familial types. All of these
are too limited in distribution and too few in the number of included
individuals to warrant taxonomic recognition. When a few families in
some isolated settlement have inbred for some generations, one or more
recognizable local types may be formed. Most of the disagreements between various schemes of racial classification arise from differences of
opinion as to taxonomic importance of the types recognized. The
tendency, on the whole, has been to exaggerate the zoological importance
of typological differences in man. At the one extreme is the discredited
view that modern man can be divided into separate species: White,
Negroid, and Mongoloid. If one starts with the supposition that the
anatomical differences between the three main modern human types are
of specific magnitude and significance, one naturally extends this exaggeration down through the various and successively finer subgroups
recognized and is likely to end up with a large array of regional and
restricted types that have been unduly promoted to the status of "races."

Such classificatory magnification is likely to lead to erroneous and vicious interpretations of the psychological and cultural implications of minor taxonomic differences. It lends itself to political exploitation and promotes "racial" discrimination, which is really not racial at all, but is socially undesirable, whatever may be the zoological status of the groups or types between which it is allowed to exist.

However, to go to the other extreme and to depreciate unduly the natural zoological differences that anyone can observe as existent in present varieties of the human species is not scientific, however laudable it may be from considerations of democracy and humanitarianism. If science obviously flies in the face of the facts and ignores or denies taxonomic differences, it merely delivers over the whole dangerous business of interpreting human group physical variation to the tender mercy of the layman, the charlatan, and the political exploiter.[78] The anthropologist who denies race leaves the house empty, swept, and garnished for the entrance of a plenty of devils.

Racial History

The first difficulty encountered in the attempt to record the ancient histories and modern distributions of human races is the devising of a valid scheme of human group classification, racial, subracial, and finer, and a technique of dividing up populations in accordance with such a scheme and of assigning individuals to their proper class. If this difficulty has been surmounted to the approximate satisfaction of the classificationist and analyst, he immediately runs upon another snag—lack of data and inadequacy of existing data. There are still many peoples of the world who have not been measured and observed by any physical anthropologist; there are more of whom only tiny and inadequate samples have been studied. Much of the information that has been collected is not only incomplete but unreliable because of rudimentary or obsolete techniques that have been employed in gathering it.[79]

[78] This situation is tantamount to that described by Christ in the parable (Mat. xii: 43–45):
   "When the unclean spirit is gone out of a man, he walketh through dry places, seeking rest, and findeth none.
   Then he saith, I will return into my house from whence I came out; and when he is come, he findeth it empty, swept, and garnished.
   Then goeth he, and taketh with himself seven other spirits more wicked than himself, and they enter in and dwell there: and the last state of that man is worse than the first."

[79] The student of history, chemistry, mathematics, economics, or of nearly any other established academic subject is likely to read with impatience a statement of the inadequacy of existing anthropological information and inquire why the anthropologists have not done a better job. The answer is simply that there have been too few anthropologists to do the job properly. In the comparatively few universities that have departments of anthropology, the staff personnel of anthropology is commonly outnumbered by that of the older vested

A puzzling and often insoluble problem confronts the racial historian when he tries to trace the antecedents of living types of man. In the classification of the latter, primary emphasis is placed upon the conformation of the soft parts of the body, pigmentation, hair form, etc. The anthropologist nearly always has to depend upon skulls and skeletal material in his reconstructions of racial history. Reliable accounts of hair color, skin color, eye color, and the rest of the variations used for racial criteria are usually missing in pre-anthropological historical records. The scattered descriptions and references that do occur are of course invaluable and are utilized to the fullest possible extent. For example, there are a few tantalizing phrases in Homer and other ancient Greek authors about blue eyes and fair or golden hair in pre-Classical and Classical Greece. Tactitus makes a few references to the physical appearance—complexion, hair color, eye color—of the Germans, and Caesar gives scraps of information about the ancient inhabitants of Britain. However, for the most part, even the relatively brief period of written records provides little information on racial criteria that can be used by the racial historian.

As soon as one familiarizes oneself with the racial variations of skulls and other bones, it becomes apparent that it is usually impossible to make any detailed and accurate deduction concerning the pigmentation and soft parts of persons represented only by skeletal remains. The determination of age, sex, stature, muscular development, shape of the head, shape of the face, projection of the jaws, general proportions of the nose, and some other physical features can be reconstructed from the bones. Pigmentation, hair form, hair quantity, eye folds, shape of the tip and wings of the nose, conformation of the lips, form of the ear, and the amount of fatty deposits on different parts of the body are not safely ascertainable from skeletal studies. All that one can do is to make inferences concerning the correlation of soft parts with skeletal material by observations on living persons with respect to the relation of their superficial anatomy to underlying skeletal structure and by studies of the skeletons of cadavers previously observed and measured.

---

interests in the curriculum in a ratio varying from 3:1 to 10:1 and even higher. In the few science museums that maintain research staffs, anthropology is somewhat better represented. Then, too, anthropologists of professional status are rarely biological or physical anthropologists. The majority of them are concerned with cultural anthropology: the study of the institutions and material culture of peoples, usually primitive peoples—their sociology, psychology, languages, arts and industries, and their past as revealed by archaeological excavations. Much more substantial contributions to the knowledge of human evolution and human biology have been made by anatomists, medical research investigators, zoologists, geneticists, and palaeontologists than by cultural anthropologists. The reason for this is that physical anthropology belongs properly with the biological sciences, whereas the rest of anthropology is a "social" science.

However, there are a few main and dependable relationships of a racial nature between skulls and heads. Typical skulls of Negroids, Mongoloids, and Whites differ from each other in a sufficient number of clear and reliable morphological variations to enable a trained craniologist to distinguish between them with a fair degree of certainty. He can be nearly sure that a skull with a certain combination of morphological and metric features belonged to an individual who in life had dark skin, woolly or frizzly hair, thick lips, heavy-tipped nose with flaring alae, and the other conventional Negroid features of the soft parts. The same is true of the recognition of Mongoloid skulls and their probably correlated variations of the soft parts. A craniologist can also identify a skull as that of a White with some precision, but he cannot ordinarily distinguish between the skull of an East Baltic and that of an Alpine, or between the skulls of Atlanto-Mediterraneans and Nordics, because such subracial differentiation depends largely upon pigmentation to which no clue is offered by the skull. Sometimes a reasonable inference about the pigmental and superficial anatomical correlates of a type of skull can be made on the basis of a more or less consistent or constant association of that skull type with specific pigment, et cetera, in living peoples. For example, there is a very long-headed and rugged type of the Mediterranean skull form, with plenty of characteristic cranial details, that is called the Upper Palaeolithic type. Persons with that type of skull (so far as may be judged from external appearance) occur frequently in Wales and Ireland and nearly always have very brunet skins and dark brown or black hair that is deeply waved or curly. This association permits a somewhat shaky inference that the same features characterized the cranial type in prehistoric times.

There are also a few composite races or primary subraces with such distinctive morphological combinations in their crania that the latter can be recognized with ease and reasonably assumed to have exhibited in life the superficial features of living types that possess such skulls. Notable among these are the skulls of Australians and of Eskimo (although the latter are probably indistinguishable from those of Chukchi and other Arctic Mongoloids).

When we get back to palaeoanthropic types of man—such as the Neanderthaloids, Sinanthropus, et cetera, we have virtually no clue as to the conformation of their soft parts, aside from the hints that may be furnished by contemporary stocks that resemble them slightly in cranial form (e.g., Australians) and we know nothing about their pigmentation. We can only assume that, since more or less heavy pigmentation seems primary and generalized in apes and man, the various steps in depigmentation that have come about as a result of mutations, mostly in the White race, probably did not affect these archaic types.

It then can be seen that the bridging of the gap in racial history between dry bones and living persons is a very precarious business. Again, it is quite probable that hybridization began very early in human history, although, of course, it could not precede racial differentiation. Hybridized racial cranial types in ancient deposits can easily be confused with generalized types that are of an earlier evolutionary status and still present prototypical blends of incipiently different racial strains. All sorts of vague suggestions of Negroid and Mongoloid features, and sometimes both together, appear in fossil skulls that seem predominantly White in type. We have experienced the arguments that arise in the interpretation of such cases in the examples of the Galilee Neanderthaloids, the Grimaldi skeletons, the skeletons from the Upper Cave at Choukoutien, and elsewhere.

When a craniologist gets hold of a skull that appears to be that of a member of some composite or secondary race, or that of an undifferentiated prototypical stock, or that of a recent hybrid, he ought to be very careful about making deductions with respect to the appearance of the owner in life in regard to pigmentation and soft parts. In the case of modern hybrids, nearly any kind of a disharmonic combination of skull, soft parts, and pigmentation can and does occur.

I have dragged out these racial methodological skeletons from the taxonomic closet because I do not want my readers to be fooled by cocksure reconstructions of racial history made by German anthropologists and others. My long and extensive experience in the fields both of skeletal raciology and of the racial classification of living peoples has made me very critical of my own efforts and those of other anthropologists. If I have achieved neither competence nor confidence, I have, at any rate, acquired candor.

RACIAL CLASSIFICATION OF MODERN MAN
(The standard of comparison is usually the adult male)

PRIMARY RACE

I. *WHITE ("EUROPEAN," "EUR-AFRICAN," "CAUCASOID")*
   Sorting Criteria:
   1. Skin color: light brown (olive), pale white, pink, ruddy
   2. Hair color: rarely dead black, all lighter shades
   3. Eye color: never black, all lighter shades
   4. Hair form: never woolly, usually wavy or straight, sometimes loosely curled

Other Characters:

5. Nose form: usually high and narrow, sometimes medium, nasal index usually leptorrhine, never platyrrhine
6. Beard and body hair: moderate or abundant
7. Facial protrusion (prognathism): usually lacking
8. Membranous lip thickness: medium to thin, little eversion
9. Chin prominence: pronounced to medium
10. Hair texture: usually medium to fine, rarely very coarse
11. Pelvis: broad in both sexes
12. Breast form (female): usually hemispherical
13. Buttocks (female): usually prominent
14. Blood group: usually much higher in A than in B
15. Palmar main line formula: most commonly 11.9.7.—

PRIMARY SUBRACES

1. MEDITERRANEAN

(Basic long-headed brunets)

Sorting Criteria:

a. Hair color: dark brown to black
b. Eye color: dark brown or medium brown
c. Head form: cephalic index less than 80

Morphological Types

1. **Upper Palaeolithic ("Galley Hill," "Combe Capelle," "Atlanto-Mediterranean")**
   a. Head form: very long, usually over 200 mm., very dolichocephalic, length-breadth index usually under 75; occiput protuberant
   b. Brow-ridges: usually large
   c. Forehead: usually receding
   d. Nasion depression: deep
   e. Hair form: usually very wavy or curly
   f. Nose form: usually straight, medium breadth and height, rather coarse
   g. Face form: often very long face, deep jaws, rather prominent malars
   h. Stature: usually tall (over 170 cm.) but may be medium, rarely short
   i. Skin color: generally dark
   Distribution: sporadic in refuge areas of Europe and the Middle East; probably commonest in Ireland, Scotland, Wales

2. **Iranian Plateau ("Indo-Afghan," "Irano-Afghan")**
   Differs from the Upper Palaeolithic type only as follows:
   a. Nose form: always high, broad or mediumly wide in root and bridge, usually convex with thin to medium, depressed tip and recurved alae
   b. Beard and body hair: usually heavy
   c. Stature and body build: usually medium height (167 cm.) and slight build
   Distribution: mostly in Iraq and Iran

3. **Classic Mediterranean**
   (Reduced derivatives of the Upper Palaeolithic and Iranian Plateau subraces)
   Two subtypes:

Characters:
  (a) Skeleton: gracile, skull smooth with small brow-ridges and mastoids
  (b) Beard and body hair: sparse
  (c) Face narrow, oval; chin pointed
  (d) Nose form: in the Upper Palaeolithic derivative, straight with medium thick tip, elevated or horizontal; in the Iran Plateau derivative, very thin, high-bridged, often aquiline nose, always convex, with thin, depressed tip and recurved alae
  (e) Stature: usually under 166 cm.
  (f) Body build: usually slender
Distribution: the hook-nosed type particularly in Arabia and the Near East among Arabs and Jews; the straight-nosed type there and in the whole Mediterranean basin, and sporadically in eastern, central, and northwestern Europe

2. AINU

(Hirsute, long-headed, mesorrhine brunets)
Sorting Criteria:
  a. Hair color: dark brown to black
  b. Eye color: dark or medium brown
  c. Head form: cephalic index less than 80 (average 76.6)
  d. Beard and body hair: excessive
  e. Nose form: nasal index mesorrhine to platyrrhine—over 70, average 83.4; root depressed, profile concave, alae flaring.
Other Characters:
  f. Skin color: light brown, grayish white
  g. Face form: short and of medium breadth (mesoprosopic), averaging about 87.
  h. Stature: short, average about 158 cm. (5 ft. 2 in.)
  i. Body build: thickset; long arms, short legs.
  j. Blood group: higher in B than in A
Distribution: Northern Japan, islands of Sakhaline and Yezo. (A recent Mongoloid admixture may be detected in many Ainu, especially noticeable in females)

3. KELTIC

(Light-eyed, dark or red-haired long-heads)
Sorting Criteria:
  a. Hair color: dark brown, medium brown, red, rarely black
  b. Eye color: blue, gray, or pale mixed
  c. Head form: cephalic index less than 80, average about 76
Other Characters:
  d. Skin color: pale white, sometimes ruddy, often freckled
  e. Face form: very long, narrow; compressed malars, long integumental upper lip, deep chin
  f. Nose form: very long, high, narrow; leptorrhine; thin long tip, compressed alae; tip sometimes depressed, sometimes snubbed; profile straight, convex, or undulating
  g. Hair form: usually wavy or curly, sometimes straight
  h. Stature tall: averaging more than 172 cm.
  i. Body build: slender, very long arms and legs, short trunk

Distribution: Concentrated in Ireland; common in Scottish Highlands and Wales; sporadic in England, Brittany, and other parts of western Europe

4. NORDIC

(Pure blond or near-blond long-heads)

Sorting Criteria:

    a. **Hair color: ash blond, ash brown, golden, golden brown**

    b. **Eye color: blue, gray, pale mixed**

    c. **Head form: cephalic index less than 80, average about 77**

Other Characters:

    d. Skin color: usually pink or ruddy, rarely creamy

    e. Nose form: usually high and narrow, leptorrhine; profile straight, aquiline or otherwise convex; tip thin, elevated or horizontal, usually not depressed; alae compressed

    f. Face form: usually narrow and relatively long, with compressed malars and gonial angles, prominent chin; but sometimes with more prominent cheek bones, squarer gonial angles, and heavier, deeper jaws with bilateral chin

    g. Mouth: long and often convex integumental upper lip, thin membranous lips

    h. Hair quantity: thin head hair with frequent baldness in males; beard and body hair medium to sparse

    i. Hair texture: prevailingly fine, often medium

    j. Hair form: wavy or straight, rarely curly

    k. Eye folds: median fold common in young adult males, external fold in old males

    l. Stature: tall, averaging 172 cm. or more

    m. Body build: slender as a rule, long extremities

The above characters combine into two well-defined Nordic subtypes. (Cf. discussion, pp. 588–589)

Distribution: Concentrated in Scandinavia, especially Sweden and uplands of Norway, common all around the Baltic and in British Isles, sporadic elsewhere in Europe. Important in United States and British colonies

5. ALPINE

(Basic brunet round-heads with medium broad noses)

Sorting Criteria:

    a. **Hair color: dark brown, medium brown, rarely black**

    b. **Eye color: dark brown, medium brown**

    c. **Head form: cephalic index over 80, averaging 85; globular heads, wide high foreheads**

    d. **Nose form: nasal index over 63, often mesorrhine; nasal profile straight or slightly concave; nose fleshy, "blobby," often with short, thick, elevated tip**

Other Characters:

    e. Skin color: olive or brunet white

    f. Hair quantity: abundant, especially heavy beard and body hair

    g. Face form: usually relatively broad and short—round or square (with prominent gonial angles)

    h. Stature: medium to short, average about 166 cm.

    i. Body build: thickset; short, thick neck; broad shoulders; deep chest; stubby extremities

Distribution: Concentrated in the central zone of Europe from France to the Urals; also southern Norway, Denmark, northern Italy, Balkans, and, sporadically in Near East; rare in northwest Africa

6. EAST BALTIC

(Blond round-heads with medium broad noses)
Sorting Criteria:
  a. Hair color: ash blond, ash brown; rarely golden or reddish
  b. Eye color: gray, light blue, rarely blue or pale mixed
  c. Nose form: nasal index over 63, often mesorrhine; nasal profile usually concave with elevated or snubbed tip, less often straight; bridge low, alae flaring
Other Characters:
  d. Skin color: creamy or ivory white, rarely ruddy
  e. Face form: square, prominent cheekbones, imparting flattish look; square gonial angles, heavy jaw with rounded, non-jutting chin
  f. Hair form: usually straight, sometimes wavy
  g. Hair texture: medium to coarse
  h. Hair quantity: heavy head hair, sparse beard and body hair
  i. Stature: extremely variable, with medium to short predominating
  j. Body build: usually thickset like Alpine
Distribution: Concentrated in Finland, Russia, Baltic states, Poland, north Germany

COMPOSITE SUBRACES

(Stabilized blends due to interbreeding of primary subraces of the White race)

7. ARMENOID

(Probably Classic Mediterranean + Alpine + Iranian Plateau; Brunet, hook-nosed, acrocephalic round-heads)
Sorting Criteria:
  a. Hair color: dark brown to black
  b. Eye color: dark brown to medium brown
  c. Head form: cephalic index over 80; high, pointed heads with flat backs; high, sloping foreheads
  d. Nose form: nasal index under 63
Other Characters:
  e. Nasal details: bridge and root high, fairly broad; profile usually convex; tip thickened and depressed, high attachment of alae; septum convex and directed downward; little nasion depression
  f. Face form: narrow and elongate, but with somewhat accentuated cheek bones; mandible usually rather small, with moderate and somewhat recessed chin eminence
  g. Lips: moderately thick with fullness and eversion of lower lip pronounced
  h. Skin color: olive, often swarthy, approaching yellow brown
  i. Hair form: usually wavy, sometimes curly, rarely straight
  j. Hair texture: coarse to medium
  k. Hair quantity: beard and body hair very abundant, eyebrows often strongly concurrent and thick; baldness frequent
  l. Stature usually medium, average 166 to 168 cm.
  m. Body build: variable, but prevailingly thickset; tendency toward obesity in middle and old age

Distribution: Concentrated in Turkey, Syria, Palestine; common in Iraq, Iran, Balkan countries, and in urban populations of eastern and central Europe

8. DINARIC

(Probably Upper Palaeolithic + Alpine + Armenoid + Nordic; mediumly to lightly pigmented, hook-nosed, acrocephalic round-heads)

Sorting Criteria:

    a. Hair color: medium to dark brown with occasional occurrence of lighter shades

    b. Eye color: brown and mixed, sometimes light

    c. Head form: cephalic index over 80, head shape as in Armenoids

    d. Nose form: nasal index under 63

    e. Stature: very tall, over 170 cm.

Other Characters:

    f. Nasal details: tip of the nose usually thinner than in Armenoids, septum less convex; nose longer and more leptorrhine

    g. Face form: face much longer and relatively narrower than in Armenoids with deeper, heavier, more projecting chin

    h. Lips thinner than in Armenoids

    i. Hair form: usually wavy

    j. Hair texture: usually medium

    k. Hair quantity: thick beards, abundant body hair

    l. Body build: tall but broad, heavy skeletal structure, very long legs

    m. Skin color: variable, usually brunet; not as dark as average Armenoids

Morphological Subtype:

British Bronze Age (Beaker Type)

Sorting Criteria: same as ordinary Dinaric

Distinguishing Characters:

    a. Head form: more massive and globular, less pointed than Dinaric

    b. Face form: broader in malar region, squarer, gonial angles more marked

    c. Nose form: fleshier than the ordinary Dinaric nose, shorter

    d. Skin color: usually florid or ruddy

    e. Hair color: oftener reddish

    f. Body build: heavier and broader than average Dinaric

Distribution:

    Dinarics: Concentrated in Dinaric Alps region of Yugo-Slavia, Austrian Tyrol; sporadic in central Europe

    British Bronze Age: mostly in the British Isles

RESIDUAL MIXED TYPES (Interbreeds)

(Sortings to include individuals of characters intermediate between the subraces above recognized)

9. NORDIC-ALPINE

(Medium- to broad-nosed round-heads of mixed or intermediate pigmentation)

Sorting Criteria:

    a. Hair color and eye color: dark hair and mixed eyes, red hair and mixed eyes, medium and red-brown hair with mixed eyes, light brown hair and dark eyes

b. **Cephalic index: 80 and over**
c. **Nasal index: 63 and over**
Distribution: This Nordic-Alpine mixed type includes 23 per cent of
9,168 United States males and 18.22 per cent of 9,395 Irish males

10. NORDIC-MEDITERRANEAN

(Long-heads of intermediate but darkish pigmentation)
Sorting Criteria:
a. **Hair color and eye color: dark hair and mixed eyes, red hair and
mixed eyes with stature under 170 cm., red-brown or medium brown
hair and mixed eyes, light brown hair and dark eyes**
b. **Cephalic index: under 80**
Distribution: This sorting includes numerically the largest group in the
United States (25 per cent) and in Ireland (28.82 per cent)

THE WHITE RACE

A generalized White race was the earliest form of *Homo sapiens,* unless the finds of fossil man in Europe, Africa, and Asia have wholly deceived us. It is possibly because of its greater antiquity that the White stock has differentiated in more subraces and morphological types than is the case with the Mongoloid and Negroid races. However, we must make the reservation that a great deal more of work has been done in studying and subdividing the White race than has been expended upon the other two.[80]

The term "White" is something of a misnomer, because the range of skin color in this race extends from light brown to ruddy, and there can be no doubt that the vast majority of White individuals have brunet skins rather than any of the lighter and more vascular complexions. Everyone agrees that early generalized and prototypical Whites must have had light brown skins, dark hair, and dark eyes, and that the processes of depigmentation leading to variations in the color of skin, hair, and eyes must have been due to subsequent repeated mutations. In this stock the presumably primitive wavy hair form predominates; the highly specialized woolly and coarse straight Mongoloid hair do not occur except as freaks or as the result of hybridization. This stock is also the most primitive in the retention of thick beard and body hair, but it is advanced in nasal evolution, in the retraction of the jaws, the prominence of the chin, and the general reduction of the teeth and dental arches. Thinning of the lips is a concomitant, if not a result, of the shrinking back of the alveolar borders in devolution of the masticatory apparatus. Magnificently unreduced, chimpanzee-like ears are found oftener in Whites than in Negroids or Mongoloids.

[80] For much more detailed discussion of the history of the White race, cf. Coon, *Races of Europe,* 1939.

The Mediterranean Subrace. Probably the name, Mediterranean, is as good as any for a designation of the great subrace of basic, long-headed brunets that constitutes the largest number of Whites, was certainly the earliest White subrace, and retains the full pigmentation of hair, skin, and eyes that was characteristic of early *Homo sapiens.* The name is adopted from the great Italian anthropologist Sergi, who used it, however, as a racial rather than a subracial title.

Certainly, the most archaic morphological type of the Mediterranean subrace is that known as Upper Palaeolithic, sometimes also called Galley Hill or Combe Capelle (or, by Coon, the "Brünn race") from type fossil finds in Europe, and also frequently referred to as Atlanto-Mediterranean (Deniker). This exceptionally long-headed type is notable for the great size of the brain-case and its rugged bony construction. The face is commonly long and massive, but it may be rather short, perhaps oftenest when bodily stature is below medium. The jaws are nearly always deep and heavy. It seems improbable that this type, when identified in Wales, Cornwall, and Ireland, or elsewhere, represents the pure lineal descendants of Upper Palaeolithic men. It is more likely to be due to recombination of genetic factors from old strains. It is hard to believe that anywhere in Europe there are inbred, unmixed survivors of Palaeolithic colonies. This type, which is easy to recognize, but does not easily lend itself to selection by any mechanical sorting process, is fairly common in Iran and Iraq and probably elsewhere in the Middle East. In Ireland, England, and the United States, a very closely similar type, that differs only in that eyes are mixed instead of dark, is sorted out as the residual Nordic-Mediterranean type, on the assumption that the lightening of eye pigmentation is due to admixture with the blond Nordic stock. This may or may not be the correct interpretation. There are virtually no pure dark eyes (medium brown, dark brown, or black) in Ireland, and hence, by sorting criteria, practically no pure Mediterraneans. However, the type, complete with dark eyes and dark hair, seems a little commoner in Britain and the United States.

A variant of this Upper Palaeolithic type in which the face is short and broad with laterally jutting cheek bones and square, flaring gonial (hinder jaw) angles is often identified as a modern Cro Magnon type. It was first thus designated by Collignon in the Dordogne region of central France, where Upper Palaeolithic man and the original Cro Magnon skeletons were found. Even here it seems probable that we are dealing with recombinations rather than pure line descendants. Other writers have recognized these so-called Cro Magnons in Scandinavia, central Europe, and elsewhere. The present writer still inclines to the belief, set forth in connection with a study of the Guanches of the Canary Islands (other alleged modern Cro Magnons), that this long-headed, short, broad-faced type ordinarily arises as a unstable hybridization product, the result of a cross between long-heads and brachycephals with short, broad faces, which latter are sometimes hafted to the long, narrow skulls of the Upper Palaeolithic type. A Mongoloid admixture often produces this combination. It may be seen in American Indians and also in the skulls of mediaeval Icelanders who are not without suspicion of having acquired a dash of Eskimo blood in connection with their colonization of Greenland. Lappish admixture might produce this type in Scandinavia.

The second morphological type of the Mediterranean subrace has recently been recognized by Henry Field under the name of the Iranian Plateau type (according to usage here it is called a type and not a race.)[81] The definition of this type, based upon very extensive anthropometric surveys of Iran and Iraq, seems to me the most important addition to the knowledge of the contemporary White race that has been made in the last few decades. It is true that Deniker recognized a somewhat similar type, which he designated as Indo-Afghan, but the pure and characteristic form of type is not Indian, nor (in all probability) Afghan, but Iranian and Mesopotamian.[82] Nor did Deniker describe and isolate the type in any really satisfactory manner. The Iranian Plateau type differs from the Upper Palaeolithic type particularly in its long, high-bridged, and boldly jutting nasal promontory. It has the same huge dolichocephalic head and massive, usually long face. The great nose may be either straight or convex, more often the latter. I have no doubt that archaeological research in the Middle East will reveal the Upper Palaeolithic antiquity of this type, which, in my opinion, is the most probable *fons et origo* of all the exuberant nasal convexity that has been distributed, not only through several White subraces and types, but by hybridization among such composite races as the American Indian, and even, perhaps, the Papuan type of Melanesia. For, high nasal elevation and convexity behave as Mendelian dominants. I incline to the theory that the original form of this magnificent nose is straight bridged and that the convexity arises initially in a bowing or buckling that takes place when it is grown on a somewhat too short face as a possibly dis-

[81] Field, *Anthropology of Iran*, p. 534.
[82] Deniker, *Races of Man*, p. 285.

harmonic feature. However, that is merely an interesting possibility. The
Iranian Plateau type is occasionally encountered in Europe, where it
may be an effect of recombination.

The brunet, long-headed, delicate and gracile type that is ordinarily
thought of under the name Mediterranean, I propose to call Classic
Mediterranean. There can be little doubt that it is a reduced, refined,
smaller-boned derivative of either or both of the massive dolichocephals
—Upper Palaeolithic and Iranian Plateau. As both J. R. de la H. Marett
and Carleton Coon argue, there has been an evolutionary tendency
toward a fineing down, almost an effeminization, of early forms of man
discernible in many modern races, both in general body build and
particularly in skeletal structure. Marett ascribes it to calcium economy
(in a brilliant book at which it is the fashion for cautious and unoriginal
scientists to sniff, but which contains more stimulating ideas and provoca-
tive theories, more suggestions for research on the relation of nutrition
to human evolution, than are encompassed in any other half-dozen books
on physical anthropology written in the last half-century).[83]

There are two variants of the Classic Mediterranean type—straight-
nosed and hook-nosed. The former is the more primitive and the more
widely distributed. It extended in prehistoric times along both shores
of the Mediterranean, into central, western, and northern Europe and
down into the Horn of Africa. Its area of characterization and source of
dissemination cannot have been far from the traditional Garden of Eden
—Mesopotamia, which archaeologists include in "the Fertile Crescent."
There is not much doubt that the eastward extension of straight-nosed
Mediterraneans of the Classic type provided the White basis of the early
populations in southeastern Asia and Indonesia. They probably were
the main carriers of the Aryan language into India at a much later date.

The expansion of the aquiline or hook-nosed Mediterranean type
seems to have been somewhat more limited and probably later than
that of the straight-nosed variant. In historical times, it was carried
into North Africa and Spain principally by the Arabs, but other Semitic-
speaking and non-Semitic peoples of prehistoric times may well have
possessed this variation. Some of this type may have reached India, but
nasal convexity there seems largely the result of infusions of the Iranian
Plateau type.

The little and lithe brunets of this Classic Mediterranean type have
disseminated their blood and their culture throughout the ancient and
modern world. Obsessed with no bigoted prejudices as to "racial purity,"

[83] Marett, *Race, Sex and Environment,* pp. 183 ff.

they have promiscuously bestowed upon the peoples with whom they have come into contact whatever of their civilization these could absorb and as many of their physical features as the recipients could retain. The Mediterraneans have mixed with the Negro peoples of central and eastern Africa so that many of the latter show the effects of the cross in their less projecting faces, narrower, longer, and higher noses, and in the diminished curve of their hair. Indeed, many classificationists recognize a "Hamitic" or "Ethiopian" race that includes such peoples as the Galla, the Somali, the Masai, the Bahima, and other peoples of East Africa who are obviously Negroids with a proportion of Mediterranean White blood varying in different groups, but amounting in general to less than one quarter. Negro Africa abounds in mulatto peoples of ancient origin and often of considerable homogeneity. Most of these are tall and slender, and from their tendency to aquiline noses seem to have acquired their White blood from the Arab or Semitic type of the Mediterranean subrace. It seems probable that most of these mixed groups originated by early contact of Mediterranean invaders into the Horn of Africa with the Negroes of East Africa and the Lake Region.

At least as early as 5000 B.C., Mediterranean race peoples in Mesopotamia and Egypt had reached a very respectable level of Neolithic civilization, had domesticated plants and animals, and were making substantial progress in arts and industries. Nomadic pastoral tribes ranged over Arabia and had probably invaded Africa by way of the Horn and mingled their blood with that of the Negro race.

In Mesolithic times, we find these ubiquitous and vivacious longheads squatting on the beaches of the Baltic and the strands of the Tagus, leaving vast residues of their shore dinners in heaps of shells and bones. In the Neolithic period, they have become skillful farmers, dexterous craftsmen, and monumental builders in stone. During the Age of Copper and Bronze, they advanced in the more favored areas to cultures of such perfumed sophistication as to involve the use of bath-tubs and drains. Crete was not only the birthplace of Zeus, but apparently also of Aesculapius and Hygeia. The first plumber probably forgot his tools in the Palace of Minos.

The Hirsute Ainu. Unshaven, unshorn, and unwashed are the Ainu, the poorest relations in the White family. The hairy Ainu, aborigines of Japan and now restricted in distribution to the northern part of Japan and its islands, are generally regarded as the remnant of an ancient, brunet white or brown stock which in former times may have extended straight across Asia into European Russia. This short, dolichocephalic or mesocephalic people is notable for the profuseness of growth of its body hair and especially for the heavy beards of the males. Obviously the Ainu have undergone a considerable dilution of their blood by recent admixture with Mongoloid strains, most apparent in the females. But the pure Ainu type, as exhibited in many males, is distinctly of the "White" variety in features and even in pigmentation. Many Ainus are almost indistinguishable from bearded Russian peasants, who perhaps carry a good proportion of the same blood. An even more remarkable resemblance, although less pronounced, is that which the Ainu bear to the natives of Australia in their large brow-ridges, depressed nasal roots, and general hairiness. Some writers consider this a mere coincidence, but I am inclined to attribute it to the common possession of an archaic White racial element which is very strong in the Ainu, perhaps almost pure, aside from recent Mongoloid admixture, but in the case of the Australians is heavily overlaid with a Tasmanian (Negritoid) admixture.

Craniologically, the Ainu are strongly reminiscent of the ancient European long-heads of the Aurignacian or Combe-Capelle type, in their rather heavy brow-ridges, depressed nasal roots, somewhat broad nasal apertures, and rather short faces. Apart from their head form, the soft parts of the Ainu face and their hairiness make them resemble Alpine types more closely than contemporary Mediterranean types. For this reason certain students are inclined to regard them as prototypes of the Alpine subrace. Their head form is, of course, distinct from the Alpine brachycephaly, although a considerable number of Ainu individuals are mesocephalic rather than frankly long-headed.

The Ainu are dirty but not disreputable, unkempt but kindly, hirsute but harmless. They worship the bear and literally kill him with kindness, organizing an annual festival in his honor, heaping encomiums upon him, and finally slaying and eating him with profuse apologies. They remind one of the Walrus and the Oysters.

The Keltics. The Keltic subrace is apparently the result of a mutation or mutations in the basic, long-headed brunet stock that affect eye color, reducing it from brown to blue, gray, or pale mixed. The same genetic changes usually lighten skin color to pale white, or even ruddy, and sometimes modify hair color from black or dark brown to medium brown, red-brown or red. Not long ago the association of fairly dark hair with blue eyes in this type was considered to have resulted from intermixture of a brunet White stock with the blond, Nordic subrace. This theory is now untenable, because the Harvard anthropometric survey of Ireland, where the Keltic subrace is at present concentrated, clearly indicates that there never could have been any such high proportion of blond Nordics in this area as would account for the tremendous segment of the population in which pure blue eyes or gray eyes are associated with dark hair. In a series of 9,521 adult Irish males, representing an adequate geographical sampling of the country, there were no less than 25.3 per cent belonging to this Keltic subrace, and no more than 5 per cent of them red-headed. As a matter of fact, red hair in Ireland is not nearly so common as is generally supposed (less than 5 per cent). On the other hand, 47 per cent of our Irish series has pure light eyes, and all but 5 per cent of these are blue. Light hair, ranging from light brown to golden blond, occurs in only about 15 per cent of these Irish as against 40 per cent of dark brown, 35 per cent of medium brown, and about 5 per cent of red brown. Mixed eyes occur in the blonds and near-blonds as often or oftener than in the brunets. The commonest effect of crossing blond, blue-eyed stocks with dark-haired, brown-eyed stocks is to produce types of intermediate pigmentation of both hair and eyes, with occasional segregation of pure blonds and pure brunets. Dark hair and blue eyes rarely result from such crossing, since some sort of broken linkage would have to occur, in all probability, to produce such a disharmonic combination. We must, then, regard the blue eyes of the Keltic subrace as the result of a mutation rather than a hybridization phenomenon. The combination of dark hair and blue eyes is so uncommon outside of the British Isles and Normandy (the former strongholds of Keltic speech) that one is almost inclined to think that the mutation took place in northwestern Europe at a relatively recent time.

There is little doubt in my mind that the term Keltic, applied to this subrace, is a sad misnomer. It is true that the type is concentrated in Keltic areas, but the anthropometric evidence in Ireland strongly indicates that the Keltic subrace was not the original carrier of Keltic speech. Furthermore, it is today far poorer in Keltic speakers than other subracial types of Ireland. Keltic speech was introduced, in all probability, by Bronze Age invaders, not earlier than 1500 to 1800 B.C. The Keltic subrace probably came in the Neolithic period, as early as 2200 or 2000 B.C. They may have been the builders of the Megalithic monuments—great, rough stone tombs and other structures. It is commonly assumed that these Neolithic immigrants came by sea, from Spain or the western Mediterranean.

In a series of 9,168 United States males, the Keltic subrace constituted about 8.5 per cent, ranking fifth among the subracial types established by sorting criteria. The Keltic type is strongly represented among the native born of native parentage, and, among the native born of foreign parentage and the foreign born, seems to have been derived primarily from Irish stock, but also from Scotch, Welsh, English, and Scandinavians.

The Red-blooded Nordics. No one knows when the peace of prehistoric Europe was first shattered by the irruptions of raw-boned ruffians from the North. The prehistoric distribution of the tall, fair-haired, blue-eyed, ruddy-skinned, and long-headed Nordic subrace is much more of a mystery than that of the Mediterraneans. The physical differences that distinguish these two races are largely a matter of size and pigmentation. Stature—gross size—is a composite and extremely variable dimension. Pigmentation of hair, skin, and eyes cannot be determined from skeletal remains. Several times I have talked with visitors to the osteological collections of Harvard who were of the impression that the bones of a Negro are black, those of an Indian red, et cetera, just as Huckleberry Finn thought that the vegetation and soil of the various states were of the several colors indicated on maps. The bones of a stunted Nordic are indistinguishable from those of an overgrown and muscular Mediterranean. The Nordic is supposed to have a longer and narrower face, larger brow-ridges and a more sloping forehead, a longer, narrower, and higher nose, and a more boldly jutting chin. But I do not believe that any physical anthropologist can with certainty distinguish the skeletal remains of the taller individuals of the subrace of Mediterraneans from those of a Nordic. He has to rely upon his impression of a brutal masculinity of bony structure in the one race in contrast to a somewhat effeminate symmetry of the other.

The sorting scheme for selecting the Nordic subrace has been somewhat liberalized in the above outline (p. 578) in comparison with the strict criteria I have employed in technical sortings of large samples of the populations of the United States and Ireland. This previous method insisted upon pure golden or ash blond hair and pure gray or pure blue eyes as prerequisites for admission to the subrace. Individuals with light eyes and golden brown or very light brown hair, or with light mixed eyes and light hair were relegated to a predominantly Nordic type, presumably tainted with some slight brunet admixture. In the present scheme, both classes are combined in criteria for selecting Nordics. The first reason for this letting down of the pigment bars is that the purely blond long-heads are numerically so few, even in countries supposed to be basically Nordic in their population, that I doubt that there are enough of them to dignify as a subracial type anywhere outside of Sweden and Norway, and perhaps not even there. These simon-pure blond long-heads in the United States constitute only 2.44 per cent of our large male series and in Ireland only 0.61 per cent. If we add in the near blond long-heads, we have an additional 17.0 per cent of Nordics in the United States and 7.0 per cent more in Ireland. However, the most important consideration leading me to lump together the two categories is the finding that the sorting out of these pure light-eyed, blond long-heads, in whatever series, generally yields a group that is decidedly below the mean age of all other racial types—usually a very young adult or a subadult group, even when, as in our samples, the entire series are supposed to be adults. This can mean only that young adult pure blonds acquire some additional pigmentation of hair and eyes after maturity, so that most of them probably are transformed into near-blonds. Personal observation leads me to conclude that "fast" blonds (whose hair and eyes do not darken) are very rare indeed. Thus, if we insist upon classifying as pure Nordic only persons with purely blue or gray eyes and ash blond or golden hair, we do not indeed empty out the Nordic baby with the bath, but rather keep the baby and empty out his mother and father.

Scandinavian anthropologists, who have carried out extensive surveys of the populations of Sweden, Norway, and Denmark, recognize several Nordic subtypes. For our purposes two are sufficient: (a) a moderately tall and rather slender type, very long-headed with somewhat gracile skeletal structure, flat temples, sloping forehead, weak brow-ridges; long, narrow, "horse face," with high thin nose, deep jaws; hair usually ash blond or light brown, skin pink, eyes light or light mixed; (b) a heavier-boned, more rugged type, with tougher-textured skin, hair color more frequently golden or golden brown than ash, eyes oftener pale mixed than pure blue; head more mesocephalic, broader, less sloping forehead; coarser nose, more prominent malars and jaw angles (Trønder type). Coon regards the more delicate, classic, ash blond Nordic type as of Iron Age origin, and the rugged, golden blond type as a blend of ethnically older elements—Upper Palaeolithic, Mesolithic, and Neolithic.[84]

The range of subtypes within the much touted Nordic "race" and the variable extent to which depigmentation of hair, skin, and eyes is seen within these subtypes lead to the suggestion that it is little more than a congeries of more or less long-headed stocks of all of the known

[84] Coon, *op. cit.*, pp. 310–319.

White varieties, bound together by a common blondism, the result, no doubt, of multiple mutations. The mutations that tend to produce partial depigmentation of skin, hair, and eyes, are probably recessive and almost certainly subject to contra-selection in any environment where the actinic rays of the sun are strong and where, consequently, melanin is necessary in the skin and the eyes for protection of the underlying tissues. However, the Baltic seems the place, *par excellence,* where selection may not discriminate against depigmentation—where, indeed, it may even confer an advantage in the struggle for survival.[85]

The Scandinavians and Germans are inclined to favor the view that the Nordic race differentiated around the Baltic, its center of distribution from early historic times. Others bring it in from the ample expanses of the Asiatic steppes. Influenced seemingly by the idea that the Nordics have always been a sporting race and fond of horses, some anthropologists have attempted to identify them with the hunters of the Aurignacian and Solutrian periods of the Upper Palaeolithic age. There seems to exist here a certain confusion of identity between peoples who are fond of horse flesh for eating and those who are addicted to the riding of horses. Because a Palaeolithic stock butchered horses for culinary purposes, it does not follow that this gastronomic interest was transmuted in their descendants into a sporting devotion to the noble equine as a beast of burden. Nor does it seem judicious to identify the Russian steppe-dwellers of the Neolithic period as descendants of the Solutrians merely because both groups were long-headed, and one ate horses and the other rode them. One might as well insist that the British are descended from the Bronze Age Cretans because the latter baited bulls and the former like roast beef.

The famous Swedish anthropologist, Retzius, maintains that the inhabitants of Scandinavia have been predominantly Nordic from Mesolithic times down to present, that the first settlers after the retreat of the ice sheet were blond Nordics.

The elaborate reconstructions of "Nordic" movements during prehistoric and protohistoric times, fabricated by European archaeologists, physical anthropologists, and even by philologists, have less of history than of fiction in their composition. If a Nordic is virtually any kind of a blond or near-blond dolichocephal or mesocephal of generally White racial antecedents, it becomes impossible to identify skeletal material

---

[85] A malicious person might define a Nordic as a dolichocephalic partial albino, preserved from the ordinary eliminatory action of natural selection by the fog and feeble sunlight of the Baltic environment.

as Nordic unless there are supporting evidences of the blondness of its owners in life. The first physical evidence of blondness in Scandinavia is furnished by certain Danish Bronze Age burials made in oak coffins. The tannic acid in the wood seems to have preserved the skins and textiles in which the bodies were clothed, and also the hair. Several of these are burials of individuals who had blond hair. The Bronze Age in Scandinavia certainly did not begin before 1800 B.C. and did not end before 750 B.C. If one could be certain that mummification and the chemical processes involved in the decay of body tissues and in the preservation of hair by tannic acid or other agencies have no bleaching effect upon hair, this evidence would be incontrovertible. I have seen numerous instances of hair naturally preserved in burials when all of the other soft parts have disappeared and when even the bones and the teeth are nearly gone. Certain soil conditions, particularly clay soils that hold the water, seem to promote this preservation of hair together with an acceleration of decay of the skeletal parts usually more lasting. In such cases, there is no usual bleaching of the hair, as far as can be observed. Black hair and dark brown hair are common enough. In the case of natural mummification or dessication and also in artificial mummification, no general bleaching effect is observable, although reddish tints, probably present in life, may be seen in some Peruvian and southwestern United States mummy hair. Therefore, on the whole, I am inclined to accept as evidence of blondness hair preserved in ancient burials.

However, an occasional Bronze Age blond mummy is a slim basis for sweeping generalizations concerning the Nordic occupation of Scandinavia from the end of glacial times onward. Mutations, or whatever may be the cause of blondness, may conceivably effect a partial depigmentation in stocks that are not dolichocephalic and leptorrhine and have no close relationship to putative Nordics. Blondness in the Baltic area is even more pronounced among Finns and other peoples of brachycephalic head-form than among the long-heads.

Invasions of Egypt by blond Libyans are reported on Egyptian monuments of the XVIIIth Dynasty (1580–1346 B.C.). The Libyan warriors terrorized the Egyptians even in the XIth and XIIth Dynasties (2400 B.C. to 2000 B.C.). The Guanches of the Canary Islands included a long-headed, blond element, attested by historical records and by blond hair in mummies. Many of their mixed descendants of today are near-blonds. Blondness occurs sporadically among Berber tribes of North Africa today, especially in the Moroccan Rif, but also in Algeria. All competent students of the peoples of this area agree that this Berber blondness is ancient and indigenous and not the result of the Vandal invasion (A.D. 428–538), although it is wholly possible that these northern bar- barians may have reinforced whatever of light hair and eyes already existed in Africa Minor. There can be little doubt that the partial de- pigmentation of the ancient Berbers operated upon a generally Mediter- ranean stock containing strains similar to, or identical with, those from which the classical Nordics developed. However, apart from the late and unimportant Vandals, there is no evidence whatsoever that the Scandi- navian, Germanic, or Baltic blonds had any historic or prehistoric con- nection with Guanches, Libyans, or modern Berber blondness. In the terminology of the cultural anthropologists, North African blondness may well have been an "independent invention" rather than the result of "diffusion."

The evidence of the existence of occasionally blond individuals among the Homeric and Classical Greeks is sufficiently clear and has been dis- cussed *ad nauseam*. It certainly does not justify inflation into pseudo- histories of conquering "Nordic" tribes invading the Greek peninsula in the Bronze Age and introducing Aryan languages, nor even such modifications as supposed incursions of brunet Alpine *hoi polloi* under the leadership of long-headed blond heroes or demigods.

The eastward extension of the Nordic subrace in ancient prehistoric times is probable. According to Haddon,[86] the Chinese annals tell of red- haired, blue-eyed tribes in central Asia, of which the Wusuns were one. Dixon believes that this subrace at a very early period had spread through most of the northern lowlands of Asia and had forced its way across the eastern plateaus to farther India and the eastern coast. He is of the opinion that one branch came through Dzungaria into China and Man- churia and passed by way of Korea into Japan. Another branch, accord- ing to this writer, followed down the great rivers and mountain ranges which spread fanwise from Thibet, thus penetrating into farther India and ultimately into Indonesia. According to Dixon, the effects of this thrust may still be seen today in parts of the borderlands, where indi- viduals of European features, with light hair and eyes and rosy cheeks are sometimes found.[87]

Guha describes a long-headed strain, with long face, narrow nose, rosy skin, lightish or gray blue eyes, chestnut hair and tall stature, among

[86] Haddon, *Races of Man and Their Distribution*, p. 49.
[87] Dixon, *The Racial History of Man*, pp. 243–244.

the northwestern Himalayan tribes of today.[88] In the prehistoric Chalcolithic (transition from stone to copper) remains from Mohenjo-daro,
in the Indus Valley, Guha recognizes a large-headed, dolichocephalic,
narrow-nosed type which he tentatively identifies with the contemporary
northwestern Himalayan blonds. It was a minor cranial element associated with another long-faced, dolichocephalic type, which he identifies
as Mediterranean. Guha thinks that these types occupied northwestern
India from the beginning of the fourth millennium B.C., but he also states
that this large-headed strain found at Mohenjo-daro probably forms one
of the constituents of the race "whose advent in India appears to syn-
chronize with the 'Aryan' invasion."

About 1500 B.C., Aryan languages are thought to have been introduced
into northwestern India, perhaps from Afghanistan. Some students
think that they were brought by blonds—"Nordics"— partly because of
the fair-complected element in this part of India and partly because of
a prior conviction that Nordics were the principal, if not original,
carriers of Aryan or Indo-European languages. Most of the German and
British anthropologists credit Nordics with the honor of being the
original "Aryans," although it is no longer fashionable to talk about an
"Aryan race." I know of no sound body of evidence—archaeological,
historical, linguistic, craniological, or anthropometric—that supports the
hypothesis that Nordics had any more to do with the origin and prehistoric diffusion of Aryan languages than had Alpines, or Dinarics, or
even the subrace that I have called Keltic. About all that we know is
that the predominantly Mediterranean types of peoples on the African
shore of the Mediterranean and on the Palestinian-Syrian shore, the
probably Armenoid inhabitants of Asia Minor, and all of the Neolithic
and earlier occupiers of the European areas bordering on the Mediterranean and in its islands certainly did not speak Aryan (Indo-European,
Indo-Germanic) languages. These languages were introduced from central Europe into Greece, Italy, and Asia Minor in the Bronze Age, probably about 1800 B.C. from central Europe by invaders of probably mixed
White subracial composition. Presumably, the Germanic branch of
Indo-European linguistic family was concentrated in Scandinavia and
North Germany at least as early as 1000 B.C., whereas the now almost
extinct Keltic languages were first concentrated somewhere in central
Europe. The latter were carried west of the Rhine and into the British
Isles in two waves, the first speaking Q dialects, which survive in Gaelic

---

[88] Guha, *Census of India*, 1931, lxii, lxx.

in Ireland, the Isle of Man, and Scotland, and the second speaking P dialects, still extant in Wales and Brittany and recently extinct in Cornwall. The Gaels reached the British Isles at the beginning of the Bronze Age in all probability (about 1800 B.C.), and the Brythons (the P-speakers) in the Iron Age, probably not before 700 B.C. to 600 B.C. The Bronze Age invaders of Britain were tall round-heads, certainly not Nordics, and the Iron Age Kelts were equally non-Nordic, if we can judge of them by their descendants in Wales and Cornwall (mostly Mediterranean) and in Brittany (predominantly Alpine). In Caesar's time, the Gauls spoke P Keltic also, and they seem to have been a mixture of White racial subtypes, including Nordic. Not even the Belgae, a Germanic-speaking people who crossed the Channel and settled in Kent in 100 B.C., were purely Nordic in physical features, although they seem to have been fairer than most of the Gauls. The movements of peoples into southern and western Europe bringing with them Aryan languages can be plausibly attributed to no single White subrace, but rather to a mixture of elements of all of them, with the possible exception of the Classic type of Mediterranean, the Upper Palaeolithic type, and the Armenoid subrace. These are more likely to have had Aryan languages imposed upon them than to have carried them.

These movements of subracially mixed peoples were only the prelude of a larger exodus of pure or nearly pure Nordics from the Baltic area. Forerunners of this advance were the Teutons and the Cimbri who fought their way from the north of Denmark into the Danube valley, turned west and ravaged Gaul, and finally were destroyed in Italy by Marius in 101 B.C. The strength of the Roman Empire kept the Nordic hordes at bay until the beginning of the third century A.D. Then the Goths, the Vandals, and other Teutonic peoples forced their way into the Balkan peninsula and adjacent areas. The Vandals in the fifth century turned westward, passed through Gaul and Spain, and formed a short-lived kingdom in West Africa. The Alemanni and the Bavarians pushed southward to the Alps. The Visigoths conquered Rome in 410 A.D. and then proceeded into the south of France and Spain and established a kingdom that lasted until the beginning of the eighth century. Meanwhile, by the end of the fifth century, the Franks had taken possession of almost the whole of Gaul. As early as the third century A.D., the Teutonic peoples began to invade Normandy and Britain. First came the Angles, Saxons, and Jutes, and after them the Danes and the Norsemen. These movements continued well into the ninth century, culminating in the conquest of Britain by the Normans, a people by this time of mixed types with Nordic blood predominant.

Evidently Nordic blood, during the first ten centuries of the Christian era, was diffused throughout Europe, and its traces may still be seen in many places remote from the Baltic Sea. The discovery of the New World and the period of colonial expansion contributed greatly to the draining of the Nordic reserve in Europe.

It is hardly surprising that German, Scandinavian, and British anthropologists, like other gentlemen, "prefer blonds." But it is unfortunate that all of the long-head adventurers of history and prehistory are rashly identified as "Nordics" on the basis only of a purely suppositional bleaching. Not all of the heroic virtues are automatically created by the deleterious mutations that are responsible for depigmentation.

The Stodgy Alpines. Brachycephaly is curiously uncommon in very archaic or palaeoanthropic types in spite of the fact that the anthropoid apes, with the single exception of the mountain variety of gorilla, are round-headed. It is true that Keith reconstructs the Piltdown skull as brachycephalic, or nearly so, and it is quite possible that some of the Krapina Neanderthaloids were relatively broad-skulled. Most of the early examples of *Homo sapiens* found in Upper Pleistocene deposits are dolichocephalic, but brachycephals do appear at Solutré in France, at Alfalou in Algeria, and elsewhere. In postglacial times, during the Mesolithic period, coarse-boned round-heads are not uncommon in Europe. In genetic terms, brachycephaly is commonly explained as the result of repeated mutations, probably involving multiple factors controlling head shape, perhaps by determining the respective growth rates of head length and head breadth. Factors repressive of increase in head length and encouraging head breadth might bring about an apparent dominance of the broad, short heads. Foetalization, or the retention of infantile features in adult life, is another favorite explanation of brachycephaly, possibly involving a shift in the endocrine balance toward a hypothyroid condition. Marett, for example, would invoke iodine deficiency as a predisposing or causal factor, operating through the ductless glands.[89]

Weidenreich stresses the reduction of massiveness and the breakdown of supporting structures of the skull—frontal and occipital torus, sagittal crest, et cetera—in the evolution of *Homo sapiens* from palaeoanthropic types of man.[90] The principal theme of Coon's findings in his very detailed study of European races is the survival to modern times of massive-skulled, Upper Palaeolithic types in refuge areas and the

[89] Marett, *op. cit.,* and *passim.*
[90] Weidenreich, *Sinanthropus,* pp. 169–176.

derivation of smaller and lighter cranial types from these rugged and ponderous precursors. Thus he lays great emphasis upon the brachy-cephals of Alfalou in Algeria, the Mesolithic skulls of Ofnet and of the so-called Borreby type—a tall, heavy-boned, brachycephalic type common in Denmark, Belgium, and the northern Scandinavian area in Mesolithic times.

There is no valid objection, in my opinion, to the derivation of modern, lighter-skulled brachycephals, such as Alpines, from ponderous ·Upper Palaeolithic precursors, but it is hard to see why modern examples of massive round-heads should be considered pure line Palaeolithic survivors of different racial antecedents from the smaller and more delicate brachycephals by whom they are, in most cases, surrounded. There are in every stock individual constitutional and familial variations in size and robustness and general body build. These we shall discuss in a later section (pp. 677–678). Naturally, the more ponderous, muscular, and heavier-boned individuals of the Alpine race more closely resemble their rugged Palaeolithic precursors. It may be desirable to recognize a more massive, Borreby morphological subtype occurring within the brunet Alpine and East Baltic brachycephalic subraces, but to accord such a subtype separate subracial or racial classification would, it seems to me, postulate an isolation of very old racial strains and a perpetuation of pure lines that is improbable in any part of modern Europe. It is, however, perfectly possible that out-of-the-way places have populations today that have been less subjected to intermixture and less affected by physiological and nutritional factors that make for type modernization than have the populations of more central areas. So, it is conceivable that some, at least, of the Borreby massive round-heads carry more unmodified Palaeolithic genes than do ordinary rugged Alpines or East Baltics.

We used to attribute some of these very tall, raw-boned brachycephalic types to interbreeding between Nordics and Alpines or between Alpines and massive dolichocephals of the Upper Palaeolithic (Combe-Capelle —Galley Hill or Brünn types). I have no doubt that many have originated in exactly this way and owe their increased size and ruggedness, in some measure, to heterosis or hybrid vigor. Actually, in a world of men who have been migratory and promiscuous for scores of thousands of years, the origin of new types through hybridization and the duplication of ancient prototypes by fresh recombinations of the same strains that were present and undifferentiated in fossil men is a much more likely phenomenon than pure line, unmodified survival of ancient forms. Atavism occurs through chance recombination of odds and ends of usually recessive genes that have been covered up in differentiated modern stocks.

It used to be the fashion to consider the round-headed Alpines as immigrants into Europe from some vast reservoir of their type, postulated to exist on the western slopes of the central Asiatic Plateau. If such a reservoir ever existed, it must have been completely emptied, because there is no considerable body of Alpine type Whites in that area today. Alpines in the Middle East are rarer by far than they are in Europe, although there is ample evidence that they have been involved in the interbreeding that has produced the secondary Armenoid subrace. It now seems probable that the tremendous increase of the Alpine type in Europe during historic times has been more a matter of selectional advantage and superior survival qualities of the type than of reinforcement through constant streams of immigration. Roundheads of obviously Alpine affinities are found in the Epipalaeolithic or Mesolithic burials in the caves at Ofnet, Würtemburg, South Germany, and in the shell heaps of Mugem on the Tagus river in Portugal. In the course of the Neolithic period, these globular-headed peoples with broad faces and short sturdy bodies established themselves in many places in Europe, as far west as Brittany, in central France, and particularly in the Alpine highlands and in the Balkan peninsula. They are also found at this early period in Denmark and in various areas of central and southeastern Europe, but not usually as the predominant element in the population. We have reason to think that the spread of Bronze Age culture up the Danubian valley and then to northern and western Europe was in considerable measure due to the industrial and commercial activity of this race, but unfortunately we are here faced by an almost insurmountable obstacle. Cremation began in Europe at some time during the Neolithic period and became more and more popular throughout the early metal ages until, at the end of the Bronze Age, it had grown to be the principal method of disposing of the remains of the dead. Nothing is more detestable to the physical anthropologist than this wretched habit of cremating the dead. It involves not only a prodigal waste of costly fuel and excellent fertilizer, but also the complete destruction of physical historical data. On the other hand, the custom of embalming and mummification is most praiseworthy and highly to be recommended. When bodies are reduced to ashes or to a heap of calcined bones, it is impossible for the anthropologists to determine anything as to their original head form or other metric characters. Brachycephals and skulls of mixed head form seem to precede and to fringe the areas in which cremation was most prevalent in Europe in the Bronze and Early Iron Ages. And these are, in general, precisely the areas in which the brachycephalic Alpine subrace is most strongly established today. Therefore, it is a justifiable inference that the spread of Alpines in Europe has been to a considerable extent conterminous with and masked by their habit, not invariable, but frequent, of burning their dead.

Throughout the Early Iron Ages and during the Roman period, cremation continued to prevail in so many areas of Europe as to obscure the racial constitution of many of the populations. This habit of cremation was not confined to Alpines; it was also taken up and practiced by Nordics and other peoples. Nevertheless, the skeletal material available for examination seems to indicate that dolichocephaly prevailed in present day Alpine strongholds, notably Czecho-Slovakia and Austria-Hungary, in Poland and Russia, until the ninth or tenth century A.D. The first historical Slavic burials, dating not earlier than 900 A.D., are predominantly those of long-headed persons, although today the Slavs are, generally speaking, brachycephalic in head form. The overwhelming numerical superiority of round-headed types in central and eastern Europe today and their increasing prevalence in western and northwestern Europe are partially explicable in the light of the historic invasions from the east. The first of the historical invasions from Asia was that of the Huns, who appeared in the latter part of the fourth century A.D. and formed a powerful kingdom in central Europe under Attila. But their disruption came about as a result of their defeat at Châlons in 451 and Attila's death in 453 A.D. These Huns could not have reinforced the Alpine race in Europe because it is now certain that they were dolichocephalic Mongoloid in racial type. In the sixth century A.D., another wave of Asiatic invaders, the Avars, brachy Mongoloids, swept into Europe, driving before them the Bulgars, the Slavs, and others. They reached the lower Danube and were given land there by Justinian. In 562 A.D., they fought the Franks on the Elbe, and later they combined with the Longobardi and crushed the Gepidae. The latter moved into Italy, leaving the Avars the masters of the greater part of the Danube valley. Later, with the Slavs, the Avars reached Hungary and overran the Balkan Peninsula. They were finally crushed in 796 A.D. by Pippin I of Italy. In 635 A.D., the Bulgars, another Asiatic group from the South Russian steppes, revolted from the Avars and entered the Balkan peninsula. The Hunagars came from the Urals to the Volga in 550 A.D. and reached the Danube about 886 A.D. With the Magyars and other Turkish tribes, they founded the kingdom of Hungary, which absorbed the remnants of the Hun and Avar empires of the fifth and sixth centuries.

It seems necessary to suppose that these successive waves of Asiatics set-
tling in Europe must have been responsible in large measure for the
brachycephalization of the modern population of central and eastern
Europe. It is hardly possible that the physical type of all of these Asiatics
could have been purely Mongoloid or we should have a more Mongoloid
population today in the areas of their settlement. Of course, Mongoloid
features are very common in these regions, but the Alpine type predominates, and Alpine physical features differ in many important respects
from those of Mongoloids.

There is, however, another possible explanation. In crosses of persons
of dolichocephalic head form with brachycephals, the offspring are more
likely to be mesocephalic or brachycephals than long-headed. In other
words, in a Mendelian sense, brachycephaly seems dominant over dolichocephaly. In a general way, this observation is well supported, but it is
hardly probable that all Alpine racial features would similarly dominate
over the distinctive features of other races. Many European subracial
types are obviously the results of an intermixture of Alpines with Nordics
or Mediterraneans, elements being blended in different proportions
and with distinct results in several subtypes. But most of these mixed
Alpine types are quite obviously *mixed* and present a mélange of Alpine
and other racial features.

If brachycephaly involves multiple, cumulative genetic factors, with
dominance of those making for short, broad heads, the amount of phenotypic or visible brachycephaly might be increased considerably in the
population, but certainly not to the extent of working a complete transformation from long-headedness to round headedness in a few centuries
in the absence of selectional forces operating to favor the latter. Dominance does not in itself increase the proportions in the population of
a dominant gene.

It therefore seems clear that the gradual increase in brachycephaly
noted from Upper Palaeolithic times to 900 A.D.—a space of at least
20,000 years—might be accountable on the basis of dominance, selectional advantage, and the creation of round-headed types from long-heads
in the interbreeding of White subraces. All of these factors put together
seem insufficient to account for the tremendous swing to round-
headedness in central and eastern Europe supposed to have taken place
in the last ten centuries. To explain this, we must invoke additional reinforcements to the round-headed population in the way of migrants
from Asia. Candela has made it clear enough that the historical invasions of Mongoloids must have brought to eastern and Central Europe
most of the high proportion of B blood group found there today (cf.

p. 547). However, not all of the Asiatic invasions brought in immigrants of purely Mongoloid types. Coon thinks that the Magyars were only partially Mongolized, though brachycephalic, and some of the Turks (the Tajiks, for example) are nearly purely Alpine.[91]

Finally, there are two considerations that must be urged in connection with this problem of modern brachycephalization of central and eastern Europe: (1) Survivals of dolichocephals and mesocephals in this area, as shown by Coon's comprehensive survey of the existing materials, are far commoner than was previously thought to be the case; (2) by no means all of the European brachycephals are Alpines; much of the increase in round-headedness may be due to infiltration of East Baltics, Dinarics, Armenoids, and partially Mongoloid elements. Thus the mystery seems to dissolve itself.

The East Baltic Tow-heads. It is no longer possible to dismiss the great group of blond round-heads around the eastern Baltic as Alpines with a dash of Mongoloid mixture who have acquired an illegitimate partial depigmentation of hair, skin, and eyes as a result of intermittent or continuous practice of the *jus primae noctis* or the *droit du seigneur* upon peasant women by noble Nordics. There are probably far more honest-to-God blonds among the eastern European round-heads than could be scraped together in any Nordic census that would include Scandinavia, Germany, the British Isles, with the United States and Canada thrown in for good measure. These round-heads are blond in their own right and not by the traditional rights of feudal lords over lower class brides. There never have been enough long-headed Nordics to confer existing East Baltic blondness upon millions of Finns, Poles, Esthonians, Lithuanians, Letts, and Russians by contributing recessive genes for pigmentation to a previously unadulterated brunet germ plasm. In any case, crosses of blonds with brunets appear to produce intermediates in pigmentation in the majority of cases, and more darks than lights.

The origin of East Baltic blondness is certainly attributable to the same causes that have produced Nordic blondness, whatever those causes may be. If the mutations making for partial depigmentation are indeed recessive, some very powerful selectional agency must have operated to preserve and to multiply blonds in this region, of whatever head-form. The true East Baltic is not simply a bleached Alpine. The head is less globular and flatter behind, the face flatter and squarer, the nose more often concave and turned up as to tip, and the chin more rounded and less prominent. There is a definite suggestion of the Mongoloid that is

[91] Coon, *op. cit.,* pp. 233–234, 636–638.

negated only in the convex upper integumental lip, the strongly biconvex blue or gray eyes devoid of internal folds, the yellowish or creamy
white and rather coarse skin, and the usually platinum, ash, or ash
brown hair. It is this ash blond, round-headed type that is vulgarly
called "a square-head." Perhaps it is most characteristically present in
Finland, but it is common enough in Sweden, Norway, and Denmark.
Sorted out with the strict prerequisites of ash or golden hair and pure
blue or gray eyes, the East Baltic type is found in only 3.02 per cent of
American males and in but 1.29 per cent of Irish. However, here again
the average age of groups so selected indicates that the rigid pigmentation requirements result in selecting mostly subadults or young adults.
Hair probably darkens somewhat after maturity in East Baltics as in
Nordics. Therefore the sorting requirements have to be liberalized to
include ash-brown hair and light mixed eyes. These near-blonds of
brachycephalic head form have usually been relegated to a Nordic Alpine residual mixed class in the Harvard sortings. Said class includes
23 per cent of American males and 18.22 per cent of Irish. Probably
all of the lighter individuals of this intermediately-pigmented sorting
class should be assigned to the East Baltic subrace.

We know practically nothing about the racial history of this type.
Cranial material that belonged to it in the older burials has probably
been attributed, for the most part, to the better known Alpine subrace,
or to some other stock. As a matter of fact, the few skulls that have been
found in the north of Russia and around the Baltic, dating back to
Neolithic times, are of diverse types, mostly dolichocephalic or mesocephalic. The brachycephals are said to have a Mongoloid appearance.[92]

East Baltic physical types speak German in Germany, Polish in
Poland, Baltic language in Lithuania and Esthonia, Finnic in Finland
and in parts of Russia, and other tongues elsewhere. The type is most
plausibly connected with the Finno-Ugrian (non-Aryan) group of
languages, but who shall say what dialect the owner of a skull employed,
especially when there are practically no skulls upon which to base a
decision?

[92] Coon, *Races of Europe*, pp. 291–292, and elsewhere in that work, wishes to give the name
"Ladogan" to the descendants of the mesocephals and brachycephals who lived in northern
Europe, east of the Baltic, from Neolithic times onward. Under this category he recognizes
two subtypes: "Neo-Danubian" and "East Baltic," without specifying, except in the most
general terms, the precise pigmental and other morphological characters that define them.
I gather that all of these are more or less blond, more or less brachycephalic, or subbrachycephalic, with a hint of Mongoloid admixture. The antecedents of these types or this type are
indeed vague, but I deprecate the multiplication of names for such nebulous anthropological
entities. Here, all blond brachycephals with broadish noses are East Baltics. That may be
oversimplification (and I am inclined to think that it is), but it is better to be simple and
clear than elaborate and turbid—at any rate, when the supporting data are scanty.

The Enterprising Armenoids. The opinion that the Armenoid race resulted from a stabilized interbreed between hook-nosed Mediterraneans and brachycephalic Alpines, expressed in the earlier edition of this book, has ben confirmed and clarified by subsequent researches. Dr. Byron L. Hughes has measured, observed, and most skillfully analyzed a series of some 1,500 adult males of Armenian origin, which he has been able to resolve into component subracial types in addition to the well-known stabilized blend.[93] The elements that enter into the interbreed are: (1) Alpine, (2) Iranian Plateau, and/or hook-nosed Classic Mediterranean, (3) a minor amount of Nordic, variable in its presence. The Armenoid type is a mosaic of dominants with some new features that emerge from the blend. The great breadth of the head is Alpine; the high sloping forehead with the especially high-rooted and salient nose with curved and depressed tip is either Classic Mediterranean or Iranian Plateau; the thickness of the tip is probably an Alpine derivative. Again, the frequently rather full and everted lips are Mediterranean, the heavy beard and body hair are Alpine or Iranian Plateau. The sugar-loaf, or pointed head, in which the forehead slopes up to an apex almost at the back of the vault and the occiput drops away so steeply as to be nearly vertical, is probably the result of disharmonic growth tendencies in the interbreed. However, in some cases the occipital flattening has been accentuated by artificial deformation. Babies are swaddled or swathed in wrappings and are thus more or less immobilized on their backs in their cradles. Pressure upon the occiput, especially if the pillow is hard, is likely to cause flattening, particularly in those infants who are undernourished or suffer from some definite deficiency disease such as rickets. There is, so far as I know, comparatively little definite information as to the extent of these cradling habits among the peoples of Armenoid head form, nor are there available ample and precise details about the cushioning of the head and other pertinent conditions. However, physical anthropologists have long worried about this possibility of artificial deformation in Armenoid heads, and their anxiety has not been alleviated by the knowledge that these extremely flat-backed, pointed, Armenoid heads are by no means as common among the offspring of Armenoid type peoples in the United States as among those born in the Near East.

The beaky, busy Armenoids emerge from their Levantine obscurity as soon as cities and civilizations arise. This subrace, characterized above all by its sugar-loaf head form and its convex nose with fleshy depressed tip and flaring wings, has its center of distribution in the Anatolian

[93] Hughes, *Physical Anthropology of Native Born Armenians.*

plateau of Asia. Little is known of its origin or prehistoric beginnings. So far as I am aware, no skulls of this type have ever been found in Palaeolithic deposits. If there were Armenoids in the Old Stone Age, I have no doubt that they monopolized the trade in mammoth wool and skin garments and were the principal dealers in necklaces of shells and teeth.

Further, physical anthropologists have not usually distinguished in their craniological studies between Armenoid skulls and other types of brachycephals. The peculiarities of the Armenoid skulls do not readily find metric expression nor are they clearly described by indices. A very high skull rising to an apex at the crown, short and broad and with extremely long and curving nasal bones associated with a long face—these are the salient cranial features. For the early historic period in the Near East, skeletal materials are as yet extremely scanty. It is not until we begin to get sculptural or pictorial representations of Asiatics on ancient monuments that we are enabled to recognize the presence of the type with certainty. According to Sir Arthur Keith, the Sumerian crania of the fourth millennium B.C. are not at all Armenoid but represent a big, dolichocephalic type of skull which must be assigned to what one may broadly call the Mediterranean subrace. It is, nevertheless, apparent from a study of sculptured remains and other representations of Sumerians of the fourth and third millennium B.C. that the characteristic Armenoid nose and head form were already well represented in that people.[94] The so-called "standard" of Ur, a panel of mosaic in shell and lapis lazuli, with figures arranged in rows and dating from about 3500 B.C., shows many human figures representing the Sumerian army.[95] Nearly all of the 50 individuals represented on this plaque show the characteristic Armenoid profile with beaky nose merging into the forehead slope. Most of the soldiers wear pointed, almost conical helmets. About one half of the men are unhelmeted prisoners. At least five of these have pointed, flat-backed heads. A statuette of a Sumerian ruler of the early part of the third millennium [96] excellently delineates this most prominent of nasal appendages and shows also the typical continuity of the slope of the nasal bridge with that of the forehead. From these and other Sumerian monuments, it is clear that the Armenoid type was represented among this ancient people long before their civilization

[94] Professor S. Landon discovered at Kish a terra-cotta portrait head belonging to the Sumerian painted ware, the last of which he places at 4000 B.C. This head (figured in *The Illustrated London News*, February 8, 1930, Plate 1) is exaggeratedly Armenoid.

[95] C. L. Woolley, *The Sumerians*, p. 51, fig. 14.

[96] *Ibid.*, p. 61, fig. 17

was overcome by the Babylonians. An even more grotesquely Armenoid type (female) is represented in a stone statuette from the temple of Khafaje, Jemdet Nasar period (before 3000 B.C.) [97]

Similarly, an Indo-Sumerian statue from Mohenjo-daro in the valley of the Indus, India, represents a bearded man with an Armenoid nose and a pointed head. This statue must go back to the second or third millennium B.C. Babylonian, Assyrian, and Hittite monuments clearly show the prevalence of these bearded Armenoids in Anatolia and Mesopotamia throughout historical antiquity. It seems altogether probable that the center of development of this subrace was in Asia Minor. From there it spread southward to Arabia and eastward at least as far as India. Writing is generally supposed to have originated from the conventionalization of pictographs having a magical or religious significance. It would, then, be the invention of holy men and priests. I should think it highly probable, however, that the necessity of keeping accounts drove inventive Armenoids to a reduction of holy to commercial writ at some very early period. It was of more importance to individuals to reckon profit and loss in business than to record victories and defeats in war. Again, prayers may well be rendered vocally, but promissory notes ought to be put in black and white.

Because of the lack of clear distinction in craniological studies between Armenoid and Alpine crania, considerable uncertainty prevails as to the prehistoric distribution of the Armenoid race in Europe. Apparently no great extension into Europe of this physical type in its purity occurred in prehistoric times, so far as can be judged from archaeological remains. It seems clear, nevertheless, that the oriental phase of the first Early Iron Age, generally called the Hallstatt period in central Europe and dating from about 700 to 500 B.C., witnessed a considerable diffusion of Armenoids from Asia Minor into the Balkan Peninsula, Greece, Italy, and probably other areas adjacent to Asia Minor. The Etruscans almost certainly came from Asia Minor and settled in Italy about the eighth century B.C. And there is reason for believing that they were in some degree Armenoid.

The Indomitable Dinarics. In Yugo-Slavia and Albania, the composite subrace known as Dinaric is the result of interbreeding of primary subraces, most of which are involved in the production of the Armenoids. The high, peaked head with flattened occiput, the long face with extremely prominent and usually convex nose are Dinaric as well as Armenoid characters. Unpublished studies of the Montenegrins by

[97] Figured in *The Illustrated London News,* Sept. 26, 1936, p. 524, Figs. 4, 5.

Robert W. Ehrich and partially published analyses of the Albanians by Coon reveal the original subracial components of the blend.[98] There are the basic brunet, round-headed Alpine, one or more types of brunet, long-headed Mediterraneans, and, in addition, a considerably stronger Nordic element than usually occurs in Armenoids. Coon regards the most important Mediterranean element involved as the so-called Upper Palaeolithic (Atlanto-Mediterranean type), which has a massive head and is particularly to the fore in those parts of Montenegro where Dinaric stature is at its maximum and the average of 177 cm. surpasses all other European means. Coon, however, is of the opinion that the convex and salient Dinaric nose comes about as a result of the shortening of the head [99] in blends of this type, and he further holds that "the principle of Dinaricization" has operated in various stocks within the White race's area of occupation, so that a group of Dinarics in one place has no necessary historical connection with a similar group elsewhere. I agree that a Dinaric-like blend has taken place in several different parts of the European area, more or less independently, but I do not consider that the Dinaric nasal convexity is of independent and multiple origin. This nasal convexity, in my opinion, goes back ultimately in every case to one of two Middle Eastern Mediterranean morphological types: the Iranian Plateau and the Classic Mediterranean with the hooked nose (which probably derived its nasality in turn from the Iranian Plateau type). In the Dinaric subrace, which is concentrated among the Montenegrins, Bosnians, northern Albanians, Serbs, Croats, and Austrians of the Tyrol region, the hooked nose element in the morphological mosaic is probably a straight Armenoid derivative.

In addition to the Iron Age invaders of this type into the Balkan area, there have been considerable historical reinforcements of Armenoids, notably by Turks. This people, coming from Turkestan, crossed the Euphrates in 1063 A.D. and in 1084 occupied Asia Minor. Two centuries later, the Ottoman Turks began to establish themselves in the Balkan peninsula, occupying Macedonia in 1372 and Constantinople in 1453. Hungary was under their domination from 1552 to 1687. There can hardly be any question of an original evolution of Dinaric or Armenoid types of nose in the Balkan peninsula when we know that the Armenoid type has been plentifully diffused into the area. The classic Dinarics of the region show a refinement of Armenoid features (cf. outline, p. 579) probably due to attenuation of Armenoid characters by

[98] Coon, *op. cit.*, pp. 587–604.
[99] *Ibid.*, explanation of Plate 35.

stronger admixture with Nordic and with the massive, tall Upper Palaeolithic (Atlanto-Mediterranean) types. Dinarics show a much greater
range of pigmentation than do most Armenoids, although out-and-out
blonds are found occasionally among persons of purely Armenian ancestry.[100]

In the Bronze Age, or just before the introduction of bronze, Britain
was invaded by tall, massive round-heads who seem to have come from
about the same area near the mouth of the Rhine and northwestern
Germany from which the later Anglo-Saxons sailed. Probably other
brachycephals came to England later during this period, but the custom of cremation obscures their racial affinities. British anthropologists
have long recognized a contemporary English and Scottish type as probably surviving from these Bronze Age invaders or as an effect of recombination of the same subracial elements. The type in question is known
as the Bronze Age, Beaker, or John Bull type. It is tall, heavy-boned,
weighty and, in middle and advanced years, obese. The skin is usually
florid or "beefy," the eyes blue or light mixed, the hair brown with
reddish mixture. Sometimes, however, and especially in Shetland, and
in parts of North England, and Scotland, and Ireland, the hair and skin
are dark. The head is massive, brachycephalic and sometimes rather
flattened behind, but more often globular. If the high, pointed
Armenoid-Dinaric brachycephaly exists in this type, it is uncommon.
Brow-ridges are heavy, malars prominent, and the face rather broad, but
not short. The nose is usually long, wide, and convex—decidedly beaky.
Beard and body hair are strongly developed. This well marked type is
found among the yeomanry, the country squires, and, according to Keith,
among the business and professional classes of Britain. It has ordinarily
been considered an Alpine-Nordic cross, and it is clear enough that
both of these elements frequently enter into its composition. However,
the nasal convexity and occasionally flattened occiput perhaps qualify
the type more correctly as Dinaric. This is the opinion of Coon, who
points out that the blend could not have been formed *in situ* in Britain
because of the absence of any antecedent Alpine type that is an essential
ingredient. As a matter of fact, Coon thinks that the brachycephalic
element in the John Bull type is closer to the ancient massive Borreby
type than to the supposedly reduced Alpine derivative.

If the Dinaric theory of British Bronze Age origins is correct, the type
harks back in respect of its nasal convexity to some ultimately Middle
or Near Eastern element, much adulterated and modified by admixture

---

[100] Coon, following Lebzelter, calls these Dinaric blonds "Norics."

with western European types. As a matter of fact, probably some of the so-called Bronze Age types are merely crosses of later Nordic long-headed blonds with the pure Alpines who certainly came into the British Isles with the later Bronze Age invasions and subsequently, in trickles, from Brittany and other points across the Channel.

In a series of 9,168 United States adult males of various national origins, 13.33 per cent were sorted out as of the Armenoid-Dinaric type, no distinction being made between the purely brunet Armenoid and the moderately dark to near-blond Dinaric. Very few of these American Dinaric-Armenoids are of Old American stocks. Most of them are of recent European derivation: Polish Austrian, Teutonic, French Canadian, Scotch, and Near Eastern. In Ireland, the Dinaric sorting selects 18.56 per cent of 9,521 adult males, all native born and of presumably Old Irish ancestry. However, these are all Dinarics and not Armenoids, in the sense that they include no individuals with black hair or with pure brown eyes. This Dinaric element is concentrated in west Ireland and may well represent, for the most part, survivors of the Bronze Age invasions.

COMPOSITE RACE
(Predominantly White)

1. AUSTRALIAN
(Archaic White + Tasmanian + recent minor fraction of Melanesian-Papuan)
Characters:
1. Hair form: low wave, curly, deep wave, rarely straight
2. Hair color: usually dark brown with reddish gold tint; sometimes medium red brown or flat brown; blondness and rufosity common in young
3. Skin color: chocolate, medium brown, light red brown, yellow brown, rarely dark brown (on unexposed parts)
4. Eye color: dark brown or medium brown, rarely light brown or black
5. Cephalic index: usually under 80; average 72.9
6. Nasal index: usually over 85; average 95.9
7. Facial index: usually under 90; average 84.3
8. Beard and body hair: moderate to pronounced
9. Head form: usually very narrow; receding foreheads with very large brow-ridges and glabella; vault gable-shaped
10. Nose form: nasion deeply depressed; nasal root medium to wide and low; bridge very wide and medium height; tip very thick; nostrils markedly oblique or transverse; alae flaring
11. Facial protrusion (prognathism); medium to pronounced
12. Chin prominence: usually negative or receding
13. Stature: extremely variable; average 164.4 cm.

Morphological Types:

1. Murrian (Southeastern)
(Most nearly White)
Characters:
    a. Hair form: 70.5 per cent low wave
    b. Skin color: on unexposed parts light red brown (36.5 per cent), medium brown (25.9 per cent), chocolate brown (21.8 per cent)—lightest skinned
    c. Eye color: more commonly medium than dark brown
    d. Hair quantity: body and beard hair strongly developed; baldness common
    e. Head form: extremely large dimensions, with somewhat higher cephalic index than most Australians
    f. Face form: more massive than in other Australians
    g. Nose form: longer, higher, than in other Australians; nasal index slightly lower
    h. Body build: broader shouldered, heavier, more lateral than in other Australians; calves well developed
Distribution: Found in purest form in southeastern Australia, but present as basic though modified type in southern and eastern coastal areas as far north as Townsville, Queensland

2. Carpentarian (Melanesian-Papuan increment)
Characters:
    a. Stature: tall, averaging 171 cm.
    b. Body build: linear, narrow hips and shoulders, short trunk (relative sitting height averaging 49.8), long legs, meager Negroid calves
    c. Skin color: dark (75.7 per cent chocolate brown, 7.3 per cent dark brown)
    d. Eye color: predominantly dark brown
    e. Hair quantity: beard medium to sparse, body hair medium to sparse, baldness rare
    f. Prognathism: more pronounced than in other Australians
    g. Relation of face breadth to head breadth: cephalo-facial index often over 100
Distribution: Northern Australia: districts adjacent to Gulf of Carpentaria, Arnhem Land

3. Tasmanoid
Characters:
    a. Stature: short, averaging 155.8 cm.
    b. Head form: all dimensions smaller than in other Australians; head relatively a little broader than in other types, averaging 73.5
    c. Face form: all dimensions reduced; relatively short
    d. Skin color: averaging darker than Murrians, lighter than Carpentarians
    e. Eye color: predominantly dark brown
    f. Hair form: oftenest curly (45.1 per cent), very crisp, pseudo-frizzly mops
    g. Hair quantity: beard and body hair relatively sparse
    h. Ears: small, close-set, small lobes soldered or attached, Negritoid
Distribution: Dense rain forest refuge areas in Cairns and Atherton Tableland districts of Queensland

COMPOSITE RACE

(Predominantly Negroid)

TASMANIAN

(Negrito + Australian)

Characters:

1. Skin color: black or dark brown
2. Hair form: woolly to frizzly, sometimes pepper-corn
3. Hair color: black
4. Beard and body hair quantity: medium to abundant
5. Nose form: nasal index hyperchamaerrhine; very short, very broad, medium height; nasal tip excessively thick; alae flaring
6. Head form: usually dolichocephalic, or subdolichocephalic, averaging about 77; skulls broader and lower than those of Australians; parietal bosses more prominent; glabella and brow-ridges strong, but not so large as those of Australians; vault gable-shaped
7. Face form: very euryprosopic; even shorter than that of Australians, medium prognathism
8. Stature: No adequate data; 23 men said to range from 5 feet, 1½ inches to 5 feet, 7½ inches (about 156.2 to 171.4 cm.)
9. Body build: said to be well developed, muscular, prominent buttocks and abdomen, slender limbs

Distribution: extinct in 1879. Formerly Tasmania and probably most parts of Australian continent

THE AUSTRALIAN LOW-BROWS

Until the British began to send out colonists who "left their country for their country's good," a very out-of-date type of man shared the island continent with the incredible duckbill, the impossible echidna, a variety of vest-pocketed marsupials, and a kind of low bred cur called the "dingo." These native Australians have chocolate skins, wavy or curly black or dark brown hair, plentiful whiskers and hairy chests, skinny legs, long thin skulls with meager cerebral contents, receding frontal bones and great brow-ridges, thrusting jaws, and hollow-backed, wide-spread noses. They have a very primitive material culture, which includes inferior weapons of wood and stone, no pottery, no domesticated plants, and habitations hardly worthy to be called "huts." They are supposed to be innocent of any accurate knowledge as to how babies come, or at any rate, as to why they come, but this report, like that of Mark Twain's death, may be exaggerated. In spite of their material simplicity, the Australians have evolved such a terrifyingly intricate system of kinship and marriage rules, such a labyrinthine maze of kin behavior patterns, that only the most gifted of anthropologists can grapple with their social organization. Australian relativity like that of Einstein is beyond the man in the street. Australians seem to be too absorbed in their kinship system to bother about developing dwellings or other creature comforts. To an Australian, his kin is his cosmos, like the Guermantes family to the puny and nameless prig immortalized by Proust.[101]

In the earlier edition of this book, the opinion was expressed that the Australian is fundamentally an archaic White modified partly by admixture with the Tasmanian who preceded him in the island continent. The Tasmanian was considered to be primarily an Oceanic Negrito, modified, in turn, by a minor infusion of Australian White. It was also suggested that in the north of Australia there has been some accession of Negroid characters through immigration of Melanesian-Papuans. These speculations have now been verified by the Harvard-Adelaide Universities Anthropological Expedition of 1938–1939, conducted by Norman B. Tindale and Joseph B. Birdsell, which traversed 16,000 miles and studied 2,458 full- and mixed-blood Australians. These anthropologists recorded the presence of a pygmoid people with crisp curly hair, on the Atherton Tableland, in the rain jungles of Queensland, inland from Cairns, and identified them as modified descendants of a Tasmanoid (Negrito stratum).[102] In his analysis of 578 full-blood male aboriginals, Birdsell has been able to prove the existence of three types, in addition to composite or blended forms: (1) Murrian or Southeastern, a heavily built, light-skinned, higher- and narrower-nosed type, with longer face and heavier beard and body hair than in most Australian aborigines; (2) Carpentarian or Northern type: tall, linear, with Negroid legs, darker skin color, sparser hair, more pronounced prognathism; (3) Tasmanoid:

---

[101] For the benefit of those of my readers who are interested in Social Anthropology, I append the following, attributed to Dr. D. O. Grell of Kurnai College, Australia. I print it in small type, because it seems to me rather trivial.

ON THE SOCIAL ORGANIZATION OF THE ARUNTA
(Dedicated to William Lloyd Warner)

Under the spreading blue-gum tree the old Arunta squats,
What makes the gin ginniferate he little cares nor wots;
His duty to his uncle's aunt wholly absorbs his thoughts.
What mammy totes to totem spots, he vaguely but surmises,
And yet he thinks he knows it all, because he subincises.
He does not waste artistic taste in building habitations;
He rather strains his microus brains remembering relations.
He scares the gins with horrid dins by whirling a churinga,
A wooden thing tied to a string swung from his greasy finger.
Throughout his life he keeps one wife, oft hospitably lent
To traveling cousins by the dozens on family business bent.
Eugenic fear makes him adhere to strict exogamy,
With sometimes, perhaps, a genial lapse to promiscuity.
Then strive and wive, old Platyrrhine, with Antipodal unction,
Though cicatrized and subincised, you've made our science function!

[102] Tindale and Birdsell, "Tasmanoid Tribes," p. 9.

very short stature, near frizzly hair, all head dimensions reduced, bulbous Negroid forehead, small Negroid ear.

Evidently the Murrian type, which is found in the south and southeast, is nearest to the archaic White prototype and least changed by Tasmanian admixture. Individuals of this type frequently look like rather coarsely bred, bulbous-nosed, low-browed Europeans, of massive build. The Carpentarian type has still bigger brow-ridges, lower forehead, more prognathism, and, in general, a much more primitive appearance. It is the closest to the Australoid types sometimes observed among the Papuans of New Guinea, and it has undoubtedly received small trickles of New Guinea Negroid blood. The Tasmanoid type is indisputably a pygmy Negrito type with some Australian admixture.

In the arid interior of Australia is Birdsell's Desert Type, a local specialized blend of Murrian and Carpentarian, which has furnished both the scientific and the general public with their idea of the conventional, "typical" Australian aborigine. It is an environmentally impoverished, inbred type that has attained a status of panmixia not realized in other parts of Australia, owing to the mechanisms of isolation. While mostly intermediate between the Murrian and Carpentarian types, it has some exaggeratedly Australoid features, such as extreme shortening of the face, reduction of head breadth relative to face breadth and forehead breadth, and excessive linearity of body build. The intriguing phenomenon of Australian juvenile blondness is centered in the western desert area.

Birdsell [103] thinks that the first wave of peoples to reach the Australian continent were pure Oceanic Negritos who spread over the whole area and reached Tasmania in the Upper Pleistocene. Then came the archaic White Murrian element, which spread through the grass lands and entirely absorbed the Negrito population except in some marginal, rain forest areas. The third and final wave to reach the Australian mainland were the tall, linear, dark-skinned Carpentarians, who came fairly recently and were still in process of infiltrating from the north when the Whites arrived in the nineteenth century. They never reached the lower Murray basin and the coastal strip behind the eastern highlands. Birdsell regards the Ainu of Hokkaido as the closest living group to the Murrian stock and thinks that, if the divergent racial adulterants that have modified Ainu and Murrians, respectively, are discounted, they are very close together. It is not his opinion that the Murrian stock is a direct derivative from the Wadjak or earlier Soloensis types of Java, because

[103] Birdsell. *Trihybrid Origin of the Australian*, pp. 213–232.

he regards the Murrian skull formation as clearly neanthropic and not palaeoanthropic, although a strain of the latter probably exists in the Murrian stock. He argues further that the Murrian stock must have left the Asiatic mainland before either Soloensis or Wadjak flourished in Java. These latter he sees as probably retarded island descendants of a common and more progressive mainland ancestral stock from which the Murrians developed. The closest affinities of the Murrian skulls are rather with the Old Man of the Upper Cave of Choukoutien.

Birdsell finds that something similar indicially and morphologically to the Carpentarian type can be isolated among the Veddah of Ceylon and such mainland aboriginal tribes as the Chenchu and the Munda. He thinks that no traces of this type are to be found in Indonesia, and if it is present in New Guinea, available anthropological material scarcely shows it.

The researches of Tindale and Birdsell demonstrate conclusively that the Australians are a composite race of archaic White stock with a considerable admixture of Negrito (through the absorption of Tasmanoids) and some modification as a result of the even more primitive Carpentarian element, which came last and brought, perhaps, added Negroid elements.

COMPOSITE RACE
(Predominantly White)

2. *INDO-DRAVIDIAN*
(Classic Mediterranean + Australoid (Veddoid) + Negrito + minor fractions of Iranian Plateau or Armenoid, Nordic, Mongoloid)
Characters:
1. Hair form: straight to frizzly, but predominantly wavy
2. Hair color: usually black
3. Skin color: varies from light brown to dark brown
4. Eye color: nearly always dark brown
5. Hair quantity: beard and body hair, usually medium to pronounced
6. Nose form: nasal index prevailingly mesorrhine (over 70); nose usually somewhat depressed at the root; root and bridge of moderate height and breadth; profile commonly straight; tip of medium thickness, alae somewhat flaring
7. Face form: usually narrow, medium length, leptoprosopic, little or no prognathism
8. Head form: cephalic index generally under 80; most group means dolichocephalic; moderate brow-ridges, rounded foreheads
9. Stature: variable, but usually medium to small
10. Body build: usually slender, linear; non-Negroid legs
Distribution: India and Ceylon
Morphological Types
1. **Classic Indo-Dravidian**

Characters:

As above but

a. Hair form: in general straight but inclined to waviness
b. Head form: usually dolichocephalic, average 74.3
c. Nasal index: mesorrhine, averaging 73
d. Stature: short, averaging 163.4 cm.

Distribution: Predominant element in lower strata of north Indian population, including to some extent the Punjab. This type approaches the Classic Mediterranean

2. Armenoid-Iranian Plateau

Characters:

a. Hair form: generally straight
b. Skin color: pale white to tawny brown
c. Head form: subbrachycephalic, averaging 81.8; high head with flattened occiput and often receding forehead
d. Face form: short face of medium breadth; total facial index averaging 86.6
e. Nose form: long, high-pitched, often convex; average nasal index 69.8
f. Body hair: beard and body hair well developed
g. Stature: medium, average 165.8 cm.

Distribution: Western littoral and Bengal

3. Indo-Nordic

Characters:

a. Hair form: generally straight
b. Hair color: usually black, sometimes dark brown
c. Skin color: from rosy white to light brown
d. Eye color: minority with gray blue or mixed eyes
e. Body hair: well developed
f. Head form: dolichocephalic, cephalic index averaging 73.1
g. Nasal index: averaging 67.1, leptorrhine
h. Stature: above medium, averaging 168.6 cm.

Distribution: In purest form in northwest Himalayan tribes: Kaffirs, Pathans, etc. Darker variants among Sikhs of the Punjab

4. Australoid (Veddoid)

Characters:

a. Hair form: wavy to curly
b. Skin color: dark chocolate brown, approaching black
c. Nose form: almost chamaerrhine, averaging 81.4 in Chenchus; root of nose broad and low
d. Head form: dolichocephalic (mean of 72.9 among Chenchus), prominent brow-ridges
e. Face form: short, narrow; moderately prognathous
f. Hair quantity: beard and body hair very sparse
g. Stature: medium, average 165 cm. in Chenchus

Distribution: Central and southern India—Bhils of the Vindhya and Chenchus of the Farhabad Hills

5. Negritoid

Characters:

a. Hair form: frizzly, or short spirals
b. Skin color: very dark
c. Head form: dolichocephalic, but with index rising as frizzly hair shortens into spirals

    d. Nose form: nasal index averaging 86.5 in Paliyan, generally chamaerrhine
    e. Lips: thick, puffy, everted
    f. Stature: short, under 160 cm., average 157.6 cm. in Paliyan and down to 152.9 cm. in other Travancore tribes
Distribution: Southern India: Kadars and Pulayans of the Peramabicullan Hills

THE INDO-DRAVIDIANS

The hundreds of millions who inhabit India are not physically homogeneous, yet various ethnic strains have fused to create a distinctive composite race that is of predominantly White origin. For this race the name Indo-Dravidian is employed here instead of the former term Dravidian. It is unfortunate that a mistake of Columbus has immovably attached to the American race the name that properly belongs to the peoples of India. "Dravidian" is a linguistic name, properly applicable to many of the darker and more primitive peoples of the southern part of the peninsula of India. The prefix "Indo-" is meant to signify that the composite race also includes the civilized peoples that speak Indo-Aryan languages, together with the Munda-speaking peoples (who, however, receive no recognition in the name of the composite race, which is long enough as it is).

The various racial types that have contributed to the Indo-Dravidian blend have long been recognized by anthropologists, but recently a survey and analysis of some 51 "racial groups" by Dr. B. S. Guha has put the entire subject of the racial composition of India upon a firmer factual foundation.[104] The basic types (for details cf. pp. 612–613) are: (1) a long-headed, short-statured, brown-skinned element predominant in the lower classes of north India and, to some extent, the Punjab (Classic Indo-Dravidian), an adulterated Mediterranean type; (2) in the western littoral and Bengal, a brunet, brachycephalic type with flattened occiput, convex nose, and heavy beard and body hair (Armenoid-Iranian Plateau); 3) a mixed Nordic type in the northwestern Himalayan area (Indo-Nordic); (4) a short-statured, curly-haired, chocolate-skinned type of dolichocephal, with prominent brow-ridges, depressed nasal root, broad nose, and prognathism (Australoid-Veddoid); (5) a submerged pygmoid strain with woolly hair and generally Negritoid features, in remote hill areas of south India; (6) intrusive Mongoloid types along the Himalayan borders and in Assam and northern Burma.

Guha's reconstruction of the prehistoric racial movements into India, based partly upon studies of the scanty skeletal material available, rest

[104] Guha, *Racial Affinities of the Peoples of India,* especially pp. lx–lxxxi.

upon the postulate that the earliest aboriginal occupants were Negritos, presumably followed and submerged by Australoid-Veddoid peoples. Numerous Palaeolithic implements have been found in India, but, up to now, no skeletal remains of Palaeolithic man, and, indeed, no skulls that can be safely attributed even to the Neolithic period. The human remains attributable to the first metal age of copper (Chalcolithic) have all been found in the sites of the Indus Valley civilization. They include skulls that approach the Classic Mediterranean and Upper Palaeolithic types of dolichocephals, and also a broad-headed skull, possibly Armenoid. Skulls from Iron Age sites are partially of the Australoid-Veddoid type, and at least one definitely Negroid cranium. Guha thinks that northwestern India from the beginning of the fourth millennium B.C. was occupied by long-headed, leptorrhine White stocks (probably Iranian Plateau and Classic Mediterranean) with a minority of Armenoids. In the Iron Age, an Upper Palaeolithic or Combe-Capelle type of primitive Mediterranean penetrated into south India. This stock may have introduced Neolithic culture in the north and subsequently may have been dislodged and driven into central and south India. Here they probably dispossessed the Australoid-Veddoid stock, who, together with the pygmoid element, were the aboriginal inhabitants.[105] These

[105] By dint of diligent search I have discovered some lines that purport to be a "poem" on the Dravidian race. I do not think much of the versification, which is wobbly, nor of the discreetly anonymous author, who seems to me to be a crude environmentalist. But here is the poem "as is":

> The heterogeneous Dravidian
> Has a skin which is black as obsidian,
> But sometimes, they say,
> It is cafe-au-lait,
> If he misses his sun bath quotidian.
>
> His locks may be wavy or curly;
> His form may be sylph-like or burly,
> His height great or stunted,
> His chin sharp or blunted
> According to meals late or early.
>
> Being somewhat absorbed in his caste
> He finds it essential to fast,
> Unless every victual
> Is cooked with due ritual,
> And so he gets thin as a mast.
>
> If he lives where the ozone is rare,
> His nose is constricted and spare;
> If he breathes air that's humid
> His beak gets quite tumid
> And his nostrils exceedingly flare.

Australoids or "pre-Dravidians" are identified by Guha as the "Nisadas" described by the Vedic Aryans as the hill- and forest-dwellers of India. The Nordic strain in northwestern India may have come in at the time of the "Aryan invasion," but certain of the earlier skulls of Mohenjo-daro might also be referable to this subrace.

COMPOSITE RACE
(Predominantly White)

3. *POLYNESIAN*
[Brunet White (Indonesian) + Mongoloid + Melanesian-Papuan]
Characters:
1. Hair form: wavy, rarely curly
2. Hair color: black, rarely reddish
3. Skin color: yellow brown
4. Head form: cephalic index usually over 80, but groups average from 74.3 to 86.5. Foreheads usually high, sloping, rather narrow; brow-ridges and glabella moderately to well developed; occiput usually rather flat and steep
5. Face form: usually wide, long, and heavy, but sometimes narrow and long. Malars moderately prominent, with some fatty padding
6. Nose form: usually long, rather broad, medium to high; straight in profile, less often convex or concave; root generally depressed; tip rather thick and elevated; alae full but not excessively flaring
7. Eyes: recessed, lids heavy, opening biconvex, sometimes slight internal fold; color medium to dark brown
8. Lips: integumental and membranous lips rather full, but not Negroid
9. Beard and body hair: always sparse, but not as meager as in Mongoloids and Negroids
10. Stature: usually tall, over 167 cm., but group means range from 167.5 cm. to 174.7 cm.
11. Body build: usually broad, muscular, mesomorphic, with tendency to corpulence
Distribution: Polynesian islands of the Pacific: Hawaii, Society Islands, Tonga, New Zealand, Samoa, etc.

THE COMELY POLYNESIANS

Polynesia is the name given to the islands of the middle Pacific scattered in groups or singly over this vast ocean. Most of these islands are included within an equilateral triangle of which the Hawaiian Islands form the apex, Easter Island the eastern angle of the base, and New Zealand its western basal point. This triangle measures about 5,000 miles on a side. To reach these islands, which are often separated from each other by hundreds of miles of open sea, primitive man had to be a skillful navigator. Polynesia must then have been peopled at a comparatively late period of human history. Palaeolithic man could never have lived there.

The inhabitants of Polynesia today constitute one of the tallest and finest-looking races of the world. They average in stature about 173 cm. In general, their skin color is yellow brown, their hair wavy and black, their head form brachycephalic, their features of moderate coarseness, and their body build sturdy, inclining to corpulency. But they show clearly the variability they owe to their composite origin. Skin color ranges from almost white to a dark brown, head form from dolicho- cephalic to brachycephalic; faces are sometimes broad and rather short but often very long and narrow; noses may be slender and high, or broad, short, and concave; the hair is prevailingly wavy, but sometimes straight and even frizzly.

Examining any considerable number of individual Polynesians, one notices some who show Mongoloid features, others in whom Negroid traits are apparent, others who approximate an European type, and a majority in whom all of these racial characteristics are blended into a harmonious and pleasing whole, distinct from the type of any of these three primary races. It is quite plain, then, that this race is made up of some sort of Negroid, Mongoloid, and White mixtures. The component elements, doubtless, have varied in their proportions in the different island groups. Polynesians are not nearly as Mongoloid as Malays and rather more Negroid than the American Indians.

However, a careful consideration of Polynesian features in the light of what is known of the behavior of Negroid and Mongoloid characters in racial crosses suggests that the White strain in this composite race must be much stronger than either of the other two elements, in spite of the apparent smoothness of the blend and the absence of segregates or re- combinations of the parental types.

None of the Negroid features that are ordinarily persistent, if not dominant, in crosses of approximately equal parts of Negro and White are apparent in most Polynesians. These are: frizzly hair, flaring alae and frontally directed nostrils, alveolar prognathism and pronounced lip eversion, relatively short trunk and long legs with attenuated calves. Similarly, the ultra-Mongoloid features ordinarily dominant in crosses with Whites are conspicuously absent. These are straight, coarse hair; narrow, slit-like eye opening with internal or complete Mongolian eye fold; low broad nasal root and concave low nasal bridge; extreme lateral and frontal jut of malars with heavy fatty padding; weak, pointed chin. Of course, there are occasional faint Mongoloid and Negroid sug- gestions in many if not most Polynesians, but they are not strong enough to indicate any but minor infusions of the blood of those races.

Crosses of Europeans with Polynesians, such as the descendants of the mutineers of the Bounty and Tahitian women, studied by Shapiro, are much more European in their physical characters than would be possible if the cross did not involve an already predominant White strain on the Polynesian side. On the other hand, crosses of Polynesians with Chinese in Hawaii are not as markedly Mongoloid as would be expected if the Chinese strain were reinforced by a strong Mongoloid element in the Polynesian. Finally, the natives of Fiji, who are the results of a Polynesian-Melanesian cross, in spite of dark skin and frizzly hair, seem to preserve an essentially White type of body build and features which are not markedly Negroid. This would hardly be the case if a strong Negroid strain already existed in the Polynesians.

There are two main theories as to the origin of the Polynesian race. One attributes the mixture which gave rise to this group to crossings of Indonesians, Mongoloids, and Negroids in the islands to the westward— Melanesia, Micronesia, and the Malay Archipelago. According to this theory, an Indonesian or fundamentally Mediterranean White group set out from Asia and in migrating eastward picked up certain Mongoloid and Negroid strains which they brought to their distant Pacific island homes. That is to say, they arrived a ready-made composite race. The other theory, ably expounded by Dixon, derives the Polynesian race from a succession of migration waves passing eastward from the Asiatic continent. He postulated, first of all, a settlement in Polynesia of a mixed "Melanesian" folk, primarily dolichocephalic, Negroid, with perhaps a dash of "Caspian" (fair dolichocephalic stock). These came from Melanesia. Then much later there came from the north a small number of long-headed invaders of "Caspian" (Nordic?) stock who first reached Samoa and Tonga and then penetrated as far as Easter Island. Finally, as late probably as the early part of the Christian era, there came, perhaps by way of Micronesia, an important body of invaders characterized by round, hypsicephalic heads and narrow noses (Dixon's "Alpine" type). These were probably mixed Mongoloids.

In favor of the multiple migration theory is the fact that the cranial evidence derived from old Polynesian graves seems to show a priority of dolichocephalic and rather Negroid-looking skulls, although brachycephalic and seemingly non-Negroid crania also occur. The populations of these islands today are predominatingly round-headed. The diversity of cranial types in the old graves is greater than one would expect from the present day population, if the ancestors of the latter had arrived in a blended state rather than in successive waves of peoples who interbred in the different islands.

The Polynesians in their consistently high stature differ markedly from the Indonesians, Malays, and other Oceanic stocks in which blends of Negroid, Mongoloid, and White have taken place. Shapiro, the leading student of the physical anthropology of Polynesians, has recently discussed the range of variation of measurements and indices in 26 Polynesian groups.[106] He finds that stature, face breadth (bizygomatic), relation of forehead breadth to head breadth (fronto-parietal), and relation of jaw breadth to forehead breadth (zygo-frontal) show a very restricted range over the vast territorial expanse, suggesting that the earliest and latest immigrants shared a basic physical community. On the other hand, head length, head breadth, cephalic index, and possibly minimum frontal diameter vary in precise geographical patterns, showing clearly that the earliest arrivals, now squeezed out into the eastern margins, had longer and narrower heads and narrower brows than the later comers. Shapiro therefore thinks that Polynesia was peopled in successive migrations of essentially the same people who had been welded into unity in Asia, but that the later migrants differed from the pioneers in cephalic features, notably in being more brachycephalic. This, for the moment, is the last word on the Polynesian race question.

PRIMARY RACE

II. NEGROID

Sorting Criteria:

1. Hair form: woolly or frizzly
2. Skin color: dark brown to black
3. Hair color: black
4. Eye color: dark brown to black
5. Nasal index: 85 and over

Other Characters:

6. Nose form: bridge and root usually low and broad; short, profile concave or straight, rarely convex; tip very thick and usually elevated; alae thick and flaring; septum usually convex
7. Lip form: integumental lips thick, upper convex; membranous lips usually puffy and everted, marked lip seam
8. Facial protrusion (prognathism): often marked in subnasal region
9. Face form: usually somewhat short in unmixed forms, with malars more prominent than in Whites, chin rounded and receding
10. Head form: prevailingly dolichocephalic with projecting occiput and rounded forehead; brow-ridges small
11. Hair quantity: usually short on head, sparse beard, little body hair
12. Ear form: usually short wide ear, with narrowly rolled helix and little or no lobe
13. Upper extremity: relatively long forearm, relatively short thumb
14. Lower extremity: usually relatively long lower leg, poorly developed calf, projecting heel, low foot arch
15. Pelvis: relatively narrow

[106] Shapiro, "Physical Differentiation in Polynesia," pp. 1–8.

16. Breast form (female): usually conical
17. Buttocks (female): usually less projecting than in Whites
18. Blood group: usually very high in O, low in A and B
19. Sweat glands: more numerous than in Whites
20. Palmar main line formula: usually 7.5.5—

PRIMARY SUBRACES

1. AFRICAN NEGRO (NEGRITIAN, FOREST NEGRO)

Sorting Criteria: **Same as above, 1–5**
Other Characters: Usually as above, 6–20
    a. Stature: extremely variable; in the rain forest of the western Sudan
       and Congo basin usually averaging from 165 cm. to 169 cm.; in the
       more open parkland and savannah areas of the Sudan, the Lake
       Region, and South Africa, often 170 cm. and higher
    b. Body build: the broad-shouldered, barrel-chested, long-armed, short-
       legged build of the so-called Forest Negro type is, apparently, an indi-
       vidual, constitutional variant and not a racial character. Relatively
       long arms are characteristic of all types, but long legs and short trunk
       of the taller types
Distribution: Sudanese and Bantu in western and central Africa, and in
    South Africa, except in Shari, Chad region, Upper Nile basin, and some
    parts of East Africa

2. NILOTIC NEGRO

[Probably has a small infusion of Hamitic (Mediterranean) blood]
Sorting Criteria: **Same as above, 1–5, except**
    a. Stature: over 170 cm. (averaging about 178 cm.)
    b. Cephalic index: under 76 (averaging about 72)
    c. Skin color: black or bluish black
Other Characters:
    d. Facial protrusion (prognathism): much reduced, often absent
    e. Nose form: probably less platyrrhine (broad-nosed) than ordinary
       Negro type
    f. Relative sitting height (height sitting as a percentage of stature: no
       adequate data, but, in view of long legs and short trunk, must average
       48 or less
    g. Lips: probably less thick, puffy, and everted than in ordinary Negroes
Distribution: Upper waters of the White Nile, especially the marshy (sudd)
    region, also upper course of the Blue Nile. Typical Nilotics are Dinka,
    Shilluk, Nuer, Lango, Acholi, Bari
    Shari Subtype
Characters: Same as ordinary Nilotics except
    a. Cephalic index: over 76 (averaging about 80)
Distribution: Shari basin of central Sudan. The best known of this type
    are the Sara, with average cephalic indices from 79.9 to 82.5 and aver-
    age statures from176.8 to 181.7 cm.

3. NEGRITO

Sorting Criteria:
    a. **Hair form: woolly, sometimes growing in pepper-corns or spiral**
       clumps
    b. **Hair color: black**
    c. **Skin color: dirty yellowish, medium brown, more rarely chocolate**
       brown

d. Stature: less than 150 cm. (4 ft., 9 in.) except when mixed

Morphological types

Infantile

Characters:

    a. Head form: subbrachycephalic, 80 or over; high with vertical forehead and little or no brow-ridges; frontal bosses prominent

    b. Face form: short, broad

    c. Nose form: narrow root; very broad, low bridge, usually concave; base of nose very broad, tip thick and directed upward; nostrils round; alae flaring

    d. Lip thickness and eversion: moderate, mouth narrow

    e. Skin color: in Africa darker than adultiform subtype—brown, eyes somewhat black

    f. Stature: somewhat taller than adultiform type

    g. Beard and body hair: sparse, but more abundant than in Negroes

    h. Body build: narrow shoulders; short trunk, often pot belly; forearms relatively shorter than in adultiform type

Distribution: Congo forest area, Andaman Islands, Malay Peninsula, Philippines, and probably interior of New Guinea

Adultiform

Characters:

    a. Head form: mesocephalic, usually under 80; low head with projecting occiput, forehead more receding, often with shield-shape central eminence, moderate brow-ridges

    b. Nose form: narrow nasal root, with low bridge broadening to funnel-shape; enormous tip, often depressed; alae very flaring, but nostrils not frontally visible; nasal index often over 100

    c. Face form: long and narrow, very receding chin

    d. Lips: upper integumental lip very long and convex; upper membranous lip very thin, lower thick; mouth slit very wide

    e. Skin color: usually grayish yellow to light brown (in Congo forests)

    f. Eye color: medium to light brown

    g. Beard and body hair: moderately developed; reddish fuzz sometimes observed on body

    h. Body build: broad shouldered, muscular; broad, very high pelvis; long torso, short legs, long arms; big hands and feet

Distribution: Congo forest area; probably also in Malay peninsula and interior of New Guinea

COMPOSITE RACE

(Predominantly Negroid)

1. MELANESIAN-PAPUAN (OCEANIC NEGROID)

(Negrito + Australoid + convex-nosed Mediterranean + minor fractions of Malay and Polynesian)

Characters:

1. Hair form: usually frizzly, sometimes tightly curled or even wavy
2. Hair color: black, oftener dark brown, sometimes reddish—"gingery," "foxy"
3. Skin color: medium to dark brown, rarely black
4. Eye color: dark brown to black
5. Facial protrusion (prognathism): not marked, sometimes absent
6. Lip thickness and eversion: never excessive, usually moderate

7. Beard and body hair: usually much thicker than in African Negro
8. Nose form: variable; the excessively thick-tipped, hyperchamaerrhine African Negro nose probably does not occur
9. Head form: very narrow, high, gable-roofed skulls common, round-heads also commoner than in African Nero
10. Extremities: typical Negroid elongation of forearms and lower legs, meager calves, low-arched feet
11. Stature: usually low, averaging less than 165 cm.

SECONDARY SUBRACES

1. PAPUAN
Characters:
    a. Hair form: oftenest frizzly, but lesser degrees of curve are common
    b. Hair color: oftener dark brown or reddish brown than dead black
    c. Skin color: medium to dark brown, rarely black
    d. Nose form: convex with thick, depressed tip and flaring alae, convex septum—"the pseudo-Semitic nose," not excessively chamaerrhine, nasal root depressed
    e. Hair quantity: beard and body hair often moderately to pronouncedly developed; frontal baldness common in males
    f. Brow-ridges: often heavy and continuous
    g. Forehead: narrow, high, rounded and sloping
Distribution: New Guinea and other islands of Melanesia, Papuan languages are oftener interior than coastal, but the subrace is not coterminous with the language

2. MELANESIAN
Characters:
    a. Hair form: usually frizzled into a mop
    b. Nose form: nasal root deeply depressed, nose often funnel-shaped, broad, low-bridged, profile straight, concave, or undulating; tip thick and elevated, nostrils circular, directed forward; nasal index higher than in Papuan subrace
    c. Head form: variable but oftener mesocephalic or brachycephalic than in Papuans, forehead wider and lower, brow-ridges less developed
Distribution: Somewhat more widely distributed in Melanesia than the Papuan subrace

THE FAR-FLUNG NEGROIDS

Narrow heads and wide noses, thick lips and thin legs, protruding jaws and receding chins, integument rich in pigment but poor in hairy growth, flat feet and round foreheads, tiny curls and big smiles—these are outstanding features of the specialized Negroid division of mankind. The Negroid races are concentrated in two widely separated areas of the Old World, namely tropical Africa and Oceania. The Negroes proper are in Africa, the composite Melanesians in New Guinea, and the pygmies or Negritos are in both areas.

The purest type of African Negro, called by Sir Harry Johnston, the "Forest Negro," is found along the coastal regions of West Africa from the Senegal river southward to the southern boundary of Portuguese

West Africa. Inland, this type predominates in the Niger Basin and in the vast area drained by the Congo and its tributaries, and is well represented in the eastern Lake region. It is especially notable for its extreme facial protrusion, its broad flattened nose, puffy and everted lips, its occasionally massive torso, invariably long arms, and relatively short legs. These Negroes have great talents for iron-working, metal-casting, and carving in wood and ivory. They are gifted in music and the dance and have evolved bloody despotic governments and decidedly unpleasant religions.

In the head waters of the Nile and in the Lake region, this type has mostly given way to a very elongated and slender, straight-faced variety of Negro, which is called the Nilotic subrace and has almost certainly some small infusion of Mediterranean White blood which has had the effect of increasing its stature, attenuating its body build, and in general modifying its type away from that of the pure Negro. In East Africa and southward to the Cape of Good Hope, the Bantu-speaking tribes also show frequently traces of admixture with some non-Negroid stock, which manifests itself particularly in the females in what Europeans consider better figures—more ample calves, thighs, and buttocks, and breasts hemispherical in shape rather than conical. The most of the Horn of Africa is occupied by mixed Negroid peoples sometimes dignified by the name of the "Ethiopian race," and showing in lighter skin color, finer cut features, and less woolly hair, evidence of the strain of hawk-nosed Mediterranean that has been mixed up with the coarser Negro type. The slender Negroid types are prone to a pastoral, cattle-breeding life, while the heavy-set, prognathous Negroes prefer agriculture and craftsmanship.

The pygmies are scattered in small groups through the Congo forests, have no language of their own, and are usually attached as hunters or pets to the full-sized agricultural Negroes of their district. They know no agriculture, have no domesticated animals, and are generally in about as primitive a state as can be imagined.

In the Pacific area, the pygmies or Negritos are found on the mainland in the Malay Peninsula (the Semang), and probably as mixed remnants in some of the hills and jungles of south India. They are the sole native inhabitants of the Andaman Islands in the Bay of Bengal, west of the Malay Peninsula; are found in the interior of New Guinea, and in certain of the Philippines, especially northern Luzon. Probably Negrito remnants occur elsewhere in the less known parts of Melanesia and the Malay Archipelago, but they have not been identified.

The full-size Negroids of Oceania are absent from the mainland of

Asia and from the Philippines and the larger islands of the Dutch East Indies. They appear in obviously mixed forms as substrata of the populations of the islands between New Guinea on the east and Java and Celebes on the west. Apart from the Negritos, they are in full occupation of the great island of New Guinea. They also exclusively inhabit the other island groups of Melanesia: the Admiralty Islands, the Bismarck Archipelago, the Solomons, the Santa Cruz Islands, New Hebrides, et cetera. In Fiji, they are mixed with Polynesian strains, and probably also in the Marshall Islands.

The question of the origin and migrations of Negroid stocks is one of the most difficult in the whole field of man's racial history and has to be discussed from several aspects: (a) unity or diversity of the Negritos and their relationship to their full grown brothers in Africa and Oceania; (b) the relation of African Negroes to Oceanic Negroids; (c) fossil evidence bearing upon all of these questions; (d) the significance of geographical distribution.

Recent researches have clarified, to some extent, the question of the physical composition of the pygmies. In Africa certainly, and in Asia and Oceania without much doubt, the Negritos consist of two distinct types: infantile and adultiform. Both types have woolly hair, bulbous foreheads; broad, flat noses, and moderate to small prognathism. The infantile type is round-headed, or nearly so; has a short broad face, with a very low-bridged, concave nose, nostrils directed forward, and wings flaring, but tip not excessively thick; lips full but not blubbery, almost no beard and body hair, narrow shoulders, pot belly; slender, short legs; medium to dark brown skin color. The adultiform type is nearly long-headed or quite so, with recessed eyes, longer, narrower face, tip of the nose remarkably thick, bulbous, and often depressed; upper integumental lip long and convex, membranous lips very thin and wide, rounded receding chin, broad shoulders, well muscled torso, lighter skin color—often yellowish—much more beard and body hair.

In the Congo forest, these two types occur together, but some pygmy groups incline more to the one than to the other. In Asia and Oceania, the infantile type seems to be exclusively represented in the Andaman Islands and in the Philippines, but Lebzelter and Schebesta claim that both forms occur among the Semang of the Malay Peninsula and, in the almost unknown pygmies of New Guinea, an exaggeratedly adultiform type of pygmy, almost pseudo-Australoid, certainly exists, together, probably, with the more usual infantile form.

As far as I can judge, the infantile type of Negrito is virtually the same in Africa and in Oceania, but I am not so sure of the identity of the adultiform types in these widely separated areas. The relationship of the two types is obscure, but it seems probable that the infantile or foetalized type represents the later development, perhaps as a result of mutations suppressing the grosser and more specialized features of the adultiform type. There can be little doubt that the Negritos sprang from a common source, probably somewhere in the intermediate area—Asia —and have been pushed out to marginal areas by larger, more powerful, and more highly evolved stocks. It is difficult to conceive of their origin either at the western or eastern extremity of their present distribution, but, if one were forced to choose, the Congo forest area would be a more plausible selection, in view of higher anthropoid evolution in this area and the probability of a differentiation *in situ* of the Forest Negro from the Congo pygmy.

In Africa, the burly, short-legged Forest Negro differs from the adulti-form pygmy in gross size, in somewhat lesser bulbousness of the forehead and bigger brow-ridges, in a more elevated nasal root and bridge and a less exaggeratedly bulbous tip, in the usual more specialized feature of thick, blubbery, and everted membranous lips, in somewhat darker skin color (not usually black, however), and possibly in scantier beard and body hair. The external ear of the Negro is like that of the pygmy, small and relatively broad, but it is much less embryonic-looking, more deli-cately sculptured.

The less primitive-looking African Negroes are more like the infantile pygmies in their nose form, dark skin color, and relative absence of body hair, but exaggerate the childish body build in short trunks, long legs, and meager calves. However, nearly all of the African Negroes tend to be markedly dolichocephalic, in contrast to the subbrachycephaly of the infantile pygmy type. There is a small center of marked brachycephaly among some enormously tall Negro tribes of the Shari Basin, but this limited round-headedness may be a local mutation. Again, even the African Negroes who are not of the coarse, Forest type have the thick everted Negro lips—apparently a mutation subsequent to, or coincident with, the development of the full grown variety of Negroes.

The scattered pygmy areas in the Congo region are surrounded by regions occupied by full-sized Negroes, many of them, however, of de-cidedly short stature (averaging between 155 cm. and 165 cm.) and show-ing pygmoid characters. Evidently, one of two phenomena, or perhaps both have occurred here: (1) an evolution of the Negro from the pygmy, (2) a hybridization of Negroes with pygmies.

Turning to the relation of the Asiatic and Oceanic pygmies to the large Negroids of that area, it is first noticeable that there are no Negroes on the mainland of southeastern Asia and not even any group that can be called Negroid (except the rather Negritoid or pygmy-like remnants in southern India). Nor are there any full-sized Negroes in the Andamans or the Philippines. Only in Melanesia are normal-statured Negroids to be found. Even these Melanesians and Papuans fail to show a full development of Negro features, such as are familiar in Africa. In the first place, Melanesian hair is apparently frizzly to curly, but never, or almost never, attains the minute spirals that are called wool. This woolly hair is without doubt an extreme specialization. Further, we do not find generally in Melanesia the characteristically full and blubbery, everted African Negro lips, although I have no doubt that they do occur sporadically. Nor is the marked total facial and alveolar prognathism of African Negroes in evidence. In the Melanesian type, the frizzled mop goes with an only moderately wide nose—of a generalized Negroidal type—a linear build (including the long legs and thin shanks), sparse beard and body hair, and a frequent infantile or even adult rufosity. Foreheads are not especially bulbous; brow-ridges are moderately developed. In the Papuan type, receding foreheads, massive brow-ridges, and grotesque, thick-tipped, hooked noses accompany hair that is often merely wavy or curly and not even frizzly—let alone woolly—and moderately to well-developed beard and body hair, often athletic build and better-developed calves.

The same alternative explanations with respect to the relationship of Negritos to Negroids present themselves in Melanesia: evolution or hybridization. In this case, contrary to the African situation, the hybridization process seems more probable; first, because Negro characters in Melanesians and Papuans are really only attenuated or adulterated Negrito features; second, because Melanesia is a way-station of Pacific migrations traversed by Australoids, Malays, Polynesians, Indonesians, etc.; third, because there is no evidence of a full-sized Negro type on the mainland where the Negrito undoubtedly evolved. Thus I am inclined to think that there are no real Negroes in Melanesia but only the hybridization products of Negritos with archaic Whites, Mongoloids, and fully evolved White subracial stocks.

However, thus far in our discussion, the whole question of the direction of descent between Negroes and Negritos has been disregarded, or rather, it has been implied that the Negrito represents the parent type. A few anthropologists think that the Negrito is a specialized and stunted off-shoot of the main Negro stem. Such an opinion disregards the position of the pygmies in marginal zones and refuge areas—a geographical circumstance that all careful students of racial movements consider irrefutable evidence of early distribution, as do also zoologists and palaeontologists in their appraisal of the spread and sequence of animal species. Again, Negritos invariably possess a far more primitive culture than the other peoples that surround them and, in Africa at least, are not known to have even a language of their own, although they do have their own language in the Andamans. If the Negritos are to be regarded as a later development than the Negroes, it is hard to see why they should have lost their language and all of the advanced elements of Negroid culture concomitantly with their decrease in bodily size.

The notion that man developed from a small ground ape into some sort of a homunculus or pygmy before he achieved the status of one of the giant primates has been popular among some students of human evolution. Kollman was an early proponent of such a theory, resting his case, to some extent, upon the analogy of the precedence of the small gibbon over the large anthropoids. In recent years, Marett has supported this supposition, which is improbable in the opinion of the author of this book. It has a little more plausibility if taken to apply to the immediate ancestry of *Homo sapiens,* anatomically modern man, as contrasted with the massive, coarse-boned palaeoanthropic specimens. For, without question, our species has undergone, to some extent, a process of refinement that amounts almost to feminization as contrasted with such specimens as Neanderthal man, Sinanthropus, and Pithecanthropus. However, transitions from the heavy skeletal structure to lighter builds occur in Upper Palaeolithic types of man without the intervention of any pygmoid form in the phylogeny. As a matter of fact, no fossil skulls of Negritos or of any sort of pygmies have been found up to now, although that proves little, since virtually no fossil finds of man of whatever kind have been made in the present habitats of Negritos. For that matter, as we have seen (pp. 375–376, 387, 392), no convincing fossil ancestor for the true full-sized Negro has yet been discovered, only two or three more or less dubious Negroids.

If we accept the present evidence of fossil forms (which seem to become more massive, even gigantic, the more of them are found), it is necessary to suppose that the Negrito has been evolved from a full-sized, heavy-boned neanthropic ancestor of an undifferentiated racial status or perhaps nearer to an archaic White than to any other existing racial stock. This foetalization and reduction may have taken place, as Marett has suggested, in response to a need for calcium and sodium economy in tropical forests where these minerals are deficient.[107] On the other hand, it may have been due to mutations not directly actuated by environ-

107 Marett, *Race, Sex, and Environment,* pp. 221–228.

mental stimuli (although it is hard to see how the biochemical change that is a mutation could originate in any other way). Some time later, in the park lands bordering the tropic forest area of the pygmy habitat in Africa, the full grown Negro may have developed from the pygmy, either through mutations in the reverse direction or by the stimulus of hybridization.

All of this is speculative stuff—hard to swallow. Any theory that can be devised to fit the present evidence is like the green spectacles that the owner put on his ass to induce him to eat shavings. It makes indigestible stuff look palatable, so that it can be gulped down. The ultimate result is likely to be a stomach ache.

COMPOSITE RACE
(Predominantly Negroid)

BUSHMAN-HOTTENTOT

(Negrito + Palaeolithic Boskop + minor fractions of Bantu Negro and Hamitic Mediterranean in Hottentots)

Sorting Criteria:
1. Hair form: tiny spirals growing in pepper-corns
2. Hair color: black
3. Eye color: dark brown to black
4. Skin color: yellow to yellow brown
5. Nasal index: over 85
6. Stature: under 160 cm.

Other Characters:
7. Cheek bones: Mongoloid lateral and frontal jut; fat padded
8. Eyes: slit-like, slanting, frequent internal epicanthus
9. Nose form: very broad, flat root; low, broad bridge; concave profile; thick, elevated tip; flaring alae
10. Forehead: bulbous, brow-ridges little developed
11. Face form: triangular; pointed, recessed chin
12. Head form: usually tending toward dolichocephaly; index under 78
13. Body hair: beard and body hair sparse or absent
14. Ear: frequent occurrence of short, square, heavily rolled Bushman ear devoid of lobe
15. Buttocks: marked steatopygia in females, slight in males
16. External genitals: horizontal penis; elongated labia minora
17. Lips: usually thick and everted with prominent lip seam

SECONDARY SUBRACES

1. BUSHMAN
Characters:
a. Stature: less than 150 cm. in unmixed individuals; average about 144 cm. (56.7 in.)
b. Head form: cephalic index usually over 75; head broader, lower, with more marked parietal bosses than in Hottentots
c. Face form: shorter, squarer, more euryprosopic than in Hottentots
d. Ear: Bushman ear commoner

e. Skin color: oftener yellow brown than yellow (?)
Distribution: Kalahari Desert, South Africa

2. HOTTENTOT
(Bushman + Bantu + Hamitic Mediterranean?)
Characters:
a. Stature: often exceeding 150 cm.
b. Head form: cephalic index usually 75 or under; head narrower, higher, with more projecting occiput than in Bushman
c. Face form: more elongate and triangular than in Bushman
d. Skin color: said to be lighter—yellower—than in Bushman
e. Steatopygia: more pronounced in Hottentot women; perhaps because of superior nutrition
Distribution: Southwest Africa; formerly also Cape Colony

THE FAT-BUTTOCKED BUSHMEN

The Bushman's stature is not great,
His jaw is quite prognathous;
Within his yellow, wool-starred pate
His skull is not capacious.
His seamed membranous lips are thick,
His malars are protrusive;
He sprays his words with dental click,
His speech is most effusive.
He squints with epicanthous eye
Across a nose prodigious;
He likes his ostrich-eggs quite high,
His women steatopygous.
—Droppings of a Moronologist.

At least fifteen thousand years ago, South Africa was peopled with dwarfish, yellow-skinned hunters who pursued the big game of the country with little bows and stone-tipped arrows, and painted or pecked on rocks and cave walls vivid scenes of the chase, realistic animals, and ceremonies of religious or secular import. After these little hunters waddled their diminutive wives, provided by nature with prodigious bustles, which doubtless undulated to their rhythmic gait and were admired in proportion to their size and mobility.

This extraordinary group of little people combines the most Negroid pepper-corn hair and the characteristically full and everted lips with the slant eyes, yellowish skin color, epicanthic folds, bridgeless nose, and projecting, fat-covered cheek bones of the Mongoloid. It possesses also the additional attraction of steatopygia, an enormous accumulation of fat localized on the buttocks and thighs and especially developed in the women, who also show a peculiar conformation of the external genital organs. Stature is little above that of the pygmies.

Every competent human taxonomist recognizes a basic affinity of the Bushmen with the Congo pygmies or Negritos. This is evidenced in body size, and, more importantly, in the pepper-corn hair—spiral clumps each consisting of a number of tiny coils not more than a millimeter in diameter, and separated from each other by bare spaces on the scalp. This pepper-corn hair is perhaps the most specialized hair growth known in the human species. It seems to be a retention of a condition frequently, if not usually, found in Negroid infants. The Bushman lips are thick and everted, not as markedly as in full-sized Negroes, but about to the extent seen in infantile types of Negritos. The special Bushman ear is clearly a modification of the short, broad, and apparently foetalized pygmy ear and is distinct from the finely cut Negro ear, particularly in that the Bushman ear has a very broad roll of the helix or outside rim, whereas that of the Negro ear is usually very narrow. The fatty accumulation on the buttocks and thighs, known as steatopygia, and enormously developed in the women, occurs at least occasionally in the Congo pygmies and in the Andamanese. Nowhere in living stocks is it so constantly and magnificently developed as in the Bushman-Hottentot race. On the whole, then, the Bushman shows undeniable Negrito affinities.

Some students want to dismiss the Mongoloid features of the Bushmen as "illusory." [108] This is merely "looking the difficulty squarely in the face and passing on." The Bushmen and Hottentots have more Mongoloid than Negroid features. Narrow eye slits with inner epicanthic folds, flat broad nasal root and low concave nasal bridge, laterally and frontally projecting malars with a fat pad covering them, yellow to yellow brown skin color—the Bushmen have all of these and lack no dependable Mongoloid criteria, save the coarse, straight hair. If one attempts to explain them as independent developments in the Bushmen stock, due to convergent evolution, he thereby qualifies himself as the world's champion camel-swallower. If the racial historian regards this astounding conglomeration of specialized Negritoid and Mongoloid features in a single race as the result of hybridization, he is faced with the difficulty of finding in Africa any Mongoloid stock, now, or at any earlier time, that could have contributed to the cross. In the first edition of this book, I tried to surmount this difficulty by postulating an early prehistoric cross of primitive Negritos with incipient Mongoloids, somewhere on the western slopes of the central Asiatic plateau. I had to pick that region because there are certainly no Bushman-like types in southeastern Asia or in Oceania; so the hybridization could not have occurred there, unless all of the mongrels subsequently trekked for Africa.

[108] Howells, *Mankind So Far*, p. 278.

I now feel obliged to reject this explanation entirely because it is incredible that such Bushman types would not exist in southeastern Asia today if they were the issue of a Mongoloid-Negrito cross. These very crosses have taken place frequently in that area. The Jakuns of the Malay Peninsula are supposed to have resulted from such a fusion (Malay-Semang), and they do not resemble Bushmen at all.

Judging from the statuettes found in European caverns from the Aurignacian onward, steatopygia was a marked characteristic of some of the late Palaeolithic peoples, and the skeletons of the old woman and boy of Grimaldi are certainly Negroid and not much unlike those of Hottentots or Bushmen of today. Further, the late Palaeolithic or Capsian art in Spain is so strikingly similar to the rock paintings made by the Bushmen in South Africa as to force the conclusion that both are the work of the same or closely allied peoples, although, probably, made at different times. Perhaps a stock ancestral to the present Bushmen-Hottentots was in northern Africa and a part of the Spanish Peninsula at the end of the glacial period, and subsequently withdrew through the whole length of the African continent, finally being reduced to its late prehistoric distribution over most of South Africa. An alternative theory is that this race occupied both North Africa and South Africa simultaneously, having invaded it from some other part of the world or having formed some center of dispersal in the African continent itself.

On the whole, I think it improbable that the ancestors of the Bushmen and Hottentot could have migrated from the extreme north of the African continent to the southern tip, passing through the tropical forest zone. It seems much more likely that they spread in both directions from some common point of departure such as might well be found in the Horn of Africa or in the Lake region of east central Africa. In any case, this race must have been differentiated before the end of the glacial period and in some unglaciated area.

If we accept the opinion of Sir Arthur Keith and most of the South African anthropologists, the Bushman-Hottentot stock of today has evolved from the Pleistocene, Middle Stone Age, large-brained Boskop type through such later types as the Fish Hoek man and the geologically recent Strandloopers (cf. pp. 394–395). This view is based upon similarity of cranial characters and postulates a radical reduction in the size of the brain among modern Bushmen and Hottentots as compared with Pleistocene ancestors. In all probability, a dwarfing of general body size is also involved. This process would be definite degeneration. Diminution of size is indeed a frequent phenomenon observed in long-continued inbreeding, particularly under adverse conditions of physical environment and, especially, with defective nutrition. If we accept the largely Boskopoid ancestry of the Bushman, we have to swallow also the degeneration theory, unless we suppose that the size reduction of the modern Bushman-Hottentots has resulted from a hybridization of the moderately-statured Boskopoids with pygmies from the Congo forest area or their relatives. A similar hybridization between Negritos and archaic Whites has produced, apparently, the small Tasmanoids of the Cairns rain forest area in northern Australia.

If the Bushman-Hottentot stock is merely a remnant of shrunken Boskopoid descendants, we have still to account both for the Negritoid and the Mongoloid features in these enigmatic, dwarfish, South African aboriginals. If we adopt the hybridization hypothesis, we may attribute woolly hair, thick lips, and perhaps steatopygia, together with the Bush-man ear, to the strong Congo pygmy strain. That would leave the Mongoloid features as a legacy from the Boskopoids. What there is of that fossil specimen looks neither definitely Negroid nor Mongoloid. Some students have thought it nearer a White type.

There is another curious complication in this African racial enigma. The Congo pygmies show a strangely high proportion of the B blood group (the gene q = .219 to .222) which is well up to Mongoloid or East Indian specifications, whereas full Negroes ordinarily run from about .11 to .16 in this gene and are much higher in O (gene r). The 268 Kung Bushmen typed by Pijper (Cf. Table 8, p. 549) are, on the contrary, very low in both A and B and consequently very high in O, like typical Negroes. However, these Bushmen must certainly be strongly mixed with Negro blood; there can hardly be that number of pure Bushmen in existence. Pijper's 506 Hottentots from Pretoria show the following gene frequencies: p = .220, q = .210, r = .590. That is very close to the Congo pygmy formula and may be duplicated among out-and-out Mongoloids, but also among Indo-Dravidians.

Now the Hottentots are ordinarily supposed to be Bushmen mixed with Bantu Negro and possibly some Hamitic Mediterranean White. Their head form is more Negroid than that of Bushmen and they are often somewhat taller. Yet they are yellower and possibly more Mongoloid in appearance than Bushmen.

The present writer can do little more than leave this racial mess in the lap of the reader, except to offer the following precarious suggestion. The ancestors of the Congo pygmies left the Asiatic area at a time prior to the full development of either Mongoloid or Negroid stocks and carrying incipient tendencies toward both of these specialized developments. The high B in the Congo pygmies and Hottentots shows Asiatic origin, but not necessarily Mongoloid inheritance. The ancestors of the Palaeolithic Boskopoids may also have carried both tendencies. In some way or other, the Congo pygmies went Negroid in their forest home, whereas the kindred stock in South Africa developed more clearly Mongoloid features disharmonically blended with Negritoid, either because of some environmental selection or because the Boskopoid strain in their ancestry reinforced the latent proto-Mongoloid potentialities derived from mixture with the pygmies.[109]

PRIMARY RACE

III. MONGOLOID

Sorting Criteria:

1. Hair form: straight, coarse texture
2. Hair color: black
3. Skin color: yellow or yellow brown
4. Eye color: medium to dark brown
5. Eye form: opening slit-like, slanting; upper lid with total Mongoloid fold, or internal epicanthic fold; heavy-lidded, fat embedded, not much recessed
6. Nose form: infantile, root very low, no nasion depression, bridge low and of medium breadth; tip short and medium in thickness; alae medium; profile variable, but usually concave or straight
7. Malars with strong frontal and lateral jut, usually covered with fat pad
8. Hair quantity: beard and body hair least developed of all races

Other Characters:

9. Body build: quite variable, but usually broad shoulders, long trunk, short extremities; calves of legs well developed
10. Stature: variable, but usually averaging under 167 cm.
11. Teeth: shovel incisors usually present
12. Sacral (Mongoloid spot): generally observable in early years
13. Blood group: usually high in B; r = .25 or more

PRIMARY SUBRACES

1. CLASSIC MONGOLOID

Sorting Criteria:

a. Cephalic index: 80 and over, averaging about 85
b. Eyefold: complete Mongolian

Other Characters: As above, 1–12

Distribution: Siberia, Amur river district, and sporadically in northern

---

[109] This laborious explanation seems to me to be even more implausible than my former simple suggestion that Bushmen are the result of an early Mongoloid-Negrito cross in Asia. However, it does take into account a considerable body of new palaeontological evidence from South Africa, as well as the blood group data. These accretions of knowledge muddy still further the already troubled waters. There is a cynical story about the old-fashioned taxonomist who found a new kind of bug that would not fit into his entomological classification. He solved his dilemma by stepping on the bug. Of course, Hottentots, Bantu, and Europeans have vied in the common cause of extinguishing the Bushmen, but their racial ambiguity will probably continue to haunt us.

China, Mongolia, Tibet. Typical peoples: Goldi, Giliak; Buriat and some other Mongol tribes; many northern Chinese, Tibetans, etc.
   2. ARCTIC MONGOLOID (ESKIMOID)
      Sorting Criteria:
         a. Cephalic index: less than 80
         b. Nasal index: usually less than 70, leptorrhine
         c. Skull vault: scaphoid, gable roof-shaped
         d. Face form: very broad, very long; exaggeration of Mongoloid jut of malars; everted gonial angles
         e. Stature: usually small, averaging under 160 cm.
         f. Eyefolds: complete Mongolian fold usually not found in adult males
      Distribution: Northeastern Asia and Arctic fringe of North America. Includes in addition to Eskimo, Chukchi, Kamtchadals, and probably Tungus and other Palaeoasiatics

THE INSCRUTABLE MONGOLOIDS

The questions: "What is a pure Mongoloid?" and "Where are the pure Mongoloids?" have vexed the author of this book over a long period of years and could not be answered satisfactorily in 1930. Research in Asia since that period has cleared up the matter, at any rate, to the partial satisfaction of the present writer. A "pure" Mongoloid is a person who presents the entire array of "spot" Mongoloid physical characters; that is, he is phenotypically pure, irrespective of what his ancestry may be. The required array of characters includes the eight listed as sorting criteria in the outline (p. 633). Groups or individuals with only part of this list of features are mixed Mongoloids of one sort or another. I completely disagree with the view of Howells [110] that Mongoloids with a full panoply of Mongoloid characters are to be regarded as "specialized" and all others who have this or that Mongoloid feature, but not all of them, "unspecialized." We are not presently in the primary race-making phase of man's evolution, nor have we been at that stage of the evolution of *Homo sapiens* for the past ten thousand years or more. Races that have been formed within that span, or are currently in process of formation, are secondary or composite races that result from the hybridization of the older primary stocks. There certainly was a period when most of *Homo sapiens* could be described as "generalized" or "unspecialized" in the sense that the members of the species carried a mélange of imperfectly differentiated physical traits—White features, associated with vague and incipient Mongoloid or Negroid tendencies. Certainly, this phase or period must have ended soon after the dispersal of the rudimentary species, *Homo sapiens*, from a common center to the outlying parts of the Eurasiatic land mass and to other

[110] Howells, *op. cit.*, pp. 250–251.

continents. The formation of the primary races was the result of isolation, inbreeding, the environmental selection of mutations within the
groups thus genetically circumscribed, and the chance dropping out
of characters. It was a phenomenon of sparse and widely separated
human stocks, not of vast populations impinging upon each other and
differentiating in little clusters within a vast area of continuous distribution. The numerical proliferation of mankind was not accelerated
until the development of agriculture and the domestication of animals
furnished a firm basis of subsistence for large groups, and the formation
of secondary races did not occur until expanding populations, aided by
the invention of devices facilitating transportation, began secondary
mass migrations that renewed the contacts between peoples that had
existed in the undifferentiated, early neanthropic phase before the
primary dispersals and formations of Negroids, Mongoloids, and Whites.
In my opinion the primary race-making phase ended at about the close
of the Pleistocene—say 15,000 to 20,000 years ago.

It is hard for me to understand how any physical anthropologists,
conversant with the multitudinous and, on the whole, very satisfactory
information gathered in the past score of years upon the results of
primary race mixtures and also upon the effects of backcrossing and
hybridization between composite races, can be so naive as to suppose
that in this promiscuous and thronged world persons who display a
disharmonic mixture of radically divergent racial characters can be
"unspecialized" or "undifferentiated." [111] The single possible exception
is the vestigial Bushman-Hottentot stock. Even here the possibility of
recent hybridization cannot be lightly dismissed.

Add to the data of race mixture the continually unfolding sequence
of archaeological discoveries in which an earlier and more primitive
racial (or at least) physical type underlies recent remains of different
culture and aspect and we have the physical types and the environmental
settings in which mixtures have taken place and composite or hybridized
types have arisen.

Peoples of the full-blown classic Mongoloid type are concentrated
in eastern Siberia along the Amur river, including such tribes as the
Goldi, Giliak, Koriak, and, farther in the interior, at least some of
the Mongols proper—notably the Buriats. The classic Mongoloid type
also occurs frequently among the northern Chinese, probably sporadi-

[111] For example, I am astounded at this statement by Howells (*op. cit.*, p. 253) with regard
to the people of China: "They do not, at any rate, appear to contain any element which is
not purely Mongoloid."

cally in Tibet, and, to a considerable extent, among such western Mongols as the Kalmucks and the Tourguts, and such northern Mongols as the Khalkas. However, there are, probably, some mixtures in most of these groups.

In addition to the brachycephalic Mongoloids, there is a long-headed group with fully Mongoloid characters in extreme northeastern Siberia, including the Tungus, the Chukchi, the Kamtchadals, and probably others. I can see no good reason for assigning the Eskimo to any separate classification of their own. As far as I am aware, they show no characters that distinguish them from the Arctic Mongoloid subrace. Particularly, the Eskimo and the Chukchi seem virtually identical craniologically and, probably, somatologically.

Explanations of the origin of the Mongoloid primary race include some of the wildest environmental fantasies that have been dreamed up by anthropologists. Here, for example, is the vision of Sir John Myres,[112] who in his own field of the history and archaeology of the Mediterranean tempers his brilliance with scientific caution and sticks closely to dependable evidence:

Rather the vast accumulation of loess, the deposit of countless dust storms, suggest a "continental" climate with wide variations, and the possibility of at least seasonal occupation by fleet grazing-animals, such as the horse. It is indeed to an intimate parasitic connexion with such an animal "host," in some such circumstances, that we have probably to ascribe the highly specialized type of man characteristic of this region now. The yellow skin-colour of the Mongoloid man gives him protective camouflage in sandy desert and dry-grass steppe; the structure of his straight, wiry hair, and its rarity except on the scalp, suggest adaptation to a continental climate; while its extreme length in both sexes serves to disguise the characteristic profile of the human head and neck, and approximate it to that of a quadruped seen from behind. From the rather prominent jaw combined with globular brain-case may be inferred long habituation of some food which minimized the pull of the muscles on the side-walls of the skull; and the only food which fulfils this condition is milk and its products, on which nomad Tartars still live almost exclusively: the absence of face-hair, the short concave nose with spread nostrils, the peculiar infantile lips, the wide flat face and obliquely set eyes, are adaptations we should expect if for ages this milk was absorbed direct from the udder; and the short legs of some Mongoloids, and poor development of the calf-muscles in all, suggest that, like Tartar infant nowadays, the parasitic proto-Mongol sat tight upon his host between meals, and shared its wanderings.

112 Myres, "Primitive Man," pp. 22–23.

Now if the reader can swallow this colossal tale, he would better close this book and seek his information on evolutionary subjects from Kipling's *Just So Stories* which explain animal adaptations quite as plausibly and much more amusingly than does this tick hypothesis of Mongoloid man. But it seems to me that the bed-time stories of the anthropogeographer, however diverting, contribute little of value to the intricate history of evolution.

Another line of interesting but somewhat fantastic speculation attempts to relate the genesis of the Mongoloid type to thyroid insufficiency. Acromegaly, a disease that involves a tumor of the anterior lobe of the pituitary and presumably excessive secretion of some of the hormones from that lobe, frequently causes gigantism, an enormous elongation of the face, and an excessively dolichocephalic head. On the other hand, a hypothyroid condition, as associated with goiter and cretinism and probably myxoedema, produces a physical type with long, heavy trunk; short, stumpy extremities; a very short broad head with bulging forehead and no brow-ridges; flat, concave nose; internal epicanthic eye folds, absence of beard and body hair, and rather straight, coarse head hair. More or less the same physical type occurs in the so-called Mongolian idiots, but these do not improve under dosages of thyroxin, whereas cretinism is virtually curable by this therapy.

Now, it is known that inland areas deficient in iodine are also the areas of cretinism and goiter. In fact, iodine deficiency seems to be the main cause of this endocrine pathology. So, it is easy enough to jump to the conclusion that the Mongoloid race has originated in some iodine-deficient, inland area of Asia and owes its brachycephaly, straight coarse head hair, scanty body hair, epicanthic folds, and all of the rest of its special characters to the fact that it is a pseudo-achondroplastic, hypothyroid race, developed, as Marett puts it, for "iodine economy." [113] If it could be established that all Mongoloids have low basal metabolism (a sign of thyroid insufficiency), this mineral deficiency theory would be considerably strengthened by the finding. However, results so far in the study of racial differences in basal metabolism are conflicting and inconclusive (cf. p. 541). The comparative sparsity of body hair in man has been guessed by many to be the result of an endocrine change in our protohuman ancestors, and it has been sugested by more than one person that human hairlessness economizes thyroid stimulus. Iodine deficiency leads to body hairlessness in animals, and Marett proposes to regard the long, coarse, straight hair of Mongoloid peoples (and also of the Himalayan ox) as economical of iodine. If iodine is responsible

[113] Marett, *Race, Sex, and Environment, passim.*

for cell proliferation, the larger the cell and the coarser the hair, the fewer hairs per unit of area will be required.[114] In this connection, also, we must not forget that the great ape of Asia, the orang-utan, is a kind of a Mongoloid in lack of brow-ridges, in presence of epicanthic folds of the eye, and long, straight, coarse body hair (although the body hair is abundant in orangs enjoying good health and adequate nutrition). Marett has brutally overworked the mineral deficiency theory as a main directive of evolution. Nevertheless, there may be something in it.

Recently a popular view of the differentiation of Homo sapiens into its three main races stresses the principle of retardation of growth or foetalization.[115] The idea is that the stocks retaining the most foetal or infantile characteristics in their adult life are the most advanced, and, possibly, the latest to be evolved. If we admit the correctness of this view (which is arguable, to say the least), the next question is to decide which race is the most foetalized. Bolk, in discussing this matter, points out that the Mongoloids have a foetal complex including brachycephaly, epicanthus, slight protrusion of the eyes (exophthalmus), and he might have added lack of development of body hair and some other characters. However, he considers the White race most foetalized in the suppression of pigmentation, retarded eruption of third molars, et cetera, and he judges the Negroes least foetalized because of black skin and infrequent suppression of third molars, et cetera. Yet he refuses to commit himself as to which race wins in this retardation contest. To my mind, these is no serious question of the primacy of the infantile Negrito in these respects. I should judge that both Mongoloids and Negroids have more claim to being called "foetalized" than any of the White subraces.

Weidenreich derives the whole process of refinement and lightening of the bones of the skeleton and skull in Homo sapiens from increase in the size of the brain relative to body bulk and the recession of the jaws. A great many of the elements of the bony reinforcement system become obsolete and disappear in this process of cerebralization. However, Weidenreich derives Homo sapiens from Sinanthropus, a coarse-boned, small-brained ancestor. His contentions as to features in Sinanthropus that foreshadow the Mongoloid have been discussed in connection with fossil man (cf. pp. 304–305) and are not convincing in the opinion of the present writer. Yet he is probably right in his view that the refinement of the skeletal framework is a phenomenon connected with the growth of the brain in the entire species of Homo sapiens.

114 Ibid., p. 161.
115 Bolk, "Origin of Racial Characteristics in Man," pp. 1–29.

We are still without a single geologically ancient find of man that is undeniably Mongoloid. The furor over the Chancelade skull (an Upper Palaeolithic specimen belonging to the French Magdalenian) still breaks out occasionally, but in a half-hearted way. The cranium does show some Eskimoid features, but these are considerably attenuated by Keith's discovery of an old photograph of the skull with the nasal bones (now gone) still intact. They were high-arched and beaky, not Eskimoid or Mongoloid. The imaginative theory, championed by Sollas and others, that the Chancelade man followed the reindeer northward in the glacial retreat and evolved into the Eskimo is hardly worthy of serious consideration. In the Upper Cave at Choukoutien, Weidenreich found another Eskimoid skull (long-headed, broad-faced, with sharply angled and jutting malars, and a slightly gable-shaped vault). It does not stretch the craniological imagination unduly to see in this specimen the prototype of an Eskimo female. However, the Old Man of the Upper Cave of Choukoutien, labelled "proto-Mongoloid" by Weidenreich, seems to me to be an out-and-out White. Hints of the coming development of Mongoloid features of the malars are not lacking in some of the Cro Magnon types and other skulls of the European Upper Palaeolithic, but whether they are rudimentary, latent, or due to early racial mixtures cannot be definitely decided. On the whole, they may well be incipient Mongoloid features in a mainly White strain. If we had the malars of the Piltdown skull (Eoanthropus), it is not improbable that some of these prototypical Mongoloid characters might be evident, judging from the conformation of the frontal bone.

It is probable that the Arctic Mongoloid type (best known in the Eskimo) may have emerged before a brachycephalic mutation took place in Mongoloid race, although it is generally supposed that the Eskimo represents the latest migration to the New World, and it is altogether certain that brachycephalic near-Mongoloids in some way by-passed the Eskimo into the New World.

COMPOSITE RACE
(Predominantly Mongoloid)
1. *INDONESIAN-MONGOLOID (INDONESIAN-MALAY)*
   (Mongoloid + primitive Mediterranean + Ainu + Negrito)
   Characters:
   1. Skin color: dark yellow brown, sometimes red brown
   2. Nose form: nasal index 80 and above, mesorrhine or chamaerrhine; nose usually low-bridged, concave with some root depression, alae flaring
   3. Hair form: usually straight and coarse, sometimes slightly wavy
   4. Hair color: black, but with occasional reddish tints

    5. Eye color: medium to dark brown, or almost black
    6. Lips: thicker than in Classic Mongoloids
    7. Prognathism: some degree of alveolar prognathism usually present
    8. Face form: Mongoloid conformation of cheek bones; faces shorter with squarer hinder jaw angles (gonial angles)
    9. Stature: under 165 cm., averaging from 155 cm. to 163 cm.
   10. Hair quantity: beard and body hair very sparse

SECONDARY SUBRACES

1. MALAY-MONGOLOID

Characters:

    a. Head form: cephalic index over 80, usually averaging 85 to 86; brow-ridges medium in development oftener than in pure Mongoloids
    b. Hair form: always straight
    c. Body build: very short and broad, mesomorphic
    d. Skin color: light yellow brown to dark yellow brown

Distribution: Indo-China, Thailand, Burma, Malay Peninsula, Dutch East Indies, Philippines, etc. This subrace includes most Japanese

2. INDONESIAN

Characters:

    a. Head form: cephalic index under 80, averaging about 78.5 mesocephalic dolichocephalic
    b. Hair form: usually slightly wavy
    c. Face form: narrower, longer, more oval than in Malay-Mongoloid subrace
    d. Nose form: higher, narrower, longer nose than in Malay-Mongoloid type; sometimes convex
    e. Body build: slender, linear
    f. Skin color: light red brown to medium brown

Distribution: Pre-Mongoloid groups in southern China, Indo-China, Burma, Thailand. Many interior tribes of Malay archipelago

THE PIRATICAL INDONESIAN-MALAYS

This highly composite race is particularly concentrated in the Malay Peninsula and in the Malay Archipelago, but many of the peoples of Indo-China, of Korea, and of Japan belong to types that may be included under this designation. The Indonesian type, often distinguished as a subrace, is generally considered to differ from the more mixed Malay type in its shorter stature, its tendency to dolichocephaly or mesocephaly, wavy hair, and less Mongoloid features, longer and narrower nose, and straighter eyes. The skin color is red-brown to brown and the hair is black. The Malay type is, on the contrary, distinctly brachycephalic with more prominent cheek bones, flatter and more concave nose, frequent Mongoloid eye, and coarser, straighter, black hair. The skin color is oftener dark than in the Indonesian type.

In the Malay Archipelago, generally speaking, the longer-headed and more wavy-haired Indonesian type tends to occur in the inland areas and the brachycephalic Malay type on the coasts. Dixon postulates for this region a succession of migrations somewhat as follows. The first inhabitants of these islands were a majority of "proto-Australoids" and a minority of Negritos. It is impossible to say which of these peoples came first from southeastern Asia, but one would incline to favor the priority of the Negritos. There arrived, considerably later, a flood of Negroid peoples, who absorbed, drove inland, or otherwise overran the more primitive populations. Soon afterward there came into western Indonesia long-headed, wavy or straight-haired peoples who were the ancestors of the Indonesians. Dixon believes these to have been a blend of Caspian ("Nordic") and Mediterranean. To me it would seem more probable that they were Mediterranean. They must have been mixed to some extent with the earlier Negrito, Australoid, and Negroid elements before reaching Indonesia. These long-heads of predominantly White stock, according to Dixon, seem hardly to have penetrated Melanesia or Australia, but reached by another route the islands of Micronesia and of central Polynesia. Next there came from southeastern Asia a population of short, yellow-skinned, straight-haired people, brachycephalic and frequently having Mongoloid eyes. These migrants pressed back into the interior the earlier population and made themselves masters of most of Indonesia. They are called by Dixon "proto-Malay." One gathers that they are supposed to have been mixed Mongoloids with some Negroid strains. Finally, at a time, according to Dixon, not much before the Christian era, there came from some portion of eastern or southeastern Asia the Malays themselves who are said to differ from the proto-Malays largely in having straighter, higher noses and a less frequent development of the Mongoloid eye. These were again a mixed Mongoloid people, but mixed with non-Negroid elements. All of this welter of peoples interbred in Indonesia to form the composite race lumped together under the name Indonesian-Malay. I am not convinced of the accuracy in detail of this account. But in general it seems undeniable that the earliest substratum of the population was Negrito-Australoid, the intermediate layer Indonesian (Mediterranean-like White), and the upper crust mixed Mongoloid (Malay). I take no stock in the issue of full-sized Negroids that Dixon and others wish to float on top of the Australoids and Negritos. My present opinion is that all Oceanic Negroids are mixed derivatives of the pygmy Negritos. Nor can I see the physical evidence for two waves of Mongoloids—proto-Malay and deutero-Malay—although some of the earlier Malay-Mongoloids probably became more mixed with ancient Negritic strains than later arrivals, and, correspondingly, some of the later Malays may have carried a fuller complement of Mongoloid features than their predecessors.

When the physical anthropology of the Malay Archipelago and of Melanesia has been properly done, I have little doubt that it will be possible to sort out in most of the island groups types representative of the earliest migrants (probably somewhat modified by admixture), together with all of the later types. Indeed, this has already been done in Australia, and in Java, where Nyèssen recognizes in the contemporary populations Australo-Dravidian, Negritic, and Mongoloid types, in addition to a "South European" element.[116] All of these strains are evident in the Philippines, both in skeletal remains and in the living population, although here again there is a dearth of large series of the living, carefully measured and adequately analyzed.

COMPOSITE RACE
(Predominantly Mongoloid)

AMERICAN INDIAN
(Mongoloid + Iranian Plateau + Australoid + very small Negritoid element)
Characters:

1. Skin color: yellow brown or red brown
2. Hair color: black, rarely dark brown
3. Eye color: dark brown to black
4. Hair form: straight, coarse; rarely wavy and of medium texture
5. Nose form: nasal index usually over 70; predominantly mesorrhine; nose very long, usually high-bridged and convex, but wide in the bridge; tip usually medium thick and depressed, alae rather flaring; lower, shorter noses occur in certain types
6. Face form: malars nearly always typically Mongoloid, but jaws deeper and chin more prominent than in typical Mongoloids; medium prognathism
7. Frontal region: brow-ridges and glabella strongly developed, foreheads more sloping than in typical Mongoloids
8. Mouth: lips thinner and mouth slit wider than in Mongoloids, but exceptions in some types
9. Beard and body hair: sparse
10. Eye folds: complete Mongolian fold lacking; internal fold rare except in women and children; external fold common
11. Teeth: shovel incisors very common
12. Blood group: usually nearly 100 per cent R, but erratic occurrence of very high A or considerable B
13. Palmar main line formula: predominantly 9.7.5.—

Morphological Types
  1. Brachycephals
     Sorting Criterion: **cephalic index 80 or over**
     Subtypes:
       Hawk-nosed

116 Nyèssen, *The Races of Java, passim.*

Characters:

a. Nose form: typically aquiline as in 5

b. Face form: broader and relatively shorter than in dolicho-cephals; malars more laterally jutting; otherwise identical

c. Body build and stature: stature varies from short to very tall; body build broad, squat; or broad and athletic in taller forms

Distribution: The commonest type in North America; perhaps also in the highland areas of Central and South America, where, how-ever, only the short, squat body build is found

Snub-nosed

Characters:

a. Nose form: broader, shorter, usually straight or concave in pro-file; alae flaring, nostrils frontally visible

b. Hair form: sometimes wavy

c. Lips: thicker integumental and membranous lips, especially lower lip; more eversion

d. Face form: more rounded, bony structure less apparent, chin much weaker

e. Body build: both tall and short; tendency toward obesity

Distribution: Sporadic in the North American area. The tall variant occurs among the Papago and other Yuman tribes of the South-west. Probably found among the Yaqui of northern Mexico and many forest tribes of Mexico and Central America. Area of char-acterization is, however, the Amazonian and Orinoco basins and most regions of South America east of the cordillera.

2. Dolichocephals

Sorting criterion: **cephalic index under 80**

Subtypes:

Hawk-nosed

Characters:

As in corresponding brachycephalic type, with longer, narrower faces, generally more linear (ectomorphic) body build. Possibly with more reddish brown than yellow brown skin color.

Distribution: Mostly in Eastern Woodlands area of the United States and Canada; sporadic elsewhere

Snub-nosed

Characters:

As in corresponding brachycephalic type, but with shorter, nar-rower face; heavier brow-ridges, depression of nasal root; marked platyrrhiny. Body build: linear; stature, short; skin color: dark yellow brown or brown.

Distribution: This type crops up in individuals in most parts of the New World. No group known to consist of a majority of this archaic type.

THE NOBLE REDSKINS

Progress toward a scientific subdivision of the American aboriginal race into clearly marked morphological types (phenotypes), the map-ping of the present distribution of these types, and their correlation with the craniological types revealed by archaeological excavations has been inexcusably retarded. The responsibility for this taxonomic lag could be laid squarely upon the shoulders of two or three great pioneers in the study of the physical anthropology of the American Indian, if it were not for reluctance to substantiate the cynical remark put by Shakespeare into the mouth of Mark Antony: "The evil men do lives after them; the good is oft interred with their bones." An almost fanatical adherence to three tenets of faith or prejudice motivated this obstructive attitude: (1) the sacred unity of the American race; (2) the denial of geological or any considerable recent antiquity of man in America; (3) the conviction that variations of physical type within the American aborigines are due to environment or to genetic factors that have neither racial nor historical significance.

If we try to approach this subject without prejudice and consider the possibility of subdividing the present American Indian into constituent types, we may be able to reach some limited, but comparatively incontrovertible, conclusions. Firstly, there can be no denying that a generally Mongoloid wash of soft part features is present in all contemporary Indian groups. Of these, the most consistently evidenced are yellow brown skin color and straight, coarse, black hair, together with the natural concomitant of purely dark eyes. The skin color is not in itself definitively Mongoloid, and it varies from an almost coppery reddish brown to some rare dark brown shades (particularly in the Yaqui of northern Mexico). However, all of the skin color variations of Indians fall within the Mongoloid range (except in cases of supposed partial albinos). Hair color is not so constant. Some tribes of the Southwest show a fair proportion of very slightly wavy hair that is dark brown or may have minor reddish tones in it. Such deviations from the Mongoloid norm are certainly commoner in Mexico, Central America, and South America, but data on their frequency are unfortunately scanty. Almost without exception, the growth of beard and body hair in American Indians is so sparse as to conform to Mongoloid (or Negroid) specifications.

The next important feature is the Mongoloid eye, marked in its fullest development by a complete fold of the upper eye lid, obscuring the free border of the lid from the outer to the inner corner, inclusive at both ends. This complete Mongoloid fold does not occur, to my knowledge, in American Indians, and I am not sure that it is found very often even in the Eskimos, whom I now judge to be out-and-out Mongoloids. An attenuated form of the upper eye fold, covering the inner corner or canthus, and loosely known as "the Mongoloid fold," is only moderately common in American Indians; it occurs often in women and children but can hardly be stated to be characteristic of Indians as a race. Moreover, the eyeball in Indians is usually deep set and not shallowly placed and embedded in fat as in model Mongoloids. The eyelids are not especially thick, the eye slits neither narrow nor slanting. In fact, the American Indian really has not a Mongoloid eye, although persistent inner epicanthi may be assumed to indicate Mongoloid admixture, as in Europeans.

The Mongoloid nose is very flat at the root and apparently very broad, although actually most of this breadth is not in the nasal bones themselves, but in the flattened frontal processes of the maxillae (upper jaws). The bridge is also characteristically low, but not especially broad; the nasal profile is predominantly concave, the tip infantile and upturned, the wings only moderately expanded, and the nostrils directed forward. Now, this kind of a nose is conspicuously absent in American Indians, except perhaps in some women and children. Several varieties of nose form occur, but none is Mongoloid. The only Mongoloid feature of Indian nose, best seen in skulls, is the lack of any depression at nasion (the juncture of nasal bones with the middle or glabellar region of the frontal bone). Even this feature is not invariable.

The Mongoloid face derives its characteristic flat appearance from a combination of skeletal structure and overlying soft parts. The malars or cheek bones are ordinarily marked in their lateral flare, in their anterior jut, and their sharp angulation (cf. p. 633). Instead of being stream-lined or rounded back below the orbits, they are squared (high cheek bones). These Mongoloid malars are usual in American Indians but absent in some of the crania from earlier archaeological strata. In the full Mongoloid type, a heavy fat pad usually overlies these squared-off malars, accentuating the forward thrust of the malars and often obscuring in profile the low root of the nose. This feature is ordinarily absent from the American face (but probably occurs as an infantile and feminine feature). The Mongoloid forehead is usually smooth and devoid of strong brow-ridges; almost all American Indian crania have strong developments of these supraorbital rims of bone.

As far as I am aware, there is nowhere in the New World an Indian group the members of which appear definitely Negroid. The closest approach is among the Yaqui of northern Mexico, who combine very dark skin with predominance of jet black hair and black eyes, very broad noses with flaring alae; thick integumental lips and puffy everted membranous lips.[117] Nor, to my knowledge, is there a tribe, group, or even individual that looks like a native Australian. Again, I am not sure that there are any pure-blooded Indians who could pass for White, either in skin color or in the configuration of the face. There are, indeed, some Indians on

[117] Seltzer, *Yaqui Indians*, pp. 101–113.

the northwest coast of Canada who, by their photographs, appear no
more Mongoloid than some of the Whites to be seen in central Europe
who have acquired a dash of the Tartar or some other Mongoloid strain.
I am not at all sure, unfortunately, that these White types are not the
result of recent European admixture. However, as one passes south
from the Eskimo fringe, a general attenuation of Mongoloid features
may be noticed, and this impression becomes stronger as one encounters
forest Indians of Central America and proceeds into the Amazon basin
and other regions of jungle-dwelling primitives. If we had adequately
studied series from these remote areas, I have no doubt that the impression could be substantiated by morphological and statistical evidence.

In general, in North America below the Arctic region, the smooth
Mongoloid foreheads, shallow eyes with epicanthic folds, and low-
rooted, saddle-backed, infantile noses frequently seen among the Eskimo
are replaced by more receding and bony brows, boldly arched salient
noses with depressed tips, massive facial skeletons with not much fat
overlay, thin lips, and deep, jutting chins. Skins become less yellow
and more coppery. Then as one goes farther south into the tropical forest areas, the picture changes again. Wavy and even curly hair is sometimes seen; skins are a darker brown with the yellow and coppery shades
less to the fore; noses become shorter, coarser, usually straight, but with
somewhat flaring wings; integumental lips are almost convex; membranous lips rather full, with the lower lip often everted; chins rounded
and weak; eyes are often deeply embedded, strongly biconvex—rather
reminiscent of Polynesian eyes. Some of these jungle types indeed
rather recall the more uncomely of the Polynesians, although of greatly
inferior stature and body build; some of them (and I am thinking particularly of the primitive Maya Lacandones in Yucatan) seem from
their photographs strikingly like Dravidians of the cruder types found
in the hill country of southern India.

When one attempts to objectify these impressions by drawing up
schemes of sorting criteria, one finds that there are no adequate data
available for such a purpose. All that I feel justified in doing is to subdivide on the basis of two well-known criteria; head form, as expressed
by the cephalic index, and nose form, crudely described as aquiline,
hooked, hawk-nosed, on the one hand, and snub-nosed (short broad,
straight or concave) on the other. With the snub-noses, whether in long-
heads or in round-heads, are ordinarily associated the complex of variations that deviate from the classic Mongoloid features. However, these
deviations—wavy or curly hair, thick lips, alveolar prognathism, heavy

brow-ridges, dark skin—are not indissolubly linked in individuals; they may occur singly or in the various possible combinations. Some of them not infrequently go with the hawk-nosed types. In the lamentably inadequate state of our knowledge (for only a very few series of the Indians south of the Mexican border have been made the subjects of anthropometric investigations), the situation suggests various degrees of fusion of more evolved with comparatively primitive types, resulting in the break-up of original linkages or their penetration by certain dominant features.

There is no longer any reasonable doubt that man reached the New World either in the Late Pleistocene or early Recent period—say 15,000 to 20,000 years ago. This moderate antiquity has been established principally by the finds of the Folsom culture in New Mexico and Colorado since 1925. In this region, a very distinctive type of fluted stone point, skilfully rechipped along the edges, is associated with the bones of an extinct species of bison and also with those of the mammoth.[118] Numerous other stone artifacts of ordinary types also belong to the culture. Unfortunately, no human skeletal remains have been associated with the Folsom implements as yet. The Minnesota Lady, of presumably comparable antiquity, remains the best authenticated of early American immigrants (cf. pp. 405–406). This 15-year old girl who fell into a lake is not an ideal subject for racial analysis because of her tender age and frail sex. Adult males show fuller development of racial characters. Dr. Jenks thinks that this Minnesota Clementine shows Mongoloid characters forestalling those of the Eskimo, along with some Australoid and Negroid features. The late Dr. Aleš Hrdlička, an irreconcilable enemy of all fossil men in the New World and a defender to the last of the faith in the racial unity of the American Indian, contended that the Minnesota girl was a modern Sioux Indian. These opinions are enough to indicate that Minne-alas was no full Mongoloid of the classic type nor yet of the Arctic type. Either her genes had not made up their minds, so that she was incompletely differentiated racially, or she was an early race mixture product. Since we have no clearly and fully Mongoloid fossil skull of greater geological antiquity than the Minnesota Lady, it is wholly possible that she represents an incipient Mongoloid.[119]

[118] Bryan, "Geology of Folsom Deposits," 139–152. Roberts, "The Folsom Problem," pp. 153–162.

[119] Privily transmitted to me by one of Professor Jenk's former students of anthropology at Minnesota is this lugubrious ballad, allegedly sung by graduate students at post-seminar carouses. The writer of the song is unknown, but suspicion rests upon an erudite faculty

Even before the discovery of the Minnesota Lady, it became clear that the solution of the problem of the racial composition of the American Indian lies in the study of the skeletal material from archaeological deposits of varying age. Unfortunately, few stratified sites yielding burials of different ages have been discovered. In a number of places in both North and South America excavation has shown that long-headed types of crania occur at the deepest levels and that these are overlaid by peoples who were brachycephalic. In the southwestern United States, the earliest population known is called the Basket Makers and consisted of slender, short persons with dolichocephalic heads, narrow and longish faces, and rather broad, low noses. They seem to show affinities with the fundamental brunet dolichocephalic type that we

wife who specializes in osteological detective stories. Well acquainted with the literary talent of this lady, the present writer considers the imputation as criminally libellous.

THRENODY FOR THE FIRST LADY OF THE LAND

On a lake shore, near a glacier
In a Minnesota clime,
Dwelt a Pleistocene old-timer
And his daughter, Clementine.

Chorus

Oh my darling, oh my darling,
Minnesota Clementine,
Parts of you are lost forever,
Dreadful sorry, Clementine.

Oh, her teeth were big as tomb-stones
And her nose was platyrrhine.
Mighty spacious and prognathous
Were the jaws of Clementine.

Drove she mammoths to the water
Every morning just at nine,
Stubbed her toe upon an esker,
Fell into the freezing brine.

Blubber lips among the cracked ice
Blowing steam and spouting slime,
But, alas, she was no whale cow,
So subsided Clementine.

On a highway, with a scraper,
Planing bumps raised by the rime,
Up they brought her, Asia's daughter,
Pleistoscenic Clementine.

Counting varves and sifting gravel,
Bones and beads, one at a time,
Papa Jenks got her together,
Fossil flapper, Clementine.

PLATE 21

a · b

Mediterranean type. Italian, stature 154 cm., cephalic index 76.5, hair dark brown, eyes brown, age 30 years

c · d

Mediterranean type. Portuguese-American, stature 172.5 cm., cephalic index 72, hair black, eyes brown, age 22 years

e · f

Alpine type. Polish-American, stature 170 cm., cephalic index 89, hair dark brown, eyes brown, age 26 years

PLATE 22

Courtesy, Peabody Museum. Photographs, H. M. Huxley

a
b

Iranian Plateau type, Samaritan

Courtesy, Peabody Museum. Photographs, H. M. Huxley

c
d

Iranian Plateau type, Samaritan

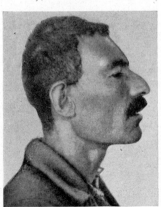 

Courtesy, Chicago Museum of Natural History. Photographs, Henry Field

e
f

Armenoid type, Kinareh, Iran

PLATE 23

Courtesy, Chicago Museum of Natural History. Photographs, Henry Field

a   b

Classic Mediterranean, convex nose, Dulaimi, Iraq

Courtesy, Peabody Museum

c   d

Ainu man

Photograph, C. W. Dupertuis

e   f

Keltic type, Irishman

PLATE 24

Courtesy of Dr. Carleton S. Coon

a   b

Riffian, Beni Urriaghel Tribe, Morocco, stature 174.7 cm., cephalic index 75.4., nasal index 61.4, facial index 97, hair light brown, eyes blue-brown

Courtesy of Dr. Carleton S. Coon

c   d

Riffian, Beni Urriaghel Tribe, Morocco, stature 171 cm., cephalic index 76.8, nasal index 55.9, facial index 86, hair light brown, eyes green-brown

e   f

American, stature 169.7 cm., cephalic index 75, nasal index 60, facial index 92, hair golden, eyes blue

NORDIC TYPES

PLATE 25

a   b

East Baltic type. Irish-American, stature 165 cm., cephalic index 84.3, hair light, eyes blue, age 27 years

c   d

Armenoid type. Russian Jew, stature 162 cm., cephalic index 83.1, hair dark brown, eyes mixed, age 24 years

Courtesy of Dr. Carleton S. Coon

e   f

Dinaric type. Albanian, stature 167 cm., cephalic index 82, nasal index 49, facial index 92, hair black, eyes dark brown

PLATE 26

Courtesy, Harvard-Adelaide Expedition. Photographs, J. B. Birdsell

a   b

Full-blood Australian, Murrian type, showing extreme of White morphology

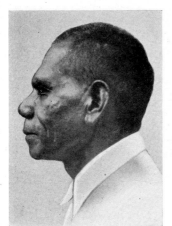

Courtesy, Harvard-Adelaide Expedition. Photographs, J. B. Birdsell

c   d

Full-blood Australian, Carpentarian type, Cape York Peninsula

Courtesy, Harvard-Adelaide Expedition. Photographs, J. B. Birdsell

e   f

Full-blood Australian man, Tasmanoid type, Cairns rain forest area, Queensland

PLATE 27

Courtesy of Dr. H. L. Shapiro and of the American Museum of Natural History

a   b

Indo-Dravidian, Singhalese

Courtesy of Dr. H. L. Shapiro and of the Bernice Bishop Museum

c   d

Polynesian, Tahitian

Courtesy of the Peabody Museum. Photograph by Dean Worcester

e   f

Indonesian-Malay. Subano man, District of Zamboango, Philippine Islands. Indonesian strain predominant

PLATE 28

a   b

American Negro, born in South Carolina, stature 170.6 cm., cephalic index 79.8

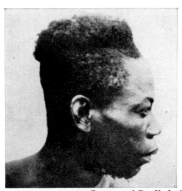

Courtesy of Dr. H. L. Shapiro and of the American Museum of Natural History

c   d

Azande, Belgian Congo, stature 161.5 cm.

Courtesy of Dr. H. L. Shapiro and of the American Museum of Natural History

e   f

Abarambo Poko, Belgian Congo, stature 175 cm.

NEGRO TYPES

PLATE 29

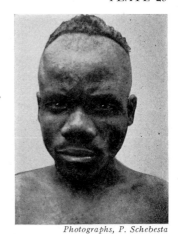

Photographs, P. Schebesta

a   b

Bakango man, adultiform type

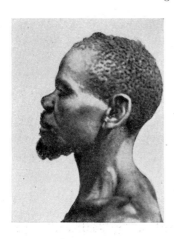

Photographs, P. Schebesta

c   d

Efé man, adultiform type

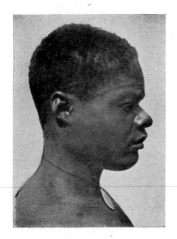

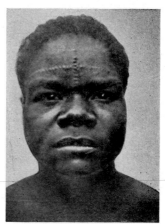

Photographs, P. Schebesta

e   f

Baćwa man, infantile type

CONGO NEGRILLOS

PLATE 30

Courtesy of the Peabody Museum

a

Solomon Islander, Melanesian type

Courtesy of the Peabody Museum. Photograph by Beattie, Hobart

b

Santa Cruz Islander, Reef Group, Papuan type, Pileni tracker

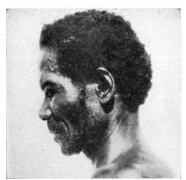

Courtesy of the Peabody Museum. Photograph by Dean Worcester

c

Philippine Negrito, chief of the Mariveles tribe

Courtesy of Dr. H. L. Shapiro and of the American Museum of Natural History

d

African Negrillo, infantile type

Courtesy of the Peabody Museum. Photograph by George Leith

e   f

Bushman, South Africa, stature 152.4 cm., Crocodile Island, Pretoria, Transvaal

PLATE 31

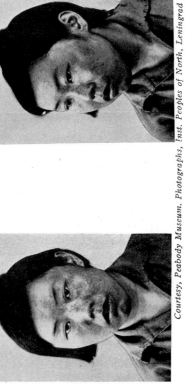

Courtesy, Peabody Museum. Photographs, Inst. Peoples of North, Leningrad

c

b

a

Pure Mongoloid type, Gilyak boy, Northeastern Siberia

Courtesy, Peabody Museum. Photographs, Inst. Peoples of North, Leningrad

f

e

d

Pure Mongoloid type, Gilyak girl, Northeastern Siberia

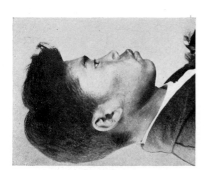

PLATE 32

Courtesy of the Museum d'Histoire naturelle de Paris

a   b

Indonesian-Malay type. Siamese showing predominant Mongoloid strain.
Muchindarak, born at Bangkok, Siam, age 23 years

Courtesy of the Museum d'Histoire naturelle de Paris

c   d

Mongoloid type. Northern Chinese, stature 165 cm., hair and eyes black

Courtesy of the American Museum of Natural History

e   f

Eskimo, Nutka, Smith Sound

PLATE 33

Courtesy of the United States Geological Survey

a   b

"Capitan," Apache, stature 172.7 cm., age about 56 years

Courtesy of the United States Geological Survey

c   d

"Bird Chief," Southern Arapahoe

Courtesy of the United States Geological Survey

e   f

"Dirty Face," Ogalalla Sioux

AMERICAN INDIANS, MIXED MONGOLOID TYPES

PLATE 34

Courtesy of the Peabody Museum. Photograph by J. Ogilvie

a   b

Wapisiana Indian, British Guiana

Courtesy of the United States Geological Survey

c   d

Ute Indian, "Graceful Walker"

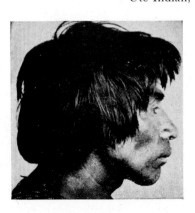 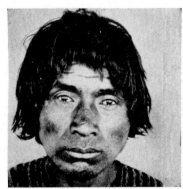

Courtesy of Frederick Starr

e   f

Tzendal Indian, Mexico

AMERICAN INDIANS SHOWING NON–MONGOLOID STRAINS

PLATE 35

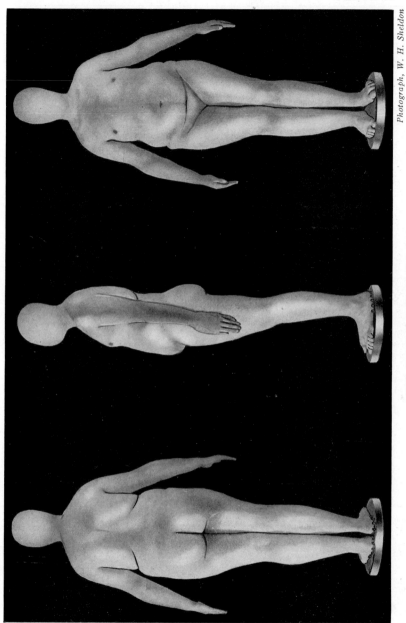

Photograph, W. H. Sheldon

THE SOMATOTYPE 721 (712)

PLATE 36

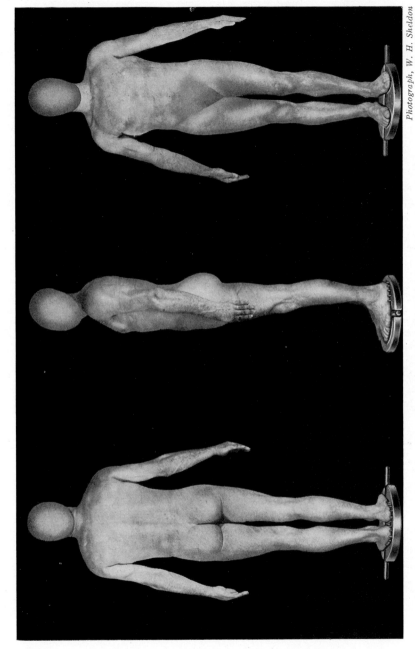

Photograph, W. H. Sheldon

THE SOMATOTYPE 171 (172)

PLATE 37

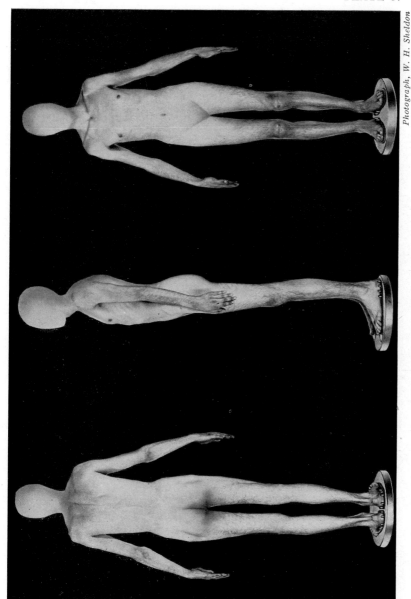

THE SOMATOTYPE 1½ 2½ 6½

Photograph, W. H. Sheldon

PLATE 38

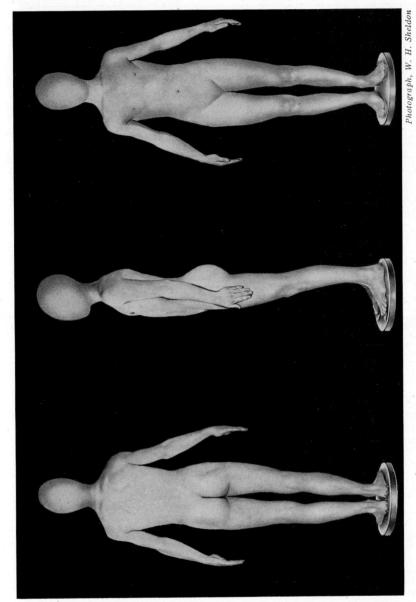

Photograph, W. H. Sheldon

THE SOMATOTYPE 344 (254)

PLATE 39

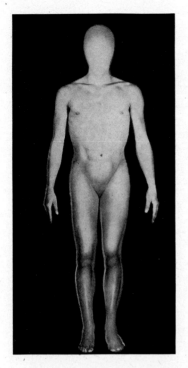
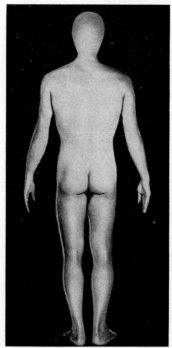

Photographs, W. H. Sheldon

THE SOMATOTYPE 261 (172), NORMALLY LOW IN
GYNANDROMORPHY

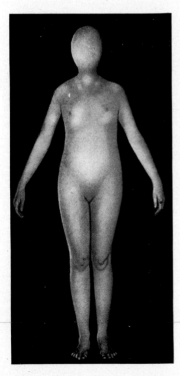
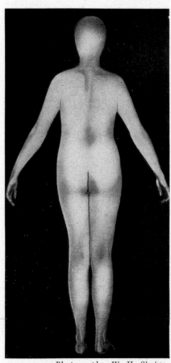

Photographs, W. H. Sheldon

THE SOMATOTYPE 523 (524), NORMALLY HIGH IN
GYNANDROMORPHY

call the Mediterranean subrace, but occasionally display also hints of Negroid admixture. Certain features of the face and skull, notably, heavy brow-ridges, depressed nasal roots, and scaphoid skulls, may indicate a strain of the archaic White race that is represented more distinctly in the Indo-Dravidians, the Australians, and the Ainu. Many of these early dolichocephals show no evidences in their cranial form of having been Mongoloid, but some other skulls of the same general type display the Mongoloid cheek bones. These small long-heads may have received some Mongoloid admixture before reaching the New World, but this is doubtful. I think it highly probable that they spread over North and South America before the period of the Mongoloid invasions. This old, long-headed type was pre-agricultural. It was probably dark-skinned and, I should guess, wavy-haired. There followed from Asia by way of Bering Straits and Alaska streams of round-headed Mongoloids, short, squarely built, and brachycephalic, with prominent cheek bones, low noses, and square jaws. These worked their way down the western coast and diffused eastward from the Rocky Mountains and the Andes. They were responsible for the highest developments of American Indian civilization. Another invasion from Asia seems to have brought a tall, long-headed type of man with a high, beaked nose. Cranial and living examples of this type show marked Mongoloid features in the cheek bones, hair form, and skin color, and it seems probable that some of these Mongoloid traits may have been acquired in Asia before the arrival of this new group in the Americas. It is possible that this group arrived before the short brachycephalic Mongoloid, since it occurs predominantly in the North America plains and woodland areas. The basic element in this stock is White, probably Iranian plateau. These stocks intermingled to form the diversified types of the American Indian today. Over all of these types there is a Mongoloid wash of dominant features, particularly observable in the cheek bones, the hair form, and the skin color.

With every sort of embryonic and matured variety of *Homo sapiens* milling around in eastern Asia at the end of the Pleistocene—Australoid-Ainu and Cro Magnon-like Whites, incipient Negritos or Negritoids, proto-Eskimoids, and odds and ends of palaeoanthropic man—it would be very strange indeed if all of the trickles of pioneers into the New World and all later immigrants were purely Mongoloid. In fact, it seems glaringly improbable that the Bering Straits and the Aleutian Islands should have strained out all prospective incomers except Mongoloids, especially when we recall the shocking racial diversity of the specimens that lay cheek-by-jowl in the one Upper Cave of Choukoutien. After all, there was no Dr. Hrdlička standing on the Aleutian equivalent of Ellis Island, acting as Prehistoric Commissioner of Immigration to enforce an alien exclusion act applicable to all save Mongoloids.

I have not mentioned heretofore the Punin skull, found in 1923 in a fossiliferous bed in the Andean highlands of Ecuador, in a stratum that yielded elsewhere bones of the extinct Andean horse, the camel, and the mastodon. It is one of those incompletely accepted fossil finds —although discovered by a reputable scientist. The point about it is that it is incontestably old in a general chronological sense, if not geologically ancient, and it is a skull that any competent craniologist would identify as Australian in type. It is easier to find Australoid-looking dolichocephals in the more ancient burials in the New World than anything in the way of a skull that resembles a Mongoloid. I found some moderately Australoid skulls among the skeletal material of the ruined pueblo at Pecos, New Mexico, which Southwestern archaeologists now say was founded not earlier than the eleventh or twelfth century A.D. There were also some strikingly Negroidal skulls in that population. I interpret such resemblances to racial types in relatively modern American Indian crania as the result of segregation and recombination of ancient racial strains that have been swamped by racially different new-comers, but crop out here and there in individuals. Call it atavism, if you like.

I suppose that no physical anthropologist who has made a special study of American material entertains the naive view held by my late colleague Dixon, that America was peopled by separate migrations, each of racially pure but different stock—first Australians, then Negritos, et cetera. Much of the mixture must have taken place before the hegira, so that the first long-heads probably carried in solution or in combination Australoid, Negroid, and I know not what other racial characters.

As for "unspecialized Mongoloids," I can only apply to them my favorite simile (borrowed from my beloved teacher of anthropology, Marett the Elder): an "unspecialized 'Mongoloid' is like a Welsh rabbit, not really a rabbit at all."

Strictures upon Race Mixture

When different races of man come into contact with each other they sometimes fight, but they always breed. Social intercourse between races always implies sexual intercourse. Even the primitive peoples who have been systematically exterminated by Europeans, such as the Tas-manians, have managed to leave some hybrid progeny begotten by the victors. Unquestionably, the races that have become extinct have passed on some of their blood to their conquerors, and it is wholly possible that in prehistoric times, when epidemics were fewer and weapons less deadly, absorption of an archaic minority race by intermarriage was the prevalent method of gaining racial supremacy. Of course, such inter-mixtures must have resulted in profound modifications of the surviving stock. Alien racial stocks cannot be digested without any more per-manent effects than a stomach ache; nor can they be grafted. Mixing the blood of two animals of different varieties may result in a hybrid resembling principally one or other of the parent stocks, but that hybrid has characters and potentialities derived from both of the lines that gave it birth.

Man is perhaps the most promiscuous animal ever evolved in the matter of indiscriminate interbreeding between races, varieties, and species (if there is more than one human species). This is why there is probably no such thing as a pure race existing today in the world. And it is for the same reason that it is necessary to recognize so many "races" —because new races have arisen from the crossings of older stocks.

In the early days of anthropology and before anthropology became a science (if it has yet attained that position), the opinion prevailed that hybridization in man was rare, unnatural, and although regrettable, nevertheless unimportant. This brings us to the necessity of recognizing two classes of race mixture: (a) mixtures between allied subraces, (b) mixtures between races physically far removed from each other, or radical mixtures. We must consider briefly the results of these two types of mixtures.

In the first place, crossings between allied subraces, as for example the Mediterraneans and Alpines, do not involve the mating of persons with markedly dissimilar physical features. Consequently, the offspring of such matings attract no attention by reason of peculiarities of ap-pearance. Hence, they are not set apart as a physical class, but easily mingle with the purer types of either parent stock. Therefore, there is little or no race prejudice involved in such miscegenation, and the interbreeds constitute no special stigmatized social group. As a result of this situation, allied and contiguous races and subraces have interbred for so many generations that there is scarcely to be found any group of people in the world that can be called racially "pure." And the closest approximation that we can make to isolating a pure race is to select from one of these adulterated groups those individuals who most closely conform to the combination of physical criteria which seems to establish the theoretically "pure" type. Improvement of means of transportation is rapidly destroying the lines of demarcation between the physical types which, under more primitive conditions, evolved in isolation into distinct but allied subracial stocks. It seems inevitable, as regards the "White" subraces in Europe and North America, that a few more cen-

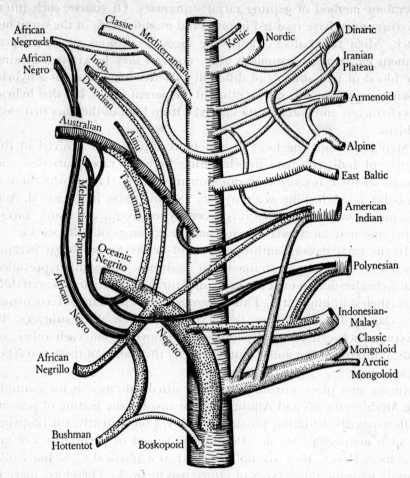

Fig. 68. Blood streams of human races.

turies will bring about the fusion of all the old types into new blends, so that it will no longer be possible to recognize Nordics, Mediterraneans, Alpines, or Armenoids. Indeed, in the United States, this process of fusion and obliteration of old race types is already far advanced.

Naturally, our practical interest in such crossings centers about their results with respect to the fertility, the vitality, the mental capacity, and the general worldly capability of the interbred offspring. In the first two of these problems, experimental biology has been able to clarify the situation by deducing principles of inbreeding and outbreeding as a result of controlled observations upon plants and animals.[120] These principles may be baldly summarized as follows:

Each separate stock, whether animal or plant, carries within its germ plasm hereditary factors that are the determinants of its physical and mental characteristics. Each stock has certain of these factors that make for strength and capability and others that conduce to weakness and incapacity. Many of the disadvantageous factors seem to be recessive and are masked by more desirable and dominant features. Nevertheless, these weaknesses are inherent in the germ plasm and may, under certain conditions, especially by the segregation of recessive traits, crop out in the individuals of the race. But, since allied stocks have tended to vary in different directions, each is likely to have a different assortment of strong points and weak points, so that, in a measure, the allied subraces supplement each other. Consequently, if such separate but allied subraces interbreed, there is a fair chance that some of the hybrid offspring will unite within themselves all or almost all of the desirable qualities of the two parent stocks. Of course, it is equally true that some of the offspring will get an unfair proportion of all of the weakness of both races and that a large number, perhaps the majority, will merely receive a random selection of virtues and vices pooled from the common resources of the parent stocks.

However, here again actual observations by animal and plant breeders indicate a better result than would be attained by mere grab-bag combinations, resulting from chance alone. For, in a general sort of a way, strong or desirable qualities seem to be, in a Mendelian sense, dominant over weak and undesirable characters. Therefore, the hybrid offspring, at least in the earlier generations, are likely to present a disproportionate number of the favorable or dominant characters of parental strains. The phenomenon known as heterosis or hybrid vigor often manifests itself in the first few generations of hybrid offspring in increased size and strength. This seems to be an effect of the attainment of a heterozygous condition in the individual with respect to many inherited characters. (A heterozygous condition is one in which factors both for dominant and recessive expressions of a trait are carried in the individual, the dominant feature being, as a rule, that which is externally manifest). When interbreeding between the hybrids is continued for a number of generations, however, hybrid vigor tends to

120 Cf. especially the excellent book *Inbreeding and Outbreeding*, by East and Jones.

diminish, owing perhaps to segregation and recombination of dominant and recessive units. At any rate, apart from the technical genetic basis of outbreeding, it is sufficiently evident that an infusion of new blood into a stock tends to reinforce its vigor, and often to increase its size. This fact has long been recognized by animal and plant breeders.

Inbreeding, on the other hand, tends to intensify the hereditary potentialities for strength and weakness already existent in the stock. This result is brought about by segregation of dominant and recessive characters. In some individuals recessive features that have been masked in their parentage are brought to light by recombination and similarly in others a purely dominant condition is reached. There is a tendency then for pure or homozygous strains to be isolated. The result of prolonged inbreeding is then to produce a number of individuals who combine the dominant (and on the whole favorable) characteristics inherent in the stock, and others who show segregated undesirable recessive traits. But, if one can eliminate these inferior inheritors by selection, there remain for future breeding those in whom the better qualities are homozygous or pure. Evidently then, inbreeding must be followed by selection in order to improve the strain. Then, if these selected individuals are bred with similarly selected members of another stock, the maximum benefits of hybrid vigor and enlargement of the range of favorable characters in the offspring may theoretically be obtained.

Let us now apply this theory to the intermixture of allied races or subraces. Obviously, these differ from each other in a number of heritable characters, some physical, and possibly, others mental. Each race has its range of potentialities for good and evil, its inherent talents and hereditary weaknesses. The crossing of such races inevitably enlarges the possibilities of favored individuals in the offspring by pooling the resources of two races. It also brings about that stimulus due to heterozygous combinations that is called hybrid vigor, frequently but not invariably manifested in the earlier generations of hybrid offspring. It affords an opportunity for the occasional production of supermen or geniuses. Of course, I do not mean that all geniuses have been the result of race mixture between allied stocks. But I do maintain that most great civilizations have been built up as a result not only of the contact of different cultures but also of the fusion of peoples and races, each bringing, no doubt, its quota of talents, and these being distributed among the mixed offspring of the cross in such a way as to enhance greatly their creative and constructive capacity. A harmonious mixture of two races is like a merger of two competitive business corporations which often produces an institution much more powerful than the combined resources of the two separate corporations. Two and two may not make four, but five or six.

The population of ancient Egypt was a fusion of a basic Mediterranean stock tinged with Negro blood, with Armenoid and possibly Nordic elements; the immortal Greeks were Mediterranean, mixed with Nordic, Armenoid, and Alpine; the Romans were Mediterranean, Nordic, and Alpine; and so the successful course of interbreeding between allied stocks might be recounted for every great civilization of which the anthropological antecedents are known to us. Unfortunately, however, we are in no position to state precisely the inheritance of physical characteristics in crosses between allied stocks, simply because such crosses have gone on for so many thousands of years that it is almost impossible to isolate pure strains of the original races involved. To study race mixture advantageously, we must have the offspring of primary crosses between the races and compare with them adequate numbers of the original pure stocks. No anthropologist has been able to unravel the snarl of mixtures and cross-bred types among European peoples. It is probably for this reason that some observers refuse to recognize the existence of subraces in what we call the "White" race. Often they perversely argue that the multiplicity of European types today is merely the result of spontaneous variation, environmental adaptation, or what not. They may pretend that the wide variability in family lines (however mixed these lines may be) is evidence of the complete erroneousness of the whole conception of race as a physical entity.

Much more ridiculous are the persons who are so uninstructed as to boast of their "pure" racial ancestry. Usually they imagine themselves to be "Nordics." There is probably not a Nordic of unmixed racial antecedents in the world, unless he is to be found in some remote and barren upland of central Sweden or at the head of some rocky Norwegian fjord. And even there he is likely to have some taint of Mongoloid Lappish blood. Persons who seem to present the combination of physical racial characters conforming to the racial ideal owe them, probably, for the most part, to segregation and recombination of characters inherited from a mixed ancestry.

In recent years a good deal of attention has been paid to the results of the second type of race mixture—that involving a radical cross between races physically far removed from each other. Such crosses involve much more obvious physical results and, consequently, much more serious social effects. The hybrid carries a mélange of contrasting physical features derived from both parent stocks and is physically distinct from each of them. When physically diverse races have crossed, the mixtures have usually taken place under conditions of social and political and economic inequality. The parental races have usually differed in language and culture as well as in physical characteristics. One of the races, usually a "White" subrace, has commonly been in the position of a dominating group, regarding the other as an inferior or even servile class of the population. Hence, the unions that have taken place between members of two such races have usually been frowned upon by society and have been more or less irregular, clandestine, and illegal. It follows that the offspring of such matings find themselves in a class that is not only physically anomalous, but socially stigmatized. They are disowned by both parent stocks or driven to throw in their lot with the socially and economically submerged racial group, unless they manage to work out their own salvation in isolation.

In order to discourage these socially difficult matings, laws have been passed in many states of this country forbidding marriages between Negroes and Whites, and there has grown up a pseudo-scientific propaganda based upon the alleged detrimental biological effects of radical crosses. This we must examine briefly. Crossings of animals of different species are not always fertile, since the species may differ too much in their structure and their physiology. In a number of other cases animal hybrids show sterility in the males and partial or complete fertility in the females. This is the condition in crosses between the buffalo, the yak, and the domestic cow.[121]

Of course, the mule is the most notorious example of a vigorous but sterile hybrid. Without troubling to survey the teeming hybrid populations of the world, certain theorists formerly maintained, ostrich-like, that wide racial crosses are either sterile or produce ornery and barren hybrids like the mule. Such being the case, radical race mixtures were unimportant. This view, however, could not be maintained for long in the face of the facts. Africa, for example, contains millions of inhabitants who may be called "Negroes" only by courtesy. They are really "Negroids" showing various proportions of White and Negro blood. These Negroids include many of the most vigorous and hardy peoples of the continent. In the United States, the so-called "mulatto" class has increased with enormous rapidity. In the population rated as "Negro" by the gatherers of the United States Census, not more than one fifth may be approximately full-blooded Negroes. Indeed, this is a most liberal estimate.

In spite of this rapid growth of the Negro-White mixed population, there has persisted in some quarters a suspicion that the offspring of such

121 *Ibid.*, p. 192.

crossing are physically inferior to the parent stocks and lacking in vitality. In the absence of reliable statistics concerning the proportions of Negro and White blood in the so-called "Negro" population and of the birth rates and death rates of mixed Negroids as compared with full-blooded Negroes, this suspicion cannot be definitely confirmed nor allayed. Nevertheless, I do not think that the notion of the physical and constitutional inferiority of the hybrid can be seriously entertained.

In 1910, the statistics of Indians of the United States, both of pure and of mixed blood, were carefully analyzed by the Bureau of the Census under the special supervision of Professor R. B. Dixon. The figures clearly demonstrate that mixed bloods show less sterility, larger numbers of children per family, and greater vitality than the pure blood Indians. Studies of the physical features of Indian-White mixed bloods carried on by Professor Franz Boas, Dr. Louis Sullivan, and others, are interesting from the point of view of the inheritance of individual physical features and give no indication whatsoever that the hybrids are physically inferior. Half-bloods are usually taller than either parent stock and thus show hybrid vigor.

Professor Eugen Fischer investigated the crosses between Hottentots and Boers in southwest Africa and found the offspring to be taller than either parent race and to exhibit a high fecundity and vitality. Rodenwald has studied the matings between the natives of Kisar, an island in the Indo-Malayan Archipelago, and Dutch soldiers. Here, again, the same results were obtained with respect to the satisfactory physical status of the hybrid. In Polynesia, Shapiro has studied the mixed bloods of Norfolk Island, descendants of the English mutineers of the warship Bounty and Tahitians. After five generations of inbreeding, these people are a physically superb group, taller than the averages of English and Polynesians. Similarly, in Hawaii, Dunn and Tozzer and Sullivan have scrutinized the intermixture of Polynesians with a number of European and Asiatic stocks. In these crosses, hybrid vigor in size is not consistently shown, but none of them indicates an inferior status on the part of the mixed bloods. The latter invariably show a high degree of fecundity and a death rate below that of the full blood Polynesians.

A detailed discussion of the fascinating subject of race mixture lies outside of the scope of this book. There are now available to the student several authoritative monographs on radical crosses and more are in process of publication. They show clearly enough that wide race mixtures produce in some instances hybrids resembling one or other of the parental stocks, but more often types displaying a combination of features drawn from all of the races involved in the cross. Occasionally, the combinations blend into new and apparently stable types. There is no doubt that new races may arise from such miscegenation. It is possible to observe offspring from the crossings of primary races who present combinations of features that are strongly reminiscent of those found in the great secondary or composite races. For example, some blends of White, Negro, and Indian blood produce individuals who closely resemble Polynesians.

Racial Quality

No physical anthropologist can rank the existing races of man within an evolutionary hierarchy in the order of their distances of departure from the anthropoid apes, because each race shows its own combination of anthropoidal, primitive human, and advanced specialized characters. There is no way of weighting these variously evolved racial features so as to arrive at a valid appraisal of the comparative evolutionary status of a particular race. The problem is somewhat easier when one deals only with skulls and bones, but even here it is a precarious business.[122] Attempts to grade types according to their evolutionary development have a certain value in studies of ancient forms of man and of the apes, but when applied to contemporary races they serve no better purpose than to stir up emotional and acrimonious controversies.

The cultural capacities, mental abilities, temperamental characters, and general behavioral tendencies of different races can hardly be determined before agreement is reached upon the hereditary physical criteria that delimit said races. Then the actual racial groups must be isolated and studied with respect to their comparative endowments of these intangible and abstract qualities. None of these prerequisites for a scientific appraisal of the varying qualities of different races has yet been realized. Particularly, there are no objective scientific techniques for the measurement of intelligence, temperament, economic capacity, et cetera, that are capable of indiscriminate application to peoples possessing radically different cultures and living under diverse conditions of economic and social environment. Some progress has indeed been made in the devising of non-literate, universal, intelligence tests applicable to all peoples in whatever environment. Results of such tests, however, cannot yet be accepted as true appraisals of racial quality.

As a matter of fact, the cultural, mental, and behavioral correlates of such broadly varying hereditary groups as races seem, in any event, to be of very slight importance. In so far as heredity is a determinant of these capacities and activities, it is one's own individual inheritance (his

122 Cf. Hooton, "The Asymmetrical Character of Human Evolution," pp. 125–134.

unique genic combination) that is all-important, and beyond that, in diminishing order, familial inheritance, geographical group inheritance, national inheritance (in so far as nations are inbred groups), and only lastly, and almost insignificantly, racial inheritance.

It is practically impossible to abstract intelligence, social efficacy, economic capacity, temperament, et cetera, from the web of cultural environment in which these qualities are entangled. The metaphor is not good; intelligence is more like a complex organic chemical compound that defies analysis and cannot easily be broken down; we know that it has heredity and environment in it, but how much of each it is impossible to say.

An inbreeding group within a certain geographical area produces a culture, partly as the result of what has been transmitted in the way of cultural knowledge handed down from one generation to the next, partly as a result of outside borrowings—the whole adapted and modified, even directed, in large measure, by the necessities of physical environment. This culture, of which the individual is a part and which his group and his ancestors have produced, moulds him into one or another of the forms acceptable to the group. Men make culture, and then culture remakes or unmakes men. It soon becomes difficult to determine which comes first—the hen or the egg.

I have spent a good deal of effort and time in selecting, by physical sorting criteria, morphological types of criminals so as to produce racial or subracial groups, and then examining these groups to ascertain whether or not they have different criminal propensities, as shown by nature of offense committed.[123] There are indeed some interesting "racial" differences, but these pale into insignificance in comparison with the remarkable variations that are correlated with nationality (or even with state of birth and incarceration). National differences in temperament, in psychology, and in behavior, are, I am sure, profoundly important, because they are the resultant of the continual interaction of cultural and biological forces. A national group is an inbred biological group, usually of mixed racial antecedents but presenting peculiar blends or specific physical and mental combinations. Such great biological entities produce a culture in conformity with their innate tendencies and with the requisites of their physical environment. This culture in turn tends to select for survival and for success within it only those to whom it is intellectually, temperamentally, and socially congenial. The culture thus accentuates the culture-making peculiarities of its own originating stock. It tends to make them culturally homozy-

_____
[123] Hooton, *Crime and the Man*, pp. 204–252.

gous, by eliminating the heterozygotes—the noncomformists in both a hereditary and an environmental sense. Thus, nationality is really more important biologically than race, because it produces culture and is made the thing of that very culture. Races have no culture.

The whole problem is no mere matter of environment; if you hope to reform the German people by changing their culture, you are up against the fact that their culture is what they themselves, by virtue of their peculiar heredity and the exigencies of their physical environment, have created and what suits them. After all, it is, in the first instance, man who creates culture, and he makes of it what he wants and he likes. Change the breed, if you want to alter its behavior.

Science can make no valid assertion that this or that race is either superior or inferior to another. For that matter, it is equally unable to put forward the claim that all races are equal biologically or in cultural capacity. We know that in every race there exists a range of mentality from idiots to geniuses, with many more of the former than the latter and a regrettable piling up of the frequency curve in the area of low intelligence. These ranges of mentality in the different races overlap to such an extent that, if we could really put an accurate and comparable test into effect whereby to determine them, we might find them to be wholly coincident. On the other hand, there might be some greater or smaller racial differences. We would better worry about the imbeciles and morons within our own race (if we happen to know what that race is) than to make specious judgments concerning the inferiority of alien races, whose members doubtless feel exactly the same about us.

In common with all reputable anthropologists, I abhor the vicious nonsense about racial inequality, and particularly "Nordic" or "Aryan" superiority, put out by German propagandists and by others under the guise of anthropology. Frankly, I do not think that the German anthropologists who emitted this stuff ever believed it themselves. They merely yielded to political pressure and wrote what they were ordered to write. No intelligent person with a scientific training in anthropology has anything but scorn for these unfounded claims, fanatical ravings, and faked facts. Their purpose is simply to arouse the prejudice of ignorant people of their own race against alien races in order to justify aggression, conquest, robbery, and murder. These absurd prevarications and foolish theories require no scientific refutation, because they are intended for consumption and belief by persons of such low intelligence that evidence, proof, reason, and truth itself mean nothing at all to them. Anthropologists only waste their time when they indulge in hysterical polemics against "racism" on the ground that it has no scientific justification. Of course it has not, nor is it intended to have; it is meant to influence minds impermeable to scientific reasoning.

Racial prejudice and racial discrimination are not likely to disappear as a result of the possible findings of scientists that all races are equal or that differences between them are insignificant. They arise from the desire of low grade human beings to dominate and exploit their fellow men, and they serve merely as convenient excuses for such evil behavior. These prejudices and discriminations can readily be transferred from race to nationality, to social class, to religious faith—wherever competition between human beings exists with resulting antagonisms. They will not be cured by preaching nor by the writing of learned treatises on racial anthropology.

Part VI. The Anthropology of the Individual

The Problem of Classification

Any kind of a human group is made up of individual units, and we cannot hope to understand group phenomena, biological or social, unless we have an accurate knowledge of the constitutional endowments, personalities, mental equipment, and social capabilities of the individuals who compose the group. The study of the anthropology of the individual may be called constitutional anthropology or constitutional psychology, but, however it is named, it requires the combined skills of the physical anthropologist, the medical practitioner, the psychologist, and the sociologist, all applied simultaneously to single individuals.

The immediate purpose of constitutional anthropology is to diagnose the capabilities of the individual from every relevant scientific approach, to the end of guiding him toward the most successful and useful life in human society that is possible within the limitations of his physical and mental endowment. An ultimate and much more important purpose is to determine the relationship between the human organism and human behavior in order to improve both. The student of the human constitution believes that the behavior of the individual is the resultant of two sets of forces—organic and environmental—of which the former is primary and the latter secondary. Every human being has organic potentialities that are limited by his heredity, but the full realization of these potentialities may be prevented by adverse environment. An improvement of the heredity of an individual already conceived and born into the world is obviously impossible; better heredity can be achieved only by an application of genetic selection to man, except in so far as an optimum environment for every individual may affect favorably his reproductive activity. It is the conviction of many a physical anthropologist, many biologists, and some psychologists that human behavior in general cannot be substantially improved unless individual human organisms are bettered in quality, either by eliminating the degenerate, inferior, and chronically diseased, or by applying the science of human genetics actually to breed stocks that are individually superior animals. The social problems of man will never be solved by merely tinkering

663

with human institutions and trying to temper the blasts of environment to hereditarily shorn lambs.

Without regard for these larger problems, it is evident that every person who manages to get along in this world has to do so on his organic own. His health and his survival depend upon his constitution, barring environmental accidents. So physicians, from the time of Hippocrates onward, have been trying to arrive at some method of classifying human physiques into types that have significance from the point of view of disease susceptibility and immunity, both organic and functional.

Now, everyone who has tackled this problem has come to about the same solution of it as you yourself (without any necessary knowledge of anthropology or medicine) would reach instantaneously if you were asked: "What are the main types of human body build?" You would answer: "Fat, medium, and thin." If you were a scientist, you might dress up these categories in high-sounding names, such as "pyknic," "athletic," and "asthenic," or "vital," "motive," and "mental," and you might elaborate their descriptions. You would probably remember the words Shakespeare put into the mouth of Julius Caesar:—rendered trite by repetition, but still the most profound constitutional observation to be found in literature. Every keen observer of men's appearance and their behavior is a constitutional psychologist without knowing it, like Monsieur Jourdain, the unwitting speaker of prose. The trouble is that Hippocrates and Shakespeare and you have all "got so far," and, until recently, no medical, anthropological, or psychological student of the human constitution has outdistanced the ancients and amateurs.

The first requirement for the science of the human constitution was to establish some simple and definite description of the human body build types, in terms of indices (or relations of one dimension to another) or in specific categories of morphological variation, or in both combined. The visual impression of obesity, or of lankiness, or of muscular and powerful build had to be reduced to some scale of measurement that would permit accurate classification of individuals. This reduction of body build types to a measurable scale proved to be a most difficult task. Many students of constitution devised all sorts of indices—some of them most elaborate and involving the mathematical manipulation of a half dozen or more of measurements—but none of these indices served satisfactorily to delimit clean cut body types. The best of them was, and is, the height divided by the cube root of weight. (Since stature is a linear measure and weight a volumetric measure, a better result is obtained by comparing stature to the cube root of weight than to raw weight.)

Most of the medical students of constitution, growing weary of taking numerous measurements and calculating indices and then finding that these tedious processes failed to differentiate the clinical types or the build types they were able to recognize at a glance, abandoned anthropometry and reverted to simple and crude judgments, placing each person in one of three, or at most four, categories. Then it was found that many persons would not satisfactorily fit into any such oversimplified scheme, and that most of the medical or psychological relationships to various build types could not be proved because of a lack of a sound and flexible scheme of classification.

It is interesting to note that the demand for a workable technique of individual anthropology arises from the needs of clinical medicine and is in no sense due to the initiative of persons professionally engaged in physical anthropology. The latter have always been few in number (and, one must admit, rather limited in their outlook), being preoccupied, for the most part, with studies of races, of fossil man, and of such phenomena as growth.[1] Diagnosticians and even good general practitioners, probably from time immemorial, have been accustomed to associate the occurrence of certain constitutional diseases with the physique or type of the patient most liable to them. Indeed, many physicians depend largely upon the body build and appearance of the patient to guide them toward a diagnosis of the malady from which he is suffering. Conscious of the inadequacy of their visual impressions of body type, but well aware that in some way or other type is directly correlated with pathological susceptibility, these clinicians sought from physical anthropologists a workable and scientific technique for determining body build type. They got virtually nothing; they asked for bread, and we gave them a stone (and right between the eyes, at that). So the medical men were forced to stumble along with their "clinical hunches," or to devise crude anthropometric methods of getting at the types they saw but could not measure.[2]

Within recent years, a clarification of the muddle of constitutional

[1] The present writer does not except himself from this stricture. In his youth (1916), he was guilty of publishing a hypercritical and cheaply facetious article upon the efforts of two distinguished Boston clinicians to establish a dichotomy of body types—"herbivorous" and "carnivorous." The classification was somewhat naïve; it postulated a long-gutted type of man with a digestive tract presumably fitted for the consumption of large amounts of coarse vegetable food, and a short-gutted type better fitted for the digestion of animal food. Subsequent studies of the length of the intestines in man have furnished a good deal of substantiation for this theory. It was not until this author had become deeply involved in the study of criminals that he began slowly to emerge from his Rip Van Winkle obliviousness to the importance of individual anthropology (about 1928).

[2] A pioneer in constitutional medicine in this country, Dr. George Draper, initiated the Constitutional Clinic at the Presbyterian Hospital in New York City and was the first to engage the services of physical anthropologists as regular members of his staff. Draper's contributions to the study of the human constitution have been numerous and valuable. (Cf. Bibliography.)

anthropology has been offered by the brilliant work of William H. Sheldon, a psychologist fully qualified also in medicine and conversant with anthropometric techniques. As yet the system of Sheldon has not been widely adopted, but, in the present writer's opinion, it is destined to form the basis of future researches in this all important field of anthropology, with, doubtless, some modifications and additions.

Sheldon's contributions to constitutional anthropology include: (a) a new concept of the interrelationship of factors or components that determine the physical type of the individual, (b) a new technique for the anthropometric and morphological classification of body types, (c) a Scale for Temperament, based upon 60 traits ascertained to be correlated with the various somatotypes (body build types).

The Sheldon System of Somatotyping

THE COMPONENTS OF SOMATOTYPES

The term "somatotype" (Greek, soma, *gen.* somatos, "body") is used by Sheldon to designate the 79 varieties of the human physique recognized under his system.[3] The different somatotypes are determined by the varying expression in the individual organism of three bodily components of structure: endomorphy, mesomorphy, and ectomorphy. Endomorphy implies a trend toward the predominance of soft roundness throughout the different regions of the body and particularly a massiveness of the digestive viscera. It is so named because the digestive viscera are derived embryologically principally from the inner germ layer, the endoderm. Mesomorphy refers to the accentuated development of certain body structures derived from the embryonic mesoderm; particularly bone, muscle, and connective tissue. Ectomorphy means predominance of surface area relative to bulk and of the brain and central nervous system relative to mass. When ectomorphy is in the ascendancy, the body build type is linear and fragile; the sensory exposure to the outside world is relatively greatest; the individual is "skinny." The skin and the nervous system take their origin from the embryonic ectoderm.

Sheldon's terminology is new, but the general ideas of the three components are not dissimilar to those of other constitutional students. Roughly, the term pyknic ("compact") used by the German, Kretschmer, corresponds to Sheldon's "endomorphic," but extremes of the development of this component (called the first component, because it is primary)

[3] Sheldon, Stevens, and Tucker, *The Varieties of Human Physique, passim.*

are not compact, but round, soft, of relatively low density, and feeble. Extreme endomorphs have small bones and loose flabby tissue; they float in water. Kretschmer's "athletic" type is equivalent to the mesomorphic predominance in body types with big bones, massive joints, and heavy muscles. The term "athletic" is functional rather than structural and lacks the precise morphological connotation of "mesomorphic." As an equivalent of types in which Sheldon's third component, ectomorphy, predominates, Kretschmer used the term "asthenic" ("weak"). It is quite unsuitable, since persons of body builds in which slenderness and linearity are marked are frequently tough, hardy, and spry.

Since all of constitutional anthropology depends upon a clear conception of the anatomical details observable in the full-blown development of the three components, when each is predominant, an abbreviated check list of the inspectional criteria for adult males is given below.[4]

Dominance: Endomorphy (first component)
  General Characters:
    Softness, roundness; lateral and antero-posterior diameters of trunk and extremities tend toward equality.
    Concentration of mass central; predominance of volume—trunk over extremities, abdomen over thorax, proximal segments of limbs over distal segments. Rounding and "hamming" of upper arms and thighs.
    Soft body contours. No muscle relief. Skin, soft, smooth.
  Head and Neck:
    Head large, often approaching spherical; face wide, lower breadth approximating upper; neck short, forming obtuse angle with chin. Short nose, close-lying ears.
  Trunk:
    Relatively long; chest wide at base, waistline high and faint; greatest body breadth above pelvis; wide angle of ribs with sternum (breastbone); some development of breasts in male; trunk looks inflated; no dimpling of sides of buttocks.
  Extremities:
    Short, tapering limbs; weak, small hands and feet; outer line of thighs and calves in frontal or dorsal view shows feminine curves.
  Skeleton:
    Small bones, with thin cortex; no external bony projections. Vertebral column appears relatively straight in profile instead of S-shaped. Hard palate wide, low, parabolic.
  Hair:
    Body hair not excessively developed; pubic hair of feminine pattern; massive chest hair rare; tendency toward premature baldness, beginning at crown and spreading into circle. Often hair is fine and lies smooth.

---

[4] Based on Sheldon, Stevens, and Tucker, *op. cit.*, pp. 37–45.

Genitalia:

Small, underdeveloped; undescended testes common.

Dominance: Mesomorphy (second component)

General Characters:

Squareness, hardness; lateral diameters large, antero-posterior much smaller. Rugged, massive muscling in high relief.

Trunk heavy, limbs massive. Skin thick and coarse with conspicuous pores; tans deeply and readily; deep, coarse wrinkles.

Head and Neck:

Head variable in size but always massive in bony structure and heavily muscled; brow-ridges, malars, and jaws thick and heavy; either brachycephalic or dolichocephalic and of variable height, but often low-browed, with relatively great facial mass as compared with brain-case; head often appears cubical.

Neck usually long with excess of lateral over antero-posterior diameter; pyramiding of powerful trapezius muscles on both sides.

Nose long and broad at base; lips thick and firm.

Trunk:

Massive and prominently muscled, but with no concentration of mass; thorax predominant over abdomen in volume, wide at top; broad shoulders, laterally projecting because of great deltoid development, often appearing low and sloping because of pyramiding of trapezius muscles; heavy, prominent clavicles; abdominal muscles thick and prominent with muscular rippling at Poupart's ligament; muscular dimpling of sides of buttocks; low waist.

Extremities:

Massive but of variable length; distal segments relatively large and heavy; thick heavy wrists, hands, fingers; forearm thickness may equal that of upper arm.

Skeleton:

Thick, heavy bones; big joints; ribs strong and heavy at intermediate angle with vertebral column and sternum; spine relatively straight in thoracic region, but sharp inward bow in lower lumbar region, accentuated by prominent muscularity of buttocks.

Hair:

Generally coarse, but may be luxuriant or sparse; hirsutism variable, usually not marked in extreme mesomorphs; masculine pattern of pubic hair; baldness variable and when present usually begins in frontal region.

Genitalia:

Well developed; thick, firm scrotum.

Dominance: Ectomorphy (third component)

General Characters:

Linearity, fragility; small delicate bones; slight, "thready" muscles; diameters sharply reduced, especially the antero-posterior; relatively short, slender trunk and long legs; stature not necessarily great; skin thin, dry, loose, sensitive to cold and heat, pale; burns and peels, does not readily tan.

Head and Neck:
 Head slight with relatively small facial mass; features small, sharp; face
 often triangular with delicately pointed chin; low, narrow, sharp nose;
 thin delicate lips; upper parts of ears projecting, lobes attached; underdeveloped jaws, constricted palate, U-shaped; light skull with small
 brow-ridges, often vertical or bulbous frontal, flat top, sometimes scaphoid; projecting occiput; usually but not invariably dolichocephalic;
 slender neck, often appearing inadequate for support of head. Neck
 projects forward; both diameters small and almost equal.
Trunk:
 Relatively long thorax; drooping, narrow, rounded shoulders, marked
 clavicular hollow; no muscle relief; flat, narrow abdomen and chest;
 under weight-gaining diet abdomen protrudes below navel.
Extremities:
 Relatively long in distal segments; weak thighs and upper arms, fingers
 and toes usually long and fragile, joints small.
Skeleton:
 Light bones; delicate prominent ribs, acute costo-vertebral angles;
 scapulae tend to wing out behind because of inadequate muscular sup-
 port and padding; high, flat lumbar curve; sharp thoracic curve.
Hair:
 Usually fine and rapid in growth; body hair sometimes abundant but
 fine-textured; baldness rare; head hair unruly, tending to grow in diverse
 directions; pubic hair variable.
Genitalia:
 Usually linear, hypertrophic; long, loose scrotum with left testicle sus-
 pended lower than right.

It is evident that the extreme developments of endomorphy, mesomorphy, and ectomorphy, respectively, as listed above, are unlikely to
occur in more than a few individuals of a population. Sheldon's theory
of somatotypes regards the three structural components as continuous
variables, each of which attains some degree of expression in every human organism. The variables are to some extent interdependent, since
it is obvious that excessive mesomorphy, for example, can only be
realized at the expense of the development of the other two components.
His scheme, therefore, provides for the classification of somatotypes according to the combination each presents of degrees of expression on a
graded scale of the three components. This conceptual advance is perhaps Sheldon's most important contribution to the study of the human
constitution, since it provides for definitely demarcated intermediate
types between the three obvious extremes. Thus, instead of dividing the
population into only three classes—forcing every individual into one of
triplet Procrustean beds—the somatotyping system recognizes as many

body build combinations as are actually encountered. An examination of the origins and application of the Sheldonian technique will demonstrate the logic and the practicability of this procedure.

THE TECHNIQUE OF SOMATOTYPING

The series upon which Sheldon established his somatotyping procedure consisted of 4,000 undergraduate male students of midwestern and eastern universities, ranging in age between 16 and 20 years. Having experimented extensively and to his complete dissatisfaction with ordinary anthropometric techniques of caliper measurements, Sheldon discarded these entirely and developed a method that relies upon standardized photographs of each subject, graded morphological observations made upon these photographs, and, as an adjunct, measurements made upon the negatives with pin-point calipers and indices derived therefrom.

The photographs consist of front, back, and side views of the nude subject taken at a standard distance, using a long focus lens (9½"), and rotating the subject on a revolving pedestal constructed to move between stops placed at intervals of 90 degrees. The photographs thus taken are practically free from optical distortion.

Since the body is obviously a composite of several discrete topographic regions, Sheldon divided it for purposes of morphological observation into five areas: (1) head, face, and neck; (2) thoracic trunk; (3) arms, shoulders, hands; (4) abdominal trunk; (5) legs and feet.

In order to ascertain the range of variation of each component in each of the five body regions, Sheldon arranged prints of his photographs of 4,000 subjects in fifteen ascending series, each series based upon a continuous gradation of the estimated value of one component in one bodily region, made by picture-to-picture comparison. He then secured a seven point scale for each component in each region, by approximating the mid-point of each range and subdividing into three equal intervals on both sides of the mid-point. Thus each component in each region is scored from a minimum of 1 to a maximum of 7, and the somatotype of the subject is determined from the average or modal score of each of the three components in the five regions combined. Each somatotype is then represented by a three digit combination, for example, 711 (extreme endomorphy), 171 (extreme mesomorphy), 117 (extreme ectomorphy), and 444 (a balanced physique falling at the mid-point of all three scales).

In order to objectify the somatotypes thus determined by morphological grading of the three structural components, Sheldon used one index derived from raw measurements (height/cube root of weight) and 17 secured by taking pin-point caliper measurements upon the photographic films and expressing each as a percentage of the stature of the subject directly measured and reduced to the size of the film. He claims for this method, when employed by an expert, an accuracy superior to that of ordinary caliper measurements on the living, and it is certain that the results thus obtained are at least as consistent, and probably more so, than measurements taken on the living subject over soft parts. Many physical anthropologists dispute the superiority of these photographic measurements over standard techniques, but the former, at any rate, provide a statistical and metric validation for the morphological or "anthroposcopic" method of scoring, since the results obtained by either method are virtually identical. Actually, the soma-totyping technique ordinarily is practised by experts without the use of the pin-point measurements, which really add nothing to the pro-cedure beyond a metric substantiation and a basis for calculating mathe-matically the significance of the differences between somatotypes in the 17 indices involved. Repeated experimentation upon adequate series by independent observers has shown that close agreement in the deter-mination of somatotypes can be secured by persons conversant with physical anthropology and anatomy after a brief acquaintance with the Sheldonian technique. The method can be employed with considerable accuracy even by individuals lacking previous training in the superficial anatomy of the human body.

Evidently, the theoretically possible number of somatotypes when each of three components is graded from 1 to 7 is the total of permuta-tions and combinations of numbers from 1 to 7, taken three at a time ($7^3 = 343$). However, it is clear that the combination or somatotype 777 could not occur, except in a superman, nor 111 in a viable individual. Sheldon, as a result of many years' work, has been able to isolate and describe only 79 somatotypes of the possible 343, although the range of his series does not probably include all non-pathological variations of the male physique, to say nothing of rare pathological and freakish body forms.[5] Because of the incompatibility of very high or very low values of all three components in one organism, the sum of the digits repre-senting the three components ranges between 9 and 12, instead of from 3 to 21. Sheldon has found that a person may score as low as 1 (the minimum) in two components, if he is 7 in the third, but he cannot reach 7 in more than one component, and usually gets no higher than

[5] Sheldon, Stevens, and Tucker, *op. cit.*, pp. 60–66.

5 in two components. The somatotypes that actually occur most frequently, by Sheldon's findings, grouped into 19 descriptive classifications, are listed in Table 10.

TABLE 10. APPROXIMATE FREQUENCIES PER 1,000 OF PRINCIPAL
SOMATOTYPES (ADULT MALES) [6]

Descriptive Classification	Somatotype	Frequency	Total
Endomorphs			
1. Extreme	711	2	
2. Strong	533	24	
3. Moderate	433	24	
4. Mesomorphic	532	18	
"	542	14	
5. Mesomorph-endomorph	442	29	
6. Ectomorphic	534	12	
7. Ectomorph-endomorph	424	13	136
Mesomorphs			
8. Extreme	171	5	
9. Strong	262	23	
"	353	49	
10. Moderate	343	47	
11. Endomorphic	452	23	
"	453	10	
12. Ectomorphic	254	16	
"	354	13	
13. Ectomorph-mesomorph	244	42	228
Ectomorphs			
14. Extreme	117	5	
15. Strong	226	25	
"	225	20	
"	335	30	
16. Moderate	334	50	
17. Endomorphic	325	21	
18. Mesomorphic	235	45	
"	245	14	210
Balanced			
19. Balanced	444	41	
"	434	35	
"	344	58	
"	443	56	190
Sporadic rare types			
(less than 10 per 1,000)			236

Only 29 of the 79 somatotypes that Sheldon has found are tabulated. These types cover 76.4 per cent of the Sheldon series of 4,000 adult males. The rest of the series is made up of sporadic rare types, none of which reaches a frequency of 1 percent. As a matter of fact, the three extreme types, 711, 171, and 117 are also extremely rare, but they have been listed because of their classificatory position at the corners of the triangular field. No single somatotype attains 6 per cent of the distribution.

[6] Data from *Varieties of Human Physique*, pp. 65, 268–269.

DYSPLASIA

Nearly every individual presents certain asymmetries or disharmonies in his body build. This union of more or less incompatible proportions in different regions of the body may be regarded as an uneven mixing of the three structural components. Sheldon calls it "dysplasia."[7] A dysplasia frequently observed in women is marked by a slender, flat, ectomorphic torso and thin arms joined to heavy, broad, obese hips and legs in which both endomorphic and mesomorphic elements are emphasized. A man with a rugged mesomorphic trunk may have elongated, fragile, ectomorphic extremities. In another, a spherical, endomorphic head and neck may be implanted upon an ectomorphic torso. These dysplasias are certainly attributable in part to separate inheritance of bodily segments in the individual from diverse ancestral strains. Your long, narrow hands and delicate, pointed fingers may have been inherited from a maternal strain, and your massive, bullet head and bull neck from a paternal strain. Undoubtedly, there are general factors operating in the direction of harmonious growth of the entire organism, but it is also certain that specific gene combinations determine the proportions of the smaller body segments, and these may be inherited separately from different strains. Some persons have such dysplastic body builds that they appear to be made of spare parts.

Of course, some dysplasias may be of functional or environmental origin. A cyclist might acquire an apparent dysplasia of the legs as a result of muscular hypertrophy caused by pedalling; a blacksmith may overdevelop his right arm. However, occupational or functional dysplasias are probably much less common and relatively unimportant in comparison with those of hereditary, constitutional origin. A great many of the somatotypes recognized in the Sheldonian scheme are often found to be markedly or radically dysplastic. In such body builds there are certainly conflicts between the opposing structural components striving for dominance. It is wholly probable that these structural dysplasias involve physiological conflicts that result in pathological susceptibilities, and it is almost certain that psychological conflicts often go with structural dysplasias. Every student of the human constitution, whether or not he uses Sheldon's system of classification, recognizes the immense importance of bodily disproportions, disharmonies, or dysplasias in the individual.

In the somatotyping system the degree of total dysplasia is simply and conveniently calculated as follows: (1) the somatotype is determined for

[7] *Ibid.,* pp. 68–72.

each of the five separate regions of the body; (2) in the case of each of the three components the sum of the differences or dysplasias is calculated by matching all of the regional combinations; (3) the dysplasias of the three separate components are added together to give a total dysplasia.[8] Sheldon found total dysplasias in his 4,000 college men to range from 0 to 38. In this series, about 49 per cent of the dysplasias ranged between 6 and 12. Dupertuis, in another series of 1,000 college freshmen, found the average dysplasia in the three components combined to be 10.22, with a mean of 2.51 for the first component, 3.47 for the second, and 4.31 for the third.[9] Extremely dysplastic or disharmonic builds occurred in 6.8 per cent of this undergraduate group. Such individuals are not only badly put together, but are likely also to be maladjusted.

GYNANDROMORPHY

Although sex is determined at conception, the differences between the primary sex organs are distinguishable externally only from the third embryonic month onward, and secondary sexual differences develop gradually through childhood with a tremendous divergence during the phase of adolescence. Each sex retains to some extent through life traits ordinarily associated with the opposite sex. The male may develop bodily characters that are excessively masculine, or may retain a physique that is slightly, moderately, or markedly feminine. Clinical anthropologists have long recognized the importance of the degree of expression of secondary features ordinarily belonging to the opposite sex. They call this mixture of masculine and feminine features gynandromorphy ("female-male-form").

In the male, the expression of feminine characteristics may be estimated by noting the following occurrences:

(1) Smallness and delicacy of facial features; slight oval eyebrows; long eyelashes; delicate alae; rosebud mouth
(2) Rounded, delicate shoulders; short, weak arms
(3) Disproportionately wide hips
(4) Hour-glass figure (viewed dorsally) involving: high waist, softly moulded shoulders, full sweeping outer curve from waist to knee,

[8] Take the following example:

I. Head and neck	353	IV Abdomen	254
II. Thorax	254	V. Legs feet	345
III. Arms, hands	244		

There are 10 combinations of each component in the five regions (I with II, III, IV, and V; II with III, IV, V; III with IV and V; IV with V). The sum of the differences of the first component is 6, of the second 6, of the third 8. The total dysplasia is 20.

[9] Sheldon, Stevens, and Tucker, op. cit., p. 71

and well developed outer curve of calf; fullness of inner contour of thighs (viewed frontally); full, inflated buttocks

(5) Sparse body hair and pubic hair feminine in arrangement

(6) Soft velvety skin with smooth subcutaneous cushioning, rounding off all body contours

(7) Fatty simulation of breast development, sometimes functional glandular tissue in the breast (gynecomasty).

Some somatotypes typically display markedly feminine characteristics (usually those carrying predominance of both ectomorphy and endomorphy over mesomorphy), but individuals belonging to the same somatotype also differ among themselves in the expression of this bisexuality.

PRESENT LIMITATIONS OF THE SOMATOTYPING TECHNIQUE

Up to now the utility of somatotyping has been restricted in its purely biological applications by inadequate knowledge of female somatotypes and their range of variation, by the question of the age stability and relative independence of nutritional fluctuations of somatotypes, by ignorance of both the racial incidence of somatotypes and the extent to which racial heredity is operative in determining the somatotype, by an insufficient exploration of the significance of the factor of gross size in the somatotypes.

Deficient knowledge of the female somatotype is due simply and solely to the impossibility of securing the required series of standardized photographs of nude women because of considerations of modesty or prudishness. Sheldon has been able to study several series of "shadow pictures" taken on female subjects for purposes of postural study, but these are relatively worthless for an exact application of the somatotyping method. Most of the somatotypes that are found in men occur also in women, but it is probable that the distribution of the female somatotypes is different. A limited amount of clinical material pertaining to female somatotypes is available for observation in hospitals, but these patients are no satisfactory substitute for a large series of "normal" females. Dysplasia is apparently more marked in females than in males, or, at any rate, it is encountered in greater extremes. Further, a scale of development of masculine traits in female somatotypes cannot be constructed upon the present basis of knowledge, although it is clear enough that masculinity in the female is to some extent related to a predominance of the mesomorphic component over the other two. All of these difficulties, stemming from deficiency of data, presently will be overcome.

The question of the permanence of the somatotype throughout the lifetime of the individual is answerable with finality only by the study of large series of different ages, from at least early childhood to old age. No extensive studies of children, adolescents, or persons well past middle age have yet been completed, although several series of boys are now under observation. The somatotyping of children is very difficult, since many of the characters of their mature physiques are merely foreshadowed, if that. Sheldon is of the opinion that the somatotype can be accurately measured at the age of 6 years and that it is probably established at birth. He maintains that it remains unchanged throughout life in spite of growth increments, increase or decrease of weight, and most maladies that are incurred from time to time.[10] It is difficult to convince the anthropological observer of long experience, who has seen his juniors change in some cases from lathes to beer-barrels between the ages of 20 and 40, that the somatotype has remained constant. Nevertheless, Sheldon argues that a 444 is not changed by age or by nutritional disturbance to a 443 or to anything else. He may change from a lean 444 to a fat 444, or from extreme obesity to emaciation, but he is still recognizable as of the original somatotype to which he was assigned at the age of 6 or of 21, if the somatotype was correctly determined on the basis of an exact knowledge of the developmental course of traits significant in somatotyping. It is easy enough to see that very many individuals—perhaps the majority—obviously do not change radically in body build from adolescence to old age. It is hard to believe that there are not at least some complete metamorphoses or transmogrifications. On the whole, I am inclined to think that Sheldon is, in the main, correct in his contention of the immutability of somatotypes, but there are probably some who really change, particularly, perhaps, if affected by endocrine disturbances. Sheldon very pertinently suggests that exactly the same question of mutability arises in racial or subracial types when, with age, a previously blond "Nordic" darkens in hair color until he might be called a "Mediterranean" or a "Keltic."

So far, the study of somatotypes has been virtually confined to the White race. No large series of Negroids or Mongoloids has been analyzed and, therefore, the range and distribution of somatotypes for these main races and for all secondary or composite races are unknown. Sheldon's system is so new and has been, as yet, employed by so few students that its universal racial applicability has yet to be demonstrated. Probably some new somatotypes will emerge when these larger investigations have been undertaken and completed. Within the White race, as the reader knows, there are a considerable number of primary and composite subraces,

---

[10] *Ibid.*, pp. 221–226.

often markedly differentiated in head form, pigmentation, hair form, and other of the criteria of race. The present somatotyping system takes no cognizance of the subracial mixtures involved in modern populations of European origin; it entirely neglects the morphological and metrical criteria that are conventionally employed by anthropologists for the distinguishing of racial types. Such a cavalier disregard of stock differences within the White race will surely not evoke the ire of the many anthropologists who seek to disparage the importance of race and, indeed, look upon it as a sort of chimaera.

For those of us who are interested from genetic and anthropological motives in isolating subracial types and analyzing their mixtures within the White race, the present disregard of these matters in the somatotyping system need not undermine its usefulness to any great extent. While the system instituted by Sheldon does involve a few racial criteria, such as relating dolichocephaly to ectomorphy, and round heads to endomorphy, it concentrates principally upon the proportions of body regions below the neck. On the contrary, the racial analyst pays particular attention to features of the head and face; he measures and observes them in great detail and includes little or nothing of body build in his sorting criteria whereby he distinguishes racial or subracial types. There is, consequently, little or no conflict between the systems but only an interlocking and overlapping in respect of cephalic or other characters neglected in somatotyping and body build features ignored in racial sortings. If the anthropologist feels a trifle scornful about the crudeness and fewness of the somatotyper's observations on head and face, the latter reciprocates when he considers the meager number and general futility of measurements and indices and observations on trunk and limbs employed by the racial anthropometrist. The somatotyper can also assert with some reason that he can hardly apply his system to racially integral groups until the anthropologists can make up their minds how to isolate such groups and by what criteria.

In general, the present writer, an anthropometrist and not a somatotyper, feels that constitution cross-cuts race, but that both racial analysis and somatotyping would be immensely illuminated by a simultaneous application of both procedures to large series of individuals. We should like to know how much of the individual variation in a supposedly racially homogeneous series is attributable to constitution—individual inheritance and familial inheritance, as contrasted with broader and vaguer racial inheritance—together with whatever of environmental adaptation or moulding may be involved in the somatotype. The con-

stitutional anthropologist or psychologist is equally desirous of ascertaining how much allowance he has to make for general racial inheritance in appraising the make-up of the individual.

The entire subject of the genetics of somatotypes or of the individual
constitution remains to be investigated. Obviously, such a research involves the study of the somatotypic resemblances between siblings and
between parents and children. It far exceeds in importance the investigation of the heredity of eye color or hair form or of most of the
racial criteria that are non-adaptive and have little or no selectional
value.

The last of the important present limitations of the somatotyping
procedure enumerated above is its as yet incomplete analysis of the
significance of gross size differences among the same and different somatotypes. The present writer feels that these cannot fail to have certain
general behavioral correlates. If two men have precisely the same body
build, say 444, and one is a five-footer who weighs 110 pounds and the
other a six-footer who weighs 200 pounds, it seems more than probable
that the personality of the runt will differ from that of the big lout. It
is not clear also in the present system whether all somatotypes come in
the same ranges of gross size—stature and weight—or whether some
somatotypes are restricted to persons of a certain size. However, Dr.
Sheldon assures me that this apparent omission has been rectified in
studies yet unpublished, that gross size is now expressed on a seven-point
scale by simple calculations, and that its implications within somatotypes are being investigated.

Body Build and Temperament

No student of the human constitution doubts the strong correlation
between the physique of the individual and his temperament. A satisfactory method of classifying human physiques is essential for a study of
these interrelationships. The Sheldon system of somatotyping is by far
the best hitherto devised and seems a fairly adequate tool for this purpose.
Doubtless it will be modified and changed somewhat in the advance of
constitutional studies, but, in the opinion of the present writer, it is
basically sound and should be utilized. However, a scale for the classification of temperament is equally necessary for the investigation of the
problem. Psychologists are as little agreed upon such a scale as have
been anthropologists and clinical students of constitution upon a method
of classifying body build.

The present writer makes no pretense of being a psychologist and cannot bring to the appraisal of schemes for the classification of tempera-ment any expert knowledge. From a perusal of various such schemes, it would appear to the anthropologist that, in spite of terminological and presumably conceptual differences, all are oriented in much the same way, or, at any rate, seem to distinguish substantially the same variations. These are differences in temperament that any lay observer of human beings can note and classify. The scale for the rating of temperament developed by Sheldon and his co-workers seems "to make sense" and has the advantage of being articulated to the system of body build classification devised by the same student. Consequently, in this case only the three structural components of the body have been correlated with constellations of temperamental traits, so that their important associ-ations are no longer a mere matter of speculation and inference.

Sheldon recognizes three primary components of temperament that are equivalents, respectively, of the three morphological components. Viscerotonia is a complex of traits so named because it is functionally and anatomically associated with predominance of the digestive viscera.[11] It is the temperamental counterpart of endomorphy. The life of a viscerotonic individual seems to be organized around his gut.

The second temperamental component is somatotonia, which cor-responds with mesomorphy on the structural side. Sheldon states that the somatotonic complex of traits is associated with the functional and anatomical predominance of the moving parts of the bodily frame, that in the somatotonic person the activity of the voluntary muscles is prepotent, in that he wishes to do something with his muscles, to indulge in assertive, combative, and adventurous movement.

The third temperamental component, cerebrotonia, involves visceral and somatic inhibition (tension), and also mental intensity and a sub-stitution of cerebration for direct action. Cerebrotonia is named from the predominance of the cerebrum in man, which is apparently associated with elaboration of "attentional consciousness" and undoubtedly exerts sharply inhibitory influences upon both soma and digestive viscera.

Prolonged research by Sheldon upon a rather small group of academic persons led to the development of his scale for temperament. A list of some 650 alleged temperamental traits was sifted down to 50, which were then subjected to an exhaustive study of their interrelationships by means of the product moment method of correlation. (The coefficient of correlation is a statistical constant that measures on a scale from 0 to 1 the extent to which a change in the value of one of a pair of variables is accompanied by a change in value, either in the same or in the opposite

---

[11] Sheldon and Stevens, *The Varieties of Temperament*, pp. 20 ff.

direction, of the other member of the pair.) This list of 50 traits was divided into three groups or clusters, which were eventually given the component designations described above. In order to be accepted for inclusion within a trait cluster, any single trait had to show a positive correlation of at least +.60 with each of the other traits in the cluster and a negative correlation of at least —.30 with every trait in each of the other two nuclear groups. (A correlation of +.60 indicates close relation between two variables, and the positive sign shows that they move in the same direction. A correlation of —.30 tends to show moderate trends in opposite directions of the members of a variable pair.) Obviously, Sheldon adopted this procedure in order to make sure that within a group of traits assigned to a single temperamental component, each single trait "goes with" every other, and is in some degree opposed to all traits in the other two components. Eventually, the scale of temperament was completed with 20 traits in each component. It is reproduced here with a brief commentary upon the three clusters of traits summarized from Sheldon's full descriptions of them.[12]

TABLE 11. SHELDON'S SCALE FOR TEMPERAMENT [13]

I	II	III
Viscerotonia	*Somatotonia*	*Cerebrotonia*
1. Relaxation in posture and movement	1. Assertiveness of posture and movement	1. Restraint in posture and movement, tightness
2. Love of physical comfort	2. Love of physical adventure	2. Physiological over-response
3. Slow reaction	3. The energetic characteristic	3. Overly fast reactions
4. Love of eating	4. Need and enjoyment of exercise	4. Love of privacy
5. Socialization of eating	5. Love of dominating, lust for power	5. Mental overintensity, hyperattentionality, apprehensiveness
6. Pleasure in digestion	6. Love of risk and chance	6. Secretiveness of feeling, emotional restraint
7. Love of polite ceremony	7. Bold directness of manner	7. Self-conscious motility of the eyes and face
8. Sociophilia	8. Physical courage for combat	8. Sociophobia
9. Indiscriminate amiability	9. Competitive aggressiveness	9. Inhibited social address
10. Greed for affection and approval	10. Psychological callousness	10. Resistance to habit and poor routinizing

[12] *Ibid.*, pp. 24–95. The reader is referred to the above work and to the preceding volume, *The Varieties of Human Physique,* for a full account and discussion of both somatotyping and temperamental rating. The present volume does not purport to be a manual of constitutional anthropology. It aims merely to give a brief account of this subject for the general reader, in the hope that he will acquaint himself more intimately with it by study of the original works.

[13] Sheldon and Stevens, *The Varieties of Temperament,* p. 26.

11. Orientation to people	11. Claustrophobia	11. Agoraphobia
12. Evenness of emotional flow	12. Ruthlessness, freedom from squeamishness	12. Unpredictability of attitude
13. Tolerance	13. The unrestrained voice	13. Vocal restraint and general restraint of noise
14. Complacency	14. Spartan indifference to pain	14. Hypersensitivity to pain
15. Deep sleep	15. General noisiness	15. Poor sleep habits, chronic fatigue
16. The untempered characteristic	16. Overmaturity of appearance	16. Youthful intentness of manner and appearance
17. Smooth, easy communication of feeling, extraversion of viscerotonia	17. Horizontal mental cleavage, extraversion of somatotonia	17. Vertical mental cleavage, introversion
18. Relaxation and sociophilia under alcohol	18. Assertiveness and aggression under alcohol	18. Resistance to alcohol, and to other depressant drugs
19. Need of people when troubled	19. Need of action when troubled	19. Need of solitude when troubled
20. Orientation toward childhood and family relationships	20. Orientation toward goals and activities of youth	20. Orientation toward the later periods of life

The Sheldon scale is not a device that can be employed by untrained persons; it is not as easily learned as is the somatotyping technique. He suggests that the user of the scale observe each subject closely for at least a year and then conduct a series of not less than 20 analytic interviews with him.[14] Ultimately, each of the 20 traits is scored on a 7-point scale. The numbered traits for each of the three components are not in every case mutually antithetical, or tri-polar. That is to say, there cannot always be two opposites to each trait. Sheldon could find only 5 sets of 3-way traits: 1. assertiveness of posture and movement, to which are opposed both relaxation and restraint; 17. extraversion of viscerotonia (free communication of feeling), to which the extraversion of somatotonia (lack of self-awareness and concentration upon the "outer reality"), and also the introversion or turning away from reality of the cerebrotonic are mutually antithetical; 18. Behavior under the influence of alcohol—relaxation and cheeriness, as opposed to quarrelsomeness, and also to general depression; 19. need of company, action, or solitude, respectively, when in trouble; 20. orientation toward family, childhood, and mother-love; as contrasted both with orientation toward the goals of youth (especially competitive sports), and orientation toward the supposed "understanding," security, and happiness of later years.[15]

[14] However, a single 20-minute interview by a practised observer gives good results.

[15] The difficulty Sheldon gets into in trying to find "three-way" sets of traits to match his three structural components reminds me of the famous three-cornered duel in "Mr. Midshipman Easy." The reader will remember that the tripartite disagreement between Mr. Easy; Mr. Biggs, the bos'n; and Mr. Eastupp, the purser's steward, was brought to issue on the field of honor in the following way. The duellists were stationed at the three points of a triangle; each faced a single opponent and turned his side elevation to another. The result

A glance at the column of 20 traits listed under viscerotonia will show that most of them are self-explanatory and need not be elaborated for purposes of the present volume. "Orientation toward people" (11) implies that the individual has something more than "a decent respect for the opinion of mankind"; he is profoundly concerned with the status, prestige, and general standing of people, and "his relative evaluation of an individual is likely to be a singularly accurate barometer of the general opinion of the community concerning that person." [16] "The untempered characteristic" (16) is explained by Sheldon as the impression of soft metal that will not take an edge and has no temper; no sparks fly; the personality is flabby, perhaps spongy.

The list of somatotonic traits includes few that require discussion here, interesting as they are. "The unrestrained voice" refers particularly to the carrying power of the voice rather than to mere volume. The somatotonic voice makes itself distinctly audible over other voices and sounds, often without perceptible effort on the part of the speaker. The general noisiness of somatotonia is partly the effect of the vigor of every movement and partly due to lack of inhibition—the heel-pounders, the door-slammers, the belly-laughers, the ack-ack coughers, and fog-horn snorers express thus their somatotonia. Sheldon states that somatotonic individuals of whatever age appear older than they really are; they mature and age rapidly in physique and deportment (but apparently not in mentality). Their primary interests are in the strenuous activities of youth and in competitive struggle; they dread advancing age and strongly encourage youthful participation and predominance in all of the affairs of the social order. They are the perennial undergraduates among college alumni, the "hearty fellows," the "go-getters," the "doers."

The physical tightness of the cerebrotonic manifests itself in stiff carriage, clenched hands, limbs tightly flexed when sitting, sphincter and general gastro-intestinal tension, fast shallow breathing, rapid pulse. The physiological over-responses include quick and violent vomiting, retching, and gagging reflexes; acute head colds of limited duration and without chest complications; general freedom from chronic infections of sinuses, throat, teeth, appendix; relative immunity to childhood diseases; but intensely irritable skins, general nervousness, frequent constipation; susceptibility to streptococcal sore throats and facile rise

---

was that Mr. Easy shot the bos'n through both cheeks, so that he couldn't pipe; the bos'n shot the steward through both buttocks, so that he couldn't sit down; and the steward missed Easy entirely.

[16] Sheldon and Stevens, *op. cit.*, p. 39.

of temperature under such infection. "Self-conscious motility of the eyes and face" implies alert, darting movements of the eyes with intense gaze and frequent blinking, together with tension of the facial musculature, which is nevertheless exceedingly mobile, alive, and responsive. Such a kaleidoscopic countenance is, however, virtually unreadable. "Inhibited social address" means lack of poise, self-conscious awkwardness, inability to "put the best foot foremost." Cerebrotonic people are prone to rapid and unpredictable changes of attitudes that lay them open to the charge of being unstable. They are, according to Sheldon, emotionally capricious.

In regard to the youthfulness of manner and appearance in the cerebrotonic, Sheldon says: [17]

If an adult, he appears to have bathed in the springs of youth. There is a strong suggestion about him that he will never grow old. The carriage of the body is youthful, as is the general expression of the face. The face lacks the hard, severe lines generally associated with somatotonic maturity. It lacks also the placid, bland relaxation associated with middle age in the more viscerotonic temperaments. There is an alert, intent, childlike or birdlike quality in the facial expression, which defines an antithesis both to the relative overmaturity of somatotonia, and to the overrelaxed, round-cheeked, suckling face of viscerotonia. The walk, the voice, the posture, the general atmosphere of suppressed intent eagerness, all suggest a singular, essential youthfulness.

Of course, the full development of the extremes of all of the traits within any of the three constellations—viscerotonic, somatotonic, or cerebrotonic—is rarely achieved in any single individual. Just as all persons present a blend of the structural components, so are the temperamental traits mixed and variable in their development. The crux of the problem is the extent to which any of the sets of 20 traits is integrated in a personality and the extent to which that integrated complex is associated or correlated with the morphological type (which is objectively classifiable).

Sheldon and Stevens are, in the opinion of the present writer, most scrupulous and rigorous in their examination of this problem and utterly disinclined toward overly optimistic and incautious interpretation of such positive results as have been found. The correlations of the three temperamental components with the corresponding structural components are about +.80 in each case (on a scale of 0 to 1), whereas the

[17] *Ibid.*, p. 87.

negative correlations between types of temperament and supposedly opposite types of body build are lower (from —.23 to —.63). The negative correlations between mesomorphy and ectomorphy (—.63) and between somatotonia and cerebrotonia (—.62) are higher than those between endomorphy and ectomorphy (—.41) and between viscerotonia and cerebrotonia (—.37); and the latter sets, in turn, higher than the negative correlations of endomorphy with mesomorphy (—.29) and of viscerotonia with somatotonia (—.34). Thus at both the physical and temperamental levels the greatest incompatibility is found between the second and third components and the least between the first and second.

Lest it should be suspected that the Sheldon Scale for Temperament has been artificially rigged to suit the somatotype component classification, it should be noted that the temperament scale was first set up, without any preconceived idea of the existence of the three main temperamental components, and later the somatotyping technique was developed as a means of seeking morphological validation for the temperamental classification. The present writer wishes to reiterate that the Sheldon-Stevens method of classifying temperament seems to him as a layman reasonable, plausible, and valid, but that he has absolutely no *locus standi* in the field of psychology. However, in morphology, as applied to Homo, he may perhaps claim some expert status, and he unequivocally asserts that the somatotype classification of Sheldon is, on the whole, scientifically sound.

When it comes to putting together the 7-point ratings on each of the 60 temperamental traits and arriving thus at a tripartite classification of personality (117, 235, 444, etc.), the difficulty of establishing any exact relationship between the two entities—physical and psychological—is painfully apparent. Thus Sheldon, in a basic study of 200 young men of academic background, found only 14 cases (7 per cent) of perfect agreement between temperament and somatotype (e.g., somatotype and index of temperament both 236). All of these occurred in fairly common somatotypes in which the first component (endomorphy) was in no case predominant, and in all cases but one was exceeded or tied by both of the other components (e.g., 344).[18] On the other hand, 11 cases (5.5 per cent) showed a radical disagreement between temperament and somatotype, amounting to at least two grades in one of the components (e.g. som. = 235, IT = 137). The dramatic disagreements generally are confined to the second and third components.

It is perhaps not surprising that in 21 cases of the 200, the Index of Temperament falls outside of the range of known somatotypes (i.e., the

18 *Ibid.*, p. 372.

IT presents permutations of numerals not found in somatotypes, for example 1–3–7). These "out-of-bounds" temperaments are probably commoner in psychopaths and maladjusted individuals than in so-called "normals" and "well adjusted" personalities. The first component is rarely involved in these disharmonies. Sheldon classifies these temperamental outsiders as 6 constitutional inferiors (especially in somatotonia), and 15 over-endowed personalities (9 with somatotonic, 6 with cerebrotonic excesses).

There are also in the 200 cases analyzed 19 (9.5 per cent) persons in whom the Index of Temperament reverses one of the morphological dominances (e.g., som. = 235, IT = 154). Nearly half of these men were involved in serious maladjustments, but the authors cautiously point out that apparent reversals of dominance may be in reality a spurious phenomenon arising from the inadequacy of the scale for temperament.

Given a considerable range of body build types and a perhaps larger assortment of temperamental types, classified according to Sheldon's system or by some other system, and correlated the one with the other, the next step is to study the relationship of these types to achievement in the world of society. Such investigations can be carried out primarily from the somatological leads—the determination of the relation of body build to achievement—or primarily from the temperamental classification. That is to say, the human material may be classified into temperamental types or categories; these subdivisions to be related to achievement. Beginning with the morphological classification is easier, because physical typing is quicker and more accurate.

Studies of the relation of individual type—physical or temperamental —to capacity for getting along in the world have been few as yet, partly because of the lack of proper scales of classification up to now, and, in greater measure, because of the reluctance of most psychologists and sociologists (the specialties particularly concerned) to recognize the importance and value of such studies. The reasons for this opposition are, in the former group, principally professional jealousy and, in the latter, downright anti-biological bias. The opportunity for students of human constitution to assist the armed services in the recent war by employing the techniques of this new science of the individual in the selection of personnel for combat and other specialized duties was wasted, for the most part, not because of the inertia of the military, but because of the obstructional tactics of fellow scientists temporarily in uniform.

Sheldon undertook the study of the relation of somatotype and Index of Temperament to achievement in his limited sample of 200 academic young men. He recognized no less than eight adaptational groups rang-

ing from a superior group to constitutional inferiors.[19] On the morphological side this admittedly insufficient investigation suggested that the
endomorph has the best chance of becoming a normal, well-adapted but
undistinguished person in an university (77 per cent). If he departs from
this category, he has a slightly better chance of being a constitutional
inferior than of rating distinguished achievement. He is unlikely to
become a troublesome misfit. A mesomorph enjoys an almost equal
chance (71.5 per cent) of being a normal, undistinguished member of
the university community, but is most likely to be a trouble-maker (21.5
per cent). He is virtually immune from constitutional inferiority, but
unlikely to be distinguished (7 per cent). The ectomorph goes to both
extremes (30 per cent distinguished achievement, 18.5 per cent of mis-
fits, and 7.5 per cent of constitutional degenerates). More and wider investigations of this nature are essential for establishment of the value
of constitutional studies.

Very recently, the Grant Study, Department of Hygiene, Harvard
University, has published preliminary findings of a six-year constitutional investigation of some 268 college undergraduates, defined as
"normal" in the sense that they were physically and mentally in good
health and in good academic standing. The anthropological techniques
employed included a partial utilization of Sheldon's somatotyping system and also more conventional anthropometric methods. The Sheldon
Scale for Temperament was not used; it was not published until the
Grant Study was far advanced. A personality rating scale devised by the
staff of the Grant Study was utilized with considerable success. The
traits included were mostly on a higher level of personality than Sheldon's temperamental characters. The Grant Study also employed psy-
chometric, physiological, medical, and sociological techniques. The results so far available are of great interest and importance, but they
cannot be summarized here. They conflict in no way with the findings
of Sheldon, but rather extend and confirm them.[20]

Body Build and Disease

The leader of clinical constitutional studies in this country for many
years has been Dr. George Draper of New York, a gifted diagnostician

[19] *Ibid.*, pp. 280–393.

[20] They are reported in detail in *"Young Man, You Are Normal,"* G. P. Putnam's Sons,
N.Y., 1945, written by the present author (who was not a member of the staff of the Grant
Study); and in a slightly later and more technical book, *What People Are,* by Clark W.
Heath and other members of the Grant Study Staff, Harvard University Press, Cambridge,
Massachusetts, 1945.

with an appreciation of the value of anthropometric techniques in medicine that is almost unique among the disciples of Aesculapius. With little support or encouragement from his own profession, Dr. Draper has conducted a constitutional clinic for nearly a quarter of a century. His contributions to the study of body build in relation to disease are of utmost importance and must be summarized here.[21]

In his studies of human constitution, Draper has used the analogy of a four-panelled screen, across the joined surfaces of which is spread the picture of man. The panels, representing anatomy, physiology, immunity, and psychology are so placed with respect to each other that the portrait is complete. Working with such a conceptual scheme, Draper has associated with himself on his clinical staff physical anthropologists, physiologists, psychologists, and statisticians. Nor has he neglected the genetic aspects of the subject.

On the anthropometric and morphological sides, Draper has used both the standardized anthropometric techniques, with many additions of his own, and, more recently, the Sheldonian technique of somatotyping. First, we shall consider results of the studies of various "disease groups" totalling 829 cases, secured by Draper by the use of anthropometry and what is sometimes called anthroposcopy (morphological observations). These are supplemented by the findings of his associate, Dupertuis, employing the Sheldon method of somatotyping.

GASTRIC ULCER AND DUODENAL ULCER

Gastric ulcer is somewhat commoner in males than in females (57 per cent of this disease group consists of males, according to Draper). Male gastric ulcer patients (25 cases) are below average in weight, slightly above in stature, and their mean ponderal index (weight/stature[3], the former in kilograms, the latter in centimeters) is the lowest of disease groups studied by Draper. They have small, narrow heads and narrow faces, with narrow, shallow chests of small circumference and narrow subcostal angles. Arm and hand dimensions are a trifle short, especially the upper arms and the fingers. The palms are somewhat narrow. These are average characters, but Draper thinks that some 75 per cent of gastric ulcer patients show distinctive bodily characteristics and that the rest may eventually prove to be capable of producing double lesions—ulcer and gall bladder pathology.

Draper's series of male duodenal ulcer patients (88) is much like the gastric ulcer group in measurements, but a little closer to the average

---

[21] Recently brought together in Draper, Dupertuis, and Caughey, *Human Constitution in Clinical Medicine*.

of all combined disease groups. Heads and upper faces are slightly longer than those of gastric ulcer patients and the relatively short arms are not in evidence. However, duodenal ulcer patients have decidedly narrower chests than those of the gastric ulcer group. The average structural component ratings, according to the Sheldon system, hardly confirm the impression of linearity and fragility of this group derived from the straight anthropometry. The third component (ectomorphy) averages 3.01 for males and 2.60 for females, which are about the same as for the totals of the Draper disease groups and below the Sheldon averages for college men and women. On the contrary, these patients are rather high in mesomorphy (males 4.51, females 4.26) as contrasted with the total disease series and with the Sheldon series. They have rather muscular physiques, which are lean but not delicate. They are somewhat low in the first component (roundness, softness—endomorphy).

GALL BLADDER

The clinical impression of gall bladder patients of both sexes emphasizes softness, roundness, and laterality of build. The males (28 cases) have wide heads, moderately short and broad faces, small gonial (jaw) angles. They also have broad, deep chests, with circumferences superior to those of other disease groups and broad subcostal angles. Arms are relatively long, but hands and fingers short and broad. The females suffering from this disease (90 cases) are well above average weight and have especially broad faces and round heads, broad deep chests of great circumference, and the broadest hips of any disease group. Their arms tend to be a little short and their hands rather large. In structural components, both male and female gall bladder patients show an excess of endomorphy (males 4.07, females 4.88). The average somatotypes for gall bladder are: males 4.4.2½, females 5.3½.2, as against the following for duodenal ulcer: males 3.4½.3, females 3½.4. 2½. Gall bladder sufferers are below average in muscularity and definitely low also in linearity and delicacy (ectomorphy).

PERNICIOUS ANEMIA

Males with pernicious anemia (31 cases) fall in average ponderal index about midway between the lighter combined ulcer groups and the stockily built gall bladder group. They have extremely short faces with very widely spaced eyes, somewhat short trunks, broad hips; short, deep, broad chests of great girth; broad pelves and long legs. The whole picture suggests to Draper an eunuchoidal trend.[22] The women (35 cases)

[22] Draper, Dupertuis, and Caughey, op. cit., pp. 122-123, 124.

are relatively the most slender of any disease group and have fairly small heads and faces. The shortness of the face is even more pronounced than in the men. Their chests are rather narrow, but very deep and short and of inferior circumference, although the subcostal angle is widest observed in any female disease group. Shoulders are narrow, pelves broad, trunk length slightly below average. Arms dimensions are average, but hands rather short. In contrast the legs appear rather long. These females confirm the eunuchoidal impression made by the males.

DIABETES MELLITUS

This disease is clinically divisible into two classes: I. Insulin-sensitive or pancreatic, II. Insulin-resistant or pituitary. In the first group are cases marked by acute onset of the disease, tendency to develop acute acidosis during periods of poor regulation, large blood sugar lowering effect of insulin, unstable equilibrium with rapid transitions from hyperglycemia and glycosuria to hypoglycemia and insulin shock. The second group is characterized by insidious onset of the disease, small tendency toward acidosis or coma, small blood sugar lowering with insulin treatment, stable equilibrium and little tendency toward insulin shock.[23] Corresponding to the two classes of diabetes, Draper and his associates found two main morphological types of diabetics (in a total of 225 cases), with the first divisible into two subclasses. Roughly, Class IA, pancreatic, shows a predominance of mesomorphy in both males and females (somatotypes: males 2½.5.3; females 4.4½.2). Pancreatic IB is higher in the first and third components and lower in the second (males 4.3.3½, females 4.3.3½). The second class, pituitary or insulin-resistant, is in both sexes strongly endomorphic (males, average somatotype 5.3.2½; females 5½.3.1½). In plain morphological terms, pancreatic IA has a marked muscular solidity with some linearity and fragility of bony structure; pancreatic IB has the same underlying skeletal structure but with a smooth overlay of fat obscuring the muscling; pituitary II is a massive, bulky group, with all breadth and volume measurements superior to those of the other two classes. It should be noted pancreatic IB consists of generally youthful patients who display a potentiality for becoming obese in later years. Draper suggests that the fat-muscle ratio is important in the two different classes of the disease. At one end of the scale preponderant muscle development is correlated with insulin-sensitiveness, severe diabetic disease, perhaps through faulty muscle-sugar combustion relationships. At the other end, massive fat component is correlated with

23 *Ibid.*, pp. 137, 179–186.

insulin-resistance, mildness of the disease, and possibly disturbance of fat-sugar storage and conversion relationships.

ACUTE RHEUMATIC FEVER

Draper's acute rheumatic fever series of males (25 cases) is characterized by long faces, with especially long and broad jaws; long trunks with broad shallow chests; broad shoulders and broad pelves, and fairly long arms and legs. Noticeable is the facial asymmetry of this group and marked irregularity of teeth and palate. Females of this group (44 cases) are below average in weight and slender in build, with narrow, shallow chests and long extremities. Asymmetries of head, face, and body are also notable. Draper suggests that mal-coordination of growth and developmental processes in this disease group may be the outstanding characteristic.[24]

ARTHRITIS

The relationship between body build and arthritis has been elucidated by Dr. Carl C. Seltzer as a result of the study of some 400 patients.[25] A prerequisite of this investigation was a proper classification of this disease into its various types: (1) *Rheumatoid*—polyarthritis with typical fusiform swelling of 6 months duration, x-ray changes, and elevated sedimentation index; (2) *Degenerative Joint Disease*—typical x-ray features including spurring, low or normal sedimentation index, etc.; (3) *Mixed;* (4) *Strumpel-Marie*—arthritis of spine, with x-rays showing fusing of sacro-iliac or calcification of spinal ligament, or both.

Rheumatoid arthritics are markedly different in body build from those afflicted by degenerative joint disease, even when allowance has been made for the much higher average age of the latter. Although the rheumatoids are more linear in body build (higher in ectomorphy), Seltzer finds that emphasis is to be placed rather upon the strong laterality, big-boned, big-muscled, highly pyknic (endomorphic) and tapering character of persons with degenerative joint disease. In males, the second component (mesomorphic or somatic) averages 4.9 in the degeneratives and 3.6 in the rheumatoids. The third component (ectomorphy) averages 3.8 in rheumatoids and only 2.4 in degeneratives. The females show somewhat similar differences, complicated by the lesser development of mesomorphy and higher endomorphic component in this sex.

Seltzer demonstrated the significant difference in body build between

24 *Ibid.*, pp. 123, 125–126.
25 Seltzer, "Anthropometry and Arthritis," pp. 163–203.

these two arthritic classes in a large number of measurements and indices. Before weight losses due to onset of the disease, rheumatoids
average nearly 30 pounds less than do degenerative joint disease patients (weights also taken prior to loss through ravages of the disease).
Rheumatoids have relatively and absolutely shorter arm spans; narrower, shallower, and generally smaller chests; smaller intercostal angles,
narrower hips, relatively narrower arm and hand dimensions, smaller
limb circumferences. The degenerative joint disease group has smaller
knee breadths and ankle breadths relative to chest circumference—
circumstances that point to a stronger tapering of their lower extremities. The rheumatoids also have narrower faces, noses, and jaws. Differentiation between the female arthritic groups closely parallels that
found in the males.

INFANTILE PARALYSIS

Some remarkable relations between physical type and susceptibility
to infantile paralysis have been uncovered by Draper in a study of
adequate series of both sexes and controls (148 paralyzed boys,
125 paralyzed girls, 229 well boys).[26] No "racial" differences in
susceptibility were found and no correlations with such characters as
the cephalic index. On the other hand, tabulation of measurements by
age groups clearly revealed that afflicted children tend to be larger than
well children in the periods before and after puberty. However, during
the period of sexual maturation there is no demonstrable difference
in growth between the sick and the well groups. Six observational peculiarities were found by Draper to show significant differences between
sick and well groups. The children who contracted the disease show
great excesses of black pigment spots, large and widely spaced central
incisor teeth, long curved eyelashes, joints capable of hyperextension,
and internal epicanthic eyefolds. Most of these characters may be regarded as foetal or infantile resemblances. In the eye-nose zone the
paralyzed children show certain retardations or foetal persistences, such
as relatively high interpupillary diameter with respect to face breadth,
and low nasal bridge (as well as the internal eye fold). There is also a
functional retardation in growth of the male genitalia and a tendency
toward feminism in body build. It then appears that susceptibility to
infantile paralysis is, as Draper says, "part of a definite type of faulty
constitution." Growth, in the sense of size augmentation, is certainly not
retarded in the polio-susceptible children, but development, in the
sense of maturation, is laggard. Children who show all or nearly all of

26 Draper, Dupertuis, and Caughey, *op. cit.*, pp. 186–206.

the five or six morphological criteria (black spots, long eyelashes, large and spaced central incisors, internal epicanthus, hyperextension of joints) are likely to contract the disease at an early age—before 7 years— and their paralyses usually involve the extremities, especially the lower. On the other hand, children with fewer of the stigmata seem more likely to contract polio between the ages of 7 years and puberty and to suffer from paralysis involving arms and trunk. Thus it appears that the age factor, together with signs of constitutional retardation, must be reckoned with in the matter of susceptibility.

Body Build and Mental Disorder

The studies of Kretschmer relating constitutional type to forms of mental disorder established an association of "pyknic" body build with manic-depressive insanity and "asthenic" build with schizophrenia. However, the Kretschmerian body build classification was inadequate for a proper investigation of these relationships. Sheldon and his associates have recently undertaken very extensive studies of large series of schizophrenes and manic-depressives, the results of which have not yet been published. Sheldon makes the preliminary notation that the most conspicuous characteristic of the schizophrenes is dysplasia rather than a concentration in any specific range of somatotypes.[27] In the schizophrenes a weakness of the second (mesomorphic) component in the thoracic region, an accentuation of the third component (ectomorphy) in the legs, and a high gynandromorphy (bisexuality) are the dysplasias manifested. Patients suffering from paranoid dementia praecox differ from the schizophrenes in being much more massive and stronger. The manic-depressives may be more mesomorphic than endomorphic, according to Sheldon. There is certainly some indication of predominant ectomorphy in schizophrenes. However, the elucidation of these relationships must await fuller applications of the somatotyping technique to adequately diagnosed mental disease groups.

Body Build and Behavior

It is inevitable that the physique of the individual influences his occupation in certain cases, his social attitudes, and his entire behavior and success or failure in society. When one stops to consider how little attention has been paid by the medical profession or by any of the

[27] Sheldon, Stevens, and Tucker, *The Varieties of Human Physique*, pp. 238–243.

"social" scientists to the effects of specific diseases upon the behavior of human beings in society, it is little wonder that the relation of physique to social activity in supposedly well and "normal" individuals has been almost entirely neglected.

No one with the merest smattering of biological science, or, in default of that, with ordinary ability to observe and pass judgment upon his fellow men, will deny the inequality of individual human physiques and the probability that many of the differences observed are of constitutional, hereditary origin. However, whether such constitutional inferiorities and superiorities are the result of genetic or environmental causes, they must influence and often determine the quality of human behavior. It is strange, then, that efforts to explore these relationships in their social implications should be opposed so bitterly by so-called social scientists and by many educators. When this opposition is not actuated by competitive jealousy or sheer ignorance, its principal source is probably the fear that the findings of investigations of such sociobiological interrelationships will result in the setting up of doctrines of biological determinism that are subversive of the principles of democracy. Such apprehension is based upon the suspicion that persons who promote the studies of the human constitution, of human genetics, and of race are not really interested in the improvement of the quality and behavior of all men, but are under-cover fascists. It is unfortunately true that German science and Nazi political and social theory have perverted the study of human improvement through biology to serve their aims of domination and oppression. However, the evil behavior of that degenerate nation should not render suspect all persons who wish to insure the future of democracy by maintaining and improving the quality of the individual human units upon which its success will depend.

Since the object of the present volume is to present an impartial, up-to-date account of human evolution for the intelligent layman and the unspecialized student, rather than to propagandize in behalf of measures designed to improve man biologically, the writer's own findings with respect to the constitutional status of criminals and insane inmates of civil and penal institutions will be neglected here. It may be mentioned, however, without fear of arousing the emotions of social equalitarians, that a crude division of native born American criminals of native parentage into nine classes according to individual combinations of height and weight yielded considerable evidence of behavioral differentiation by body build. Six of nine body build subgroups showed statistically significant differentiation in the nature of offenses committed, six of nine occupational differentiation, four of nine educational differentiation.[28] The classes were made by dividing the entire series of 3,910 males into three stature subgroups based upon the mean—short, medium, and tall—and then further subdividing each statural subgroup on the basis of its own mean weight—light, medium, and heavy. The nine subgroups thus distinguished varied continuously upward in gross size (stature and weight) and showed considerably more sociological than anthropological differentiation. The Sheldon system of somatotyping was not then available; hence no appraisal of structural components was made. This system of individual sortings by combinations of stature and weight has, however, the advantage of taking into consideration gross size, which seems to be very important behaviorally. Sheldon's system will acquire added usefulness when this size factor is adequately analyzed in its relationships both to somatotype and to temperament.

Sheldon's preliminary remarks upon his study of juvenile criminals, as yet unpublished, emphasize in these boys distinctly high gynandromorphy, as well as other dysplasias, and, on the motivational side, a driving somatotonia, poorly sustained and complicated by sensitive cerebrotonic characteristics.[29]

The Stages and Status of Human Evolution

It is possible tentatively to describe stages in the evolution of man from an anthropoid ape status down (or up) to his present evolutionary position and, in most cases, to give some sort of approximate chronology of this development—at least in geological terms. It is futile to attempt prophesies of the future course of human evolution, because that course depends largely upon the policies adopted by putatively civilized nations. If the sciences (biological and social) particularly concerned with man are given a plain mandate first to discover methods of correcting downward trends in human evolution and, second, to apply these methods to populations under the necessary social sanctions, we may perhaps look forward to considerable improvement in the organic quality of man and in his behavior. However, we shall never achieve an applied science of man until both biological scientists (geneticists, physical anthropologists, physiologists, psychologists, and various medical specialists) and social scientists (social anthropologists and sociologists) stop

28 Hooton, *Crime and the Man*, pp 84–100; *The American Criminal*, I, pp. 159–187, 281–283.
29 Sheldon, Stevens, and Tucker, *op. cit.*, pp. 254–259.

fighting each other or ignoring each other's findings and get down to work together at the exigent task that confronts them both and that cannot be accomplished by either separately. Isolationist attitudes and behavior in the science of man are just as foolish and impracticable as in international affairs under modern conditions of transportation and communication.

We shall begin our outline with the development of the apes, since the stages prior to that are not human at all but merely lower primate, insectivore, and so on down to the amoeba.

1. Lower Oligocene (35,000,000 years). First tiny, unspecialized anthropoid ape, possible precursor of gibbon or common ancestor (Propliopithecus).

2. Lower Miocene (19,000,000 years). First generalized giant apes, not strictly specialized for arboreal life, combining in dental, mandibular, and pedal characters resemblances to chimpanzee, orang, gorilla, man. (Proconsul of the Dryopithecus Family.)

3. Lower Pliocene (7,000,000 years). Terrestrial, bipedal, short-jawed apes with non-protrusive canines and generally humanoid dentitions (Australopithecinae), and probably terrestrial, bipedal, short-jawed proto-hominids with enlarging brains.

4. Lower Pleistocene (1,000,000 years). Fully erect, bipedal, prognathous, low-browed, massive-boned palaeoanthropic men, with brain volume midway between present gorilla and present man; large anthropoidal teeth; probably carnivorous, certainly tool-using (Pithecanthropus erectus).

5. Middle Pleistocene (500,000 years). Conservative and Progressive Neanderthaloids; brains of modern volume; some recession of jaws, incipient chin; highly evolved stone-chipping industry. Thick-skulled, big-brained chimpanzee-jawed precursor of Homo sapiens (Eoanthropus).

6. Upper Pleistocene (100,000 years). Gradual disappearance of palaeo-anthropic types of man, except in Java and Australia, through absorption by racial mixture with Homo sapiens forms, extermination, and replacement by mutants. Dominance of a robust-boned crude and somewhat generalized Homo sapiens type of predominantly White affinities, but with incipient Negroid and Mongoloid characters. Continued size reduction of teeth, jaws, and structures reinforcing face and brain-case —frontal and occipital tori.

7. Early Holocene (25,000 years). Primary races of Homo sapiens already differentiated as a result of dispersion of generalized types, isolation, inbreeding, mutations, natural selection of types suited for survival in various types of physical environment. In the White race little effeminization of skeletal type but incipient formation of primary subraces, partial depigmentation of stocks dwelling farthest north. Foetalization and dwarfing of certain tropic-dwelling and specialized proto-Negroids

resulting in formation of Negritos, followed by development of full-sized Negroes through mutation and possibly intermixture. Partial foetalization and specialization of Asiatic, desert-dwelling proto-Mongoloids. Beginning of the formation of secondary races by intermixture of primary races; Australian secondary race already established by Australoid-Tasmanoid fusion. Early migrants into America and begining of formation of American secondary race.

8. Early Neolithic (8,000 B.C. in Middle East). Beginning of domestication of plants and animals—change from natural collecting to artificial basis of subsistence. Increasing reliance upon agricultural and pastoral food acquisition. Beginning of sedentary communal life in fixed dwellings. Increase in epidemic and endemic diseases owing to lack of sanitation and closer and continuous personal contacts. Beginning of nutritional deficiencies due to unbalanced diets.

9. Early Bronze (4,000 B.C. in Middle East). Rise of urban life, division of labor, occupational selection of constitutional types, uneven distribution of wealth, rise of warfare for acquisition of territory, goods, and labor; differentiation of physical types by class and caste owing to slavery, with resulting intermixture of primary races; rapid increases of interbreeds between primary subraces and formation of secondary races. Some physical and cultural heterosis.

10. Second Early Iron Age (500 B.C. in the Mediterranean). Deterioration of sedentary urban populations through crowded and unsanitary living conditions with consequent spread of disease; unbalanced diets and malnutrition common. Beginning of development of relative immunities to certain diseases in stocks continuously subjected to their ravages. Migrations and incursions of warlike and tough barbarians, partly as a result of their obtaining efficient iron weapons. Panmixia of White subraces in urban European centers.

11. Migration Period (A.D. 500 in Europe). Decay and overthrow of Classic Mediterranean civilizations complete. Large infusions of vigorous and undeteriorated barbarian stocks. Widespread interbreeding, Mongoloid admixtures.

12. Middle Ages (A.D. 1000 in Europe). Spread of urban civilization and slum living conditions. Frequent urban malnutrition and depression of stature. More rapid transmission of epidemics.

13. Colonization Period (A.D. 1500). Formation of stabilized secondary races (e.g., Polynesian, American Indian, Indo-Dravidian) completed. Diffusion of pioneering European stocks to New World and elsewhere, with new hybridization. Beginning of wholesale decimation of primitive peoples by warfare, enslavement, and introduction of European culture and European diseases.

14. Period of Industrialization (A.D. 1800). Rapid increase of unhealthy occupations and bad, congested living conditions. Proliferation of occupational and constitutional diseases. Beginning of medical control of epidemics and effective surgery. Spread of tuberculosis, syphilis, dental disease, etc.

15. Period of Mechanization (A.D. 1900). Excessive dependence upon effort-saving devices tending to initiate functional atrophy—physical and mental—in urban populations. Increased nervous tension as a result of modern living conditions; insufficient maintenance of organic tone through healthy manual labor and outdoor exercise. General proliferation of the psychoses of civilization.

Vitaminic deprivation as a result of subsistence upon processed food; rampant dental caries and deficiency diseases; visual deterioration. Rapid decrease of infant mortality as a result of advance of sanitation and medical science; preservation and fostering of the physically and mentally ill-endowed with consequent reproduction of inferior off-spring; prolongation of life of the aged without rejuvenation of main-tenance of their bodily and mental powers. Support and proliferation of the socially incapable, feeble-minded, insane, and criminalistic through public and private charity. Obsolescence of natural selection; lack of effective genetic or environmental control of the population. Effects of modern facilities in transportation and communication: world wide dissemination of previously localized epidemics and agencies of infection; gradual break-down of isolating mechanisms of biological evolution (as well as social and cultural evolution); widespread and radical race mixtures with resultant potentialities both for good and for evil; marked changes in offspring of races and stocks that have emigrated from one environment to another—often in the direction of size increase.

Effect of modern mechanized warfare: negation of natural selection by use of physically and mentally best endowed young males for combat with consequent depletion of finest breeding stock; war neuroses of home front population as a result of aerial attacks with probably deleterious effects upon reproductive powers, previously limited to males, but now extended to females. Chronic malnutrition of in-habitants of subjugated areas; undue aggrandizement of mesomorphy and somatotonia—structural and temperamental components par-ticularly valuable for combat personnel.

General tendency in civilized countries (under peace conditions) toward increase of stature and linearity (ectomorphy) with narrowing and elongation of face and jaws and excessive disturbance of dental occlusion.

There are some disquieting and somber findings in latter stages of human evolution which the reader may ignore or disbelieve (if he thinks that they are based upon unsound evidence). It is not within the scope of the present work to discuss them in detail or to suggest remedies.[30] If there are any evidences of positive and progressive evolution of the physical man since Neolithic times, say 10,000 years ago, I am ignorant of them. On the other hand, it is easy enough to point out the appearance

[30] The present writer has dealt with these problems in several books: *Apes, Men, and Morons, Twilight of Man, Crime and the Man, Why Men Behave Like Apes and Vice Versa.*

and multiplication of retrogressive and degenerative characters. Some of these, such as the reduction and suppression of the wisdom teeth and the shrinking and malformation of the little toes, are trivial enough. What seems to me important is not the alteration of this or that anatomical detail that has lost its function, but rather the choice of selective breeding for sound human quality or for weakness and inferiority. Natural selection has been largely nullified by man's ignorant and purposeless monkeying with his own biological evolution, although most of this interference has been primarily exerted through cultural and social agencies. However, natural selection has never been purposeful, nor intelligent, nor, perhaps, altogether effective. Cannot man, with his vaunted intelligence and his ever-increasing control over everything in nature except himself, learn how to become a better animal? His evolutionary future is in his own hands, and, if they continue to be dirty and inept, he will re-infect it and himself. The prognosis would then be unfavorable.

Bibliography

Aberle, S. B. D. "Maternal Mortality among the Pueblos," *Amer. J. Phys. Anth.,* Vol. XVIII (1933).

Adam, William, "The Keilor Fossil Skull: Palate and Upper Dental Arch," *Mem. Nat. Mus. Melbourne,* No. 13, 1943.

Arambourg, C., Boule, M., Vallois, H., and Verneau, R. "Les Grottes Paléo-lithiques des Beni Segoual (Algérie)," *Arch. L'Inst. Paleon. Hum.,* Mem. XIII, 1934.

Bauman, John E. "The Strength of the Chimpanzee and Orang." *Scien. Month.,* Vol. XVI, 1923.

————. "Observations on the Strength of the Chimpanzee and Its Implications," *J. Mammal.,* Vol. VII, 1926.

Benedict, Francis G. "The Basal Metabolism of Some Browns and Blacks in Jamaica," in *Race Crossing in Jamaica.* Washington, D.C.: Carnegie Institution of Washington, 1929, Pub. 395.

Berckhemer, F. "Ein Menschenschädel aus den diluvialen Schottern von Steinheim," *Anth. Anz.,* X, 1932.

Bernstein, M., and Robertson, S. "Racial and Sexual Differences in Hair Weight," *Amer. J. Phys. Anth.,* Vol. X, 1927.

Bingham, H. C. *Sex Development in Apes.* Baltimore: The Johns Hopkins Press, 1928. Comp. Psychol. Mono., Vol. V, No. 1, Ser. no. 23.

Birdsell, Joseph B. *The Trihybrid Origin of the Australian Aborigine,* a thesis submitted in partial fulfillment for the degree of Doctor of Philosophy, Harvard University, 1941.

Bolk, A. "Origin of Racial Characteristics in Man," *Amer. J. Phys. Anth.,* Vol. XIII, 1929.

von Bonin, Gerhardt. "European Races of the Upper Palaeolithic," *Human Biol.,* Vol. VII, 1935.

Boule, Marcellin. *Les Hommes Fossiles.* 2nd. ed.; Paris: Masson, 1923.

Boule, Marcellin, and Vallois, H. "L'Homme Fossile d'Asselar (Sahara)," *Arch. L'Inst. Paleon. Hum.,* Mem. IX, 1932.

Bowles, Gordon T. *New Types of Old Americans at Harvard.* Cambridge: Harvard University Press, 1932.

Boyd, William C. "Blood Groups," *Tab. Biol.,* Vol. X, 1939.

Broom, Robert. "A Contribution to the Craniology of the Yellow-Skinned Races of South Africa," *J. Royal Anth. Inst.,* Vol. LIII, 1923.

Broom, Robert. "On Australopithecus and Its Affinities," in *Early Man*. Philadelphia: J. B. Lippincott Co., 1937. Ed. by G. G. MacCurdy.

——. "The Dentition of the Transvaal Pleistocene Anthropoids, *Plesianthropus* and *Paranthropus*," *Ann. Transvaal Mus.*, Vol. XIX, 1939.

——. "A Restoration of the Kromdraai Skull," *Ann. Transvaal Mus.* Vol. XIX, 1939.

——. "The Milk Molars of Man and the Anthropoids," *So. African Dent. J.*, Vol. XV, 1941.

——. "South Africa's Part in the Solution of the Problem of the Origin of Man," *So. African J. Scien.*, Vol. XL, 1943.

Brues, Alice M. *Sibling Resemblances as Evidence for the Genetic Determination of Traits of the Eye, Skin, and Hair in Man*. (Ms.) 1944.

Bryan, Kirk. "Geology of the Folsom Deposits in New Mexico and Colorado," in *Early Man*. Philadelphia: J. B. Lippincott, 1937, ed. by G. G. MacCurdy.

Candela, P. B. "The Introduction of Blood-Group B into Europe," *Human Biol.*, Vol. XIV, 1942.

——. *New Data on the Blood Groups of Apes and Monkeys*, paper read before the Amer. Ass'n. Phys. Anth., Apr. 16, 1942.

Carpenter, C. R. *A Field Study of the Behavior and Social Relations of Howling Monkeys (Alouatta Palliata)*. Baltimore: The Johns Hopkins Press, 1934. Comp. Psychol. Mono., Vol. X, No. 2, Ser. No. 48.

——. "Behavior of Red Spider Monkeys in Panama," *J. Mammal.*, Vol. XVI, 1935.

——. *A Field Study in Siam of the Behavior and Social Relations of the Gibbon (Hylobates Lar)."* Baltimore: The Johns Hopkins Press, 1940 Comp. Psychol. Mono., Vol. XVI, No. 5, Ser. No. 84, 1940.

Chen, K. K., and Poth, E. J. "Racial Differences in Mydriatic Action of Cocaine, Euphthalmine, and Ephedrine," *Amer. J. Phys. Anth.*, Vol XIII, 1929.

Clark, W. E. LeGros. "General Features of the Swanscombe Skull Bones, and the Endocranial Cast of the Swanscombe Bones," in "Report on the Swanscombe Skull," *J. Royal Anth. Inst.*, Vol. LXVIII, 1938.

Clark, W. E. LeGros, Cooper, D. M., and Zuckerman, S. "The Endocranial Cast of the Chimpanzee," *J. Royal Anth. Inst.*, Vol. LXVI, 1936.

Clark, W. E. LeGros and Morant, G. M. "Report on the Swanscombe Skull." *J. Royal Anth. Inst.*, Vol. LXVIII, 1938.

Clements, Forrest. "Racial Differences in Color Blindness," *Amer. J. Phys. Anth.*, Vol. XIV, 1930.

——. "Racial Differences in Mortality and Morbidity," *Human Biol.*, Vol. III, 1931.

Cohn, Alfred E. "Cardiovascular System and Blood," in *Problems of Ageing*. Baltimore: The Williams & Wilkins Co., 1939. Ed. by E. V. Cowdry.

Cook, Robert. "The Rh Gene as a Cause of Mental Deficiency," *J. Hered.*, Vol. XXXV, 1944.

Cooke, H. B. S., Malan, B. D., and Wells, L. H. "Fossil Man in the Lebombo Mountains, South Africa: The 'Border Cave,' Ingwavuma District, Zululand." *Man,* Vol. XLV., Nos. 1–18, London, 1945.

Coon, Carleton S. *The Races of Europe.* New York: The Macmillan Company, 1939.

Crawford, O. G. S. *Man and His Past.* Oxford: Oxford University Press, 1921.

Cummins, Harold. "Methodology in Palmar Dermatoglyphics," in *Measures of Men.* New Orleans: Mid. Amer. Res. Ser. Pub. No. 7, 1936.

Cummins, Harold, and Midlo, Charles. *Finger Prints, Palms and Soles, an Introduction to Dermatoglyphics.* Philadelphia: The Blakiston Company, 1943.

Cummins, Harold, and Spragg, S. D. S. "Dermatoglyphics in the Chimpanzee: Description and Comparison with Men," *Human. Biol.*, Vol. X, 1938.

Danforth, C. H. *Hair, with Special Reference to Hypertrichosis.* Chicago: American Medical Association, 1925.

Dankmeijer, J. "Some Anthropological Data on Finger Prints," *Amer. J. Phys. Anth.*, Vol. XXIII, 1938.

Dart, Raymond A. *"Australopithecus africanus:* The Man-Ape of South Africa," *Nature,* Vol. CXV, 1925.

———. "Recent Discoveries Bearing on Human History in South Africa," *J. Royal Anth. Inst.*, Vol. LXX, 1940.

———. "The Status of Australopithecus," *Amer. J. Phys. Anth.*, Vol. XXVI, 1940.

Darwin, Charles. *The Descent of Man.* London: J. Murray, 1909.

Davenport, C. B., and Danielson, F. H. *Heredity of Skin Color in Negro-White Crosses.* Washington, D.C.: Carnegie Institute of Washington, 1913. Pub. No. 108.

Davies, A. "A Re-Survey of the Morphology of the Nose in Relation to Climate," *J. Royal Anth. Inst.*, Vol. LXII, 1932.

Deniker, J. *The Races of Man.* New York: Charles Scribner and Sons, 1900.

Dixon, R. B. *The Racial History of Man.* New York: Chas. Scribner's Sons, 1923.

Dobzhansky, Theodosius. *Genetics and the Origin of Species.* 2nd. ed. rev.; New York: Columbia University Press, 1941.

Draper, George, Dupertuis, C. W., and Caughey, J. L. Jr. *Human Constitution in Clinical Medicine.* New York and London: P. B. Hoeber, Inc., 1944.

Drennan, M. R. "An Australoid Skull from the Cape Flats," *J. Royal Anth. Inst.*, Vol. LIX, 1929.

———. "Pedomorphism in the Pre-Bushman Skull," *Amer. J. Phys. Anth.*, Vol. XVI, 1931.

Drennan, M. R. "The Florisbad Skull and Brain Cast," *Trans. Royal Soc. So. Africa,* Vol. XXV, Pt. 1, 1937.

Dreyer, T. F. "A Human Skull from Florisbad, Orange Free State, with a Note on the Endocranial Cast," *Proc. Acad. Scien. Amster.,* Vol. XXXVIII, 1935.

Dublin, Louis I. "Longevity in Retrospect and in Prospect," in *Problems of Ageing.* Baltimore: The Williams & Wilkins Company, 1939. Ed. by E.V. Cowdry.

Duckworth, W. L. H. *Morphology and Anthropology.* Cambridge: Cambridge University Press, 1915. 2nd. ed.; Vol. I.

East, E. M., and Jones, D. F. *Inbreeding and Outbreeding.* Philadelphia: J. B. Lippincott Co., 1919.

Edwards, Edward A., and Duntley, S. Quimby. "An Analysis of Skin Pigment Changes after Exposure to Sunlight," *Science,* Vol. XC, No. 2332, 1939.

———. "The Pigments and Color of Living Human Skin," *Amer. J. Anat.,* Vol. LCV, 1939.

Ellis, Havelock. *Man and Woman.* 4th. ed.; London: The Walter Scott Publishing Co., Ltd., 1912.

Field, Henry. *Contributions to the Anthropology of Iran.* Anth. Series, Field Mus. Nat. Hist., Vol. XXIX, No. 2, Pub. No. 459, 1939.

Finch, Glen. "The Bodily Strength of Chimpanzees," *J. Mammal.,* Vol. XXIV, 1943.

Friedenwald, Jonas S. "The Eye," in *Problems of Ageing.* Baltimore: The Williams & Wilkins Co., 1939. Ed. by E. V. Cowdry.

Galloway, Alexander. "The Characteristics of the Skull of the Boskop Physical Type," *Amer. J. Phys. Anth.,* Vol. XXIII, 1937.

———. "The Nature and Status of the Florisbad Skull as Revealed by Its Non-Metrical Features," *Amer. J. Phys. Anth.,* Vol. XXIII, 1937.

Gardner, B. B., and MacAdam, D. L. "Colorimetric Analysis of Hair Color," *Amer. J. Phys. Anth.,* Vol. XIX, 1934.

Garner, R. L. *Apes and Monkeys: Their Life and Language.* Boston: Ginn and Company, 1900.

Gates, R. Ruggles. "Blue Eyes in Natives of Ceylon," *Brit. Med. J.,* Vol. I, 1938.
———. Ms., 1944.

Glaser, S. "Sweat Glands in the Negro and the European," *Amer. J. Phys. Anth.,* Vol. XVIII, 1934.

Glodt, Herbert R. *Melanogenesis: A Review,* thesis submitted for Honors in Anthropology, Harvard College, 1937.

Goodwin, A. J., and Lowe, C. van Riet. *The Stone Age Cultures of South Africa,* Ann. So. African Mus., Vol. XXVII, 1929.

Gregory, William King. *The Origin and Evolution of the Human Dentition.* Baltimore: Williams & Wilkins Co., 1922.

———. *Our Face from Fish to Man.* New York: G. P. Putnam's Sons, 1929.

Gregory, William King, and Hellman, Milo. "Evidence of the Australopithecine Man-Apes on the Origin of Man," *Science*, Vol LXXXVIII,
No. 2296, 1938.

———. "The Dentition of the Extinct South African Man-Ape *Australopithecus (Plesianthropus) transvaalensis* Broom, A Comparative and
Phylogenetic Study," *Ann. Transvaal Museum,* Vol. XIX, Pt. 4, 1939.

———. "The South African Fossil Man-Apes and the Origin of the Human
Dentition," *J. Amer. Dent. Assn.,* Vol. XXVI, 1939.

———. "The Upper Dental Arch of *Plesianthropus transvaalensis* Broom, and
Its Relations to Other Parts of the Skull," *Amer. J. Phys. Anth.,* Vol.
XXVI, 1940.

Gregory, William King and Hellman, Milo. "Revised Reconstruction of the
Skull of *Plesianthropus Transvaalensis* Broom." *Amer. J. Phys. Anth.,*
Vol. III, n.s. 1945.

Gregory, William King, Hellman, Milo, and Lewis, G. Edward. *Fossil Anthropoids of the Yale-Cambridge India Expedition of 1935.* Washington,
D.C.: Carnegie Institute of Washington, 1937. Pub. No. 495.

Greulich, W. W., and Thoms, Herbert. "The Growth and Development of
the Pelvis of Individual Girls before, during, and after Puberty." *Yale
Jr. Biol. & Med.,* Vol. XVII, No. 1, 1944.

Guha, B. S. *Census of India, 1931, Vol. I—India, Part III—Ethnographical.
A. Racial Affinities of the Peoples of India.* Simla: Government India
Press, 1935.

Guild, Stacy R. "The Ear," in *Problems of Ageing.* Baltimore: The Williams
& Wilkins Co., 1939. Ed. by E. V. Cowdry.

Haddon, A. C. *Races of Man and Their Distribution.* New York: The Macmillan Co., 1925.

Heath, Clark W. *What People Are.* Cambridge: Harvard University Press,
1945.

Honoré, F. "Un Nouveau Singe à Facies Humaine," *L'Illustration,* Apr. 13,
1929.

Hooton, Earnest A. "The Asymmetrical Character of Human Evolution,"
Amer. J. Phys. Anth., Vol. VIII, 1925.

———. "Methods of Racial Analysis," Vice-presidential address to Section
H, A.A.A.S., *Science,* Vol. LXIII, No. 1621, 1926.

———. "Note on the Anthropometric Characters of the Yahgan and the
Ona," in *Indians of Tierra del Fuego.* New York: Museum of the American Indian, Heye Foundation, Vol. X, 1928.

———. *Apes, Men, and Morons.* New York: G. P. Putnam's Sons, 1937.

———. *The American Criminal.* Cambridge, Mass.: Harvard University
Press, 1939.

———. *Crime and the Man.* Cambridge, Mass.: Harvard University Press,
1939.

———. *Twilight of Man.* New York: G. P. Putnam's Sons, 1939.

Hooton, Earnest A. *Why Men Behave Like Apes and Vice Versa.* Princeton: Princeton University Press, 1940.

———. *Man's Poor Relations.* Garden City, New York: Doubleday, Doran & Co., Inc., 1942.

———. *Young Man, You Are Normal.* New York: G. P. Putnam's Sons, 1945.

Howells, W. W. *Mankind So Far.* Garden City, New York: Doubleday, Doran & Co., Inc., 1945.

Hrdlička, Aleš. *Skeletal Remains Suggesting or Attributed to Early Man in North America.* Washington, D.C.: B.A.E., 1907. Bull. 33.

———. *Physiological and Medical Observations among Indians of Southwestern United States and Northern Mexico.* Washington, D.C.: B.A.E., 1908. Bull. 34.

———. *Early Man in South America,* Washington, D.C.: B.A.E., 1912. Bull. 52.

———. *The Skeletal Remains of Early Man.* Washington, D.C.: Smith. Miscl. Coll., 1930. Pub. No. 3033, Vol. LXXXIII.

———. *Children Who Run on All Fours.* New York: Whittlesey House, 1931.

Hughes, B. L. *The Physical Anthropology of Native Born Armenians,* thesis submitted for degree of Doctor of Philosophy, Harvard University, 1938.

Humphry, G. M. *Old Age.* Cambridge: Macmillan & Bowes, 1889.

Huxley, T. H. "On the Relations of Man to the Lower Animals," in *Man's Place in Nature.* New York: E. P. Dutton and Co., 1902.

Ivanovsky, A. "Physical Modifications of the Population of Russia under Famine," *Amer. J. Phys. Anth.,* Vol. VI, 1923.

Ivy, A. C. "Digestive System," in *Problems of Ageing.* Baltimore: The Williams & Wilkins Co., 1939. Ed. by E. V. Cowdry.

Jenks, Albert Ernest. *Pleistocene Man in Minnesota, a Fossil Homo Sapiens.* Minneapolis: The University of Minnesota Press, 1936.

Joleaud, L. "Remarques sur l'Evolution des Primates Sud-Américains à Propos du Grand Singe du Venézuéla," *Rev. Scien.,* May, 1929.

Jones, F. Wood. *Arboreal Man.* London: E. Arnold, 1916.

———. *Man's Place among the Mammals.* New York: Longmans, Green & Co., 1929.

Keith, Sir Arthur. "The Suppression and Transmutation of Lower Vertebral Segments," *J. Anat.,* Vol. XXXVII, 1903.

———. *The Human Body.* London: Williams and Norgate, 1912.

———. *The Antiquity of Man.* 2nd. ed.; Philadelphia: J. B. Lippincott Co., 1925.

———. *New Discoveries Relating to the Antiquity of Man.* New York: W. W. Norton & Co., Inc., 1931.

———. "A Resurvey of the Anatomical Features of the Piltdown Skull with

Some Observations on the Recently Discovered Swanscombe Skull," *J. Anat.*, Vol. LXXIII, 1938–39.

Kingsley, J. S. *The Vertebrate Skeleton from the Developmental Standpoint.* Philadelphia: P. Blakiston's Sons & Co., 1925.

von Koenigswald, G. H. R. "Eine fossile Säugetierfauna mit Simia aus Südchina," *Konin. Neder. Akad. Weten. Amster., Proc.*, Vol. XXXVIII, 1935.

——. "Ein fossiler Hominide aus dem Altpleistocän von Java," in *Die Ingenieur in Nederlandsch-Indië*, Vol. IV, 1936.

——. "Erste Mitteilung über einen fossilen Hominiden aus dem Altpleistocän Ostjavas," *Konin. Neder. Akad. Weten. Amster., Proc.*, Vol. XXXIX, 1936.

——. "Ein Unterkieferfragment des Pithecanthropus aus den Trinilschichten Mitteljavas," *Konin. Neder. Akad. Weten. Amster., Proc.*, Vol. XL, 1937.

——. "A Review of the Stratigraphy of Java and Its Relations to Early Man," in *Early Man.* Philadelphia: J. B. Lippincott Co., 1937. Ed. by G. G. MacCurdy.

——. "Ein Neuer Pithecanthropus-Schädel," *Konin. Neder. Akad. Weten. Amster., Proc.*, Vol. XLI, 1938.

——. "Anthropological and Historical Studies Relating to the Earliest Evidence of Man." Washington, D.C.: Carnegie Institute of Washington, 1939. *Year Book*, No. 38.

——. *The South African Man-Apes and Pithecanthropus.* Washington, D.C.: Carnegie Institute of Washington, 1942. Pub. No. 530.

von Koenigswald, G. H. R., and Weidenreich, Franz. "The Relationship between Pithecanthropus and Sinanthropus," *Nature,* Vol. CXLIV, 1939.

Köhler, Wolfgang. *The Mentality of Apes.* New York: Harcourt, Brace and Co., 1925.

von Krogh, Chr. "Serologische Untersuchungen über die stammesgeschichtliche Stellung einiger Primaten," *Anth. Anz.*, Vol. XIII, 1937.

Krogman, W. M. *A Bibliography of Human Morphology, 1914–1939.* Chicago: The University of Chicago Press, 1941.

Leakey, L. S. B. *The Stone Age Races of Kenya.* London: Oxford University Press, 1935.

——. "A Miocene Anthropoid Mandible from Rusinga, Kenya," *Nature,* Vol. CLII, 1943.

Lewis, G. Edward. "Preliminary Notice of New Man-like Apes from India," *Amer. J. Scien.*, Vol. XXVII, 1934.

Lewis, Julian Herman. *The Biology of the Negro.* Chicago: The University of Chicago Press, 1942.

Lothrop, S. K. *The Indians of Tierra del Fuego.* New York: Mus. Amer. Ind., Heye Found., Contr., Vol. X, 1928.

de Loys, Francis. "A Gap Filled in the Pedigree of Man?" *Illus. London News,* June 15, 1929.

Macalister, A. "Physiognomy," *Ency. Brit.* 1911, 11th. ed., Vol. XXI.

MacConaill, M. A. "The Stature of Male School Children in Relation to Hair and Eye Colour," *Ann. Eugen.,* Vol. VIII, 1937–38.

————. "The Classification of Hair and Eye Colour upon Developmental and Genetic Bases," *Ann. Eugen.,* Vol. XI, 1941–42.

MacConaill, M. A., and Ralphs, F. L. "Post-Natal Development of Hair and Eye Colour, with Special Reference to Some Ethnological Problems," *Ann. Eugen.,* Vol. VII, 1936.

MacCurdy, G. G. *Human Origins.* New York: D. Appleton and Co., 1924.

MacInnes, D. G. "Notes on the East African Miocene Primates," *J. E. Africa and Uganda Nat. Hist. Soc.,* Vol. XVII, 1943. London.

Mahony, D. J. "The Keilor Fossil Skull: Geological Evidence of Antiquity," *Mem. Nat. Mus. Melbourne,* No. 13, 1943.

————. "The Problem of Antiquity of Man in Australia," *Mem. Nat. Mus. Melbourne,* No. 13, 1943.

Marcais, J. "Decouverte de restes humains fossiles dan les gres quaternaires de Rabat (Maroc)," *L'Anth.,* Vol. XLIV, 1935.

Marett, J. R. de la H. *Race, Sex and Environment, a Study of Mineral Deficiency in Human Evolution.* London: Hutchinson's Scientic and Technical Publications, 1936.

Marston. A. T. "The Swanscombe Skull," *J. Royal Anth. Inst.,* Vol. LXVII, 1937.

Martin, R. *Lehrbuch der Anthropologie.* Jena: Gustav Fischer, 1928.

Maslow, A. H., and Harlow, H. F. "Comparative Behavior of Primates, II, Delayed Reaction Tests on Primates at Bronx Park Zoo," *J. Comp. Psychol.,* Vol. XIV, 1932.

McCown, Theodore D., and Keith, Sir Arthur. *The Stone Age of Mount Carmel. The Fossil Human Remains from the Levalloiso-Mousterian.* London: Oxford University Press, 1939. Vol. II.

Mohr, O. L. "Woolly Hair, a Dominant Mutant in Man." *Jr. Hered.,* Vol. XXIII, No. 9, 1932.

Mollison, Theodor. "Die Verletzungen am Schädel und den Gliedmassenknochen des Rhodesiafundes," *Anth. Anz.,* Vol. XIV, 1938.

Mollison, Theodor, and Giesler, W. "Untersuchungen über den Oldoway Fund," *Verhand. Gesell. für Phys. Anth.,* Vol. III, 1929.

Montandon, George. "Un Singe Actuel en Amérique," *Rev. Scien.,* May 11, 1929.

Morant, G. M. "Studies of Palaeolithic Man, IV. A Biometric Study of the Upper Palaeolithic Skulls of Europe and of Their Relationships to Earlier and Later Types," *Ann. Eugen.,* Vol. IV, 1930.

————. "The Form of the Swanscombe Skull," in "Report on the Swanscombe Skull," *J. Royal. Anth. Inst.,* Vol. LXVIII, 1938.

Morton, D. J. "The Evolution of the Human Foot," *Amer. J. Phys. Anth.*, V (1922), VI (1924).

———. "Evolution of Man's Erect Posture," *J. Morph. Physiol.*, Vol. 43, 1926

Myres, J. L. "Primitive Man in Geological Time, Mongoloid Man," in *Cambridge Ancient History*, Vol. I, 2nd ed., The Macmillan Co., N.Y., 1923.

Nissen, Henry W. *A Field Study of the Chimpanzee*, Baltimore: The Johns Hopkins Press, 1931. Comp. Psychol. Mono., Vol. VIII, No. 1, Ser. No. 36, 1931.

Nyèssen, D. J. H. *The Races of Java*. Weltevreden, D.E.I.: Indisch Comité voor Wetenschappelijke Onderzoekingen, 1929.

Okladnikov, A. P. "Neanderthal Man and His Culture in Central Asia," *Asia*, Vol. XL, 1940.

Oppenoorth, W. F. F. "Ein neuer diluvialer Urmensch von Java," *Nat. und Mus.*, Vol. LXII, 1932.

———. "The Place of Homo Soloensis among Fossil Men," in *Early Man*. Philadelphia: J. B. Lippincott Co., 1937, ed. by G. G. MacCurdy.

Pearl, R. "The Biology of Death," *Scien. Month.*, Vol. XII, 1921.

Pei, W. C. "A Preliminary Report on the Late-Palaeolithic Cave at Choukoutien," *Bull. Geol. Soc. China*, Vol. XIII, No. 3, 1934.

———. "On the Upper Cave Industry," *Peking Nat. Hist. Bull.*, Vol. 13, Pt. 3, 1939.

Pipkin, S. B., and A. C. "Hair of Albino Negroes," *J. Hered.*, Vol. 35, No. 7, 1944.

Pycraft, W. P. "Description of the Human Remains" in *Rhodesian Man and Associated Remains*. London: The British Museum, 1928.

Quenstedt, W. and A. *Hominidae Fossiles*, Fossilium Catalogus; I: Animalia, pars 74, Apr. 15, 1936.

Reynolds, E. *Evolution of the Human Pelvis in Relation to the Mechanics of Erect Posture*, Papers, Peabody Mus. Amer. Arch. Ethnol., Vol. XI, 1931.

Roberts, Frank H. H. Jr. "The Folsom Problem in American Archaeology," in *Early Man*. Philadelphia: J. B. Lippincott Company, 1937, ed. by G. G. MacCurdy.

Schiff, Fritz. "Racial Differences in Frequency of the 'Secreting Factor,'" *Amer. J. Phys. Anth.*, Vol. XXVII, 1940.

Schiff, Fritz, and Boyd, William C. *Blood Grouping Technic*. New York: Interscience Publishers, Inc., 1942.

Schokking, C. P. "Another Woolly-Hair Mutation in Man." *J. Hered.*, Vol. XXV, No. 9, 1934.

Schultz, Adolph H. "Embryological Evidence of the Evolution of Man," *J. Wash. Acad. Scien.*, Vol. XV, No. 12, 1925.

———. "The Skeleton of the Trunk and Limbs of Higher Primates," *Human Biol.*, Vol. II, 1930.

Schultz, Adolph H. "Die Körperproportionen der erwachsenen catarrhinen Primaten, mit spezieller Berücksichtigung der Menschenaffen," *Anth. Anz.,* X, 1933.

―――. "Eruption and Decay of the Permanent Teeth in Primates," *Amer. J. Phys. Anth.,* Vol. XIX, 1935.

―――. "Characters Common to Higher Primates and Characters Specific for Man," *Quart. Rev. Biol.,* Vol. II, 1936.

―――. *Growth and Development of the Chimpanzee.* Washington, D.C.: Carn. Inst. of Wash., 1940. Pub. No. 518, Cont. to Embry., No. 170.

Seltzer, Carl C. "Anthropometry and Arthritis, I, Differences between Rheumatoid and Degenerative Joint Disease: Males; II, Females." *Medicine,* Vol. XXII (1943), No. 2.

―――. *Physical Characteristics of the Yaqui Indians, in Studies of the Yaqui Indians of Sonora, Mexico,* Texas Technological College Bulletin, Vol. XII, (1936), No. 1.

Senyürek, Muzaffer Süleyman. "Pulp Cavities of Molars in Primates," *Amer. J. Phys. Anth.,* Vol. XXV, 1939.

―――. "The Dentition of *Plesianthropus* and *Paranthropus,*" *Ann. Transvaal Mus.,* Vol. XX, 1941.

Shapiro, Harry L. *Migration and Environment,* New York and London: Oxford University Press, 1939.

―――. "Physical Differentiation in Polynesia," in *Studies in the Anthropology of Oceania and Asia,* Papers, Peabody Mus. Amer. Arch. Ethnol., Vol. XX, 1943.

Sheldon, W. H., and Stevens, S. S. *The Varieties of Temperament.* New York: Harper & Brothers, 1942.

Sheldon, W. H., Stevens, S. S., and Tucker, W. B. *The Varieties of Human Physique.* New York: Harper & Brothers, 1940.

Smith, Geoffrey. *Primitive Animals,* The Cambridge Manuals of Science and Literature. Cambridge: Cambridge University Press, 1911

Smith, Grafton Elliot. "The Natural Subdivision of the Cerebral Hemisphere," *J. Anat. Physiol.,* Vol. XXXV, 1901.

―――. "The Evolution of Man." *Smithsonian Institution Annual Report.* Washington, D.C.: Smithsonian Institution, 1912.

―――. *Essays on the Evolution of Man.* Oxford: Oxford University Press, 1927.

Snyder, L. H. *The Principles of Heredity.* 2nd. ed.; New York: D. C. Heath and Co., 1940.

Snyder, L. H., Schonfeld, M. D., and Offerman, E. M. "The RH Factor and Feeblemindedness," *J. Hered.,* Vol. 36, No. 1, 1945.

Sonntag, C. F. *The Morphology and Evolution of Apes and Man.* London: John Bale, Sons, and Danielsson, Ltd., 1924.

Steggerda, Morris. *Maya Indians of Yucatan.* Washington, D.C.: Carnegie Institute of Washington, 1941. Publication No. 531.

Steggerda, Inez D. and Morris, and Lane, Mary Steele. "A Racial Study of Palmar Dermatoglyphics with Special Reference to the Maya Indians of Yucatan," in *Measures of Men*. New Orleans: Mid. Amer. Res. Ser., 1936. Pub. No. 7.

Straus, William L., Jr. "The Posture of the Great Ape Hand in Locomotion and Its Phylogenetic Implications," *Amer. J. Phys. Anth.*, Vol. XXVII, 1940.

Suk, V. "Anthropological and Physiological Observations on the Negroes of Natal and Zululand," *Amer. J. Phys. Anth.*, Vol. X, 1927.

Swanscombe Committee of the Royal Anthropological Institute. "Report on the Swanscombe Skull," *J. Royal Anth. Inst.*, Vol. LXVIII, 1938.

Taylor, Griffith. *Environment, Race, and Migration*. Chicago: The University of Chicago Press, 1937.

de Terra, Helmut. "The Siwaliks of India and Early Man," in *Early Man*. Philadelphia: J. B. Lippincott Company, 1937, ed. by G. G. Mac-Curdy.

Thoms, Herbert. "Newer Aspects of Pelvimetry," *Amer. J. Surg.*, n.s. Vol. XXXV (1937), No. 2.

Thomson, A., and Buxton, L. H. D. "Man's Nasal Index in Relation to Certain Climatic Conditions," *J. Royal Anth. Inst.*, Vol. LIII, 1923.

Tilney, F. *The Brain from Ape to Man*. New York: Paul B. Hoeber, Inc., 1928.

Tindale, Norman B. "The Antiquity of Man in Australia," *Aust. J. Scien.*, Vol. III, 1941.

Tindale, Norman B., and Birdsell, Joseph B. "Results of the Harvard-Adelaide Universities Anthropological Expedition, 1938–1939, Tasmanoid Tribes in North Queensland." Adelaide: *Rec. S. Aust. Mus.*, 1941. Vol. VII, No. 1, 9 pp.

Todd, T. Wingate. "Skeletal Records of Mortality," *Scien. Monthly*, Vol. XXIV, 1927.

————. "Ageing of Vertebrates," in *Problems of Ageing*. Baltimore: The Williams & Wilkins Co., 1939. Ed. by E. V. Cowdry.

Trotter, Mildred. "The Form, Size, and Color of Head Hair in American Whites," *Amer. J. Phys. Anth.*, Vol. XIV, 1930.

Weidenreich, Franz. "The Sinanthropus Population of Choukoutien (locality 1) with a Preliminary Report on New Discoveries," *Bull. Geol. Soc. China*, Vol. XIV, 1935.

————. *The Mandibles of Sinanthropus pekinensis: A Comparative Study*, Palaeon. Sin., Ser. D, Vol. VII (1936), fasc. 3.

————. *Observations on the Form and Proportions of the Endocranial Casts of Sinanthropus pekinensis, Other Hominids and the Great Apes: A Comparative Study of Brain Size*, Palaeon. Sin., Ser. D, Vol. VII (1936), fasc. 4.

————. "*Sinanthropus pekinensis*, and Its Position in the Line of Human Evolution," *Peking Nat. Hist. Bull.*, Vol. X (1936), Pt. 4.

Weidenreich, Franz. "*Sinanthropus pekinensis*—A Distinct Primitive Hominid," *Proc. Anth. Soc. Tokyo, and Jap. Soc. Ethnol.*, 1936.

———. "The New Discoveries of *Sinanthropus pekinensis* and Their Bearing on the *Sinanthropus* and *Pithecanthropus* Problems," *Bull. Geol. Soc. China*, Vol. XVI, 1936–37.

———. *The Dentition of Sinanthropus pekinensis: A Comparative Odontography of the Hominids*, Palaeon. Sin., n.s. D, No. 1, whole ser. 101, 1937.

———. "The Forerunner of *Sinanthropus pekinensis*," *Bull. Geol. Soc. China*, Vol. XVII (1937), No. 2.

———. "The New Discovery of Three Skulls of *Sinanthropus Pekinensis*," *Nature*, Vol. CXXXIX, 1937.

———. "Reconstruction of the Entire Skull of an Adult Female Individual of *Sinanthropus pekinensis*," *Nature*, Vol. CXL, 1937.

———. "The Relation of *Sinanthropus pekinensis* to *Pithecanthropus, Javanthropus* and Rhodesian Man," *J. Royal Anth. Inst.*, Vol. LXVII, 1937.

———. "Discovery of the Femur and the Humerus of *Sinanthropus pekinensis*," *Nature*, Vol. CXLI, 1938.

———. "The Duration of Life of Fossil Man in China and the Pathological Lesions Found on His Skeleton," *Chinese Med. J.*, Vol. LV, 1939.

———. "On the Earliest Representatives of Modern Mankind Recovered on the Soil of East Asia," *Peking Nat. Hist. Bull.*, Vol. XIII (1939), Pt. 3.

———. *The Skull of Sinanthropus pekinensis, A Comparative Study on a Primitive Hominid Skull*, Palaeon. Sin., n.s. D, No. 10, whole ser. 127, 1943.

———. *Giant Early Man from Java and South China*, Anth. Papers, Amer. Mus. Nat. Hist., Vol. 40, Pt. 1, New York, 1945.

Weinert, Hans. *Ursprung der Menscheit*. Stuttgart: Ferdinand Enke verlag, 1932.

———. "Africanthropus: Der erste Affenmenschenfund aus dem Quartär Deutsch-Ostafrikas," *Quartär I*, 1938.

———. "Der erste afrikanische Affenmensch, *Africanthropus njarasensis*," *Der Biol.*, Vol. VII, 1938.

———. "Africanthropus njarasensis, beschreibung und phyletische Einordnung des ersten Affenmenschen aus Ostafrika," *Zeit. Morph. Anth.*, Vol. XXXVIII, 1939.

Westermarck, E. *The History of Human Marriage*. London: Macmillan and Co., Ltd., 1921.

Wiener, A. S. "Evolution of the Human Blood Group Factors," *Amer. Nat.*, Vol. LXVII (1943), No. 770.

———. "Nomenclature of the Rh Blood Types," *Science*, Vol. XCIX (1944), No. 2583.

Wiener, A. S., Belkin, R. B., and Sonn, E. B. "Distribution of the A_1-A_2-B-O, M-N, and Rh Blood Factors among Negroes in New York City," *Amer. J. Phys. Anth.*, Vol. II, n.s., 1944.

Wiener, A. S., Sonn, E. B., and Chien, L. Yi. "Blood Groups, Subgroups, M-N and Rh Types of Chinese," *Amer. J. Phys. Anth.*, Vol. II, n.s., 1944.

Wiener, A. S. and Wade, Dorothy. "Rh and Hr Factors in Chimpanzees." *Science,* Vol. CII, No. 2642, 1945.

Wilder, H. H. "Racial Differences in Palm and Sole Configuration," *Amer. J. Phys. Anth.*, Vol. V, 1922.

Williams, George Dee. *Maya-Spanish Crosses in Yucatan,* Papers Peabody Mus. Amer. Arch. Ethnol., Vol. XIII (1931), No. 1.

Wood, E. J. *Giants and Dwarfs.* London: R. Bentley, 1869.

Woolley, C. L., *The Sumerians,* London: Oxford University Press, 1928.

Wunderly, J. "The Keilor Fossil Skull: Anatomical Description," *Mem. Nat. Mus. Melbourne,* No. 13, 1943.

Wylie, Philip. *Generation of Vipers.* New York: Farrar & Rinehart, 1942.

Yearsley, Macleod. "Pathology of Left Parietal Bone," in *Rhodesian Man and Associated Remains.* London: The British Museum, 1928.

Yerkes, Robert M. *Almost Human.* New York: The Century Co., 1925.

———. *Chimpanzees.* New Haven: Yale University Press, 1943.

Yerkes, Robert M. and Ada W. *The Great Apes.* New Haven: Yale University Press, 1929.

Zeuner, Frederick E. *The Age of Neanderthal Man, with Notes on the Cotte de St. Brelade, Jersey, C.J.* London: Arch. Inst. London, 1940. Occas. Papers No. 3, Geochro. Tab. No. 2.

Zuckerman, S. *The Social Life of Monkeys and Apes.* London: Kegan Paul, Trench, Trubner and Co., 1932.

———. *Functional Affinities of Man, Monkeys, and Apes.* New York: Harcourt, Brace and Co., 1933.

Appendix. Elementary Anthropometry

Contents

Appendix

Elementary Anthropometry

The brief descriptions of anthropometric technique included in this Appendix are intended for students who wish to acquaint themselves with the rudiments of laboratory procedure in the study of the human skeleton and with the basic measurements and observations taken upon living subjects. The pages that follow do not purport to be a comprehensive laboratory manual of physical anthropology; such a work would be a full-sized volume in itself.[1] The student who is willing to read the directions carefully and practise assiduously can learn the measuring techniques by himself, but it is highly desirable that his methods be checked by a professional physical anthropologist before he embarks upon original research. Masses of anthropometric data painstakingly collected by insufficiently instructed persons have had to be discarded because of deficiencies in the techniques of the worker.

Morphological observations upon qualitative features of bones or of living persons cannot be learned satisfactorily from any existing textbook. Satisfactory grading of attributes, such as size of brow-ridges, requires extensive morphological experience on the part of the observer or else personal tuition by a physical anthropologist whose ideal standards of rating have already been fixed by such experience. Even veteran anthropologists have difficulty in maintaining consistency in these subjective ratings and still greater difficulty in equating their standards with those of other equally experienced observers. For·this reason, no

---

[1] The standard textbook of physical anthropology, which contains descriptions of all of the ordinary measurements employed in the study of the skeleton and of the living subject is Rudolf Martin, *Lehrbuch der Anthropologie,* 2nd ed., 3 vols., Jena, 1928.

Useful laboratory manuals published in English are:

Aleš Hrdlička, *Practical Anthropometry* (Philadelphia, Wistar Institute of Anatomy, 1939).

Charles B. Davenport, *Anthropometry and Anthroposcopy* (Cold Spring Harbor, N.Y.: Eugenics Research Association Handbooks, 1927).

Louis P. Sullivan, and H. L. Shapiro, *Essentials of Anthropometry* (New York: American Museum of Natural History, 1928).

The last two mentioned are pocket manuals devised for the use of explorers and field-workers. They deal exclusively with measurements and observations to be taken upon living subjects.

attempt has been made in the following pages to enter into the intricacies of the grading of morphological attributes. The number and complexity of these morphological observations may be judged from the Harvard blanks, here reproduced as text figures. The beginning student is advised to confine himself to caliper measurements and to such observations as fall into "present" or "absent" categories, or into such definite classes as present themselves in the case of eye color and hair color.

The Human Skeleton

MATERIALS AND INSTRUMENTS

The minimum requirements of material for the study of the human skeleton include an articulated skeleton and at least several disarticulated skeletons or archaeological remains of complete or fragmentary human burials. If the bones recovered from archaeological excavations are dry and fragile, they should be washed carefully, dried slowly (not in the sunlight), and then treated with alvar.[2] This preparation will harden them so that they can be handled with impunity. If skulls and bones are not too fragmentary and in too poor condition, they can be reconstructed from pieces, and there is no better way to learn the human skeleton than by mending bones. Do not throw away odd fragments and isolated small bones and teeth; they can be used for practise in identification. In the Harvard laboratory course in physical anthropology, a weekly bone quiz is given in which numbered fragmentary specimens are rotated through the class, with approximately one minute allotted to the identification of each bone or part of a bone, half credit being awarded for correctly identifying the bone by name and the other half for naming the side of the body to which it belongs. Human skeletons do not come into the hands of the physical anthropologist wired together, nor, for the most part complete, unless they are derived from dissecting-room material.

The instruments necessary for the study of the skeleton include a sliding caliper, a spreading caliper, a steel metric tape, a measuring board, a goniometer, and a skull pad.

The sliding caliper is equipped with sharp points at one end of its arms, for use in measuring bones, and blunt tips at the other end of its arms, for measuring the living. It is graduated in centimeters and millimeters up to 25 cm. A much larger sliding caliper, or an anthropometer, is useful in measuring articulated pelves. The spreading caliper has a

2 Cf. G. Woodbury, "The Use of Polymerised Vinyl Acetate and Related Compounds in the Preservation and Hardening of Bone," *Am. J. Phys. Anthrop.*, 1936, Vol. XXI, pp. 449–450.

hinge in the middle and curved arms facing each other and terminating in rounded tips. It is graduated in centimeters and millimeters up to 30 cm. These instruments are not made by American manufacturers. Before the war they could be obtained from Rickenbach & Sohn, Zürich, and from Alig and Baumgärtel, Berlin. However, it is possible to find utilizable substitutes by looking through the catalogs of tool-makers and the manufacturers of medical and surgical instruments. Steel spring metric tapes are obtainable at hardware stores.

Satisfactory measuring boards can be made of ⅞" seasoned lumber. Those used in the Harvard laboratory are 22½" long and 12" wide. At one end is mortised an upright 8½" high, at a precise right angle. The surface of the measuring board is covered with millimeter paper upon which are tacked at intervals of 7 cm. three parallel cardboard strips, 50 cm. long, graduated in millimeters and centimeters, which are furnished by the U.S. Bureau of Standards. A sheet of celluloid tacked over the millimeter paper and the measuring strips prevents soiling and wear of the graduated surfaces. An L-shaped wooden square, made of two pieces mortised together at a precise right angle, completes the measuring device. The dimensions of the squares used in the Harvard laboratory are 9¼" long, 1¼" wide, 4½" high, and ½" thick. The moveable square is placed against one end of a bone, the other end of which abuts against the upright of the measuring board. The length is read off the graduated surface of the board from the edge of the square.

A goniometer for the measurement of angles may be constructed by hinging a small wooden flap to a bottom board and affixing to edge of the latter a metal or a celluloid protractor. The hinged flap moves through 180° and the angle is read from the position of its edge against the upright protractor.

The skull pad is a flattened ring or doughnut stuffed with hair or some other packing material and covered with canvas or leather. Its outside diameter is 8½" and the diameter of the enclosed hole is 3¼", the thickness of the pad 1¼". A skull may be rested in almost any position upon this pad, so that the hands of the operator are free for the manipulation of the caliper or other measuring device.

HOW TO LEARN THE SKELETON

The student should begin by reading the descriptions of the various bones contained in any standard text-book of human anatomy and checking these descriptions against actual specimens of the bones themselves, both loose and in the articulated skeleton. He should learn the names of the various parts of each bone and the principal muscular attachments, the centers of ossification, the ages at which the epiphyses unite, etc. Drawing the bones is very helpful, as is also the identification of broken fragments. The anthropologist must be able to visualize the entire bone from any of its identifiable parts. Fragments may be identified by checking them against complete bones or articulated skeletons. The student is advised to begin with the vertebral column, learning the regional differences first, then the distinctive vertebrae. He may then begin to practise the measurements of the lumbar column. Next come the pelvis and sacrum; then the femur and the rest of the lower extremity. The shoulder girdle and sternum, the upper extremity, and the skull, follow in that order. Foot- and hand-bones are learned most easily by the help of specimens in which the numerous small bones of these extremities are loosely strung on cat-gut. These are obtainable at anatomical supply houses. In studying the skull, begin with the bones of the brain-case; then proceed to the facial bones, and end with the teeth. The broken skull fragments from archaeological excavations are invaluable for the learning of cranial variations.

For laboratory exercises in anthropometry, series of bones already measured and observed by the instructor should be set out for measurement and observation by the student. His results can then be handed in and corrected. In the basic laboratory course in physical anthropology at Harvard University, the instructor lectures upon a specific region of the skeleton or a single bone, while in the laboratory the students are learning the morphology of that bone, practising its measurements, the calculation of necessary indices, and the requisite observations, and at the same time are undergoing weekly bone quizzes on the parts currently studied. These bone identification quizzes are cumulative, in that they include all areas of the skeleton previously covered, and they increase in difficulty, in as much as smaller and trickier fragments of the various bones are presented from time to time. A full term of 12 weeks with a minimum of 4 laboratory hours per week and 3 hours of lectures should acquaint the student with the osteology and osteometry of the skeleton, except the skull. In this space of time he should also be familiarized with all essential details of cranial variation. However, an elementary knowledge of craniometric technique and observations upon cranial morphology requires another half-term.

The Sex of the Skeleton

The determination of the sex from the postcranial skeleton in adults is easy and certain in about 80 per cent of cases, difficult but possible in another 10 per cent of cases, and quite dubious in the remainder. In general, males have larger and heavier bones than females, with the ridges that mark the muscular attachments much more prominent. The articular heads of the humerus and the femur are larger in males and the acetabulum is larger and deeper. However, the best criteria of differentiation are in the pelvis (cf. pp. 253–254). In the mounted pelvis, the brim or inlet has a greater posterior breadth in the female and often a greater antero-posterior length, so that the entire cavity of the true pelvis is roomier. The outlet of the male pelvis is much more constricted, because the ischia converge downward, instead of diverging, as in females. The distance between the ischiatic spines is thus reduced in the male. The lower portion of the male sacrum is not bent backward and upward sharply, as in the female, so that the entire pelvic aperture is much smaller in the male. On the complete pelvic bone (the innominate bone), the sacro-sciatic notch is characteristically deep and narrow in the male, wide and shallow in the female. Just behind the sacro-sciatic notch on the ilium and just in front of the articular surface for the sacrum, the female bone usually shows a deep, wide, pitted groove or sulcus, of considerable extent. In the typical male bone this pre-auricular sulcus is usually only a faint groove.

The body of the pubic bone, where the two halves of the pelvis meet in front (the symphysial region), is lower and broader in the female than in the male. Below this region, the pubic arch in the female is Norman, in the male Gothic. The sub-pubic angle made by these descending branches of the two pubic bones and by their union with the ascending branches of the ischia is much narrower in the male than in the female. Also, in the female the descending branches of pubis are lipped outward and there is usually a constriction or waist in the ramus of the pubis just below the broad symphysial body. In the male, the descending branch of the pubis is broader, flatter, usually uneverted, and without the constriction at its upper end. The false pelvis, formed by the hollowing of the ilia above the pelvic brim or inlet, is usually wider in the male; the male ilia flare much more laterally and the iliac crest is more rugged, with a prominent tuberosity near the middle of its course. The female ilia rise more nearly vertically and are more gracile. The female sacrum is relatively broader and shorter than that of the male.

Some of these differences are ascertainable in the pelves of foetuses, children, and adolescents. However, a certain proportion of adult pelves show no clear differentiation of the sexual characteristics or display contradictory combinations. The honest anatomist admits his inability to sex such skeletons with any certainty.

The Age of the Postcranial Skeleton

The age of the individual at death is ascertainable with a fair degree of accuracy in immature skeletons from the extent of ossification of bones and epiphyses (and in the skull from the eruption of the teeth, for which cf. pp. 234–235, 732). In adult skeletons the determination of age is precarious and approximate.

At birth, every vertebra consists of three pieces, the body and the two halves of the vertebral arch. The halves of the arches unite behind in the first year of life, beginning in the lumbar region and extending upward. About the third year, the bodies of the upper cervicals are joined to their arches; in the lower lumbars, this union is not completed until the sixth year. The sacral vertebrae are formed from central bodies, each with an upper and lower epiphysial plate, lateral parts (which also have epiphyses), and the vertebral arches. The vertebral arches are united with their bodies between the second and fifth or sixth years, beginning with the lower sacrals. The epiphysial plates for the bodies appear about the sixteenth year, those for the lateral parts between the eighteenth and twentieth years. The intervertebral fibrocartilages that separate the bodies of the sacral vertebrae begin to disappear from the eighteenth year in the lowest sacral vertebrae. All segments of the sacrum are united between the twenty-fifth and thirtieth years of life. The segments of the coccyx do not usually begin to join until after maturity. Late in life they are often fused together and united with the sacrum.

At birth, the three parts of the pelvic bone—ilium, ischium, and pubis—are united only by cartilage. By the seventh or eighth year the inferior branches of the pubis and ischium are almost completely united by bone. The articulation of the three bones in the acetabulum forms a Y-shaped cartilage. The ossification of this cartilage begins in the pubis-ischium branch of the Y at about 12 years and fuses at about 15–16 years.

The age order of the union of epiphyses has been determined accurately by Stevenson from large series of skeletons of known age in the collection of Western Reserve University.[3] The sequence is definite and constant for man, apparently irrespective of sex and race. As a matter of fact, the same sequence is found fairly generally throughout other mammalian forms. Stevenson's findings are summarized in the following table.

[3] Paul H. Stevenson. "Age Order of Epiphyseal Union in Man," *Am. J. Phys. Anthr.*, 1924, Vol. VII, pp. 53–93.

AGE ORDER OF EPIPHYSIAL UNION IN MAN
(Data from Stevenson)

Order	Begins	Completed
1. Distal extremity of humerus.	15 y. (?)	Before 17 y.
(a) Medial epicondyle	16 y. (?)	Before 17 y.
2. Coracoid process of scapula	15 y.	Before 16 y.
3. Three elements of innominate	15 y. (?)	Before 17 y.
4. Head of radius	Beginning of 18 y.	End of 18 y.
(a) Olecranon of ulna	16 y. (?)	17 y.
5. Head of femur	Beginning 18 y.	18 y.
(a) Lesser and greater trochanters	Lesser slightly earlier, greater same as head	18 y.
6. Tuberosities of ribs	18 y.	22 y. (very unreliable)
7. Distal extremities of tibia and fibula	18 y.	End of 18 y.
8. Proximal extremity of tibia	Beginning 18 y.	Beginning 20 y.
(a) Proximal extremity of fibula	" "	" "
9. Distal extremity of femur	Beginning 19 y.	Beginning 20 y. (or earlier)
10. Tuberosity of ischium	Beginning 18 y.	Beginning 19 y.
11. Distal extremities of radius and ulna	Beginning 19 y.	19 y.
12. Head of humerus	19 y.	20 y.
13. Crest of ilium	19 y.	21 y.
14. Heads of ribs	20 y.	22 y. (very unreliable)
15. Ramal epiphysis of pelvis	19 y.	22 y.
16. Clavicle	22 y. (?)	28 y.

The determination of age at death from the postcranial skeleton is much more difficult in mature individuals. The most reliable indicators are the face of the pubic symphysis, certain features of the scapula, the closing of the cranial sutures, and the wear of the teeth. (For cranial sutural obliteration and teeth, cf. pp. 145–146, 734.)

In general, the adult individual approaching middle age begins to develop bony outgrowths at the sites of attachments for muscles and ligaments. Increase of the definition of so-called muscular ridges is due to aging rather than to muscular power. The texture of bones becomes less ivory-like after 25 years, and, particularly in the skull, more "matte," and eventually pitted and granular. "Moth-eaten" patches appear in certain bones. Demineralization takes place, especially in the spongy tissue of the bone. This is a phenomenon of middle and advanced age, irregular in its progression and often complicated by nutritional and pathological conditions.

Todd has recognized the following phases of appearance and ossification of the face of the pubic symphysis in mature skeletons:

1. Age 18–19. Symphysial surface traversed by horizontal ridges separated by well marked grooves; no definite delimiting margins, no definition of extremities.

2. Age 20–21. Surface still grooved, but grooves toward dorsal margin beginning to be filled with fine textured bone; dorsal limiting margin begins to develop; no delimitation of extremities; foreshadowing of ventral bevel.

3. Age 22–24. Progressive obliteration of ridge and furrow system; dorsal margin becoming more defined; ventral beveling more pronounced; no delimitation of extremities.

4. Age 25–26. Great increase of ventral beveled area; complete definition of dorsal margin through formation of dorsal plateau; commencing delimitation of lower extremity.

5. Age 27–30. Little change except sporadic and premature attempts at formation of ventral rampart; lower extremity and dorsal margin increasingly definite; commencing formation of upper extremity.

6. Age 30–35. Increasing definition of extremities; development and completion of ventral rampart; absence of lipping of symphysial margin.

7. Age 35–39. Face changes from granular to finer texture; commencing bony outgrowths into tendons and ligaments.

8. Age 39–44. Symphysial face smooth and inactive; oval outline complete; extremities clearly defined; no rim; no lipping.

9. Age 45–50. Symphysial face presents a marked rim; dorsal margin uniformly lipped; ventral margin irregularly lipped.

10. Age 50– . Symphysial face eroded and showing erratic ossification; ventral margin more or less broken down.

The above phases of metamorphosis of the symphysial face have been determined from a study of adult male White pelves. In the White female, the ridge and furrow system is somewhat more delicate and there is some retardation in the first two phases (1. Age 16–?; 2. Age ?–25; 3. Age 25–26?, 4. Age 26–27; 5. Age 27–30; 6. Age 30–36; 7. Age 36–40; 8. Age 40–45; 9. Age 45–50; 10. Age 50–). In the female a delay of two or three years occurs in the consolidation of the ventral aspect of the bone, so that the symphysial face is already complete and quiescent before the ventral aspect. Ossifications of tendinous and ligamentous attachments begin about 5 years later in the female. Lipping of the margins and pathological erosion of the symphysial surface are less extensive. However, altogether the differences are so slight that they would be of little utility in sex determination.

Todd also studied the changes in the symphysis of the Negro-White hybrids of both sexes. The differences from the Whites are not important. The formation of a symphysial rim begins in the Negro-White male some 10 years earlier than in Whites, but the rim formation tends to be aborted. Lipping of the dorsal margin begins 5 years earlier, but is also arrested. The ventral erosion and surface rarefaction characteristic of the last phase in Whites also commences some 5 years earlier, but is not so marked.

On the whole, the elementary student is advised not to devote too much attention to these details of difference, but merely to place any pelvis that he has to examine within the White male schema, so far as he can.

The age changes in the adult scapulae are clearly defined by Graves, but without the multiplicity of chronological phases described by Todd for the pubic symphysis.[4] They consist of: (a) lipping of the glenoid fossa, beginning in the early thirties at the notch at the juncture of the upper and middle thirds of the ventral glenoid margin; (b) similar lipping of the clavicular facet; (c) development of a plaque of bone on the under surface of the tip of the acromion process; (d) granulation or scale-like proliferation of the smooth trapezial surface of the scapula below the spine; (e) roughening and increase in size of the ridges running across the scapula; (f) development of atrophic spots or "moth-eaten patches," especially in the thin area below the scapular spine; (g) buckling, pleating, or wrinkling of the dorsal surface. All of these changes begin in the thirties and become more apparent with advancing age. The warping or distortion rarely is pronounced before the fortieth year.

READING CALIPERS AND RECORDING MEASUREMENTS

Standard anthropometric instruments are graduated in centimeters and millimeters. It is sufficient to read to the nearest millimeter. The use of a Vernier scale for finer readings is inadvisable, since the anatomical points to be measured cannot be located precisely enough to warrant the splitting of millimeters. If the scale of the caliper seems to read exactly halfway between the two divisions marking a millimeter, add or drop the half millimeter to make an even number. In measurements of the skeleton it is most convenient to record in millimeters rather than in centimeters and decimals. In grosser measurements, such as stature, it is customary to record in whole centimeters, followed by the decimal point and the millimetric fraction (e.g., 175.6 cm.) Actually, in such large measurements, sufficient accuracy is obtained even by reading to the nearest whole centimeter.

The Most Important Measurements and Observations upon the Postcranial Skeleton

LUMBAR VERTEBRAE

Measurements

1. *Vertical ventral diameter of centrum.* From the middle point of

[4] W. W. Graves, "Age Changes in the Scapula," *Am. J. Phys. Anthr.*, Vol. V, 1922, pp. 21–23.

the superior ventral border of the vertebral body (centrum) to the middle point of the inferior ventral border.
Sliding caliper.

2. *Vertical dorsal diameter of centrum.* From the middle point of the superior dorsal border of the vertebral body to the middle point of the inferior dorsal border.
Sliding caliper or spreading caliper.

Vertical lumbar index:

$$\frac{\text{Sum of dorsal vertical diameters of centra} \times 100}{\text{Sum of ventral vertical diameters}}$$

Divisions of index:

Kurtorachic　(convex forward)　　x– 97.9
Orthorachic　(straight)　　　　　98–101.9
Koilorachic　(concave)　　　　　102– x

THE PELVIS AND SACRUM

Measurements

On each of the mounted pelves take the following measurements and calculate the indices given below:

1. *Pelvic height:* Distance from highest point of iliac crest to deepest point of ischial tuberosity—right side, left side, mean. Large sliding caliper.
2. *Greatest pelvic breadth:* Maximum diameter outside of iliac crests.

Breadth-height index: $\dfrac{(1)\ \text{Height} \times 100}{(2)\ \text{Greatest breadth}}$

3. *Sagittal diameter of pelvic inlet:* Middle point of edge of sacral promontory to middle of posterior ridge of upper symphysial border. Small sliding caliper.
4. *Transverse diameter of pelvic inlet:* Maximum transverse diameter of pelvic inlet between *Liniae arcuatae* perpendicular to preceding measurement.

Index of the pelvic inlet: $\dfrac{(3) \times 100}{(4)}$

Platypellic　　　x — 89.9
Mesatipellic　　90 — 94.9
Dolichopellic　95 — x

5. *Greatest breadth of the ischiatic notch:* From the ischiatic spine to the posterior inferior iliac spine. Sliding caliper.
6. *Anterior length of sacrum:* From middle anterior point of promontory to middle anterior point of lower border.

7. *Sacral breadth:* Greatest breadth of sacrum at level of anterior projection of the auricular surfaces.

Length-breadth index of sacrum: $\dfrac{(7) \times 100}{(6)}$

Dolichohieric	x — 99.9
Subplatyhieric	100 — 105.9
Platyhieric	106 — x

Observations

(1) *depth* and

(2) *breadth of ischiatic notch* (e.g. depth: sm., medium, deep)

(3) *pre-auricular sulcus:* width and depth [5]

(4) *sub-pubic angle:* sm., medium, large

(5) *phase of pubic symphysis:* (approximate) [6]

(6) *ischia:* parallel, converging, diverging

THE FEMUR

Measurements

1. *Length bicondylar:* Length of the femur in natural position with the condyles resting against the vertical wall of the measuring board and the movable square tangent to the extremity of the femoral head.

2. *Length maximum:* Greatest length from the internal condyle to the extreme point of the head on the measuring board.

3. *Diameter of the head, maximum:* Taken with the sliding caliper.

4. *Sub-trochanteric diameter, antero-posterior:* Sagittal diameter of the shaft below the lesser trochanter at the level of the greatest transverse diameter. (Sliding caliper)

5. *Sub-trochanteric diameter, lateral:* Transverse diameter perpendicular to the preceding.

Index of platymeria — $\dfrac{\text{Antero-posterior diameter (4)} \times 100}{\text{Lateral diameter (5)}}$

Hyperplatymeric	x — 74.9
Platymeric	75 — 84.9
Eurymeric	85 — 99.9
Stenomeric	100 — x

6. *Middle shaft diameter, antero-posterior:* Diameter between the dorsal and ventral surfaces of the femur at the middle of the shaft, perpendicular to the ventral surface. (Sliding caliper)

[5] Cf. D. E. Derry, "Sexual and Racial Characters of the Human Ilium," *J. Anat.*, Vol. LVIII, 1923, pp. 71–83.

[6] Cf. T. W. Todd, "Age Changes in the Pubic Bone," *Am. J. Phys. Anthr.*, Vol. III, 1920, pp. 285–334; Vol. IV, 1921, pp. 1–70, 333–406, 407–424.

7. *Middle shaft diameter, lateral:* Transverse diameter at the same point, perpendicular to the preceding. (In this and in the preceding avoid oblique measurements.)

$$\text{Middle index } \frac{\text{Middle diameter, lateral (7)} \times 100}{\text{Middle diameter, antero-posterior (6)}}$$

Observations

(1) *Sex:* Arrange male and female femora in separate columns, also lefts and rights, paired and odd.

Sex determined by size, robusticity, diameter of head. Below 46 mm. generally female.

(2) *Sub-trochanteric region:* [7]

 (1) Crista hypotrochanterica: absent, submedium, medium, pronounced, very pronounced.

 (2) Fossa hypotrochanterica: the same as above.

 (3) Third trochanter: the same as above.

(3) *Middle shaft:* [7]

 (1) Shape: oval, elliptical, prismatic, quadrilateral.

 (2) Linea aspera: absent, submedium, medium, slight pilaster, medium pilaster, pronounced pilaster.

(4) *Degree of torsion of the upper portion:* Observed by laying the femur on the table and noticing the angle of the head and the neck with the plane of the posterior surface of the condyles: negative torsion, neutral, slight (less than 10 degrees), medium torsion (10–20 degrees), pronounced torsion (20–30 degrees), very pronounced. In paired femora, notice differences in torsion between right and left.

THE TIBIA

Measurements

1. *Maximum length (minus spine):* Osteometric board. Place the tibia with the malleolus against the vertical wall of the osteometric board and with the long axis of the bone parallel with the long axis of the board. The tibia should rest on its dorsal surface. Place the square against the anterior edge of the lateral condyle external to the tibial spine.

2. *Middle diameter (antero-posterior):* Sliding caliper. Mark the middle point on the tibial crest. Measure antero-posterior diameter.

3. *Middle diameter (lateral):* Perpendicular to preceding. Place tibial crest against graduated bar of caliper.

[7] Cf. Aleš Hrdlička, "Shape of Shaft," *Am. J. Phys. Anthr.*, Vol. XIX, 1934, pp. 477–479, 479–481, "Sub-trochanteric region," *op. cit.*, Vol. XIX, 1934, pp. 17–37; Vol. XXIII, 1937, pp. 127–198

Middle Index $= \dfrac{(3) \times 100}{(2)}$

4. *Nutritive foramen diameter (antero-posterior):* Antero-posterior diameter at level of base of nutritive foramen on external surface of bone. Sliding caliper.
5. *Nutritive foramen diameter (lateral):* Perpendicular to preceding. Sliding caliper.

Index of platycnemia $- \dfrac{(5) \times 100}{(4)}$

Hyperplatycnemic	x — 54.9
Platycnemic	55 — 62.9
Mesocnemic	63 — 69.9
Eurycnemic	70 — x

Observations

(1). *Shape of shaft at middle.*[8] Use Hrdlička's set of mounted casts of tibia at middle of shaft and classify according to type: (1) ordinary prism, (2) lateral prism, (3) external surface concave, (4) posterior surface divided in two by vertical ridge (more or less quadrilateral), (5) interior border indistinct, posterior half of bone oval, (6) plano-convex, (7) indefinite.

(2) *Retroversion of head:* Absent, submedium, medium, pronounced.

(3) *Lateral condyle:* Convex or concave.

(4) *Squatting facets:* Extensions of inferior articular surface above anterior lip of tibia. Present or absent.

THE SCAPULA

Measurements

1. *Morphological breadth:* Diameter between the highest point of the superior angle and the lowest point of the inferior angle. (Sliding caliper)
2. *Morphological length:* Diameter between the middle point of the glenoid fossa and the point on the vertebral border midway between the two ridges terminating the scapular spine. (Spreading caliper) Mark point on vertebral border with pencil.
3. *Breadth of infra-spinous fossa:* Diameter between the inferior angle of the scapula and the point on the vertebral determined in No. 2. (Sliding caliper)
4. *Breadth of supra-spinous fossa:* Diameter between the superior angle of the scapula and the point on the vertebral border determined in No. 2. (Sliding caliper)

[8] Aleš Hrdlička, "Study of the Normal Tibia," *Am. Anthr.*, Vol. XI, 1898, pp. 307–312.

Indices

1. Scapular index: $\dfrac{\text{Morphological length (2)} \times 100}{\text{Morphological breadth (1)}}$

2. Infra-spinous index: $\dfrac{\text{Breadth of infra-spinous fossa} \times 100}{\text{Morphological length}}$

3. Supra-spinous index: $\dfrac{\text{Breadth of supra-spinous fossa} \times 100}{\text{Morphological length}}$

Observations

(1) *Vertebral border* [9] (from scapular spine to inferior angle): Convex, straight, concave.

(2) *Scapula notch:* Absent, slight, medium, deep, foramen.

(3) *Shape of acromion process:* Sickle, triangular, quadrangular, intermediate.

(4) *Age changes:* [9] Lipping of glenoid fossa, pleating, buckling, atrophic patches. Classify each in following categories: absent, sub-medium, medium, pronounced.

THE HUMERUS, THE RADIUS, THE ULNA

The elementary student is advised to confine his measuring to the maximum lengths of these bones and to the maximum diameter of the humeral head. The former are of use in reconstructing stature and limb proportions, the latter in the determination of sex.

STATURE RECONSTRUCTION FORMULAE

Male Stature

(a) $81.306 + 1.880$ Femur
(b) $70.641 + 2.894$ Humerus
(c) $78.664 + 2.376$ Tibia
(d) $85.925 + 3.271$ Radius
(e) $71.272 + 1.159$ (Femur + Tibia)
(f) $71.443 + 1.220$ Femur + 1.080 Tibia
(g) $66.855 + 1.730$ (Humerus + Radius)
(h) $69.788 + 2.769$ Humerus + .195 Radius
(i) $68.397 + 1.030$ Femur + 1.557 Humerus
(k) $67.049 + .913$ Femur + .600 Tibia + 1.225 Humerus — .187 Radius

Female Stature

(a) $72.844 + 1.945$ Femur
(b) $71.475 + 2.754$ Humerus
(c) $74.774 + 2.352$ Tibia
(d) $81.224 + 3.343$ Radius
(e) $69.154 + 1.126$ (Femur + Tibia)
(f) $69.561 + 1.117$ Femur + 1.125 Tibia

[9] Cf. W. W. Graves, "Types of Scapulae," *Am. J. Phys. Anthr.*, Vol. IV, 1921, pp. 111–128.
——, "Age Changes in the Scapula," *op. cit.*, Vol. V, 1922, pp. 21–34.

(g) 69.911 + 1.628 (Humerus + Radius)
(h) 70.542 + 2.582 Humerus + .281 Radius
(i) 67.435 + 1.339 Femur + 1.027 Humerus
(k) 67.469 + .782 Femur + 1.120 Tibia + 1.059 Humerus — .711 Radius

The formulae above were developed by Professor Karl Pearson for the reconstruction of stature from dry bones.[10] The best results are obtained from formulae (e), (f), and (i). The length of the femur used is maximum length. In using these formulae, be careful to express the lengths of long bones in centimeters and decimal fractions thereof.

The Cranium

PRELIMINARY REMARKS

A great deal of damage may be done to skulls, especially fragile archaeological specimens, by inexpert and careless handling. Never lift a skull by taking hold of any part of the facial skeleton, or the zygomatic arches, or by hooking your finger through the foramen magnum. Carry the skull as you would a thin bowl, resting the vault in your cupped hands (both of them). If you have to lift the skull with one hand, in no case put your thumb and forefinger into the orbits and attempt to raise it by a grip on the inner walls of the orbits. If you do, you will certainly crush the paper-thin lachrymal bones. The only proper way to lift a skull with one hand is to place your thumb on one temporal region, just above the external orbital process and your first, second, and third fingers in a corresponding position on the other temporal region. In so doing, you will not injure the skull, unless you drop it.

If you possess a skull with its teeth in place, be sure to glue them into their sockets, if they are loose; especially the single-rooted teeth—incisors, canines, premolars, and (usually) third molars.

A skull complete with the facial portion attached and the lower jaw present is called a *cranium;* a skull minus the lower jaw, but otherwise intact, is a *calvarium;* a skull minus lower jaw and facial skeleton, but with brain-case intact, is called a *calvaria.* A skull cap with the base broken away is called a *calva.* This terminology may seem pedantic to you, but it would not if you came into charge of a museum collection in which everything from a few broken bits to a complete cranium had been cataloged indiscriminately as a "skull" or a "cranium."

In the lists of skull measurements that follow, you may have to omit

[10] K. Pearson, "Mathematical Contributions to the Theory of Evolution. V. On the Reconstruction of the Stature of Prehistoric Races," *Phil. Trans.,* Vol. CXCII, 1899, p. 169–244.

auricular height and the various facial angles, since these measurements ordinarily require the use of craniophores and goniometers. You can rig home-made substitutes, if you are ingenious. The standard position of the skull in measuring facial angles is the eye-ear plane (the tops of the ear-holes and the lower rims of the orbits in the same horizontal plane). This eye-ear plane is a close equivalent to the poise of the head in the living when the eyes are fixed upon the horizon. In order to fix the skull in this position, you must have a device that holds up the skull by rods thrust into the ear-holes, with a pointer at the level of the tops of the ear-holes that can rest on the lower rim of one or other of the orbits. You will also need some sort of a prop against the roof of the hard palate to prevent the skull from doing a nose-dive around the ear axis.

Here is also omitted a description of the method of measuring the cubic capacity of a skull, because it involves the use of special apparatus (control skull of known water capacity, glass tube graduated to 2,000 cc., quarts of mustard seed, and other accessories). However, there is a still more cogent reason for that omission: the unending and tedious controversy in which physical anthropologists have indulged (and are still engaged) about the accuracy of various techniques of measuring cranial capacity. I suggest that the elementary student content himself with calculating the cubic capacity of the brain-case by using Pearson's formula (cf. p. 739).

Many of the morphological observations taken upon crania (see pp. 741–743 in which the Harvard blanks are reproduced) require whole lecture periods for their explanation and demonstration, as well as series of carefully selected crania that exhibit the variations in question. These morphological observations are not dealt with in this brief treatise. The anthropologist adheres to a fixed ideal standard of comparison of "medium" development, on the basis of his experience as to what is "medium" in the typical skull of an adult European male of northwestern European extraction. There is no double standard for the two sexes and all of the grading is done against this ideal standard of "medium" in the European male. It is so difficult for any experienced craniologist to be consistent in such grading that some evade the task. Also, there are some variations that do not ordinarily occur in European crania and these have to be rated against an ideal universal standard— which is even harder to acquire.

Craniology is not easy, but skulls are interesting and congenial specimens with which to work. They are easier to get along with than people and can be measured and observed more accurately.

THE SEX OF THE CRANIUM

Sex is also determinable from the skull in the majority of cases—more easily in Whites than in Negroids or Mongoloids. The male skull is, in general, larger, heavier, more rugged in the relief of its muscular markings and processes (or projections). Notably more prominent in the male are the temporal crests and the lines of attachment of the neck muscles and ligaments and the external occipital protuberance. Every anthropologist looks at once at the mastoid processes and the brow-ridges in order to sex a skull. In the male, the mastoids are bigger in every way, more massive and projecting than in the female, and the supramastoid crests are generally well marked. The styloid processes in males are often long and strong, but never so in females.

The brow-ridges in the female skull are ordinarily but little developed and the glabella eminence on the frontal bone (just above the root of the nose) is usually only moderately convex. These features in males are variable in development, but usually far more prominent. The male forehead is generally more sloping than that of the female. The latter often has an erect or even bulbous frontal region with the bosses of the frontal bone prominent. The edges of the female orbits are ordinarily sharper and more delicate than those of the male; the zygomatic arches thinner and more fragile, the malars less massive, the entire facial skeleton smaller and relatively shorter and broader, the nasal skeleton more infantile. The male has a bigger palate and larger teeth. Particularly, the lower jaw or mandible in the male is heavier, much deeper in the chin region, with a stronger forward projection of the bony eminence of the chin. The latter is often bilobate or bilateral in males (cf. pp. 168–169) but usually pointed or median in the female.

In spite of all of these criteria of distinction, it is sometimes impossible to fix the sex of a skull with certainty. Sexual differences are minimized in Negroids and Mongoloids, in which races the frontal region tends to be infantile in both sexes, and in Australoids, among whom the crania of females often have bigger brow-ridges and teeth than ordinarily are found in White European males. Small, gracile individuals of the male sex of any race are likely to be mistaken for females, and large, rugged females for males. No dependable sex differences in the skull are apparent until puberty is reached, often not even then.

In such archaic palaeoanthropic types as Pithecanthropus and Sinanthropus, the sex of specimens is particularly puzzling because the range of sexual differentiation in the skeletons of races represented only by a few isolated specimens is incompletely known.

THE AGE OF THE CRANIUM

There are some ossificatory processes of the immature skull that are of use in ascertaining the age of the individual at death. The frontal bone at birth consists of two halves which usually begin to unite during the second year of life. However, in a considerable proportion of cases, this median frontal or metopic suture remains open throughout life. The occipital bone at birth is in four parts: an upper part, two lateral portions, and a basilar segment. The upper portion, called the squama, is usually united to the lateral portions by the end of the fifth year; the lateral parts join the basilar part before the seventh year. The basilar part is united to the sphenoid bone by a strip of cartilage up to the twentieth year. Union begins at about that time and is completed in the course of two or three years. The closure of the basilar suture is a good indication that the skull is that of an adult.

However, the eruption of the temporary and permanent dentitions is a much better guide to the age of the individual at death. The teeth erupt in a stated order and at average ages for each tooth that are substantially the same for both sexes and all races of modern man that have been studied. Sexual and racial variations in the age of the eruption of teeth are so much less than individual variation that they can be disregarded in attempting to age specimens. Some individuals are precocious and others retarded, so that the determination of chronological age from physiological age is not absolute, but merely approximate.

USUAL AGES OF TOOTH ERUPTION

Deciduous or Milk Dentition

Lower central incisors	6 to 9 months
Upper incisors	8 to 10 months
Lower lateral incisors and first molars	15 to 21 months
Canines	16 to 20 months
Second molars	20 to 24 months

Permanent Dentition

First molars	6th year
Central incisors	7th year
Lateral incisors	8th year
First premolars	9th year
Second premolars	10th year
Canines	11th to 12th year
Second molars	12th to 13th year
Third molars	17th to 25th year

In the eruption of both sets of teeth, the lowers tend to be cut a little before the corresponding teeth of the upper jaw. The beginning student should note that the milk teeth total 20, viz.: $I\frac{2}{2}C\frac{1}{1}MM\frac{2}{2}$ (2 incisors,

1 canine, 2 milk molars on each side and in each jaw). The dental formula for the permanent dentition is $I\frac{2}{2}C\frac{1}{1}PM\frac{2}{2}M\frac{3}{3}$, or 32 teeth in all. The permanent molars erupt in the growing alveolar processes of the jaws back of the milk molars. The permanent premolars therefore replace the milk molars. For detailed description of the various teeth, the student should refer to any text-book of human anatomy.

In the skulls of mature individuals, little more than a guess at the age at death can be made from the condition of the teeth. The wear of the teeth depends upon their hardness (partly a matter of individual constitution) and the amount of abrasive material in the diet (sand, grit, et cetera), as well as upon the nature and amount of food consumed and the length of time that the teeth have been in use. In civilized persons who live upon diets of soft, cooked foods, there is often little wear of the teeth, even late in life. Other persons living upon the same diets wear down their teeth markedly, presumably because of bio-chemical deficiencies. Many primitive groups who chew vigorously upon gritty food wear down the teeth to mere stumps by the time they attain moderately advanced years.

The occlusion or closing of the cranial sutures and their external obliteration are the best criteria of the age at death of mature skulls, but they are erratic and unreliable in comparison with the epiphysial unions, the eruption of teeth, and even with the age changes in the pubic symphysis. The following summary of ectocranial suture closure in adult male Whites is gathered from the work of Todd and Lyon, the best authorities on this subject.[11] Each cranial suture presents two aspects: that seen on the inside of the skull (endocranial) and that seen on the outside (ectocranial). Closure begins approximately at the same time in both aspects, but endocranial closure is more regular and reliable. However, the ordinary observer has difficulty in observing the closure of sutures inside the skull unless the latter is sawed in half. This procedure is undesirable in the case of fragile skulls that come out of archaeological burials. Therefore, the ectocranial suture closure is most likely to be useful to the anthropologist. Todd and Lyon studied both White and Negro skulls, but the differences in sutural closure are almost negligible and certainly of no importance in determining the age of a specimen. Sex differences are equally unimportant. The most disconcerting phenomenon of sutural closure is "lapsed union"—in

---

[11] T. W. Todd and D. W. Lyon, II "Ectocranial Closure in Adult Males of White Stock," *Am. J. Phys. Anthr.* Vol. VIII, 1925, pp. 23–46; cf. also *op. cit.*, Vol. VII, 325–384; Vol. VIII, 47–71, 149–168.

which bone heaps up along the edges of a suture without closure of the suture taking place. This lapsed union may affect a part of a suture or all of it and is especially common in the sagittal and lambdoid sutures. When lapsed union develops, the suture may never close.

In the following scheme, numbers designate approximate degree of sutural closure: O = open or patent, 1 = one quarter, 2 = one half, 3 = three quarters, 4 = complete closure.

CRANIAL SUTURE CLOSURE IN MALE WHITES
(Data from Todd and Lyon)

Suture	Commencement and Course	Termination or Peak
Sagittal		
pars óbelica	20; rise to 2.1 at 23; slow to 26, then rapid	29 to 3.9
pars lambdica	21; steady to 1.2 at 24; pause until 27	29 to 2.4
pars verticis	21; 0.7 at 25	29 to 2.7
pars bregmatica	26; rapid	29 to 2.9
Coronal		
pars bregmatica	26; rapid	29 to 2.3
pars complicata	26; steady	29 to 0.9
pars pterica	22; 0.4 at 26; 2.3 at 29	50 to 3.8
Lambdoid		
pars lambdica	21 to 26	30 to 2.3
pars media	21 to 26	30 to 1.9
pars asterica	26	30 to 0.6
Masto-occipital		
pars superior	28; to 0.8 at 32	old age to 3.0
pars media	" " 1.0 "	old age to 3.5
pars inferior	26 " 1.4 at 33	62 to 3.6
Spheno-temporal	36 to 37	65
Squamous	38	39 at 0.6, secondary activity in the sixties
Parieto-mastoid	39; slow until late fifties	64 to 1.2
Spheno-parietal	28; rise to 0.5 at 31; 2.0 at 38	early sixties
Spheno-frontal		
pars temporalis	28; gradual rise to 0.7 at 31; sharp rise to 2.1 at 38	65 up to 4.0
pars orbitalis	28; rise to 2.3 at 31	46 to 3.8

The discerning student will note that the details of the above table actually are of little use in the precise aging of crania except in the third decade of life. The present writer, utilizing all criteria of age, from whatever part of the skeleton, is accustomed to commit himself no farther than the placing of a cranium that is adult in one of the following categories: Young adult (21–35); Middle-aged adult (36–55); Old adult (56–75); Very old adult (75–x).

Granularity of the skull surface, thickening or thinning of the bones of the vault, multiple vascular pitting of the parietal bones, are all changes that are often seen in adult crania, but, according to Todd, are referable to chronic nutritional defect or other constitutional defect rather than to age.

CRANIAL LANDMARKS

Brain-case

1. *Glabella*	Most prominent point on the middle of the frontal bone between the brow-ridges and just above the naso-frontal suture.
2. *Bregma*	Meeting place of the coronal and sagittal sutures.
3. *Opisthocranion*	The most posterior point on the occiput in the median sagittal plane.
4. *Inion*	The meeting point of the *Liniae nuchae superiores* (superior curved lines) in the median sagittal plane. Also called the external occipital protuberance.
5. *Opisthion*	The middle point on the posterior border of the foramen magnum.
6. *Basion*	The middle point on the anterior border of the foramen magnum.
7. *Pterion*	The region on the side of the cranial vault where the frontal, parietal, temporal, and sphenoid bones meet.
8. *Porion*	The middle point on the upper border of the auditory meatus.

Facial skeleton

9. *Nasion*	The middle point of the naso-frontal suture. Usually the point where the nasal suture meets the naso-frontal suture.
10. *Naso-spinale*	Deepest or lowest point on the inferior border of the nasal aperture in the median sagittal plane. In crania with strongly developed nasal spines the point is determined by a line uniting the lowest points on the right and left sides of the lower border of the aperture.
11. *Prosthion*	In measurements of facial height this is the lowest point on the alveolar border of the maxilla between the central incisor teeth. In measurements of facial projection it is usually taken as the most anterior point on the maxilla in the median sagittal plane.
12. *Dacryon*	Point on the inner wall of the orbit where the frontal, lachrymal, and maxillary bones meet.
13. *Gnathion*	Middle point on the lower border of the mandibular symphysis.
14. *Gonion*	Point on the external border of the mandible that marks the juncture of the horizontal and ascending rami. In measurements the most lateral point is selected.

CRANIAL MEASUREMENTS

[The letters in parentheses before the various cranial measurements are those given to the corresponding measurements on the Harvard craniological blanks reproduced in Charts 1–4. The letters are used as symbols in giving the formulae on the blanks for calculating the most important cranial and facial indices, in which one measurement is expressed as a percentage of another. The cranial measurements here listed without letters in parentheses before them are those not ordinarily used in the calculation of indices. The measurements as listed below are not always in alphabetical sequence or in the same precise order as they are given on the charts that reproduce the Harvard blanks. The reason for the change in order is that a considerable saving of time is effected if all of the measurements that have to be taken with a specific instrument—such as the spreading caliper or the sliding caliper—are done in sequence—whether or not they follow a natural anatomical order. Thus, the observer need not waste time by laying down one caliper and picking up another every few measurements. Of course, this economy of time is effected only when one has a recorder to write down the measurements on the blanks as one reads them from the instrument. If you have to lay down your instrument and pick up a pen to write down your measurement, and then lay down the pen and take up a caliper to make the next measurement, you will hardly save much time by using the revised and more efficient order of measurements.]

(a) *Glabello-occipital Length* (Spreading caliper)
Place the skull on the pad on its right side. Hold the left point of the caliper on glabella and move the right point up and down the occiput in the median line, watching the scale. Record the maximum measurement (opisthocranion).

(b) *Maximum Width* (Spreading caliper)
Place the skull on the pad resting on its occiput or on its base. Take the greatest breadth perpendicular to the median sagittal plane wherever the greatest breadth occurs, avoiding the supra-mastoid crest and making due allowance for any warping outward of the temporal squama.

(c) *Basion-Bregma Height* (Spreading caliper)
Place skull on pad on its right side. Fix left caliper point on basion and right point on bregma.

(d) *Thickness of Left Parietal above Temporo-Parietal Suture* (Spreading caliper)
Place skull on right side. Introduce left arm of caliper through foramen magnum. Take three readings on left parietal 1 cm. above squamous suture; anterior inferior angle, middle, posterior inferior angle. Record average. Do not compress the caliper arms.

(e) *Minimum Frontal Diameter* (Spreading caliper)
Minimum breadth between the temporal crests on the frontal bone.

(f) *Maximum Diameter Bi-zygomatic* (Spreading caliper)
Greatest breadth between zygomatic arches, perpendicular to the median sagittal plane.

(g) *Menton-Nasion Height* (Total facial height) (Sliding caliper)
Place skull on pad in norma facialis (with face upward). With left hand adjust mandible so that teeth are in occlusion. With sliding caliper in

right hand read height from nasion to gnathion (menton). This measurement cannot be taken unless the teeth occlude.

(h) *Prosthion-Nasion Height* (Upper facial height) (Sliding caliper)
Fixed point of sliding caliper is placed on nasion and sliding point adjusted to prosthion.

(i) *Basion-Nasion* (Spreading caliper or sliding caliper)
Place skull in norma basilaris (with base upward). The fixed caliper point (left) is placed upon nasion and the movable point adjusted to basion.

(j) *Basion-Prosthion* (Spreading caliper or sliding caliper)
Place skull in norma basilaris. Note that prosthion may lie above the lowest point on the alveolar process between the incisor teeth. In such cases the spreading caliper may be used. The sliding caliper is here preferred.

(k) *Nasal Height* (Sliding caliper)
Height from nasion to subnasal point. Take the mean of the heights to lower borders of the nasal aperture on each side of the spine.

(l) *Nasal Breadth* (Sliding caliper)
Maximum breadth of nasal aperture perpendicular to height.

(p) *Nasalia–Upper Breadth* (Sliding caliper)
Distance between the two points of juncture of the naso-frontal and naso-maxillary sutures.

(q) *Nasalia–Lower Breadth* (Sliding caliper)
Distance between the two points of meeting of naso-maxillary suture and piriform aperture.

(m) *Orbits–Height* (Sliding caliper)
Consider the orbit as a rectangle. The height is taken from the upper to the lower border in the middle of the orbit and perpendicular to the long axis. Measure and record right and left orbits separately.

(n) *Orbits–Breadth* (Sliding caliper)
Consider the orbit as a rectangle. The breadth is measured from dacryon to the middle of the external border (ectoconchion). (Right and left orbits).

(r) *Interorbital Breadth* (Sliding caliper)
Breadth between the two dacryon points.

(s) *Bi-orbital Breadth* (Sliding caliper)
Breadth between the two ectoconchia.

(t) *Palate–External Length* (Sliding caliper)
Length from prosthion to the points tangent to the posterior edges of the alveolar borders. Cannot be taken upon edentulous palates.

(u) *Palate–External Breadth* (Sliding caliper)
Maximum external breadth of palate on the outside of the alveolar borders. This is usually at the level of the second molars. Cannot be taken upon edentulous palates.

(w) *Bi-condylar Width* (Sliding caliper or measuring board)
Diameter between most external points of mandibular condyles.

(x) *Height of Symphysis* (Sliding caliper)

Distance between gnathion and infra-dentale (point on alveolar border between middle incisor teeth of mandible.)

(y) *Bigonial Diameter* (Sliding caliper)
Diameter between gonia (most external points of juncture of ascending ramus and horizontal ramus).
Minimum Breadth of Ascending Ramus (Sliding caliper)
Smallest distance between anterior and posterior borders of left ascending ramus. Taken perpendicular to height.
Mean Diameter Foramen Magnum (Sliding caliper)
Mean of maximum length (basion-opisthion) and maximum transverse diameter.

(v) *Condylo-symphysial Length* (Measuring board)
Place the mandible on the measuring board with the condyles tangent to the upright plane. Measure with the square to the most anterior point of the mental process.
Height of Ascending Ramus (Measuring board)
Place the mandible on the measuring board with the horizontal rami against the upright plane. Measure the height of the condyles with the square. Record the height of the left condyle.
Mean Angle of the Lower Jaw (Mandibular goniometer)
Place the mandible on the goniometer in natural position and raise the inclined plane so that it is tangent to the posterior edges of both ascending rami. Read the angle.
Maximum Circumference (Above brow-ridges) Steel tape.
Place skull on pad in norma frontalis. Hold zero point of tape between left thumb-nail and index finger. Place zero point on right temporal crest just above brow ridge. With right hand pass tape around most protruding point of occiput, back on the left side, across left temporal crest at level corresponding to zero point on right crest, and across frontal bone to right frontal crest. Read circumference at overlap of tape. The tape should pass above the brow-ridges, not across the brow-ridges. This measurement should be tried two or three times in order to insure obtaining the maximum. Especial care must be taken to have the tape rest on the most protuberant point of the occiput. If you have a recorder, have him (or her) hold the tape on the occiput.
Arc–Nasion Opisthion (Steel tape)
Lay skull on pad on right side. With left hand fix zero point of tape at nasion. With right extend tape along sagittal suture and over occiput in median line to opisthion. Before recording measurement, make sure that zero point has not moved from nasion.
Arc–Transverse (Steel tape)
Place skull on pad in norma basalis (resting on occiput with skull base presented toward observer). With left hand hold zero point upon right porion and pass tape over bregma, recording distance to left porion. Make sure that the zero point does not move.

(c') *Auricular Height* (Ranke's craniophore or Mollison's)
(a) *Ranke.*
Adjust skull in eye-ear plane and read height to vertex.

(b) *Mollison*

Adjust skull in eye-ear plane. With spreading caliper record breadths between poria and from each porion to bregma. The height may be read from a table.

CRANIAL CAPACITY

When the apparatus for measuring cranial capacity is not available, the student may approximate the cubic contents of the brain case by employing the Lee-Pearson formulae.[12] There are a number of these formulae calculated for different "races." Here only the "interracial" formulae are given. All formulae are based upon maximum length of the skull, maximum breadth, and either basion-bregma or auricular height. It is considered that the auricular height (height from the top of the ear-holes) gives a better result than the basion-bregma height. However, auricular height usually requires a craniophore and accessories, if it is to be measured quickly and accurately.

A rough approximation to auricular height may be obtained as follows. Prop up the skull in the eye-ear plane and mark the point on the sagittal suture that lies in the same vertical plane with the poria (middle points on the lower edge of the upper border of the tympanic bones). Now, with a caliper measure the distance across the skull base between the two poria and take half of it. Measure the distance from each porion to the point marked on the sagittal suture. Take a mean of these two measurements. You now have approximately the hypotenuse and the base of a right triangle. Calculate the upright side by the formula you recall from your plane geometry. Here are the Pearson formulae:

Basion—Bregma Height
Males: Capacity $= 524.6 + 0.000266 \times L \times B \times H$
Females: Capacity $= 812.0 + 0.000156 \times L \times B \times H$
Auricular Height
Males: Capacity $= 359.34 + 0.000365 \times L \times B \times H$
Females: Capacity $= 296.40 + 0.000375 \times L \times B \times H$

If the mean thickness of the left parietal bone exceeds 6 mm., you may obtain a better result by subtracting 50 cc. from the total. If the mean thickness falls below 4 mm., it may be well to add 50 cc. to the total.

The present writer does not guarantee the accuracy of any of these results. In his opinion, cranial capacity can be measured by a well-trained student, using mustard seed and the ordinary apparatus, with an error of no more than 10 cc. The cranial module gives a fair estimate

[12] For descriptions of all of the current methods of calculating cranial capacity, cf. Martin, *Lehrbuch*, II, pp. 643–648. This reference also includes a description of the more or less standard method of actually measuring cranial capacity.

of the outside size of the cranium, when capacity cannot be measured, or when one lacks faith in calculations of cranial capacity.

NOTE ON THE HARVARD CRANIAL BLANKS

Specimens of the blanks used for cranial measurements and observations at Harvard University are reproduced—largely for the purpose of indicating the scope of the morphological observations not discussed here. These blanks are designed for coding and punching in cards used by the International Business Machines. Each card has 80 columns, with 12 holes to a column. It is for this reason that the observations are arranged by columns with numbers ranging up to 12. In the case of measurements, the observer records the measurement on the dotted lines and it is subsequently coded in the boxes to the right. If the measurement is a 3 digit figure, only the last two digits are coded, since the first digit is nearly always 1. Two cards are used for cranial measurements and observations, but some basic data are repeated on the second card for convenience in machine correlation and sorting. Similar blanks are used for the postcranial skeleton.

Hints upon the Determination of Race from the Skeleton

An experienced physical anthropologist ought to be able to determine from the examination of the skeleton whether it belonged to a "civilized" or an "uncivilized" person, and whether that person was a White, a Negroid, or a Mongoloid. There are also some especially distinctive races, subraces, or peoples that are usually identifiable from the skeletal characteristics. Here, again, we must content ourselves with a few helpful clues.

If the jaws of a skull are large, the teeth in perfect occlusion and devoid of dental caries and other signs of disease, the betting odds are heavily in favor of the individual's "primitive" or "savage" status. The evidence is more convincing still when the crowns of the teeth are heavily worn—usually an indication of a primitive, abrasive diet. The skeletons of many, if not most, primitive peoples also show in the tibiae and the femora the signs of a bent-knee gait—platycnemia (cf. p. 340) and platymeria, and, very commonly, squatting facets on these bones and on the neck of the astragalus. If the palate and jaws are constricted, the teeth crooked and irregularly erupted; if there are signs of multiple dental caries, pyorrhoea, and abscesses, the skeleton is usually that of a person who has enjoyed the blessings of modern civilization. The

PEABODY MUSEUM OF HARVARD UNIVERSITY — CRANIAL MEASUREMENTS

Catalogue No.................... Sex....................

Area.................... Special Locality.................... Tribe....................

Observer.................... Date....................

1 Description

1 Cranium
2 Calvarium
3 Calvaria
4 Calva

Condition

5 Poor
6 Fair
7 Good

Sex Criteria

8 Uncertain
9 Certain

Muscularity

10 Small
11 Medium
12 Large

2 Age

1 Infant (x–3)
2 Child (4–6)
3 Child (7–12)
4 Adolescent (13–17)
5 Subadult (18–20)
6 Young Adult (21–35)
7 Middle-aged Adult (36–55)
8 Old Adult (56–75)
9 Very Old (76–x)

Weight

10 Light
11 Medium
12 Heavy

3 Deformation

1 Occipital
2 Right Occipital
3 Left Occipital
4 Lambdoid
5 Fronto-occipital
6 Other

Degree Deformation

7 Trace
8 Small
9 Medium
10 Pronounced

Cause Deformation

11 Artificial
12 Pathological

a	Glabello-occipital Length	4 5
b	Maximum Width	6 7
c	Basion-Bregma Height	8 9
d	Mean Thickness Left Parietal	10
e	Minimum Frontal Diameter	11 12
c′	Auricular Height	13 14
	Frontal Height	15 16
	Frontal Angle	17 18
	Total Facial Angle	19 20
	Mid-facial Angle	21 22
	Alveolar Angle	23 24
f	Bizygomatic Diameter	25 26
g	Nasion-Menton Height	27 28
	Nasion-Prosthion Height	29 30
h	Basion-Nasion Length	31 32
	Basion-Prosthion Length	33 34

k	Nasal Height	35 36
l	Nasal Breadth	37 38
m	Orbital Height — Left	39 40
n	Orbital Breadth — Left	41 42
m′	Orbital Height — Right	43 44
n′	Orbital Breadth — Right	45 46
p	Nasalia — Upper Breadth	47 48
q	Nasalia — Lower Breadth	49 50
r	Interorbital Breadth	51 52
s	Biorbital Breadth	53 54
t	Palate — External Length	55 56
u	Palate — External Width	57 58

v	Condylo-symphysial Length	59 60
w	Bicondylar Width	61 62
x	Height of Symphysis	63 64
y	Bigonial	65 66
	Minimum Br. Ascending Ramus	67 68
	Mean Angle Mandible	69 70
	Stature — Pearson Formula:	71 72
	♂ 71.272 +1.159 (Femur + Tibia)	
	♀ 69.154 +1.126 (Femur + Tibia)	
	Morphological Type	73

	Cranial Capacity	74 75
		76 77
	Sex	78 79
		80

Chart 1

PEABODY MUSEUM OF HARVARD UNIVERSITY—CRANIAL OBSERVATIONS AND INDICES

Catalogue No. .... Sex ....

Area .... Special Locality .... Tribe ....

Observer .... Date ....

1 Description
Cranium
1 Cranium
2 Calvarium
3 Calvaria
4 Calva
Condition
5 Poor
6 Fair
7 Good
Sex Criteria
8 Uncertain
9 Certain
Muscularity
10 Small
11 Medium
12 Large

2 Age
1 Infant (x–3)
2 Child (4–6)
3 Child (7–12)
4 Adolescent (13–17)
5 Subadult (18–20)
6 Young Adult (21–35)
7 Middle-aged Adult (36–55)
8 Old Adult (56–75)
9 Very Old (76–x)
Weight
10 Light
11 Medium
12 Heavy

3 Deformation
1 Occipital
2 Right Occipital
3 Left Occipital
4 Lambdoid
5 Fronto-occipital
6 Other ....
Degree Deformation
7 Trace
8 Small
9 Medium
10 Pronounced
Cause Deformation
11 Artificial
12 Pathological

4 Form
1 Ellipsoid
2 Ovoid
3 Spheroid
4 Pentagonoid
5 Rhomboid
6 Sphenoid
7 Brisoid
Sex
10 Male
11 Female
12 Doubtful

5 Frontal Region
Brow Ridges
1 Median
2 Divided
3 Continuous
Brow Ridges Size
4 Trace
5 Small
6 Medium
7 Large
8 Very Large
Glabella
9 Small
10 Medium
11 Large
12 Very Large

6 Frontal Region
Height
1 Very low
2 Low
3 Medium
4 High
5 Very High
Slope
6 None, Bulging
7 Slight
8 Medium
9 Pronounced
10 Very Pronounced
Metopism
11 Traces
12 Complete

7 Frontal Region
Postorbital Constriction
1 Small
2 Medium
3 Large
4 Very Large
Bosses
5 Small
6 Medium
7 Large
Median Crest
8 Small, Medium
9 Large
Breadth
10 None
11 Small, Medium
12 Large

8 Parietal Region
Sagittal Elevation
1 Small
2 Medium
3 Large
4 Very Large
Postcoronal Depression
5 Small
6 Medium
7 Large
Bosses
8 Small, Medium
9 Large
Foramina
10 None
11 Small, Medium
12 Large

9 Temporal Region
Fullness
1 Flat
2 Small
3 Medium
4 Large
Mastoids
5 Small
6 Medium
7 Large
Supramastoid Crest
8 Small
9 Medium
10 Large
Sphenoid Depression
11 Small
12 Medium, Large

10 Occipital Region
Curve
1 None
2 Small
3 Medium
4 Pronounced
Inion
5 None
6 Small
7 Medium
8 Large
Torus
9 Absent
10 Small
11 Medium
12 Large
Shape of Torus
4, 8 Ridge
4, 9 Mound

11 Lambdoid Flattening
1 None
2 Small
3 Medium
4 Pronounced
Transverse Suture
5 Absent
6 Present
Serration
Lambdoid
7 ?
8 Simple
9 Submedium
10 Medium
11 Pronounced
12 Very Pronounced

12 Serration
Coronal
1 ?
2 Simple
3 Submedium
4 Medium
5 Pronounced
6 Very Pronounced
Serration
Sagittal
7 ?
8 Simple
9 Submedium
10 Medium
11 Pronounced
12 Very Pronounced

Chart 2

CRANIAL OBSERVATIONS (*Continued*)

13 External Occlusion
Coronal
1 Open
2 Beginning
3 Medium
4 Advanced
5 Complete
External Occlusion
Sagittal
5 None
6 Open
7 Beginning
8 Advanced
10 Complete
Os Incae
11 Single
12 Multipartite

14 External Occlusion
Lambdoid
1 Open
2 Beginning
3 Medium
4 Advanced
Wormian Bones
Lambdoid
5 None
6 Few (1-3)
7 Medium (4-6)
8 Many (7-x)
Wormian Bones
Others
9 Absent
10 Temporo-occipital

15 Pterion Form
Right
1 H
2 K
3 X
4 Retourné
5 Epipteric
Pterion Form
Left
6 H
7 K
8 X
9 Retourné
10 Epipteric
Median Occipital Fossa
11 Small
12 Medium, Large

16 Condyles Elevation
1 Small
2 Medium
3 Large
Basion
4 Low
5 Medium
6 High
Styloids
7 Small
8 Medium
9 Large
Pharyngeal Tubercle
10 Absent, Submedium
11 Medium
12 Large

17 Pharyngeal Fossa
1 None, Submedium
2 Medium
3 Large
Lacerate Foramina
4 Small
5 Medium
6 Large
Glenoid Fossa Depth
7 Small
8 Medium
9 Large
Postglenoid Process
10 Small
11 Medium
12 Large

18 Tympanic Plate
1 Thin
2 Medium
3 Thick
4 Very Thick
Auditory Meatus
5 Round
6 Oval
7 Ellipse
8 Slit
Petrous Depression
9 Absent
10 Small
11 Medium
12 Large

19 External Pterygoid
Plate
1 Small
2 Medium
3 Large
Internal Pterygoid Plate
4 Small
5 Medium
6 Large
Pterygo-basal Foramina
Right
7 Absent
8 Indicated
9 Complete
Pterygo-basal Foramina
Left
10 Absent
11 Indicated
12 Complete

20 Orbits Shape
1 Oblong
2 Rhomboid
3 Square
4 Ellipse
5 Round
Orbits Inclination
6 None
7 Small
8 Medium
9 Pronounced
Lacrimo-ethmoid
Articulation
10 Absent
11 Small
12 Medium, Large

21 Infra-orbital Suture
Right
1 None
2 Facial
3 Orbital
Infra-orbital Suture
Left
4 None
5 Facial
6 Orbital
Suborbital Fossa
7 Absent
8 Slight
9 Medium
10 Deep
Os Japonicum
11 Absent
12 Present

22 Malars Size
1 Small
2 Medium
3 Large
4 Very Large
Malars Lateral Projection
5 Small
6 Medium
7 Large
Malars Anterior Projection
8 Small
9 Medium
10 Large
Marginal Process
11 Absent, Submedium
12 Medium, Large

23 Zygomatic Process
Thickness
1 Small
2 Medium
3 Pronounced
Nasion Depression
4 Absent
5 Small
6 Medium
7 Deep
Nasal Root Height
8 Very Low
9 Low
10 Medium
11 High
12 Very High

24 Nasal Root Breadth
1 Very Small
2 Small
3 Medium
4 Large, Very Large
Nasal Bridge Height
5 Very Low
6 Low
7 Medium
8 High
9 Very High
Nasal Bridge Breadth
10 Small
11 Medium
12 Large

25 Nasal Profile
1 Straight
2 Concave
3 Concavo-convex
4 Convex
Nasal Sills
5 Absent
6 Dull
7 Medium
8 Sharp
Nasal Spine
9 Absent
10 Small
11 Medium
12 Large

26 Subnasal Grooves
1 Absent
2 Small
3 Medium
4 Pronounced
Mid-facial Prognathism
5 Absent
6 Slight
7 Medium
8 Pronounced
Alveolar Prognathism
9 Absent
10 Slight
11 Medium
12 Pronounced

27 Total Prognathism
1 Absent
2 Slight
3 Medium
4 Pronounced
Alveolar Border
Absorption
5 None
6 Slight
7 Medium
8 Pronounced
Alveolar Border
Preservation
9 Poor
10 Fair
11 Good
12 Perfect

28 Palate Shape
1 Parabolic
2 Hyperbolic
3 Elliptical
4 Small U
5 Large U
Palate Height
6 Low
7 Medium
8 High
9 Very High
Palatine Torus Form
10 Ridge
11 Mound
12 Lump

29 Palatine Torus Size
1 Absent
2 Small
3 Medium
4 Large
Palatine Transverse
Suture
Direction
5 Median
6 Anterior
7 Posterior
Postnasal Spine
8 Absent
9 Small
10 Medium
11 Large

30 Mandible Size
1 Small
2 Medium
3 Large
4 Very Large
Chin Form
5 Median
6 Bilateral
Chin Projection
7 Negative
8 Neutral
9 Small
10 Medium
11 Large

Chart 3

Catalogue No.................................

Area.................................

Sex.................................

Special Locality.................................

Observer.................................

Tribe.................................

Date.................................

31 Mandible
Alveolar Prognathism
1 None
2 Slight
3 Medium
4 Pronounced
Genial Tubercles
5 Absent, Pit
6 Small
7 Medium
8 Large
Mylo-hyoid Ridge
9 Absent
10 Slight
11 Medium
12 Pronounced

32 Gonial Angles
Pterygoid Attachment
1 Small
2 Medium
3 Pronounced
4 Very Pronounced
Gonial Angles Eversion
5 None
6 Small
7 Medium
8 Pronounced
Tooth Eruption
9 Incomplete
10 Complete
11 3rd Molar Suppressed
12 Other

33 Teeth Lost
Ante-mortem
1 0
2 1-4
3 5-8
4 9-12
5 13-16
6 17-20
7 21-24
8 25-28
9 29-32
Teeth Lost
Post-mortem
Mandibular Torus
10 Small
11 Medium
12 Large

34 Teeth Wear
1 None
2 Slight
3 Medium
4 Pronounced
5 Very Pronounced
Teeth Quality
6 None
7 Poor
8 Medium
9 Good
10 Excellent
Accessory Cusps

35 Teeth Caries
1 None
2 1-4
3 5-8
4 9-16
5 17-x
Abscess
6 None
7 1-3
8 4-x
Abscess Size
9 Small, Medium
Pyorrhea
10 Large
11 Absent
12 Present

36 Shovel Incisors
1 Absent
2 Slight
3 Medium
4 Pronounced
Bite
5 Under
6 Edge
7 Slight Over
8 Medium Over
9 Pronounced Over
Crowding
10 Absent, Slight
11 Medium
12 Pronounced

37 Molar Cusps
Upper
1 4-4-4
2 4-4-3
3 4-4-2
4 4-3-2
5 4-3-1
6 Other
Lower
7 5-5-5
8 5-5-4
9 5-4-4
10 4-4-4
11 4-4-3
12 Other

38 Morphological Type
1
2
3
4
5
6
7
8
9
10
11
12

b/a	Cranial Index	39 40
c/a	Height-Length	41 42
c/b	Height-Breadth	43 44
e/b	Fronto-parietal	45 46
c'/a	Auricular Height-Length	47 48
(a+b+c)/3	Cranial Module	49 50
g/f	Facial	51 52
h/f	Upper Facial	53 54
f/b	Cranio-facial	55 56
l/k	Nasal	57 58

m/n	Left Orbital	59 60
p/q	Nasalia-Transverse	61 62
r/s	Interorbital	63 64
u/t	External Palatal	65 66
v/w	Mandibular	67 68
y/f	Zygo-gonial	69 70
y/e	Fronto-gonial	71 72
e/t	Zygo-frontal	73 74
	Horizontal Circumference	75 76
	Nasion-Opisthion	77 78
	Transverse Arc	79 80

Chart 4

case is clinched if the teeth are filled or dental plates are present. The Maya Indians sometimes put in ornamental fillings of jade or gold in the anterior teeth, but these are unmistakable.

SKELETONS OF WHITES

The postcranial bones of Whites are usually heavier, thicker, more massive than those of non-Whites, with some individual and group exceptions. Particularly, the joints of the long bones in Whites are larger, the bones of the wrist and of the tarsus less rounded and with better defined articular surfaces. White pelves are considerably wider and more rugged than those of most non-Whites. Muscular markings on the bones of Whites are likely to be more prominent, partly because these are in considerable measure features of advanced age, and civilized Whites survive longer than do the bulk of primitive peoples.

The skulls of Whites, especially Europeans, are most readily recognizable by small jaws, pinched palates, and frequently high, narrow nasal bones and sharp lower borders of the nasal aperture with well developed nasal spine. The chin eminence is bigger than in most non-Whites, partly because the alveolar borders have shrunk more, throwing the bony chin into prominence. A diagnostic feature of White skulls, more marked in males than in females, is a depression of the naso-frontal suture below the level of the convex glabella (the eminence in the frontal bone just above the root of the nose). This depression of nasion is exaggerated in aboriginal Australian skulls and in the skulls of some Papuans and Melanesians. The brow-ridges in Whites again particularly in the males, are bigger and more developed laterally than in Negroids or pure Mongoloids, but Australians surpass, and American Indians at least equal, Whites in this feature. Correspondingly, receding foreheads are oftener observed in Whites than in Negroids or most pure Mongoloids, but this criterion is not very dependable. Very intricate and tortuous cranial sutures are rarely seen outside of the White race, but medium to simple sutural serration is common enough in Whites, especially in prehistoric skulls. On the whole, mastoid processes and styloid processes are likely to be bigger in Whites than in non-Whites; the external occipital protuberance is often a conical elevation and sometimes a bony hook, whereas a swollen transverse ridge or torus occurs more frequently in Mongoloids, Australoids, and American Indians. In the mandible, the genial tubercles are usually better marked in Whites than in non-Whites. Straight or orthognathous faces, devoid of prognathism, are most commonly diagnostic of White racial ancestry.

NEGROIDS

Most Negroids have slender long bones with rather small articular heads and joint surfaces. Strongly bowed femora with marked pilasters are rare. The pelvis is narrow and high; that of the female is less well differentiated from that of the male than in Whites. The bones of the forearm and of the leg are long relative to the bones of the upper segments of their respective limbs.

The texture of the Negro skull, when in a relatively fresh condition, seems closer, denser, and more ivory-like than the skull texture of Whites and Mongoloids. The Negroid face is usually marked by strong alveolar prognathism—a particular bulging of the jaws in the subnasal region —by a poorly developed chin, and by the low, broad nasal bridge and exaggeratedly broad nasal aperture. The latter usually has dull or indistinct lower borders and a rudimentary nasal spine. The longitudinal nasal suture is fused or obliterated not infrequently in adult Negroids. This fusion is very rare in non-Negroids. The palate and dental arches of the Negroid skull are commonly long and somewhat narrow. The teeth are not especially large, although they exceed in size those of Whites. Often there is a space in the alveolar processes behind the third molars, and impacted wisdom teeth (tilted against the second molars in the mandible or backward in the maxilla) are rare in Negroids. The face of the pure Negro is usually quite short, but mixed Negroids often have long, deep faces and jaws. Negro malars are not ordinarily massive, deep, or flaring, but they are more sharply angled than those of most Whites. The Negroid orbit tends to be low and rarely is tilted downward and outward. The glabella is often as prominent as in Whites who show medium development of this feature; it is hardly ever swelling and protrusive, and the brow-ridges are considerably below modal White development. The typical Negroid forehead is symmetrically rounded— from side to side and from front to back—it inclines to narrowness and is not very high; in females the forehead is often bulbous.

In the male forehead, a median frontal ridge or elevation often may be seen along the lines of juncture of the two halves of the frontal bone; in the more bulging female forehead the frontal bosses—one in the middle of each half of the frontal bone—are often conspicuous. The temporal region of the Negroid skull is almost always flat, particularly because most Negroid crania are long-headed and owe their dolichocephaly principally to narrowness. An annular or ring-like constriction across the skull just behind the coronal suture is often marked. The occiput is usually protuberant and symmetrically convex; the attachments of neck muscles and ligaments ordinarily are not strongly developed.

MONGOLOIDS

I do not know of any postcranial skeletal features that are distinctively Mongoloid. The primary diagnostic feature in the skull is the size and shape of the malar. If you look at the skull from the basal view, you will see that the lower border of the malar or cheek-bone consists of a frontal and almost transverse edge and a lateral edge that breaks away from the frontal edge at a very sharp angle, nearly a right angle. This angulation is in strong contrast to the ordinary stream-lined White malar, viewed from below, which presents a smooth curving around from the front to the side. The Negroid malar is often intermediate in angulation, but nearer to the White form. The entire medial part of the Mongoloid malar is pushed forward, so that the portion of it that forms the lower rim of the orbit is often advanced farther forward than the upper orbital rim. The body of the malar is also deeper, broader, and more massive than in the White or the Negroid. Both anterior jut and lateral flare are inescapable. The forward thrust of the malar contributes to the flat-faced appearance of the Mongoloid skull. In conformity with this architecture, the suborbital or canine fossa (a depression in the maxilla below the middle of the orbit) is often very slight in Mongoloids or entirely absent. It is usually fairly well developed in Whites and often deep in Negroids. There is ordinarily no depression whatsoever of the nasion region (the naso-frontal suture) below the feeble glabellar eminence of the Mongoloid. This is one of the best diagnostic features of Mongoloid skulls. The root of the nose is usually very flat and broad, but the tops of the nasal bones themselves may be quite narrow. Almost always, the nasal root of the Mongoloid is deeply depressed *below* the nasion region and this concavity may carry down to the middle of the bridge, or may give way to a convexity (particularly in mixed Mongoloids). The nasal bridge is nearly always low in pure Mongoloids, but it is not very wide, nor is the nasal aperture. The latter is inclined to infantile conformation, with dull borders and a small nasal spine. Mongoloid facial skeletons usually show some alveolar prognathism of both jaws, but not nearly so much as is usual in Negroid or Australoid skulls. The palate and dental arcades are likely to be short and wide. Correspondingly, the lower jaw is ordinarily wide with flaring hinder angles, and somewhat short antero-posteriorly. The chin eminence is better developed than in typical Negroids, but not so prominent as in most Whites. Shovel-shaped incisors (scooped out behind) are certainly characteristic of Mongoloids, but they may occur in other races. Weiden-reich regards the bony swellings on the palate and on the inside of the mandibular corpus (the palatine and the mandibular tori) as Mongoloid features. They are most common in the Eskimo, who are indubitable Mongoloids. However, they occur in non-Mongoloids. The pterygoid plates of the Mongoloid skull are likely to be large and flaring, especially in strong jaws with everted gonial angles.

The part of the tympanic plate that forms the back wall of the glenoid fossa often exhibits irregular holes or gaps, due to imperfect ossification. These dehiscences are especially common in immature and female skulls and may be regarded as infantile characters. On the whole, Mongoloid glenoid fossae are likely to be shallower than those of Whites.

The frontal region of the Mongoloid skull is usually not provided with large brow-ridges or a prominent glabella. Characteristically, it presents a rather flat surface, sloping gently to moderately. The forehead is not low. Nor is it narrow, except in comparison with the great breadth of the brain-case across the parietals (in brachycephals only). The temporal region is rarely full or bulging, even in the round-heads. Brachycephalic Mongoloid skulls tend to be more wedge-shaped or sphenoidal than brachycephalic White skulls, which are often more nearly globular. This difference of appearance results from the lesser breadth of the Mongoloid frontal, in comparison with maximum breadth of the skull back on the parietals, from the flatter temporal region of the Mongoloid and the lesser convexity of the occipital region. Mongoloid skulls often present a ridge-pole-like elevation in the sagittal region, where the parietal bones meet in the center. However, this sagittal elevation occurs often in absolutely non-Mongoloid crania—both long-headed and round-headed. Weidenreich regards it as a Mongoloid feature. I do not. Flat occiputs and marked occipital tori occur together at a maximum in brachycephalic Mongoloids.

The sutures of the Mongoloid skulls are, on the whole simpler in pattern than those of Whites or Negroids. Sometimes they are almost linear. They are rarely complicated. In the Eskimo, a peculiar feature is the tremendous thickening of the tympanic bone, which forms a part of the auditory meatus. This special feature is not diagnostic of Mongoloid skulls in general. A vertical, slit-like auditory opening or meatus, liable to blocking by bony overgrowths in the form of irregular nodules (exostoses), is very common among American Indians (who constitute a secondary race with Mongoloid features predominant). I do not know how far this peculiar formation of the auditory meatus characterizes pure Mongoloids as a race.

Measuring the Living

INSTRUMENTS

In addition to the metric tape and the small sliding and spreading calipers used in measuring bones, the anthropometrist who measures living subjects requires an anthropometer and scales for recording the body weight. In any sort of laboratory it is essential to use a beam scale, which is the most accurate kind. In the field a portable spring scale—of the type just large enough for the subject to stand upon—may be employed, but its accuracy should be checked at frequent intervals.

The anthropometer is a tubular instrument, usually made of brass, nickel-plated, and graduated by centimeters and millimeters up to 2 meters. It comes in three sections that have to fit together very accurately, so that the sliding sleeve will pass over the joints. At the top of the anthropometer is a fixed sleeve that takes a graduated arm with a bevel point. This arm can be moved in and out of the sleeve so that the measuring point is at any desired distance from the graduated rod or tube. Below the fixed sleeve is a sliding sleeve, also carrying a retractible measuring arm. This sleeve moves up and down the entire anthropometer. The uppermost segment of the anthropometer can be detached and used as a very large sliding caliper for chest measurements, etc. These anthropometers are not made in this country at present. Before the war they could be procured from the firms that make spreading and sliding calipers (cf. p. 717). If an anthropometrist or a laboratory is so fortunate as to possess a good anthropometer, it should be handled with caution. Keep a light film of oil on it when it is not in use and be particularly careful to prevent sand and grit from getting into the tightly fitting joints and warping them. Do not assemble the anthropometer and then leave it leaning up against the wall in a corner. Such treatment will warp it. Do not drop the measuring arms on the floor; they are made of soft metal and will bend and then fail to fit the sleeves for which they are intended.

None of the various scales used by European anthropologists for matching skin color, hair color, and eye color are now obtainable. In any event, none of them were satisfactory. A good and experienced observer could make a better qualitative judgment as to shade of skin color, etc., than the results obtained by trying to use any of those inadequate matching gadgets. Front and profile photographs of the head of each subject taken at a standard distance are invaluable adjuncts of measurements and observations.

HARVARD UNIVERSITY — ANTHROPOMETRY

Place .... No. ....
Date .... Occupation .... Birthplace .... Group or Tribe .... Name ....
Office, Rank .... Sex .... Father's Group or Tribe .... Mother's ....
Kinship with .... Brothers .... Sisters .... Sons .... Daughters ....
Reel .... Frames .... Marital State, sing, mar, div, wid ....

Observer .... Recorder 1

Age	5
Weight	6 7
Stature	8 9
Tragion	
Acromion	
Dactylion	10 11
Span	
Biacromial	12
Bi-iliac	13
Chest Breadth	14
Chest Depth	15
Sitting Ht.	16
Blood Group I, II, III, IV .... R .... M	47

Head Circum.	17
Head Length	18 19
Head Breadth	20 21
Head Height	22
Minimum Frontal	23
Bizygomatic	24
Bigonial	25
Total Face Ht.	26
Upper Face Ht.	27
Nose Ht.	28
Nose Br.	29
Rel. Sh. Ht.	
Rel. Span 10, 11/8, 9	30
Rel. Sh. Br. 12/8, 9	31

Sh.-Hip. 13/12	32
Thoracic 15/14	33
Rel. Sit. Ht. 16/8, 9	34
Ceph. 20, 21/18, 19	35
Length-Ht. 22/18, 19	36
Breadth-Ht. 22/20, 21	37
Fronto-Par. 23/20, 21	38
Cephl-Fac. 24/20, 21	39
Zygo-Fr. 23/24	40
Fronto-Gon. 25/23	41
Zygo-Gon. 25/24	42
Facial 26/24	43
Upper Facial 27/24	44
Nasal 29/28	45 46

48 Skin color Forehead	49 Skin color Breast or in. arm	50 Vascularity	51 Hair form	52 Head hair, quan.	53 Body hair, quan.	54 Hair color Head	55 Hair color Beard, mustache
1 Pale	1 Pale	1 Abs.	1 Str.	1 Sm.	1 Abs.	1 Black 27	1 Black 27
2 Pink 3	2 Pink 3	2 Sm.	2 L.W.	2 +	2 Sm.	2 Dk. br. 4-5	2 Dk. br. 4-5
3 Brunet 7, 8, 9	3 Pink 3	3 +	3 D.W.	3 ++	3 +	3 Brown 7-9	3 Brown 7-9
4 Swarthy 10, 11	4 Swarthy 10, 11	Freckles	4 Cur.	Baldness	4 ++	4 Red br. 6, 10	4 Red br. 6, 10
5 Rd. br. 12-14, 16	5 Rd. br. 12-14, 16	5 Abs.	5 Friz.	4 Abs.	Grayness, Head	5 Gld. br. 11-16	5 Gld. br. 11-16
6 Lt. br. 15-17, 18	6 Lt. br. 16, 17, 18	6 Sm.	6 Wool.	5 Sm.	5 Abs.	6 Ash br. 22-26	6 Ash br. 22-26
7 Lt. y. br. 4, 5	7 Lt. y. br. 4, 5	7 +	Texture	6 +	6 Sm.	7 Golden 17-19	7 Golden 17-19
8 Y. br. 19-20, 6	8 Y. br. 19-20, 6	8 ++	7 Coar.	7 ++	7 +	8 Ash 20, 21	8 Ash 20, 21
9 Med. br. 21-25	9 Med. br. 21-25	Moles	8 Med.	8 +++	8 ++	9 Red 1-3	9 Red 1-3
10 Choc. 26-29	10 Choc. 26-29	10 Abs.	9 Fine	Beard, quan.	Grayness, Beard	10 White	10 White
11 Dk. br. 30-35	11 Dk. br. 30-35	11 Few	Handedness	9 Sm.	9 Abs	11	11
12 Black 36	12 Black 36	12 Many	10 Right	10 +	10 Sm.	12	12
			11 Left	11 ++	11 +		
			12 Ambi.	12 +++	12 ++		

Chart 5

750

ANTHROPOMETRY (Continued)

56 Eye Color
1 Black
2 Dk. br. 2, 3
3 Dk.-lt. br.
4 Lt. br. 4
5 Gy. br. 11
6 Gr. br. 6
7 Bl. br. 5 {7-10, 12-14}
8 Gray 16
9 Gy. blue
10 Blue 15
11 Unmatched
12 Other

57 Pigment
Mixed eyes
1 ++ dk. 5
2 ++ dk. 6
3 Even 7, 8
4 ++ lt. 9, 11
5 +++ lt. 12, 14
Iris
6 Clear
7 Rayed
8 Zoned
9 Spotted
10 Diffuse
11 Scalloped
12 Other

58 Eyefolds
External
1 Abs.
2 Sm.
3 ++
4 ++
Median
5 Abs.
6 ++
7 ++
8 +++
Internal
9 Sm.
10 Sm.
11 ++
12 ++

59 Eye
Obliquity
1 Abs.
2 Sm.
3 ++
4 +++
5 Down
Opening ht.
6 ++
7 ++
8 +++
Eyebrow thickness
9 ++
10 +
11 ++
12 +++

60 Eyebrows
Concurrency
1 Abs.
2 Sm.
3 +
4 ++
Brow Ridges
5 Abs.
6 ++
7 ++
8 +++
Forehead ht.
9 +++
10 Sm.
11 ++
12 ++

61 Forehead
Slope
1 Forward
2 Abs.
3 Sm.
4 ++
5 +++
Nasion dep.
6 ++
7 Abs.
8 Sm.
9 ++
10 +
11 ++
12 +++

62 Nasal
Root ht.
1 Ssm.
2 Sm.
3 ++
4 +++
5 +
Root br.
6 Ssm.
7 Sm.
8 ++
9 +++
Septum
10 +++
11 Str., conc.
12 Convex

63 Nasal
Bridge ht.
1 Ssm.
2 +
3 ++
4 +++, ssm.
Bridge br.
5 Sm.
6 Sm.
7 ++
8 +++, ssm.
Profile
9 Concave
10 Straight
11 Convex
Tip
12 Snub

64 Nasal tip
Thickness
1 Sm.
2 Sm., +
3 ++
4 +++, ssm.
Inclination
5 Up, +
6 Up, sm.
7 Horiz.
8 Down, sm.
9 Down, +
Wings
10 Compr.
11 ++
12 Flaring

65 Nostrils vis. fr.
1 Abs.
2 Sm., +
3 ++
4 Abs.
5 Present
Lateral
Shape
6 Thin
7 Medium
8 Round
Axes
9 Parallel
10 Obl. sm.
11 Obl. +
12 Transv.

66 Lips
Integumental
1 Abs.
2 Sm.
3 ++
Memb. upper
4 Ssm.
5 ++
6 +++
7 ++
Memb. lower (if diff.)
8 Abs.
9 Sm.
10 +
11 ++
12 +++

67 Lips
Eversion
1 Abs.
2 Sm.
3 ++
4 +++
Lip seam
5 Sm.
6 Sm.
7 ++
8 +++
Mid-fac. prog.
9 Abs.
10 Sm.
11 ++
12 +++

68 Alv. prog.
1 Abs.
2 Sm.
3 ++
4 +++
Chin prom.
5 Sm.
6 Sm.
7 ++
8 +++
Chin type
9 Median
10 Bilat.
11 Complete
12 Partial

69 Bite
1 Under
2 E-to-E
3 Sm.-over
4 ++-over
Loss
5 None
6 Ssm. 1-4
7 Sm. 5-8
8 ++ 9-16
9 ++ 17-
Wear
10 Abs. Sm.
11 ++
12 ++, +++

70 Caries
1 Abs.
2 Ssm. 1-4
3 Sm. 5-8
4 + 9-16
5 ++ 17-
Shortening
6 Abs.
7 Sm.
8 ++
Crowding
9 +++
10 Abs.
11 +
12 ++

71 Malars
Front. projection
4 Abs.
5 Sm.
6 ++
7 +++
Lat. projection
4 Abs.
5 Sm.
6 ++
7 +++
Gonial angles
9 Sm.
10 ++
11 +++
12 ++

72 Ear
Helix
1 Sm.
2 +
3 ++
4 +++
Antihelix
5 Abs.
6 Sm.
7 ++
8 +++
Dar's pt.
9 Abs.
10 Sm.
11 ++
12 ++

73 Ear lobe
1 Soldered
2 Attached
3 Free
Size
4 Abs.
5 Sm.
6 ++
7 +++
Protrusion
8 Abs.
9 ++
Slant
10 +++
11 Sm.
12 ++

74 Fullness
Temporal
1 Sm.
2 Sm.
3 ++
Occ. protrusion
4 Abs.
5 Sm.
6 ++
7 +++
Lamb. flattening
8 Abs.
9 Sm.
10 ++
11 ++
12 Disharmony

75 Occ. Flattening
1 Abs.
2 Left
3 Right
Cran. asymmetry
4 Abs.
5 Left
6 Right
Fac. asymmetry
7 Abs.
8 Left
9 Right
Body build
10 Linear
11 Medium
12 Lateral

76 Race
1
2
3
4
5
6
7
8
9
10
11
12

77
1
2
3
4
5
6
7
8
9
10
11
12

78
1
2
3
4
5
6
7
8
9
10
11
12

79
1
2
3
4
5
6
7
8
9
10
11
12

80
1
2
3
4
5
6
7
8
9
10
11
12

Chart 6

THE SUBECT'S CLOTHING

For purposes of ordinary anthropometric measurements and observations, the male subject need only remove his hat, coat, waistcoat, shoes and the heavy contents of his pockets, if any. Women remove hat, shoes, and coat.

AGE

It is usually sufficient to record the age of the subject to the nearest birthday, unless that age is below 6 years or measurements are to be repeated at intervals of less than a year. The ages of children under 6 years may be recorded in months, and of those under 2 years in weeks.

MEASUREMENTS TAKEN WITH THE SUBJECT STANDING

Weight. See that the subject stands still on the middle of the scale platform. In the case of very young children or infants in arms, it is easiest to weigh the adult with the child in arms and then subtract the weight of the adult. Weights of adults need be recorded only to the nearest pound. Weigh to the nearest ounce in infants and very young children. In the case of babies weighed with some clothes on, subsequently subtract the weight of similar or identical articles of clothing. For adult males of medium size, clothing consisting of flannel trousers and belt, tie, cotton shirt, sheeveless cotton undershirt, and heavy cotton socks weighs about 2 pounds, 14 ounces. A medium weight woollen sweater-vest weighs 1 pound. Cotton trousers weigh about 4 to 6 ounces less than medium weight woollen trousers. It is safe to subtract 3 pounds for medium weight clothing (minus, of course, hat, coat, shoes, waistcoat and pocket contents) for adult males and 4 pounds for heavier articles of the same description.

Women's clothing, consisting of rayon blouse, medium weight short woollen skirt, brassiere, rayon slip, light elastic girdle, garters, and rayon stockings, weighs 1 pound 12 ounces. If a rayon dress is substituted for the blouse and woollen skirt, the total clothing weighs 2 ounces more. Thus 2 pounds is enough to allow for the weight of ordinary female clothing. However, older women and women of great bulk and/or stature, wear clothing that weighs more. Probably 3 pounds should be allowed for such subjects.

In any event, the diurnal variation of weight in the individual is likely to exceed 2 pounds, even in sedentary adult males weighing 150 pounds. In heavy persons who are physically active—doing manual labor or exerting themselves in strenuous sports—the daily weight fluctuation is much greater. Hence there is no particular point in worrying about the inaccuracy in the recording of total weight that results from an over-estimate or an under-estimate of clothing weight, when these errors amount to less than 1 pound.

Stature (Anthropometer or wall scale and anthropometric square). The subject should stand as erect as possible, the arms hanging at the sides (thumbs forward), the heels together, the head held so that the eyes are directed upon the horizon. Place the anthropometer directly in front of the subject about 1 foot away, taking care that it is kept absolutely vertical. The observer stands a little in front and to the side of subject and with one hand holds the anthropometer and lowers the sliding sleeve, while with the other he feels that the descending horizontal measuring arm makes contact *lightly* with the vertex of the subject's head. Record in centimeters and millimeters (although in analysis the figures will be reduced to the nearest centimeter).

Acromion-Dactylion (See Total Arm Length).

Span. This is the measurement between the tips of the middle fingers when the arms are extended sideways horizontally from the body. Hold the anthropometer horizontally with its long bar flat against the chest of the subject slightly below shoulder level. Let the middle finger of the extended right hand of the subject touch the inner surface of the fixed sleeve at the end of the anthropometer, while the middle finger of the left hand pushes the sliding sleeve toward the butt end of the anthropometer up to maximum reach. Note that in most anthropometers the span has to be read by subtracting the position of the upper edge of the sliding sleeve from 2 meters.

Arm Length (Acromion-Dactylion) (Upper segment of anthropometer). Acromion is the most lateral point on the acromion process of the scapula, found by palpating with the finger and following the outer edge of the scapular spine forward until the most lateral point of its extension is discovered and can be marked with a crayon or skin pencil. Dactylion is the tip of the middle finger. The acromion-dactylion measurement, when the arm is hanging down with the palm inward, is total arm length. Some anthropometrists take this measurement projectively, by measuring the height of acromion from the ground with the anthropometer and then dropping the sliding sleeve and measuring the height of dactylion from the ground. This method is not recommended because movement of the subject makes it inaccurate. The preferred method is to use the uppermost segment of the anthropometer as a sliding caliper. With one hand, hold the point of the top measuring arm against acromion and with the other depress the sliding sleeve until the middle finger tip of the subject just touches the point of the lower measuring arm.

Biacromial Diameter (Upper segment of anthropometer). This measurement is the maximum breadth of the bony shoulder girdle. The observer stands behind the subject and holds the 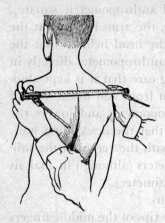 upper section of the anthropometer (used as a sliding caliper) with the measuring arms retracted to a length of about 4 inches. He can then move the sliding sleeve of the anthropometer with the heel of the hand. If the measuring arms are pulled out too far, this cannot be done, because the points of each measuring arm must be held between the tips of the thumbs and the sides of the index fingers while the tips of the index fingers are advanced beyond the points of the measuring bar, palpating for the acromia. When the two acromion points are found by following along the outside edge of the scapular spine, the measuring point of the left hand bar (in the fixed sleeve at the top of the anthropometer) is pressed firmly against the left acromion; the heel of the right hand presses the sliding sleeve inward and the point of that measuring bar is applied firmly to the right acromion. This measurement requires moderate pressure— enough to indent the deltoid muscle, but not enough to cause discomfort to the subject.

Bi-iliac Diameter or *Pelvic Breadth* (Upper segment of anthropometer). The observer stands behind the subject holding the fixed sleeve of the anthropometer in his left hand, the sliding sleeve in his right. The measuring arms are well extended (or pulled out), because this measurement is to be taken against the inner edges of the measuring arms, not at their points. As in the case of biacromial diameter, the forefingers of the operator are used to palpate (feel for) the most lateral points on the iliac crests. In slender males, these points are often prominent bony bumps, upon which the belt rests if the subject holds up his trousers by a belt. Avoid the belt and the pocket seam, either by loosening the belt and lowering the trousers an inch or two, or by getting the subject to hitch up his trousers. In obese male subjects and in most females, the points on the iliac crest between which the measurement is to be made are deep and hard to find, partly because of overlying tissue and partly because of a lack of lateral flare of the iliac crests. They are usually at about the level of the waistline (if any), and below rather than above it.

When the points are located, press the measuring arms firmly against them, if necessary indenting the skin and fatty and muscular tissue quite deeply. Take the reading on the caliper when it is in measuring position, since removing it from the body of the subject will alter the position of the sliding arm. This measurement can hardly be taken with an accuracy finer than 1 cm.

Chest Breadth (Upper segment of anthropometer as sliding caliper). Pull out the measuring arms to their full extension in the sleeves. Most tubular anthropometers have a flattened seg-  ment on one side. Place this flattened surface of the anthropometer across the subject's chest at nipple level (in males). Since the sternum and chest slope down and forward, the extended measuring arms of the anthropometer will now project diagonally downward and backward be- low the subject's arm-pits. The arms of the sub- ject are hanging, but held slightly away from the sides of the chest. Apply the left measuring arm (the one in the fixed sleeve) to the right wall of the chest, but without exerting more than enough pressure to make a light contact. With the right hand, now push in the sliding sleeve until mere contact is made with the left wall of the chest. As the subject inhales and exhales, move the sliding sleeve in and out and take a mean between expiration and inspiration. Let the subject breathe naturally; do not encourage him to maximum puffing out of the chest and extreme defla- tion. The measurement is difficult and relatively inaccurate. One can hardly hope to attain an accuracy better than 1 cm.

Chest Depth (Upper segment of anthropometer as sliding caliper). This measurement is even more difficult and less accurate than the pre- ceding. With the left hand hold the inner edge of the fully extended top measuring arm (the one in the fixed sleeve) across the chest of the subject at nipple level. The graduated tube of the anthropometer passes diagonally downward and backward below the left arm-pit of the subject, whose left arm hangs outside the tube. With the right hand, push in the sliding sleeve against the back of the subject at the level of the lower tip of the scapula (shoulder-blade).

Compress the tissues until the inside edge of the measuring arm is in contact with the skin overlying the spine in the mid- dle line. Take the reading with the anthropometer in position. This chest depth can be measured much more easily with a large spreading chest- or pelvic-caliper with curving arms, if such an instrument is available. Its limit of accuracy with the sliding caliper is not much less than 1.5 cm.

In many mature females, the breasts interfere with the taking of these measurements. The present writer does not attempt to take the chest diameters of female subjects.

MEASUREMENTS TAKEN WITH THE SUBJECT SITTING

Sitting Height (The two lower segments of the anthropometer). This is the height of the head, neck, and trunk of the subject in an erect sitting position. Subtracted from stature, it gives the best approximation to total length of the lower extremities. The subject must sit upon a flat, hard surface with the thighs horizontal and the legs vertical. I prefer to take this measurement with the subject sitting on a table, well back, so that the table edge practically touches the backs of the dangling legs. Since the feet are unsupported, the subject is thereby prevented from artificially increasing his sitting height by contracting the buttock muscles. If a table is unavailable, a box must be used. In this case it is desirable to have a number of boards that can be placed upon the box to adjust the height of the latter to the position in which the thighs are horizontal and the legs vertical in the sitting position. If the position of the lower limbs varies—if the seat is too low so that the knees are elevated and the thighs partially flexed, or if the legs are stretched out—the tilt of the pelvis and the lumbar curve are altered, so that they are quite different from the positions obtaining in the erect standing individual. What is required is the nearest possible sitting equivalent to the position of the pelvis and the degree of lumbar curvature and the consequent total trunk length of the person standing up. Consequently, when the subject is seated with thighs horizontal and legs dangling or, if resting on the ground, vertical, feel of the small of his back to ascertain that the lumbar curve is not flattened, but concave from behind. If the subject has slumped, so that the lumbar curve is flattened, push in his lumbar region or even give him a smart rap with the side of the hand to make him straighten up and flex his lumbar spine. This is most important. The anthropometer is then placed upon sitting surface, just behind the subject, and the sliding sleeve with its extended measuring arm is lowered until the observer feels the usual light contact of the lower edge of the measuring arm with the vertex of the subject's head. The head is erect, with the gaze fixed upon the horizon, as in the measurement of stature. This important measurement can be taken accurately (to less than 1 cm.), if all of the directions are carefully followed. Otherwise, extremely variable and unreliable results may be obtained.

Head Circumference (Metric spring tape). The operator stands in front of the seated subject, or to the left. Hold the zero point of the spring tape on the right temporal crest of the subject just above the lateral end of the brow-ridge, or just above and inside of the external angular process of the frontal bone. With the right hand pass the tape around the most projecting part of the occiput, back along the left side of the head, over the corresponding point on the left temporal, and across the frontal bone, until it overlaps the zero point. Pull the tape tight if the head hair is thick, so as to get as close as possible to the scalp. Repeat the measurement three times, using slightly different levels of the tape on the back of the head in order to be sure that you have found the level of maximum circumference. Since this measurement ordinarily exceeds 500 mm. in adult male Whites, you need not worry unduly about the discrepancies of your three trials, if they do not amount to more than 3 mm.

Head Length (Spreading caliper). Operator at left of subject. Hold the rounded tips of the caliper arms between the thumbs and index fingers (or second fingers). Place the left hand tip lightly on the most forward eminence of the glabella, holding it there without exerting pressure. Now, with the right hand, pass the tip of the other arm of the caliper lightly over the occiput of the subject in the middle line, exerting no pressure and watching the caliper reading. Record the maximum glabello-occipital length in the median or middle line. Make several trials on the occiput, holding the left hand tip steady on glabella

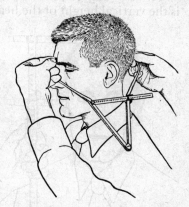

throughout. Some observers prefer to work from the left side, holding the caliper horizontally with its hinge toward themselves. In this way the scale is read most easily. However, there is some advantage in holding the caliper vertically so that its hinge is above the subject's head and the horizontal scale falls in the sagittal or median front-to-back line of the head. A skewed or diagonal measurement is less likely to result from this technique, because the horizontal scale of the caliper helps align the points in the median sagittal plane. However, in the upright position, the scale of the caliper must be read upside down. Both techniques should yield the same result. There should be no more than 1 mm. of deviation in readings of head length.

Head Breadth. The operator stands behind the seated subject. Holding the tips of the caliper arms between his thumbs and forefingers, he applies them lightly to the sides of the subject's head, just above the ears, and moves them forward and backward and up and down in elliptical patterns, making sure that both caliper points are kept in the same horizontal and transverse plane, exactly at right angles to the plane of measurement of head length. While the observer is finding the maximum transverse breadth, he is watching the caliper-scale and records the maximum when it is attained. The caliper can be held horizontally with the hinge toward the observer, or vertically with the hinge above the head of the subject. Especial care must be taken to find the greatest transverse breadth, which is usually slightly above the ears and nearly above the middle of the top of the ear rim (the helix). Further precaution must be taken against exerting pressure on the caliper tips (this is a contact measurement). Any anthropometrist ought to be able to make this measurement with an error not exceeding 1 mm.

Head Height (Upper section of anthropometer). This measurement is the vertical height of the head above tragion. Tragion is a notch at the

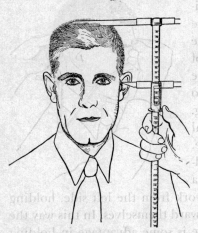

juncture of the anterior, inferior root of the helix (the rolled outer rim of the ear) with the tragus (a flap of cartilage that overhangs the ear-hole). This tragion point corresponds very closely to porion, the point on the lower border of the upper rim of the tympanic bone from which auricular height of the skull is measured. The subject sits with the eyes directed toward the horizon, and, for the measurement of head height on the left side, with the head turned well to the right. This turning of the head prevents the shoulder from interfering with the vertical position of the tubular upper section of the anthropometer. Pull out the upper measuring arm to its fullest extension; retract the lower measuring arm so that it projects about 3 inches from the sliding sleeve with its measuring point on the upper edge of the arm. Now place the upper arm across the head of the subject above tragion in the transverse plane and allow it to rest there lightly while most of the weight of the instrument is supported by the grip of the left hand on the lower part of the vertically held tubular shaft of the anthropometer. With the right hand, raise or lower the sliding sleeve that carries the lower measuring arm until the measuring point of the arm just touches tragion. Now make certain that the shaft of the anthropometer is absolutely vertical. Get your recorder or any bystander to help you check its position. If the upper measuring arm that rests across the head of the subject is not horizontal, and the tubular shaft of the anthropometer is not vertical, the measurement will be hopelessly inaccurate. After you have measured the height from the left ear-hole, repeat the procedure on the right side and record as head height the mean of the readings of the two sides. Measuring both sides and taking the average is recommended because the two ear-holes are often at different levels with reference to the point in the sagittal plane on top of the head from which height is measured. This head-height measurement is difficult and must be practised assiduously. A skilled person can reduce his error, or the variation in repeated readings of this measurement, to 3 mm. or even less.

The present writer has had ample experience with other techniques of measuring head height, including the utilization of a head-spanner, but recommends the method described above as the easiest and most accurate when employed by a practised operator.

Minimum Frontal (Spreading caliper). Minimum frontal diameter is the least breadth of the forehead, taken where the temporal crests are closest together, just above and inside of the external angular processes of the frontal bone. The observer stands in front of the seated subject, holding the tips of the arms of the caliper between his thumbs and second fingers, thus leaving the forefingers free for palpating the subcutaneous bony temporal crests. When the points on the crests have been found by the forefinger tips, advance the tips of the caliper and record the reading, using moderate to light pressure. This measurement seems easy, but great care must be taken not to allow the tips of the calipers to slip down below the temporal crests on to the temporal muscles. The convenient hollow in the temples at this point is likely to be utilized for reception of the caliper tips by the unpractised or hurried observer. The result is a minimum frontal diameter that includes the anterior thickness of both temporal muscles and may exceed the correct dimension by 10 mm. or more. This measurement ought to have an accuracy of 1 mm.

Bizygomatic (Spreading caliper). The bizygomatic diameter, which is maximum face breadth, is taken on the zygomatic arches where these project most laterally. Holding the tips of the caliper arms between the thumbs and index or second fingertips, run the caliper points forward and backward over the zygomatic arches, without exerting pressure, and making sure that the caliper tips are kept in the same transverse plane, so as to avoid a diagonal measurement. The hinge of the caliper is toward the observer so that he can look down and read the scale. Record the maximum. This is an easy measurement. Its average error ought to be less than 1 mm.

Bigonial Diameter (Spreading caliper). Bigonial diameter is the outside breadth of the lower jaw at its hinder angles. Gonion is the most

laterally projecting point on the outside of the angle of the jaw. Hold the caliper tips between thumbs and second fingertips and use the index fingers for palpation. Allow the hinge of the caliper to hang down to a nearly vertical position. The gonia are much lower and deeper than you would expect them to be from observation. In persons with muscular jaws, the rounded angle of the mandible is often somewhat everted and several nodules or bumps can be felt on its outer and lower surface. Find the points for maximum breadth in the transverse plane, and take the reading with the caliper in place, exerting firm pressure on account of the thickness of the overlying soft tissues. Error should not exceed 2 mm.

Total Face Height (Sliding caliper). The upper landmark from which this measurement and the two following are taken is nasion. It is the middle point on the naso-frontal suture—the juncture of the longitudinal nasal suture with the transverse naso-frontal suture. Locating this point on the living is considered to be difficult by all anthropologists, and, in some cases, almost impossible. It is usually slightly above the deepest depression of the root of the nose; it is well above the level of the inner corners of the eyes; it is nearly and often exactly at the level of the tangent to the summits of the arches made by the superior palpebral furrows or sulci—the wrinkle on the upper eyelid above the free edge that carries the eyelashes and almost parallel with that edge, visible when the eyes are wide open (Ashley-Montagu). Nasion is usually at about the level of the lowest inner eyebrow hairs (Connolly).

In order to find nasion by palpation, place your right thumbnail almost flat upon the bridge of the subject's nose and move it upward until the edge of the thumb nail feels beneath the skin the transverse groove that marks the fronto-nasal suture. When you are sure that you have found the right point, indent the skin with the edge of the thumbnail and mark the middle of the indentation with a skin pencil or crayon before the indentation disappears. Be careful not to push up or ripple the skin in this process of palpation. In most women and children and in many males—especially Mongoloids and Negroids—there is virtually no eminence of glabella above the nasal root and the naso-frontal suture is not depressed and cannot be palpated. In such cases, use the superior palpebral level, the inside lower eyebrow hair level, and the inner corners of the eyes as guides, remembering that nasion is above the deepest depression of the nasal root—called by me the subnasion dip. You ought not then to miss nasion by more than 1 mm. or at most 2 mm.

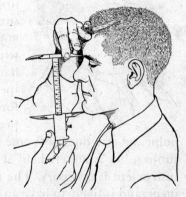

The observer stands or kneels in front of the seated subject and to the right. It is easier to get at the subject if the latter is standing, but the advantage is offset by the likelihood that the subject will move his head or sway, thus impairing the accuracy of the measurement. The observer holds the top arm of the sliding caliper at its juncture with the bar, using thumb and finger tip of the left hand and resting the inner or ulnar edge of his palm against the forehead of the subject, so as to steady the instrument. The blunt tips of the caliper arms are used, not the sharp points. The tip of the upper arm is held in position barely touching the point on the subject's skin that has been marked as the nasion. With the right hand, the observer adjusts the lower sliding arm of the caliper so that it makes a firm contact with the middle point on the under jaw of the subject just below the chin. Make sure that the subject's mouth is closed and that his teeth are in occlusion. If he wears dental plates or has lost his teeth so that there is no molar occlusion, omit the measurement. Do not thrust the lower arm of the caliper too far back under the chin; otherwise you will not get the vertical distance from the nasion tip to the menton or gnathion (the point on the lower surface of the mandible just mentioned), but the length of the leg of a right triangle of which you require the hypotenuse length. Accuracy, 2 mm.

Upper Face Height (Sliding caliper). Taken immediately after the preceding with the upper arm of the caliper still held upon nasion. The lower landmark of this measurement is the lowest projection of the gums of the subject between the upper middle incisor teeth. In order to get the tip of the lower caliper arm into this position, it is necessary to raise the upper lip of the subject. The easiest way of doing this is to push up the upper lip with the flat edge of the lower measuring arm of the caliper. However, if you employ this method, you must have a sterilizing solution of some sort, into which to dip the caliper points after use upon each subject. If you ask the subject to grimace, baring the teeth, the point

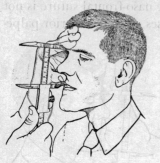

on the gum desired will be exposed, but the contraction of the facial muscles will probably displace the point on the skin marked as the site of nasion. It is usually possible for the operator to push up the upper lip of the subject with the tip of the second finger of his right hand, while the sliding lower arm of the caliper is manipulated between the thumb and forefinger. This is the method used by the present writer. In this way, the lower caliper point and arm does not come into contact with the lip or the gum of the subject, but is merely held at the desired level, and no cleansing of the instrument is necessary. The upper face height is an awkward measurement, and is likely to have an error of 2 mm. to 3 mm. Do not take it on subjects with dental plates or missing upper central incisors.

Nose Height (Sliding caliper). A very simple measurement, taken immediately after upper face height and with the upper tip of the sliding caliper still held at nasion. The lower landmark is the juncture of the nasal septum with the upper lip. Usually, the measurement can be taken with the caliper arms more or less perpendicular to transverse plane of the face, as in the two preceding measurements. Sometimes the subject has a long and depressed nasal tip, so that the juncture of the lip and the septum has to be measured from the side. In this case, the caliper bar is held on the right or left side of the face, with its flat surface toward the face, instead of in the middle line of the nasal bridge with its edge directed toward the subject's face.

Nose Breadth (Sliding caliper). The maximum breadth of the nose between the alae (wings). This measurement must be taken without the slightest compression of the alae. In order to steady the instrument, the tips of the third and fourth fingers of the left hand may rest against the right side of the subject's face. Error should be less than 1 mm.

Ear Length (Sliding caliper). Measure the left ear only. Hold the caliper against the side of the subject's head with the measuring edge of the fixed arm tangent to the uppermost part of the rim of the ear (the helix), the inside edge of the flat, graduated bar of the caliper tangent to the anterior implantation of the ear. Now raise the lower sliding bar of the caliper until it just touches the lowermost point of the ear lobe or the juncture of ear lobe with cheek if the lobe is soldered. Be extremely careful not to compress the ear.

Ear Breadth (Sliding caliper). The measurement is taken at right angles to the preceding measurement. In this case the inner edge of the upper, fixed measuring arm is held against the

anterior implantation of the ear and the horizontal bar of the caliper is above the ear. The plane of the measurement depends upon the ear—whether it is almost flat against the side of the head or projects outward to a varying extent. In any event, get the distance from the anterior implantation to the most backward projection of the ear rim (the helix). This is the maximum breadth of the ear. Again, be most careful not to compress the ear.

Statistics

For the analysis of data on groups of people or on series of bones and skulls, statistical methods must be used. Statistics are merely mathematical devices for the elucidation of quantitative data or qualitative data that can be classified and counted. The statistical procedures that the anthropometrist must employ are few and comparatively simple. Firstly, when he has assembled a series of measurements of a dimension, for example, stature, he must arrange his observations by classes with equal values in each class, beginning with the lowest stature unit or class and recording the number of stature observations that fall within it, then proceeding to the next, and so on. When the process of classification and enumeration (seriation) is finished, the student will know the range of his series, how many individuals fall in each stature class, and whether the series clumps up in the middle or is irregularly distributed. He then calculates the arithmetical mean, the standard deviation, the coefficient of variation, and the standard or probable error of the mean and perhaps of these other constants. The standard and probable errors allow the student to gauge the extent to which his means and other constants are likely to be unreliable as a result of the limited size of the sample he has studied. The use of these standard or probable errors also permits a judgment as to the significance of differences between means of different samples. The product moment coefficient of correlation has a limited utility in the treatment of anthropological data and the student should learn how to calculate it and what it means. This device has been abused, overworked, and misinterpreted in an outrageous fashion.

In the statistics of attributes—qualitative categories that do not lend themselves readily to measurement—the percentage frequency is still the most useful as well as the simplest method of treatment. It is necessary to learn the calculation and use of the probable and standard errors of percentages. Beyond that, the method of calculating the coefficient of mean square contingency, and, more particularly, the use of what is called chi-square, are invaluable in appraising the significance of the association of attributes.

All of these methods can be learned quickly and easily by the student who knows arithmetic and algebra. Many excellent statistical text-books are available. Some of those found most useful by the present writer are listed in the footnote.[13]

A SIMPLE METHOD OF SOMATOTYPING

A simple and objective method of somatotyping according to the system developed by Sheldon is a prime desideratum of constitutional anthropology. An abbreviated scheme of somatotype rating is given here, preceded by Sheldon's latest instruction sheet relative to the posing of subjects for the essential photographs.

Somatotyping is an average rating of the development of each of the three structural components—endomorphy, mesomorphy, and ectomorphy—based upon the mean scores of five principal regions of the body. The scheme set forth below involves rating of the structural components in three or five features of each of the five body regions—head and neck, thoracic trunk, shoulders and arms, abdominal trunk, legs and feet. The independent ratings of each region are averaged to give the regional somatotype, and the five regions averaged to give the total

---

[13] G. Udny Yule and M. G. Kendall, *An Introduction to the Theory of Statistics* (11th ed.; London: C. Griffin & Company, Ltd., 1937). (The most comprehensive and the most useful to the physical anthropologist.)

G. W. Snedecor, *Statistical Methods* (3rd. ed.: Ames, Iowa: Collegiate Press, Inc., 1940). (Especially useful in its simple and up-to-date treatment of the statistics of attributes.)

H. Arkin and R. R. Colton, *An Outline of Statistical Methods* (New York: Barnes and Noble, Inc., 1934). (The handiest ready-reference book).

L. L. Thurstone, *The Fundamentals of Statistics* (New York: The Macmillan Company, 1925. (A clear and simple exposition of the elementary statistics of variables.)

somatype. The first development of this point-by-point rating system resulted from the work of Adelaide Bullen, of the Harvard Fatigue Laboratory, upon female subjects, for whom no somatotyping standards had been established. Subsequent developments of the abbreviated rating system for male subjects were made by the author and by Dr. Carl C. Seltzer and were revised and brought into close co-ordination with previous ways of somatotyping by Dr. William H. Sheldon, himself. This method is now being taught by the author to his classes in constitutional anthropology. The system of pin-point caliper measurements upon negatives and the use of indices derived therefrom is excessively time-consuming and, in any event, refers the observer back to his original all-over morphological rating.

In this new abbreviated rating system the student is advised not to make a preliminary, all-over judgment of the total somatotype of the subject, whose photograph he is studying. If he does, this is likely to influence and prejudice his rating of individual features. It is better to start right out on the first point in the first area and try to rate each point independently, letting the chips fall where they may.

The extreme developments of the point or subregion to be rated are listed under the headings of each of the three structural components. The student reads across the paper and then examines the three photographs, in order to determine which is the first dominant of the structural components. He then makes up his mind which component is second in order of dominance. Next he decides how far up on the scale of 1 to 7 the primary dominant should be rated for the point or subregion, then the value of the secondary dominant, and finally the rating of the third component. If he cannot decide between the dominance of two structural components, he gives them equal rating—usually 4–4 if the third structural component is obviously weaker, and rarely, if ever, more than 5–5. (According to Sheldon's system, the highest sum of the ratings of the 3 components is 12, and the least rating of any component is 1. Therefore a 5–5–1 might occur, but hardly a 6–6–1. However, on the individual point system, the present writer could easily imagine a rating of 6–6–1 on a quite extraordinary development of some isolated character, but not, of course, for the whole subject, or even for a whole region of the body.)

In points where there is an overwhelming dominance of a single component, it is often difficult to assign values to the subordinate components since their development is masked. Then it is necessary to make an appraisal of these subordinate values by reference to their general development in some other region of the body in which the subordinate structural component is more easily observed. For example, if we have a highly endomorphic abdomen—say a 6 or a 7, we have to judge the value of the supporting mesomorphy in that region partly from the bony and muscular development of adjacent regions, because we cannot actually see *any* muscular relief in the belly itself.

Remember that the least value of any structural component, even on any individual point, is 1. The least sum of the three component values, even on an individual point or subregion, is nearly always 9 in an adult subject. Hence, if you can rate the dominant component no higher than 4, and the secondary component only 3, the third component ought to be given a rating of 2, even when it is obviously the least in development. You may be inclined to regard this procedure as a mystic game of numbers, but it really is not. It is merely a conformity to a system of classification that is somewhat arbitrary in its limits, as all taxonomic schemes are. If it appears that there really are 8's in mesomorphy, or in any structural component, they will eventually turn up and demand an extension of the scale. So far they have not.

This very new and abbreviated somatotyping has proved very satisfactory so far, when used upon males of college age and older. It has not been applied extensively to immature individuals of either sex or to females of adult years. The adaptation of this rating scale to these categories of subjects raises questions that cannot be discussed here.

Eventually (and soon, it is to be hoped) there will be published albums of photographs with the exact point-by-point, regional, and total somatotyping ratings, to show the range of variation within single somatotypes and in all of the commoner types. At present, the beginner really needs the instruction of an experienced somatotyper. If you want to start by yourself, use the photographs in Sheldon's works as models and bear in mind the following pitfalls:

(1) The amount of endomorphy in slender individuals is likely to be underestimated. Endomorphy is often a smooth blanketing of fatty tissue in immature individuals and in some mature subjects. It is not always great masses of localized fat.

(2) High mesomorphy often, and perhaps usually in mature individuals, is likely to have a considerable endomorphic overlay. Look at the size and ruggedness of the joints and of the hands and feet in subjects whose component dominance bothers you.

(3) Ectomorphy can perhaps be detected better from wrists, ankles, hands, feet, and neck than from general body build. Ectomorphic dysplasias in dominant endomorphs or dominant mesomorphs are likely to crop out in these places.

(4) In the opinion of the present writer the features of the face and head are likely to be unsafe guides in somatotype rating. They are determined in considerable part by racial and other hereditary factors that are not closely correlated with body build. The neck is much more dependable for the somatotyper.

DIRECTIONS FOR POSING SUBJECT IN SOMATOTYPE PHOTOGRAPHY
(W. H. Sheldon)

1. Feet against back of outline on pedestal.
2. Stand erect but naturally, *shoulders not raised.*

Frontal Picture:

1. Arms straight, fully extended (elbows locked). Fingers together, wrist bent so that fingers point down in plane with external malleolus.
2. Hands five inches out from thighs.[14]
3. Face looking directly at camera.
4. Shoulders down.

Profile Picture:

1. Arms straight and locked, fingers as above. Arm in center of body outline so that no protrusion of elbow behind or hand in front—i.e., preserve back and front body outline.
2. Knees must be perfectly in line; relaxed.
3. Chest must be in natural position (not inflated).
4. Face in perfect profile.

Dorsal Picture:

1. As front, but arms carried a little farther forward to prevent shadow on flanks.
2. No turning of head.

ABBREVIATED SOMATOTYPE RATING
(The sign ÷ means "approximately equals.")

I. HEAD AND NECK

Endo	Meso	Ecto
1. Little bony relief; (pneumatic fullness) basket-ball head and face	Muscular, rugged, bony face; square or oblong tendency in head and face.	Thin, fragile-boned face (often environmentally malformed); oval or hatchet face (but highly variable)
2. Chin-neck angle blunted	Sharp chin-neck angle; heavy, square chin	Pointed, or weak, light chin; sharp chin-neck angle

[14] In subjects with broad, fat chests and narrow hips, increase distance so that upper arms will clear sides of chest.—E. A. H.

Endo	*Meso*	*Ecto*
3. Pudgy features; often short, pointed nose with conical tip; thick, loose lips; tendency toward "suckling" lips	Heavy, broad nose of variable length; firm, large mouth	Delicate features, especially nose and mouth
4. Smooth, cylindrical neck (not necessarily short); AP (antero-posterior) $=$ T (transverse)	Heavily muscled, "bull" neck; pyramiding of trapezius; AP less than T	Thin, long neck; often inclined forward; $AP = T$
5. Soft-padded clavicles	Heavy, strong clavicles	Delicate, sharp clavicles; (sternal ends often dropped); marked clavicular hollows.

II. THORACIC TRUNK

Endo	*Meso*	*Ecto*
1. Back: smooth, no muscle relief	Back: rugged, high muscular relief	Sharp bony relief; little muscular relief; scapulae often winged
2. Back: markedly broad; faint and sometimes reversed taper (even absent)	Back: markedly broad; sharp taper (disappears in 6's and over)	Narrow back; slight to medium but highly variable taper
3. Side: deep, puffy chest; lower depth exceeds upper; elastic (high expansibility, big lift)	Deep muscular chest: lower depth $\div$ upper	Flat, shallow, non-muscular chest
4. Side; abdomen predominant over thorax; both deep and wide	Thorax predominant over muscle-controlled abdomen	Thorax either predominant over small, compressed abdomen or subordinated to small convexity (indicative of mesopenia)
5. Front: high, wide, faint rib angle; relatively short chest cage	Heavy, well-muscled ribs; moderate rib angle; chest long relative to abdomen	Skinny ribs; sharp rib angle; total trunk short, but thorax relatively medium or long

III. ARMS, SHOULDERS, HANDS

Endo	*Meso*	*Ecto*
1. Shoulders square, high fat-blanketed	Shoulders prominent, broad, muscular, often sloping	Shoulders, narrow, bony, thin; height variable; often rounded
2. Proximal hamming; thickness proximal exceeds distal segment; little muscle relief; smooth, tapering forearm; small rounded wrists; AP $\div$ T	Rugged deltoid, triceps, biceps; massive, muscular forearm nearly as thick as upper arm; heavy, square bony, muscular wrists; superficial veins marked	Stringy, thready muscles; low relief; long, weak, bony forearm; thin, fragile, bony wrists
3. Tendency toward short-fingered, pudgy, small-boned hands (marked dysplasias frequent)	Massive, heavily muscled, square, bony hands	Thin, narrow hands; slender digits

IV. ABDOMINAL TRUNK

Endo	*Meso*	*Ecto*
1. Full, large, inflated abdomen; AP ÷ T; often transverse folds in 6's, 7's, and middle-aged	Compact, well-muscled abdomen; frequent rectus relief; AP less than T	Under-developed, non-muscular, small abdomen; frequently with slumped convexity or otherwise variable
2. Broad, high, indistinct waist; (sometimes ant. and post. transverse folds in 6's, 7's)	Sharp, low, well-muscled waist of variable breadth	Small, fragile, non-muscular waist
3. Broad pelvis with fat pads and greatest breadth above crests (when well nourished)	Heavy, bony pelvis; muscle markings over Poupart's ligament	Narrow, sharp-boned pelvis; conspicuous anterior iliac spines
4. High, flat, lumbar curve	Sharp, low lumbar curve	High, deep lumbar curve
5. Inflated, soft, large buttocks; angle with gluteal fold part obliterated in lateral view	Muscular, laterally dimpled buttocks (due to endopenia); sharp angle with gluteal fold	Flat, thin, non-muscular buttocks (micropygy due to mesopenia)

V. LEGS AND FEET

1. Soft, pneumatic fullness; proximal predominance and hamming of thighs	Thick, ruggedly muscled, heavy-boned legs; solid, even development of segments	Thin, non-muscular, bony legs, with delicate, elongated distal segments
2. Approximation of thighs when heels together (knock-knees in mesopenia); predominance of outer calf curve (weakness of inner); small, rounded ankles	Prominent muscular relief of massive thighs, conspicuous inner calf curve; gastrocnemius calf shadow; ankles massive, bony	Weak muscling of thighs; marked interspace; relatively little muscling or curvature of calves; fragile, sharp-boned, thin ankles
3. Small-boned, pudgy feet; toes usually short but frequent dysplasias	Large, heavy, bony feet; toe length variable	Long, thin, delicate feet; (dysplasias frequent)

Index

Aqueous humor, 475. *See also* Eye structure

Arboreal life, importance to preprimates, 67; modes of locomotion, 68-69; grasping ability, 69-70; changes in brain organization, 71; olfactory sense, 72; "emancipation of the fore limbs," 74; reduction of litters, 74; brain changes, 79-80; theories on man's ancestral abandonment of, 105-106

Arboreal preprimate stage, 67; evolution of climbing, 67; specialization of limbs, 67-69

Arch, 201, 523. *See also* Touch pads and friction skin, and Finger, palm, and sole prints

Archaeozoic (or Azoic) era, 51. *See also* Table 2, 62

Arches and whorls, percentage frequencies in finger prints of man and chimpanzee, Table 6, 524

Areola, 245

Armenoid (composite subrace), sorting criteria and other characters, 579; distribution, 580; description, 602; history, 602-603

Armenoid-Iranian Plateau (morphological type), characters, 613; distribution, 613; description, 614. *See also* Indo-Dravidian (composite race)

Armenoids, nose, 518

Arrector pili muscle, 193. *See also* Hair

Arthritis, 690. *See also* Body build and disease

Aryan languages, introduction of, 593

Asselar Man, description, 385; site, date, and remains, 385-86; cranial capacity, 386; Negroid characters, 387

Association areas, importance of, 149-50, 152

Ateles, 19. *See also* Spider monkey

Atlanto-Mediterranean type, 582

Auditory bulla, 188. *See also* Ear

Aurignacian industries, distribution, 365; tools, art, and associated animal and human remains, 366; in Africa, 387, 390; steatopygia, in statuettes, 613. *See also* Pleistocene culture sequences, and Combe-Capelle, Cro Magnon

Australia, geologic history and correlations with European glaciations, 353; Keilor skull, 354; Talgai skull, 356; Cohuna skull, 357

Australians, compared with Wadjak and Tasmanian, 352-53; compared with Keilor skull and Cohuna specimen, 355-57

Australians (composite race), characters, 607; morphological types (Murrian, Carpentarian, Tasmanoid), 607-609; description, 609-12

Australoid or Veddoid (morphological type), characters and distribution, 613; description, 614-15. *See also* Indo-Dravidian (composite race)

Australopithecus africanus, age and remains, 281; as ancestral to orang and chimpanzee, 281-82; cranial capacity, 283; description and conclusions, 281-84

Axial or carpal triradius, 526. *See also* Finger, palm, and sole prints

Aye-aye (Cheiromyidae), 16. *See also* Lemuroidea

Azygos lobe, evolutionary significance, 224-25

Baboons, distribution, 23; description, 23; social organization and intelligence, 24; evolution, 25; Hamadryas baboon, 25; ground-dwelling specializations, 84, 107; menstruation, 251-52; Hamadryas family life, 261-62; skin pigmentation, 466. *See also* Cercopithecidae

Barbary "apes," 23. *See also* Cercopithecidae

Basal metabolism, pulse, temperature, racial differences, 541-42

Basic pad systems, 200. *See also* Touch pads and friction skin

Beaker type, British Bronze Age, sorting criteria and characters, and distribution, 580; description, 606

Behavior and body build, 692. *See also* Body build and disease

Biceps muscle, 226

Bipedal gait, 107, 130

Birth, weight comparisons in men, chimpanzees, orangs, gorillas, and macaques, 237-38; in men, 256; uterine and pelvic changes, 256; in chimpanzees, 256-57; nursing and menstruation, 258-59

"Black Apes" of Celebes, 23. *See also* Cercopithecidae

Blastophore, 207. *See also* Embryology

Blastula, 207. *See also* Embryology

Blood groups, serology of man, apes, monkeys, 44-45; shared by man, apes, monkeys, 45-46, 552; and multiple alleles, 428-29; genetics of, and distribution, 544-46; and morphological characters, 557; Rh factor and genetics, 558

Body build and disease, 686; gastric and duodenal ulcer, 687; gall bladder and pernicious anemia, 688; diabetes mellitus, 689; acute rheumatic fever, arthritis, 690; infantile paralysis, 691; and mental disorder, and behavior, 692

Body build and temperament, 678. *See also* Somatotyping

Body size and proportions in primates, 100-101

Body stalk, 209. *See also* Embryology